The
Which?
Good F
Guide 2006

The Which? Good Food Guide 2006

Edited by
Andrew
Turvil

Which?

Which? books are commissioned by
Consumers' Association and published by
Which? Ltd, 2 Marylebone Road, London NW1 4DF
Email: *books@which.co.uk*

Distributed by Littlehampton Book Services Ltd
Faraday Close, Durrington, Worthing, West Sussex
BN13 3RB

British Library Cataloguing in Publication Data
A catalogue record for this book is available from the
British Library

ISBN 1 84490 002 9

Contributing writers: Elizabeth Carter, Bill Evans, Kieran Flatt, David Kenning, John Kenward, David Mabey, Allen Stidwell and Stuart Walton

Sub-editors and proofreaders: Andrew Grice, Hugh Morgan, Katherine Servant, and Richard John Wheelwright

Editorial and production: Angela Newton and Ian Robinson
Cover design: Adrian Morris and Mark Latter
Cover photographs: Getty images/Zephyr
Photograph of Michael Palin (page 17): Basil Pao
Typeset by Saxon Graphics Ltd, Derby
Printed and bound by Bookprint S L, Barcelona

For a full list of Which books, please call 01903 828557, access our website at www.which.co.uk, or write to Littlehampton Book Services. For other enquiries call 0800 252100.

To submit a report on any restaurant, please visit *www.which.co.uk/gfgfeedback*

Contents

Independent, reliable, unbiased ...

The Good Food Guide has been a champion of high standards and culinary integrity ever since it first began in 1951. Published by Which?, it shares the organisation's aim 'to help consumers choose the best goods and services - and avoid the worst'. As you would expect, it is entirely independent and accepts no sponsorship, advertising or payment for inclusion. All restaurants are visited anonymously by our team of experienced and knowledgeable inspectors, consisting of many food writers and ex-chefs who pay for their meals in exactly the same way as their fellow diners.

Any establishment that appears in this book has been endorsed by our readers and inspectors, and their inclusion is based on the level of cooking skill displayed and quality of produce. We do not inspect for hygiene, however, as this role is carried out by local authorities. At the time of writing, not all local authorities make this information public though Which? is campaigning for this to happen.

The Good Food Guide:

- provides comprehensive guidance on restaurant details such as smoking restrictions, children's meal options, vegetarian meal options, wheelchair access, service charges and information on chefs/ownership
- gives real, first-hand insight into atmosphere, service and general dining experience
- awards detailed score gradings for each main entry
- shows accurate price ranges for a three course meal plus wine and service
- includes a broad range of cuisine styles
- covers the entire country

We're passionate about good food and good service, and we know that you are too. To share your dining experiences with us, log on to our new GFG website at www.which.co.uk/gfgfeedback.

How to use The Good Food Guide

Finding a restaurant

The Good Food Guide's entries are divided into six sections: London, England, Scotland, Wales, Channel Islands and Northern Ireland. In the London section, restaurants are listed alphabetically *by name*; in all other sections, they are listed *by locality* (usually the name of the town or village).

- If you know the name of the restaurant: go to the *index* at the back of the book.
- If you are searching for restaurants in a particular area: first go to the *maps* at the front of the book, just after page 32. Once you know the location (or, for London, the restaurant's name), go to the relevant section of the book to find the entry for the restaurants shown.
- If you are seeking award-winning restaurants, those with outstanding wine cellars, etc: make use of the *lists* starting on page 26.

Reading a Good Food Guide entry

The Good Food Guide 2006 aims to provide as much information on each establishment as possible. At the top of each entry you will find the restaurant's name, map reference and location, address, telephone and fax numbers, its email or website address, as well as any symbols that may apply to the establishment. The cuisine style is also given; this is not meant to be a comprehensive assessment of cooking style, but rather to act as a helpful pointer. At the top of entries you will also find the cooking mark, from 1 to 10 (see below) and the cost range for one person having a three-course meal including wine. The middle part of the entry describes food, wines, atmosphere and so on, while the final section gives some additional details you might find useful.

Entries that have not been allocated a score are marked AR (Also Recommended). These provisionally recommended establishments (known as 'round ups' in previous editions) are now integrated with main entries throughout the book. The name of the restaurant appears in italic and the description is shorter than a main entry. These establishments provide further gastronomic possibilities, whether they are food-focused pubs, Thai cafes or Indian restaurants. Some are new openings yet to be fully assessed, and others are old-stagers that have proved themselves valuable local assets over time. Where subsequent reports and inspections merit it, such establishments may progress to a full entry in future editions.

The following pages show a sample entry and give a brief guide to the cooking marks and various symbols used throughout the book:

Cooking marks

Every restaurant allocated a mark out of ten has been endorsed by readers and our own independent inspectors. These scores are meant as an indication of the level of skill demonstrated in the cooking, and ALL restaurants listed are among the best in the UK. Establishments marked AR (Also Recommended) are not graded but may also be of interest.

1–2 **Competent cooking** Sound, capable cooking

3–4 **Competent to good cooking** Fine ingredients cooked appropriately, although there may be occasional inconsistencies

5–6 **Good to very good cooking** High-quality ingredients, consistently good results

7–8 **Very good to excellent cooking** High level of ambition, finest ingredients consistently treated with skill and imagination

9–10 **The best** The top restaurants in the country, highly individual and displaying impressive artistry

Symbols

The following symbols are used throughout this guide:

NEW ENTRY New main entry 2006 (may have been a 'round up/also recommended' in previous editions)

AR Not a full entry but provisionally recommended (known as 'round-ups' in previous editions, these 'also recommended' establishments are now integrated throughout the book)

Chef changed since last year's entry

Wine list well above average

Outstanding wine cellar

Smoking banned in all eating areas

Smoking restricted, but permitted in some eating areas

Budget dining possible (£30 or less per person for three-course meal, including coffee, a half-bottle of wine and service charge)

Participating restaurant in *The Good Food Guide* £5 voucher scheme (see page 11 for details)

Accommodation available

Cost

The price range given is based on the cost of a three-course meal (lunch and/or dinner) for one person, including coffee, house wine, service and cover charge where applicable, according to information supplied by the restaurant. The lower figure is the least you are likely to pay, from either á la carte or set-price menus, and may apply only to lunch. The higher figure indicates a probable maximum cost, sometimes based on a set-price meal of more than three courses, if that is what is offered. This figure is inflated by 20 per cent to reflect the fact that some people may order more expensive wine, extra drinks and some higher-priced 'special' dishes, and that price rises may come into effect during the lifetime of this edition of the Guide.

map reference and restaurant locality

MAP 3 Brighton EAST SUSSEX

name of establishment

Headless Chicken

address, telephone number (and website if known)

1 High Street, Brighton, BN1 3FG
Tel: (01000) 818181
Website: www.headlesschicken.co.uk

cooking mark, type of cuisine and average per-person cost for a three course meal including wine and service

Cooking 1 | Modern British | £27--£68

symbols can denote exceptional wine, smoking restrictions, new chef, budget dining and participation in the £5 voucher scheme. See page 8 and the inside front cover for a full list

This is what we call the narrative part of the entry, where we give you the low-down on each establishment. We will tell you whether it is a smart country house hotel standing in splendid isolation, a lively city Italian restaurant, or a seafood café overlooking the sea.

The food references come from readers' reports, official inspections, or from menus sent in by the restaurant. Specific dishes mentioned in the entries are not guaranteed to be on the menu at the time of a visit, rather they are intended as an indication of what the restaurant has delivered over the previous year, and are good examples of the style of food you can expect. Comments appearing in 'quotation marks' are generally verbatim comments from readers or inspectors that we considered suitably appropriate to quote in full.

We also write about the kind of service you can expect, again based on the experiences of the readers and inspectors, and most entries finish with details on the drinks available. Restaurants given the Glass or Bottle award get in-depth write-ups on their wine lists; these awards are not given to restaurants that we consider do not offer value for money, or a decent range of choice at the cheaper end of the spectrum.

other details can include opening time, prices, service, seating, disabled facilities and much more

Chef: Fred Smith **Proprietors:** John and Josephine **Open:** Sun L 12.30 to 1.30, Mon to Sat D 7.30 to 9 **Closed:** 25 and 26 Dec **Meals:** alc (main courses £16.50 to £19.50). Set L Sun £23.50, Set D £39.50 **Service:** not inc **Cards:** Amex, Delta, Diners, MasterCard, Maestro, Visa **Details:** 80 seats. Private parties: 40 main room, 25 to 30 private rooms. Car park. Vegetarian meals. Children's helpings. No smoking. Wheelchair access (not WC). No music. No mobile phones **Accommodation:** 16 rooms, all with bath/shower. TV. Phone. B&B £90 to £175. Rooms for disabled. Baby facilities. Fishing

Meals

At the bottom of each entry, information on the types of meals is given, with any variations for lunch (L) and dinner (D), together with details of availability. An á la carte menu is signified by the letters *alc*. This is followed by a range of prices for main courses, rounded up to the nearest 50p. *Set L* denotes a set-price lunch; *Set D* means set-price dinner. Set meals usually consist of three courses, but can include many more. If a set meal has fewer than three courses, this is stated. If there is a cover charge, this is also indicated. Brief details of other menus, such as light lunch or bar snacks, are also given. If there is a cover charge, that is also mentioned here.

Service

Net prices means that prices of food and wine are inclusive of service charge, and this is indicated clearly on the menu and bill; *not inc*, that service is not included and is left to the discretion of the customer; *10%* that a fixed service charge of 10 per cent is automatically added to the bill; *10% (optional)*, that 10 per cent is added to the bill along with the word 'optional' or similar qualifier; and *none*, that no service charge is made or expected and that any money offered is refused. *Card slips closed* indicates that the total on the slips of credit cards (or chip and pin machine) is closed when handed over for signature or authorisation.

Other details

Information is also given on *seating*, *outside seating* and *private parties*. We say *car park* if the restaurant provides free parking facilities for patrons (*small car park* if it has only a few spaces), and say *vegetarian meals* only if menus list at least one vegetarian option as a starter and one as a main course (if this is not noted, a restaurant may still be able to offer vegetarian options with prior notice – it is worth phoning to check).

Any restrictions on children are given, such as *no children* or *no children under 6 after 8pm*; otherwise, it can be assumed that children are welcome. In addition *children's helpings* are noted if smaller portions are available at a reduced price; *jacket and tie* if it is compulsory for men to wear a jacket and tie to the restaurant. *No smoking* means just that; smoking is not permitted in any of the eating areas. In some restaurants the less stringent *smoking restricted* applies and, where possible, we give details of these restrictions. *Wheelchair access* means the proprietor has confirmed that the entrance is at least 80cm wide and has passages at least 120cm wide in accordance with the Royal Association for Disability and Rehabilitation (RADAR) recommendations. *Also WC* means that the proprietor has assured us that toilet facilities are suitable for disabled people (*not WC* that these are not available or the proprietor is not sure). *Music* indicates that live or recorded music is usually played in the dining-room; *occasional music* that it sometimes is; *no music* that it never is. *No mobile phones* means the restaurant requests that these are switched off. At the end of London entries the nearest Underground station is given, where appropriate.

Accommodation

For establishments offering overnight accommodation, the number of rooms, along with facilities provided in the rooms (e.g. bath/shower, TV, phone), is set out. Prices are usually given for bed and breakfast (*B&B*). *D, B&B* indicates that the price also includes dinner. The first figure given is the lowest price for one person in a single room, or single occupancy of a double, the second is the most expensive price for two people in a double room or suite. *Rooms for disabled* means the establishment has stated that its accommodation is suitable for wheelchair-users. Restrictions on children, and facilities for guests with babies, are indicated.

Good Food Guide £5 voucher scheme

Restaurants that have elected to participate in *The Good Food Guide* £5 voucher scheme are indicated by a £5 symbol. Each voucher is redeemable against a pre-booked meal for a minimum of two people, provided the customer highlights the intention to use the voucher at the time of booking. Only one voucher may be used per table booked. For further details please see the reverse side of the vouchers themselves.

Good Food Guide Online

An online version of *The Good Food Guide* is available on the Internet to Which? Online subscribers; for details see www.which.co.uk.

Sending us your feedback

The Good Food Guide began life in the 1940s as a series of magazine articles, written by Raymond Postgate, the author, classicist and wine enthusiast. He took eating-out recommendations from friends and wrote regular features about different establishments. Eventually, these articles were published in book form for the first time in 1951; since 1962 the Guide has been published by Which?

More than fifty years on, the same principle of restaurant recommendations based on personal opinion and experience remains. *The Good Food Guide* receives thousands of reader reports and feedback about all kinds of establishments, throughout the year. All of those forms, emails and letters are recorded and logged, helping to provide a picture of where the good restaurants really are. This feedback also helps us to identify new establishments that have recently opened and may be worthy of inclusion. Our anonymous inspectors are sent to restaurants only after places have been recommended - so your feedback is very important to us.

This year, to coincide with the new-look Guide, we've decided to build a website dedicated to reader feedback. You can go on-line and register your experiences - good or bad - about a restaurant you've recently visited, and make suggestions about new establishments that you think should be included. Whether it's a quick business lunch, routine dinner with a friend, birthday or anniversary dinner, or once-in-a-lifetime celebratory meal, we'd like to hear from you. All of your comments will be recorded and logged and, who knows, some of you may see a snippet of your thoughts in next year's Guide.

To log on to the dedicated reader feedback site, please go to:

www.which.co.uk/gfgfeedback

When you visit our site, you'll be asked a number of questions about your dining experience. These questions will cover all aspects of the meal, including the quality of the food and drink, the service you received and the general setting. In particular, please consider the following points:

Setting

This can include comments on views from the restaurant, as well as the décor and ambience inside. In particular, we'd like to hear about how the restaurant is decorated, how it feels and what the general atmosphere is like.

Menus

We'd like to know about the kind of food that is served at the restaurant and any specific influences on the menu. In particular, what did you and the other diners eat? Were you impressed by the range of choice, and the ingredients used? Does the restaurant pride itself on using local suppliers? Is the food organic? Was it well-prepared and well-presented? What did you think about the quality of the cooking? Would you say the food was value for money?

Drinks

We'd like to know about the range of drinks available in the restaurant. Is the wine list well-informed and/or extensive? Has it been put together with an eye to the dishes on the menu? Is it well-priced? Are there plenty of wines available by the glass, as well as by the bottle? Please also tell us about the other drinks. For example, the selection of aperitifs and after-dinner drinks available, as well as the selection of soft drinks. Would you say the drinks were value for money?

Service

Bad service can ruin a good meal, but good service and a fine meal can combine to create a fantastic dining experience. Please tell us about the efficiency and friendliness of the service you received and how it contributed to your meal.

Other points of interest

This is an opportunity for you to tell us anything else that you think might be useful or of interest. In particular, if a restaurant has changed hands and/or acquired a new chef, we'd like to hear about it. Similarly, if you believe some of the other services at the restaurant, such as children's meals, disabled facilities, seating arrangements or dining policy are worthy of note, then please let us know.

In addition to these categories, we'll be asking you whether you would recommend the restaurant and whether you'd return for another meal.

All of this feedback helps us to form a picture of each establishment and create a shortlist for inspections and possible inclusion in the book. No restaurant can ever elect to be included in the Guide - only after sufficient reader feedback do we consider an establishment ready for inspection. So please do log-on and tell us about your different dining experiences throughout the year.

Alternatively, if you do not have computer access, please write to us at The Good Food Guide, Which? FREEPOST, 2 Marylebone Road, London, NW1 4DF, and we'll send you some report forms.

We look forward to reading your comments!

One further note

The overwhelming majority of reader's reports we receive are genuine, unsolicited accounts of their restaurant experiences. It is surprisingly easy to spot when, on very rare occasions, we receive a report that has been orchestrated by a restaurateur and, needless to say, this is of no benefit to anybody. When you log onto the site, we shall ask you to confirm that you have no connection with the restaurant management or proprietors in any way, and that you have not been asked, by them, to contact us. It is only through maintaining these strict rules that we can confirm our status and integrity as truly independent.

Introduction

Welcome to the new look *Good Food Guide.* We've embraced the twenty-first century with a brighter and livelier page design, improved the quality of the paper, and integrated all the entries into a single section for ease of use. Now every recommended restaurant appears under its location in the main body of the book. What hasn't changed is our unswerving independence – restaurants pay no fee for entry, and our inspectors pay the bill at the end of every meal. This rigorous inspection programme combined with the feedback from thousands of readers forms the bedrock of over 1200 restaurant reviews, covering everything from the best pubs, via seafood cafes, to the very top dining rooms in the country.

Thank you to everyone who has written to us during the course of this edition. These stories of great discoveries and big disappointments, alongside the everyday ups-and-downs of eating in UK restaurants, are fuel for *The Good Food Guide.* This is truly a guidebook borne out of the experiences of people who are passionate about food and restaurants, and the level of detail, enthusiasm and knowledge shown in many of these reports (as we call them) is quite outstanding. This year sees the dropping of the list of contributors from the back of the book, not because we are unappreciative, but simply that we would rather make use of the space for restaurant reviews, articles and useful lists. Those of you who continue to feed us with information know who you are, and we are very grateful that you do so; the book would not exist without your input. The founding principles of Raymond Postgate's original idea remain unchanged – readers share their knowledge of where the best eating is to be had across the country, and the inspectors ratify the recommendations. See page 12 for the best ways to get in touch and make your voice heard.

A survey by Yell.com in 2005 revealed that the most misspelled word on the internet is restaurant. That could be seen as mixed news for us in the restaurant guidebook business, but worse still for those in education. What this does show is that UK consumers are looking for information on where to eat. A survey in the hospitality trade magazine *Caterer and Hotelkeeper* (28th July 2005 edition) of 1000 people revealed that 44 per cent of them would use *The Good Food Guide* over any other guidebook – that put us on top of the list and some 14 per cent ahead of our nearest rival. The internet is an increasingly popular source of information for all areas of our lives, and increasingly those seeking restaurants are heading for the super-highway. So you may find it useful to know that *The Good Food Guide* is available to Which? subscribers online at www.which.co.uk.

On your doorstep

The boom in the organic food market in the UK is well documented. The environmental case for organic food is a strong one, with any reduction in chemicals surely a good thing, but not everyone can afford the price premium charged for much of the organic-branded produce filling the shelves. As the significance of chemical residues on non-organic food is debated, consumers make choices based on their ability to pay the premium, their willingness to put the environment at the top of the agenda, and, hopefully, on matters of taste and flavour. Interestingly enough, organic is not a word seen as often as you might think on the menus of restaurants in the guide. By far the biggest trend is for naming the producers, suppliers, or in the case of meats, the breed of animal. This traceability brings peace of mind, and confidence. Restaurants should take the time to source produce with care, of course, and those that do so rightly want us to know they are dedicated to finding the very best quality produce: Herdwick lamb, for example, born and bred on the fells of the Lake District, is worth shouting about. These foods are available to us as consumers (ie not just as wholesale to businesses), but few of us have the time to shop from a dozen different suppliers over the internet and wait around for deliveries. The UK has a wealth of great supplies and it helps raise awareness and knowledge when beef appears on the menu not just as beef, but as Welsh black or Aberdeen Angus.

In for the long haul

There is no food more natural and healthy than the fruits of the sea, but the waters have been muddied over recent years by the very serious issues of long-term sustainability. It can be confusing to know what is the right thing to do as far as being a responsible consumer is concerned. The Marine Conservation Society (MSC) lists on its website (www.fishonline.org) species at risk, and they provide clear advice on what to avoid as well as viable alternatives.

Some restaurants are taking a responsible attitude, including Christian Sandefelt's new restaurant 'Deep' in London (see entry). Here sustainability is a clear goal, and it does give the customers the opportunity to try less commonly known fish. It is fair to say that many chefs play it very safe with fish, and stick to a few popular species they know won't challenge the diners. Quite a few of these are on the at risk list, including turbot from the North Sea, for example, and monkfish. If you are not sure where a fish comes from, and therefore whether it is at risk, ask, and if the waiter doesn't know, request that they go and ask the chef. And if the chef doesn't know, that tells you something about the care and attention they are paying to the provenance of their supplies.

Chip on your shoulder

What is 12½ per cent of £81.50 – quickly, come on, I haven't got all day. This year some readers have reported their brushes with the Chip and Pin payment system. No longer left with a receipt on the table and plenty of time to consider a fair tip, the new machine is now presented, and a sum must be calculated while a staff member hovers at your shoulder. Does 12½ sound like too much trouble when under pressure? 10 per cent is certainly easier – round it up, round it down, but it is certainly easy to be flustered into paying more than you intended.

Many restaurants will automatically add a gratuity, of course, usually 12½ per cent these days. Where do you think the money is going? Straight to the waiting staff, right? The truth is an employer does not have to pass all of the tips on to the staff. The Tronc system (for pooling tips) exists so that all tips collected are distributed among the waiting and kitchen staff, but, and it is a big but, the employers are not legally obliged to pass this on to the staff. And you can be assured that if they are not legally obliged to do so, some are probably not going to bother. The money collected as a 'gratuity' can go towards salaries, or even paying the credit card charges. This lack of clarity does not help us consumers feel comfortable or confident in the whole tipping process.

Dish of the day

Chefs can be as fashion conscious as everybody else, and while some strive for individuality and personal resonance, others play it safe with dishes they think won't scare the horses. Prime cuts of meat and familiar fish are the way for so many, with some chefs taking the easy option. Every year, though, an ingredient or two comes to prominence, something we managed without for years will become an essential part of the foodies larder. The ingredient for the 2006 edition has to be the tonka bean. You might be unfamiliar with it now, but we'll all be scouring the shelves for them before too long. Reminiscent of vanilla, the tonka has hints of cloves, almonds and cinnamon to boot, and it appears in a number of entries this year. How about honey cheesecake with tonka bean ice cream and butterscotch sauce (Pink Geranium, Melbourn), or rice pudding infused with tonka beans (Treacle Moon, Newcastle upon Tyne), or crème brûlée flavoured with rhubarb and tonka beans (Dinham Hall, Ludlow)? And, in case you're wondering, no, I don't have shares in a plantation.

The key to success

The basic principles of *The Good Food Guide* have not changed over the 54 years of its existence. We still strive to find the best cooking in the UK, regardless of the smartness of the setting, or the style of the food on the plate. If it is cooked with skill and prepared from good, fresh ingredients, we are interested. The internet has helped us become more efficient in keeping in touch with you, the reader, and that is why we have set up a special website – www.which.co.uk/gfgfeedback – so as to more effectively process all this information. You are still welcome to write in, send us menus etc., but contact can be just a keystroke away.

In early 2005 the US food magazine, *Gourmet*, voted London 'the best place to eat in the world right now'. We shouldn't get complacent until that award is given to Croydon.

Good eating

Andrew Turvil, *Editor*

A moveable feast

Food is a two-edged sword for the traveller, bringing euphoria and vengeance, delight and desperation, in equal measure. Not only does it have a profound effect on group morale (like an army, a film crew marches on its stomach) it is also an essential part of communication. The offer of refreshment to a guest is an almost universal phenomenon and the sharing of it makes a connection which overcomes language barriers.

This can be a mixed blessing. Had the language barrier been lower I might never have gulped down a gourd of fermented palm wine in an Indian village in Peru, only to learn that it had been fermented by the saliva from the old ladies of the village. If I'd known the Arabic for "No, thanks I'm full", when offered a suspiciously heady piece of camel liver in Algeria, I might have avoided twenty-four hours of quite spectacular eruptions.

Meals can make good television as the participants are relaxed and more likely to open up, though there are exceptions to the rule. In traditional Muslim communities meals with foreigners tend to be eaten swiftly, purposefully and not lingered over. The women do the cooking but do not join their men at the table. Nor is there any alcohol to lower the inhibitions.

I enjoy my food so much that I get quite depressed if there is no sense of celebration involved in the despatching of it. It reminds me of those arid power lunches in Manhattan where diners vie with each other as to who can eat and drink the least.

Eating and working is not always easy. On Japan's Sado Island my hungry crew had to end a long day by filming a feast prepared for me by the proprietress of a *ryokan*, a small traditional inn. Cameras turned and microphones were trained on me as I put away a succession of pure delights – seafood with garlic; bream, tuna and squid sashimi; vegetables in bean curd; abalone steak in soy sauce; fried sea-bream with limes; teriyaki of tuna stomach and rice pickles in bean paste. For my tired crew's sake I tried to pretend it was all pretty average, but I'm not that good an actor.

Another time it was my turn to suffer. I was in a Dogon village in south-eastern Mali, sitting with the men-folk around a communal bowl of millet porridge, stained vivid green with baobab leaf sauce, at the bottom of which nestled a chicken, aubergine and onion stew. This doesn't sound like hardship except that the outside temperature, and we *were* outside, was 55 degrees centigrade. I was required to eat with the fingers of one hand, squeezing the millet into a ball and dipping it into the stew. It was like picking up hot coals and my yelps of discomfort caused much mirth among the Dogon, where the ability to eat hot food is a sign of sexual prowess.

One advantage of the cuisine in sub-Saharan Africa is that you can be pretty sure your food is fresh, as it's been running about the yard an hour earlier. One night we came upon a dimly lit restaurant with wooden booths around a clay courtyard. It all seemed delightfully atmospheric with the sounds of goats and chickens rising into the night air. A wooden signboard hung above the door, creaking gently in the breeze.

We ordered fresh goat. Moments later there was a flurry of hysterical bleatings, followed by a thud and silence. The sound of fresh goat. And the crash of romantic illusions.

The opposite of the plain and simple meals of Africa were the banquets of China. The Chinese adore their food and believe there is nothing that moves that can't be devoured. I learned this in a Guangzhou restaurant where snake was the house speciality.

We gamely ordered cobra, which was brought to our table in a basket. The basket was then opened and the creature presented to us. That was alarming but worse was to come. The chef interpreted our nervous smiles as a cue to insert a knife into the still-wriggling snake and remove its gall bladder. Then, as other diners gathered round, nodding appreciatively, he skinned it with impressive speed and craftsmanlike precision.

My feeling is that it is marginally more healthy to see the animal you are about to eat killed before you, but this was clearly not the feeling of a body calling itself The Reptile Protection Trust, who bombarded us with angry letters after transmission.

I can't think what the Trust would have made of the banquet laid on for us after the filming. After a liqueur of fresh gall bladder and rice wine (good for rheumatism, we were told) there followed cat and snake soup, fruit-eating fox (reared on bananas), shredded snake with broccoli, ginseng and mushroom, and rice birds. At the end of this last course the Chinese plates were completely clean, those of the British all circled with a neat ring of rice-bird's heads.

I have been served maggots, beetles, ant's eggs and armadillo with beans in a restaurant in Mexico City and I have been offered dried reindeer heart with my coffee in a tent in Lapland, but some of the best food experiences have not involved exotic food but plain food in exotic locations. Fresh pasta and Chilean red wine never tasted better than in a tent in Antarctica, nor salmon stew (laced, I have to say, with vodka) in a woodcutter's hut in Siberia.

The wonderful thing about food is its universality. Like sex and sore throats it is something common to us all, transcending boundaries of wealth, class and nationality. . When it pretends otherwise, like those neo-colonial champagne breakfasts beloved of African safari parks, it can be a depressing experience.

Most of my favourite meals have been in unpretentious surroundings and a gastronomic highlight of our Himalaya journey was on a rickety old boat on the delta in Bangladesh. All our boatmen had to work with was a calor gas ring, a galley the size of a Portaloo and whatever they could procure from the fishermen whose canoes we passed on the edge of the mangrove forest. They produced only one dish. A stew of crab, prawn and river lobster flavoured with turmeric, quince, chilli, coriander, onions and ginger. There were no napkins and all the glasses were chipped, but if there were any justice it could have won our tottering craft The Good Food Guide Floating Restaurant of the Year Award.

Michael Palin

Food and flavour

The next time you go to a restaurant, remember that eating is a multi-modal process (involving all the senses). Any notion that food is simply about *taste* is misguided. Try eating a beautifully cooked piece of fish off a paper plate with a plastic knife and fork, or drinking fine wine from a polystyrene cup – it is not the same. Both physiological and psychological factors come into play and, in many cases, they cannot be separated. The shape of the cup will affect the perceived smell and flavour of the wine and the material will affect the feel of the cup in the hand and on the lips.

Taste is one of the six senses, the others being: touch, sound, sight, smell and proprioception, (the sense of 'ourselves'). The sense of taste can be broken down into five basic categories, all of which happen in the mouth and nowhere else. These categories are: salt, sweet, sour, bitter and umami (the most recently identified taste, named by Ikeda in Japan in 1908). There is a current theory that fat is actually a taste but this has yet to be proved. We have up to ten thousand taste buds on the tongue and in the mouth. These regenerate, so the receptors that we use today will not be the same as were used a couple of days ago. Although different parts of the tongue can register different tastes, the classic 19th century drawing of the tongue, showing it divided into different sections for the four different tastes is totally wrong.

When we eat, taste buds on our tongue pick up only taste but no flavour. The molecules in food that provide flavour (known as odour or aroma molecules) pass up into the olfactory bulb situated between the eyes at the front of the brain. It contains hundreds of receptors that register aroma molecules contained in everything that we eat and smell. This is where the flavour of the food is registered.

There is a simple but effective and enjoyable way of demonstrating that smell and taste are registered in different parts of the head:

Have ready some table salt and biscuits, fruit or anything easy to eat. Squeeze your nostrils tightly enough to prevent breathing thorough them, but not so tight as to hurt. Take a good bite of biscuit or fruit and start chomping, making sure that the nostrils remain clenched.

You will notice that it is impossible to perceive the flavour or aroma of the food being eaten.

Now, with nostrils still squeezed and food still in the mouth, lick some salt. Although it was impossible to detect the flavour of the food that was being eaten with clenched nostrils, the taste of the salt is unhindered.

Finally, let go of your nostrils and notice the flavour of the food come rushing into your headspace.

As if this distinction between taste and smell wasn't enough, the brain also has to process information given to it by the other senses while we are eating, sometimes with surprising results. Here are just a few examples of the senses' influence on determining what we taste and our emotional response to it.

A few years ago at a Sommelier school in France, trainee wine waiters were put through a routine wine tasting. Unknown to them, a white wine that they had just tasted had been dyed red with a non-flavoured food dye then brought back out to taste and evaluate. Something very interesting happened. They all made notes on the assumption that the wine was what it looked like – red. In this case, the eyes totally influenced flavour perception.

A couple of years ago, I developed a simple appetiser inspired by this very experiment; orange and beetroot jelly. The dish consists of just two squares of jelly, one orange and the other beetroot. The jellies however are not what they appear to be. What looks like orange is, in fact, yellow beetroot juice, and what looks like beetroot is blood orange. The expected flavours are therefore reversed without tampering with the colours.

Back to taste, and another quirk of perception. We all know that chewing gum loses its flavour after a certain period of time. But it does not become tasteless as quickly as we might think. What happens is that, when we chew, the sweetening agent in the gum gradually dissolves in the mouth and is then swallowed, reducing the gum's sweetness. The brain tracks the sweetness and as this reduces so too does the perception of the mint and menthol flavours. In reality however, it has been proven that these aromas are still in our headspace for several hours.

One way to avoid this satiated effect, where flavours cease to register, is to create bursts of flavour. At the restaurant, we do this by using small cubes of jelly that literally burst in the mouth. It is actually quite easy to create the same effect while cooking at home. Certain spices, coriander seed for example, can give wonderful bursts of flavour, making the dish much more exciting than one that incorporates the same amount of coriander powder.

Another way to demonstrate this is to make a cup of coffee with a single ground bean – it will be most insipid. Now take a coffee bean whole and pop it into your mouth. Crunch it several times and then knock back a cup of water. When served like this, the same amount of coffee and water will provide a far greater burst of coffee that will last in the mouth.

It is this principle that was the catalyst for the Fat Duck's much publicised bacon and egg ice cream. The idea with this dessert was not to create a dessert that was based on breakfast but to play with the whole concept of encapsulation.

Eggs thicken ice cream custard because the proteins in the egg coil up and thicken the mix when subjected to heat. The coiled up proteins are now in an encapsulated form and can have a tendency to make the resulting ice cream taste of egg by supplying bursts of egg flavour. In order to avoid this potential egg flavour, I reduced the cooking temperature of the custards, resulting in incredibly clean ices.

I then started to wonder what would happen if I made custard loaded with egg yolk and overcooked it, to the point of scrambling. If the mix was then pureed and passed through a fine mesh sieve before churning, what would the ice cream taste like? The first mouthful transported me back to my youth and the fond memory of Saturday mornings when my mother used to make fried egg on toast. Although a study in the science of ice cream making and flavour encapsulation, this ice cream had created the emotion of an English breakfast!

As well as allowing us to enjoy food, the senses act as warning systems, taste being the last of the sensory barriers, and bitterness the last of the taste barriers. A natural aversion to bitterness can prevent us from eating foods that could be harmful, although it appears that we have the ability to be able to modify such basic likes and dislikes. For example, we generally grow to like bitter foods such as tea, coffee and beer as we grow older.

I began thinking about this whole subject a couple of years ago when I noticed that more and more customers were commenting on the fact that the red cabbage with grain mustard ice cream served as an appetiser just got better each time they ate it. Interestingly enough, this was the only dish on the menu whose recipe had not changed over the past year. It seemed that the barrier being presented (unintentionally) with this dish was the vivid purple colour of the cabbage; a colour not normally associated with food. To some diners, the initial difficulty of accepting this colour interfered with the appreciation of the dish but as they got used to it they lost their inhibition and simply enjoyed its flavour .

Smell is the most powerful memory trigger of all of the senses but we differ so greatly in what smells hit the right or wrong notes. As well as our emotions and associations differing greatly from person to person, we all live in our own sensory world. Each of us hears and smells things differently.

It was-up until quite recently-considered that we had around three hundred receptors that between them were responsible for registering all aroma molecules on earth. It is now thought that we have some four hundred but only use about three hundred of them. We do not all use the same receptors and therefore register flavour molecules differently. Two people tasting the same banana will not necessarily register the same flavour. The same goes for sight and sound.

The whole process of flavour perception is multi-sensory. We all have our own perception of life. Not only do we see, hear and taste differently but we have our own, individual personal experiences, emotion and memory. As long as this continues, the world of eating will be a very exciting place.

Heston Blumenthal

Choosing from the wine list

We've all had 'em – bad wine list moments. Perhaps a strange, almost eerie, selection of nameless generic bottles, with no vintages or producers listed. Anyone for 'Sancerre: £26.50'? Or maybe the house red turned out to be a volatile stinker – but the waiter refused to take it back. Or it was simple – the mark-ups on wine were so terrifyingly high you plumped straight for a double gin.

Actually, my biggest disappointment over a restaurant wine list was none of the above. It happened in a promising local restaurant, where I was handed a smart black laminated book. I opened it eagerly to find just four words, two on each side of a single page. 'House red' and 'house white' were the only choices – the wine 'list' was a joke.

It isn't actually very funny to land up in a restaurant which doesn't give a hoot about wine. Take note, proprietors. The vast majority of us care about the range, quality and good value of our vino – and these days the average punter knows a lot more about the subject than in the past. Often, we look forward not only to the fabulous marinated duck, but also to choosing a silky-smooth New Zealand Pinot Noir to go with it.

Happily, there are fewer truly dismal lists around. James Hocking should know. He runs The Vineyard Cellar, which supplies 250 restaurants and pubs, and he showcases premium Californian wine on his own restaurant list at The Vineyard at Stockcross. 'There has been a huge leap forward in recent years,' he says, of wine lists in general. 'Owners, sommeliers and the diners themselves seem much more interested in unusual wines, not simply the same old grape varieties and big names. So it's not all Cabernet and Chardonnay any more, it's Mourvedre or Marsanne, or wines from regions off the beaten track, finally getting on to restaurant wine lists.'

Although the variety may have improved, rip-off prices, a major cause of restaurant rage, are, unfortunately, still around. James Hocking has seen 'shocking' mark-ups recently of 700 per cent + VAT on certain restaurant wine lists, and once spotted a Spanish red listed for £85 that he 'knew for certain was available in wine shops for just £7'.

But it's hard to pinpoint high mark-ups unless you know retail prices well. The best hope is to look for a well-known wine on the list – say, Moet & Chandon Brut Imperial Champagne, or Tio Pepe fino sherry, or (always a good touchstone, this) Cloudy Bay Sauvignon Blanc. Try to remember roughly what your familiar bottle costs in Oddbins or Tesco or Corney & Barrow, and see if the restaurant price seems unreasonably high. If they are pushing it with one listing, the whole lot is likely to be over-inflated.

Matthieu Longuere, head sommelier at London's La Trompette restaurant – part of a loosely linked group that includes The Square and Chez Bruce which has been praised for keeping wine lists fair – comes clean on pricing. 'The costs on most basic wines need to be around a 65 per cent gross mark-up,' he says. 'And we have a fixed mark-up on top-end bottles of around £40 per bottle, no matter what that bottle cost us.'

Interestingly, John Gilchrist of gastro-pub The Crooked Billet, in Newton Longville, Bucks, comes up with a near-identical answer. '10 per cent profit is acceptable. To get that, we need to make 65 per cent gross profit across the board.' He also believes that more expensive wines should carry lower mark-ups and, like Hocking, has been horrifed by wines marked up by 600 per cent or 700 per cent in other restaurants.

Gilchrist, who made his name with a mould-breaking and exciting wine list at Brown's Hotel in London in the 1990s, says today the 'worst rip-offs' are in 'large, upmarket hotels, particularly big London ones'. 'They might typically source a house wine in bulk, paying just £2 a bottle, and selling it on in the restaurant for £20 or more. It's probably not even very good wine, but some people will still buy it because of where they are.'

The Crooked Billet makes a virtue of selling every one of its 300 wines by the glass, as well as the bottle. How on earth does it make a profit? 'I don't worry about waste, as I drink up the best bottles!' comes the answer. More seriously, the average spend *per glass* at the Crooked Billet is £20; and Gilchrist sells a fair amount of venerable old Petrus at £400 *a glass*, so this pub is clearly not your typical boozer...

And that's just great! How refreshing it is to be able to walk into gastro-pubs around the country and find inspiring, fairly-priced premium wines on the list, rather than the warm Liebfraumilch and oxidised Muscadet of old. Indeed, gastro-pubs can take plenty of credit for pushing wine lists to new limits, often charging decent prices to boot. Several restaurateurs and sommeliers I spoke to for this feature felt that, currently, the best-value wines to be had when eating out are in wine-friendly, innovative, modern food-friendly pubs.

So, we now know to look out for a) a wide variety of wines on the list and b) down-to-earth prices. What else should be on a decent wine list?

- A wide selection of wines by the glass is important, and this should be a range that changes fairly frequently, to add depth and interest for the regular customer. Drinking wine by the glass is increasingly popular, especially where there are tasting menus, when a different glass per course makes perfect sense.

- As well as offering wines by the glass, there should be an appealing range of half-bottles, magnums and even different glass sizes.
- Freshness is all – light whites (except Riesling, which does age well), rosés, cheaper sparkling wines and non-vintage Champagnes and pale dry sherries MUST be young and in tip-top fresh condition.
- The list should be ordered in logical, clear and helpful way. Some choose to group wines by country, others by grape variety or style ('light and aromatic whites'; 'rich and powerful reds' and so on). Style is the best, in my view, as it helps you tease out a wine of the right structure and weight to match a particular dish, whereas a group from, say, Italy, could encompass almost anything. Succinct, intelligent tasting notes and some (unbossy) links to the menu are other pluses. If it is a long selection, a 'short-list' of around a dozen wines at the front is a must.
- The list must suit the area where the restaurant is located – what the locals enjoy and what suits their average spend. Gilchrist went round all the local wine shops and supermarkets near his pub before planning the wine list. 'I saw what people were buying – for example, lots of South African wine – then I put better examples of it on the list.'
- The wines must suit the food. Sounds obvious, perhaps, but there are still one or two fish restaurants offering rich red wines galore and only one Riesling…
- An approachable, helpful sommelier is a huge plus. Long, impressive wine lists, however well put-together, will always seem daunting to some, so use a friendly sommelier if you find one and pick his or her brain. Sommelier Matthieu Longuere promises that 'we are more approachable these days – more positive and diplomatic!' Find out if he's right.
- Finally, when looking for a great wine list, always search for signs of real passion about wine. This will show in an area of special interest. Perhaps the restaurant owner loves fine ports and madeiras, and has a selection of fifteen by the glass. Or there might be an extraordinary set of mature Rieslings, or an amazing group of wines from one region, like Piedmont or Margaret River (even better when that region makes particularly food-friendly wines). This shows the restaurant really cares about wine and almost certainly has got to some effort with the entire list.

If no such enthusiasm shines out, and the list is dominated by one or two brands or producers (watch out for the same names repeating across a range of wine styles), all from the same supplier, or if there's a big emphasis on trendy cult wines at astronomic prices at the top end, and a couple of sad, unnamed house reds and whites at the bottom, then vote with your feet. Get to the off-licence before tracking down the nearest BYO. At least then, only *you* can be blamed for a poor choice of wine.

Susy Atkins

The top-rated restaurants 2006

Every restaurant allocated a mark out of ten has been endorsed by readers and our own independent inspectors. These scores are meant as an indication of the level of skill demonstrated in the cooking. The list below shows the higher-scoring restaurants this year.

Mark 9 for cooking

London
Gordon Ramsay, SW3

England
Fat Duck, Bray
Le Manoir aux Quat' Saisons, Great Milton
Winteringham Fields, Winteringham

Mark 8 for cooking

London
The Capital, SW3
Pétrus, SW1
Pied-à-Terre, W1
Square, W1
Tom Aikens, SW3

England
Le Champignon Sauvage, Cheltenham
Hibiscus, Ludlow
Waterside Inn, Bray

Wales
Ynyshir Hall, Eglwysfach

Mark 7 for cooking

London
Le Gavroche, W1
Ledbury, W11

England
Black Pig, Rock
Castle Hotel, Taunton
Chester Grosvenor, Arkle, Chester
L'Enclume, Cartmel
Fischer's Baslow Hall, Baslow
George, Yarmouth
Gidleigh Park, Chagford
Hambleton Hall, Hambleton
Harry's Place, Great Gonerby
Holbeck Ghyll, Windermere
Old Vicarage, Ridgeway
Mr Underhill's, Ludlow
Pool Court at 42, Leeds
Restaurant Sat Bains, Nottingham
St Ervan Manor, St Ervan
Vineyard at Stockcross, Stockcross
Whatley Manor, Easton Grey

Scotland
Andrew Fairlie at Gleneagles, Auchterarder
The Creel, St Margaret's Hope
Restaurant Martin Wishart, Edinburgh

Wales
Tyddyn Llan, Llandrillo

To submit a report on any restaurant please visit *www.which.co.uk/gfgfeedback*

Special awards 2006

These awards do not necessarily go to the restaurants with the highest mark for cooking, but rather to the ones which have shown particular merit or achievement during the year. It may go to an old favourite or to a new entry, but in either case the places listed below have been singled out because they have enhanced the eating-out experience in some special way.

London

Ledbury, W11	*London Restaurant of the Year*
Bellamy's, W1	*London Newcomer of the Year*
Brackenbury, W6	*London Commended*
Coach and Horses, EC1	*London Commended*
Chisou, W1	*London Commended*
Hakkasan, W1	*London Commended*
Rasoi Vineet Bhatia, SW3	*London Commended*

Rest of England

Chester Grosvenor Hotel, Arkle, Chester	*Cheshire Restaurant of the Year*
Coachman Inn, Snainton	*North Yorkshire Newcomer of the Year*
Entropy, Leicester	*Leicestershire Newcomer of the Year*
George Hotel, Codford St Peter	*Wiltshire Restaurant of the Year*
Edmunds, Henley-in-Arden	*Warwickshire Restaurant of the Year*
Elephant, Torquay	*Devon Newcomer of the Year*
Establishment, Manchester	*Manchester Restaurant of the Year*
5 North Street	*Gloucestershire Restaurant of the Year*
Fish Café, Rye	*East Sussex Newcomer of the Year*
Goodfellows, Wells	*Somerset Restaurant of the Year*
Hand & Flowers, Marlow	*Buckinghamshire Newcomer of the Year*
Midsummer House, Cambridge	*Cambridgeshire Restaurant of the Year*
St Ervan Manor, St Ervan	*Cornwall Newcomer of the Year*
Sir Charles Napier, Chinnor	*Oxfordshire Restaurant of the Year*
Three Fishes, Mitton	*Lancashire Restaurant of the Year*
Three Lions, Stuckton	*Hampshire Restaurant of the Year*
Weavers Shed, Golcar	*West Yorkshire Restaurant of the Year*

Scotland

Restaurant Martin Wishart, Edinburgh	*Scotland Restaurant of the Year*
Buttery, Glasgow	*Scotland Commended*
Inverlochy Castle, Fort William	*Scotland Commended*

Wales

Ynyshir Hall, Eglwysfach	*Wales Restaurant of the Year*
St Tudno Hotel, Llandudno	*Wales commended*
Tan-y-Foel, Capel Garmon	*Wales commended*

Northern Ireland

Roscoff Brasserie, Belfast	*Northern Ireland Restaurant of the Year*

The Guide's longest-serving restaurants

The Guide has seen many restaurants come and go. Some, however, have stayed the course with tenacity. (Qualification for this list is that the restaurant has been in each edition of the Guide subsequent to its first entry.)

Connaught, London W1	53 years
Gay Hussar, London W1	49 years
Gravetye Manor, East Grinstead	49 years
Porth Tocyn Hotel, Abersoch	49 years
Sharrow Bay, Ullswater	45 years
Walnut Tree Inn, Llandewi Skirrid	41 years
Black Bull Inn, Moulton	39 years
Rothay Manor, Ambleside	37 years
Le Gavroche, London W1	36 years
Summer Isles Hotel, Achiltibuie	36 years
The Capital, London SW3	35 years
Miller Howe, Windermere	35 years
Old Fire Engine House, Ely	34 years
Ubiquitous Chip, Glasgow	34 years
Druidstone, Broad Haven	33 years
Peat Inn, Peat Inn	33 years
Plumber Manor, Sturminster Newton	33 years
Waterside Inn, Bray	33 years
White Moss House, Grasmere	33 years
Isle of Eriska, Eriska	32 years
Airds, Port Appin	30 years
Farlam Hall, Brampton	29 years
Corse Lawn House, Corse Lawn	28 years
Gidleigh Park, Chagford	28 years
Hambleton Hall, Hambleton	27 years
Pier Hotel, Harbourside Restaurant, Harwich	27 years
Sabras, London NW10	27 years
Grafton Manor, Bromsgrove	26 years
Magpie Café, Whitby	26 years
Champany Inn, Linlithgow	25 years
Drum and Monkey, Harrogate	25 years
Royal Crescent, Pimpernel's, Bath	25 years
RSJ, London SE1	25 years
Seafood Restaurant, Padstow	25 years
Sir Charles Napier, Chinnor	25 years
Y Bistro, Llanberis	25 years
Le Caprice, London SW3	24 years
Kalpna, Edinburgh	24 years
Little Barwick House, Little Barwick	24 years
Moss Nook, Manchester	24 years
Neal Street Restaurant, London WC2	24 years
Sportsman's Arms, Wath-in-Nidderdale	24 years

Restaurants with outstanding wine cellars

Marked in the text with a 🍷

London

Bibendum, SW3
Bleeding Heart, EC1
Cambio de Tercio, SW5
Chez Bruce, SW17
The Don, EC4
Enoteca Turi, SW15
Fifth Floor, SW1
Le Gavroche, W1
Gordon Ramsay, SW3
Gordon Ramsay at Claridge's, W1
Great Eastern Hotel, Aurora, EC2
Greenhouse, W1
Greyhound, SW11
Ledbury, W11
Maze, W1
Mirabelle, W1
Orrery, W1
Oxo Tower, SE1
Pétrus, SW1
Pied-à-Terre, W1
Ransome's Dock, SW11
Roussillon, SW1
RSJ, SE1
Square, W1
Tate Britain Restaurant, SW1
Tom Aikens, SW3
La Trompette, W4
Zaika, W8

Rest of England

Barwick, Little Barwick House
Birmingham, Hotel du Vin & Bistro
Bolton Abbey, Devonshire Arms, Burlington Restaurant
Bristol, Hotel du Vin & Bistro
Brockenhurst, Le Poussin at Whitley Ridge
Chagford, Gidleigh Park
Chinnor, Sir Charles Napier
Corse Lawn, Corse Lawn House
East Grinstead, Gravetye Manor
Faversham, Read's
Grasmere, White Moss House
Great Milton, Le Manoir aux Quat' Saisons
Harrogate, Hotel du Vin & Bistro
Huntingdon, Old Bridge Hotel
Kew, Glasshouse
Leeds, Fourth Floor Café and Bar
Leeds, Sous le Nez en Ville
Lewdown, Lewtrenchard Manor
Manchester, Second Floor
Newton Longville, Crooked Billet
Petersfield, JSW
Ridgeway, Old Vicarage
Southwold, Crown Hotel
Stockcross, Vineyard at Stockcross
Tunbridge Wells, Hotel du Vin & Bistro
Ullswater, Sharrow Bay
Winchester, Hotel du Vin & Bistro

Scotland

Achiltibuie, Summer Isles Hotel
Edinburgh, Forth Floor
Edinburgh, Valvona & Crolla Caffè Bar
Edinburgh, Witchery by the Castle
Glasgow, Ubiquitous Chip
Gullane, Greywalls Hotel
Linlithgow, Champany Inn
Peat Inn, Peat Inn

Wales

Aberdovey, Penhelig Arms Hotel
Llandrillo, Tyddyn Llan
Llandudno, St Tudno Hotel, Terrace
Pwllheli, Plas Bodegroes
Reynoldston, Fairyhill
Skenfrith, Bell at Skenfrith

London restaurants by cuisine

Boundaries between national cuisines can be blurred, so the restaurants listed below are classified by the predominant influence, although there may be some crossover. The headings are in many cases more generalised than the brief cuisine descriptions given at the tops of the entries themselves, and restaurants without a single overriding influence are not included on the list at all.

British

Franklins, SE22
Medcalf, EC1
Rhodes Twenty Four, EC2
Rivington Bar and Grill, EC2
Rules, WC2
St John, EC1
Smiths of Smithfield: Top Floor, EC1
Tate Britain Restaurant, SW1
Wiltons, SW1

Chinese

Chinese Experience, W1
ECapital, W1
Four Seasons, W2
Fung Shing, WC2
Golden Dragon, W1
Hakkasan, W1
Hunan, SW1
Mandarin Kitchen, W2
Mr Kong, WC2
New World, W1
Nyonya, W11
Phoenix Palace, NW1
Royal China, E14, NW8, W1, W2
Yauatcha, W1

Danish

Lundum's, SW7

East European/Eurasian

Baltic, SE1
Gay Hussar, W1
Potemkin, EC1

French

Admiralty, WC2
Almeida, N1
L'Auberge, SW15
Aubergine, SW10
Bellamy's, W1
Berkeley Square Café, W1
Bistro Aix, N8
Bleeding Heart, EC1
Bonds, EC2
Brasserie St Quentin, SW3
The Capital, SW3
Le Cercle, SW1
Le Chardon, SE22
Chez Kristof, W6
Club Gascon, EC1
Le Colombier, SW3
Le Coq d'Argent, EC2
Crowthers, SW14
Drones, SW1
L'Escargot, Ground Floor, W1
L'Escargot, Picasso Room, W1
L'Estaminet, WC2
L'Etranger, SW7
Food Room, SW8
La Galette, W1
Le Gavroche, W1
Gordon Ramsay, SW3
Gordon Ramsay at Claridge's, W1
Incognico, WC2
Maze, W1
Mirabelle, W1
Mon Plaisir, WC2
Morgan M, N7
Orrery, W1
Patterson's, W1
Pearl, WC1
Le Petit Max, SW11
Pétrus, SW1
Pied-à-Terre, W1
Plateau, E14
La Poule au Pot, SW1
Racine, SW3
Roussillon, SW1
RSJ, SE1
Savoy Grill, WC2
Sketch, Gallery, W1
Sketch, Lecture Room and Library, W1
South, EC2
Square, W1
Swissôtel The Howard, Jaan, WC2
Tom Aikens, SW3
Les Trois Garçons, E1
La Trompette, W4
La Trouvaille, W1
Le Vacherin, W4
Wells, NW3

Fusion/pan-Asian

e&o, W11
Eight Over Eight, SW3
Great Eastern Dining Room, EC2
Pengelley's, SW1
Providores, W1

Greek

Lemonia, NW1
Real Greek, N1
Real Greek Souvlaki and Bar, EC1

Indian/Pakistani/Bangladeshi

Amaya, SW1
Babur Brasserie, SE23
Benares, W1
Café Spice Namaste, E1
Calcutta Notebook, SW18
Chor Bizarre, W1
Chowki, W1
Chutney Mary, SW10
Cinnamon Club, SW1
Deya, W1
Ginger, W2
Great Nepalese, NW1
Haandi, SW3
Kasturi, EC3
Lahore Kebab House, E1
Masala Zone, W1
Mehek, EC2
Mela, WC2
Mint Leaf, SW1
Mirch Masala, SW16
Old Delhi, W2
Painted Heron, SW10
Parsee, N19

Portes des Indes, W1
Radha Krishna Bhavan, SW17
Rasa Samudra, W1
Rasa Travancore, N16
Rasa W1, W1
Rasoi Vineet Bhatia, SW3
Red Fort, W1
Salloos, SW1
Sarkhel's, SW18
Tamarind, W1
Tandoor, NW9
Vama, SW1
Veeraswamy, W1
Yatra, W1
Zaika, SW7

Indian vegetarian

Diwana Bhel Poori, NW1
Kastoori, SW17
Rani, N3
Rasa, N16
Sabras, NW10

Indonesian/Straits/Malaysian

Champor-Champor, SE1
Singapore Garden, NW6

Italian

Al Duca, SW1
Alloro, W1
Al San Vincenzo, W2
Arancia, SE16
Ark, W8
Assaggi, W2
Bertorelli's, WC2
Camerino, W1
Carluccio's Caffe, W1
Cecconi's, W1
Cipriani, W1
Il Convivio, SW1
Eddalino, W1
Enoteca Turi, SW15
Giardinetto, W1
Green Olive, W9
Locanda Locatelli, W1
Metrogusto, N1
Neal Street Restaurant, WC2
Olivo, SW1
Passione, W1
Philpott's Mezzaluna, NW2
Phoenix, SW15
Quo Vadis, W1
Refettorio, EC4
River Café, W6
Salusbury, NW6
Sardo, W1
Sardo Canale, NW1
Tentazioni, SE1
Timo, W8
Vasco & Piero's Pavilion, W1
Zafferano, SW1

Japanese

Café Japan, NW11
Chisou, W1
Ikkyu, W1
Itsu, SW3, W1
Kiku, W1
K10, EC2
Kulu Kulu Sushi, W1
Matsuri High Holborn, WC1
Moshi Moshi Sushi, EC2
Miyama, W1
Nobu, W1
Roka, W1
Sumosan, W1
Sushi-Hiro, W5
Sushi-Say, NW2
Tokyo Diner, WC2
Tsunami, SW4
Ubon by Nobu, E14
Umu, W1
Yoshino, W1
Zuma, SW7

North African/Middle Eastern

Adams Café, W12
Al Hamra, W1
Momo, W1
Noura Brasserie, SW1
Numidie, SE19

Seafood

Back to Basics, W1
Brady's, SW18
Chez Liline, N4
Deep, SW6
fish!, SE1
Fish Hoek, W4
Fish Shop, EC1
FishWorks, W1, W4
J. Sheekey, WC2
Lobster Pot, SE11
Lou Pescadou, SW5
Manzi's, WC2
One-O-One, SW1
Two Brothers, N3

South American

Armadillo, E8
Cantaloupe, EC2
Fina Estampa, SE1

Spanish

Cambio de Tercio, SW5
Cigala, WC1
Fino, W1
Moro, EC1
Olé, SW6
Rebato's, SW8

Swedish

Glas, SE1

Thai

Blue Elephant, SW6
Mango Tree, SW1
Nahm, SW1
Patara, W1
Thai Bistro, W4
Thai Garden, E2

Turkish

Efes, W1
Istanbul Iskembecisi, N16
Iznik, N5
Sofra, WC2
Tas, SE1

Vegetarian

Gate, W6
Manna, SW1

Vietnamese

Huong-Viet, N1

New entries

These restaurants are new main entries in the Guide this year, although some may have appeared in previous years, or in the 'Round-ups' last year.

London

Amaya, SW1
Bellamy's, W1
Bonds, EC2
Chancery, EC4
Chez Kristof, W6
Chinese Experience, W1
Coach and Horses, EC1
Deep, SW6
Deya, W1
Emile's, SW15
Farm, SW6
Food Room, SW8
Greyhound, SW11
The Gun, E14
Hunan, SW1
Ledbury, W11
Maze, W1
Medcalf, EC1
Mint Leaf, SW1
Ottolenghi, N1
Patara, W1
Pengelley's, SW1
Rivington Bar and Grill, EC2
Roka, W1
Rules, WC2
Sardo Canale, NW1
Sketch, Gallery, W1
Umu, W1
Le Vacherin, W4

Rest of England

Ambleside, Drunken Duck Inn
Arundel, Arundel House
Awre, Red Hart Inn
Aylesford, Hengist
Barnsley, Barnsley House
Bath, King William
Birchover, Druid Inn
Birmingham, Simpsons
Bray, Hinds Head
Brighton, Gingerman at Drakes
Bruton, Bruton House
Buckminster, Tollemache Arms
Corbridge, Angel of Corbridge
Cranbrook, Apicius
Crockerton, Bath Arms
East Coker, Helyar Arms
East Lavant, Royal Oak
Farnham Royal, King of Prussia
Fowey, Old Quay House
Haddenham, Green Dragon
Henley-on-Thames, Hotel du Vin
Highclere, Marco Pierre White's Yew Tree
Huddersfield, Vanilla
Hull, Boars Nest
Hunsdon, Fox & Hounds
Ilfracombe, The Quay Restaurant
Ilkley, Box Tree
Knightwick, The Talbot
Ledbury, Malthouse
Lower Oddington, Fox Inn
Leicester, Entropy
Ludlow, Overton Grange
Marlow, Hand & Flowers
Marton, MacCallums Restaurant, Lowfield Inn
Marton, Sun Inn
Mawgan, New Yard
Mistley, Mistley Thorn
Mitton, Three Fishes
Munslow, Crown
Newton Poppleford, Moores'
Norwich, Mad Moose Arms, One Up Restaurant
Nottingham, Geisha
Oaksey, Wheatsheaf
Oxford, Liaison
Penzance, Bay Restaurant
Pershore, Belle House
Richmond, Restaurant at the Petersham
Rye, Fish Café
St Ervan, St Ervan Manor
Shinfield, L'Ortolan
Snainton, Coachman Inn
Southall, Three Tuns Hotel, Mehfil
Southampton, White Star Tavern
Southrop, Swan at Southrop
Stanton Fitzwarren, Stanton House Hotel, Rosemary
Stoke-sub-Hamdon, Priory House Restaurant
Stow-on-the-Wold, Unicorn Hotel
Tetbury, Calcot Manor
Torquay, Elephant
Warwick, Rose and Crown
Wells, Goodfellows
Whitley, Pear Tree Inn
Whitstable, JoJo's
Wickham, Old House
Wrightington, Simply Heathcotes

Scotland

Ballater, Green Inn
Edinburgh, Rhubarb at Prestonfield
Glasgow, No. Sixteen
Glasgow, Rococo
Inverness, Glenmoriston Town House

Wales

Beaumaris, Café Neptune
Capel Dewi, Y Polyn
Cardiff, Brazz
Cardiff, Gilby's
Conwy, Castle Hotel, Shakespeare's Restaurant
Llanarmon Dyffryn Ceiriog, West Arms
Solva, Old Pharmacy

Northern Ireland

Belfast, James Street South
Belfast, Roscoff Brasserie
Kircubbin, Paul Arthurs

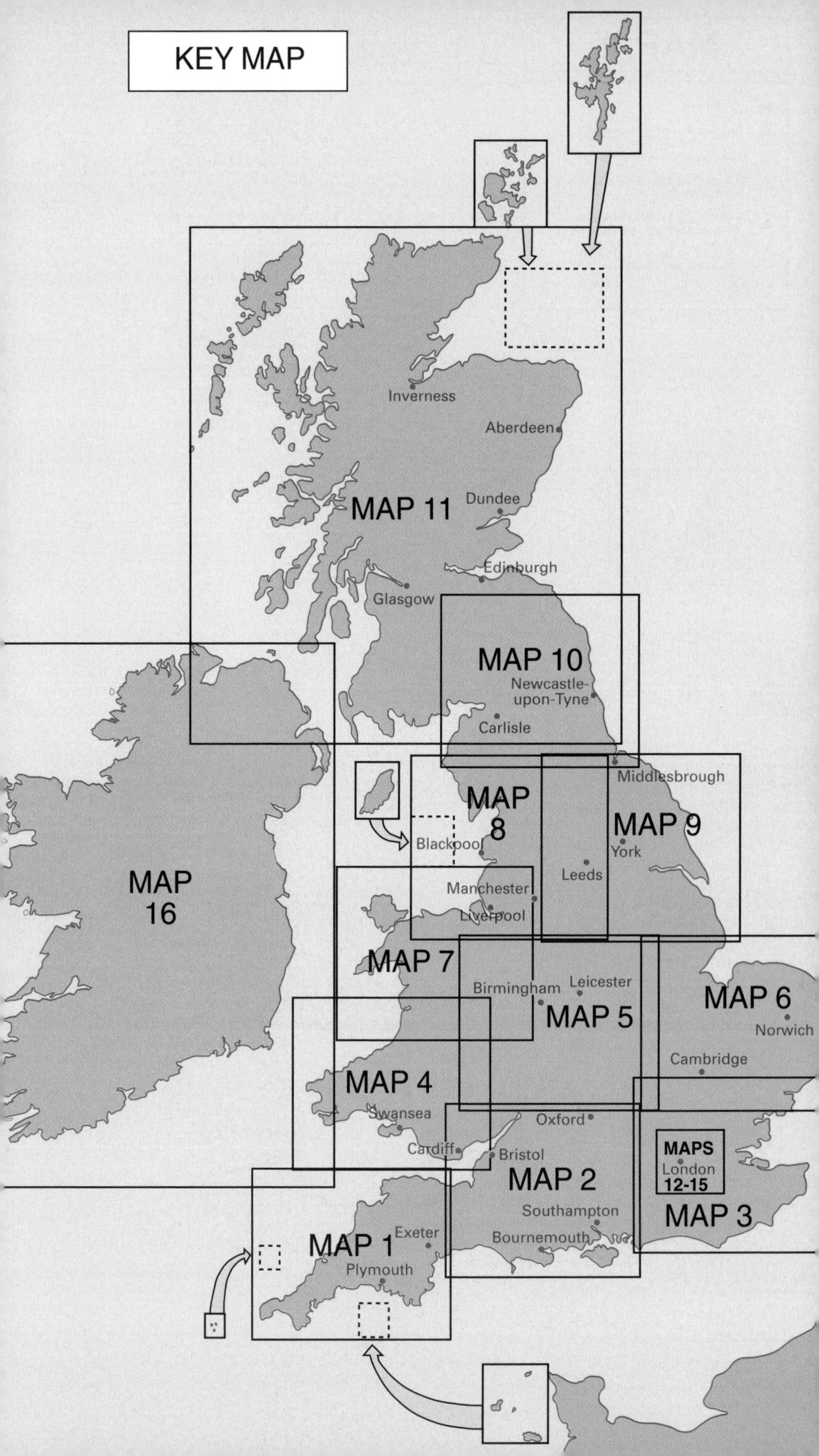
KEY MAP
MAP 11
Inverness
Aberdeen
Dundee
Edinburgh
Glasgow
MAP 10
Newcastle-upon-Tyne
Carlisle
MAP 16
MAP 8
Blackpool
MAP 9
Middlesbrough
York
Leeds
Manchester
Liverpool
MAP 7
Birmingham
Leicester
MAP 5
MAP 6
Norwich
Cambridge
MAP 4
Swansea
Cardiff
Oxford
Bristol
MAP 2
MAPS
London
12-15
Southampton
MAP 3
Bournemouth
MAP 1
Exeter
Plymouth

MAP 1

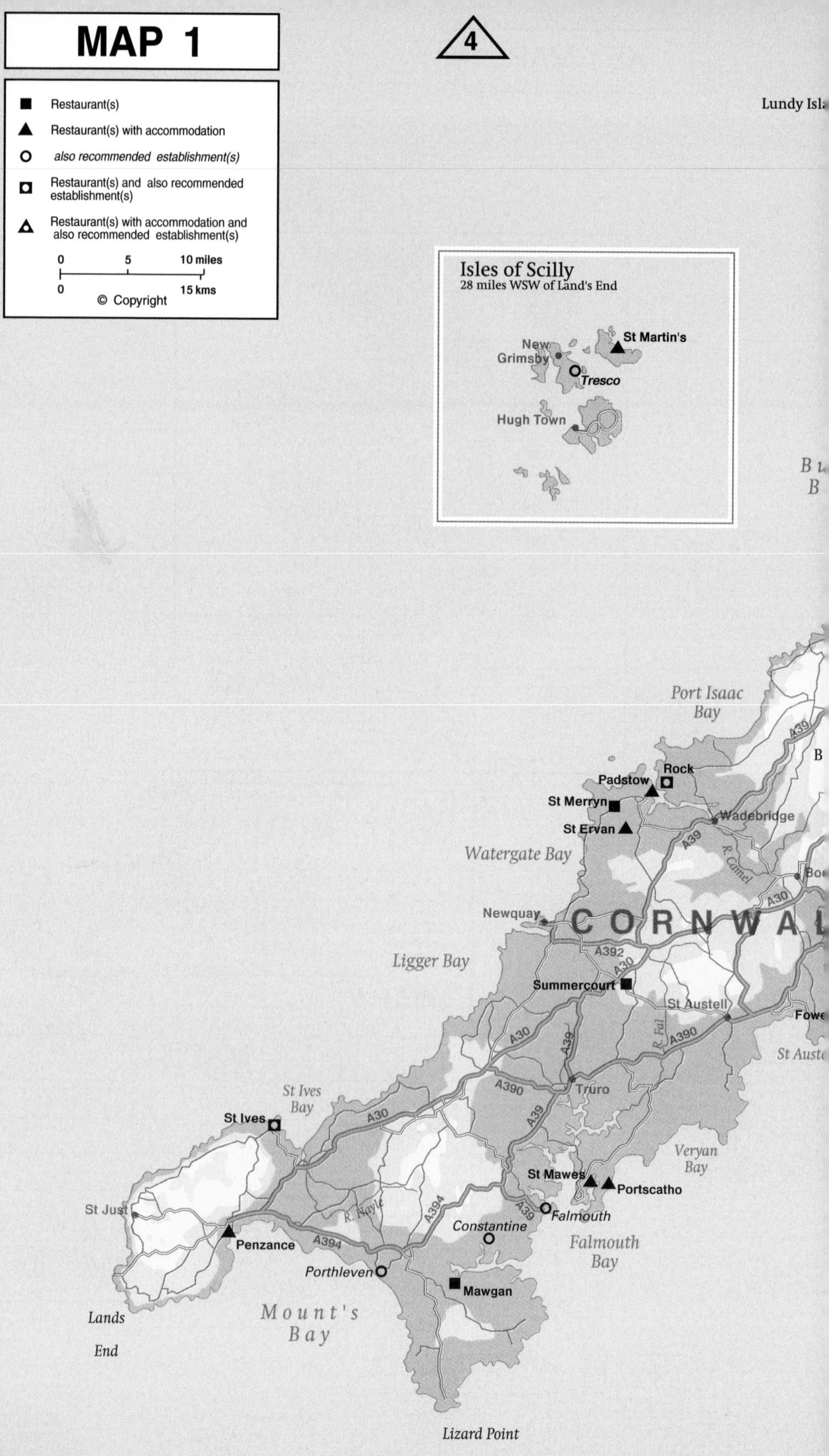

■ Restaurant(s)

▲ Restaurant(s) with accommodation

○ *also recommended establishment(s)*

Restaurant(s) and also recommended establishment(s)

Restaurant(s) with accommodation and also recommended establishment(s)

0 5 10 miles

0 15 kms

Lundy Isl

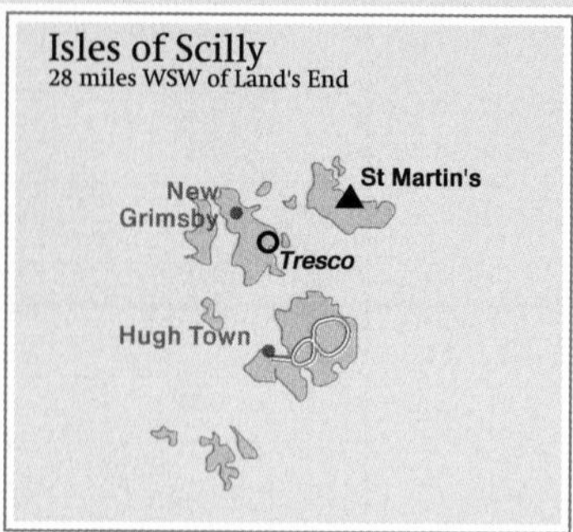

Port Isaac Bay

Rock

Padstow

St Merryn

Wadebridge

St Ervan

Watergate Bay

R. Camel

A39

A30

Newquay

CORNWAL

A392

Ligger Bay

Summercourt

St Austell

Fowe

St Aust

R. Fal

A390

Truro

St Ives Bay

St Ives

Veryan Bay

St Mawes

Portscatho

St Just

R. Hayle

A394

Falmouth

Constantine

Penzance

Falmouth Bay

Porthleven

Mawgan

Mount's Bay

Lands End

Lizard Point

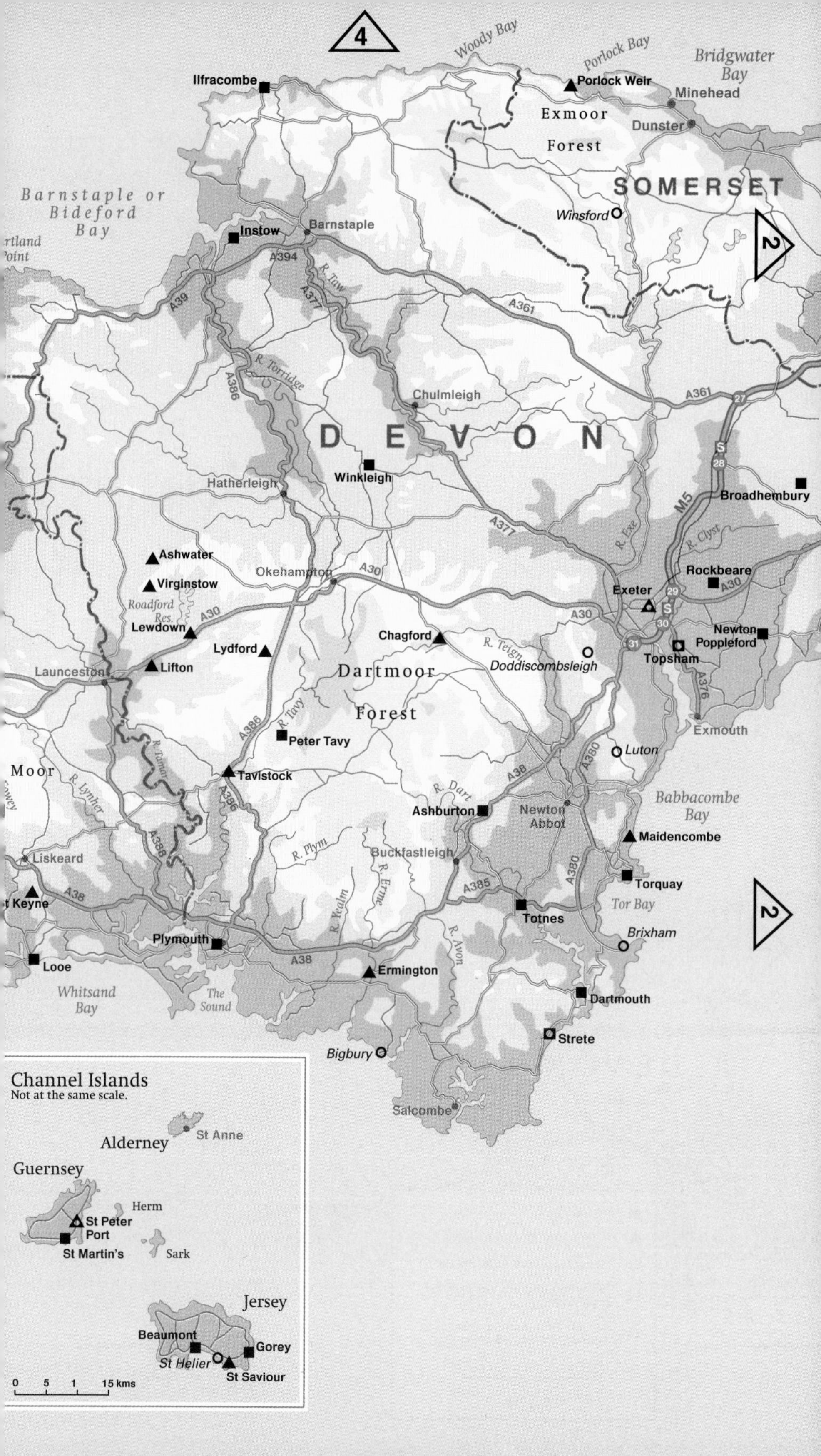
4
Woody Bay
Porlock Bay
Bridgwater Bay
Ilfracombe
Porlock Weir
Minehead
Exmoor Forest
Dunster
SOMERSET
Barnstaple or Bideford Bay
Winsford
Instow
Barnstaple
2
A394
R. Taw
A377
A361
A39
R. Torridge
A386
Chulmleigh
A361
DEVON
Winkleigh
Broadhembury
Hatherleigh
M5
A377
R. Exe
R. Clyst
Ashwater
Okehampton
A30
Rockbeare
Virginstow
Exeter
A30
Roadford Res.
A30
Lewdown
Chagford
Newton Poppleford
Lydford
R. Teign
Topsham
Launceston
Lifton
Doddiscombsleigh
Dartmoor Forest
A376
R. Tavy
A386
Exmouth
Peter Tavy
Luton
R. Tamar
A380
Moor
R. Lynher
Tavistock
A38
R. Dart
Babbacombe Bay
A386
Ashburton
Newton Abbot
Maidencombe
A388
R. Plym
Buckfastleigh
R. Erme
Liskeard
A385
A380
Torquay
St Keyne
A38
R. Yealm
Totnes
Tor Bay
2
R. Avon
Plymouth
Brixham
Looe
A38
Ermington
Whitsand Bay
The Sound
Dartmouth
Strete
Bigbury
Salcombe
Channel Islands
Not at the same scale.
Alderney
St Anne
Guernsey
Herm
St Peter Port
St Martin's
Sark
Jersey
Beaumont
Gorey
St Helier
St Saviour
0 5 1 15 kms

4
5
1
Crickhowell
Llandewi Skirrid
Skenfrith
Rockfield
Monmouth
Gloucester
GLOUCESTERSHIRE
Arlingham
Awre
BLAENAU GWENT
Merthyr Tydfil
TORFAEN
Nantyderry
Clytha
Whitebrook
Pontypool
MONMOUTHSHIRE
Tredunnock
CAERPHILLY
Bassaleg
Newport
NEWPORT
CARDIFF
St Fagans
Cardiff
VALE OF GLAMORGAN
Mouth of the Severn
Portishead
BRISTOL
Bristol
NORTH SOMERSET
SOUTH GLOUCESTERSHIRE
Cotswolds
Colerne
Bath
BATH & N.E. SOMERSET
Weston-Super-Mare
Shipham
Mendip Hills
Burnham-on-Sea
Bridgwater Bay
Dunster
Wells
Shepton Mallet
Upton Scudamore
Glastonbury
Bridgwater
Bruton
SOMERSET
Taunton
South Cadbury
Gillingham
Stoke sub Hamdon
Yeovil
Sherborne
Sturminster Newton
Barwick
East Coker
DEVON
Chard
Broadhembury
Corscombe
N. Dorset Downs
DORSET
Honiton
Gittisham
Maiden Newton
Rockbeare
Bridport
West Bay
Dorchester
Newton Poppleford
Weymouth
Weymouth Bay
Bill of Portland
Restaurant(s)
Restaurant(s) with accommodation
also recommended establishment(s)
Restaurant(s) and also recommended establishment(s)
Restaurant(s) with accommodation and also recommended establishment(s)
0 5 10 miles
0 15 kms
© Copyright

Bourton-on-the-Water
R. Evenlode
5
Aylesbury
BUCKINGHAMSHIRE
Long Crendon
Dinton
Haddenham
Wytham
Oxford
Barnsley
Southrop
Chiltern Hills
3
Cirencester
Tadpole Bridge
Great Milton
Poulton
Fairford
R. Thames
Chinnor
Buckland
Abingdon
Britwell Salome
Dorchester
High Wycombe
Oaksey
Stanton Fitzwarren
OXFORDSHIRE
Didcot
Ardington
Nettlebed
Marlow
Swindon
Stoke Row
Moulsford
M4
Cray's Pond
Henley on Thames
Goring
Maidenhead
Chieveley
Yattendon
Reading
Stockcross
Marsh Benham
Kintbury
Newbury
BERKSHIRE
Rowde
Devizes
Old Burghclere
Highclere
WILTSHIRE
Salisbury Plain
Basingstoke
M3
Aldershot
Odiham
Andover
Whitchurch
Alton
Longstock
HAMPSHIRE
Stockbridge
Teffont Evias
Winchester
Salisbury
R. Test
Petersfield
Romsey
R. Itchen
Farnham
M27
M271
R. Meon
Chilgrove
Stuckton
R. Avon
Southampton
Wickham
A3(M)
Funtington
West Stoke
R. Beaulieu
Emsworth
M275
Chichester
Brockenhurst
Bucklers Hard
Southsea
Portsmouth
New Milton
The Solent
Christchurch
Lymington
Barton on Sea
Seaview
Selsey Bill
Poole
Bournemouth
Yarmouth
Newport
Poole Bay
The Needles
Isle of Wight
Studland
Swanage
Bonchurch
Ventnor
St Catherine's Point
MAP 2

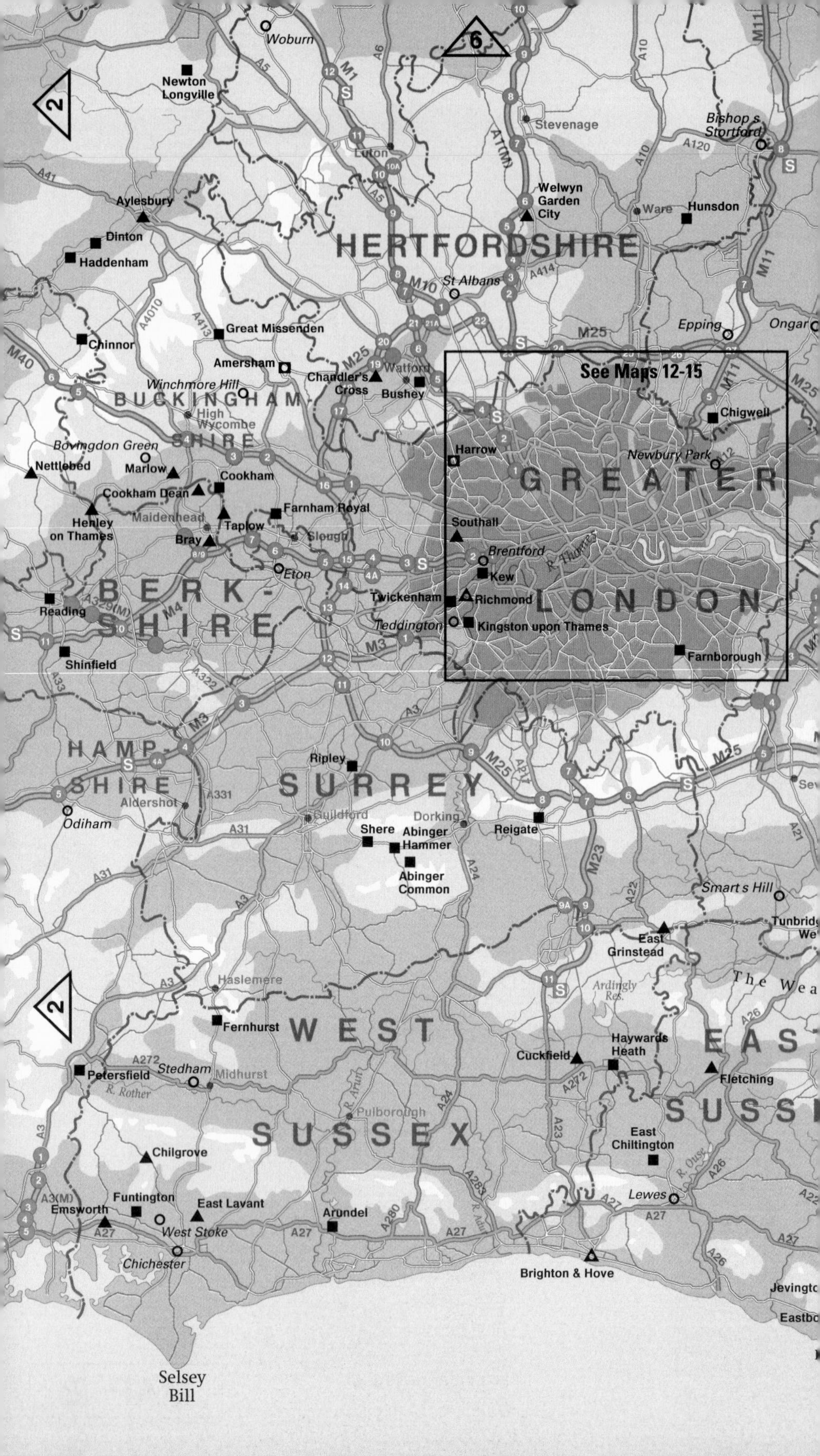

Woburn
6
2
Newton Longville
Stevenage
Bishop s Stortford
Luton
Aylesbury
Welwyn Garden City
Ware
Hunsdon
Dinton
Haddenham
HERTFORDSHIRE
St Albans
Great Missenden
Chinnor
Epping
Ongar
Amersham
Chandler's Cross
Watford
Bushey
See Maps 12-15
Winchmore Hill
BUCKINGHAMSHIRE
High Wycombe
Chigwell
Bovingdon Green
Harrow
Newbury Park
Nettlebed
Marlow
Cookham
GREATER LONDON
Cookham Dean
Henley on Thames
Maidenhead
Farnham Royal
Taplow
Southall
Bray
Slough
Brentford
R. Thames
Eton
Kew
Twickenham
Richmond
Reading
BERKSHIRE
Teddington
Kingston upon Thames
Shinfield
Farnborough
HAMPSHIRE
Ripley
SURREY
Odiham
Aldershot
Guildford
Dorking
Reigate
Shere
Abinger Hammer
Abinger Common
Smart s Hill
Tunbridge Wells
East Grinstead
Haslemere
Ardingly Res.
The Weald
2
Fernhurst
WEST SUSSEX
Cuckfield
Haywards Heath
EAST SUSSEX
Fletching
Petersfield
Stedham
Midhurst
R. Rother
Pulborough
R. Arun
East Chiltington
Chilgrove
R. Ouse
Lewes
Funtington
Emsworth
East Lavant
Arundel
West Stoke
Chichester
Brighton & Hove
Jevington
Eastbourne
Selsey Bill

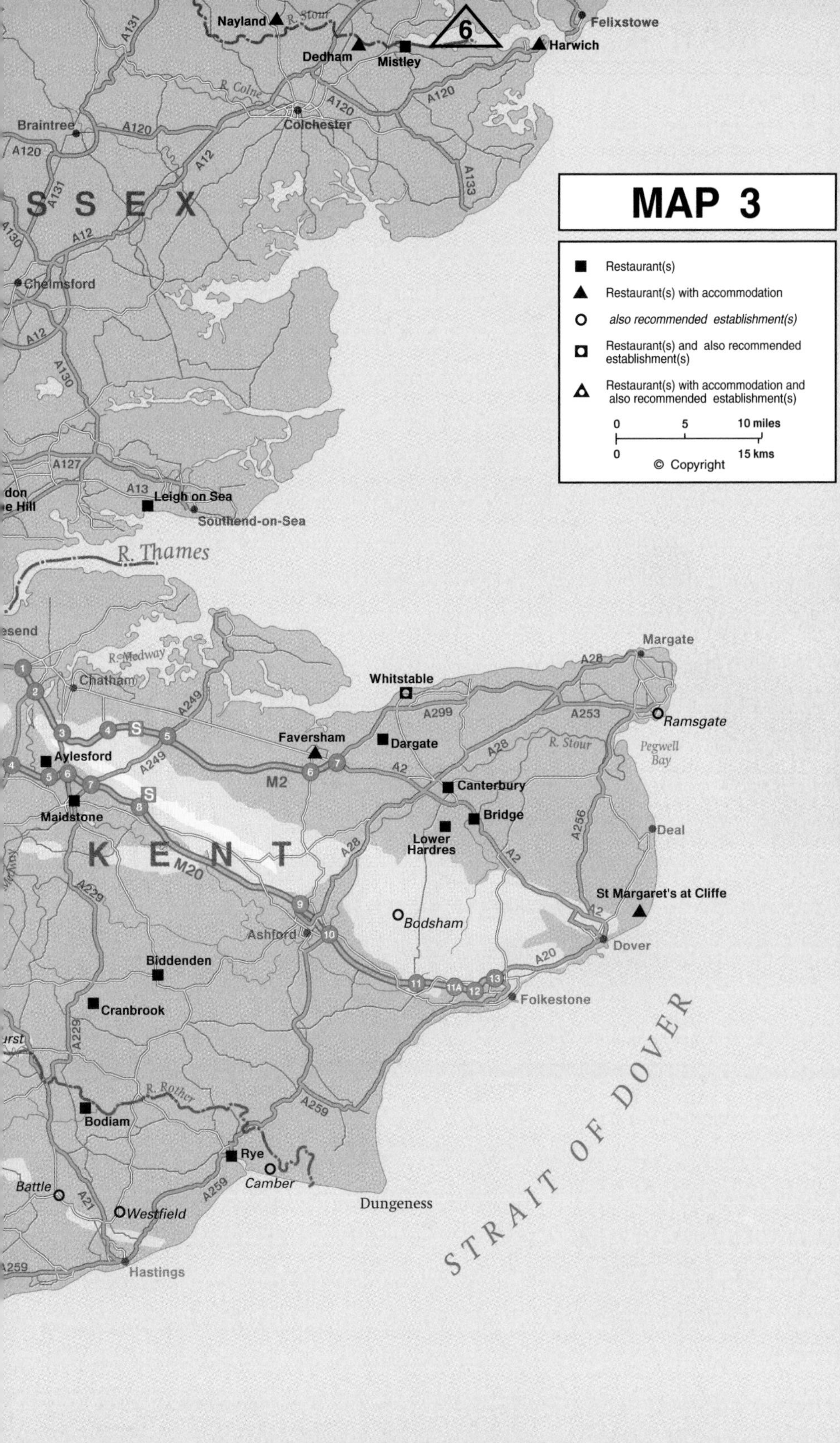
MAP 3
Restaurant(s)
Restaurant(s) with accommodation
also recommended establishment(s)
Restaurant(s) and also recommended establishment(s)
Restaurant(s) with accommodation and also recommended establishment(s)
0
5
10 miles
0
15 kms
© Copyright
Nayland
Dedham
Mistley
Harwich
Felixstowe
Colchester
Braintree
Chelmsford
Leigh on Sea
Southend-on-Sea
R. Thames
Whitstable
Margate
Ramsgate
Pegwell Bay
Chatham
Faversham
Dargate
Aylesford
Maidstone
Canterbury
Bridge
Lower Hardres
Deal
St Margaret's at Cliffe
KENT
Bodsham
Ashford
Dover
Biddenden
Cranbrook
Folkestone
Bodiam
Rye
Camber
Battle
Westfield
Hastings
Dungeness
STRAIT OF DOVER

MAP 4

■ Restaurant(s)
▲ Restaurant(s) with accommodation
○ *also recommended establishment(s)*
◘ Restaurant(s) and also recommended establishment(s)
△ Restaurant(s) with accommodation and also recommended establishment(s)

0 5 10 miles
0 15 kms

CARDIGA
BAY

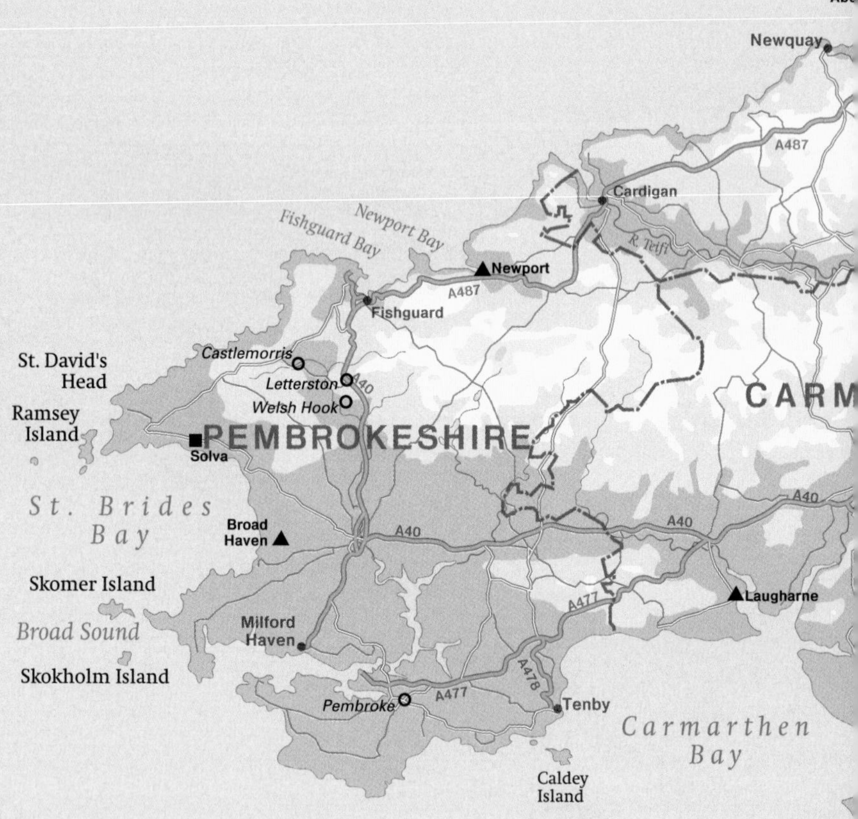

BRISTOL

1

Barmouth
Penmaenpool
Dolgellau
Cader Idris
893
7
Afon Dyfi
Machynlleth
Aberdovey
Eglwysfach
Cambrian Mountains
Newtown
SHROPSHIRE
5
Llangurig
Llanfair Waterdine
POWYS
Presteigne
Titley
Kington
CEREDIGION
Llandrindod Wells
Lampeter
Llanwrtyd Wells
Llangammarch Wells
Builth Wells
Cwmbach
Llandovery
Felinfach
R. Usk
Brecon
R. Monnow
CARMARTHENSHIRE
Salem
R. Tywi
Brecon Beacons
Crickhowell
Llandewi Skirrid
BLAENAU GWENT
Nant-y-derry
Clytha
Merthyr Tydfil
NEATH PORT TALBOT
RHONDDA CYNON TAFF
MERTHYR TYDFIL
CAERPHILLY
TORFAEN
Tredunnock
SWANSEA
Swansea
Port Talbot
Swansea Bay
BRIDGEND
Bassaleg
Newport
NEWPORT
CARDIFF
Cardiff
St Fagans
Southerndown
VALE OF GLAMORGAN
CHANNEL
Mouth of the Severn
2

MAP 5
Restaurant(s)
Restaurant(s) with accommodation
also recommended establishment(s)
Restaurant(s) and also recommended establishment(s)
Restaurant(s) with accommodation and also recommended establishment(s)
0 5 10 miles
0 15 kms
© Copyright
WREXHAM
Wrexham
Worleston
Crewe
Nantwich
Newcastle Under Lyme
Llanarmon Dyffryn Ceiriog
Oswestry
Llanfyllin
STAFFORDSHIRE
Stone
Stafford
Shrewsbury
Telford
Ironbridge
Norton
Marton
SHROPSHIRE
Wolverhampton
Church Stretton
Newtown
Munslow
Llanfair Waterdine
Ludlow
Kidderminster
Chaddesley Corbett
Holy Cross
POWYS
Brimfield
Bromsgrove
Dunhampton
Ombersley
Presteigne
Titley
Leominster
WORCESTERSHIRE
Knightwick
Kington
HEREFORDSHIRE
Worcester
Ullingswick
Pershore
Hay-on-Wye
Colwall Stone
Hereford
Ledbury
Corse Lawn
GLOUCESTERSHIRE
Clifford's Mesne
Crickhowell
Skenfrith
Cheltenham
Llandewi Skirrid
Gloucester
Shurdington
Abergavenny
Rockfield
Monmouth
MONMOUTHSHIRE
Arlingham
Nantyderry
Clytha
Whitebrook
Awre
Painswick

Birchover
9
Caunton
Newark
DERBYSHIRE
NOTTINGHAMSHIRE
Ashbourne
Nottingham
Great Gonerby
Derby
Grantham
Langar
Plumtree
Stathern
Burton on the Wolds
Buckminster
9
Loughborough
Clipsham
LEICESTERSHIRE
Oakham
Knossington
Rutland Water
Hambleton
Lichfield
RUTLAND
Leicester
Medbourne
Kibworth Beauchamp
Nuneaton
Market Harborough
Lowick
Kettering
Coventry
Dorridge
Pitsford Res.
Kenilworth
Wellingborough
Warwick
Bishop's Tachbrook
Daventry
Northampton
Fawsley
WARWICKSHIRE
Stratford-upon-Avon
NORTHAMPTONSHIRE
Roade
Paulerspury
Chipping Campden
Ilmington
Hanwell
Banbury
Paxford
Buckingham
Woburn
Newton Longville
Chipping Norton
Kingham
Lower Oddington
Upper Slaughter
Bicester
BUCKINGHAMSHIRE
3
OXFORDSHIRE
Aylesbury
2
Dinton
Long Crendon
Haddenham
Oxford

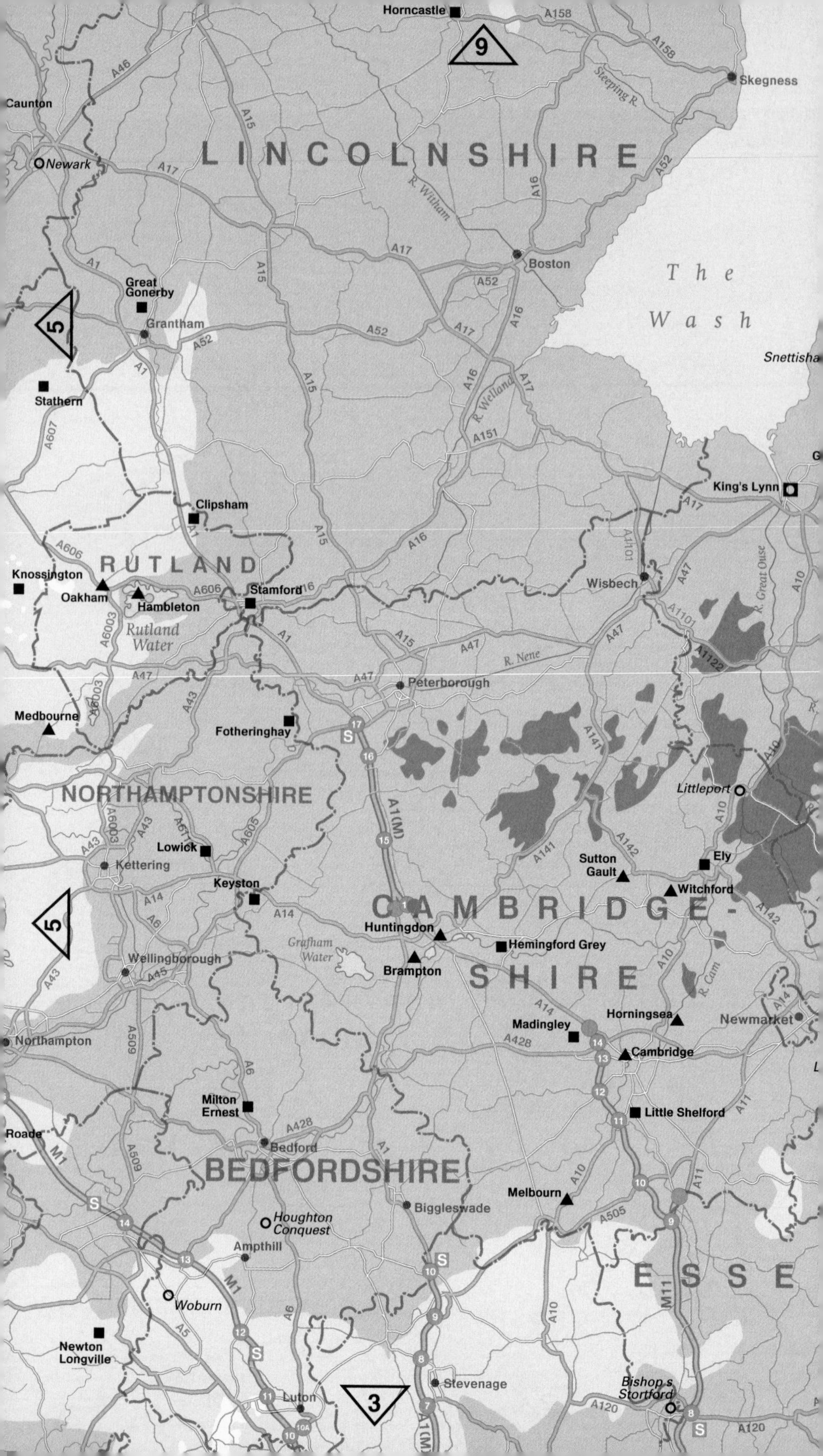

LINCOLNSHIRE
RUTLAND
NORTHAMPTONSHIRE
CAMBRIDGE-SHIRE
BEDFORDSHIRE
ESSE
The Wash
Horncastle
Skegness
Caunton
Newark
Boston
Great Gonerby
Grantham
Stathern
Snettisha
King's Lynn
Clipsham
Knossington
Oakham
Hambleton
Rutland Water
Stamford
Wisbech
Peterborough
Medbourne
Fotheringhay
Littleport
Lowick
Kettering
Keyston
Sutton Gault
Ely
Witchford
Huntingdon
Hemingford Grey
Brampton
Grafham Water
Wellingborough
Horningsea
Newmarket
Madingley
Cambridge
Northampton
Milton Ernest
Little Shelford
Roade
Bedford
Melbourn
Houghton Conquest
Biggleswade
Ampthill
Woburn
Newton Longville
Stevenage
Luton
Bishop's Stortford
R. Witham
R. Welland
R. Nene
R. Great Ouse
R. Cam
Steeping R.
9
5
5
3

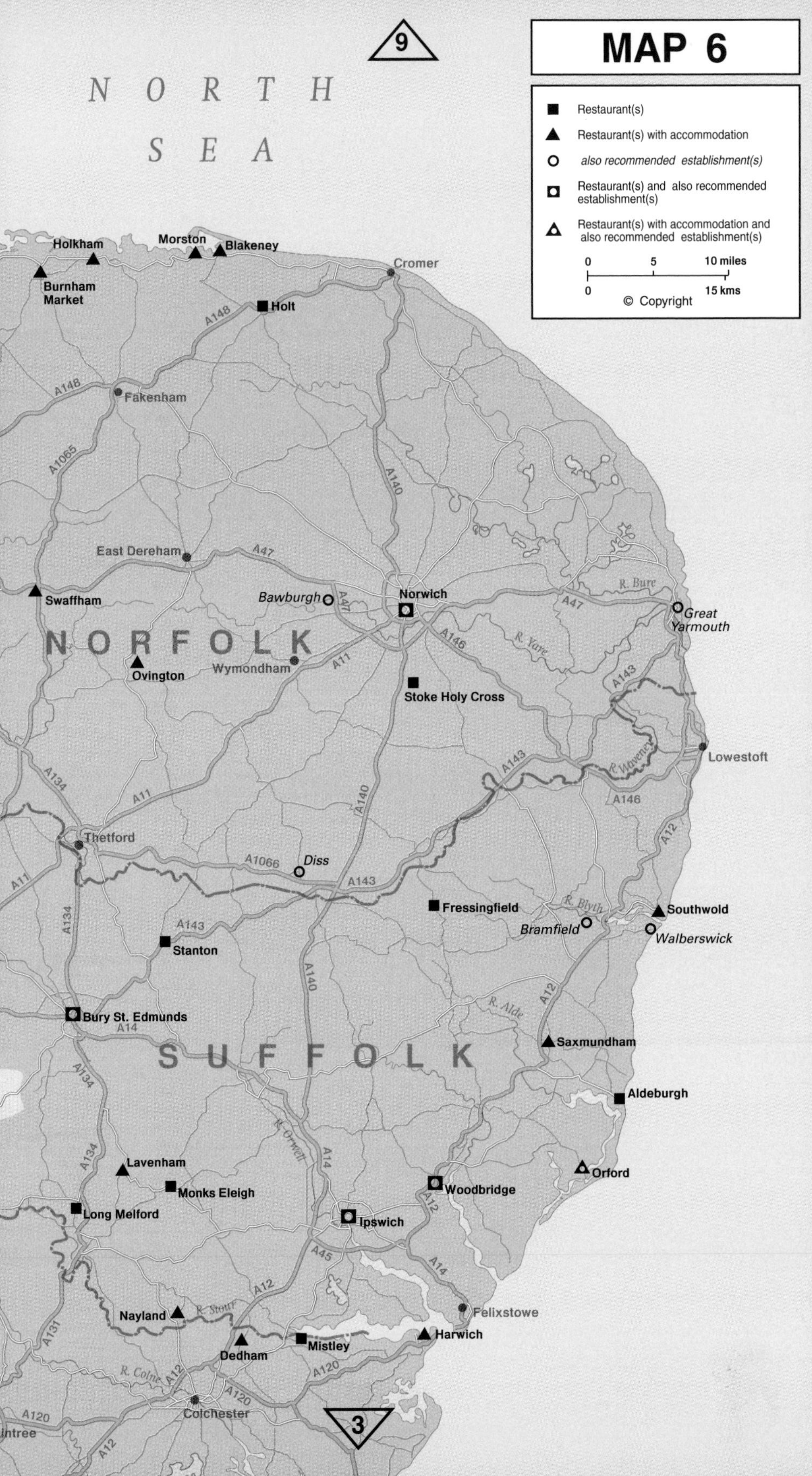

9
MAP 6
Restaurant(s)
Restaurant(s) with accommodation
also recommended establishment(s)
Restaurant(s) and also recommended establishment(s)
Restaurant(s) with accommodation and also recommended establishment(s)
0 5 10 miles
0 15 kms
© Copyright
NORTH SEA
Holkham
Morston
Blakeney
Burnham Market
Cromer
Holt
A148
Fakenham
A1065
A140
East Dereham
A47
Swaffham
Bawburgh
Norwich
R. Bure
Great Yarmouth
NORFOLK
Ovington
Wymondham
A11
A146
R. Yare
Stoke Holy Cross
A143
Lowestoft
R. Waveney
A134
Thetford
A1066
Diss
A12
Fressingfield
R. Blyth
Southwold
Bramfield
Walberswick
Stanton
R. Alde
Bury St. Edmunds
A14
Saxmundham
SUFFOLK
Aldeburgh
R. Orwell
Lavenham
Orford
Monks Eleigh
Woodbridge
Long Melford
Ipswich
A45
Felixstowe
Nayland
R. Stour
Harwich
Dedham
Mistley
A131
R. Colne
A120
Colchester
3
aintree

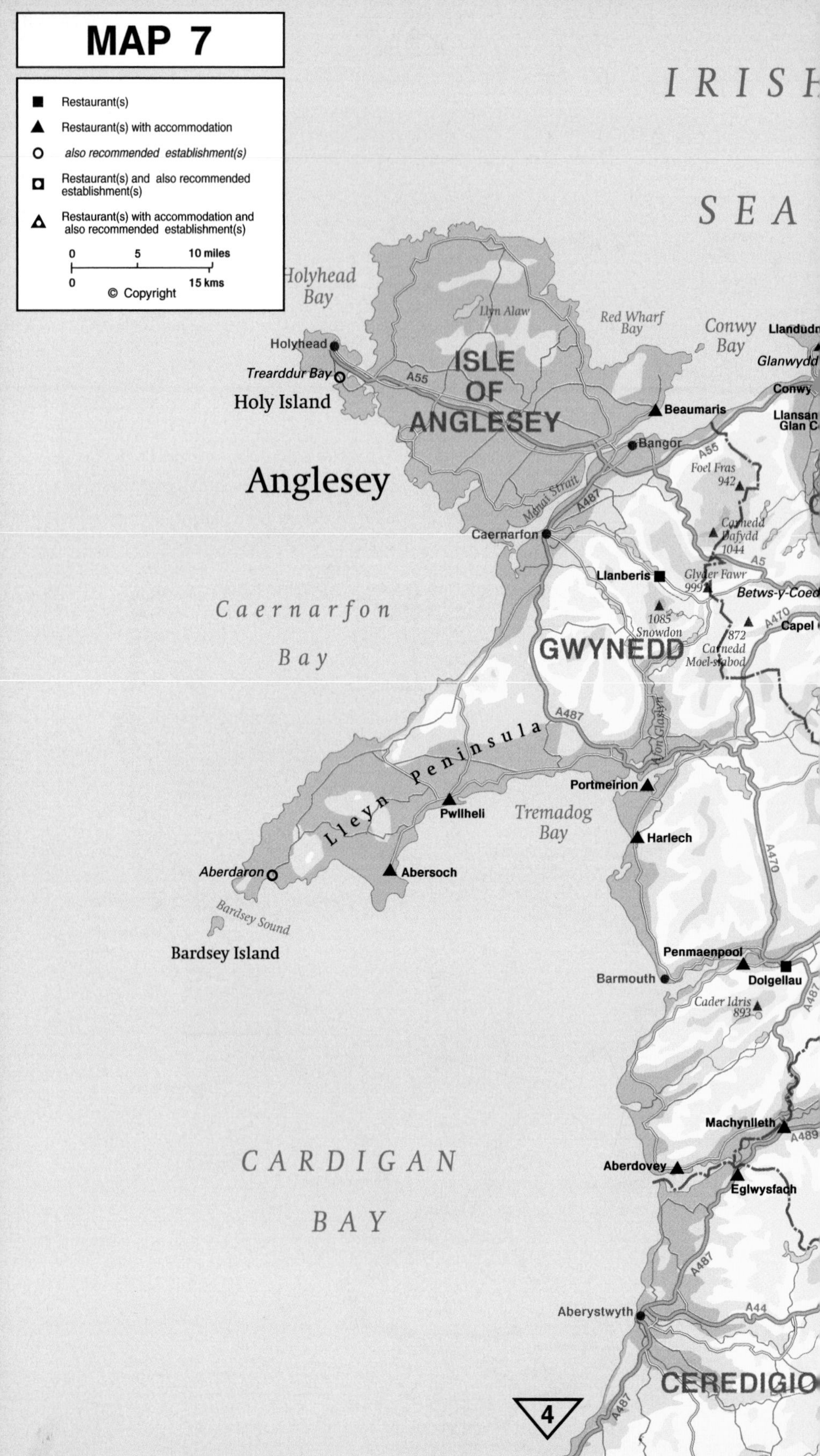

MAP 7
Restaurant(s)
Restaurant(s) with accommodation
also recommended establishment(s)
Restaurant(s) and also recommended establishment(s)
Restaurant(s) with accommodation and also recommended establishment(s)
0
5
10 miles
0
15 kms
© Copyright
IRISH
SEA
Holyhead Bay
Llyn Alaw
Red Wharf Bay
Conwy Bay
Llandudno
Glanwydden
Conwy
Holyhead
Trearddur Bay
Holy Island
ISLE OF ANGLESEY
A55
Beaumaris
Llansanffraid Glan Conwy
Bangor
Anglesey
Menai Strait
A487
A55
Foel Fras 942
Carnedd Dafydd 1044
Caernarfon
A5
Llanberis
Glyder Fawr 999
Betws-y-Coed
1085 Snowdon
872
A470
Capel
Caernarfon Bay
GWYNEDD
Carnedd Moel-siabod
A487
Afon Glaslyn
Lleyn Peninsula
Portmeirion
Pwllheli
Tremadog Bay
Harlech
A470
Aberdaron
Abersoch
Bardsey Sound
Bardsey Island
Penmaenpool
Barmouth
Dolgellau
Cader Idris 893
A487
Machynlleth
A489
CARDIGAN BAY
Aberdovey
Eglwysfach
A487
A44
Aberystwyth
CEREDIGION
A487
4

Southport
8
Wrightington
Bispham Green
Ramsbottom
Bolton
Ormskirk
Skelmersdale
Wigan
GTR
MANCHESTER
MERSEYSIDE
Wallasey
Liverpool
St Helens
Oxton
Sale
Altrincham
Warrington
Widnes
Runcorn
R. Mersey
Colwyn Bay
Prestatyn
Rhyl
R. Weaver
CHESHIRE
Chester
FLINTSHIRE
Hawarden
Denbigh
Hendrerwydd
DENBIGHSHIRE
Alwen
Llyn Brenig
Worleston
Crewe
Nantwich
Wrexham
WREXHAM
R. Dee
Whitchurch
Llandrillo
Llanarmon Dyffryn Ceiriog
Bala Lake
Oswestry
L. Vyrnwy
Llanfyllin
R. Severn
Telford
Ironbridge
Norton
SHROPSHIRE
Church Stretton
Newtown
Munslow
POWYS
Llanfair Waterdine
Ludlow
5
Brimfield

MAP 8
Restaurant(s)
Restaurant(s) with accommodation
also recommended establishment(s)
Restaurant(s) and also recommended establishment(s)
Restaurant(s) with accommodation and also recommended establishment(s)
0 5 10 miles
0 15 kms
© Copyright
10
CUMBRIA
Ennerdale Water
Scafell Pike 977
Wast Water
Grasmere
Ambleside
Troutbeck
Windermere
Hawkshead
Bowness-on-Windermere
Near Sawrey
R. Esk
R. Duddon
A595
A5092
A590
A591
Ulverston
Cartmel
Barrow-in-Furness
Isle of Walney
Morecambe
Heysham
Morecambe Bay
Forton
Fleetwood
R. Wyre
A585
Blackpool
M55
Kirkham
A583
Lytham St Anne's
Point of Ayre
Ramsey Bay
Ramsey
Kirk Michael
Isle of Man
Laxey Bay
Douglas
Glenmaye
Port Erin
Port St Mary
Calf of Man
A59
A565
Southport
A570
Wright
Ormskirk
Skelmersdale
M58
M57
A580
MERSEYSIDE
Wallasey
Liverpool
Oxton
M53
R. Mersey
M56
7
Colwyn Bay
Conwy Bay
Llandudno
Glanwydden
Colwyn Bay
Prestatyn
Rhyl
Conwy
Llansanffraid Glan Conwy
A55
CONWY
A470
Denbigh
7
FLINTSHIRE
Hawarden
Chester

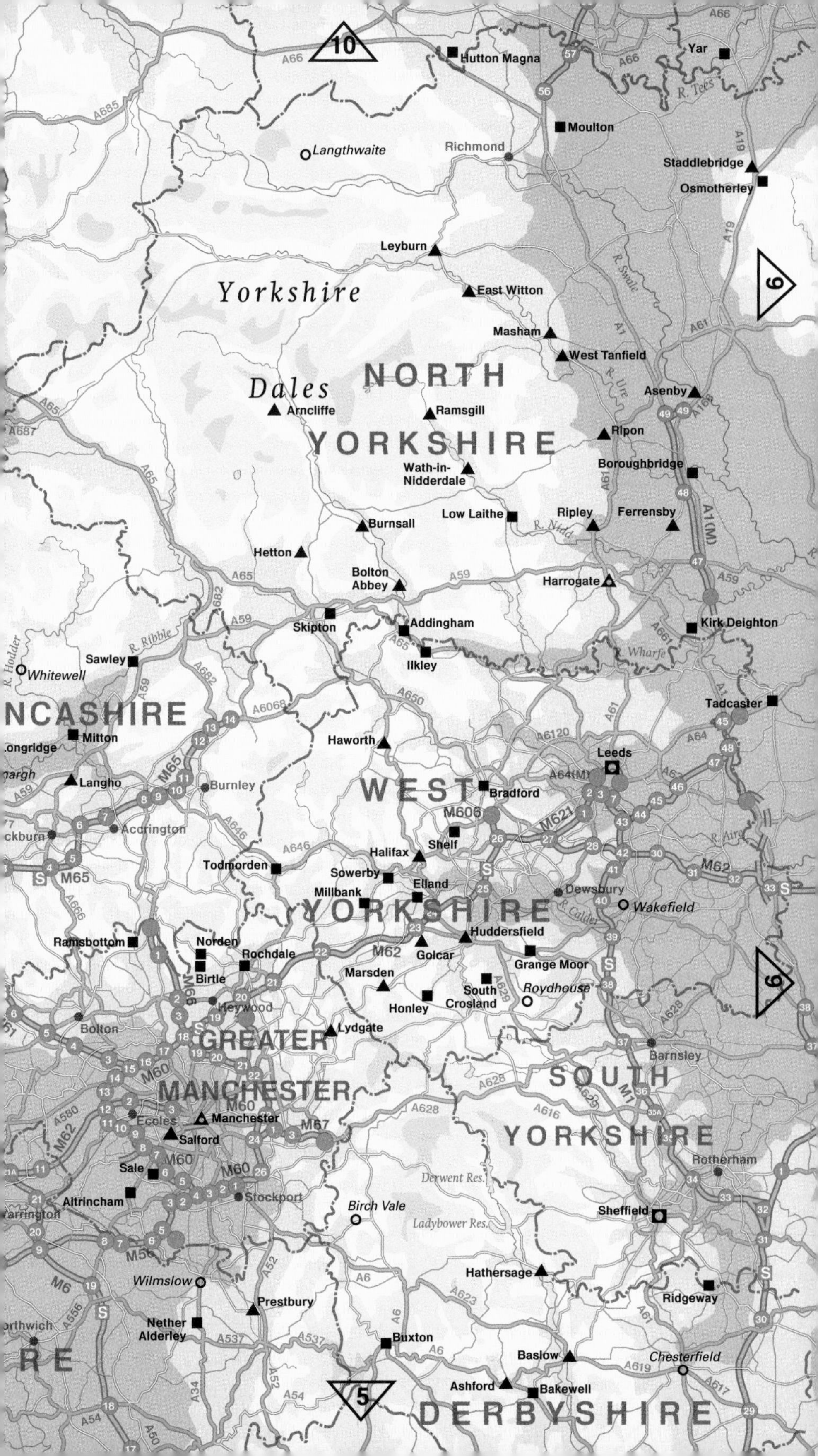

10
Hutton Magna
Yar
R. Tees
Moulton
Langthwaite
Richmond
Staddlebridge
Osmotherley
Leyburn
R. Swale
6
Yorkshire
East Witton
Masham
West Tanfield
NORTH
Dales
R. Ure
Asenby
Arncliffe
Ramsgill
YORKSHIRE
Ripon
Wath-in-Nidderdale
Boroughbridge
Low Laithe
Ripley
Ferrensby
R. Nidd
Burnsall
Hetton
Bolton Abbey
Harrogate
Skipton
Addingham
Kirk Deighton
R. Ribble
R. Hodder
Whitewell
Sawley
Ilkley
R. Wharfe
NCASHIRE
Tadcaster
Mitton
Longridge
Haworth
Leeds
Langho
Burnley
WEST
Bradford
Accrington
Shelf
R. Aire
Halifax
Todmorden
Sowerby
Elland
Dewsbury
Millbank
YORKSHIRE
Wakefield
R. Calder
Huddersfield
Ramsbottom
Norden
Golcar
Grange Moor
Rochdale
Birtle
Marsden
South Crosland
Roydhouse
Honley
6
Heywood
Bolton
Lydgate
GREATER
Barnsley
SOUTH
MANCHESTER
Eccles
Manchester
Salford
YORKSHIRE
Derwent Res.
Rotherham
Sale
Altrincham
Stockport
Birch Vale
Sheffield
Warrington
Ladybower Res.
Hathersage
Wilmslow
Ridgeway
Prestbury
Nether Alderley
Northwich
Buxton
RE
Baslow
Chesterfield
Ashford
Bakewell
5
DERBYSHIRE

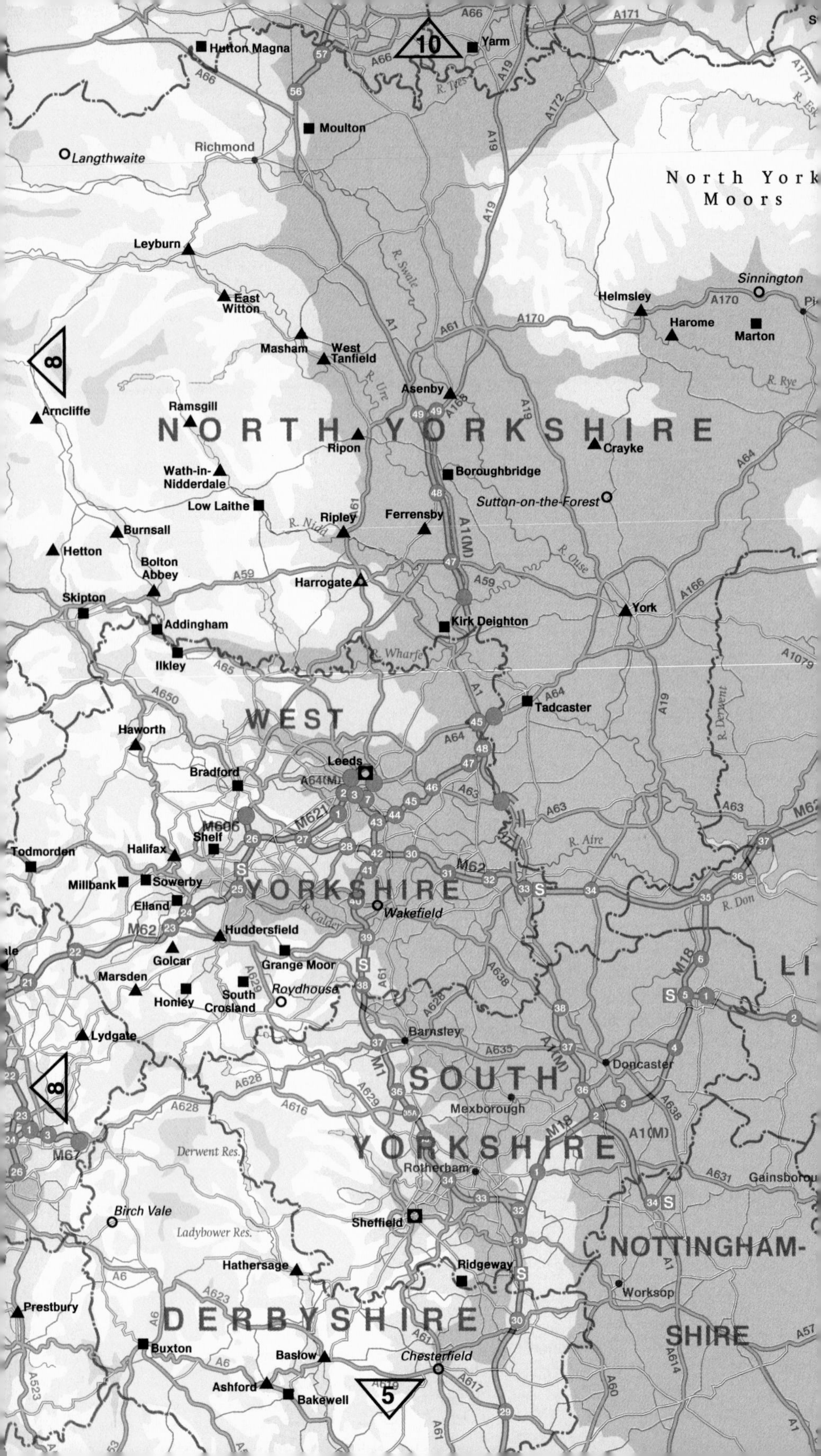

10
Hutton Magna
Yarm
Moulton
Richmond
Langthwaite
North York Moors
Leyburn
East Witton
Masham
West Tanfield
Helmsley
Sinnington
Harome
Marton
8
Arncliffe
Ramsgill
Asenby
NORTH YORKSHIRE
Ripon
Crayke
Wath-in-Nidderdale
Boroughbridge
Sutton-on-the-Forest
Low Laithe
Ripley
Ferrensby
Burnsall
Hetton
Bolton Abbey
Harrogate
Skipton
York
Addingham
Kirk Deighton
Ilkley
Tadcaster
WEST
Haworth
Leeds
Bradford
Shelf
Halifax
Todmorden
Millbank
Sowerby
YORKSHIRE
Wakefield
Elland
Huddersfield
Golcar
Grange Moor
Marsden
Honley
South Crosland
Roydhouse
Lydgate
Barnsley
Doncaster
SOUTH
8
Mexborough
YORKSHIRE
Derwent Res.
Rotherham
Gainsborough
Birch Vale
Sheffield
Ladybower Res.
NOTTINGHAM-
Hathersage
Ridgeway
Worksop
Prestbury
DERBYSHIRE
SHIRE
Buxton
Baslow
Chesterfield
Ashford
Bakewell
5
R. Tees
R. Swale
R. Ure
R. Nidd
R. Ouse
R. Wharfe
R. Rye
R. Esk
R. Derwent
R. Aire
R. Calder
R. Don
A66
A171
A19
A172
A1
A61
A170
A168
A64
A59
A166
A1079
A65
A650
A63
M62
M621
M606
A64(M)
A1(M)
M18
M1
A629
A628
A616
A635
A638
A631
A6
A623
A523
A614
A60
A617
A619
A57
M67

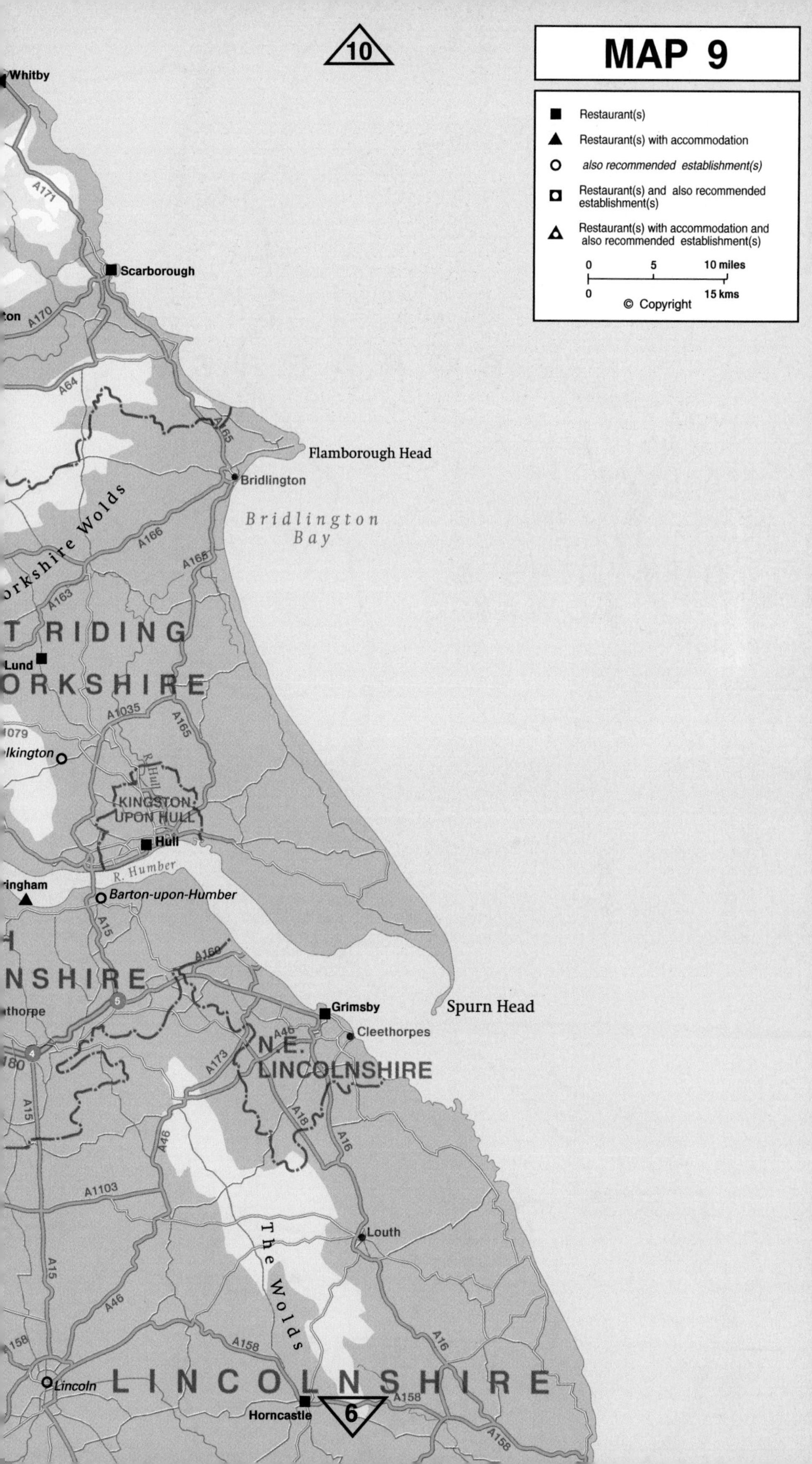

MAP 9
10
Restaurant(s)
Restaurant(s) with accommodation
also recommended establishment(s)
Restaurant(s) and also recommended establishment(s)
Restaurant(s) with accommodation and also recommended establishment(s)
0 5 10 miles
0 15 kms
© Copyright
Whitby
Scarborough
Flamborough Head
Bridlington
Bridlington Bay
Lund
KINGSTON UPON HULL
Hull
R. Humber
Barton-upon-Humber
Spurn Head
Grimsby
Cleethorpes
N.E. LINCOLNSHIRE
Louth
The Wolds
Lincoln
LINCOLNSHIRE
Horncastle
6
A171
A170
A64
A165
A166
A163
A1035
A160
A15
A46
A173
A18
A16
A1103
A158

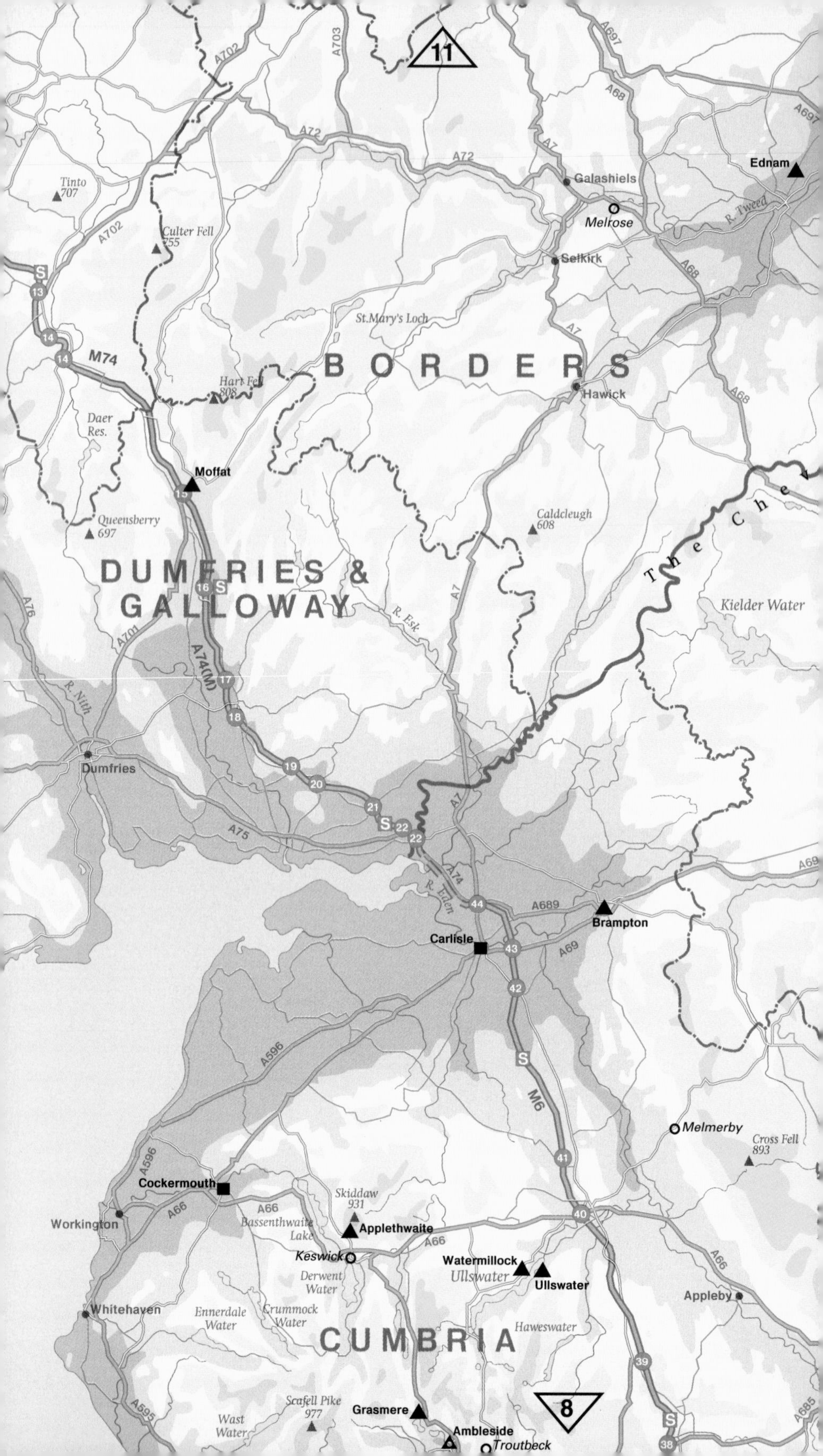

11
A703
A702
A697
A68
A72
A7
Galashiels
Melrose
Ednam
R. Tweed
Tinto 707
Culter Fell 755
Selkirk
M74
St.Mary's Loch
BORDERS
Hart Fell 808
Hawick
Daer Res.
Moffat
Queensberry 697
Caldcleugh 608
The Chev
DUMFRIES & GALLOWAY
A76
A701
R. Esk
Kielder Water
A74(M)
R. Nith
Dumfries
A75
A74
R. Eden
A689
Brampton
Carlisle
A69
A596
M6
Melmerby
Cross Fell 893
Cockermouth
Workington
A66
Skiddaw 931
Bassenthwaite Lake
Applethwaite
Keswick
Watermillock
Ullswater
Derwent Water
Appleby
Whitehaven
Ennerdale Water
Crummock Water
Haweswater
CUMBRIA
Scafell Pike 977
Grasmere
8
Wast Water
A595
Ambleside
Troutbeck
A685

MAP 10
Restaurant(s)
Restaurant(s) with accommodation
also recommended establishment(s)
Restaurant(s) and also recommended establishment(s)
Restaurant(s) with accommodation and also recommended establishment(s)
0 5 10 miles
0 15 kms
© Copyright
Berwick-upon-Tweed
Holy Island
Farne Is.
The Cheviot 815
Alnwick
Alnmouth
R. Aln
R. Coquet
NORTHUMBERLAND
R. Blyth
Ponteland
R. Pont
Tynemouth
Newcastle upon Tyne
Corbridge
R. Tyne
Gateshead
TYNE & WEAR
Stanley
Derwent Res.
Consett
Chester-le-Street
Seaham
Durham
DURHAM
Hartlepool
HARTLEPOOL
Tees Bay
Redcar
Aycliffe
STOCKTON-ON-TEES
Romaldkirk
Middlesbrough
MIDDLESBROUGH
REDCAR
Hutton Magna
Yar
Pinchinthorpe
R. Tees
Moulton
A1
A697
A1068
A189
A696
A68
A19
A69
A194(M)
A692
A690
A167
A688
A1(M)
A179
A689
A66
A171
A172
11
9

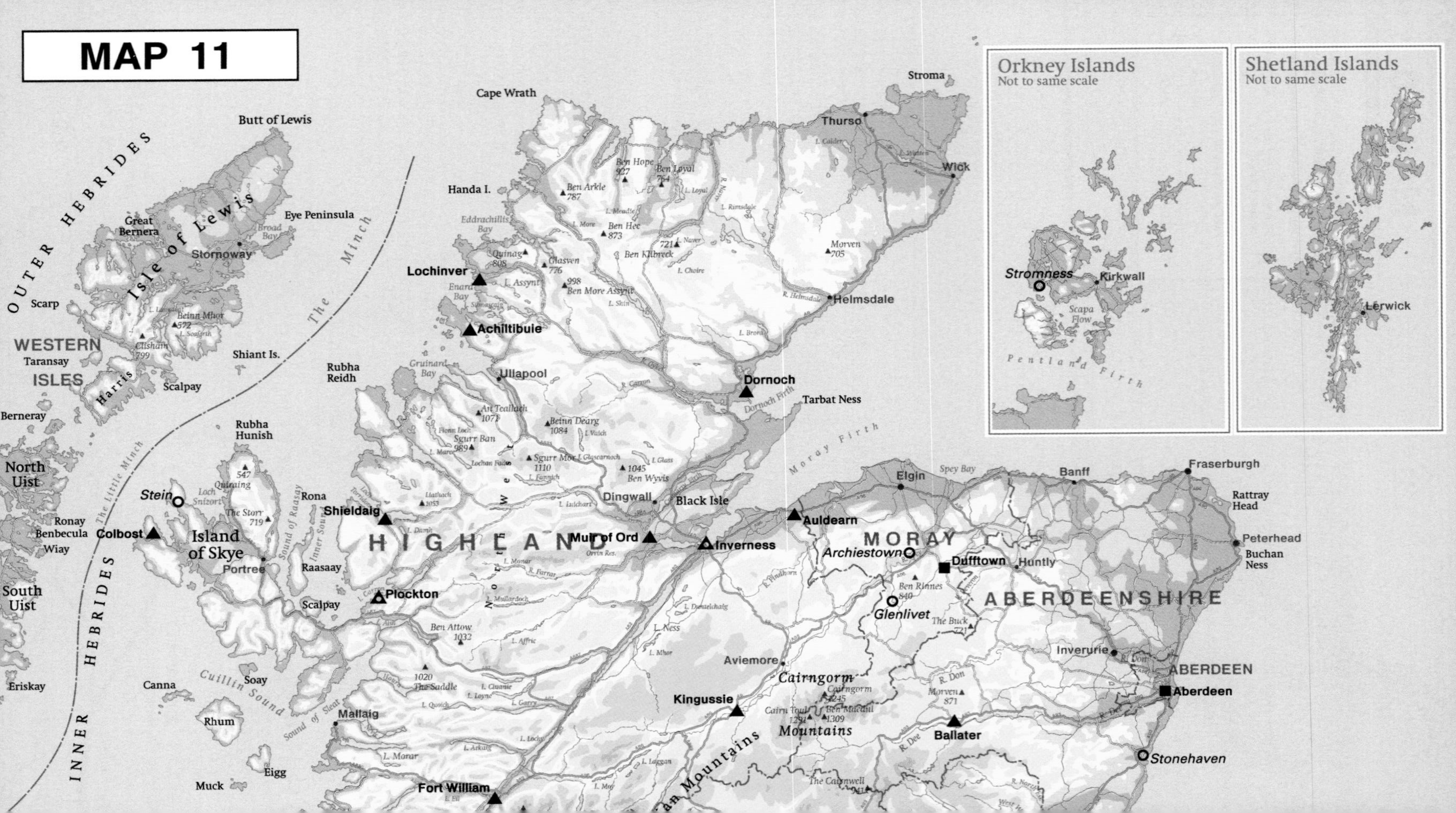
MAP 11
Orkney Islands
Not to same scale
Stromness
Kirkwall
Scapa Flow
Pentland Firth
Shetland Islands
Not to same scale
Lerwick
OUTER HEBRIDES
Butt of Lewis
Isle of Lewis
Great Bernera
Stornoway
Eye Peninsula
Broad Bay
Scarp
Beinn Mhor 572
Clisham 799
WESTERN ISLES
Taransay
Harris
Scalpay
Shiant Is.
The Minch
Berneray
North Uist
Ronay
Benbecula
Wiay
South Uist
Eriskay
The Little Minch
INNER HEBRIDES
Rubha Hunish
Stein
Colbost
Island of Skye
Portree
The Storr 719
Quiraing
Rona
Raasaay
Sound of Raasay
Inner Sound
Scalpay
Soay
Canna
Cuillin Sound
Rhum
Eigg
Muck
Sound of Sleat
Mallaig
Rubha Reidh
Cape Wrath
Handa I.
Eddrachillis Bay
Lochinver
Quinag 808
Glasven 776
998 Ben More Assynt
Achiltibuie
Gruinard Bay
Ullapool
An Teallach 1071
Sgurr Ban 989
Beinn Dearg 1084
Sgurr Mor 1110
1045 Ben Wyvis
Shieldaig
Plockton
HIGHLAND
Ben Attow 1032
1020 The Saddle
L. Morar
Fort William
Ben Arkle 787
Ben Hope 927
Ben Loyal 764
Ben Hee 873
721
Ben Klibreck
Morven 705
Thurso
Stroma
Wick
Helmsdale
Dornoch
Dornoch Firth
Tarbat Ness
Moray Firth
Dingwall
Black Isle
Muir of Ord
Inverness
L. Ness
Auldearn
Aviemore
Kingussie
Cairngorm
Cairngorm 1245
Cairn Toul 1291
Ben Macdui 1309
Mountains
Elgin
Spey Bay
MORAY
Archiestown
Dufftown
Ben Rinnes 840
Glenlivet
The Buck 721
Banff
Huntly
ABERDEENSHIRE
Inverurie
Morven 871
Ballater
R. Dee
Fraserburgh
Rattray Head
Peterhead
Buchan Ness
ABERDEEN
Aberdeen
Stonehaven
The Cairnwell

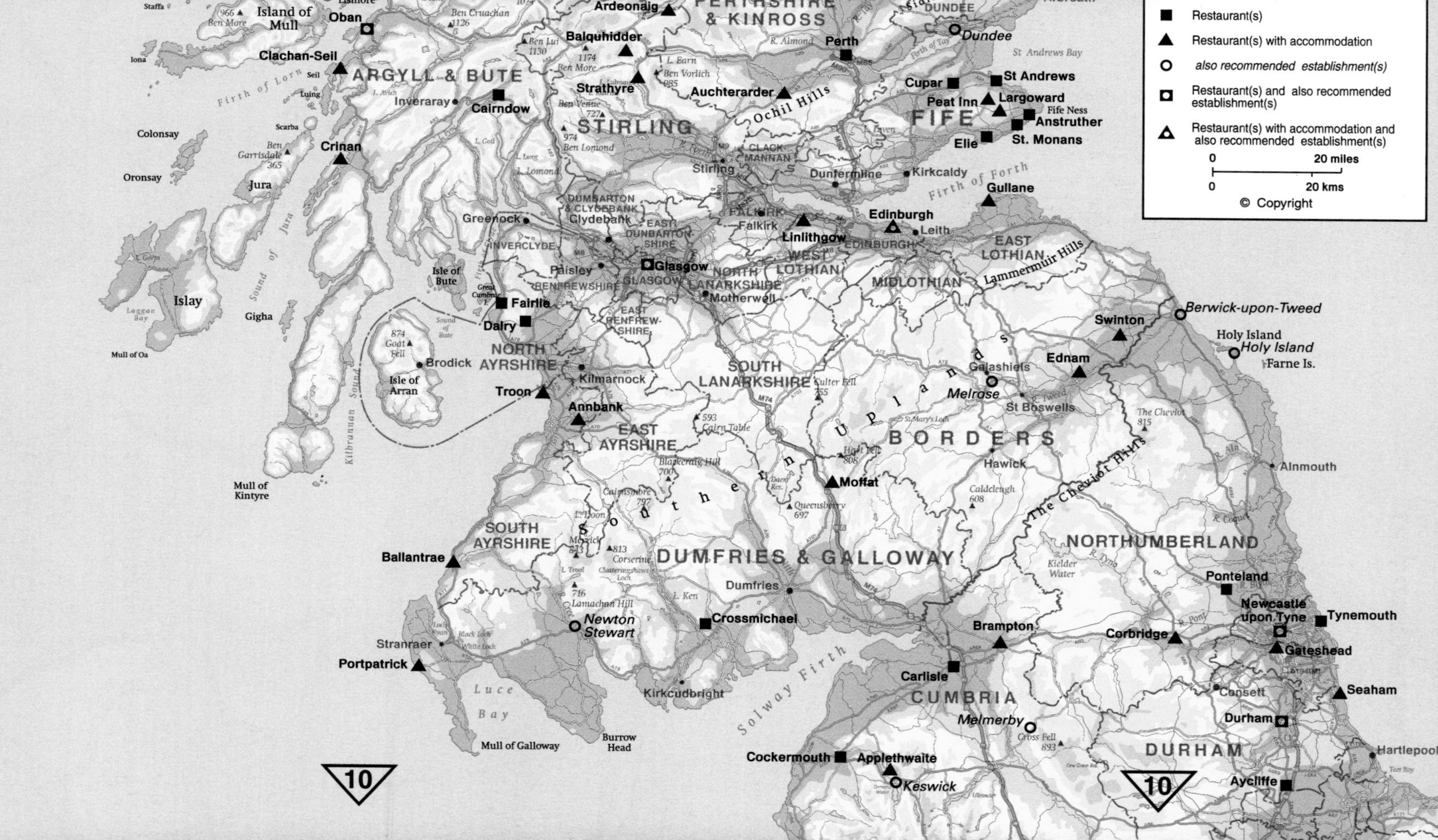Restaurant(s)
Restaurant(s) with accommodation
also recommended establishment(s)
Restaurant(s) and also recommended establishment(s)
Restaurant(s) with accommodation and also recommended establishment(s)
0 20 miles
0 20 kms
© Copyright
Island of Mull
Oban
Clachan-Seil
ARGYLL & BUTE
Inveraray
Cairndow
Crinan
Ardeonaig
Balquhidder
Strathyre
STIRLING
PERTHSHIRE & KINROSS
Perth
Auchterarder
Ochil Hills
Dundee
Cupar
St Andrews
Peat Inn
Largoward
FIFE
Anstruther
Elie
St. Monans
Kirkcaldy
Dunfermline
Stirling
Firth of Forth
Gullane
Edinburgh
Leith
Linlithgow
Falkirk
Greenock
Clydebank
Glasgow
Paisley
Fairlie
Dalry
Isle of Bute
Isle of Arran
Brodick
NORTH AYRSHIRE
Kilmarnock
Troon
Annbank
EAST AYRSHIRE
Motherwell
SOUTH LANARKSHIRE
EAST LOTHIAN
Lammermuir Hills
MIDLOTHIAN
WEST LOTHIAN
Berwick-upon-Tweed
Holy Island
Farne Is.
Swinton
Ednam
Galashiels
Melrose
St Boswells
BORDERS
Southern Uplands
Hawick
Moffat
The Cheviot Hills
Alnmouth
NORTHUMBERLAND
Ponteland
Newcastle upon Tyne
Tynemouth
Gateshead
Corbridge
Brampton
Seaham
Consett
Durham
DURHAM
Hartlepool
Aycliffe
Carlisle
CUMBRIA
Melmerby
Cockermouth
Applethwaite
Keswick
Solway Firth
DUMFRIES & GALLOWAY
Dumfries
Crossmichael
Kirkcudbright
Newton Stewart
SOUTH AYRSHIRE
Ballantrae
Stranraer
Portpatrick
Luce Bay
Mull of Galloway
Burrow Head
Islay
Jura
Colonsay
Oronsay
Gigha
Mull of Kintyre
10
10

Greater London
BARNET
Stanmore
Finchley
Rani
Two Brothers
Tandoor & Great Eastern Bar
Hendon
HARROW
The Wells
Café Japan
Parsee
Mosaica @the Factory
Bistro Aix
Philpott's Mezzaluna
Hampstead
See Map 13
CAMDEN
WEMBLEY
Willesden
Sushi-Say
Sabras
BRENT
William IV
A40(M)
Sushi-Hiro
HAMMERSMITH AND FULHAM
See Map 15
CITY OF WEST-MINSTER
Ealing
Acton
Anglesea Arms
Ealing Park Tavern
FishWorks
Adams Café
Le Vacherin
Fish Hoek
La Trompette
Thai Bistro
Brackenbury
Havelock Tavern
Cotto
Popeseye
Snows on the Green
Chez Kristof
KENSINGTON AND CHELSEA
See Map 14
HAMMERSMITH
Brentford
Burlington
Gate
River Café
Sonny's
MVH
Redmonds
Ole Tapas
Blue Elephant
Ransome's Dock
Salisbury Tavern
Chutney Mary
Greyhound
Deep
Food Room
Le Petit Max
Tsunami
Fulham
Emile's
Phoenix
Enoteca Turi
L'Auberge
Brady's
The Victoria
Crowthers
RICHMOND
Wandsworth
WANDSWORTH
Earl Spencer
Chez Bruce
Balham Bar &
Calcutta Notebook
Sarkhel's
Twickenham
Kastoori
Radha Krishna Bhavan
Light House
Wimbledon
Merton
Kingston upon Thames
Morden
Mitcham
KINGSTON UPON THAMES
Malden
MERTON
M1
A1
A41
A5109
A109
A1000
A410
A406
A504
A5
A4
A4140
A4008
A404
A40
A4020
A315
A307
A306
A205
A3205
A316
A3
A217
A214
A24
A218
A216
A236
A308

MAP 12
Mosaica @ the Lock
Rasa Travancore
Istanbul Iskembecisi
Armadillo
Thai Garden
Wapping Food
Royal China
Plateau
The Gun
Ubon
Inside
Chapter Two
Franklins
The Green
Le Chardon
Babur Brasserie
CHIGWELL
EDMONTON
Woodford
Hainault
REDBRIDGE
Walthamstow
WALTHAM FOREST
ILFORD
HACKNEY
Barking
NEWHAM
BARKING & DAGENHAM
East Ham
TOWER HAMLETS
Poplar
R. Thames
Thamesmead
Woolwich
Greenwich
GREENWICH
Lewisham
Eltham
Dulwich
Catford
LEWISHAM
Sidcup
Crystal Palace
BROMLEY
Beckenham
A102(M)
Restaurant(s)
Restaurant(s) with accommodation
also recommended establishment(s)
0 5km
0 4 miles
© Copyright

Mezzaluna
HAMPSTEAD HEATH
FORTUNE GREEN
Hampstead
Hampstead Heath
Gospel Oak
Belsize Park
West Hampstead Thameslink
Finchley Road & Frognal
West Hampstead
Finchley Road
Kentish Town W.
Kilburn
Brondesbury
Chalk Farm
Swiss Cottage
Singapore Garden
Bradley's
Manna
Lemonia
Primrose Hill
Lansdowne
Odettes
Sardo Canale
Camden Town
South Hampstead
PRIMROSE HILL
Kilburn High Road
Royal China
St John's Wood
London Zoo
Salusbury
Kilburn Park
Queens Park
REGENT'S PARK
Lord's Cricket Ground
Maida Vale
BBC Studios
Madame Tussauds Planetarium
Marylebone
Phoenix Palace
Warwick Avenue
Green Olive
Edgware Road
Chapel
Old Delhi
Paddington
Ledbury
Cow Dining Room
Royal Oak
Ladbroke Grove
Ginger
E & O
Montcalm, Crescent
Al San Vincenzo
First Floor
Electric Brasserie
Assaggi
Bayswater
Four Seasons
Mandarin Kitchen
Porte des Indes
Marble Arch
Notting Hill Brasserie
Nyonya
Royal China
Queensway
Lancaster Gate
Notting Hill Gate
HYDE PARK
See Map 15
Holland Park
Ark
KENSINGTON GARDENS
Clarke's
Kensington Place
The Serpentine
Round Pond
Albert Memorial
Hyde Park Corner
Belvedere
Royal Albert Hall
Knightsbridge
Zaika
Victoria & Albert Museum
High Street Kensington
Science Museum
Timo
Natural History Museum
South Kensington
Kensington (Olympia)
Ebury Wine Bar
Gloucester Road
Cumberland Arms
Earls Court
Sloane Square
See Map 14
West Kensington
Lou Pescadou
West Brompton
Chelsea Royal Hospital
Eight over Eight
Vama
Farm
Chelsea FC
The Painted Heron
Fulham Broadway
BATTERSEA

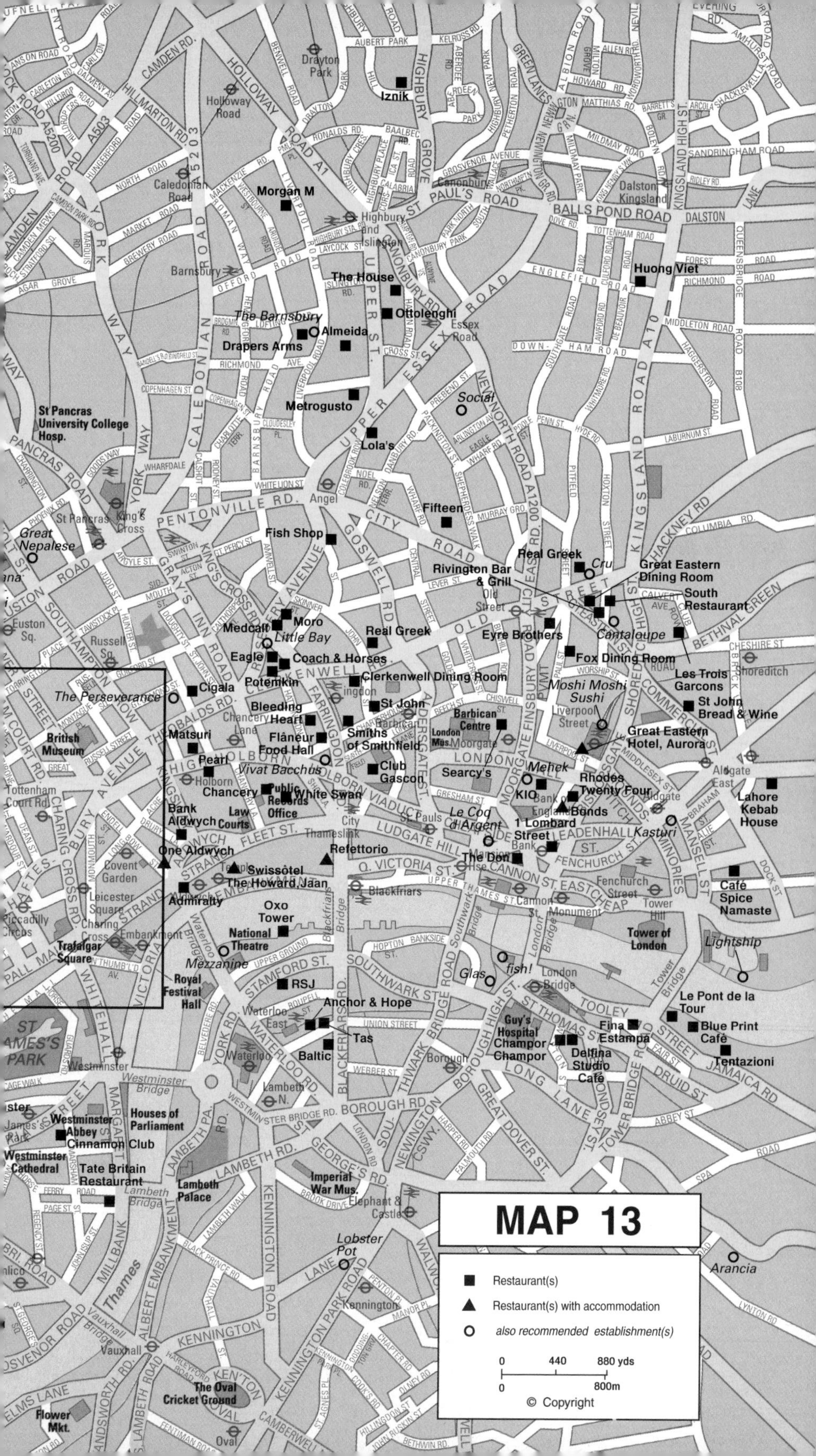

MAP 13
Restaurant(s)
Restaurant(s) with accommodation
also recommended establishment(s)
0
440
880 yds
0
800m
© Copyright
Iznik
Morgan M
The House
Ottolenghi
The Barnsbury
Almeida
Drapers Arms
Metrogusto
Social
Lola's
Huong Viet
Fifteen
Fish Shop
Real Greek
Cru
Rivington Bar & Grill
Great Eastern Dining Room
South Restaurant
Cantaloupe
Eyre Brothers
Fox Dining Room
Les Trois Garcons
St John Bread & Wine
Moshi Moshi Sushi
Great Eastern Hotel, Aurora
Moro
Medcalf
Little Bay
Eagle
Coach & Horses
Potemkin
Clerkenwell Dining Room
St John
Cigala
The Perseverance
Bleeding Heart
Flâneur Food Hall
Smiths of Smithfield
Club Gascon
Barbican Centre
Searcy's
Matsuri
Pearl
Vivat Bacchus
Chancery
White Swan
Mehek
KIO
Rhodes Twenty Four
Bonds
1 Lombard Street
Kasturi
Lahore Kebab House
Bank Aldwych
One Aldwych
Le Coq d'Argent
The Don
Refettorio
Swissôtel The Howard, Jaan
Admiralty
Café Spice Namaste
Oxo Tower
National Theatre
Mezzanine
Lightship
Glas
fish!
RSJ
Anchor & Hope
Tas
Baltic
Royal Festival Hall
Champor Champor
Fina Estampa
Delfina Studio Café
Le Pont de la Tour
Blue Print Café
Tentazioni
Westminster Abbey
Cinnamon Club
Houses of Parliament
Tate Britain Restaurant
Lambeth Palace
Imperial War Mus.
Lobster Pot
Arancia
The Oval Cricket Ground
Great Nepalese
St Pancras University College Hosp.
British Museum
Tower of London
Westminster Cathedral

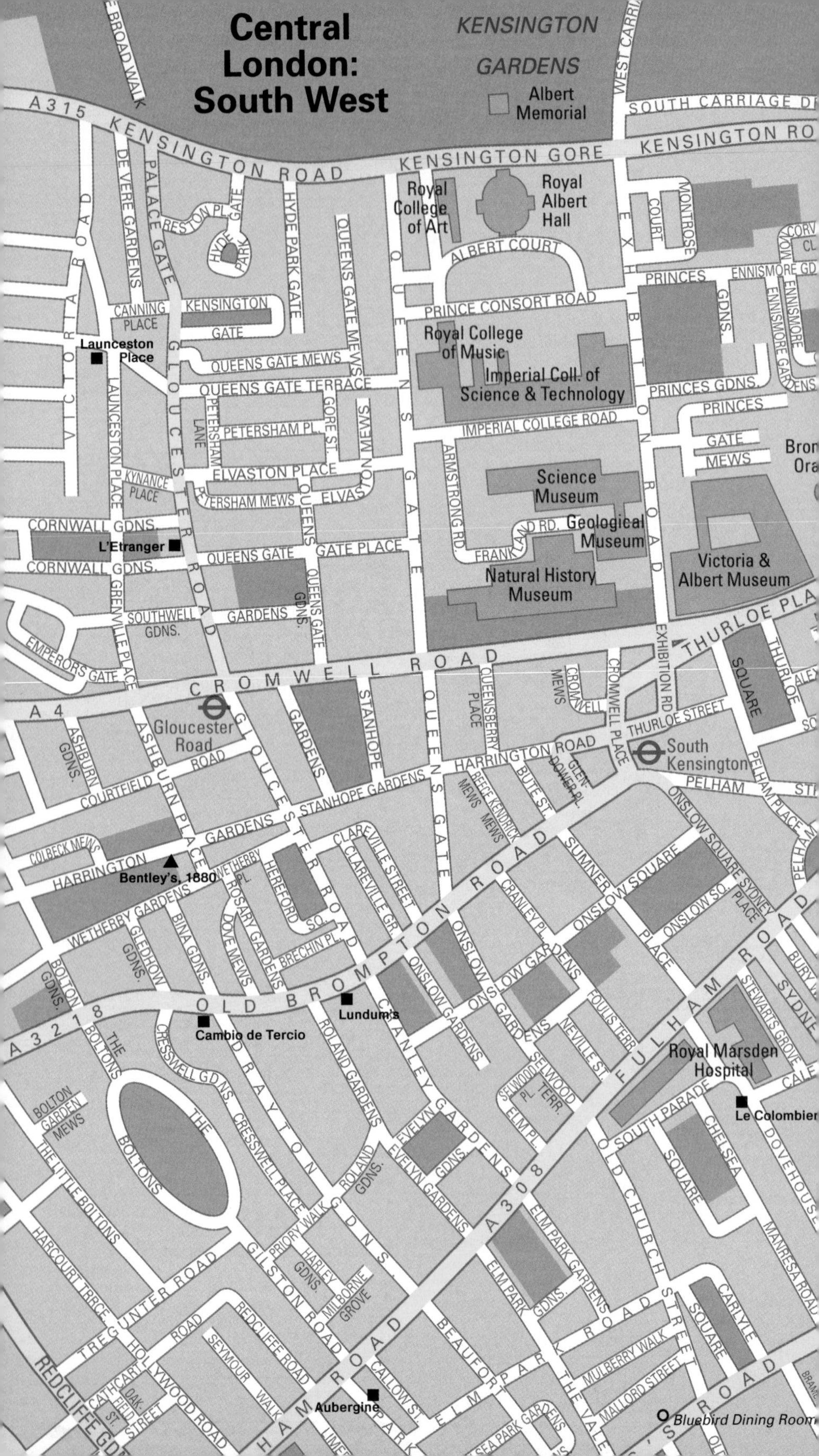

Central London: South West
KENSINGTON GARDENS
Albert Memorial
BROAD WALK
WEST CARRIAGE
SOUTH CARRIAGE DR
A315 KENSINGTON ROAD
KENSINGTON GORE
KENSINGTON RO
Royal College of Art
Royal Albert Hall
ALBERT COURT
PRINCE CONSORT ROAD
Royal College of Music
Imperial Coll. of Science & Technology
IMPERIAL COLLEGE ROAD
Science Museum
Geological Museum
Natural History Museum
Victoria & Albert Museum
FRANKLAND RD.
ARMSTRONG RD.
EXHIBITION ROAD
PRINCES GDNS.
PRINCES GATE MEWS
ENNISMORE GDNS.
MONTROSE COURT
VICTORIA ROAD
DE VERE GARDENS
PALACE GATE
HYDE PARK GATE
RESTON PL.
CANNING PLACE
KENSINGTON GATE
QUEENS GATE MEWS
QUEENS GATE TERRACE
QUEENS GATE
Launceston Place
LAUNCESTON PLACE
KYNANCE PLACE
PETERSHAM LANE
PETERSHAM PL.
PETERSHAM MEWS
GORE ST.
ELVASTON PLACE
ELVASTON MEWS
GLOUCESTER ROAD
CORNWALL GDNS.
L'Etranger
QUEENS GATE PLACE
QUEENS GATE GDNS.
SOUTHWELL GDNS.
GARDENS
EMPERORS GATE
GRENVILLE PLACE
A 4 CROMWELL ROAD
THURLOE PLACE
Gloucester Road
ASHBURN GDNS.
ASHBURN PLACE
COURTFIELD ROAD
STANHOPE GARDENS
QUEENSBERRY PLACE
CROMWELL MEWS
CROMWELL PLACE
EXHIBITION RD
THURLOE STREET
THURLOE SQUARE
HARRINGTON ROAD
South Kensington
PELHAM STREET
PELHAM PLACE
BUTE ST.
GLENDOWER PL.
REECE MEWS
KENDRICK MEWS
COLBECK MEWS
HARRINGTON GARDENS
Bentley's, 1880
WETHERBY PL.
WETHERBY GARDENS
HEREFORD SQ.
CLAREVILLE STREET
CLAREVILLE GR.
BRECHIN PL.
ROSARY GARDENS
DOVE MEWS
BINA GDNS.
GLEDHOW GDNS.
BOLTON GDNS.
SUMNER PLACE
ONSLOW SQUARE
ONSLOW SQ.
SYDNEY PLACE
CRANLEY PL.
ONSLOW GARDENS
A3218 OLD BROMPTON ROAD
Lundum's
Cambio de Tercio
CRANLEY GARDENS
FOULIS TERR.
NEVILLE ST.
SELWOOD PL.
SELWOOD TERR.
ELM PL.
FULHAM ROAD
A308
Royal Marsden Hospital
Le Colombier
SOUTH PARADE
CHELSEA SQUARE
DOVEHOUSE
STEWARTS GROVE
BURY
SYDNEY
THE BOLTONS
BOLTON GARDEN MEWS
THE LITTLE BOLTONS
CRESSWELL GDNS.
CRESSWELL PLACE
DRAYTON GDNS.
ROLAND GARDENS
ROLAND GDNS.
EVELYN GARDENS
EVELYN GDNS.
PRIORY WALK
HARLEY GDNS.
MILBORNE GROVE
GILSTON ROAD
HARCOURT TRRCE.
TREGUNTER ROAD
REDCLIFFE GDNS.
HOLLYWOOD ROAD
SEYMOUR WALK
REDCLIFFE ROAD
CATHCART RD.
OAKFIELD ST.
FULHAM ROAD
Aubergine
CALLOW ST.
BEAUFORT STREET
ELM PARK GDNS.
ELM PARK GARDENS
ELM PARK ROAD
OLD CHURCH STREET
MULBERRY WALK
MALLORD STREET
THE VALE
CARLYLE SQUARE
MANRESA ROAD
Bluebird Dining Room

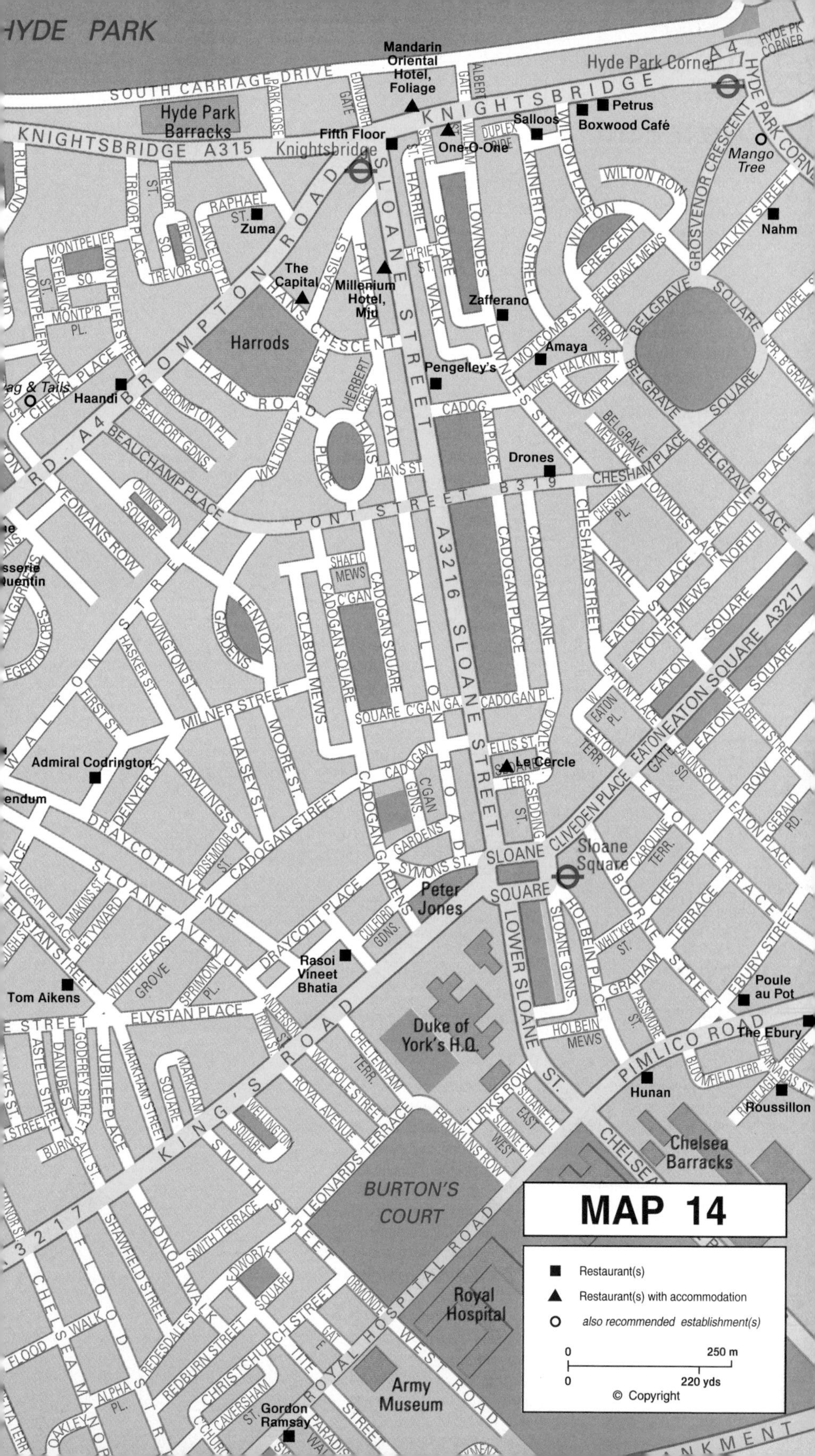

MAP 14
HYDE PARK
Hyde Park Corner
Hyde Park Barracks
Mandarin Oriental Hotel, Foliage
Fifth Floor
One-O-One
Salloos
Petrus
Boxwood Café
Mango Tree
Zuma
Nahm
The Capital
Millenium Hotel, Mid
Zafferano
Harrods
Amaya
Pengelley's
Haandi
Drones
Admiral Codrington
Le Cercle
Sloane Square
Peter Jones
Rasoi Vineet Bhatia
Tom Aikens
Duke of York's H.Q.
Poule au Pot
The Ebury
Hunan
Roussillon
Chelsea Barracks
BURTON'S COURT
Royal Hospital
Army Museum
Gordon Ramsay
KNIGHTSBRIDGE A315
BROMPTON ROAD
SLOANE STREET
PONT STREET
CADOGAN SQUARE
BELGRAVE SQUARE
EATON SQUARE
KING'S ROAD
ROYAL HOSPITAL ROAD
PIMLICO ROAD
Restaurant(s)
Restaurant(s) with accommodation
also recommended establishment(s)
0 250 m
0 220 yds
© Copyright

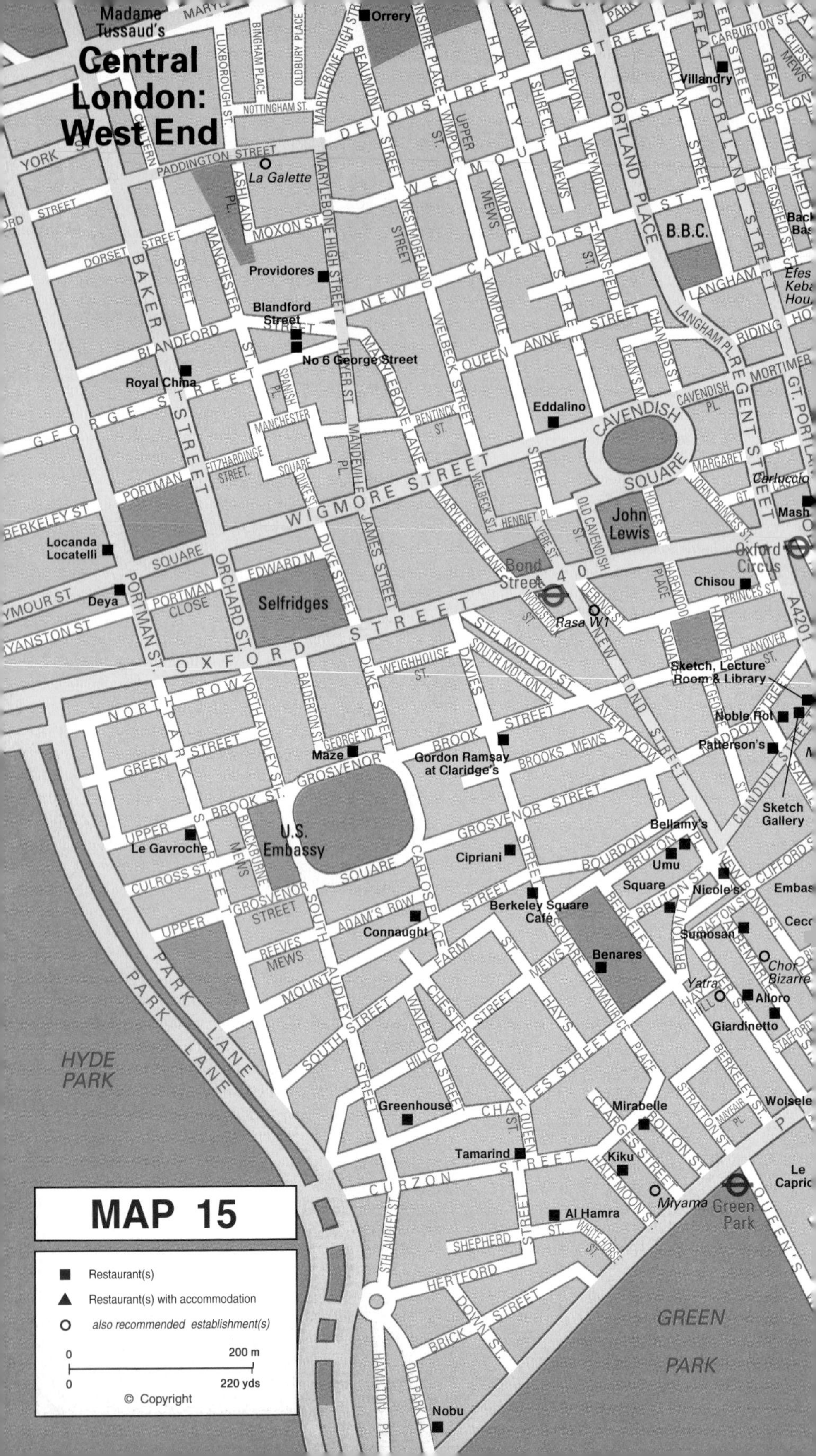

Central London: West End
MAP 15
Restaurant(s)
Restaurant(s) with accommodation
also recommended establishment(s)
0
200 m
0
220 yds
© Copyright
Madame Tussaud's
Orrery
Villandry
La Galette
B.B.C.
Providores
Blandford Street
No 6 George Street
Royal China
Eddalino
Carluccio
Mash
John Lewis
Locanda Locatelli
Deya
Selfridges
Bond Street
Rasa W1
Oxford Circus
Chisou
Sketch, Lecture Room & Library
Noble Rot
Patterson's
Sketch Gallery
Maze
Gordon Ramsay at Claridge's
U.S. Embassy
Le Gavroche
Cipriani
Bellamy's
Umu
Nicole's
Berkeley Square Café
Connaught
Benares
Sumosan
Chor Bizarre
Yatra
Alloro
Giardinetto
Greenhouse
Mirabelle
Wolseley
Tamarind
Kiku
Miyama
Green Park
Al Hamra
Nobu
HYDE PARK
GREEN PARK
PARK LANE
OXFORD STREET
WIGMORE STREET
BAKER STREET
GEORGE STREET
CAVENDISH SQUARE
GROSVENOR SQUARE
BERKELEY SQUARE
CURZON STREET
PICCADILLY
REGENT STREET
NEW BOND STREET
PORTLAND PLACE
MARYLEBONE HIGH STREET
MARYLEBONE LANE
SOUTH AUDLEY STREET
NORTH AUDLEY ST.
MOUNT STREET
BROOK STREET
CHARLES ST.
HALF MOON ST.
CLARGES STREET
BOLTON ST.
DOVER ST.
ALBEMARLE ST.
CONDUIT STREET
HANOVER SQUARE
PRINCES ST.
MADDOX STREET
DAVIES STREET
DUKE STREET
JAMES STREET
ORCHARD ST.
PORTMAN SQUARE
MANCHESTER SQUARE
DORSET STREET
BLANDFORD STREET
PADDINGTON STREET
NEW CAVENDISH STREET
WEYMOUTH STREET
DEVONSHIRE STREET
QUEEN ANNE STREET
WELBECK STREET
WIMPOLE STREET
HARLEY STREET
MORTIMER ST.
LANGHAM PL.
A40
A4201

Russell Square
National Childrens Hospital
University of London
British Museum
Goodge St.
Ikkyu
Roka
Fino
Pied-à-Terre
Passione
Camerino
Rasa Samudra
Hakkasan
Tottenham Court Road
Gay Hussar
Quo Vadis
L'Escargot
Red Fort
Patara
Alastair Little
Lindsay House
Incognico
Mela
Mon Plaisir
Neal Street Restaurant
Le Deuxieme
Vasco & Piero's Pavilion
Masala Zone
Trouvaille
Yauatcha
Itsu Soho
Bertorelli's
Covent Garden
Ivy
Chinese Experience
ECapital
New World
Tokyo Diner
Randall & Aubin
Circus
Kulu Kulu Sushi
Le Cafe du Jardin
COVENT GARDEN
L'Estaminet
Sofra
Golden Dragon
Mr. Kong
Fung Shing
Manzi's
Chuen Cheng Ku
Chowki
Atlantic Bar and Grill
Trocadero
Rules
Leicester Square
J.Sheekey
Savoy Grill
Piccadilly Circus
Yoshin
National Portrait Gallery
Portrait Restaurant, National Portrait Gallery
National Gallery, Crivelli s Garden
TRAFALGAR SQUARE
Nelson's Column
Charing Cross
Charing Cross Station
Al Duca
Mint Leaf
Embankment
W'Sens
Admiralty Arch
Ministry of Defence
Marlborough House
Horse Guards Parade
Banqueting House
ST JAMES'S PARK
Inn the Park
River Thames
TORRINGTON
MALET STREET
BLOOMSBURY STREET
MONTAGUE PLACE
RUSSELL SQUARE
SOUTHAMPTON ROW
BEDFORD PLACE
MONTAGUE ST.
GT. ORMOND
BOSWELL STREET
OLD GLOUCESTER STREET
QUEEN SQUARE
BLOOMSBURY WAY
BLOOMSBURY SQUARE
BURY
MUSEUM ST.
COPTIC ST.
GREAT RUSSELL STREET
NEW OXFORD ST.
HIGH HOLBORN
A40
TOTTENHAM COURT ROAD A400
TOTTENHAM ST.
HOWLAND ST.
CHARLOTTE STREET
GOODGE ST.
MORTIMER ST.
NEWMAN STREET
BERNERS STREET
RATHBONE PL.
STORE STREET
CHENIES STREET
BEDFORD AVENUE
BEDFORD SQUARE
PERCY ST.
WINDMILL ST.
STEPHEN ST.
HANWAY ST.
BAINBRIDGE ST.
DYOTT ST.
OXFORD STREET
SOHO SQUARE
SOHO ST.
SUTTON ROW
ST GILES HIGH ST.
EARNSHAM ST.
SHAFTESBURY AV.
ENDELL STREET
STUKELEY ST.
MACKLIN ST.
PARKER ST.
DRURY LANE
NEAL ST.
MONMOUTH STREET
SHORTS GDNS.
SHELTON ST.
LONG ACRE
FLITCROFT ST.
NEW COMPTON ST.
CHARING CROSS ROAD
EARLHAM ST.
WEST ST.
LITCHFIELD ST.
CARLISLE ST.
DEAN STREET
FRITH STREET
GREEK ST.
WARDOUR STREET
POLAND STREET
NOEL ST.
BERWICK ST.
BROADWICK ST.
MEARD ST.
OLD COMPTON STREET
SHAFTESBURY AVENUE
LEXINGTON ST.
PETER ST.
BEAK ST.
GOLDEN SQUARE
WARWICK ST.
BREWER STREET
GERRARD ST.
LISLE ST.
LEICESTER ST.
CRANBOURN STREET
GT. NEWPORT ST.
ST MARTINS LANE
NEW ROW
GARRICK ST.
FLORAL ST.
JAMES'S ST.
KING ST.
HENRIETTA ST.
MAIDEN LANE
TAVISTOCK ST.
BEDFORD ST.
BEDFORDBURY
CHANDOS PLACE
THE STRAND
WILLIAM IV ST.
JOHN ADAM ST.
VILLIERS STREET
GLASSHOUSE STREET
COVENTRY ST.
HAYMARKET A4
JERMYN ST.
REGENT ST.
ORANGE STREET
PANTON ST.
WHITCOMB ST.
SUFFOLK ST.
IRVING ST.
CHARLES II ST.
PALL MALL EAST
COCKSPUR ST.
PALL MALL
ST JAMES'S SQUARE
KING STREET
DUKE OF YORK ST.
WATERLOO PLACE
CARLTON HOUSE TERR.
CARLTON
THE MALL
NORTHUMBERLAND AV.
WHITEHALL A3212
GT. SCOTLAND YD.
WHITEHALL PLACE
HORSEGUARDS AVE.
VICTORIA EMBANKMENT
HORSE GUARDS ROAD
MARLBOROUGH

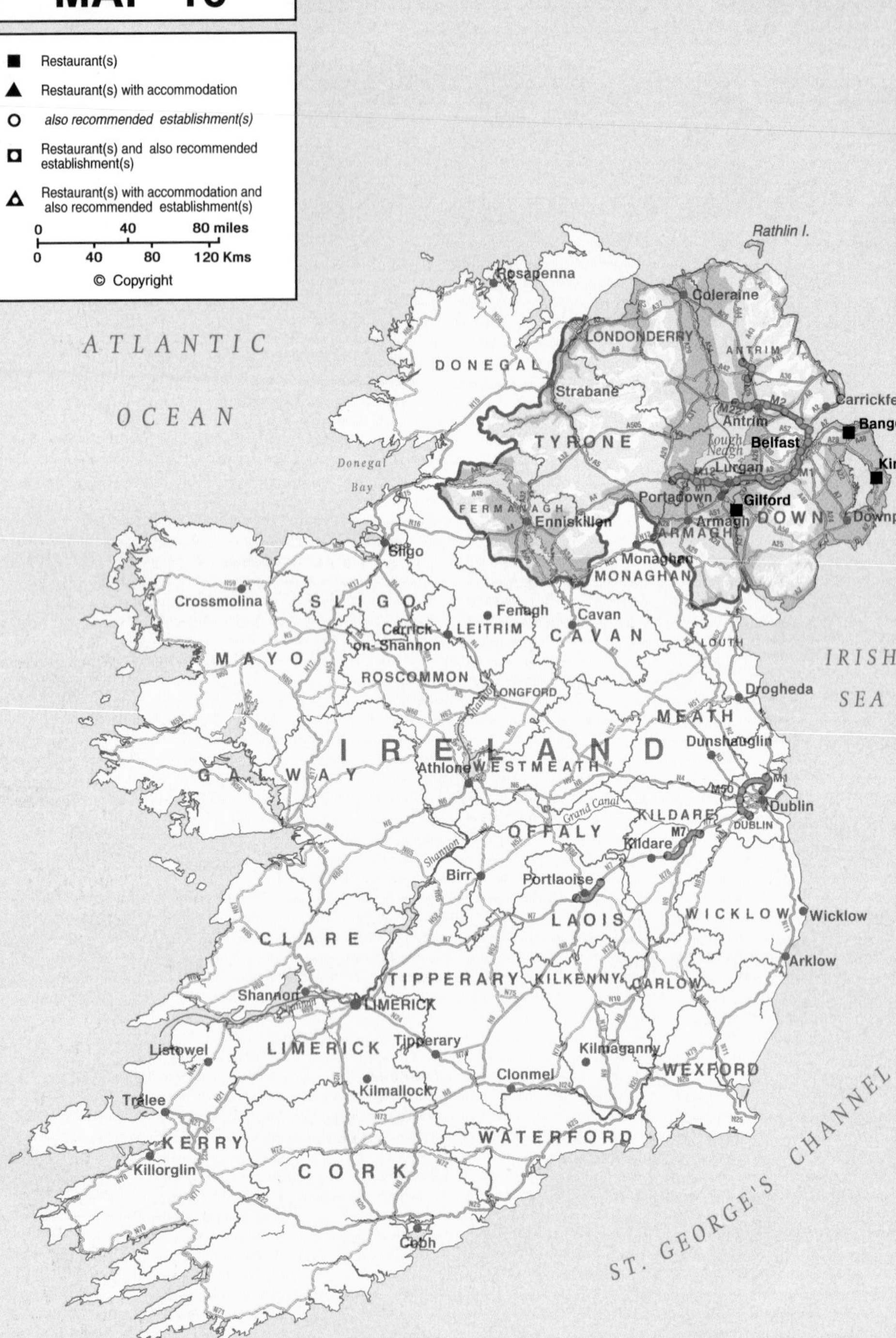

ATLANTIC

OCEAN

MAP 12

Adams Café

77 Askew Road, W12 9AH
Tel: (020) 8743 0572

Cooking 3 | North African | £24–£31

By day, Adams is a café, but at night this buzzy neighbourhood venue changes tack and heads for North Africa. Over the years it has become a past master at tempering the fire and aromatic headiness of genuine ethnic cooking with some refined, mollifying touches. Traditional tagines bursting with 'immense flavour' are one of the highlights (chicken with pickled lemons and green olives has been singled out); the kitchen is also famed for its couscous (eight versions in all) and grills ranging from tuna or red mullet to merguez sausages. Meals begin with a plate of invigorating nibbles, starters range from brik to briouats (triangular seafood pastries), and proceedings conclude with authentic sweetmeats. The cheap and cheerful wine list (from £9) has some gluggable North African bottles plus Ch. Musar.

Chef: Sofiene Chahed **Proprietors:** Abdel and Frances Boukraa **Open:** Mon to Sat D only 7 to 11 **Closed:** Christmas to New Year, bank hol Mon **Meals:** Set D £10.50 (1 course) to £15.50 **Service:** 12.5%, card slips closed **Cards:** Amex, Delta, Maestro, MasterCard, Visa **Details:** 60 seats. Private parties: 24 private room. Vegetarian meals. Wheelchair access (not WC). Music **Tube:** Ravenscourt Park

MAP 14

Admiral Codrington

17 Mossop Street, SW3 2LY
Tel: (020) 7581 0005
Website: www.theadmiralcodrington.co.uk

Cooking 3 | Modern European | £39–£55

This may look like a Sloaned-up Victorian pub, with smart people shoulder-to-shoulder in the bar, but when it comes to food things are different. A conservatory-style dining room at the back, with pale wood floor, retractable roof and nautical undertones sets off bright, modern food. Crispy baby squid comes with lemon mayonnaise, or try foie gras and chicken liver parfait with Muscat jelly. 'The Admiral's Cod' (with tomatoes, mushrooms and a herb crust) may be the kitchen's pride and joy, but higher ambitions show in seared loin of blue-fin tuna with cannellini beans and basil, or slow-roast shoulder of lamb with spiced aubergine caviar and mint dressing. Finish with, say, blood orange and vanilla cheesecake. The competitively priced global wine list includes house South Africans at £12.50.

Chef: John Rotherham **Proprietor:** Longshot Plc **Open:** all week 12 to 2.30 (3.15 Sat, 4.15 Sun), 7 to 10.30 (10.15 Sat) **Closed:** 24 to 26 and 29 Dec **Meals:** alc (main courses £11 to £15). Cover 80p. Bar menu available **Service:** 12.5% (optional), card slips closed **Cards:** Amex, Delta, Maestro, MasterCard, Visa **Details:** 55 seats. 20 seats outside. Private parties: 20 to 60 private rooms. Vegetarian meals. Children's helpings. Music **Tube:** South Kensington

MAP 13

Admiralty

Somerset House, Strand, WC2R 1LA
Tel: (020) 7845 4646

Cooking 5 | French | £49–£79

The setting is an impressive high-ceilinged room in Somerset House done out in turquoise and ochre, but it is the 'ocean-going memorabilia' that catches the eye – chandeliers of ships in full sail, a full-size crocodile pinned to the wall, a display case of baby sea horses. Daniel Groom has taken over the kitchen, and while he uses many classic combinations – Sauternes jelly with ballottine of foie gras, for example – he brings a contemporary slant to the menu with the likes of crab risotto with avocado ice cream. For main courses, saddle of rabbit stuffed with spinach and pancetta and wrapped in Parma ham may come perched on a spoonful of tomato-flavoured couscous with cannelloni of morels on the side.

Cheeses, 'mainly French', are kept in fine fettle, and puddings tend to be rich: even a rice pudding is made with cream, topped off with cherries preserved in syrup and served with blackcurrant sorbet. There are one or two minor let-downs (including bread), service is 'friendly but slightly awkward', and anyone hoping to counter the menu prices by choosing something modest from the wine list faces a difficult task – only a couple of bottles are under £20.

Chef: Daniel Groom **Proprietor:** Restaurant Associates **Open:** all week L 12 to 2.15, Mon to Sat D 6 to 10.15 **Closed:** Christmas, D bank hols **Meals:** alc (main courses £17.50 to £23) **Service:** 12.5% (optional) **Cards:** Amex, Delta, Diners, Maestro, MasterCard, Visa **Details:** 55 seats. Private parties: 60 main room, 15 to 30 private rooms. Vegetarian meals. No smoking in 1 dining room. Wheelchair access (also WC). Music **Tube:** Temple, Covent Garden

MAP 15

Alastair Little

49 Frith Street, W1D 4SG
Tel: (020) 7734 5183

Cooking 4 | Modern European | £46–£65

In the late 1980s Alastair Little (the chef and the restaurant) was in the vanguard of a move to a more straightforward style of cooking than London was then, by and large, being treated to. The spare, minimal dining room, the daily-changing menus written in plain English, and the naked simplicity of the food have all stood the test of time. Twenty years on, the kitchen guard has changed – Little is no longer associated – but the ideals have not been lost under the guidance of Sue Lewis. No matter how simple the dish – sizzling prawns with parsley, chilli and garlic, for example – they apply a combination of skill, good materials and sound judgement. Light treatments (mostly searing and roasting) are hallmarks, seen in an inspector's main course of fillet steak, 'much better than several I have had in the preceding months', teamed with chips and 'well-made' béarnaise, and by roast wild sea bass with Puy lentils and a mustard sauce. Meals begin with bread – anything from crusty brown to focaccia – and finish with crème brûlée, or chocolate bavarois. 'Hard to find any fault' and 'effortless' describe the service, and the wine list, a page each of globetrotting whites and reds, runs from £17.50.

Chef: Sue Lewis **Proprietors:** Mercedes André-Vega and Kirsten Tormod Pedersen **Open:** Mon to Fri L 12 to 3, Mon to Sat D 6 to 11.30 **Closed:** bank hols **Meals:** Set L £31, Set D £38 **Service:** not inc **Cards:** Amex, Delta, Diners, Maestro, MasterCard, Visa **Details:** 60 seats. 4 seats outside. Private parties: 10 main room, 25 private room. No cigars/pipes in dining room. Wheelchair access (not WC). No music. Air-conditioned **Tube:** Tottenham Court Road

MAP 15

Al Duca

AR

4–5 Duke of York Street, SW1Y 6LA
Tel: (020) 7839 3090

Smart Italian in the heartland of gentrified West End retail therapy, behind Fortnum and Mason. Tidy fixed-price menus (from £17.50 lunch, from £20 dinner) promise unfussily composed, workmanlike dishes such as marinated salmon with citrus, herbs and pear sauce, pappardelle with duck ragù, and baked poussin with rosemary potatoes, chilli and brandy sauce, before simple desserts like tiramisù. Service gets mixed reports, but the comprehensive, well-considered Italian wine list more than makes amends (prices from £16). Closed Sun.

MAP 15

Al Hamra

31–33 Shepherd Market, W1J 7PT
Tel: (020) 7493 1954
Website: www.alhamrarestaurant.com

Cooking 2 | Lebanese | £42–£75

A familiar presence on Shepherd Market since the mid-1980s, Al Hamra still exudes a certain Middle Eastern aura, whether you are eating amid potted plants in the plush dining room or sitting on the patio. The mammoth menu doesn't change much and neither have the prices in the last year. Meze open the show, and the range extends far and wide, from barassia (leeks in olive oil and lemon juice) and sawda dajaj (fried chicken livers with sour Grenadine sauce) to the anatomical delights of lamb's sweetbreads and testicles. The chargrill is deployed for high-protein kebabs, and there are everyday Lebanese desserts to finish. France and the Lebanon loom large in a wallet-stretching list of wines from £15. An offshoot called Brasserie Al Hamra Express was opening as we went to press at 52 Shepherd Market, W1; tel: (020) 7493 1068.

Chef: Mahir Abboud **Proprietor:** S. and A.H. Fansa **Open:** all week noon to 11.30 **Closed:** 24 Dec to 2 Jan **Meals:** alc (main courses £13 to £22.50). Cover £2.50 **Service:** not inc **Cards:** Amex, Delta, Diners, Maestro, MasterCard, Visa **Details:** 65 seats. 24 seats outside. Private parties: 70 main room. Vegetarian meals. Children's helpings. Wheelchair access (not WC). Music. Air-conditioned **Tube:** Green Park

MAP 13

llium

olphin Square, Chichester Street, SW1V 3LX
l: (020) 7798 6888
/ebsite: www.allium.co.uk

ooking 5 | Modern European | £45–£77

x-Savoy chef Anton Edelmann pitched his camp this independent restaurant within Dolphin quare in 2003, taking over the venue from Gary hodes. The décor is a sultry deep blue, set off by e gleam of chrome, and the cooking – under the gis of head chef Peter Woods – aims for a high egree of refinement.

A trio of cep tortellini sitting on a piece of celeac filled with chicken mousse, over which a rich d-wine reduction was poured at the table, was a bour-intensive starter that certainly impressed e summer visitor. The now familiar meaty wrapng of monkfish powerfully reminded the same porter what the point of such a preparation origally was, as a bandaging of Ardennes ham was plied to it, the earthy accompaniment of crushed oad beans only adding to the depth of the dish. nother way through the menu might be seared allops on carrot and cardamom purée with ervil froth, and then roast partridge with two rvings of cabbage (sautéed and braised), creamed rolles and a haggis spätzli. A wait of twenty inutes will be rewarded with a raspberry soufflé, rved with matching sorbet, to finish, or there uld well be a whole baked peach seasoned with nger and lemon. Service is generally commended exemplary. The wine list contents itself with a ndful of happy choices from most French regions d a few other countries, starting at £15.50.

Chef/Proprietor: Anton Edelmann **Open:** Tue to Fri and Sun L 2 to 3 (2.30 Sun), Tue to Sat D 6 to 10 **Meals:** alc (main ourses £17.50 to £24.50). Set L £17.50 (2 courses) to £22.50. Bar menu available **Service:** 12.5% (optional) **Cards:** Amex, Delta, Diners, Maestro, MasterCard, Visa **Details:** 90 seats. Private parties: 90 main room, 12 to 70 private rooms. Vegetarian meals. Children's helpings. Wheelchair access (also WC). Occasional music. No mobile phones. Air-conditioned **Tube:** Pimlico

MAP 15

Alloro

19–20 Dover Street, W1S 4LU
Tel: (020) 7495 4768

Cooking 4 | Italian | £43–£67

In a swanky location just off Piccadilly near the Ritz, Alloro is every inch the archetypal Mayfair Italian, from its discreet frontage to its marble floors, earthy colour schemes and 'alloro' (laurel leaf) motifs highlighted on decorative plaster casts. Top-drawer imported ingredients stand tall on the menu and the kitchen makes the most of what it has to hand without gilding the lily. Genuine regional antipasti like Piedmontese Tomino cheese with speck, sauté trevisano and balsamic vinegar set the tone before home-made fish tortelli with fennel sauce or indulgences like quail and foie gras risotto, while big flavours and earthy rusticity define centrepiece dishes such as pan-fried cod fillet with chickpea stew and Ligurian olive oil or roast squab with spinach, girolles and black truffles. Tiramisù with dark chocolate or hot rhubarb sfogliatina (flaky pastry) bring up the rear, along with Italian cheeses and home-made pear mustard. Quality control is impressive on the all-Italian wine list, with lavish collections of mature bottles in Piedmont and Tuscany. Prices have a Mayfair ring, but good Sicilian house is £16.50 and 11 come by the glass.

Chef: Marzio Zacchi **Proprietor:** A–Z Restaurants Ltd **Open:** Mon to Fri L 12 to 2.30, Mon to Sat D 7 to 10.30 **Closed:** Bank hols, 2 weeks Christmas **Meals:** Set L £25 (2 courses) to £28, Set D £27.50 (2 courses) to £35 **Service:** 12.5% (optional), card slips closed **Cards:** Amex, Delta, Diners, Maestro, MasterCard, Visa **Details:** 70 seats. No cigars/pipes. No music. Air-conditioned **Tube:** Green Park

MAP 13

Almeida

30 Almeida Street, N1 1AD
Tel: (020) 7354 4777
Website: www.conran.com

Cooking 4 | French Bistro | £33–£69

Sir Terence Conran's smart, five-year-old restaurant opposite the theatre of the same name is a relaxed place: somewhere to enjoy rather than worship food, and very popular. Its Francophile directive is apparent in a carte that weaves together

French regional and classical threads with fresh ingredients at the heart of things, showing to good effect in a 'salade de betteraves rôties et fromage de chèvre', and grilled herring with warm potato and mustard salad. A largely conservative culinary approach at main course – grilled halibut with sauce hollandaise, fillet steak with pepper sauce – is offset by scallops teamed with black pudding, or roast Anjou pigeon with petits pois. At dessert stage it's hard to resist the famed trolley of tarts (there's a similar one dealing in charcuterie for first courses), but rum baba and chocolate soufflé are worthy competitors. A tapas menu is served all day in the bar.

The short wine list, with around 20 options all available by bottle (from £14.50), glass or pot lyonnais (two thirds of a bottle) makes a tempting little bistro range. The weighty full version runs to rare and old bottles, with the usual Conran focus on southern France and a welcome slate of top-class South African wines.

Chef: Ian Wood **Proprietor:** Conran Restaurants **Open:** all week 12 to 2.30 (3 Sun), 5.30 to 11 (6 to 10.30 Sun) **Closed:** 25 and 26 Dec, 1 Jan **Meals:** alc (main courses £14.50 to £19.50). Set L £14.50 (2 courses) to £17.50, Set D £14.50 (2 courses, not 7 to 10pm) to £17.50. Bar tapas menu available **Service:** 12.5% (optional), card slips closed **Cards:** Amex, Delta, Diners, Maestro, MasterCard, Visa **Details:** 95 seats. 20 seats outside. Private parties: 8 to 20 private rooms. Children's helpings. No-smoking area. Wheelchair access (also WC). No music. Air-conditioned **Tube:** Angel/Highbury and Islington

MAP 13

Al San Vincenzo

30 Connaught Street, W2 2AF
Tel: (020) 7262 9623

Cooking 2 | Italian | £38–£71

This pint-sized Italian restaurant occupies the ground floor of a narrow terraced house not far from Marble Arch. Comfortable high-backed chairs and flowers help to create a welcoming feel, and Giorgio the ginger tom certainly looks at home. Vincenzo Borgonzolo's cooking aims to satisfy rather than push out any boundaries, and a high level of satisfaction is certainly occasioned. Smoked haddock fishcakes on a sauce of purée fagioli with garlic and lemon has been a successful February starter, while main courses of rabbit stifado with cabbage and lentils, and richly commendable calf's liver with beetroot agrodolce and mash have been classic winter fare. Finish with chocolate semifreddo, or a pairing of fresh mango and dolcelatte. A tiny list of Italian wines leads o with Venezia varietals at £16.

Chef: Vincenzo Borgonzolo **Proprietors:** Elaine and Vincenzo Borgonzolo **Open:** Mon to Fri L 12.30 to 1.30, Mon to Sat D 7 to 9.30 **Meals:** alc (main courses £13 to £18) **Service:** not inc, 12.5% for parties of 5 or more **Cards:** Delta, Maestro, MasterCard, Visa **Details:** 24 seats. Private parties: 20 main room. Vegetarian meals. No smoking. Music **Tube:** Marble Arch

MAP 14

Amaya

NEW ENTRY

15 Halkin Arcade, Motcomb Street, SW1X 8JT
Tel: (020) 7823 1166
Website: www.realindianfood.com

Cooking 3 | Indian | £33–£82

The latest venture from the owners of Chutne Mary (see entry) occupies a slice of prim Belgravia real estate overlooking Halkin Arcad It's an ambitious affair with a huge triangul dining area and 'insanely eclectic' décor. The idea to select several items from the list of tandoor sigri (charcoal grill) and tawa (skillet) specialiti and finish with a curry. Piquant tandoori duc with tamarind glaze has been highly impressiv likewise Punjabi chicken wing 'lollipops Following on, there are enticingly described dish such as nimboo gosht (lamb osso buco fragra lime curry), plus vegetables including two 'thum width strips' of spiced grilled aubergine. Chutne are excellent, and there are some gems among t desserts, including grilled mango with passion fruit fool. The wine list flaunts its Belgravia pric (from £17.05), although it's a good match for t food. The service didn't impress at inspection.

Chef: Karunesh Khanna **Proprietors:** Ranjit Mathrani, and Namita and Camellia Panjabi **Open:** all week 12 to 2.30 (2.15 Sat and Sun), 6.30 to 11.15 (10.15 Sun) **Closed:** D 25 Dec **Meals:** alc (main courses £12.50 to £24). Set L £14 to £25, Set D £26 to £55 **Service:** 12.5% (optional), card slips closed **Cards:** Amex, Delta, Diners, Maestro, MasterCard, Visa **Details:** 90 seats. Private parties: 8 to 14 private rooms Vegetarian meals. No-smoking area. Wheelchair access (also WC). Music. Air-conditioned **Tube:** Knightsbridge

NEW ENTRY	This appears after the restaurant's name if the establishment was not a main entry in last year's Guide, although it may have been a 'round-up/also recommended' in previous editions.

MAP 13

Anchor & Hope

36 The Cut, SE1 8LP
Tel: (020) 7928 9898

Cooking 5 | Traditional European | £30–£59

What the Anchor & Hope is offering is very much in tune with the London times, at least to those who don't expect three lots of appetisers and a pre-dessert with their dinner. The venue is a big, babbling bar with a dining area, the latter screened off from view by a tatty red curtain at service times. There is no booking. Turn up, be nice to the staff and wait for a table. The food makes a virtue of rustic simplicity. One reporter started with big chunks of octopus with aubergine on toast and loved every mouthful. Another was brought up short by the oily allure of a heap of 'excellent' smoked sprats seasoned with a blob of horseradish cream. Raw materials are almost eerily fine, the eloquent flavour of fat-fringed beef rump singing out next to a bundle of anchovy-seasoned green beans and beetroot, while fish might be sea bass with fennel and aïoli. Duck confit is the real thing, served with a square of semolina gnocchi bursting with buttery richness, and meals end strongly with the likes of fig and vanilla anglaise tart ('predictably, it was first-rate,'), or chocolate pot. The wine list stays mostly in Europe, and the listings are gutsy enough to accompany the food. (The Bandol is 15 per cent abv.) Prices start at £10 for Vins de Pays d'Oc.

Chefs: Harry Lester and Jonathon Jones **Proprietors:** Robert Shaw, Harry Lester, Jonathon Jones and Mike Belben **Open:** Mon 6 to 10.30, Tue to Sat 12 to 2.30, 6 to 10.30 **Meals:** alc (main courses £10 to £21). Bar menu available **Service:** not inc **Cards:** Delta, Maestro, MasterCard, Visa **Details:** 80 seats. 9 seats outside. No cigars in dining room. Wheelchair access (not WC). No music **Tube:** Waterloo, Southwark

MAP 12

Anglesea Arms

35 Wingate Road, W6 0UR
Tel: (020) 8749 1291
Email: angleseaarms@hotmail.com

Cooking 2 | Modern European | £25–£50

'The Anglesea Arms can still show the younger upstarts a thing or two,' observed a fan of this pioneering London gastro-pub. It remains a highly accessible neighbourhood eating place with a laid-back attitude (no bookings), great hospitality and a daily menu that makes a virtue of flexibility. The cooking is simple, precise and – like the pub itself – unfussy: poached skate wings are served in a 'well-meaning' fashion with potato salad, horseradish and chives, while top-quality breast of organic chicken receives support from braised Jerusalem artichokes, Savoy cabbage, French beans and tomato confit. To finish, opt for cheese or a dessert such as lemon posset with raspberry coulis and biscotti. The wine list is a short, tidy, globetrotting slate with plenty by the glass and bottle prices from £11.50.

Chef: Henrik Ritzen **Proprietor:** Fiona Evans **Open:** all week 12.30 to 2.45, 7 to 10.45 **Closed:** 1 week at Christmas **Meals:** alc (main courses £8.50 to £14.50). Set L Mon to Fri £9.95 (2 courses) to £12.95 **Service:** not inc **Cards:** MasterCard, Visa **Details:** 40 seats. 16 seats outside. Vegetarian meals. Children's helpings. No smoking. Wheelchair access (not WC). No music. **Tube:** Ravenscourt Park

MAP 13

Arancia

AR

52 Southwark Park Road, SE16 3RS
Tel: (020) 7394 1751

Strong colours and contemporary art set the mood at this informal neighbourhood Italian, noted for its buzz and fair prices. Expect gutsy regional dishes in the shape of, say, spaghettini with crab, red chillies and garlic (£4.75), or carpaccio, before bollito misto (£9.50), or pea risotto with marjoram. Poached spiced pears with mascarpone is a typical pudding. Exclusively Italian wines from £9.50. Closed Sun and Mon.

MAP 13

Ark

122 Palace Gardens Terrace, W8 4RT
Tel: (020) 7229 4024
Website: www.thearkrestaurant.co.uk

Cooking 1 | Italian | £36–£67

Close to Notting Hill tube, with a few pavement-side tables outside, this unassuming, neighbourhood Italian is fashionably taupe inside, with splashes of colour from soft furnishings. Large mirrors at either end amplify it into an 'appealing and attractive' space. In June, English asparagus with truffled hollandaise and fried quail's eggs went down well, then there are pasta dishes in starter or main sizes (veal and chicken-liver ravioli with Barolo jus, say), plus maybe fried John Dory with treviso and salsify, or osso bucco with saffron risotto. Desserts are in the lemon tart or panna-cotta (with prune and Armagnac coulis) mould. An all-Italian list, arranged from north to south, offers a dozen by glass, with bottles from £13.50.

Chef: Steve Moran **Proprietor:** Louise Mayo **Open:** Tue to Sat L 12 to 3, Mon to Sat D 6.30 to 11 **Closed:** bank hols **Meals:** alc (main courses £10 to £20). Light L menu available **Service:** 12.5% (optional), card slips closed **Cards:** Amex, Delta, Maestro, MasterCard, Visa **Details:** 55 seats. 12 seats outside. Private parties: 60 main room. Vegetarian meals. Children's helpings. Wheelchair access (not WC). Music. Air-conditioned **Tube:** Notting Hill Gate

MAP 12

Armadillo

41 Broadway Market, E8 4PH
Tel: (020) 7249 3633

Genuine South American home cooking in downtown South Hackney. The décor is spartan and the food can seem a touch rough-hewn, but the kitchen delivers a fair range of authentic dishes from esmeraldas (steamed plantain dumplings with peanut sauce; £5) to grilled steaks, or roast suckling pig with criolla cabbage and chestnuts (£14). Try chocolate and chilli truffles (£2.50) to finish. Affordable South American and Iberian wines from £11. Open Tue to Sat D only.

MAP 13

Assaggi

The Chepstow, 39 Chepstow Place, W2 4TS
Tel: (020) 7792 5501

Cooking 4 | Italian | £45–£67

Sitting pretty above a Notting Hill pub, the Chepstow, Assaggi is an intimate, laid-back Italian restaurant of the domestic school, with spare décor and a broadly smiling, friendly approach. Let it be said once more: book well ahead. Sardinian carta da musica breads (think Mediterranean pop-padoms) whet the appetite for the robustly satisfying southern Italian cooking to come. Fat prawns on a bed of pea purée with crisp-cooked pancetta was a big hit at inspection, the several flavours counterpointing each other well, after which you may opt for a traditional intermediate pasta course, such as tagliolini with herbs and walnuts, or perhaps light-textured gnocchi, which may come with forthright sausage ragù. Fritto misto is more than capably rendered as a main course, comprised of turbot, squid and prawns, while the more capacious appetite might opt for grilled venison with chestnuts and perhaps a side order of spinach. Desserts might include a plain, well-made bavarois with espresso poured over it, or flourless chocolate cake with smooth, paradoxically tasty, unflavoured ice cream. The short Italian wine list piles on the pounds but opens at £17.95 with Monica, a little-known light red from Sardinia.

Chef: Nino Sassu **Proprietors:** Nino Sassu and Pietro Fraccari **Open:** Mon to Sat 12.30 (1 Sat) to 2.30, 7.30 to 11 **Meals:** alc (main courses £17 to £20) **Service:** not inc, card slips closed **Cards:** Delta, Diners, Maestro, MasterCard, Visa **Details:** 40 seats. Vegetarian meals. Children's helpings. No music. Air-conditioned **Tube:** Notting Hill Gate

MAP 15

Atlantic Bar and Grill

20 Glasshouse Street, W1B 5DJ
Tel: (020) 7734 4888
Website: www.atlanticbarandgrill.com

Cooking 4 | Modern European | £39–£95

The Atlantic is a vast, designer-led subterranean room, and though it may lack the allure of a decade ago, it's an impressive place, with drinks and decibels still setting the tone in the bar. The restaurant is less frantic, with well-spaced tables and pleasant service. The menu deals in contemporary foods and places particular emphasis on Welsh Black beef and upon fish. Combinations are generally well-established, thus terrine of foie gras with brioche and muscat to start, and mains of chargrilled tuna with spiced roasted vegetables and tahini, or pot-roasted shoulder of milk-fed lamb with gratin dauphinoise. There are occasional forays into less familiar territory – a lobster ceviche, for example, or Cornish crab spaghettini with monk's beard, tomato and chill.

A contemporary list of food-friendly wines from £14 is arranged by style, with a reserve list of more serious bottles adding depth. There are no bargains but worthwhile options under £25 include Joguet's light red Cuvée Terroir (£24) from the Loire and Chilean Sauvignon Blanc by Errázuriz (£18.50).

Chef: Ben O'Donoghue **Proprietor:** Oliver Peyton **Open:** Mon to Fri L 12 to 3, Mon to Sat D 6 to 12 **Closed:** 25 Dec, 1 Jan, bank hols **Meals:** alc (main courses L £7 to £19.50, D £8 to £32). Bar menu available 12 to 3am **Service:** 12.5% (optional) **Cards:** Amex, Delta, Diners, Maestro, MasterCard, Visa **Details:** 120 seats. Vegetarian meals. Wheelchair access (not WC). Occasional music. Air-conditioned **Tube:** Piccadilly Circus

MAP 12

L'Auberge

AR

22 Upper Richmond Road, SW15 2RX
Tel: (020) 8874 3593

A little corner of France now well established on the Putney scene. Pascal and Christine Ardilly serve a classic repertoire: try a starter of assiette landaise (£5.50), followed by fillet of halibut with sauce bretonne (£14.50) and, for dessert, a mousse of pain d'épice accompanied by caramelised poached pear (£5) or a plate of proudly unpasteurised French cheeses. A £16 three-course set menu offers three starters and four main courses. Good French wines start at £11.50. Open Tue to Sat D only.

MAP 14

Aubergine

11 Park Walk, SW10 0AJ
Tel: (020) 7352 3449
Email: auberginerestaurant@yahoo.co.uk

Cooking 5 | Modern French | £38–£127

The discreet aubergine-coloured canopy announces the presence of this long-standing Chelsea restaurant, where seasonally based modern French cuisine is the business. It seems an age since Gordon Ramsay cut his teeth here, but successive incumbents have largely maintained the formidable pace set in the early years. A light colour scheme and skylights to the rear make the room feel pleasantly airy and relaxed.

William Drabble favours an earthy approach to the repertoire, with translucent poached lobster tail with leeks and black truffle in a 'scintillating' crustacean sauce, classically accompanying plump seared scallops with pea purée and smoked bacon jus, and adding densely creamy smoked garlic mash to a main course of well-timed roasted brill. A certain tendency to sweetness in reduction sauces upset the balance of one or two dishes at inspection, but techniques are otherwise generally sound. Poached collar of bacon makes an interesting main-course choice, and is garnished with baby carrots and a sauce of foie gras. Fruit is used to good effect in desserts such as orange cream with refreshing citrus salad, or figs poached in red wine and served with pannacotta-textured set yoghurt, while French cheeses come with excellent nut and raisin bread.

The wine list deals mainly in smart bottles from France, with classed-growth clarets running to multiple vintages. Less illustrious offerings are nonetheless respectable – Faugères by Gilbert Alquier (£20) or St-Nicolas-de-Bourgueil from Mabileau (£23) – and half-bottles are taken seriously.

Chef: William Drabble **Proprietor:** A to Z Restaurants **Open:** Mon to Fri L 12 to 2, Mon to Sat D 7 to 11 **Closed:** 24 Dec to 4 Jan **Meals:** Set L £34 (inc wine), Set D £60 to £74 **Service:** 12.5% (optional), card slips closed **Cards:** Amex, Delta, Diners, Maestro, MasterCard, Visa **Details:** 52 seats. Private parties: 64 main room. Vegetarian meals. No cigars/pipes. Wheelchair access (not WC). No music. No mobile phones. Air-conditioned **Tube:** South Kensington/Fulham Broadway

MAP 15

Avenue

AR

7–9 St James's Street, SW1A 1EE
Tel: (020) 7321 2111

Still chic and elegant after a decade, this veteran of the contemporary brasserie scene keeps up appearances with a textbook, across-the-globe menu. Take your pick from Vietnamese-style prawn and papaya salad (£9), spaghetti with meatballs, confit of duck with braised chicory and orange (£14.50), and – for true Brits – calf's liver with bubble and squeak and devils on horseback. Finish with passion-fruit and pineapple rum baba (£6.50). Set meals £17.95/£19.95. Steeply priced but classy modern wine list from £16. Closed Sat L.

MAP 12

Babur Brasserie

119 Brockley Rise, Forest Hill, SE23 1JP
Tel: (020) 8291 2400
Website: www.babur-brasserie.com

Cooking 2 | Indian | £25–£50

Enam Rahman has been running the kitchen in this enterprising suburban Indian for two decades, and his culinary intent has always been to promote the regional traditions of Indian cooking. Classic ideas are given a few twists and fish looms large on the menu. Ros-tos crab (cooked in white wine and mango juice and topped with cheese) and beef salan (flavoured with a cashew nut and yoghurt purée) are listed as specialities, and Mr Rahman also rings the changes with malai pheasant tikka and John Dory Madras. Among desserts, look for hot chocolate and coconut samosas. House wine is £10.95. The restaurant was closed for refurbishment as our deadline approached, but hopefully the life-size effigy of a Bengal tiger on the roof will survive as a notable local landmark.

Chef: Enam Rahman **Proprietor:** Babur 1998 Ltd **Open:** Sat to Thur L 12.15 to 2, all week D 6.15 to 11 **Closed:** 25 and 26 Dec **Meals:** alc (not Sun L; main courses £7 to £13). Sun buffet L £9.25 **Service:** not inc **Cards:** Amex, Delta, Diners, Maestro, MasterCard, Visa **Details:** 56 seats. Private parties: 32 main room. Vegetarian meals. Children's helpings. Wheelchair access (not WC). Music. Air-conditioned

MAP 15

Back to Basics

21A Foley Street, W1W 6DS
Tel: (020) 7436 2181
Website: www.backtobasics.uk.com

Cooking 1 | Seafood | £32–£58

Customers are offered a plastic bib to wear before tackling the gargantuan 'fisherman's fish soup' in this blue-painted Fitzrovia bistro. It's typical of the happy-go-lucky mood of the place – made even more appealing by the tables outside. Fish is the business here, although non-piscine alternatives are available. A few doubts about freshness and flair have surfaced of late, and some ideas (for example, grilled tuna steak topped with goats' cheese) seem 'doomed to failure'. That said, home-cured gravlax is pleasingly light, and the kitchen keeps things simple with dishes like sea bass with spring onions and ginger, or cod with crispy bacon and mushy pea salsa. 'Table Wines' (from £13) are augmented by an 'Alternative Cellar' of fine French vintages.

Chef: Stefan Pflaumer **Proprietor:** Ursula Higgs **Open:** Mon to Sat 12 to 3, 6 to 10.30 **Closed:** Christmas, bank hols **Meals:** alc (main courses £11 to £18.50) **Service:** 12.5% (optional), card slips closed **Cards:** Amex, Delta, Diners, Maestro, MasterCard, Visa **Details:** 40 seats. 60 seats outside. Private parties: 45 main room, 6 private room. Vegetarian meals. Children's helpings. No smoking in 1 dining room. Music **Tube:** Oxford Circus

MAP 12

Balham Bar & Kitchen AR

15–19 Bedford Hill, SW12 9EX
Tel: (020) 8675 6900

Breakfast starts the day at this ultra-trendy, glass-fronted rendezvous. Beyond that, the menu takes a chic brasserie view of things, offering 'small plates' of nibbles, salads and sandwiches as well as dishes like tomato tartare with basil purée (£7.50), fillet of sea bass with fennel and citrus fruits (£12.50) or rump of lamb 'pot-au-feu'. Finish with lemon tart or crème brûlée (£5). Sunday brunch from noon to 5. Glamorous cocktails and eclectic wines from £12.95. Open all week.

MAP 13

Baltic

74 Blackfriars Road, SE1 8HA
Tel: (020) 7928 1111
Website: www.balticrestaurant.co.uk

Cooking 2 | East/North European | £24–£57

Opposite Southwark Tube station, 'Baltic taps into the themes conjured by the name': trendy vodkas, a cool, 'striking' minimalist interior and cold-climate food from Eastern Europe. Beyond the mineral-toned, high-volume bar, the white-painted restaurant has close-packed tables, a high ceiling and skylights that let daylight pour in. Start with hearty Siberian dumplings filled with beef and pork, or Polish black sausage with braised Puy lentils and bacon. Then fennel-poached hake with spring vegetables and herbs offers an alternative to mostly meaty mains (perhaps salt beef with pickled vegetables and horseradish dumplings), while naleski (crêpes filled with sweet cheese, almonds and raisins) figure among the puddings. Wines are a fashionable global assemblage ordered by price from £12.50.

Chef: Mark Parris **Proprietor:** Jan Woroniecki **Open:** all week 12 to 3, 6 to 11.15 **Meals:** alc (main courses £10 to £15). Set L £11.50 (2 courses) to £13.50, Set D 6 to 7 £11.50 (2 courses) to £13.50 **Service:** 12.5% (optional), card slips closed **Cards:** Amex, Delta, Diners, Maestro, MasterCard, Visa **Details:** 100 seats. 15 seats outside. Private parties: 120 main room, 12 to 30 private rooms. Vegetarian meals. Wheelchair access (also WC). No music. Air-conditioned **Tube:** Southwark, Waterloo

AR	Not a full entry but provisionally recommended (known as 'round-ups' in previous editions, these 'also recommended' establishments are now integrated throughout the book).

MAP 13

Bank Aldwych/Bank Westminster

1 Kingsway, Aldwych, WC2B 6XF
Buckingham Gate, SW1E 6BS
Tel: (020) 7379 9797 (centralised number)
Website: www.bankrestaurants.com

Cooking 3 | Modern European | £32–£84

There are two Bank branches in London. The original in Aldwych is now ten years old and occupies most of the ground floor of an Art Deco-style office block, while its younger sibling at Buckingham Gate sits at the rear of the Crowne Plaza hotel. Both offer modern brasserie food of considerable liveliness and flair. Start perhaps with ham hock, Serrano and foie gras terrine with celeriac rémoulade, before going on to herb-crusted halibut with broad beans, or rump of lamb with mushroom duxelles, but note that more demotic dishes, such as fishcakes on spinach with butter sauce, receive good notices too. Finish with a roast pear served with pecan cake and bourbon cream, or satisfying autumn fruit compote with sablé biscuits and mascarpone cream. Service is reassuringly attentive. The Aldwych branch has the larger wine selection but the idea is the same in both: lively, brief selections balanced between classic and modern flavours and arranged by style, with smart bottles for high days and a healthy range by the glass. Eponymous house wines are £14.

Chef: Damien Pordevie (Aldwych), Matt Dawson (Westminster) **Proprietor:** Bank Restaurant Group plc **Open:** Mon to Fri L 12 to 2.45, Mon to Sat D 5.30 to 11; Aldwych also open Sat L 12 to 2.45 and Sun brunch 11.30 to 5 **Meals:** alc (main courses £12.50 to £28). Set L £13.50 (2 courses) to £16, Set D £13.50 (2 courses) to £17.95. Bar and (Aldwych only) breakfast menus available **Service:** 12.5% (optional) **Cards:** Amex, Delta, Diners, Maestro, MasterCard, Visa **Details:** 200 seats (Aldwych), 150 seats (Westminster). Private parties: 200 Adwych, 150 Westminster main room, 15 to 30 Aldwych, 22 to 44 Westminster private rooms. Vegetarian meals. Children's helpings. Wheelchair access (also WC). Music. Air-conditioned **Tube:** Holborn, St James's Park

MAP 13

Barnsbury

AR

209–211 Liverpool Road, N1 1LX
Tel: (020) 7607 5519

Regular art exhibitions catch the eye in this no-frills Islington gastro-pub, but the food is also worth attention. 'The kitchen knows its stuff and buys well', and new chef John O'Riordan has the pedigree to back it up. Open with scallops and Thai fragrant salad (£6.50), move on to roast chicken breast with Catalan broad beans and chorizo (£11.50), and finish nearer home with rhubarb and ginger crumble (£4.50). Organic wines make their mark on the enterprising wine list (prices from £12). Open all week. Reports, please.

MAP 15

Bellamy's

NEW ENTRY

18–18A Bruton Place, W1J 6LY
Tel: (020) 7491 2727

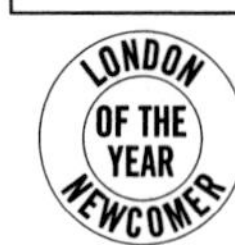

Cooking 5 | Brasserie | £45–£87

Bruton Place, off the north side of Berkeley Square, is shaping up to be quite a little gastronomic enclave. As well as Umu (see entry), it boasts this new French deli/brasserie. Look for the dark green canopies and exterior foliage, and proceed through the shop to the glass double doors that lead into the restaurant itself. With a bar at the back, comfortable banquettes and large framed art posters, the ambience seems spot-on, even though there is a faintly more pronounced sense of elegance than might be the case in the genuine Parisian article.

A fixed-price menu deals in the likes of oeufs mimosa, rock salmon with lemon and capers, and wild strawberry tart, while the carte furnishes scrambled eggs with summer truffles, caviar served straight, shellfish salads, red mullet with tapenade, roast guinea fowl provençale, and, of course, steak and chips. Good things at inspection included jelly-topped smoked eel mousse of great intensity and balance, navarin of spring lamb that delivered well-seasoned tender chunks of meat in a rounded tomato-based broth, and carefully made chocolate mousse that steered a course between 'airy nothingness and solid pastiness'. 'Polished and professional' service takes an interest, while avoiding the napkin-twirling reflex. Wines, printed on the reverse of the menu, are entirely French, as is only natural in the setting. Prices are steep, ascending like a sheer rock face from their base of £18 for Mâcon-Villages and Bordeaux Supérieur. There are plenty by the glass, though, from £4.75.

Chef: Stéphane Paloud **Proprietor:** Gavin Rankin **Open:** Mon to Fri L 12 to 2.15, Mon to Sat D 7 to 10.15 **Closed:** 24, 25 and 31 Dec, bank hols **Meals:** alc (main courses £16 to £22.50). Set L and D £22.50 (2 courses) to £26. Cover £1.50 **Service:** 12.5% (optional), card slips closed **Cards:** Amex, Delta, Maestro, MasterCard, Visa **Details:** 80 seats. Private parties: 80 main room. Vegetarian meals. Wheelchair access (not WC). No music. Air-conditioned

MAP 13

Belvedere

Off Abbotsbury Road, Holland Park, W8 6LU
Tel: (020) 7602 1238
Website: www.whitestarline.org.uk

Cooking 4 | Anglo-French | £34–£68

Stroll in Holland Park, or spend hours at the opera in summer, before making for the stylish Belvedere with its flamboyantly elegant dining hall. The menu stays mainly with classical brasserie favourites – parfait of foie gras and chicken livers, for example, or rillettes of duck with mixed leaves, cornichon and Poilâne toast – and breaks little new ground. Billy Reid's touch, though, is confident and sure, ranging from smoked haddock with warm potato salad and mustard butter, to calf's liver and bacon with sage jus. Desserts are equally reassuring, perhaps lemon tart or a tarte Tatin of pears. Set-price menus (lunchtime and early evening, two choices per course) are good value: potted shrimps; herb-battered fillet of whiting, broken peas, French fries and tartare sauce; treacle tart with clotted cream, say, all for £17.95. The wine list is arranged by grape variety, and engineers a reasonable balance between New and Old World styles, but there is little under £25; ten come by the glass from £4, and house wines start from £17.

Chef: Billy Reid **Proprietor:** Jimmy Lahoud **Open:** all week L 12 to 2.30 (3.15 Sun), Mon to Sat D 6 to 11 **Meals:** alc (main courses £13 to £19). Set L Mon to Sat £14.95 (2 courses) to £17.95, Set D 6 to 7 £14.95 (2 courses) to £17.95 **Service:** 12.5% (optional), card slips closed **Cards:** Amex, Delta, Diners, Maestro, MasterCard, Visa **Details:** 144 seats. 20 seats outside. Private parties: 60 main room. Vegetarian meals. Music. Air-conditioned **Tube:** Holland Park/High Street Kensington

MAP 15

Benares

12A Berkeley Square House, Berkeley Square, W1J 6BS
Tel: (020) 7629 8886
Website: www.benaresrestaurant.com

Cooking 3 | Modern Indian | £67–£104

Named after the holy city of Benares (now Varanasi), this glitzy contemporary Indian puts on the style with its tiled floor, staircase and lily ponds. The kitchen blends traditional ideas with contemporary flavours, jazzing up chicken curry with basil and straw mushrooms and serving grilled lamb chops with mustard and potato salad. The list of appetisers ranges from a mixed tandoori platter of lamb, chicken and salmon kebabs to jal tarang (a salad of scallops, prawns and oyster fritters with grapes and ginger dressing), while main courses offer sea bass poached in coconut milk and turmeric broth as well as classic rogan josh. Desserts can also turn up a few surprises like crisp date pastry with toasted cumin and kumquat juice. The cheapest bottle of wine on the patrician list is £23, although plenty are offered by the glass.

Chef/Proprietor: Atul Kochhar **Open:** Mon to Fri L 12.30 to 2.30, all week D 5.30 to 11 (6 to 10.30 Sun) **Meals:** alc (main courses £12 to £25). Set L £14.95 (2 courses), Set D 5.30 to 7.30 £17.95, Set D £59. Bar menu available **Service:** 12.5% (optional), card slips closed **Cards:** Amex, Delta, Diners, Maestro, MasterCard, Visa **Details:** 150 seats. Private parties: 100 main room, 12 to 22 private rooms. Vegetarian meals. No children after 8pm. No smoking. Music. Air-conditioned **Tube:** Green Park

MAP 14

Bentley, 1880

27–33 Harrington Gardens, SW7 4JX
Tel: (020) 7244 5361
Website: www.thebentley-hotel.com

Cooking 6 | Modern European | £65–£91

There are one or two comparably grand edifices in the environs of the Bentley, just off Gloucester Road, but none can surely have such a jaw-dropping effect as this one. One wonders whether there is an inch of marble left in Italy on progressing down the stairs to the basement restaurant, where a dazzling chandelier overhangs a gold-panelled room with large gilt mirrors and upholstered chairs that could seat minor royalty at a state occasion.

Andrew Turner has devised a series of menus for 'grazing' through his food. Comprised of seven to ten mini courses, these represent a good way of sampling the range. For only slightly more than the cost of the standard three-course structure, you might opt for a parade of seven, beginning at a soup of mushrooms and truffles, and then travelling through dishes of lobster, lasagne, and a seared Celtic scallop, to roast breast of Challans duck with confit leg and Savoy cabbage, before French cheeses presage the finishing line – lemon tart with almond ice cream. Presentation is as minutely considered as the surroundings seem to mandate, and if the odd dish suffers from overelaboration there is no questioning the soundness of flavours and combinations. Essaying a journey through the main carte might take you from smoked royal salmon fillet to pear soufflé à notre façon, via tournedos Rossini. Informative and friendly service assists relaxation. The wine list aims to inspire rather than overawe, so you will find good Côtes du Rhône by Guintrady (£21) alongside mature Hermitage from Chave at £380 and a vast list of wines by the glass from around £5 to £30.

Chef: Andrew Turner **Proprietor:** ILH Ltd **Open:** Tue to Sat D only 6 to 10 **Closed:** 10 days from 25 Dec, bank hols **Meals:** Set D £45 to £60 **Service:** not inc, card slips closed **Cards:** Amex, Delta, Diners, Maestro, MasterCard, Visa **Details:** 60 seats. Private parties: 70 main room, 12 to 14 private rooms. Vegetarian meals. No children under 10. No smoking. Wheelchair access (also WC). Music. No mobile phones. Air-conditioned **Accommodation:** 64 rooms, all with bath/shower. TV. Phone. Room only £199 to £350. Rooms for disabled. Baby facilities

MAP 15

Berkeley Square Restaurant

7 Davies Street, W1K 3DD
Tel: (020) 7629 6993
Website: www.theberkeleysquare.com

Cooking 6 | Modern French | £34–£84

Dropping 'Café' from this restaurant's name better represents its nature. These are cool, smart, understated premises off the north-west corner of Berkeley Square, with bright modern artworks enlivening the muted colour scheme. A black-tiled terrace with awning entices summer diners, and is heated when the weather turns nippier.

Steven Black's metropolitan restaurant food is slick, polished, artfully composed. The cheaper fixed-price menus – three choices per course and excellent value – may take in duck pressé with dried fruit chutney, then perhaps salmon fillet with sautéed potatoes, baby leeks and a mussel and saffron dressing, with dessert or cheese to finish. If your purse-strings are looser, though, the six choices per course can surprise with combinations like venison loin served with liquorice-scented pumpkin and preserved lemon purée, braised chicory and juniper berries. The odd over-exuberance can be forgiven and there are understated dishes too: fillet of Aberdeen Angus is served relatively plain with a medley of shredded wild mushrooms and shallots cooked in red wine. Desserts such as sweet-and-sour plum compote with hazelnut shortbread and ginger ice cream are followed by good coffee and petits fours, and service is generally praised.

The substantial wine list is French-led, with good coverage elsewhere, and a fine selection of dessert wines. Prices reflect the post-code, but there is an impressive opening list of 14 by the 150ml glass from £5.50.

Chef: Steven Black **Proprietors:** Vince Power and Steven Black **Open:** Mon to Fri 12 to 2.30, 6 to 10 **Closed:** 25 Dec, bank hols, last 2 weeks Aug **Meals:** Set L and D £12.95 (2 courses) to £45 **Service:** 12.5% (optional), card slips closed **Cards:** Amex, Delta, Diners, Maestro, MasterCard, Visa **Details:** 70 seats. 14 seats outside. Private parties: 60 main room, 8 to 14 private rooms. Vegetarian meals. Children's helpings. Occasional music. Air-conditioned

MAP 15

Bertorelli's

AR

44A Floral Street, WC2E 9DA
Tel: (020) 7836 3969

At this typically Italian restaurant the buzz is audible, service 'smooth and professional', and the menu plunders the Italian regional larder voraciously: buffalo mozzarella (in a salad with chargrilled vegetables; £6), prosciutto, risottos and linguine with clams (£11.50) all find their way on to the plate. Set-price lunch and a pre-theatre deal (£18.50 for three courses) and a lighter café, menu are notable options. The all-Italian wine list offers a fair choice under £20. Closed Sun L. Branches at 19 Charlotte Street, W1, tel: (020) 7636 4174, and 11 Frith Street, W1, tel: (020) 7494 3491.

MAP 14

Bibendum

Michelin House, 81 Fulham Road, SW3 6RD
Tel: (020) 7581 5817
Website: www.bibendum.co.uk

Cooking 3 | Modern British | £47–£111

Ascend the chrome-banistered stairway to the first-floor restaurant, and the view – particularly on a sunny daytime visit – is ravishing indeed. A tall, tunnel-vaulted, stained-glass window looks out over the Fulham Road, and the cream-painted walls, with their Michelin Man cartoons, contribute to the feeling of lightness. Highly polished renditions of European rustic cooking are what Bibendum has always been about, and some dishes are convincing. Grilled fillet of bream with Jerusalem artichoke purée, strozzapreti dumplings and garlicky greens delivered ample flavour at inspection, and generously served guinea fowl with porcini cannelloni and peas was rich and filling. Other dishes – overly gelatinous fish soup, an attempt at a tarte fine aux pommes that missed by a long way through undercooked pastry and unadorned apple – suggest a lack of adequate concentration for the prices.

The wine list remains a star, although service has been found wanting. Inspiring ranges from the French regions culminate in a lavish showing of Bordeaux and Burgundy, while Australia leads the charge for the New World. Ritzy bottles are part and parcel of the experience, but Tim Adams Riesling looks good value at £19.95 and there is no shortage of options in the £20 to £30 range.

Chef: Matthew Harris **Proprietors:** Sir Terence Conran, Simon Hopkinson, Michael Hamlyn and Graham Williams **Open:** all week 12 to 2.30 (12.30 to 3 Sat and Sun), 7 to 11.30 (10.30 Sun) **Closed:** D 24 Dec to 27 Dec **Meals:** alc D (main courses £16.50 to £29). Set L £28.50 **Service:** 12.5% (optional) **Cards:** Amex, Delta, Diners, Maestro, MasterCard, Visa **Details:** 88 seats. Private parties: 90 main room. Children's helpings. No music. No mobile phones. Air-conditioned

MAP 12

Bistro Aix

54 Topsfield Parade, Tottenham Lane, N8 8PT
Tel: (020) 8340 6346
Website: www.bistroaix.co.uk

Cooking 3 | French | £26–£61

This quirkily furnished neighbourhood bistro offers warm colours, friendly service and food that certainly appeals to Crouch End residents. Classic onion soup or house pâté with cornichons and salad might be followed by wild mushroom and white truffle risotto ('excellent – full of flavour'), or roast sea bass with citrus and coriander sauce, grilled avocado, spinach and pine nuts. Tender lamb shank with celeriac mash is praised and 'the best venison I have tasted', with whisky sauce, parsnip chips and leek mash. Desserts ensnared one party, who, with 'much exchanging of spoonfuls', demolished an apple tarte Tatin, citron tart, and warm chocolate moelleuse with griottines, vanilla ice cream and chocolate sauce. The good-value set lunch has also been endorsed. A short list of fair-value wines (mostly French) opens at £12.

Chef: Lynne Sanders **Proprietors:** Lynne Sanders and Andrew Schutt **Open:** Tue to Sun; 12 to 2.30, 6.30 to 10.30 **Closed:** 26 Dec, 1 Jan **Meals:** alc (main courses £10.50 to £18). Set L £11.50 (2 courses) to £16.50, Set D Tue to Fri and Sun £13.50 (2 courses) to £16.50 **Service:** 12.5% (optional), card slips closed **Cards:** Amex, Delta, Diners, Maestro, MasterCard, Visa **Details:** 70 seats. Private parties: 50 main room, 24 private room. Vegetarian meals. No cigars/pipes. Wheelchair access (not WC). Music. Air-conditioned

MAP 15

Blandford Street

5–7 Blandford Street, W1U 3DB
Tel: (020) 7486 9696
Website: www.blandford-street.co.uk

Cooking 3 | Modern European | £33–£73

'Has the edge for relaxing atmosphere and décor and sophisticated food,' writes an enthusiast. Others have concurred, liking the colour scheme and decent space between tables. The food takes a broadly European perspective, with a carte that starts with Jerusalem artichoke tartlet with a salad of endive and orange, gravad lax with pickled cucumber and dill mustard, and grilled fillets of red mullet with fennel and cuttlefish paella. Main dishes are mostly classics with a modern touch: a well-reported slow-roast shoulder of lamb with flageolet beans, roast garlic, glazed carrots and button onions, for example, or roast rare-breed pork chop with Riesling choucroute, frankfurters, bacon and parsley potatoes. The daily-changing set menu is good value, 'friendly, attentive' describes the service, and wines are divided almost evenly between France and the rest of the world. House vins de pays are £16.

Chef: Martin Moore **Proprietor:** Nicholas Lambert **Open:** Sun to Fri L 12 to 2.30, Mon to Sat D 6.30 to 10.30 **Closed:** Christmas, bank hols **Meals:** alc (main courses £11 to £20). Set L Mon to Fri £15 (2 courses) to £19.50, Set L Sun £20 (2 courses) to £25, Set D £15 (2 courses) to £19.50 **Service:** 12.5% (optional), card slips closed **Cards:** Amex, Delta, Diners, Maestro, MasterCard, Visa **Details:** 50 seats. 10 seats outside. Private parties: 50 main room, 12 to 18 private rooms. Vegetarian meals. No-smoking area. Wheelchair access (not WC). Occasional music. Air-conditioned **Tube:** Bond Street, Baker Street

MAP 13

Bleeding Heart

The Cellars, Bleeding Heart Yard, Greville St, EC1N 8SJ
Tel: (020) 7242 8238
Website: www.bleedingheart.co.uk

Cooking 2 | French | £39–£66

Tucked down a little alley, Bleeding Heart looks as if it could be that elusive thing in the City: a great little local restaurant. Indeed, with its three-pronged operation – tavern, bistro, restaurant – relaxed feel and considerable charm, it certainly draws a loyal following. Whatever else, the kitchen is a busy one, delivering strident Anglo-French cooking to the pretty basement restaurant. Luxuries include foie gras with a winter fruit compote, and truffled mushrooms in a wild mushroom risotto, but no attempt is made to shock with outrageous ingredients. Classical foundation is evident – duck terrine en croûte, chateaubriand with sauce béarnaise – and combinations can be as simple as roast breast of chicken with sautéed tagliarini and Parmesan. Desserts include pear tarte Tatin with honey ice cream, and warm chocolate pudding with pistachio ice cream. Bordeaux and Burgundy cater to a clientele who know their vintages, but the special strength of the global wine collection is New Zealand, including the house bottles from Trinity Hill (£16.45 for white, £19.95 for red). Magnums and larger bottles for celebratory dining are a speciality, while around 20 come by the glass.

Chef: Pascal Even **Proprietors:** Robert and Robyn Wilson **Open:** Mon to Fri 12 to 2.35, 7 to 10.30 **Closed:** 10 days at Christmas **Meals:** alc (main courses £12 to £21.50). Set L £29.95 **Service:** 12.5% (optional), card slips closed **Cards:** Amex, Delta, Diners, Maestro, MasterCard, Visa **Details:** 150 seats. 40 seats outside. Private parties: 150 main room, 30 to 60 private rooms. Vegetarian meals. No children under 7. No-smoking area. No pipes in dining room. No music. No mobile phones. Air-conditioned **Tube:** Farringdon

MAP 14

Bluebird Dining Room AR

350 King's Road, SW3 5UU
Tel: (020) 7559 1129

Majestic, awesomely designed Conran outpost crowned by a sleek skylit roof running the length of the vast room. A 'handsome crowd' packs the place for oysters, crustacea and starters like potted poultry livers with onion marmalade (£6.50), while creditable main courses range from grilled Charolais sirloin with herb butter (£17) to pan-fried wild sea bass with parsley salad and tapenade. Rhubarb and vanilla fool (£6) is a typical pudding. Eclectic, realistically priced wines from £16. Open Sun L and Mon to Sat D.

To submit a report on any restaurant, please visit *www.which.co.uk/gfgfeedback*.

MAP 12

Blue Elephant

3–6 Fulham Broadway, SW6 1AA
Tel: (020) 7385 6595
Website: www.blueelephant.com

Cooking 1 | Thai | £36–£80

London's most extravagant Thai restaurant is certainly out to impress, with its ornate bar, carp ponds, waterfalls and luxuriant floral displays. The menu is equally flamboyant, dressing up classic dishes with exotic titles and offering full measure for vegetarians. Familiar items like fishcakes, somtum salad and roast duck curry are augmented by eyebrow-raising crossovers including seared foie gras with tamarind sauce, British rack of lamb with kapraow sauce, wild rice and fried basil, or stir-fried black spaghetti with seafood, tomatoes and garlic. Desserts range from coconut-based sodsai to jackfruit cheesecake, while Sunday brunch is a buffet bonanza complete with 'live cooking demonstrations and face-painting for children'. The lengthy, global wine list opens its account at £17.

Chef: Somphong Sae-Jew **Proprietor:** Blue Elephant International plc **Open:** Mon to Fri L 12 to 2.30, Sun brunch 12 to 3.30, all week D 7 (6.30 Fri and Sat) to 12 (10.30 Sun) **Closed:** 25 to 28 Dec **Meals:** alc (main courses £10 to £19.50). Set L Mon to Fri £10 (2 courses), Set D £33 to £53 **Service:** 12.5% (optional), card slips closed **Cards:** Amex, Delta, Diners, Maestro, MasterCard, Visa **Details:** 350 seats. Private parties: 350 main room, 10 to 350 private rooms. Vegetarian meals. Children's helpings. Wheelchair access (also WC). Music. Air-conditioned **Tube:** Fulham Broadway

MAP 13

Blueprint Café

Design Museum, 28 Shad Thames, SE1 2YD
Tel: (020) 7378 7031
Website: www.conran.com

Cooking 2 | Modern European | £40–£69

'Next-to-river' tables are highly sought after in this light, airy restaurant on the first floor of the Design Museum, and mini-binoculars are provided for diners to savour the stunning views over the Thames from London Bridge to Canary Wharf. Upfront culinary ideas, from a starter of preserved garlic, goats' cheese and tapenade to main-dish poached ox tongue with beetroot and horseradish, suit the tone of the place, although results can be 'hit-and-miss'; vegetables are extra. Recent successes have included razor clams with a parsley crust, and braised mutton stew with broad beans, bacon and mint, followed by rich apricot and plum tart with Jersey cream. The main wine list opens with house selections from £15.

Chef: Jeremy Lee **Proprietor:** Conran Restaurants Ltd **Open:** all week L 12 to 3, Mon to Sat D 6 to 11 **Meals:** alc (main courses £12.50 to £19.50). **Service:** 12.5% (optional), card slips closed **Cards:** Amex, Delta, Diners, Maestro, MasterCard, Visa **Details:** 120 seats. 16 seats outside. Private parties: 120 main room. Vegetarian meals. Children's helpings. Wheelchair access (not WC). No music **Tube:** Tower Hill/London Bridge

MAP 13

Bonds

NEW ENTRY

Threadneedle Hotel, 5 Threadneedle Street, EC2R 8AY
Tel: (020) 7657 8088
Website: www.theetoncollection.com

Cooking 6 | Modern European | £47–£92

The Threadneedle Hotel was formerly the headquarters of Citibank, making this another palatial temple to Mammon now wholesomely rededicated to hospitality. It's worth having a quick sashay around the sensational lobby, even if you aren't a resident, before heading for the more understated restaurant, where walnut panelling and subtle lighting make for a muted atmosphere, and tables are widely enough spaced.

Barry Tonks took over the kitchen in summer 2004, having previously worked at McClements in Twickenham (see entry). The style is modern European, with a pronounced French accent, with prices reflecting the ambience. A tian of Cornish crab has been a triumph, not overpowered by mayonnaise but successfully partnered by pink grapefruit jelly and a bavarois of peas and pistachios. That seam of considered innovation also runs through dishes such as sautéed foie gras with pain d'épice, mango confit and a syrup of Banyuls, and in main courses such as sea bass with mirepoix of earthy vegetables and stringy mozzarella. More mainstream has been an 'assured and confident' serving of tender noisettes of lamb with sweetbreads and new season's garlic. Tarte Tatin with Calvados crème fraîche is a benchmark rendition of a classic dessert, avoiding over-caramelisation. Fine coffee is served in classy cobalt-blue crockery, with seductive dark chocolates to accompany. Service, sad to say, needs a lot more training to begin to be commensurate with the surroundings. A clued-up wine list leans towards quality French estates with a modern outlook, offering the likes of Cristia's supple Châteauneuf or Nozay's super-ripe Sancerre. Prices reflect the location, but there are drinkable bottles for under £20 and an inspired range of 18 by the glass.

Chef: Barry Tonks **Proprietor:** Peter Tyrie **Open:** Mon to Fri 12 to 2.30, 6 to 10 **Closed:** 24 Dec, 4 Jan **Meals:** alc (main courses £17.50 to £27). Set L £23.50 (2 courses) to £29.50, Set D £60. Bar menu available **Service:** 12.5% (optional), card slips closed **Cards:** Amex, Delta, Maestro, MasterCard, Visa **Details:** 80 seats. Private parties: 6 to 16 private rooms. Vegetarian meals. Children's helpings. No smoking. Wheelchair access (also WC). Music. Air-conditioned **Accommodation:** 69 rooms, all with bath/shower. TV. Phone. B&B £305 to £535. Rooms for disabled **Tube:** Bank

MAP 14

Boxwood Café

The Berkeley, Wilton Place, SW1X 7RL
Tel: (020) 7235 1010
Website: www.gordonramsay.com

Cooking 3 | Modern British | £38–£90

Like its neighbour Pétrus elsewhere in the building (see entry), the Boxwood falls within the Gordon Ramsay aegis, but, despite the address, its main entrance is on Knightsbridge. It's a split-level basement venue, with a bustling bar, smart table settings and properly attentive staff. Stuart Gillies cooks an extensive menu of fairly simple brasserie dishes, the range running from pickled Arctic herrings with new potatoes and crème fraîche to chargrilled veal rump with roast ceps and herb-crusted vine tomatoes. Barely seared yellowfin tuna with fennel, red onion and black pepper sauce is served only just warm, like much else, but is well timed and impeccably fresh. Desserts take in blood orange and vanilla cheesecake, and rice pudding with Armagnac prunes. A well-selected, Knightsbridge-priced wine list is supplemented by a reserve list of bottles mostly in three or more figures. Drink by the glass from £4.75.

Chef: Stuart Gillies **Proprietor:** Gordon Ramsay Holdings Ltd **Open:** all week 12 to 3 (4 Sat and Sun), 6 to 11 **Meals:** alc (main courses £8.50 to £25). Set L Mon to Fri £21, Set L Sat and Sun £18.50. Cover £2 **Service:** not inc **Cards:** Amex, Delta, Maestro, MasterCard, Visa **Details:** 140 seats. Private parties: 120 main room, 12 to 16 private rooms. Vegetarian meals. Children's helpings. No smoking. Wheelchair access (not WC). Music. Air-conditioned **Tube:** Knightsbridge

This symbol means that the restaurant has elected to participate in *The Good Food Guide's* £5 voucher scheme (see 'How to Use the Guide' for details).

MAP 12

Brackenbury

129–131 Brackenbury Road,
W6 0BQ
Tel: (020) 8748 0107

Cooking 4 | Modern European | £25–£51

At the far end of a residential street off Goldhawk Road, with a terrace for summer dining, the Brackenbury really delivers the goods. It specialises in a straightforward style with terrines, omelettes and steaks, as well as straight-up dishes of scallop and leek risotto and confit duck leg with chorizo hashed potatoes. The pattern is eight choices per course at dinner and at lunchtime a slightly shorter carte with a three-course fixed-price menu as an alternative. Salad combinations like the one of pear, beetroot, pistachio nut, Roquefort and mixed leaves should fire up the appetite. Richer fare might be loin of pork with choucroute, sauce soubise, straw potatoes and apple purée, or roast cod with spinach, forestière potatoes and red wine jus; vegetarians could pick a mushroom duxelles and spinach tart with a truffled poached egg and hollandaise. Puddings bring on Agen prune and brandy crème brûlée, or white chocolate mousse with champagne jelly and raspberries. The short, global wine list opens with southern French vins de pays at £12.

Chef: Noel Capp **Proprietor:** Lisa Inglis **Open:** Sun to Fri L 12.30 to 2.45 (3.30 Sun) Mon to Sat D, 7 to 10.45 **Closed:** 25 Dec, 1 Jan, Easter **Meals:** alc (main courses £9.50 to £16). Set L Mon to Fri £12.50 (2 courses) to £14.50 **Service:** 12.5% (optional), card slips closed **Cards:** Amex, Delta, Maestro, MasterCard, Visa **Details:** 65 seats. 20 seats outside. Private parties: 65 main room, 20 to 40 private rooms. Vegetarian meals. Children's helpings. No smoking at D, no smoking in 1 dining room at L. No music **Tube:** Hammersmith

MAP 13

Bradleys

25 Winchester Road, NW3 3NR
Tel: (020) 7722 3457

Cooking 3 | Modern French | £28–£74

This contemporary dining room on a quiet street behind Swiss Cottage has a 'quite luxurious feel'. The cuisine – unashamedly French, and modern but not aggressively so – has a backbone of fairly conservative dishes enlivened by surprise elements like spiced crushed black truffle potatoes and cardamom oil with scallops, and seared foie gras and spinach and grappa sauce with Barbary duck breast and confit leg. Highlights have included a sole soufflé with foaming chive sauce; a caramelized chicory Tatin accompanying saddle of rabbit; and roast halibut delicately smoked with Australian paperbark chips, giving an 'elusive, aromatic, wonderful flavour'. Vegetables are extra. Rhubarb savarin with rhubarb ice cream, and an orange and almond flour-free cake, have been appreciated, and reporters hail the 'friendly, courteous' service. The French-led wine list is arranged by style, has plenty by the glass and emphasizes affordable bottles like the straightforward Loire white, Petit Bourgeois (£17.50).

Chef: Stephen Englefield **Proprietors:** Simon and Jolanta Bradley **Open:** Tue to Fri and Sun L 12 to 3, Tue to Sat D 6 to 11 **Closed:** 1 week Christmas, bank hols **Meals:** alc (not Sun L; main courses £12 to £25.50). Set L £12 (2 courses) to £16, Set Sun L £18 (2 courses) to £22, Set D £23 **Service:** 12.5% (optional), card slips closed **Cards:** Amex, Delta, Maestro, MasterCard, Visa **Details:** 60 seats. Private parties: 60 main room. Vegetarian meals. No cigars/pipes. Wheelchair access (not WC). Music. No mobile phones. Air-conditioned **Tube:** Swiss Cottage

MAP 12

Brady's

AR

513 Old York Road, SW18 1TF
Tel: (020) 8877 9599

Now in its sixteenth year, this family-run Wandsworth fish-and-chip restaurant continues to be popular with locals who know a good piece of haddock when they see one. The formula remains the same, with choice running from cod, plaice or skate, done in the lightest batter (from £8), to grilled mackerel, Dover sole (£13), or swordfish. Start with salmon fishcake (£2.50), or potted shrimps (£3.50), and finish with apple crumble (£2.25). House wine £9.95. Open Mon to Sat D only.

MAP 14

Brasserie St Quentin

243 Brompton Road, SW3 2EP
Tel: (020) 7589 8005
Website: www.brasseriestquentin.co.uk

Cooking 3 | Modern French | £30–£75

More Parisian Left Bank than Brompton Road south side (opposite the Oratory), this characteristic French brasserie has burgundy banquettes, dark-wood floor, etched mirrors, buzzy atmosphere and pleasant staff. Friendly, relaxed and with a warm welcome from an 'urbane' maître d', the setting perfectly fits the archetypal brasserie menu of unpretentious cuisine and top-quality ingredients. Classics – like seared foie gras with caramelised apples and green peppercorns, feuilletté d'escargot à la crème d'ail, or grilled ribeye with sauce béarnaise and pommes frites – rub shoulders with more contemporary influences, perhaps scallops served with pancetta, green beans and sesame dressing, or steamed salmon with sweet ginger and chilli dressing. The likes of hot chocolate fondant (with orange ice cream) or passion-fruit brûlée return to classic mode at dessert, while the patriotically French-dominated wine list (helpfully annotated) offers a good selection by the glass and half-bottle, with house kicking things off at £14.50 (£4.25 by the glass).

Chef: Gary Durrant **Proprietor:** Brasserie St Quentin Ltd **Open:** all week 12 to 3, 6 to 10.30 (10 Sun) **Meals:** alc (main courses £11.50 to £23.50). Set L £15.50 (2 courses) to £17.50, Set D 6 to 7.30 £15.50 (2 courses) to £17.50 **Service:** 12.5% (optional) **Cards:** Amex, Delta, Diners, Maestro, MasterCard, Visa **Details:** 60 seats. 4 seats outside. Private parties: 12 main room, 6 to 20 private rooms. Vegetarian meals. No cigars/pipes. Occasional music. Air-conditioned **Tube:** Knightsbridge, South Kensington

MAP 12

Burlington

AR

1 Station Parade, W4 3HD
Tel: (020) 8995 3344

Redmond and Pippa Hayward's second neighbourhood bistro (see Redmond's) sees them opting for a similar style of contemporary British cooking. Typical dishes might be cep and red wine risotto (£5.75), braised lamb shank with rosemary gratin dauphinois (£12), and organic salmon with caponata, smoked salmon fritter and lemon dressing, while a reporter was particularly pleased to round things off with passion-fruit pannacotta (£5.25). Service was slow for one reader. About 50 wines rise from £12. Closed Sat L, Mon L and Sun D.

🍷	This symbol means that the wine list is well above the average.
🍾	This symbol means that the restaurant has a truly outstanding wine cellar.

MAP 15

Café du Jardin

28 Wellington Street, WC2E 7BD
Tel: (020) 7836 8769/8760
Website: www.lecafedujardin.com

Cooking 2 | Modern British | £23–£62

Covent Garden eating places come and go, but this remains a sought-after destination for theatre-goers, tourists and others seeking fun and eclectic food. That is due largely to Tony Howorth, who has been at the stoves since 1993. Brasserie old-stagers like Caesar salad and ribeye steak with frites and béarnaise sauce share the stage with pasta, risottos and a mixed bag of dishes from boudin blanc with braised red cabbage and morels, or grilled loin of venison with balsamic-glazed carrots and madeira jus, to seared smoked salmon and juniper-scented vegetables, or fillet of sea bass with sweet-and-sour fennel and brown butter vinaigrette. Vegetables are extra. Dependable desserts like raspberry cheesecake and sticky toffee pudding with caramel sauce close the show.

Italy and Australia look particularly tempting on an international list packed with good wines at fair prices, starting with house bottles at £11.50. France appeals too, and for enthusiasts there's a much pricier fine wine list. Note the 15% service charge.

Chef: Tony Howorth **Proprietors:** Robert Seigler and Tony Howorth **Open:** all week 12 to 3, 5.30 to 12 (noon to 11 Sun) **Closed:** 24 and 25 Dec **Meals:** alc (main courses £9.50 to £16). Set L £10.95 (2 courses) to £14.50, Set D Mon to Sat 5.30 to 7.30 and 10 to 12 (noon to 11 Sun) £10.95 (2 courses) to £14.50 **Service:** 15% (optional), card slips closed **Cards:** Amex, Delta, Maestro, MasterCard, Visa **Details:** 110 seats. 22 seats outside. Private parties: 60 main room. Wheelchair access (not WC). Occasional music. Air-conditioned **Tube:** Covent Garden

MAP 12

Café Japan

626 Finchley Road, NW11 7RR
Tel: (020) 8455 6854

Cooking 4 | Japanese | £20–£52

Koichi Konnai's likeable Japanese eating house has something of the bustle and enthusiasm of a café/deli, with its rows of utilitarian pine tables and busy counter. Sushi plays a major role here, and a brigade of cooks deliver a vast range: tuna, sea bass, flying fish roe, and more, have all passed the quality test. The menu also takes in various 'inside-out' rolls, sashimi, and a number of hot dishes, including salt-grilled salmon neck (with 'delicious' skin) and a version of that fusion legend, grilled miso-marinated black cod. Familiar appetisers, from edamame beans to age-tofu (fried bean curd), start the ball rolling, and ice creams (perhaps aduki red bean or kuri chestnut) are a fine way to finish. House wine is £8.50; otherwise drink tea, beer or saké. Note that it's cash only and no bookings at lunchtime, when the menu has been expanded to include a few more cooked dishes and specials.

Chef/Proprietor: Koichi Konnai **Open:** Sat and Sun L 12 to 2, Wed to Sun D 6 to 10 (9.30 Sun) **Closed:** 3 weeks Aug **Meals:** alc (main courses £4.50 to £20). Set L £8.50 (2 courses), Set D £12 (2 courses) to £18 **Service:** not inc **Cards:** Maestro, MasterCard, Visa **Details:** 39 seats. No smoking. Music. Air-conditioned **Tube:** Golders Green

MAP 13

Café Spice Namaste

16 Prescot Street, E1 8AZ
Tel: (020) 7488 9242
Website: www.cafespice.co.uk

Cooking 2 | Indian | £37–£70

Vibrant colours define the cavernous interior, and visitors can expect to be cosseted in Cyrus Todiwala's high-profile contemporary Indian. The menu reads well, and the food shows a fair degree of subtlety: 'while there were some hot dishes, the emphasis seemed to be on spice and full flavour,' noted one couple. All manner of British regional ingredients can appear in unexpected guises: samosas are filled with Cheltenham beetroot and coconut; Suffolk wild boar chipolatas are cooked in vindaloo masala. Elsewhere, sea bass is given an Indo-Chinese twist with sweet-and-sour chilli and garlic sauce, and guinea fowl is used for a rich korma. Desserts have included a comforting warm 'custard' pudding spiced with nutmeg, ginger and cardamom. Wines have been chosen to complement the food, with prices starting at £14.50. Parsee is under the same ownership (see entry).

Chef: Angelo Collaco **Proprietor:** Cyrus Todiwala **Open:** Mon to Fri L 12 to 2.45, Mon to Sat D 6.15 to 8.30 **Meals:** alc (main courses £8 to £18). Set L and D £30 to £40 **Service:** 12.5% (optional), card slips closed **Cards:** Amex, Delta, Diners, Maestro, MasterCard, Visa **Details:** 120 seats. 60 seats outside. Private parties: 90 main room, 30 to 40 private rooms. Vegetarian meals. Music. Air-conditioned **Tube:** Tower Hill

MAP 12

Calcutta Notebook

201 Replingham Road, SW18 5LY
Tel: (020) 8874 6603
Website: www.sarkhels.com

Cooking 3 | Bengali | £28–£53

In 2003 Udit Sarkhel opened this specialist Bengali restaurant right next door to Sarkhel's itself (see entry), having drawn inspiration from his grandmother's classical cooking and also from his mother's more frugal approach to things culinary. The result is a menu that kicks off with a fascinating collection of Calcutta street snacks, including such rare delights as mochar chop (potato croquettes filled with chopped banana flowers), and ghugni (spiced curried peas topped with date chutney and roast cumin). More substantial dishes run to kakrar jhal (chilli-hot blue swimming crab and green onion stew), goat curry, and chicken rezala (cooked with almonds, dried plums, and shallots). There are also meatless 'niramish' specialities like potoler dolma (wax gourd stuffed with cottage cheese and raisins). 'Canteen refreshments' are available from noon to 6pm. House wine is £10.90.

Chef: Udit Sarkhel **Proprietors:** Udit and Veronica Sarkhel **Open:** Tue to Sun 12 to 2.30, 6 to 10.30 (11 Fri and Sat) **Meals:** alc (main courses £7.50 to £10). Set L and D £18 **Service:** not inc **Cards:** Maestro, MasterCard, Visa **Details:** 28 seats. Private parties: 36 main room. Vegetarian meals. Children's helpings. No smoking. Music. Air-conditioned **Tube:** Southfields

MAP 14

Cambio de Tercio

163 Old Brompton Road, SW5 0LJ
Tel: (020) 7244 8970
Website: www.cambiodetercio.com

Cooking 3 | Modern Spanish | £44–£72

Right down to the bold décor of the national colours, matador paintings and a warm, lively atmosphere, this is clearly a place proud of its Spanish accent. White-clothed tables are closely packed, and there's an airier conservatory back room, a polished metal bar upfront and a few pavement tables outside under an awning for fair-weather dining. The food has authenticity but ambition and modern style too, with vibrant flavours and some stunning presentation gracing a lengthy repertoire packed with interest. Roast piquillo peppers stuffed with monkfish, or perhaps fried cakes of Majorcan sobrasada (local soft chorizo) in a white-wine sauce could catch the eye to begin with, while among hearty, rustic mains, a loin and rack of lamb with a stew of its sweetbreads, mushrooms and chard might vie for attention. To finish, a hot liquid hazelnut chocolate cake with creamy mint ice cream will keep the crowds flocking back. Service is suitably swift, professional and eager.

Wine is an all-Spanish affair and the list naturally opens with an inspired range of sherries by the glass. The main selection gives a superb account of traditional and modern Spain, starting with the finest bottles (including some long-cellared Riojas) and working its way down to more everyday drinking from £16.75.

Chefs: Alberto Criado and Javier Jimenez **Proprietor:** Abel Lusa **Open:** all week 12.15 to 2.30, 6.45 to 11.30 **Closed:** 2 weeks at Christmas **Meals:** alc (main courses £14 to £17) **Service:** not inc, card slips closed, 12.5% for parties of 6 or more **Cards:** Amex, Delta, Maestro, MasterCard, Visa **Details:** 45 seats. 8 seats outside. Private parties: 80 main room, 20 private rooms. Wheelchair access (not WC). Music. Air-conditioned **Tube:** Gloucester Road

MAP 15

Camerino

16 Percy Street, W1T 1DT
Tel: (020) 7637 9900
Website: www.camerinorestaurant.com

Cooking 3 | Italian | £35–£60

Despite its name change, the erstwhile Paolo hasn't altered in any material respect. From the start it gained plaudits – and crowds of diners – for its 'modern setting' and for serving Italian food to an appreciated formula: a concise menu that follows the Italian style (four courses, with pasta for the second) and juxtaposes classics like venison bresaola (with rocket salad, celeriac and mayonnaise) with trendier offerings including ravioli of pheasant with rosemary sauce. Reporters have been generous in praise of grilled scallops with grilled radicchio, or organic chestnut tagliatelle with mixed wild mushrooms, and of mains of veal kidneys with artichokes and lentils, and baked sea bream with spinach and olive paste. 'Pleasantly efficient' staff work the tables with consummate skill, uncorking bottles from an all-Italian list that opens in Sicily and Puglia at £13.50, but only hits its stride above £20.

Chef: Valerio Daros **Proprietor:** Paolo Boschi **Open:** Mon to Fri L 12 to 3, Mon to Sat D 6 to 11 **Closed:** 24 to 26 Dec, 1 Jan, Easter Mon **Meals:** Set L £17.50 (2 courses) to £25.50, Set D £23.50 (2 courses) to £31.50 **Service:** 12.5% (optional), card slips closed **Cards:** Amex, Delta, Diners, Maestro, MasterCard, Visa **Details:** 65 seats. 8 seats outside. Private parties: 80 main room. Vegetarian meals. Children's helpings. No pipes/cigars. Wheelchair access (not WC). Music. Air-conditioned **Tube:** Tottenham Court Road, Goodge Street

MAP 13

Cantaloupe

AR

35–42 Charlotte Road, EC2A 3PD
Tel: (020) 7613 4411

Trendy Hoxton rendezvous serving a fiery assortment of Iberian and Latin American dishes in high-decibel surroundings. The open-to-view kitchen delivers dishes like fish, potato and parsley croquetas with saffron aïoli (£5), grilled steaks from Brazilian beef, and breast of duck with pomegranate and walnut sauce (£12.50). Finish with Peruvian dark chocolate and coffee pot with pistachio ice cream. All-day tapas bar menu, cocktails, trendy beers and gluggable wines from £12.50. Closed Sat L and Sun L.

MAP 14

The Capital

22–26 Basil Street, SW3 1AT
Tel: (020) 7591 1202
Website: www.capitalrestaurant.co.uk

Cooking 8 | French | £52–£174

The Capital dining room was born again in 2004. What was felt by some to have been a rather dated ambience previously has been given a gentle makeover, with the predominant hue still muted fawn, the necessary splash of colour coming in the form of mid-blue seating, upholstery and drapes. Never the grandest of grand-hotel dining rooms in dimension, it seems, if anything, more intimate still, an impression reinforced by the closing off of the little hatchway that used to allow a discreet glimpse into the kitchen.

For the rest, the ship sails on. The extravagantly talented Eric Chavot has been here since 1999, and the cooking occupies a rarefied niche at the top end of modern French haute cuisine. Menus are in English and not in the slightest given to flights of gastronomic rhetoric, although the quality of what turns up on the plate is such that we might forgive

Chavot if they were. Lunch seems a relative bargain, as was discovered again by a reporter who began with langoustine tortellini in matching consommé, a 'terrifically subtle warm broth that revealed more layers of complexity with each spoonful'. A main course of halibut was boldly partnered with tempura-style battered slices of chorizo, a small piece of belly pork and a meaty jus. Alongside it was a separate bowl of braised choucroute in lightly truffled velouté, with a tower of fondant potato.

In the evenings, the cooking moves up another gear but remains hearteningly willing to use more rustic ingredients as well as the expected luxuries. Snails (with scallops), frogs' legs with veal sweetbreads in a fricassee, and Puy lentils with sautéed foie gras all appear among starters, while main courses might take in a serving of rabbit saddle provençale with white beans and a risotto of seared calamari and tomato. Risotto might also be on offer at dessert stage, an orange and chestnut version with chestnut ice cream being the highlight of one reporter's January visit. Other dishes are tantalisingly terse, leaving you to discover for yourself what 'pineapple and tarragon' or 'texture of apple and ginger' might bring. An assiette of miniatures is available for the indecisive. Service is routinely commended as flawless.

As always, our postbag is full of complaints about the wine mark-ups. There is nothing of interest under £25 and, as one reporter advises, 'it is probably best to ignore the French classics'. For the handsomely resourced, the choice is magnificent, but for mere mortals even the wines by the glass are served in a parsimonious 125ml measure and start at £6.

Chef: Eric Chavot **Proprietor:** David Levin **Open:** all week 12 to 2.30, 7 to 11 **Meals:** Set L £29.50, Set D £48 (2 courses) to £115 (inc wine) **Service:** 12.5% (optional) **Cards:** Amex, Delta, Diners, Maestro, MasterCard, Visa **Details:** 33 seats. Private parties: 35 main room, 24 private room. Vegetarian meals. No children under 10. No smoking. Wheelchair access (not WC). No music. Air-conditioned **Accommodation:** 49 rooms, all with bath/shower. TV. Phone. Room only £175 to £275. Baby facilities **Tube:** Knightsbridge

MAP 15

Le Caprice

Arlington House, Arlington Street, SW1A 1RT
Tel: (020) 7629 2239
Website: www.caprice-holdings.co.uk

Cooking 4 | Modern British | £39–£86

Monochrome pictures, a black carpet, glitzy mirror-backed bar, and flattering up-lighters create a 'slightly dated effect but not jarringly so'. The atmosphere is busy and bustling, and every care is taken with ingredients – one reporter, though, rightly described the cover charge of £2 a head as 'particularly cheeky'. The menu is a greatest-hits list of modern brasserie cooking: eggs Benedict, dressed crab with celeriac rémoulade, salmon fishcake with sorrel sauce, steak tartare, and calf's liver with champ and crispy bacon. The output is consistent, and good quality is to the fore – for instance, the girolles in the risotto with wild garlic. Choose elderflower jelly with seasonal fruits, treacle tart and clotted cream, or cheeses to finish. Espresso is excellent, especially when teamed with 'unbelievably rich' chocolate cookies and brownies, and service is 'fabulously pampering', although some have been frustrated by the time-limit on tables. Good producers feature on the sharply chosen wine list. Although prices are highish, there's a good selection by the glass from £4.75. Bottle prices start at £13.25.

Chef: Kevin Gratton **Proprietor:** Caprice Holdings Ltd **Open:** all week 12 to 3.30, 5.30 to 12 **Closed:** 25 and 26 Dec, Aug bank hol **Meals:** alc (main courses £12.50 to £25). Cover £2 **Service:** not inc, card slips closed **Cards:** Amex, Delta, Diners, Maestro, MasterCard, Visa **Details:** 90 seats. Vegetarian meals. Children's helpings. Wheelchair access (not WC). Music. No mobile phones. Air-conditioned **Tube:** Green Park

MAP 15

Carluccio's Caffé AR

8 Market Place, W1
Tel: (020) 7636 2228

The original branch of Antonio Carluccio's chain of fashionable Italian caffés is just what is needed 'on busy London sightseeing days'. Fans love the vibrant atmosphere and the 'unfailingly welcoming staff' and the kitchen does its job with excellent breads and pastries (from £1.25), salads, plenty of pasta (Neapolitan spaghetti with clams and chilli, £7.25) and desserts like coffee pannacotta with caramel sauce (£4.25). Short list of regional Italian wines from £10.95. Open all week. (See www.carluccios.com for other addresses across the country.)

AR	Not a full entry but provisionally recommended (known as 'round-ups' in previous editions, these 'also recommended' establishments are now integrated throughout the book).

MAP 15

Cecconi's

5A Burlington Gardens, W1S 3AZ
Tel: (020) 7434 1500
Website: www.cecconis.co.uk

Cooking 5 | Italian | £47–£89

A warm, discreet feel pervades the low-lit dining room, where diverting modern art hangs on mushroom-grey walls and a bare wooden floor somehow manages not to echo too much noise. This makes a restrained backdrop to well-wrought, modish Italian cooking built around fine ingredients and accomplished technique.

Three scallops make an inviting first course, served with puntarelle, bitter shoots of the chicory family, and a saffron-scented dressing. Intermediate rice or pasta dishes have taken in good broad bean and pecorino ravioli, and generous porcini risotto, while main courses partner star proteins – usually roasted – with fitting fresh vegetables: roast saddle of rabbit with prosciutto, leeks and sage, or rack of Welsh lamb with cannellini beans and garlic leaves. Dish of the evening at inspection was a whole Dover sole on the bone, impeccably timed and eloquent of flavour, even though it was adorned with nothing more radical than butter and a clump of rather acidulous shallots. Our correspondents are split about the tiramisù – some find it exemplary, others disappointing – and the deconstructive take on zabaglione involves pouring the emulsion over serried ranks of pear slices. Service builds from early longueurs to a sprint finish, when robust espresso and excellent dark chocolate truffles should rev up the diners too. 'Good but expensive' is the general conclusion on the Italian wine list. It is strongest in fine Tuscans and Barolos, but there is room too for good affordable options like Capezzana's fruity Barco Reale (£23), and a dozen come by the glass.

Chef: Nick Freeman **Proprietors:** Soho House Ltd **Open:** all week 12 to 3 (10 to 4 Sat/Sun) **Meals:** alc (main courses £11 to £26) **Service:** 12.5% (optional), card slips closed **Cards:** Amex, Delta, Diners, Maestro, MasterCard, Visa **Details:** 80 seats. Private parties: 90 main room. Vegetarian meals. Wheelchair access (also WC). Occasional music. Air-conditioned **Tube:** Green Park, Piccadilly Circus

MAP 14

Le Cercle

1 Wilbraham Place, SW1X 9AE
Tel: (020) 7901 9999
Email: info@lecercle.co.uk

Cooking 5 | French | £23–£67

An elegant basement restaurant with marble floor and neutral colour scheme, not far from Sloane Square, Le Cercle is an offshoot of Club Gascon (see entry). The approach is similar: a menu, on brown parcel paper, is classified into sections running from Végétal to sweet Gourmandises, the dishes served in small tasting portions, so that a range of creations may be tried. Regional dishes from around France are reinvented and celebrated with infectious fervour, and, despite the wealth of choice, most things reveal a high degree of precision. Ravioles de Romans are cheese-filled pasta parcels in a creamy sauce strewn with chopped black truffle and shredded chicory, cooked fennel is pertinently dressed in a thick orange vinaigrette, while braised oxtail is 'meltingly tender', and nicely matched with Jerusalem artichoke purée. Indeed, dishes often score highly for their textures, among them a croustillant of pig's trotter, the flaky pastry supporting a generous quantity of properly gelatinous foot. An acclaimed gourmandise has been well-made miniature crêpes served with a first-rate Amaretto-glazed plum compote. Black-clad staff are pleasant and discreet.

The all-French wine list forthrightly lays out a quality selection from all regions, including the oft-neglected South-West, that also encompasses some serious bottles from mature vintages. A trio of suggestions by the glass for each section of the menu provides a smart way to keep pace with the food flavours. Bottles from £11.50.

Chef: Thierry Beyris **Proprietor:** Vincent Labeyrie and Pascal Aussignac **Open:** Tue to Sat 12 to 3, 6 to 11 **Meals:** alc (main courses £6.50 to £15). Set L £15 to £19.50. Bar menu available **Service:** 12.5% (optional), card slips closed **Cards:** Amex, Delta, Maestro, MasterCard, Visa **Details:** 65 seats. Private parties: 80 main room, 20 private room. Vegetarian meals. Wheelchair access (also WC). Music. Air-conditioned **Accommodation:** 33 rooms, all with bath/shower. TV. Phone. Room only £135 to £265. Rooms for disabled. **Tube:** Sloane Square

NEW ENTRY	This appears after the restaurant's name if the establishment was not a main entry in last year's Guide, although it may have been a 'round-up/also recommended' in previous editions.

MAP 13

Champor-Champor

62–64 Weston Street, SE1 3QJ
Tel: (020) 7403 4600
Website: www.champor-champor.com

Cooking 3 | Malaysian/Asian | £33–£59

Vivid colours, bric-à-brac and tribal artefacts define the mood in this busily decorated restaurant whose Malay name, fittingly, equates to 'mix-and-match'. The cooking does that too, grafting a range of Asian influences onto Malaysian *kampong* (village) roots, and shows no fear of taking risks or crossing borders. Menus are fixed-price and change every few months. Unusual breads and canapés lead on to venison satay, shiitake congee with truffle oil or a salad of green mango, water chestnut and kangkung (swamp cabbage). An 'inter-course' granita then precedes dishes like poached sea bass with vermicelli salad and pineapple red curry, or roast ostrich fillet with perchik sauce and taro chips. To finish, expect such exotic novelties as tropical fruit soup, or steamed ginger cake with smoked banana ice cream. The shortish wine list offers interesting possibilities and there's an eclectic choice of 'Asia-Pacific' beers, to boot.

Chef: Adu Amran Hassan **Proprietors:** Charles Tyler and Adu Amran Hassan **Open:** Mon to Sat D only 6.15 to 10.30, L by appointment for groups **Closed:** 2 weeks at Christmas, 5 days at Easter, most bank hols **Meals:** Set L £21.50, Set D £20 (2 courses) to £35 **Service:** 12.5% (optional), card slips closed **Cards:** Amex, Delta, Maestro, MasterCard, Visa **Details:** 38 seats. Private parties: 18 main room, 4 to 8 private rooms. Vegetarian meals. Wheelchair access (not WC). Music. Air-conditioned **Tube:** London Bridge

MAP 13

Chapel

AR

48 Chapel Street, NW1 5DP
Tel: (020) 7402 9220

Lively everyday boozer favoured by drinkers and eaters around Edgware Road tube station. Blackboard menus are in the global gastro-pub mould of tortilla with chorizo (£5.50) and baked goats' cheese with honey and rosemary before roast crocodile fillet with noodles, orange and ginger marmalade and pak choi (£13) and pan-fried plaice fillet with mash, French beans, cherry tomato compote and tsatsiki. Short international wine list from £2.90 a glass, £10.90 a bottle. Open all week.

MAP 13

Chancery

NEW ENTRY

9 Cursitor Street, EC4A 1LL
Tel: (020) 7831 4000
Website: www.thechancery.co.uk

Cooking 4 | Modern European | £44–£53

Tucked away just off Chancery Lane, this moderately attractive building is sister to Andrew Thompson's and Zak Jones's Clerkenwell Dining Room (see entry). The décor is crisp, clean, modern and unobtrusive, with plenty of natural light from large windows. The dining space is split into two sections with arched openings, the floors are mahogany parquet, and the walls (brown and white) are hung with modern abstract art. The food is in the same vogue style as the Clerkenwell's, so expect confident, well-executed, modern cooking. Fish is handled well, from seared salmon crumbled into chilled cucumber soup with dill for a spring starter to a main course of roast monkfish 'saltimbocca', of impeccable quality and perfectly timed, with mousseline potato, broad beans and spinach. A trio of pork – a cube of boneless belly, braised cheek on celeriac purée, and a miniature stuffed cabbage on caramelised apples has also impressed. Desserts have fared less well, although a mille-feuille of caramelised apples with custard has hit the mark. Service is friendly and courteous but can be slow. The compact wine list, as crisply scripted as the menu, rolls out a balanced international spread, opening at £14.50.

Chef: Andrew Thompson **Proprietors:** Andrew Thompson and Zak Jones **Open:** Mon to Fri 12 to 2.30, 6 to 9.30 **Meals:** Set L and D £32 **Service:** 12.5% (optional), card slips closed **Cards:** Amex, Delta, Diners, Maestro, MasterCard, Visa **Details:** 45 seats. Private parties: 60 main room. Vegetarian meals. Children's helpings. No smoking in 1 dining room. Wheelchair access (not WC). Music. Air-conditioned **Tube:** Chancery Lane

MAP 12

Chapter Two

43–45 Montpelier Vale, SE3 0TJ
Tel: (020) 8333 2666
Website: www.chaptersrestaurants.co.uk

Cooking 4 | Modern European | £32–£60

A two-storey restaurant on the edge of the heath, this is the sibling of Chapter One (see entry,

Farnborough). Duskily lit, comfortably appointed, with a dish of olives on each table, the place is smart and chic. Trevor Tobin calls his seasonally changing dishes 'modern European comfort food', but that doesn't preclude a certain desire to surprise. Honey-roast quail with celeriac and apple rémoulade and hazelnut vinaigrette is a lush way to start, as is sweet-and-sour mackerel with prawn beignets, spiced aubergine and a 'pesto' incorporating coriander and pecans. Vinaigrettes and foams take the place of sauces in the modern way, although a main course might manage both a mushroom cappuccino and sherry vinegar caramel to go with confit of brisket, accompanied by pearl barley, celery and carrots. 'Israeli couscous' is a new one, seen here with a duo of steamed halibut and braised squid. Go one better with a finishing trio of rum babas, in hazelnut, chocolate and kumquat variations. The shortish wine list packs in France, Italy, Spain and the New World, with house wines from £15.50 for a South African Chenin Blanc.

Chef: Trevor Tobin **Proprietor:** Selective Restaurants Group **Open:** all week 12 to 2.30, 6.30 to 10.30 **Meals:** Set L £14.50 (2 courses) to £18.50, Set D Sun to Thur £16.95 (2 courses) to £19.95, Set D Fri and Sat £23.50 **Service:** 12.5% (optional), card slips closed **Cards:** Amex, Delta, Diners, Maestro, MasterCard, Visa **Details:** 75 seats. Private parties: 50 main room. Vegetarian meals. Children's helpings. No smoking. Wheelchair access (also WC). No music. Air-conditioned

MAP 12

Le Chardon AR

65 Lordship Lane,SE22 8EP
Tel: (020) 8299 1921

Cheery neighbourhood bistro in a former greengrocer's with a large patio for al fresco eating. The kitchen turns out French classics from noon to 11pm, including starters such as onion soup, foie gras terrine, and escargots vol-au-vent in Meaux mustard sauce (£4.25), followed by sole meunière (£12.50), or duck leg confit (£10.75). To finish, there might be tarte Tatin, or rich chocolate pot (£4.50). Serviceable, mainly French wine list from £10.95. Open all week. Related to the Green (see entry).

AR	Not a full entry but provisionally recommended (known as 'round-ups' in previous editions, these 'also recommended' establishments are now integrated throughout the book).

MAP 12

Chez Bruce

2 Bellevue Road, SW17 7EG
Tel: (020) 8672 0114
Website: www.chezbruce.co.uk

Cooking 6 | Modern British | £39–£82

Bruce Poole's restaurant, facing Wandsworth Common, exudes an understated, grown-up feel, with muted colours and a prevailing sense of airiness contributing to a relaxed tone. There isn't much room between tables, but staff go about their business carefully, so there is no feeling of jostle. An attractive menu positions the cooking style squarely within the rustic French ambit, and dishes are put together with a high degree of refinement and a focus on textural contrast. A supremely successful first course has combined neatly cubed smoked haddock and potato with leek, gratinated with Beaufort cheese and breadcrumbs, while an autumnal boudin of grouse and quail is kitted out with foie gras and Jerusalem artichoke purée (and a surcharge), and proved to be hugely satisfying. Offal is well handled generally, as is evidenced by a main course of grilled calf's kidney with anchovy butter and green beans, topped with (that textural note again) feathery strands of crisp potato galette. Classy desserts include a well-made honey and walnut tart, or a harmoniously balanced assemblage of warm orange and almond cake with citrus salad and passion-fruit sorbet. The set lunch has been described as 'one of the little treasures of London'.

Through France, Italy, Spain, Germany, Austria, Australia, and the US, quality on the wine list never stints, and it always stays on top of emerging trends: witness a handful of bottles from Jura and Savoie. With house white at £16.50, this is not a place for budget drinking, but halves abound and a vast array of options comes by the glass.

Chefs: Bruce Poole and Matthew Christmas **Proprietors:** Bruce Poole and Nigel Platts-Martin **Open:** Mon to Fri 12 to 2, 6.30 to 10.30, Sat 12.30 to 2.30, 6.30 to 10.30, Sun 12 to 3, 7 to 10 **Closed:** 24 to 26 Dec, 1 Jan **Meals:** Set L Mon to Fri £23.50, Set L Sat £25, Set L Sun £29.50, Set D £35 to £45 **Service:** 12.5% (optional), card slips closed, 15% for parties **Cards:** Amex, Delta, Diners, Maestro, MasterCard, Visa **Details:** 85 seats. Private parties: 70 main room, 16 to 22 private rooms. Vegetarian meals. No children under 7 at D. No smoking. Wheelchair access (not WC). No music. Air-conditioned **Tube:** Balham

MAP 12

Chez Kristof

NEW ENTRY

111 Hammersmith Grove, W6 0NQ
Tel: (020) 8741 1177
Website: www.chezkristof.co.uk

Cooking 5 | French | £26–£59

Jan Woroniecki's latest venture occupies a prominent corner site in an area short of good eateries - - it's a white-walled, zinc-barred, halogen-lit brasserie whose hard-edged modernism is offset by trailing fairy-lights at the window. Jan brought Polish cooking to Kensington (at Wodka) and Nordic chic to Southwark (Baltic, see entry); here he essays French demotic.

Nibble on anchoïade and crudités at the bar while planning your meal. Expect main dishes like lamb shank with ratatouille, braised rabbit with chanterelles and asparagus, and ox cheek daube with prunes and Armagnac, with moules marinière or steak tartare to start, and île flottante to finish. At a May dinner a salad of ceps and chicken livers made a toothsome, if not quite seasonal, combination. A tranche of monkfish on the bone followed, served with armoricaine sauce and ripped basil, with the alternative of a plump, whole Bresse pigeon with peas, and more springtime ceps providing fullness and balance. Gratin dauphinois as a side-order should be sought out for its properly cheesy, garlicky richness. French cheeses are well-kept, and desserts might include beautifully oozy chocolate fondant, or poached pear with bitter chocolate sorbet. Wines are all French, with prices to suit every budget and a good showing of those top-value regional wines that offer unfamiliar flavours to those weary of New World varietals. Prices open at £12 (£3.50 a glass).

Chef: Zac El Hamdou **Proprietor:** Jan Woroniecki **Open:** all week 12 to 3 (4 Sat/Sun), 6.30 to 11.15 (10.30 Sun) **Meals:** alc (main courses £11.50 to £16.50). Set L £12 (2 courses) to £15 **Service:** 12.5% **Cards:** Amex, Delta, Diners, Maestro, MasterCard, Visa **Details:** 120 seats. 25 seats outside. Private parties: 1 to 50 private rooms. Vegetarian meals. Children's helpings. Wheelchair access (also WC). Music. Air-conditioned **Tube:** Hammersmith

MAP 12

Chez Liline

AR

101 Stroud Green Road, N4 3PX
Tel: (020) 7263 6550

Exotic Mauritian seafood cookery in revamped surroundings on the fringe of Finsbury Park. Raw materials are from the fishmonger next door, and the kitchen adds a French accent to dishes like moules à la mauricienne (mussels with tomatoes, chilli and thyme; £4.75), lotte braisé et fèves épicés (braised monkfish with spiced broadbeans; £14.25), and lobster cooked three ways (perhaps with ginger and pickled lime). French and New World wines from £10.75.

MAP 15

Chinese Experience

NEW ENTRY

118 Shaftesbury Avenue, W1
Tel: (020) 7437 0377
Website: www.chineseexperience.com

Cooking 2 | Chinese | £24–£64

One of the newest kids on the Soho Chinatown block, this young blood aims for sleek minimalism, eschewing red and gold dragons in favour of white or muted orange walls and pots of striking paper orchids. Authenticity and innovation are the kitchen's watchwords and dim sum are a feature; reporters have praised Shanghai-style steamed pork buns and deep-fried shredded turnip cakes and it's worth investigating the Chinese-only list. The kitchen flirts (rather unconvincingly) with new-wave gimmicks such as 'neo-modernist' strawberry spare ribs, but it's on surer ground when it comes to classics like sea-spice aubergine with bean curd. Impeccable steamed whole sea bass with ginger and spring onion proves the axiom that 'simple is best' – especially when the juicy liquor is 'yummy enough to drink on its own'. Service is smiley and the minimal wine list starts at £12.50.

Chef: Gun Leung **Proprietor:** Linfox Ltd **Open:** all week 12 to 11 (11.30 Fri and Sat) **Closed:** 25 and 26 Dec **Meals:** alc (main courses £7 to £22). Set L £19 (min 2), Set D £23 (min 2) **Service:** not inc **Cards:** Amex, Delta, Maestro, MasterCard, Visa **Details:** 130 seats. Private parties: 100 main room, 30 private room. Vegetarian meals. Wheelchair access (also WC). Music. Air-conditioned **Tube:** Leicester Square

MAP 15

Chisou

4 Princes Street, W1B 2LE
Tel: (020) 7629 3931

Cooking 4 | Japanese | £25–£85

'Cries of welcome in Japanese' greet customers as they enter this modest but very authentic restaurant in Mayfair's 'Little Japan'. 'Chisou' translates as 'spirit of the feast', and the extensive menu encompasses all manner of traditional and contemporary dishes, backed up by a list of chef's specials (tiny pieces of simmered belly pork with boiled spinach and mustard, for example). Sushi is reckoned to be 'among the best in town', thanks to superb ingredients and good rice: braised eel and 'fattest' (as the menu phrases it) tuna have excelled from a list that also includes maki rolls. Delicacy, balance and fine technique also underpin feather light gyu tataki (seared beef fillet with garlic and ponzu sauce), mixed tempura, and steamed tofu wrapped in bean curd with king prawns and shiitake. For a finale, reporters suggest home-made sweet red bean or Japanese chestnut ice cream. Service is ever courteous and full of smiles. The short wine list begins with Chilean house selections at £13.

Chef: Mr Funakoshi **Proprietor:** David Leroy **Open:** Mon to Sat 12 to 2.30, 6 to 10.15 **Closed:** Easter **Meals:** alc (main courses £6.50 to £27). Set L £9.90 to £15.90 **Service:** not inc L, 12.5% D **Cards:** Amex, Delta, Diners, Maestro, MasterCard, Visa **Details:** 56 seats. Private parties: 20 main room, 4 to 14 private rooms. No cigars. Occasional music. Air-conditioned **Tube:** Oxford Circus

MAP 15

Chor Bizarre

AR

16 Albemarle Street, W1H 4HW
Tel: (020) 7629 9802

Plush Indian cluttered with artefacts gleaned from ethnic bazaars. The menu is an adventurous – but far from cheap – trek through the Subcontinent, stopping off for street snacks and tak-a-tak nibbles like South Indian crab cakes (£7) as well as tandooris and regional dishes like Malabar prawns (£15) or Kashmiri goshtaba ('velvety spheres' of minced lamb in yoghurt sauce). Thalis ('the grand repast') from £23. Knowledgeably selected wines, with prices from £16. Downstairs is Chai Bazaar, an Indian Tea Bar. Closed Sun L.

MAP 12

Chutney Mary

535 King's Road, SW10 0SZ
Tel: (020) 7351 3113
Website: www.realindianfood.com

Cooking 2 | Indian | £31–£87

The opulent décor recalls the Raj, but the wide-ranging menu pulls together dishes from all over the Subcontinent. A selection of Indian street food appears as a starter, alongside a Malabar-inspired dish of scallops with coconut and ginger, and Goan-style stuffed crab. Chilli and cheese naan makes an appearance (there's also the more familiar peshawari), and side orders of spring onion bread, and yellow tur lentils with garlic and tomato are worth trying. Main courses include green chicken curry from Goa, roast duck with black pepper sauce from Kerala, and a Punjabi vegetarian selection: malai kofta curry, bhindi singara dopiaza, and dhal makhani, for example. The tandoor supplies interestingly marinated chicken, lamb and poussin, plus prawns with mustard and dill, while desserts follow an East-meets-West theme, teaming a cinnamon-flavoured dark chocolate fondant with an orange blossom-flavoured lassi, and orange and cardamom sorbet with ginger bread-and-butter pudding. House wines start at £16.25.

Chef: Nagarajan Rubinath **Proprietors:** Ranjit Mathrani, and Namita and Camellia Panjabi **Open:** Sat and Sun L 12.30 to 3, all week D 6.30 to 11.30 (10.30 Sun) **Meals:** alc D (main courses £15.50 to £25.50). Set L £16.50 **Service:** 12.5% (optional), card slips closed **Cards:** Amex, Delta, Diners, Maestro, MasterCard, Visa **Details:** 110 seats. Private parties: 110 main room, 12 to 30 private rooms. Vegetarian meals. Children's helpings. No-smoking area. Wheelchair access (not WC). Occasional music. Air-conditioned **Tube:** Fulham Broadway

MAP 15

Chowki

AR

2–3 Denman Street, W1D 7HA
Tel: (020) 7439 1330

'Home-style Indian food' on a shoestring is the attractive deal at this cheerful diner off Piccadilly Circus. Customers sit at traditional wooden tables ('chowki'), and the food 'has its moments'. Menus draw on regional recipes for, say, Kashmiri deep-fried lotus stems (£2), Maharashtran lamb curry or fish poached with fennel and coconut (£8.50), and almond pudding with cardamom from Chettinand. Three-course 'feasts' £12; house wines from £9.95. Open all week. Under the same ownership as Mela (see entry).

MAP 15

Christopher's

18 Wellington Street, WC2E 7DD
Tel: (020) 7240 4222

Bullish transatlantic bar/grill in a prime Covent Garden site once occupied by London's first casino. America goes head to head with Europe for a menu that jets from Nantucket lobster and prawn fritters (£11) and grilled New York strip steak with fries (£22.50) to roast fillet of sea bass with leek confit. Order tobacco onions or Monterey mash on the side, and finish with honeycomb and bay leaf parfait (£6.50). Theatre menus and weekend brunch. Majestic wine list with California and France sharing most of the spoils; prices from £14. Closed Sun D.

Chef/Proprietor: Jake Hodges **Open:** all week 12 to 10.45 (9.45 Sun) **Closed:** D 24 Dec, 25 and 26 Dec, 1 Jan, Easter Sun **Meals:** alc (main courses £10 to £21). Set L Mon to Sat £15 (2 courses) to £18, Set L and D Sun £10.50 (1 course). Tapas menu available **Service:** 12.5% (optional), card slips closed **Cards:** Amex, Delta, Diners, Maestro, MasterCard, Visa **Details:** 60 seats. 20 seats outside. Private parties: 75 main room, 40 private room. Vegetarian meals. Children's helpings. Wheelchair access (not WC). No music. Air-conditioned **Tube:** Holborn

MAP 15

Chuen Cheng Ku

AR

17 Wardour Street, W1V 3HD
Tel: (020) 7734 3281

A veteran of Chinatown, this three-storey giant is noted for its dim sum, which are dispensed from a cavalcade of heated trolleys. All the favourites are here, from steamed dumplings, deep-fried morsels and slithery steamed cheung fun to roast meats and bowls of soup noodles – plus specials to keep the regulars interested. The full menu is a Cantonese monster (appetisers from £4, main courses from £7) backed up by set banquets. House wine £9.95. Open all week.

MAP 13

Cigala

54 Lamb's Conduit Street, WC1N 3LW
Tel: (020) 7405 1717
Website: www.cigala.co.uk

Cooking 2 | Spanish | £31–£71

A 'delightful, completely unpretentious little restaurant' in an interesting street off Holborn, Cigala offers a warm welcome and authentic Spanish cooking at good-value prices. The plainly decorated dining room, its tables adorned smartly and simply with linen cloths, is all the more pleasant for eschewing cheesy Spanish theming. The menus change twice daily and have a good balance of meat and seafood dishes, with staples from the Spanish repertoire such as sopa de ajo (garlic soup with a poached egg), or chicken croquettes with green salad for starters, and main courses of roast suckling pig with patatas a los pobres and quince aïoli, or grilled sea bream with broad beans, peas and asparagus. To finish, chilled rice pudding topped with grated nutmeg is both simple and 'simply delicious'. Spanish house wines are £13.50.

MAP 13

Cinnamon Club

Old Westminster Library, Great Smith Street, SW1P 3BU
Tel: (020) 7222 2555
Website: www.cinnamonclub.com

Cooking 4 | Modern Indian | £35–£128

Books still line the shelves of this 'beautiful, historic' former library, where high-backed tan leather banquettes add to the drama of this formal and imposing room. Elegant mahogany panels add further to the sense of history. The twenty-first century role of this fine building is as host to a top-drawer Indian restaurant. Chef Vivek Singh starts things off with an amuse-bouche of, say, a potato fritter served with pumpkin chutney, before starters such as tandoori king prawns with mint and coriander, or English asparagus with smoked aubergine and curried yoghurt. Tandoori Nile perch with carom seeds and a little mango, red onion, and yoghurt has impressed, while Charolais fillet steak, slow cooked with onion sauce, saffron potatoes, and spinach and mushrooms stir-fried with spices was the stellar dish for one luncher. Bread are good – garlic nan, for example – and desserts extend to semolina halwa with caramelised pineapple. The wine list is a good match for the food. Prices start at £14.

Chef: Vivek Singh Proprietor Iqbal Wahhab **Open:** Mon to Fri L 12 to 2.30, Mon to Sat D 6 to 11. Breakfast available 7.30 to 9.30 **Closed:** 25 and 26 Dec, 1 Jan **Meals:** alc (main courses £11 to £31). Set L and D 6 to 7 £19 (2 courses) to £22, Set D £60 to £96 (inc wine). Bar D menu available **Service:** 12.5% (optional), card slips closed **Cards:** Amex, Delta, Diners, Maestro, MasterCard, Visa **Details:** 220 seats. Private parties: 40 main room, 40 to 80 private rooms. Vegetarian meals. No music. Air-conditioned **Tube:** Westminster

MAP 15

Cipriani

25 Davies Street, W1K 3DE
Tel: (020) 7399 0500
Website: www.cipriani.com

Cooking 3 | Italian | £50–£122

In 2004 the Ciprianis brought Venetian grand dining to London, opening this opulently appointed restaurant modelled on the original Harry's Bar. There's a little more elbow room here, and the much less mixed clientele reflects the high cost of the fairly simple, old-wave Italian cooking. Tuna tartare at £17 makes a light starter; there are plain grills such as lamb chop or Scottish ribeye, and classics like risotto alla primavera, calf's liver with polenta, and (oddly) chicken curry with rice pilaff. Reporters haven't had much luck here this year, but there may be salvation in main courses such as halibut with cherry tomatoes and capers, and the ices, mousses and cakes that round it all off. A good, Italian-led wine list starts with branded house wines at £3.50, or £26 a bottle.

Chef: Giuseppe Marangi **Proprietor:** Arrigo Cipriani **Open:** all week 12 to 3, 6 to 11.45 **Meals:** alc (main courses £15 to £42). Set L £28 to £35, Set D £35 to £40. **Service:** 12.5% (optional), card slips closed **Cards:** Amex, Delta, Maestro, MasterCard, Visa **Details:** 120 seats. Private parties: 30 main room, 12 to 20 private rooms. Vegetarian meals. Children's helpings. Wheelchair access (also WC). No music. Air-conditioned **Tube:** Bond Street

MAP 15

Circus

1 Upper James Street, W1F 9DF
Tel: (020) 7534 4000
Website: www.circusbar.co.uk

Cooking 3 | Modern European | £30–£75

On a large corner site with huge glass windows, Circus still feels contemporary and appealing eight years after opening. The cooking is broadly European, but occasionally features ideas from further afield: you might find Thai red curry with chicken, choi sum and jasmine rice, or seared tuna with wakame, cucumber and soy on the carte. Roast Gressingham duck with lemon, mint and watercress, or sirloin steak with roast tomato and béarnaise sauce are more typical though, with vegetables extra. Elsewhere, bright Mediterranean flavours surface in starters of oak-aged feta with roast red peppers and rocket salad, or scallops baked in their shells with globe artichoke purée and garlic butter. Finish, perhaps, on a traditional note with raspberry pavlova. The varied wine list starts at £16, but there is little under £20.

Chef: Richard Lee **Proprietor:** Mirror Image Group **Open:** Mon to Fri L 12 to 3, Mon to Sat D 5.45 to 12 **Meals:** alc (main courses £10.50 to £22). Set L £14.50 (2 courses) to £16.50, Set D 5.45 to 7.15 and 10.30 to 12 £14.50 (2 courses) to £16.50. Bar menu available **Service:** 12.5% (optional), card slips closed **Cards:** Amex, Delta, Diners, Maestro, MasterCard, Visa **Details:** 140 seats. Private parties: 50 main room, 12 to 20 private rooms. Vegetarian meals. Children's helpings. Wheelchair access (not WC). No music. Air-conditioned **Tube:** Piccadilly Circus

MAP 13

Clarke's

124 Kensington Church Street, W8 4BH
Tel: (020) 7221 9225
Website: www.sallyclarke.com

Cooking 4 | Modern British | £36–£68

After 22 years, Sally Clarke's formula has changed – slightly. Set in a row of expensive antique shops and estate agents, the low-lit basement restaurant, with an open-plan kitchen and smaller ground-floor dining room, still serves a no-choice dinner menu, but the 'four-courses-or-nothing rule' has been relaxed, and the menu is now priced for two, three or four courses. The kitchen's emphasis remains on the best seasonal ingredients simply prepared, and a meal often starts with a salad – perhaps peas, grilled spring onions and pea shoots, and a dressing of mustard and tarragon accompanying San Daniele ham. This could be followed by fillet of Cornish sea bass with a sauce of Prosecco, chives and dill, or roast breast of corn-fed chicken with a creamy sauce of field mushrooms and tarragon. Vegetable accompaniments are usually imaginative, and first-class cheeses precede unusual desserts: say, bitter chocolate and prune soufflé cake with espresso cream.

Lunch is a selection of four starters, three main courses, and either cheese or a couple of puddings, and brunch is served on Saturday. There's something to please all palates in the short, hand-picked wine list, from mature claret to super-fresh New Zealand Sauvignon by Kim Crawford (£20). Look out for Alsace from Ostertag and a great range from California. House white is £15.

Chefs: Sally Clarke and Liz Payne **Proprietor:** Sally Clarke **Open:** Mon to Sat L 12.30 (11 Sat) to 2, Tue to Sat D 7 to 10 **Closed:** 10 days at Christmas, bank hols **Meals:** alc L (main courses £14 to £16). Set D £36 (2 courses) to £49.50 **Service:** net prices, card slips closed **Cards:** Amex, Delta, Diners, Maestro, MasterCard, Visa **Details:** 85 seats. No smoking. Wheelchair access (not WC). No music. No mobile phones. Air-conditioned **Tube:** Notting Hill Gate

MAP 13

Clerkenwell Dining Room

69–73 St John Street, EC1M 4AN
Tel: (020) 7253 9000
Website: www.theclerkenwell.com

Cooking 4 | Modern European | £33–£67

'CDR' can still show a clean pair of heels to most of its nearby rivals and has blossomed into a mature, confident restaurant – despite its unpromising location on the ground floor of an office block. Chef Nelson Reposo has settled into his stride and is now capable of creating flavours that 'shout': expect food that is a palate-challenging amalgam of 'rich, soft, dark, sweet, gutsy'. Scallops with baby squid, chorizo, aubergine, rocket and pine-nut salad is a harmonious combination, while braised oxtail enjoys an equally forthright partnership with black pudding, parsnip purée and bordelaise jus. In a more exotic vein there might be caramelised duck breast with confit spring roll and stir-fried vegetables, and the kitchen does a good line in terrines. Desserts aim for gently flavoured richness rather than extravagant presentation, as in coffee and mascarpone meringue with Amaretto parfait and pistachio ice cream. The well-chosen wine list favours Europe over the New World, with prices from £13.50. The same team also runs the Chancery (see entry).

Chefs: Andrew Thompson and Nelson Reposo **Proprietors:** Zak Jones and Andrew Thompson **Open:** Sun to Fri L 12 to 3, Mon to Sat D 6 to 11 **Closed:** 24 to 31 Dec, 1 and 2 Jan **Meals:** alc (main courses £15 to £19.50). Set L Sun £15.50 (2 courses) to £19.50 **Service:** 12.5% (optional), card slips closed **Cards:** Amex, Delta, Diners, Maestro, MasterCard, Visa **Details:** 100 seats. Private parties: 70 main room, 1 to 40 private rooms. Vegetarian meals. Children's helpings. No smoking in 1 dining room. Wheelchair access (also WC). Music. Air-conditioned **Tube:** Farringdon

MAP 13

Club Gascon

57 West Smithfield, EC1A 9DS
Tel: (020) 7796 0600

Cooking 5 | French | £48–£106

Club Gascon and its sister Le Cercle (see entry) have created for themselves a niche that didn't previously exist. The formula is a multi-sectioned menu of avant-garde, 'tapas' dishes based on or derived from the cuisine of South-west France; this is the kind of place where you eat a taster portion of pressed duck foie gras with crab claws and pipérade, and then perhaps a mini-casserole of turbot 'plancha', with pork belly and wild mushrooms. Much of the food succeeds by ambushing preconceptions: 'the keynote to the whole dining experience here is surprise,' observed a pair who were suddenly brought a scoop of salted peanut ice cream they weren't expecting. Tellingly, the simpler ideas seem to work best, among them a 'delightfully smooth' celeriac and prawn bisque, or a side-plate of 'beautifully crisp and tasty' turnip chips. Where doubts surface, the fault tends to lie in over-elaboration: a mass of flavours doesn't quite come off in a dessert of confit of citrus fruits, toasted pine nuts, lime sorbet and bergamot. Chocolate mousse on a thick biscuit base accompanied by top-notch coffee ice cream scored more highly, as does the polished service from ladies in long black ties.

All the South-west's big wine names are here – Brumont, Berthoumieu, Triguedina, etc. – along with much that's less familiar and some good Languedoc bottles. Pricey Bordeaux classed growths make up the balance. Bottles start at £15, and a dozen come by the glass.

Chef: Pascal Aussignac **Proprietors:** Vincent Labeyrie and Pascal Aussignac **Open:** Mon to Fri L 12 to 2, Mon to Sat D 7 to 10.30 **Closed:** 23 and 24 Dec to 4 Jan, bank hols **Meals:** alc (main courses £9 to £19). Set L and D £38 **Service:** 12.5% (optional), card slips closed **Cards:** Amex, Delta, Maestro, MasterCard, Visa **Details:** 48 seats. Private parties: 48 main room. Vegetarian meals. Children's helpings. No-smoking area. Wheelchair access (not WC). Music. Air-conditioned **Tube:** Barbican, Farringdon

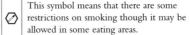

⊘	This symbol means that smoking is not permitted.
	This symbol means that there are some restrictions on smoking though it may be allowed in some eating areas.

MAP 13

Coach and Horses

NEW ENTRY

LONDON GFG 2006 COMMENDED

26–28 Ray Street,
EC1R 3DJ
Tel: (020) 7278 8990
Website: www.thecoachandhorses.com

Cooking 4 | Modern British | £29–£49

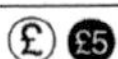

The corner-sited pub may look traditional from the outside, but the acres of wood within – floor, panelling, tables, chairs – bear all the hallmarks of a modern-day gastro-pub. The menu changes daily, delivering refreshingly robust and uncomplicated combinations that at a spring inspection opened with crubeens (pig's trotter formed into little patties, breadcrumbed and fried) served with dandelion and sorrel, a slice of 'pungent, cheesy' Irish Desmond tart, and a tangle of tender squid, parsley and lemon, and finished with a just-set rhubarb jelly. In between was 'so simple, so delicious' Goosnargh chicken leg with cannellini beans, fennel, wild garlic and tarragon, six big, fat roast scallops with split peas and a lick of lemony beurre blanc, and perfectly timed cod with mushrooms, bacon and a 'dab of well-tempered' aïoli. The style of cooking is light – some may say healthy – and its simplicity and clear flavours reflect prime materials treated confidently. 'It is democratic, it is honest, it is straightforward,' adds an enthusiastic regular, who also raises a cheer for the knowledgeable staff. The wine list covers a good range of styles and prices, starting with house French at £11.90.

Chef: Andy Tyrell **Proprietors:** Giles Webster and Juliet Peston **Open:** Sun to Fri L 12 to 3, Mon to Sat D 6 to 10 **Closed:** 24 Dec to 2 Jan, bank hols **Meals:** alc (main courses £10.50 to £16). Bar menu available Mon to Fri **Service:** not inc, 12.5% for parties of 6 or more **Cards:** Amex, Delta, Maestro, MasterCard, Visa **Details:** 50 seats. 86 seats outside. Private parties: 40 main room. Vegetarian meals. No-smoking area. Wheelchair access (not WC). Occasional music

MAP 14

Le Colombier

145 Dovehouse Street, SW3 6LB
Tel: (020) 7351 1155

NEW CHEF | French | £31–£67

This French neighbourhood bistro, with its crisp white table linen, comfortable seating and straightforward cooking, keeps regulars coming back year after year. We learned of the chef change here too late for an inspection. Previously, however, we had had good reports of the value-for-money set lunch, and sound à la carte options like goose rillettes and scallops with wild mushrooms, and the menu remains strewn with Gallic classics. Expect the likes of soupe de poissons, Dover sole meunière, steak tartare, côte de veau, carré d'agneau, and crème brûlée and crêpes suzette. Taking its lead from the cooking, the French-only wine list offers a no-nonsense spread of options from £13.90.

Chef: C. McLean **Proprietor:** Didier Garnier **Open:** all week 12 to 3 (3.30 Sun), 6.30 to 10.30 (10 Sun) **Meals:** alc (main courses £13.50 to £21.50). Set L £14.50 (2 courses) **Service:** 12.5% (optional), card slips closed **Cards:** Amex, Delta, Maestro, MasterCard, Visa **Details:** 70 seats. 30 seats outside. Private parties: 10 main room, 10 to 30 private rooms. Vegetarian meals. Wheelchair access (not WC). No music **Tube:** South Kensington

MAP 15

The Connaught, Angela Hartnett's Menu

16 Carlos Place, W1K 2AL
Tel: (020) 7592 1222
Website: www.angelahartnett.com

Cooking 5 | Modern European | £50–£113

The subtle shift of emphasis that took place within the redesigned confines of the Connaught after the Ramsay group took over in 2002 has been well maintained. There are bright modern paintings hanging on the old mahogany panelling now, and a muted cream and tawny colour scheme to lighten the ambience, but the approach of the service is as old-school as ever, which perhaps explains the lack of buzz in the atmosphere that ought to accompany the cooking.

A Franco-Italian bent informs Angela Hartnett's menus, with pasta and gnocchi in evidence among starters. Tortelli of pumpkin with mustard fruits and sage butter is one way to begin, duck consommé with tortellini of confit duck on Swiss chard another. Sauces and dressings play a significant role in deepening the impact of main courses, so smoked red wine is the lubricant for fillets of John Dory with sautéed potato and cauliflower purée, while a single-estate olive oil dresses sea bass, served with tomatoes and aubergine crisps. Cheeses from Italy, France and the British Isles crowd the board, and the Italian note is heard again in roasted figs with zabaglione and spiced tapioca. Trend-setters might go for the baked vacherin dessert with confit new potatoes.

The wine list is strong in classic names and top vintages, with Italy and France the leading players – but the range has now broadened to include options under £20 in both countries. Upmarket short selections are the name of the game elsewhere. A well-chosen 14 come by the glass.

Chef: Angela Hartnett **Proprietor:** Gordon Ramsay Holdings Ltd **Open:** all week 12 to 3, 5.45 to 11 **Meals:** Set L £30, Set D £55 to £70. Bar menu available **Service:** 12.5% (optional), card slips closed **Cards:** Amex, Delta, Diners, Maestro, MasterCard, Visa **Details:** 70 seats. Private parties: 70 main room, 14 to 22 private rooms. Vegetarian meals. Children's helpings. No smoking. No music. No mobile phones. Air-conditioned **Tube:** Bond Street/Green Park

MAP 13

Il Convivio

143 Ebury Street, SW1W 9QN
Tel: (020) 7730 4099
Website: www.etruscarestaurants.com

Cooking 2 | Modern Italian | £31–£73

This spacious, light, basement dining room with warm colours and cool tiled floor offers a contemporary version of Italian food. The menu is sensibly compact, and starters invariably include a few salads – rocket leaf with figs, Parmesan and pine nuts, say – while pasta dishes come in starter, middle or main sizes. Seafood runs from cod and salmon skewer with caramelised chicory, to cep-crusted monkfish medallion with sautéed courgette. Counterpointing such appealing diversity, are more traditional Buccleuch rib steak with red onion marmalade, or fillet of veal with sautéed wild mushrooms. Desserts include chestnut semifreddo, or pineapple carpaccio with exotic fruit and vanilla syrup. The all-Italian wines include some interesting bottles, but mark-ups are fairly severe; house wine is £13.50.

Chef: Lukas Pfaff **Proprietors:** Enzo and Piero Quaradeghini **Open:** Mon to Sat 12 to 2.45, 7 to 10.45 **Closed:** bank hols **Meals:** alc (main courses £13.50 to £18). Set L £15.50 (2 courses) to £19.50, Set D £26.50 (2 courses) to £38.50 **Service:** 12.5% (optional), card slips closed **Cards:** Amex, Delta, Diners, Maestro, MasterCard, Visa **Details:** 65 seats. Private parties: 70 main room, 14 private room. Vegetarian meals. No cigars. Music. Air-conditioned **Tube:** Victoria, Sloane Square

To submit a report on any restaurant, please visit *www.which.co.uk/gfgfeedback.*

MAP 13

Le Coq d'Argent

No. 1 Poultry, EC2R 8EJ
Tel: (020) 7395 5000

Spectacular location, awesome cityscapes from the rooftop garden, and suave trademark Conran interior. Broadly based French regional cooking with plenty of flexible options: oysters, caviar, and crustaceans are fixtures, but the kitchen also produces workmanlike renditions of venison tartare with celeriac, apple and hazelnut salad (£9.25), and fillet of beef Rossini (£23) before desserts like bitter chocolate fondant with coffee ice cream (£6.75). Blockbuster wine list, but 'truly knee-trembling prices'. Open Sun to Fri L and Mon to Sat D.

MAP 12

Cotto

44 Blythe Road, W14 0HA
Tel: (020) 7602 9333
Email: bookings@cottorestaurant.co.uk

Cooking 2 | Modern British | £30–£52

This neighbourhood venue in a quiet location behind Olympia is unflashily decorated, with plain plum-coloured walls, chrome and black chairs, and white-clothed tables. The short, fixed-price menu is reckoned good value and takes in fish soup with gurnard and brown shrimp tortellini as well as well-timed seared scallops with cauliflower purée and beignets, and main courses of cod poached in bouillabaisse sauce with mussels, brown shrimps, and rouille. The kitchen has also produced a fine sea bream with braised fennel, crushed potatoes and five-spice jus, a well-made hot chocolate fondant – the central liquid chocolate nicely rich – with Banyuls syrup, and bitter chocolate tart with a good, thin pastry base. The wine list is a sensible slate with plenty of New World offerings. Prices open at £12.90.

Chef: James Kirby **Proprietors:** James and Jane Kirby, and Warren Barton **Open:** Mon to Fri L 12.30 to 2.30, Mon to Sat D 7 to 10.30 **Closed:** 1 week at Christmas, bank hols **Meals:** Set L £14.50 (2 courses) to £17.50, Set D £18 (2 courses) to £20.50 **Service:** 12.5% (optional), card slips closed **Cards:** Amex, Delta, Maestro, MasterCard, Visa **Details:** 70 seats. 12 seats outside. Private parties: 80 main room, 10 to 35 private rooms. Children's helpings. No cigars/pipes in dining room. Music. Air-conditioned **Tube:** Kensington (Olympia)

MAP 13

Cow Dining Room

AR

89 Westbourne Park Road, W2 5QH
Tel: (020) 7221 0021

Guinness with oysters is a best seller in the packed Saloon Bar of this 'in-the-know' West London boozer, but there's plenty more to enjoy in the tiny upstairs dining room. The menus are in the gastro-pub mould of braised ox tongue with salsa verde (£7.50), wild sea bass with roast fennel, artichoke hearts and tapenade (£17), and rump of lamb with butter-bean and chorizo stew. Finish with, perhaps, rhubarb cheesecake (£5.25). Wines from £13.75. Dining room open Sat and Sun L and all week D.

MAP 12

Crowthers

481 Upper Richmond Road West, SW14 7PU
Tel: (020) 8876 6372

Cooking 2 | Modern British/French | £39–£47

Philip and Shirley Crowther have been feeding the locals of East Sheen and beyond since 1982, and their neighbourhood restaurant seldom deviates from its stated aims. Fixed-price dinner menus are biased towards typically Gallic dishes such as best end of lamb with a provençale herb crust and rosemary and redcurrant sauce, or calf's liver with onion, sage and madeira, although the kitchen occasionally ventures further afield for grilled aubergine with tomato, feta and pesto, or grilled fillet of turbot with crispy curly kale and Thai spices. Desserts are mostly Anglo-French classics like caramelised lemon tart, or sticky toffee pudding with hot butterscotch sauce. The short, fairly priced wine list opens with George Kinross house selections at £12.75.

Chef: Philip Crowther **Proprietors:** Philip and Shirley Crowther **Open:** Tue to Sat D only 7 to 10.30. L bookings only **Meals:** Set D £21.50 (2 courses) to £26.50 **Service:** not inc **Cards:** Delta, Maestro, MasterCard, Visa **Details:** 35 seats. Private parties: 35 main room. Children's helpings. Wheelchair access (not WC). No music. Air-conditioned **Tube:** Richmond

This symbol means that the restaurant has elected to participate in *The Good Food Guide's* £5 voucher scheme (see 'How to Use the Guide' for details).

MAP 13

Cru

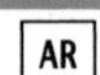

2–4 Rufus Street, N1 6PE
Tel: (020) 7729 5252

Chefs may come and go, but the trans-ethnic menu of this warehouse conversion in one of London's trendiest artists' quarters continues to offer new-wave tapas (chilli prawns with kai lan), platters of fish, meat, vegetables and cheese (from £12), and evening specials like bouillabaisse (£15.25). The carte deals in king prawn cocktail, yellowfin tuna niçoise (£15.25), and chicken with cannellini beans and peas, and there's a good-value set lunch (£10 for two courses). Finish with fudge brownies (£5). The global wine list opens at £12. Closed Mon.

MAP 13

Cumberland Arms

29 North End Road, W14 8SZ
Tel: (020) 7371 6806

Wooden floors and uncomplicated décor strike the right note at this relaxed gastro-pub where much of the attraction is focused on the food. Choose from short, daily-changing menus that drift around Mediterranean ideas like pancetta risotto with melted leek, rosemary and Parmesan (£6.50), grilled sea bass with lemon and thyme, aïoli and salsa fresca (£12.50), and ribeye steak with borlotti bean stew and salsa verde. Finish with something sweet like chocolate and almond cake (£4). House Italian is £10.50. Open all week.

MAP 12

Deep

NEW ENTRY

The Boulevard, Imperial Wharf, SW6 2UB
Tel: (020) 7736 3337
Website: www.deeplondon.co.uk

Cooking 3 | Seafood | £35–£97

Deep opened in April 2005, part of a newly built development in a waterside setting that may require a little effort to find. Once there, an impeccably contemporary scene greets the eye, with plain cream walls, clean lines and low-slung furniture. This is a lounge bar as well as restaurant. Fish and seafood are the orientation, and the owners are sufficiently abreast of marine ecological developments to trade only in non-threatened species. That, of course, means no cod, but who needs that when wild salmon, zander and perch are among the main courses, the last appearing with onion gnocchi, morels and vanilla bisque? Seafood and meat combinations are enthusiastically tried, so a gently flavoured first-course terrine is comprised of both lobster and veal sweetbreads. Calamari braised in port have a soup of Jerusalem artichoke poured over them at table to make an exhibition starter. A main course of turbot, grilled on the bone, has delivered immaculate fish, with haricots blancs and a citrus salad. If desserts are often the weak point in a fish restaurant, fear not. Here you can finish royally with the likes of caramelised pineapple with fennel ice cream and coconut.

The Sandefeldts are Swedish, and the drinks list contains a large selection of aquavits in 25ml shots, as well as a cosmopolitan, varietally classified wine list of more than sound pedigree but of uncomfortable mark-ups. South African house wines are £14.50.

Chefs: Christian Sandefeldt and Fredrik Bolin **Proprietors:** Christian and Kerstin Sandefeldt **Open:** Tue to Sun L 12 to 3 (4 Sat and Sun), Tue to Sat D 7 to 11 **Meals:** alc (main courses £15 to £24). Set L £15.50 (2 courses) to £19.50. Cover £1. Bar menu available **Service:** 12.5% (optional), card slips closed **Cards:** Amex, Delta, Maestro, MasterCard, Visa **Details:** 80 seats. 40 seats outside. Private parties: 100 main room. No smoking. Wheelchair access (also WC). Music. Air-conditioned

MAP 13

Delfina Studio Café

50 Bermondsey Street, SE1 3UD
Tel: (020) 7357 0244
Website: www.delfina.org.uk

Cooking 4 | Global | £33–£49

Contemporary artists work in the studios above this highly colourful and entertaining venue not far from London Bridge. It's a fruitful symbiotic relationship that ensures plenty of visual impact and atmosphere for visitors who come to this large, white-walled, pine-floored space seeking something a bit different at lunchtime (and on Friday evenings). Opening times may be limited, but invention abounds. The chargrilled fish of the day comes all the way from Australia, and the rest of the menu draws from right across the world. Scallop carpaccio is served with watermelon, shiso sprouts, green chilli and lime, while venison steak is partnered by rosemary mash, raspberry chilli jam, chocolate oil and watercress; side orders of vegetables, like herb and artichoke dauphinoise are £3.50. Meatless options are equally outré – perhaps miso-glazed aubergines with sesame sticky rice, pickled ginger and cucumber salad – and desserts run to chocolate and herb samosas with mango salad. The neat, modern wine list is peppered with options by the glass; bottle prices start at £12.50.

Chef: Maria Elia **Proprietors:** Digby Squires and Bruce Watson **Open:** Mon to Fri L 12 to 3, Fri D 7 to 10 **Closed:** 24 Dec to 2 Jan **Meals:** alc (main courses £10 to £13.50) **Service:** 12.5% (optional), card slips closed **Cards:** Amex, Delta, Diners, Maestro, MasterCard, Visa **Details:** 140 seats. Private parties: 300 main room, 5 to 500 private rooms. Vegetarian meals. No cigars. No-smoking area. Wheelchair access (also WC). Occasional music **Tube:** London Bridge

MAP 15

Le Deuxième

65A Long Acre, WC2E 9JH
Tel: (020) 7379 0033
Website: www.ledeuxieme.com

Cooking 2 | Modern European | £26–£62

The décor is simple at this relative of the Café du Jardin (see entry), while service has the brisk efficiency of a well-oiled machine. There's skill in the kitchen, too, with food well timed and attractively presented. Flavour and textural combinations are well conceived, but a few peripheral elements let the side down at inspection. Begin with an attractively stacked assembly of smoked goose breast on potato galette and pickled leeks, drizzled with pumpkin oil, or seared scallops with pea fritter and vermouth beurre blanc. Some dishes have oriental leanings, as with a main-course seared tuna with choi sum, water chestnuts and sesame glaze. To finish, try lavender pannacotta with mixed berries. The set menu appears to offer best value, and wine mark-ups seem fair, but make budgetary allowance for vegetables, charged extra, and the 15% service charge. The wine list is full of good ideas both in France and further afield. Bottles start at £12.50 and a good number come by the glass. There's also a smart list of fine wines.

Chef: Geoffrey Adams **Proprietors:** Robert Seigler and Tony Howorth **Open:** Mon to Fri 12 to 3, 5 to 12, Sat 12 to 12, Sun 12 to 11 **Closed:** 24 and 25 Dec **Meals:** alc (main courses £9.50 to £16.50). Set L and D 5 to 7 and 10 to 12 (11 Sun) £10.95 (2 courses) to £14.50 **Service:** 15% (optional), card slips closed **Cards:** Amex, Delta, Maestro, MasterCard, Visa **Details:** 58 seats. Private parties: 58 main room. Vegetarian meals. Wheelchair access (not WC). No music. Air-conditioned **Tube:** Covent Garden

MAP 15

Deya

NEW ENTRY

34 Portman Square, W1H 7BY
Tel: (020) 7224 0028
Website: www.deya-restaurant.co.uk

Cooking 4 | Modern Indian | £43–£65

Success breeds success, and this new venture, backed by the team behind Zaika, is off to a cracking start. Deya is definitely not a clone, even though ideas resonate here and there. Proceedings take place in a grand room with a lofty Georgian ceiling, ornate plasterwork and fashionably subdued lighting. The menu is a heady amalgam of classic (rogan josh) and modern (goats' cheese samosas with sweet-and-sour potatoes), and the kitchen makes impressive use of high-quality raw materials: bluefin tuna is marinated in ginger and chilli then cooked with mustard seeds, while tandoori prawns arrive on a golden crisp uthappam pancake with a trendy salad and a pot of coconut chutney. Details and incidentals count for a great deal, from superb chutneys and amuse-bouche (a tiny puri topped with chickpeas and yoghurt) to stir-fried green vegetables, exemplary rice and breads and a European-style pre-dessert (lychee granita). An excellent global wine list capably juggles contemporary and classic names and budget and smarter bottles, with France and Italy leading the way. Prices start at £13.50, and the dozen by the glass include Sauvignon Blanc from India.

Chef: Veerapan Muruggapam **Proprietors:** Sir Michael Caine, Claudio Pulze and Raj Sharma **Open:** Mon to Fri L 12 to 2.45, Mon to Sat D 6 to 11 **Closed:** Christmas and New Year **Meals:** alc (main courses £10.50 to £15). Set L £14.50 (2 courses), Set D £24 to £30. Bar menu available **Service:** 12.5% (optional), card slips closed **Cards:** Amex, Delta, Diners, Maestro, MasterCard, Visa **Details:** 70 seats. Vegetarian meals. Children's helpings. No cigars/pipes in dining room. Music. Air-conditioned

MAP 13

Diwana Bhel Poori

AR

121 Drummond Street, NW1 2HL
Tel: (020) 7387 5556

The vegetarian frontrunner in Drummond Street's 'Little India', a stone's throw from Euston Station. It's 'the best-value restaurant in London', according to a fan, who added that 'things are getting pricey, with snacks now as much as £3 and main courses weighing in at £5.50'. Starters and snacks eclipse most other dishes: eponymous bhel puris, aloo papri chat, bhajias and chunky samosas are all firm favourites with regulars. Unlicensed, but soothing lassi does the trick. Open all week, noon to midnight.

MAP 13

The Don

The Courtyard, 20 St Swithin's Lane, EC4N 8AD
Tel: (020) 7626 2606
Website: www.thedonrestaurant.co.uk

Cooking 2 | Modern European | £39–£70

Like its stablemate Bleeding Heart (see entry), this venerable City institution (once owned by Sandeman) is equally valued for its aristocratic wine list and reliable modern cooking. It's 'a regular place for corporate entertainment', according to a Barbican 'power-luncher' who praised the pressed terrine of foie gras and duck confit with orange and beetroot dressing, and a top-drawer risotto of artichokes, mushrooms and figs. Visitors to the ground-floor restaurant can also expect scallops baked en croûte with lime and vanilla, and grilled calf's liver with sage polenta, curly kale and glazed shallots, followed by banana tarte Tatin with rum and raisin ice cream. The basement bistro has a separate menu promising more straightforward dishes like smoked haddock Mornay. The very fine wine list focuses on France but picks blue-chip names everywhere – including Argentina (Yacochuya) and Chile (Antiyal) – and culminates in long selections of port and madeira. Those not on City salaries are well catered for by the proprietors' own Trinity Hill wines (£16.45 for white, £19.95 for red) and numerous options by the glass.

Chef: Matt Burns **Proprietors:** Robert and Robyn Wilson **Open:** Mon to Fri 12 to 2, 7 to 10 **Closed:** 10 days at Christmas **Meals:** alc (main courses £12.50 to £23) **Service:** 12.5% (optional) **Cards:** Amex, Delta, Diners, Maestro, MasterCard, Visa **Details:** 45 seats. Private parties: 18 to 24 private rooms. Vegetarian meals. No children under 7. No-smoking area. No music. Air-conditioned **Tube:** Bank

	This symbol means that the wine list is well above the average.
	This symbol means that the restaurant has a truly outstanding wine cellar.

MAP 13

Drapers Arms

44 Barnsbury Street, Islington, N1 1ER
Tel: (020) 7619 0348
Website: www.thedrapersarms.co.uk

Cooking 3 | Modern British-Plus | £32–£54

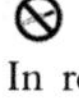

In recent years, this Islington watering hole has become an assured, sophisticated establishment, much favoured by a young, affluent crowd. The bar (where you can eat lunch most days) buzzes with noise and chatter, while the upstairs restaurant is a 'lovely, symmetrical space' with draped blinds, a fireplace at either end and duck-egg-blue walls. The kitchen turns out generous helpings of classic gastro-pub food: white gazpacho with chilli tiger prawns kicked off one enjoyable meal, before a comforting dish of slow-cooked lamb kleftiko with garlicky new potatoes, aubergine salsa and mint aïoli. Other options might range from caramelised five-spice pork belly with Thai green salad to wild boar sausages with bubble and squeak, while desserts are old faithfuls like mixed-berry pavlova. The all-purpose, global wine list opens with house French at £12.

Chef: Mark Emberton **Proprietors:** Paul McElhinney and Mark Emberton **Open:** Sun L 12 to 3, Mon to Sat D 7 to 10.30 **Closed:** 25 to 28 Dec, 1 and 2 Jan **Meals:** alc (main courses £10.50 to £15). Bar menu available **Service:** 12.5% (optional), card slips closed **Cards:** Amex, Delta, Maestro, MasterCard, Visa **Details:** 100 seats. 50 seats outside. Private parties: 40 main room. Vegetarian meals. Children's helpings. No smoking. Music **Tube:** Highbury & Islington

MAP 14

Drones

1 Pont Street, SW1X 9EJ
Tel: (020) 7235 9555
Website: www.whitestarline.org.uk

Cooking 4 | Anglo-French | £33–£81

In one form or another, Drones has been a popular Belgravia haunt for more than three decades. The carte reflects the influence of Marco Pierre White in both scope and culinary style, combining classic French dishes such as parfait de foie gras en gelée and paillard of veal à la forestière with British favourites of potted shrimps and what the menu describes as 'properly garnished' roast chicken. In all this the kitchen keeps a sense of balance – between smoked haddock with grain mustard beurre blanc on the one hand and more substantial braised oxtail alla romana on the other – and the food aims to provide sustenance in the most comforting way. Desserts are from the MPW back list: old favourites like lemon tart and champagne gelée of red fruits. The wine list spans the world fairly democratically. All but two Vins de Pays d'Oc, at £16, are over £20, but there is an interesting selection by the glass.

Chef: Joseph Croan **Proprietor:** White Star Lines Restaurants **Open:** Sun to Fri L 12 to 2 (3 Sun), Mon to Sat D 6 to 11 **Meals:** alc (main courses £12.50 to £24.50). Set L Mon to Fri £14.95 (2 courses) to £17.95, Set L Sun £19.50 **Service:** 12.5%, card slips closed **Cards:** Amex, Delta, Diners, Maestro, MasterCard, Visa **Details:** 96 seats. Private parties: 12 main room, 12 to 40 private rooms. Vegetarian meals. No pipes in dining room. Wheelchair access (not WC). Music. Air-conditioned **Tube:** Sloane Square, Knightsbridge

MAP 13

e&o

14 Blenheim Crescent, W11 1NN
Tel: (020) 7229 5454
Website: www.eando.nu

Cooking 3 | Asian/Fusion | £29–£69

From its fashionable lower-case logo to trademark accessories, everything about this ultra-hip Notting Hill place catches the eye. 'Great-looking staff' mingle with even greater-looking glitterati, and energy levels are off the scale. Some say e&o helped to pioneer the notion of oriental grazing food, and – despite ever-higher expectations – it still excites. The menu (plus helpful glossary) scours the Far East, and it's sliced up into soups, salads, curries et al. The results can be uneven, but few would argue with copybook prawn and chive dumplings, or rock shrimp tempura with yuzu (citron) aïoli ('devastatingly fresh' crustacea, 'fabulous' batter). There are also sure-fire winners among newcomers like 'perfectly tuned' scallop tartare with oba crisps. Egg-fried rice is faultless, although desserts have impressed less. The sexy globetrotting wine list rounds off the package, although prices are a tad high. House wines are £13.50. Will Ricker also owns Eight Over Eight and Great Eastern Dining Room (see entries).

Chef: Simon Treadway **Proprietor:** Will Ricker **Open:** Mon to Sat 12.15 to 3 (4 Sat), 6.15 to 11, Sun 1 to 4, 6.15 to 10.30 **Closed:** 25 and 26 Dec, 1 Jan, Aug bank hol **Meals:** alc (main courses £9.50 to £21.50) **Service:** 12.5% (optional), card slips closed **Cards:** Amex, Delta, Diners, Maestro, MasterCard, Visa **Details:** 82 seats. 20 seats outside. Private parties: 6 main room, 10 to 20 private rooms. Vegetarian meals. No cigars/pipes in dining room. Wheelchair access (not WC). No music. Air-conditioned **Tube:** Ladbroke Grove

MAP 13

Eagle

159 Farringdon Road, EC1R 3AL
Tel: (020) 7837 1353

Cooking 2 | Mediterranean | £22–£43

This pioneer of food pubs hasn't changed much over the years. 'Good pub food, huge portions, good service, relaxed atmosphere', is how one regular sums it up, adding 'it can get very busy indeed'. A short Anglo-Mediterranean menu is chalked up on small boards, and much of the cooking is done on the chargrill behind the bar. Squid with tomato, parsley, fennel, garlic and basmati rice was bursting with flavour, and pumpkin and wild garlic risotto was a 'huge steaming portion'; or there might be roast lamb with green lentils and mixed leaves. This is not the place for a three-course meal – starters are limited, and there are only a couple of desserts – but prices are very reasonable. Beers are on tap or bottled, and a compact blackboard list of global wines starts at £11, all available by the glass.

Chef: Ed Mottershaw **Proprietor:** Michael Belben **Open:** all week L 12.30 to 3 (3.30 Sat/Sun), Mon to Sat D 6.30 to 10.30 **Closed:** 3 days Christmas, bank hols **Meals:** alc (main courses £8 to £14) **Service:** not inc **Cards:** Delta, Maestro, MasterCard, Visa **Details:** 65 seats. 24 seats outside. Vegetarian meals. Children's helpings. Wheelchair access (not WC). Music **Tube:** Farringdon

MAP 12

Ealing Park Tavern

222 South Ealing Road, W5 4RL
Tel: (020) 8758 1879

Cooking 2 | Modern British | £28–£45

When the gastro-pub bandwagon turned off the M4 and headed for Ealing, it set up camp in this lively corner pub. Crowds pack into the vast bar area and dining room, where decibel levels can be high: 'not the place for an intimate tête-à-tête,' thought one visitor. The weekly-changing menu puts its faith in big-hearted dishes, which means bourride, confit of belly pork with bubble and squeak and lentil jus, and home-made burger with pancetta, chips and tomato relish. Starters might include duck liver parfait with pickled cucumber, while desserts are robust offerings like sticky date pudding. The concise, all-European wine list promises enjoyable quaffing at reasonable prices. House French is £11.50.

Chef: Vincent Morse **Proprietors:** Nick Sharpe and Vincent Morse **Open:** Tue to Sun L 12 to 3 (3.45 Sun), all week D 6 to 10.15 (9 Sun) **Closed:** 25 and 26 Dec, 1 Jan **Meals:** alc (main courses £8.50 to £13.50). Bar tapas menu available **Service:** not inc, card slips closed, 12.5% for parties of 5 or more **Cards:** Amex, Maestro, MasterCard, Visa **Details:** 68 seats. 40 seats outside. Vegetarian meals. No children after 8pm. No smoking. Occasional music **Tube:** South Ealing

MAP 12

Earl Spencer

AR

260–262 Merton Road, SW18 5JL
Tel: (020) 8870 9244

Revitalised Southfields watering hole that has been given a contemporary makeover without sacrificing any of its traditional pubby character. The daily-changing menus focus on global dishes like Moroccan-style marinated quail with rocket, red pepper and chilli dressing (£5), eggs Mornay with purple-sprouting broccoli, and beef kofta with bulgur wheat salad, yoghurt and mint (£8.50), followed by, say, buttermilk pudding with rhubarb compote (£4). Appealing choice of wines from £10. Open all week.

MAP 14

The Ebury

11 Pimlico Road, SW1W 8NA
Tel: (020) 7730 6784
Website: www.theebury.co.uk

Cooking 2 | Modern European | £37–£65

This former pub got a smart makeover in 2003 when Tom Etridge took it over, with the clever blending of old and new including impressive chandeliers. The operation has been simplified somewhat, offering just one menu throughout, with the ground-floor brasserie operating on a no-booking basis and the bookable first-floor dining room opening for dinner only. The menu reads simply and enticingly and delivers the flavours it promises with creditable panache. A May dinner for one party provided satisfaction in the form of a fairly thick slicing of carpaccio of beef with salsa verde, a generous goats' cheese salad with roasted red peppers, pine nuts and pomegranate, fine grilled calf's liver and bacon, and a very fresh piece of black bream served with crushed, marinaded potatoes and saffron vierge. Finish with chocolate and almond terrine with pistachio ice cream.

Service is attentive, and wines are a reasonably well chosen bunch, fairly spread between France and the New World. House wines sell at £12.95 a bottle, and eleven wines are available by the glass from £3.50.

Chef: Andrew Donovan **Proprietor:** Tom Etridge **Open:** all week 12 to 3.30 (4 Sat and Sun), 6 to 10.30 (10 Sun). Dining room: Mon to Sat D only 6 to 10.30 **Closed:** 24 to 31 Dec **Meals:** alc (main courses £10 to £22) **Service:** 12.5% (optional), card slips closed **Cards:** Amex, Delta, Maestro, MasterCard, Visa **Details:** 65 seats (60 brasserie). Private parties: 150 main room. Vegetarian meals. Wheelchair access (also WC). Music. Air-conditioned **Tube:** Sloane Square

MAP 13

Ebury Wine Bar

AR

139 Ebury Street, SW1W 9QU
Tel: (020) 7730 5447

Veteran among London's wine bars, much cherished for its well-worn décor and 'faded atmosphere'. Current owners aren't about to change anything – including the 'great honest food'. Reports have praised deep-fried rock oysters in beer batter with pickled fennel, but the repertoire extends to crab and ricotta tart (£6.50), braised rabbit leg with caramelised apples (£14), and desserts like hot chocolate and praline cake (£5.25). Pedigree wine list, with prices from £12 and around 30 by the glass. Closed Sun L.

MAP 15

ECapital

AR

8 Gerrard Street, W1D 5PJ
Tel: (020) 7434 3838

Cheerful, smart Chinatown address that promotes the little-known regional cuisine of Shanghai. Starters are particularly intriguing, from Yang Chau pork terrine (£5) to Arctic clam with jellyfish. The bulk of the menu mixes a few esoteric ideas (sea cucumber and shark's fin on a bed of sizzling rice biscuits; £15) with more familiar staples such as braised duck in plum sauce (£6.50) and beef with green pepper and black-bean sauce. Unusual teas. Open all week.

AR	Not a full entry but provisionally recommended (known as 'round-ups' in previous editions, these 'also recommended' establishments are now integrated throughout the book).

MAP 15

Eddalino

10 Wigmore Street, W1U 2RD
Tel: (020) 7637 0789
Website: www.eddalino.co.uk

Cooking 3 | Italian | £36–£65

There may be the look of an old-fashioned trattoria to Eddalino, with its arched brick wall dividing the glass-fronted dining room in two, but it is also home to Francesco Pesce's gently innovative Italian cooking. Sea bass is served carpaccio-fashion, dressed with baby fennel, grapefruit and dill, or there may be honey-glazed pigeon to start, with a herbed tartlet of baby veg. A choice from various pasta and risotto options might then intervene before mains such as veal fillet served with a gratin of fennel and sheep's-milk grana sardo, or rabbit with agrodolce peppers, potatoes and olives. As well as the more unusual offerings, however, it is quite possible to dine on cured meats and fritto misto, and end with something like chocolate torta accompanied by properly made toffee ice cream.

The wine list is an earnest all-Italian affair. Masses of Piedmont and Tuscan reds culminate in a range of vintages of Sassicaia, while other regions reliably turn up top producers from the £17.50 Colterenzio Pinot Bianco onwards.

Chef: Francesco Pesce **Proprietor:** Piero Zanelli **Open:** Mon to Sat 12 to 3, 6 to 10.30 **Meals:** Set L £23, Set D £27.50 (2 courses) to £36.50 **Service:** 12.5% (optional) **Cards:** Amex, MasterCard, Maestro, Visa **Details:** 55 seats. 8 seats outside. Private parties: 50 main room, 15 to 30 private rooms. Vegetarian meals. Children's helpings. No-smoking area. Wheelchair access (not WC). Music. Air-conditioned **Tube:** Oxford Street

MAP 15

Efes

AR

80–82 Great Titchfield Street, W1W 7QT
Tel: (020) 7636 1953

Well-liked Turkish stalwart that has been delivering the goods for more than three decades. Menus kick off with a fair choice of meze (around £4), from biber dolma (stuffed green peppers) to chicken with walnut sauce. Main courses are mostly variations on high-protein kebabs and grills (£7 to £9), ranging from kofte (minced lamb) and ciger patlican soslu (liver with aubergine sauce) to more expensive steaks. Baklava, kadeyif and other desserts (£3) from the trolley. Efes beer and Turkish wines (£15). Useful for take-aways. Closed Sun.

MAP 13

Eight Over Eight

392 King's Road, SW3 5UZ
Tel: (020) 7349 9934
Website: www.eightovereight.nu

Cooking 2 | Asian/Fusion | £33–£71

Will Ricker's King's Road venue throbs with business, which seems to divide equally between bar and dining area. Against the background of a diverting, quasi-oriental design scheme, the cooking is pan-Asian, and the menu has a helpful ingredient glossary on the back, taking you from 'albacore' to 'yuzu' with concision. Dim sum, salads and sashimi are the name of the game, with options such as Korean-style beef bulgogi and green peppercorns, or chicken and physalis 'jungle curry', broadening the range. Technique is versatile enough to attempt tempura-battered rock shrimp with yuzu aïoli. Finish with lychee granita and champagne float. The drinking is fun, too, with inventive cocktails and a list of non-alcoholic juice blends supporting an exciting wine list that moves swiftly from £14 Italian basics and ten sound options by the glass to a host of desirable bottles cherry-picked from around the world. The Great Eastern Dining Room and e&o are under the same ownership (see entries)

Chef: Andy Vassetter **Proprietor:** Will Ricker **Open:** Mon to Sat L 12 to 3, all week D 6 to 11 (10.30 Sun) **Closed:** 25 to 28 Dec, bank hols L **Meals:** alc (main courses L £9 to £15, D £9 to £26). Set L £15 (2 courses, inc glass of wine). Bar menu available **Service:** 12.5% (optional), card slips closed **Cards:** Amex, Delta, Diners, MasterCard, Maestro, Visa **Details:** 95 seats. Private parties: 8 to 14 private rooms. Vegetarian meals. Wheelchair access (not WC). No music. Air-conditioned **Tube:** Sloane Square

MAP 13

Electric Brasserie

AR

191 Portobello Road, W11 2ED
Tel: (020) 7908 9696

The Electric Cinema complex includes this smart brasserie and bar combo, which generates a lively buzz. The repertoire is a promising mix of classic recipes, ranging from foie gras with Sauternes jelly (£8.50) to fillet steak Diane and chicken Kiev (£15.50), jazzed up with a few voguish flourishes like scallop carpaccio with lemon marmalade, and duck cottage pie (£12). Alternatively, you might consider small plates (£5) of chorizo, crispy squid, or snails in garlic, or the evening trolley (all day Sun), which wheels out the roast of the day. Finish with peach melba or Sussex pond pudding (£6). Open all week.

MAP 15

Embassy

29 Old Burlington Street, W1S 3AN
Tel: (020) 7851 0956
Website: www.embassylondon.com

Cooking 4 | Modern British | £37–£85

There is a distinct touch of retro about the Embassy concept, a two-floored venue where you dine at street level before descending (if you're a member) to the nightclub below to continue drinking and perhaps shake the odd leg. The VIP lounge sits above the dance floor, the better to absorb the vibe. Garry Hollihead, a chef with a wealth of London experience, offers a style of food that blends up-to-date concepts with a strong note of the vernacular. Smoked salmon with pickled cucumber, lemon and capers, or egg cocotte with chicken livers and spinach might precede main courses designed to indulge, such as salmon and crab fishcake, lobster thermidor with tagliatelle, or Buccleuch fillet steak with wild mushrooms and garlic. End with cherry and almond tart, or chocolate fondant with pistachio ice cream. The wine list is a concise selection that will appeal to those who go clubbing in Mayfair. Prices open at £16.50 for a pair of Vins de Pays d'Oc blends.

Chefs: Garry Hollihead and Mark Grogan **Proprietors:** Mark Fuller and Garry Hollihead **Open:** Tue to Fri L 12 to 3, Tue to Sat D 6 to 11.30 **Meals:** alc (main courses £14.50 to £26). Set L £16.95 (2 courses) to £25, Set D £35 **Service:** 12.5% (optional), card slips closed, 15% for parties of 8 or more **Cards:** Amex, Delta, Maestro, MasterCard, Visa **Details:** 120 seats. 24 seats outside. Private parties: 120 main room, 40 to 50 private rooms. Vegetarian meals. No children under 18. Wheelchair access (not WC). Music. Air-conditioned **Tube:** Green Park, Piccadilly Circus

MAP 12

Emile's

NEW ENTRY

96–98 Felsham Road, Putney, SW15 1DQ
Tel: (020) 8789 3323
Website: www.emilesrestaurant.co.uk

Cooking 2 | Modern European | £32–£45

Set in a residential area a short walk from Putney High Street, an understated frontage singles ou

this 'truly neighbourhood' restaurant. Inside there's a light and airy feel, the deep-green carpet, pale avocado walls, white-clothed tables and bamboo-style chairs setting a somewhat retro 'colonial look', while modern gold-leaf wall panels add style. The monthly-changing, fixed-price menus offer plenty of choice (with just one or two supplements) and a surprising modern-European edge, though the individual fillet of beef Wellington always finds a place as a house favourite. Otherwise, expect the likes of roast fillet of sea bream served with prawn tortellini, braised spring onions and a citrus vinaigrette, and for traditional desserts, like treacle tart with vanilla ice cream, to line up alongside more esoteric offerings, perhaps strawberry jelly served with balsamic ripple and black-pepper crème fraîche ice cream. A compact, global wine list offers reasonably priced drinking with house from £10.95.

Chefs: Sam Stafford and Andrew Sherlock **Proprietors:** Emil Fahmy and Andrew Sherlock **Open:** Mon to Sat D only 7.30 to 11 **Closed:** 2 Jan, bank hols **Meals:** Set D £19.50 (2 courses) to £22.50 **Service:** not inc **Cards:** Delta, Maestro, MasterCard, Visa **Details:** 100 seats. Private parties: 36 main room, 35 to 45 private rooms. Vegetarian meals. Wheelchair access (not WC). Music **Tube:** Putney Bridge

MAP 12

Enoteca Turi

28 Putney High Street, SW15 1SQ
Tel: (020) 8785 4449

Cooking 3 | Italian | £28–£55

'Italian cuisine evolved in the home', says Giuseppe Turi, who since 1990 has brought a slice of the mother country to Putney. He imports a whole larder of authentic regional ingredients and aims to recreate the 'casalinga' cooking style, second nature to generations of Italian housewives. Inspiration comes from the gastronomic heartlands of Umbria, Puglia, Sardinia and beyond, and the specials list tells the tale: grilled asparagus comes with a Parmesan-coated deep-fried egg, while vegetarians might also enjoy a risotto of celery, Taleggio and black truffle. Seasonality defines dishes like venison with white cabbage, fonduta (warmed Fontina cheese whisked with eggs and butter), gnocchi and quince preserve, or a crab salad with chickpea purée and samphire, while desserts are mostly in the classic vein of tiramisù, pannacotta and hot chocolate fondant.

Wines sourced from A-list merchants survey the current Italian wine scene from good, straightforward Orvieto to a host of top Barolos in classic and modern styles. House wines are £13.50, and every dish comes with a wine recommendation from the affordable end of the list.

Chef: Kodajo Ginevry **Proprietor:** Giuseppe Turi **Open:** Mon to Sat 12 to 2.30, 7 to 11 **Closed:** 25 and 26 Dec, 1 Jan, bank hols L **Meals:** alc (main courses £8.50 to £17.50). Set L £13.50 (2 courses) to £16.50 **Service:** 12.5% (optional), card slips closed **Cards:** Amex, Delta, Diners, Maestro, MasterCard, Visa **Details:** 85 seats. Private parties: 40 main room, 28 private room. Vegetarian meals. Children's helpings. No smoking in 1 dining room. No cigars/pipes. Wheelchair access (also WC). Occasional music. Air-conditioned **Tube:** Putney Bridge

MAP 15

L'Escargot, Ground Floor

48 Greek Street, W1D 4EF
Tel: (020) 7439 7474
Website: www.whitestarline.org.uk

Cooking 3 | Modern French | £28–£53

Much about L'Escargot feels old-fashioned, but then there has been a restaurant on this central site since the 1920s – it can certainly claim to be a Soho institution. Traditionally, the ground floor has always been a brasserie, and it offers a comfortably short menu that's a fair mix of classic and modern brasserie dishes, the gamut running from blinis with smoked salmon and fromage blanc via omelette Arnold Bennett to crisp fillets of red mullet with tabbouleh and tomato essence, and chocolate fondant with milk ice cream and raspberry coulis. Good raw materials are more often than not improved by the treatment they receive – roast pork cutlet and braised pork belly complemented by a well-judged marjoram jus and 'not too sweet' apple sauce, for example – but on the downside flavours don't always pack a punch. Service is friendly and well drilled. Wines aim for the upper end of the market, so those without financial restrictions can enjoy themselves hugely. For the rest of us, house French is £14.

Chef: Dominic Teague **Proprietors:** Jimmy Lahoud and Marco Pierre White **Open:** Mon to Fri L 12 to 2.15, Mon to Sat D 6 to 11.15 **Closed:** D 25 Dec, 26 Dec, 1 Jan **Meals:** alc (main courses £13 to £15). Set L and D 6 to 7 £14.95 (2 courses) to £17.95 **Service:** 12.5% (optional) **Cards:** Amex, Delta, Diners, Maestro, MasterCard, Visa **Details:** 80 seats. Private parties: 10 to 60 private rooms. Vegetarian meals. No pipes in dining room. Music. Air-conditioned **Tube:** Tottenham Court Road, Leicester Square

MAP 15

L'Escargot, Picasso Room

48 Greek Street, W1D 4EF
Tel: (020) 7439 7474
Website: www.whitestarline.org.uk

NEW CHEF | Modern French | £42–£87

The Picasso Room is the calm oasis above the bustling Ground Floor at L'Escargot (see entry above). It's an L-shaped space with deeply recessed Art Deco light fittings, and pride of place is given to a display of original ceramics by the twentieth-century master. An air of relaxed hedonism prevails, enhanced by the lightly worn formality of black-tied waiters.

The style is modern French, with plenty of menu lingo to prove it. Escargots sautéed bourguignonne come with a chausson of spinach, fresh ceps get piled on to a tarte fine, and pithiviers of wood pigeon comes with roast chestnuts and a game jus – all for starters. Not all raw materials are French – among the foie gras and Challans duck are Dorset crab, Aberdeen Angus and Balmoral venison – but the preparations leave you in no doubt which way the compass needle points. That venison comes with creamed Savoy cabbage and a jus of bitter chocolate, while poulet rôti en cocotte is served with broad beans, roast salsify and sauce Albufera. A sorbet of Granny Smith apple is the crowning glory to a blackberry soufflé, or there might be coconut crème brûlée, or a biracial cheese selection. Prices on the French-led wine list are pumped up by both pedigree and location, and the house 'regrets any disappointment' occasioned by the vintages turning out to be inaccurate. House Chardonnay and Merlot are £14, or £5 a glass. As the Guide went to press chef Jeff Galvin left to set up his own restaurant, and Warren Gerahty took over at the stoves of the Picasso Room. Reports, please.

Chef: Warren Gerahty **Proprietors:** Jimmy Lahoud and Marco Pierre White **Open:** Tue to Fri L 12 to 2, Tue to Sat D 6 to 11 **Closed:** 25 and 26 Dec, 1 Jan, 2 weeks Aug **Meals:** Set L £19.50 (2 courses) to £42, Set D £42 **Service:** 15% (optional) **Cards:** Amex, Delta, Diners, Maestro, MasterCard, Visa **Details:** 30 seats. Private parties: 40 main room. No cigars/pipes in dining room. No music. Air-conditioned **Tube:** Leicester Square, Tottenham Court Road

MAP 15

L'Estaminet

14 Garrick Street, WC2E 9BJ
Tel: (020) 7379 1432

Cooking 2 | French | £25–£72

For thirteen years this cheerily informal restaurant has been flying the tricolour for rustic French food. The cooking is deep-rooted bourgeois; there may be a starter of king prawns stir-fried with capsicum and ginger tossed in for good measure, but there's a foie gras terrine as well; on the whole L'Estaminet knows its customers and doesn't seek to inflict shocks to their systems. Marinated herring fillets on a warm potato salad, or a dozen Burgundy snails with Pernod, garlic and parsley butter indicate the palette of flavours, followed by grilled fillet of turbot with a shallot sauce, and a grilled fillet of beef, or magret de canard. Old faithful puddings take in mousse au chocolat, and crème brûlée, and the selection of unpasteurised cheeses might entice the adventurous. Wines are French, of course, and house bottles are £11.50.

Chef: Phillippe Tamet **Proprietor:** Cassis Ltd **Open:** Mon to Fri L 12 to 2.30, Mon to Sat D 5.45 to 10.45 **Closed:** bank hols, last 2 weeks Aug, Dec 24 to Jan 3 **Meals:** alc (main courses £14 to £20). Set D 5.45 to 7.30 £14.99 to £16.50 **Service:** 12.5%, card slips closed **Cards:** Amex, Delta, Maestro, MasterCard, Visa **Details:** 55 seats. Private parties: 14 main room. Wheelchair access. Music. No mobile phones. Air-conditioned **Tube:** Leicester Square, Covent Garden

MAP 14

L'Etranger

36 Gloucester Road, SW7 4QT
Tel: (020) 7584 1118
Website: www.etranger.co.uk

Cooking 2 | Modern French-Plus | £27–£84

'Pan-fried foie gras with beetroot jus, tempura and tamarind sauce' sums up the Franco-Asian complexion of the food at this modernist venue done out in shades of grey and aubergine. The name itself suggests 'strangeness' and the short menu doesn't disappoint: here you will find tuna spring rolls with ginger and coriander pitched alongside Charolais beef tartare as well as lobster tempura with ponzu and wasabi mayonnaise in company with peppered steak with home-made sumo chips. If you are seeking simplicity you might be torn between caviar with crème fraîche and blinis or a platter of sashimi, while the choice of desserts spans everything from a trio of summer black truffles with pandan leaves and wasabi crème brûlée to thoroughly European apple tart with caramel fudge and vanilla ice cream. Grazing dishes for 'finger', 'chopstick' and 'spoon' are available until midnight. Old World classics abound on the wine list, and the New World gets good consideration too. There are good things to be had around the £20 mark.

Chef: Jerome Tauvron **Proprietor:** Ibi Issolah **Open:** Sun to Fri L 12 to 2.30, Mon to Sat D 6.30 to 10.45 (Sun L 11.45-3) **Meals:** alc (main courses £15.50 to £42.50). Set L £14.50 to £16.50 **Service:** 12.5%, card slips closed **Cards:** Amex, Delta, Maestro, MasterCard, Visa **Details:** 60 seats. Private parties: 10 to 20 private rooms. Vegetarian meals. No-smoking area. Wheelchair access (not WC). Music. Air-conditioned **Tube:** Gloucester Road

MAP 13

Eyre Brothers

70 Leonard Street, EC2A 4QX
Tel: (020) 7613 5346
Website: www.eyrebrothers.co.uk

Cooking 2 | Iberian | £37–£76

The Eyre Brothers is a combination of lively City watering hole and full-dress restaurant, combining a neutral, contemporary look with lots of mahogany, black walnut and leather. It is also one of the few Iberian restaurants in London, where Spanish and Portuguese dishes are given equal billing, featuring ingredients like jamon and morcilla, bacalao and corn milhos. Among starters might be Portuguese spring cabbage, chouriço and potato soup, or pulpo a la gallega (octopus with smoked paprika, olive oil, potatoes, parsley and onion). Main courses have included grilled rump of lamb with rosemary and garlic, accompanied by patatas velhas, and fried grouper fillet on roast tomato, olive, caper and anchovy montada. Wines (from £14.95) show the modern face of Iberia, with a quality international cast in support.

Chefs: David Eyre and João Cleto **Proprietors:** David and Robert Eyre **Open:** Sun to Fri L 12 to 2.30 (4 Sun), Mon to Sat D 6 to 10.30 **Meals:** alc (main courses £12 to £21). Tapas menu available **Service:** 12.5% (optional), card slips closed **Cards:** Amex, Delta, Diners, Maestro, MasterCard, Visa **Details:** 70 seats. Private parties: 70 main room. Vegetarian meals. No-smoking area. Music. Air-conditioned **Tube:** Old Street

MAP 13

Farm

NEW ENTRY

18 Farm Lane, SW6 1PP
Tel: (020) 7381 3331
Website: www.thefarmfulham.co.uk

Cooking 2 | Modern European | £30–£52

The red-brick building off Fulham Broadway looks boozer-like outside, and sounds it in the bar, but there's a smart dining room behind. Paul Merrett, formerly of the Greenhouse (see entry), cooks a short menu of modern crowd-pleasers like chargrilled ribeye steak, béarnaise and chips, or fish pie with mushy peas. Oak-smoked eel with treacle-cured bacon, caramelized apple and herb oil might precede baked salmon en croûte with potato salad, pea cress and mustard and honey dressing. A simple apple tarte fine with vanilla ice cream and caramel sauce was a highlight at inspection, as was rhubarb bavarois with ginger ice cream, orange sorbet and poached rhubarb. The short wine list is modern and easy-going like the surroundings, but prices (from £13) are highish for a gastro-pub; ten come by the glass (£3.50 to £8.50).

Chef: Paul Merrett **Proprietor:** Tom Etridge **Open:** all week 12 to 3 (3.30 Sun), 6 to 10.30 (6.30 to 10 Sun) **Meals:** alc (main courses £10 to £14) **Service:** 12.5% (optional) **Cards:** Amex, Delta, Maestro, MasterCard, Visa **Details:** 76 seats. 8 seats outside. Vegetarian meals. Wheelchair access (not WC). Music. Air-conditioned **Tube:** Fulham Broadway

MAP 13

Fifteen

15 Westland Place, N1 7LP
Tel: (0871) 330 1515
Website: www.fifteenrestaurant.com

Cooking 3 | Modern European | £42–£135

The former warehouse in Hoxton is still as full as ever, and the cooking steers the course set at the beginning: a bright, modern, seasonal blend of Italian influences. Jamie Oliver's Fifteen Foundation is a training programme for underprivileged youngsters, and while television exposure may be partly responsible for the popularity, and thus a convoluted booking system, the ground-floor trattoria seeks to redress this by making half of its tables available on a first-come basis. Here a menu offering risotto of ham hock, gnocchi with Gorgonzola dolce and treviso, and pan-fried calf's liver with oozy polenta and crispy sage gremolada sets out the prospectus clearly.

Those with a hard-won reservation in the basement restaurant can expect a menu of Jamie-speak – 'fantastic salad', 'funky leaves', 'sexy sea kale' and so on – but what matters is that ingredients are first-rate and, in general, the cooking works: simple food, boldly handled, with Mediterranean flavours, as in ravioli of pork, tomato and mascarpone with cinnamon, butter and Parmesan sauce, or chargrilled marinated leg of Welsh lamb with braised celeriac, purple-sprouting broccoli and an anchovy and rosemary dressing. Bittersweet chocolate tart with cherries poached in vanilla and Valpolicella is a wicked way to finish. The restaurant's extensive wine list, organised by grape varieties, opens at £21 and climbs quickly; the trattoria offers a shorter, all-Italian list.

Chef: Jamie Oliver **Proprietor:** The Fifteen Foundation **Open:** trattoria all week L 12 to 3 (5 Sun), Mon to Sat D 6 to 10; restaurant all week L 12 to 2.30, Mon to Sat D 6.30 to 9.30 **Meals:** trattoria alc (main courses £12 to £15); restaurant alc L (main courses £19.50 to £25). Set D £60 **Service:** 12.5% (optional), card slips closed **Cards:** Amex, Delta, Maestro, MasterCard, Visa **Details:** trattoria 40 seats; restaurant 72 seats. Vegetarian meals. No smoking. Wheelchair access (also WC). No music. Air-conditioned **Tube:** Old Street

MAP 14

Fifth Floor

Harvey Nichols, 109–125 Knightsbridge, SW1X 7RJ
Tel: (020) 7823 1839
Website: www.harveynichols.com

Cooking 4 | Modern British | £31–£72

The top-floor restaurant at Harvey Nichols has been something of a Knightsbridge institution since the early 1990s, much frequented by dedicated shoppers and ladies who lunch. Indeed, lunch may still be the best time to catch it, when the ambience in the large, comfortably appointed room has its own restrained buzz, away from the commotion of the adjoining food court.

New chef Helena Puolakka arrived in the spring of 2005, and has maintained the style of uptown brasserie cooking for which the place has always been renowned. Successes have included an 80s-style courgette flower filled with vibrantly flavoured lobster mousse, sauced with lobster cream, a 'keenly balanced' main course of milk-fed Anjou pork with caramelised apples and wild rice, and another of tournedos Rossini, a dead-on rendition using Aberdeen Angus, topped of course with a piece of luscious foie gras. Vegetable sides are competently cooked, and coffee is as it should be. Desserts have impressed less. The wine list has been a star from the word go and has accumulated numerous iconic bottles from the likes of Comtes Lafon, Harlan, Cheval Blanc and Pétrus. Own-label bottles kick things off with Sauvignon Blanc and Merlot at £14.50 and there are oodles of options by the glass.

Chef: Helena Puolakka **Proprietor:** Harvey Nichols **Open:** all week L 12 (11 Sun) to 3.30, Mon to Sat D 6 to 10.30 **Meals:** alc (main courses £9.50 to £16.50). Set D 7 to 10.30 £10 (2 courses) to £13. Bar menu available **Service:** 12.5% (optional) **Cards:** Amex, Delta, Diners, Maestro, MasterCard, Visa **Details:** 110 seats. 40 seats outside. Private parties: 250 main room, 100 to 500 private rooms. Vegetarian meals. Children's helpings. No-smoking area. Wheelchair access (also WC). Music. Air-conditioned **Tube:** Knightsbridge

MAP 13

Fina Estampa

150–152 Tooley Street, SE1 2TU
Tel: (020) 7403 1342

Cooking 2 | Peruvian | £28–£53

Bianca Jones continues to deliver her own version of Peruvian home cooking in this amenable neighbourhood restaurant, which adds a shot of South American vitality to the somewhat austere environs of Tooley Street. Prices have stayed the same 'for the last five years', say the owners – and so has the décor, with its collection of native artefacts, plates and gold-framed mirrors. Potatoes are at the heart of the cuisine – perhaps layered with avocado and tuna in causa rellena or jazzed up with a sauce of fromage frais and mild yellow chillies. Mains range from chicken seco (with coriander sauce, Peruvian-style beans and salsa criolla) to baked salmon sudado, while desserts are mostly ice creams and sorbets. The wine list was due to be updated with a clutch of new Argentinian imports as we went to press.

Chef: Bianca Jones **Proprietors:** Richard and Bianca Jones **Open:** Mon to Fri 12 to 10.30, Sat D only 6.30 to 10.30 **Closed:** 24 to 26 Dec, bank hols **Meals:** alc (main courses £7.50 to £16) **Service:** 10% (optional), card slips closed **Cards:** Amex, Delta, Diners, Maestro, MasterCard, Visa **Details:** 80 seats. Private parties: 65 main room, 25 to 65 private rooms. Vegetarian meals. Children's helpings. No-smoking area. Occasional music. Air-conditioned **Tube:** London Bridge

MAP 15

Fino

33 Charlotte Street (entrance in Rathbone Street), W1T 1RR
Tel: (020) 7813 8010
Website: www.finorestaurant.com

Cooking 3 | Spanish | £30–£74

Head into Rathbone Street to find the discreet entrance to this slick modern tapas joint. In the stylishly designed basement you can graze your way through an extensive menu of authentic morsels ranging from crisp fried shrimps and jamon de Jabugo to clams with sherry and ham, buñuelos de bacalao (salt cod fritters) with tartare sauce, and meats such as marinated grilled quail and sucking pig. Desserts take in shots of crème Catalan foam, Santiago tart, and chocolate fondant with pistachio ice cream. Some things have failed to impress, but reporters approve of the concept, and service wins points for its friendliness and accuracy. Sherries are given proper consideration, and the wine list seldom strays far from its Iberian roots; prices start at £16.

Chef: Jean Phillipe Patruno **Proprietors:** Sam and Eddie Hart **Open:** Mon to Sat 12 to 2.30, 6 to 10.30 **Closed:** 25 Dec, bank hols **Meals:** alc (main courses £5.50 to £15.50). Set L £14.50 (2 courses) to £28, Set D £17.95 (2 courses) to £28 **Service:** 12.5% (optional), card slips closed **Cards:** Amex, Maestro, MasterCard, Visa **Details:** 90 seats. Private parties: 90 main room. Vegetarian meals. Wheelchair access (also WC). No music. Air-conditioned **Tube:** Goodge St/Tottenham Court Road

MAP 13

First Floor

186 Portobello Road, W11 1LA
Tel: (020) 7243 0072

A candlelit dinner in this theatrically decorated room with music pumping from antique speakers is a definitive Portobello Road experience. Look for energetic and seasonal flavour combinations like a springtime fennel and blood orange salad (£6), followed by roast rump of lamb with asparagus and wild garlic leaf (£16), then freshen your palate with a selection of home-made sorbets (£5). Ten wines come by the glass, with bottle prices from £12. Open all week L and Tue to Sat D.

MAP 13

fish!

AR

Cathedral Street, SE1 9AL
Tel: (020) 7407 3803

Contemporary steel and glass pavilion hard by Southwark Cathedral and in the heart of the wonderful Borough food market. With an ecological attitude and commitment to fish from sustainable stocks, available species are ticked on the menu. Choose steamed or grilled and pick your sauce or accompaniment – say, sea trout with hollandaise, or John Dory with spicy salsa (£17). Start with organic smoked salmon (£8) and finish with tiramisù (£5). House wine £13.95. Open all week. fish! Kitchen is next door to Jarvis fishmonger's at 56–58 Coombe Road, Kingston-upon-Thames, Surrey; tel: (020) 8546 2886.

MAP 12

Fish Hoek

8 Elliott Road, W4 1PE
Tel: (020) 8742 0766
Email: info@fishhoek.co.uk

Cooking 2 | Seafood/South African | £28–£71

Housed in a double-fronted building in a quiet residential street, this is a 'slick, bright and unfussy' restaurant 'clearly popular even in midweek'. The kitchen delivers a wide range of South African and other exotic fish, as well as a few native offerings, almost all of them available in either half or full portions. Searing and roasting of meaty white fish like whole stumpnose, or Indonesian barramundi, the latter accompanied by sautéed garlic potatoes and green bean and shallot salad – a hit at inspection – are done well, and reports have praised simply conceived starters like crabmeat salad with lemon mayonnaise. Brandy-soaked berries teamed with chocolate sorbet is a good way to finish. Bread has been praised, service is swift, friendly and knowledgeable, and fish-friendly whites from South Africa dominate the short list. House wine is £17.50.

Chef: Andrew Bellew **Proprietor:** Pete Gottgens **Open:** Tue to Sun 12 to 2.30, 6 to 10.30 **Closed:** 23 Dec to 8 Jan **Meals:** alc (main courses £10 to £25). Set L £12 (2 courses) to £14.50 **Service:** not inc, card slips closed, 12.5% for parties of 6 or more **Cards:** Delta, Maestro, MasterCard, Visa **Details:** 52 seats. Private parties: 50 main room. No smoking in 1 dining room. Music. Air-conditioned **Tube:** Turnham Green

MAP 13

Fish Shop

360–362 St John Street, EC1V 4NR
Tel: (020) 7837 1199
Website: www.thefishshop.net

Cooking 2 | Seafood | £29–£74

The basement area opens on to a walled patio garden, while the ground floor offers split-level eating, in this tall neo-Georgian building near the Angel and Sadler's Wells. Imaginatively treated seafood is the order of the day, although if you aren't feeling that adventurous, it's worth knowing that fish and chips – fresh haddock in crisp, thin batter, crunchy, well-seasoned chips and fine tartare sauce – are highly rated. Otherwise, prepare for grilled langoustines in Pernod and tarragon butter, red snapper with clams, seaweed mash and saffron jus, or seared tuna with celeriac and wasabi rémoulade. Side orders include mushy peas, the crusty country bread is fabulous, and if you've eaten all your greens, there's sticky toffee pudding to look forward to. The wine list sticks mostly to whites, but looks well beyond mainstream Sauvignons and Chardonnays, with lots to try by the glass. Bottles start at £13.95.

Chef: Didier Leberre **Proprietor:** John Moyle **Open:** Tue to Sun 12 to 2.30, 5.30 to 10.30 (6.30 Sun) **Meals:** alc (main courses £11 to £29.50). Set L Tue to Sat £13.50 (2 courses) to £17, Set D Tue to Sat 5.30 to 7 £13.50 (2 courses) to £17 **Service:** 12.5% (optional), card slips closed **Cards:** Amex, Delta, Diners, Maestro, MasterCard, Visa **Details:** 80 seats. 20 seats outside. Private parties: 80 main room, 10 to 40 private rooms. Vegetarian meals. Children's helpings. No smoking in 1 dining room. Wheelchair access (also WC). No music **Tube:** Angel

MAPS 12 AND 15

Fishworks

6 Turnham Green Terrace, W4 1QP
Tel: (020) 8994 0086
89 Marylebone High Street, W1U 4QW
Tel: (020) 7935 9796
Website: www.fishworks.co.uk

Cooking 2 | Seafood | £33–£69

The attraction of Fishworks is freshness: as one reporter noted, 'you see items on sale alive in the shop... so you know what you will be served inside.' Having set the ball rolling in Bath, Bristol and Christchurch (see entries), Mitchell Tonks is now spreading his message across the capital: there are currently two outlets (Marylebone being the newest) and more are in the pipeline. A fixed menu focuses on crustacea and 'classics' like steamed Fowey mussels, but the best bets are the daily specials: braised Start Bay crab with tomato and chilli might vie for attention with pollack fillet, split peas, pancetta and mint. Fish-friendly European whites (from £15.25) dominate the wine list.

Chefs: Jack Scarterfield (Turnham Green) and Thomas Hill (Marylebone Road) **Proprietor:** Fishworks plc **Open:** Tue to Sun L 12 to 2.30, Tue to Sat D 6 to 10.30 **Closed:** 24 Dec to early Jan, day after bank hols **Meals:** alc (main courses L £7 to £25, D £11 to £25) **Service:** not inc **Cards:** Amex, Delta, Maestro, MasterCard, Visa **Details:** 48 seats, 22 seats outside (Turnham Green); 62 seats (Marylebone Road). Vegetarian meals. Children's helpings. No smoking. Music. Air-conditioned **Tube:** Turnham Green/Regent's Park

MAP 13

Flâneur

41 Farringdon Road, EC1M 3JB
Tel: (020) 7404 4422
Website: www.flaneur.com

Cooking 2 | Modern European | £35–£55

Through 'sheer flamboyance and nerve' Flâneur's warehouse conversion marries industrial scale with domestic feel in a conflation of high-class deli and a restaurant providing simple brasserie cooking with a strong Italian influence. Treatments are straightforward: salt cod, rocket, white beans, capers and chilli, say, or parsnip and chestnut soup, being typical starters. Mains take in tender and flavoursome boiled organic gammon well complemented by lentils and parsley sauce – our inspection's high spot – or fried sea bass with saffron, mussels and shallots. Desserts, mainly cakes and tarts, disappointed at inspection, but service is knowledgeable and enthusiastic. The wine list, nearly all French, starts at £14.50, with a dozen or so by the glass from £3.90.

Chef: Simon Phelan **Proprietors:** Mike Metcalfe and Chris Fraser **Open:** all week L 12 to 3, Mon to Sat D 6.30 to 10.30 **Meals:** alc (main courses £12 to £14) **Service:** 12.5% (optional) **Cards:** Amex, Delta, Maestro, MasterCard, Visa **Details:** 55 seats. Vegetarian meals. No smoking. Wheelchair access (not WC). Occasional music **Tube:** Farringdon

MAP 12

Food Room

NEW ENTRY

123 Queenstown Road, SW8 3RH
Tel: (020) 7622 0555
Website: www.thefoodroom.co.uk

Cooking 3 | French/Mediterranean | £28–£56

Home to a succession of upscale restaurants over the last 20 years, these Battersea premises now play host to a new venture by Eric and Sarah Guignard, who also run the French Table in Surbiton (see entry). The kitchen goes all out on the presentation front, with plenty of sculpted towers and drizzles, and the cooking style is resolutely French. Start with Jerusalem artichoke and goats' cheese mille-feuille, or an unusual but effective velouté of smoked haddock with miniature fish beignets, mussels and finely chopped broccoli. Lasagne of mackerel, tomato confit, beetroot and horseradish cream has also passed muster. Main courses might run from saddle of rabbit with cocoa bean purée, prunes, crisp ham and madeira sauce to pan-fried halibut with roast leeks, asparagus and langoustine froth. Finish with banana mousse with spun sugar and coconut sorbet – 'a very good concoction'. France is given a slight advantage over the New World and the rest of Europe on the wine list of 50-odd bottles. Bottle prices open at £12.50, and half a dozen come by the glass from £3.50.

Chef: Eric Guignard **Proprietors:** Sarah and Eric Guignard **Open:** Wed to Fri L 12 to 2.30, Tue to Sat D 7 to 10.30 **Closed:** 25 and 26 Dec, first week Jan, last 2 weeks Aug **Meals:** Set L £13.50 (2 courses) to £16.50, Set D £19.50 (2 courses) to £24.50 **Service:** 12.5% (optional), card slips closed **Cards:** Delta, Maestro, MasterCard, Visa **Details:** 68 seats. Vegetarian meals. Children's helpings. No smoking in 1 dining room. Wheelchair access (also men's WC). Music. Air-conditioned

MAP 13

Four Seasons

84 Queensway, W2 3RL
Tel: (020) 7229 4320

Cooking 2 | Cantonese | £22–£56

Those who are 'chronically addicted' to the pleasures of succulent, honeyed roast meats habitually seek solace here. Crowds gather outside and block the entrance; others cluster in homage around the meat preparation area ('a zone of almost religious significance to the restless faithful'). Things are hardly less frantic in the main dining room, where service can be erratic and the food can miss its target. That said, the kitchen wins the day with 'sinfully gratifying' roast duck and specials like whole sea bass flavoured with curry paste, black beans, preserved vegetables and coriander (an odd idea, but stunningly good); reporters have also enjoyed vegetable spring rolls, sizzling aubergine with clumps of crispy pork in spicy sauce, and 'superior' Singapore noodles. House wine is £9.90.

Chef: Mr Tong **Proprietor:** Paul Chung **Open:** all week 12 to 11.15 **Closed:** 23 to 25 Dec **Meals:** alc (main courses £6 to £20). Set L and D £13.50 to £18 (all min 2 or more) **Service:** 12.5% **Cards:** Delta, Maestro, MasterCard, Visa **Details:** 60 seats. Vegetarian meals. Music. Air-conditioned **Tube:** Bayswater, Queensway

MAP 13

Fox Dining Room

28 Paul Street, EC2A 4LB
Tel: (020) 7729 5708
Email: fox.ph@virgin.net

Cooking 3 | Modern European | £31–£39

'We never forget it's a pub,' writes Trish Hilferty, and indeed that's just what you get when you enter: a bare-boarded bar with a casual atmosphere; those wishing to eat head upstairs to the darkly Gothic dining room. Here, the menus are short and descriptions terse, for the kitchen emphasises simplicity and clear flavours, which reflects well on the contemporary European style. There is nothing flashy about the presentation, and no gimmicks, just prime materials confidently treated. Starters of watercress soup, or smoked haddock cakes with aïoli lead on to, say, hare with pappardelle, or poussin with swede and carrot mash, and for dessert there could be blood orange posset, or prune and ginger pudding.The compact, modern wine list runs in price order, starting at £11 a bottle, £2.75 a glass.

Chef: Trish Hilferty **Proprietor:** Michael Belben **Open:** Mon to Fri 12.30 to 3, 6.30 to 10.30 **Closed:** 24 Dec to 3 Jan, bank hols **Meals:** Set L and D £15 (2 courses) to £19.75. Bar menu available **Service:** not inc, 10% for parties of 6 or more **Cards:** Amex, Delta, Maestro, MasterCard, Visa **Details:** 34 seats. 20 seats outside. Private parties: 40 main room. Vegetarian meals. Children's helpings. No music **Tube:** Old Street, Liverpool Street

MAP 12

Franklins

157 Lordship Lane, SE22 8HX
Tel: (020) 8299 9598
Website: www.franklinsrestaurant.com

Cooking 2 | British | £21–£56

Franklins, on busy Lordship Lane, presents a blue-tiled frontage to the world, and inside, beyond the buzzy, pubby bar, is an airy dining room where food is taken seriously in foursquare British manner. Bare brick walls are hung with large mirrors, floors and chairs are dark wood, tables come with white paper cloths, efficient staff wear long white aprons, and there's a view into the tiny kitchen, all cultivating that gastro-pub vibe. Honest, generous British food using sound ingredients is described with deadpan economy on a weekly-changing seasonal carte; perhaps devilled kidneys, or pheasant and porcini terrine to start, then saddleback pork loin with snails and black pudding, or smoked haddock with mussels and sprouting broccoli. Finish with faithful rhubarb crumble or bread-and-butter pudding, or maybe Scotch woodcock. There's also a value, no-choice fixed-price lunch menu, and a compact, mostly French wine list starts at £11 (£2.75 a glass).

Chefs: Tim Sheehan and Phil Greene **Proprietors:** Rodney Franklin and Tim Sheehan **Open:** all week 12 to 4, 6 to 10.30 **Closed:** 25 to 26 and 31 Dec, 1 Jan **Meals:** alc (main courses £10 to £18). Set L £9 (2 courses) to £12. Bar menu available **Service:** not inc, 10% (optional) for parties **Cards:** Amex, Delta, Maestro, MasterCard, Visa **Details:** 67 seats. Private parties: 42 main room, 25 private room. Children's helpings. No-smoking area. Wheelchair access (also WC). No music

MAP 15

Fung Shing

15 Lisle Street, WC2H 7BE
Tel: (020) 7437 1539
Website: www.fungshing.co.uk

Cooking 2 | Chinese | £34–£69

Tourists peering through the steamy windows are likely to be reassured by Fung Shing's neat aquamarine tablecloths, Chinese paintings and smart-suited waiters. Like many of its neighbours, this one-time superstar seems to court trade from Westerners rather than concentrating on the intricacies of authentic cuisine. That said, some still vigorously applaud its cooking, especially when dishes are from the familiar world of hot-and-sour soup, aromatic crispy duck, and steamed sea bass with ginger and spring onions. The kitchen also flexes its muscles for specials like prawns with fried lotus roots, and crispy-roast pigeon. Steamed pork dumpling was a notable disappointment at inspection, as was a main course hot-pot of belly pork with yam. Wines (from £14.50) are a cut above the Soho Chinese norm.

Chef: Frankie Cheung **Proprietor:** Fung Shing Partnership **Open:** all week 12 (6 bank hols) to 11.15 **Closed:** 24 to 26 Dec **Meals:** alc (main courses £8 to £19). Set L and D £17 to £30 (all min 2 or more) **Service:** 10%, card slips closed **Cards:** Amex, Delta, Diners, Maestro, MasterCard, Visa **Details:** 100 seats. Private parties: 50 main room, 20 to 50 private rooms. Vegetarian meals. Music. Air-conditioned **Tube:** Leicester Square

MAP 15

La Galette

AR

56 Paddington Street, W1U 4HY
Tel: (020) 7935 1554

Drink cider from Brittany and Normandy from the bolée (porcelain bowl) for that authentic feeling at this cheerful Marylebone crêperie. Start with something like salmon rillettes served with toast before moving on to the eponymous buckwheat pancakes. Fillings range from Normandy butter (£3.95) to forestière (mixed forest mushrooms with crème fraîche and parsley; £7.90), or complète (ham, cheese and egg; £6.50). Finish with sweet fillings such as chocolate sauce or chestnut cream (£3.50). Open all week.

MAP 12

Gate

51 Queen Caroline Street, W6 9QL
Tel: (020) 8748 6932
Website: www.thegate.tv

Cooking 2 | Vegetarian | £30–£43

If the restaurant itself is nothing out of the ordinary to look at, it's the wide-reaching cooking that's the draw – unusual ingredients, vivid colours and flavours all testify to the fact that vegetarian cookery need not be dull. A typical diverse menu may feature chargrilled, skewered halloumi in a tikka marinade with red onions, peppers, courgettes and a butterbean salsa, and a version of tagine made with root vegetables, dates and pickled lemon. Pancakes are popular, perhaps flavoured with coriander and mustard seed and filled with spiced cauliflower, butternut squash and cashew nuts, then served with lentils, okra and mango and coconut compote. Chocolate fondant laced with Kirsch-marinated black cherries is a good bet for dessert, or there's a cheese plate with date and fig compote and oatcakes. A single page wine selection offers a few organics, starts at £11 and stays mostly under £20, with glass prices from £3.

Chef: Jo Tyrrell **Proprietors:** Michael and Adrian Daniel **Open:** Mon to Fri L 12 to 2.45, Mon to Sat D 6 to 10.45 **Closed:** 25 Dec, 1 Jan, bank hols **Meals:** alc (main courses £8 to £13) **Service:** 12.5% (optional), card slips closed **Cards:** Amex, Delta, Maestro, MasterCard, Visa **Details:** 60 seats. 25 seats outside. Private parties: 80 main room. Vegetarian meals. No smoking. Music **Tube:** Hammersmith

MAP 15

Le Gavroche

43 Upper Brook Street, W1K 7QR
Tel: (020) 7408 0881
Website: www.le-gavroche.co.uk

Cooking 7 | French | £50–£186

The name appears in bold black lettering above the otherwise discreet canopied entrance in a Mayfair apartment mansion. There is a small, clubby lounge and bar area for aperitifs and menu perusal, after which you are led down to the low-lit basement dining room, which is decorated in deep green and hung about with small paintings and photographic highlights of the restaurant's history. A business that has been an established name for as long as the Gavroche needs to manage a fine balancing act between not alienating customers who may have been coming here since the 1960s and continuing to expand its client base. Thus it is that a lady in lamé may find herself at an adjacent table to a young lad who has to be reminded smilingly not to take his jacket off, while Albert Roux himself – who handed over the kitchen baton to his son Michel in 1991 – still pops in for lunch.

There are novelties on the menu, although only a few: stuffed rabbit appears with ratatouille in a salad dressed with cep oil; a main course of lobster comes strewn with chanterelles on a vaporously light Jerusalem artichoke purée, served in very lightly chillied pan juices; mille-feuille of pears, sandwiched with a cream filling radiant with eau-de-vie, is garnished with crumbled toasted pistachios and sauced with salty-buttered caramel. Otherwise, it's kitchen luxuries all the way, with the spirit of Escoffier alive and wafting over dishes such as coeur d'artichaut Lucullus (an artichoke heart stuffed with truffled foie gras and chicken mousse), and caviar grains sprinkled like hundreds and thousands into a butter sauce to accompany a fine, and hugely generous, first course of salmon and broad bean tartare. Jugged hare is properly blood-drenched and rich. Go with the ostentatious flow, and the experience is rewarding indeed.

Staff are so numerous that a visit to the lavatories might create momentary gridlock. They know what they're doing, though. 'From the moment of our arriving to our departure, service was exceptional in its polite friendliness, unobtrusive attention and seamless efficiency.' You can gawp at page after page of leading French wines from Bordeaux and Burgundy, with a whole spread devoted to vintages from the first-growth châteaux and Dom. de la Romanée-Conti, but unless your budget stretches that far it is more rewarding to scour other regions, where well-chosen and affordable bottles from £17 mingle unabashed with the stars. Beyond France, only Italy is covered in any depth.

Chef: Michel Roux **Proprietor:** Le Gavroche Ltd **Open:** Mon to Fri L 12 to 2, Mon to Sat D 6.30 to 11 **Closed:** Christmas, New Year, bank hols **Meals:** alc (main courses £27 to £49). Set L £44 (inc wine), Set D £86 **Service:** 12.5% (optional), card slips closed **Cards:** Amex, Delta, Diners, Maestro, MasterCard, Visa **Details:** 70 seats. Private parties: 80 main room. Vegetarian meals. Jacket. No-smoking area. No music. Air-conditioned **Tube:** Marble Arch

MAP 15

Gay Hussar

2 Greek Street, W1D 4NB
Tel: (020) 7437 0973
Website: www.simplyrestaurants.com

Cooking 1 | Hungarian | £31–£56

The Hussar rides on regardless of London's happening restaurant scene. Opened in 1952, it has 'old timer' written all over it, from the red banquettes and wood panelling, via its loyal customers, to the unchanging list of Hungarian dishes. Expect wild cherry soup, or marinated fillets of herring with soured cream to start, then wiener schnitzel, goulash, or fresh duck foie gras in Tokaji with mashed potato. Poppy-seed strudel and vanilla ice cream, or chestnut purée could round the meal off. Standards may be variable; one who first ate here thirty years ago 'and was impressed' now feels the place is 'resting upon its laurels'. Bull's Blood and Tokaji feature on a half-Hungarian wine list that opens with house wine at £13.50.

Chef: Carlos Mendoca **Proprietor:** Restaurant Partnership plc **Open:** Mon to Sat 12.15 to 2.30, 5.30 to 10.45 **Closed:** 25 to 28 Dec and 1 to 3 Jan **Meals:** alc D (main courses £9.50 to £16.50). Set L £16.50 (2 courses) to £18.50 **Service:** 12.5% (optional), card slips closed **Cards:** Amex, Delta, Diners, Maestro, MasterCard, Visa **Details:** 82 seats. Private parties: 10 main room, 6 to 24 private rooms. Vegetarian meals. No cigars or pipes in main room. Music. Air-conditioned **Tube:** Tottenham Court Road

MAP 15

Giardinetto

39–40 Albemarle Street, W1S 4TE
Tel: (020) 7493 7091

Cooking 2 | Italian | £45–£96

Maurizio Vilona's distinctive Italian cooking has upped sticks since last year's Guide and made a bold journey from Charlotte Street into the heart of Mayfair. Here, stylish minimalism is the prevailing tone, with light plank flooring and plain white walls, and smartly dressed staff swish up and down the split-level dining areas. The intention is to create a liaison of traditionalism and modernity, as is apparent in 'fresh and vibrant' carpaccio of monkfish garnished with grapefruit and dressed in a green vinaigrette, or in bright green chlorophyll tagliolini with chunks of lobster and a bare spoonful of crustacean sauce. As well as inventive meat dishes such as roast pigeon in orange and sage sauce, one or two Ligurian specialities remain on the menu – trofiette al pesto, for example, or caramella ripiena, a candy-shaped pasta parcel stuffed with shrimps and chickpeas in a cherry tomato sauce – and meals conclude with the likes of a pyramid of chocolate mousse with red berry coulis. A generous choice of wines by the 150ml glass starts at £5 and introduces a list that gives an exhaustive picture of what's happening in Italian viticulture nowadays. Prices are thoroughly Mayfair, starting at £15.

Chef/Proprietor: Maurizio Vilona **Open:** Sun to Fri L 12.30 to 3 (12 to 3.30 Sun), all week D 7 to 11 (10.30 Sun) **Meals:** alc (main courses £15 to £23). Set L and D £60 **Service:** 12.5% (optional), card slips closed **Cards:** Amex, Delta, Diners, Maestro, MasterCard, Visa **Details:** 50 seats. Private parties: 8 to 14 private rooms. Vegetarian meals. Wheelchair access (also WC). Music **Tube:** Green Park

MAP 13

Ginger

115 Westbourne Grove, W2 4UP
Tel: (020) 7908 1990
Website: www.gingerrestaurant.co.uk

Cooking 2 | Bangladeshi | £20–£56

Ginger celebrates the traditions of Bangladeshi home cooking in surroundings that are vivid and contemporary, although its menu also cuts a broad swath through the regions of the Subcontinent. Bengali street snacks like shingara (vegetable 'samosas') and Calcutta's favourite katti kebab cones (shredded lamb in a wholewheat wrap) appear among the starters, while the rest of the menu ranges from Goan king prawn balchao (with pickled peppers and dried shrimps) and kashi (goat) bhuna to an unusual fish biryani and crossovers like hashon raja (grilled Barbary duck breast with spicy orange zest sauce). Pumpkins, plantains and karela feature among the vegetables, while desserts range from classic Bengali sweetmeats to pink champagne sorbet. The thoughtfully assembled wine list suits the food. Prices start at £11.95.

Chef: Cruz Gomes **Proprietor:** W. Rahman **Open:** Mon to Thur 5 to 10.45, Fri 5 to 11.45, Sat noon to 11.45, Sun noon to 10.45 **Closed:** 25 Dec **Meals:** alc (main courses £7.50 to £13). Set L and D noon (5 Mon to Fri) to 7.30 £9.95 **Service:** 12.5% (optional) **Cards:** Amex, Delta, Maestro, MasterCard, Visa **Details:** 56 seats. Private parties: 80 main room, 15 to 36 private rooms. Vegetarian meals. No smoking in 1 dining room. Music. Air-conditioned **Tube:** Notting Hill Gate

MAP 13

Glas

AR

3 Park Street, SE1 9AB
Tel: (020) 7357 6060

Just a stone's throw from Borough Market, this new Swedish restaurant offers much more than 101 ways with herrings. Small, light and contemporary inside, the menu offers a range of grazing dishes, including crayfish salad (£5.45), seasoned with lemon and lots of black pepper, and baked beetroot with goats' cheese, walnuts and green leaves. Spiced venison comes with mash and a well-balanced liquorice jus (£6.45), and desserts run to saffron pancake with blackberries and buttermilk sorbet (£3.95). Herrings do make an appearance, perhaps with vodka and lime, or herbs and garlic (£3.95). House wine starts at £13.95. Reports, please. Open Tue to Sat.

MAP 15

Golden Dragon

28–29 Gerrard Street, W1V 7LP
Tel: (020) 7734 2763

Cooking 2 | Chinese | £21–£51

Effigies of dragons and staff in gold waistcoats emphasise the name of this big, bold and colourful Chinatown address. Like many of its neighbours it deals in broadly based Cantonese cooking, although the encyclopaedic menu also branches out for Peking duck and stir-fried Szechuan prawns. Roast meats (including pigeon and marinated duck, 'served warm') are among the high points, hot-pots are earthy assemblages of – say – braised lamb belly with dry bean curd, and one-plate rice and noodle dishes are in plentiful supply. Seafood also shows up strongly, from clear steamed crab to deep-fried squid with garlic and chilli. Lunchtime crowds flock in for the comprehensive selection of dim sum, which runs from lobster dumplings with salad cream to char sui bau (steamed buns filled with jammy roast pork). House wine is £9.

Chef: Mr Man **Proprietor:** Grandpord Ltd **Open:** all week 12 (11 Sun) to 11.15 (11.45 Fri and Sat, 10.45 Sun) **Meals:** alc (main courses £5.50 to £18). Set L and D £12.50 (2 courses, min 2) to £23.50 (min 5) **Service:** 10% **Cards:** Amex, Delta, Diners, Maestro, MasterCard, Visa **Details:** 200 seats. Private parties: 200 main room, 10 to 40 private rooms. Vegetarian meals. Wheelchair access (not WC). Music. Air-conditioned **Tube:** Leicester Square, Piccadilly Circus

MAP 14

Gordon Ramsay

68–69 Royal Hospital Road, SW3 4HP
Tel: (020) 7352 4441
Website: www.gordonramsay.com

Cooking 9 | French | £56–£144

World domination may not be the ultimate goal of Gordon Ramsay, but with Tokyo and New York joining Dubai and London in the fold, it is looking increasingly likely. With TV commitments in the USA to boot, his contribution to the airline industry over the last year has doubtless been significant. He may never have got to hear the faithful at Ibrox chanting 'There's only one Gordon Ramsay', but it is worth pointing out the truth of the matter. One of Ramsay's great skills, however, seems to be an ability to delegate to trusted lieutenants, prodigious talents themselves, who carry forward the mission.

Royal Hospital Road remains the flagship among the London operations. A refurbishment of the dining room is due to take place during the life of this Guide, with the relatively small room presenting a challenge for design guru David Collins. Doubtless it will remain an appropriate space for what amounts to just about the best cooking in the capital.

Service is charming and professional, and the maître d', Jean-Claude Breton, deserves a name-check once again for his passion and consummate skill. Do not worry if you can't decide what to choose from the menu, as M. Breton will run through the options and inspire you one way or another. Amuse-bouche have included a delicate pastry filled with smoked salmon, some taramasalata and garlic ('a striking combination') before a pre-starter soup (consommé of potato, bacon and smoked eel, perhaps). Changes on the menu are introduced at a gentle pace – not fast enough for some – with signature dishes like ravioli of lobster, langoustine and salmon poached in a light bisque with lemongrass and chervil velouté a fixture among starters, with perhaps only the slightest of tweaks from time to time. A first-course slice of foie gras terrine impressed an inspector with its 'silky-smooth texture and intense flavour', served with a few wild mushrooms and leaves, and pan-fried Isle of Skye scallops are paired with Peking duck (alongside charlotte potatoes and a green salad) in a rich, piquant oriental sauce. The quality of the produce shines throughout, whether a main course of perfectly timed sea bass with celeriac purée, or Cornish lamb cooked three ways (best end, leg and shoulder). A daily special of fillet of Kobe beef has arrived topped with Périgord truffles and served on some onion and spinach with girolles, artichoke and pomme purée in a divinely indulgent main course.

The name Assiette de l'Aubergine harks back to a time when Ramsay was a man without an empire and is a godsend to those who can't decide how to finish: 'what a great selection, which amounted to just about every dessert on the menu.' Among the items are a chocolate and hazelnut soufflé, served in a mini pan straight from the oven, a triumph of lightness and delicate flavour, a tiptop tarte Tatin, and an orange parfait with a chocolate madeleine and almond feuilleté, which hit all the right flavour and texture buttons.

The wine list succeeds brilliantly as a showcase for the world's finest – if you have the budget for Ch. Latour you can select any of the top vintages back to 1945 (£6,200, if you were wondering). Equally impressive is the sense of balance, with quality and fair prices from the £12 Côtes de Gascogne upwards and an imaginative global selection to complement the detailed coverage of France. A delectable dozen come by the glass.

Chef: Gordon Ramsay **Proprietor:** Gordon Ramsay Holdings Ltd **Open:** Mon to Fri 12 to 2.30, 6.45 to 11 **Closed:** 2 weeks at Christmas **Meals:** Set L £40, Set D £70 to £90 **Service:** not inc **Cards:** Amex, Delta, Diners, Maestro, MasterCard, Visa **Details:** 44 seats. Private parties: 44 main room. Vegetarian meals. Children's helpings. No smoking. Wheelchair access (not WC). No music. No mobile phones. Air-conditioned **Tube:** Sloane Square

MAP 15

Gordon Ramsay at Claridge's

Brook Street, W1A 2JQ
Tel: (020) 7499 0099
Website: www.gordonramsay.com

Cooking 6 | French | £48–£121

If you're entering the hotel from the Davies Street entrance (beneath the canopy on which the master's name is inscribed), you'll need to head along the corridor, turn right into the lounge and then right again for the restaurant. This perambulation through a bygone world of tinkling and chintz should set the mood, although it won't quite prepare you for the dimly lit, orangey-brown murk of the dining room itself, with its colossal three-tiered light fittings seemingly modelled on the Guggenheim Museum in New York.

Mark Sargeant produces a menu that fits seamlessly into the Ramsay group mould, with a wide variety of choice, virtually no supplements, and the option of a table in the kitchen if you'd like to have a chat with him while you eat. There are extravagant successes: braised Gloucester Old Spot belly pork comes crowned with roast langoustines, fixed to it with a cladding of truffled white-bean purée, with a couple of loosely crumbed quail's egg beignets into the bargain, to make a majestic opening course. Purées are clearly in, a cauliflower variation appearing with scallops and a caramelised sauce of sherry vinegar, but main courses aim for substantial impact even where the ideas are quite familiar, as in monkfish wrapped in Parma ham accompanied by top-notch herb risotto. Not everything quite fits the opulent bill: a starter consisting of broccoli purée scattered with almonds with a poached duck egg in it seems a dowdy effort for a £60 menu, even taking into account its two slivers of truffle, and an inspection main course of sea trout offered a fine piece of brilliantly timed fish with fresh-tasting tomato butter sauce, but only a sparse underlay of under-seasoned crushed potatoes, some cherry tomatoes and a few spears of asparagus for company. Pre-desserts may well be as artfully composed as the dessert itself, the latter perhaps offering chocolate crème brûlée with a slice of caramelised pear and a tiny squidge of pear sorbet. Legions of staff provide service at varying levels of ability.

The 'telephone book' wine list offers phenomenal quality with prices to match but turns up creditable options under £25 in minor appellations, such as benchmark Côtes du Ventoux from Domaine de Fondrèche (£24). There's decent Muscadet and other French basics for £18, and 12 options are promised by the glass.

Chef: Mark Sargeant **Proprietor:** Gordon Ramsay Holdings Ltd **Open:** all week 12 to 3, 5.45 to 11 **Meals:** Set L £30 to £60, Set D £60 to £70 **Service:** not inc **Cards:** Amex, Delta, Diners, Maestro, MasterCard, Visa **Details:** 100 seats. Private parties: 100 main room, 6 to 60 private rooms. Vegetarian meals. Children's helpings. No smoking. Wheelchair access (not WC). No music. No mobile phones. Air-conditioned **Tube:** Bond Street

MAP 13

Great Eastern Dining Room

54–56 Great Eastern Street, EC2A 3QR
Tel: (020) 7613 4545
Website: www.greateasterndining.co.uk

Cooking 3 | Pan-Asian | £32–£58

This sleek and stylish warehouse conversion has settled into the pan-Asian style that is Will Ricker's trademark (see also e&o and Eight Over Eight). The menu is the kind that encourages sharing – 'and a bit of exploration' – with a useful lexicon of Asian dishes and their descriptions on the flip side. Highlights at inspection were dim sum of caramelised braised oxtail, and a silky 'East-meets-West' coconut and rhubarb pannacotta – and the roll-call of dishes ranges from tuna sashimi, red shrimp tempura, and tea-smoked salmon and green papaya salad, to crisp-skinned chicken with black vinegar. The bar next door is a popular hangout for affluent City types and adds to the buzzy atmosphere, and the 'fittingly stylish' wine list leans towards the New World, with prices starting at £13.

Chef: Mark Adler **Proprietor:** Will Ricker **Open:** Mon to Fri L 12 to 3, Mon to Sat D 6.30 to 11 **Meals:** alc (main courses £8 to £14.50). Bar menu available **Service:** 12.5% (optional), card slips closed **Cards:** Amex, Delta, Diners, Maestro, MasterCard, Visa **Details:** 65 seats. Private parties: 90 main room. Vegetarian meals. No cigars/pipes in dining room. No music. Air-conditioned **Tube:** Old Street

MAP 13

Great Eastern Hotel, Aurora

Liverpool Street, EC2M 7QN
Tel: (020) 7618 7000
Website: www.aurora-restaurant.co.uk

Cooking 4 | Modern European | £42–£81

Hard by Liverpool Street Station, the Great Eastern's Aurora restaurant offers the chance of dining in the grand style, then boarding the commuter train home when there is a seat to be had. The room's well-bred good looks derive in no small part from the vast stained-glass dome that rises above it, back-lit after dark to create a dream-like ambience.

Drawing on the best of European tradition – anything from masterly boeuf en daube to innovative pavé of sea bass with trompettes and Sauternes sauce – Allan Pickett offers fixed-price or à la carte options, plus a seven-course tasting menu. The first might embrace honey-glazed gammon carved on a trolley, or a fillet of gilthead bream with braised fennel, while the second offers dishes like ballottine of quail and boudin blanc with truffle-dressed herb salad, then perhaps best end of Dornoch lamb with Parmesan gnocchi in a rosemary bouillon. Among the desserts, three types of crème brûlée could be one option, or cheeses from another of those trolleys.

The wine list strikes a winning balance between numerous fabulous bottles and a healthy number of options under £20. The fertile middle-ground encompasses southern-hemisphere delights such as Hunter's New Zealand Pinot Noir (£31) and offbeat French bottles like Jurançon Vitatge Vielh from Clos Lapeyre (£33). A host of choices by the glass ranges from £4.95 to £14.95.

Chef: Allan Pickett **Proprietor:** Conran Holdings **Open:** Mon to Fri 12 to 2.30, 6.45 to 10 **Closed:** 2 weeks at Christmas, bank hols **Meals:** alc (main courses £16 to £25). Set L £23.50 (2 courses) to £28 (3 courses), Set L 12 to 2 £50 (7 courses) Set D 6.45 to 9 £50 (7 courses) **Service:** 12.5% (optional) **Cards:** Amex, Delta, Diners, Maestro, MasterCard, Visa **Details:** 100 seats. Private parties: 100 main room. Vegetarian meals. No pipes. Wheelchair access (also WC). Music. Air-conditioned **Accommodation:** 267 rooms, all with bath/shower. TV. Phone. Room only £225 to £575. Rooms for disabled. Baby facilities **Tube:** Liverpool Street

MAP 13

Great Nepalese

48 Eversholt Street, NW1 1DA
Tel: (020) 7388 6737

Gopal Manandhar's exceedingly likeable, family-run restaurant within earshot of Euston remains a godsend for commuters and others. The menu has its quota of curry-house staples, but it pays to explore the ever-increasing list of Nepalese specialities. Look for momo (steamed dumplings; £4), bhutuwa chicken with green herbs (£5.25) and the duck dishes, as well as intriguing vegetables and side dishes ranging from aloo bodi tama (potatoes, bamboo shoots and beans; £3.50) to dhaniya achar (coriander pickle). Drink Nepalese Gurkha beer, lassi or house wine (£8.95). Open all week.

MAP 12

The Green

58–60 East Dulwich Road, SE22 9AX
Tel: (020) 7732 7575
Website: www.greenbar.co.uk

Cooking 2 | Modern European | £21–£53

An end-of-terrace shop premises beside a green is the setting for this neighbourhood venue, which tries to look cool with its beige décor, abstract artwork and wooden floor. Live jazz on Tuesday and Thursday evenings reinforces the groovy image, and the kitchen serves classic UK brasserie fare. Pan-fried chicken livers with tarragon, cream and cognac have been 'properly homemade', and reporters have also praised baked cod fillet with shrimp, mussel, Noilly Prat and lemon sauce. Vegetarian options could include spinach gnocchi, while desserts are valiant attempts at, say, Calvados, apple and pear tart with vanilla ice cream. Breakfast and all-day snacks are a bonus. The affordable wine list fulfils its purpose, with cheap and cheerful house recommendations at £9.95. Related to Le Chardon in nearby Lordship Lane (see entry).

Chef: Damien Gillespie **Proprietors:** Heather and Robert Benyayer **Open:** all week 12 to 3.30, 6 to 11 **Meals:** alc (main courses £9 to £12.50). Set L £8.50 (2 courses) to £11.50 **Service:** 10% (optional) **Cards:** Amex, Delta, Maestro, MasterCard, Visa **Details:** 120 seats. 30 seats outside. Private parties: 100 main room. Vegetarian meals. Children's helpings. No smoking in 1 dining room. Wheelchair access (also WC). Music

MAP 15

Greenhouse

27A Hays Mews, W1J 5NY
Tel: (020) 7499 3331
Email: reservations@greenhouserestaurant.co.uk

Cooking 6 | Modern European | £54–£136

'It is a pleasant restaurant,' writes a reporter, 'approached through a rather Hollywood-like avenue of wooden boards, plants, fountains, designed I think to distract you from the fact that this restaurant is actually in the basement of a pretty grotty-looking block of Mayfair flats.' Serious intent is apparent from the well-spaced tables and plush surrounds, and the place is awash with well-drilled staff.

Tasting menus of seven small courses are a speciality, but there is also a three-course carte for those who like choosing for themselves. Bjorn van der Horst's innovative concepts are supported by sound techniques and unusual flavourings that bring vigour and surprise. Fine breads give an initial hint of the quality-consciousness that underscores the cooking, while one diner's 'unique and superb' lobster with caramelised endive and vanilla brown butter set the tone for an autumn tasting menu that included a serving of foie gras with espresso syrup and Amaretto foam that was a 'quite extraordinary combination of flavours'.

This is accomplished, complex and ambitious food handled with assurance, well illustrated by an inspection dinner of a starter of heirloom tomatoes baked in a puff pastry case with goats' cheese and pesto, and main courses of poached halibut with a sweet pea sabayon and liquorice and red wine sauce, and grilled Limoux veal chop with swede purée, spring radishes and bagna cauda. Outstanding pre-desserts give notice that impeccable technique and spot-on flavours carry on right through to desserts: perhaps a rustic dish of baked apricots with a 'clafoutis sponge-like pastry', or white chocolate mousse with black olive toffee, 'a quite unbelievable mixture of flavours'.

Masterful wine service is on hand to guide diners through the epic list, whether matching a series of glasses (£7 to £19) to your meal or helping to navigate the reams of top-class Bordeaux and Burgundy. There are no budget options, but £25 will turn up something really interesting like Delatite Dead Man's Hill Gewürztraminer from Australia or a range from South-west France.

Chef: Bjorn van der Horst **Proprietor:** Marc Group **Open:** Mon to Fri L 12 to 2.45, Mon to Sat D 6.45 to 10.45 **Meals:** Set L £28 (2 courses) to £85, Set D £52 (2 courses) to £85 Service: 12.5% (optional), card slips closed **Cards:** Amex, Delta, Diners, Maestro, MasterCard, Visa **Details:** 70 seats. Private parties: 4 to 10 private rooms. Vegetarian meals. No-smoking area. No music. No mobile phones. Air-conditioned **Tube:** Green Park

MAP 13

Green Olive

5 Warwick Place, W9 2PX
Tel: (020) 7289 2469

Cooking 2 | Italian | £35–£62

In a residential enclave of Little Venice, this green-painted Italian restaurant is a genuine neighbourhood venue with rustic décor and an unstuffy lack of pretence. Flexible fixed-price menus are beefed up with supplements, and a few Tuscan influences show up here and there. The kitchen procures unusual ingredients and tackles interesting modern ideas, as in a dish of baccala ('tossed cod') with marinated vegetables and black-olive pâté or pan-fried duck livers with peaches, brioche and passito wine sauce. Main courses are divided equally between meat and fish, from classic osso buco to tuna steak with casseroled aubergines, while desserts include workmanlike renditions of, say, hazelnut parfait with chocolate sauce. The wine list looks to Italy for some promising stuff, although mark-ups are high; prices start at £16.

Chef: Andrea Vercelli **Proprietor:** Ferridale Ltd **Open:** all week 12 to 2.30, 6.30 to 11 **Closed:** 25 and 26 Dec, 1 Jan, Good Friday **Meals:** Set L £15 (2 courses) to £18, Set D £21 (2 courses) to £26 **Service:** 12.5% (optional), card slips closed **Cards:** Amex, Delta, Maestro, MasterCard, Visa **Details:** 55 seats. 12 seats outside. Private parties: 20 main room. Vegetarian meals. No smoking in 1 dining room. No cigars/pipes. Music. No mobile phones. Air-conditioned **Tube:** Warwick Avenue

MAP 12

Greyhound

NEW ENTRY

136 Battersea High Street, SW11 3JR
Tel: (020) 7978 7021
Website: www.thegreyhoundatbattersea.co.uk

Cooking 3 | Modern British-Plus | £25–£51

Occupying a corner site, the grey-painted exterior gives way to a light, airy but warm interior with

dark timber flooring, leather chairs and simple unclothed wooden tables. Although still a pub, the serious surroundings and informed service reflect the quality of the food. Given the complexity of the cooking, menus are kept sensibly short, and are based on well-sourced ingredients. Serious intention is shown in a soup of haddock and mushroom, which has been given the frothy treatment and is topped with a fried quail's egg. A lot can happen in a dish: witness Label Anglais chicken breast with baked beans – cannellini beans in a seriously reduced tomato sauce – chorizo and Scotch egg, and timing can be perfect, as in melting collops of mutton with a light but intense reduction.

This intention to introduce multiplicities of flavours and textures pervades throughout, and works a treat in a white-chocolate cake with silky horseradish ice cream and finely diced mango. The varietally arranged wine list gets off to a flying start with 16 interesting options by the glass and goes the distance, all the way up to a 'super-rare' list of individual iconic bottles with four-figure price tags. Burgundy and Alsace show up as favourite regions and this is a great place for *Sideways*-inspired Pinot fans. Prices are fair, with plenty of basics under £20 and a baseline of £11.40.

Chef: Tomislav Martinovic **Proprietors:** Sharlyn and Mark van der Goot **Open:** Tue to Sun L 12 to 2.30 (3 Sun), D 7 to 9.30 **Closed:** 23 to 26 Dec, 30 Dec to 3 Jan **Meals:** Set L £12 (2 courses) to £15, Set D £26 (2 courses) to £29.50 **Service:** 10%, card slips closed **Cards:** Amex, Delta, Maestro, MasterCard, Visa **Details:** 37 seats. 20 seats outside. Private parties: 40 main room, 8 to 25 private rooms. Children's helpings. No smoking in 1 dining room. Wheelchair access (also WC). Music. No mobile phones

MAP 12

The Gun

NEW ENTRY

27 Coldharbour, E14 9NS
Tel: (020) 7515 5222
Website: www.thegundocklands.com

Cooking 3 | Modern British | £33–£75

Out of the stable that owns the White Swan (see entry), this rejuvenated eighteenth-century dockers' pub benefits from a fabulous Thames-side location: 'it would be great to come here and drink a merchant banker's salary on their champagne terrace,' mused one correspondent. Scott Wade worked at the Mirabelle (see entry), and there are signs of serious culinary intent here: roast quail is paired with black pudding, prune and almond jam and apple aqua dolce, while ribeye steak with chips is perked up by chopped snails. Fish ranges from Dover sole meunière to braised hake with grilled chorizo and a tomato and chickpea stew, and desserts take inspiration from points as far apart as the Lake District (sticky toffee pudding) and India ('intriguing' kulfi with Goan mango and edible silver leaf). The manageable wine list is helpfully categorised by style. Prices start at £12.50.

Chef: Scott Wade **Proprietors:** Tom and Ed Martin **Open:** Mon to Fri 12 to 3, 6 to 10.30, Sat and Sun 10.30 to 4.30, 6 to 10.30 **Closed:** 25 and 26 Dec, 1 Jan **Meals:** alc (main courses £11 to £23). Bar menu available **Service:** 12.5% (optional), card slips closed **Cards:** Amex, Delta, Maestro, MasterCard, Visa **Details:** 85 seats. 40 seats outside. Private parties: 55 main room, 12 to 20 private rooms. Vegetarian meals. Children's helpings. Wheelchair access (also WC). Music. Air-conditioned **Tube:** Canary Wharf DLR

MAP 14

Haandi

136 Brompton Road, SW3 1HY
Tel: (020) 7823 7373
Website: www.haandi-restaurants.com

Cooking 4 | Indian | £37–£73

Haandi made its name in Nairobi and Kampala before moving to London in 2000. The restaurant, a stylish but unostentatious place opposite Harrods, is reckoned by some to be the equal of any Indian in the capital, and its reputation hinges on consistency, top-quality raw materials and spot-on spicing – not to mention 'remarkably fair prices'. Tandooris form the backbone of the menu, among them rich, complex chicken burra tikka ('suffused with spices from the marinade and brushed with more marinade'). The kitchen also soaks up influences from elsewhere, offering baby corn bhajias, South Indian chicken chennai (with coconut, curry leaves and mustard seeds), and Goan fish curry made with tilapia. 'Fabulous' vegetables range from aloo gobi and chana masala to tawa mushrooms seared on an iron griddle. Romali roti is the pick of the breads, and desserts include pistachio kulfi topped with rose syrup and falouda. House Italian is £11.50. There's a second London branch at 301–303 Hale Lane, Edgware, tel: (020) 8905 4433.

Chefs: Ratan Singh and Arjun Singh **Proprietor:** Haandi Restaurants Ltd **Open:** all week 12 to 3, 6 to 11 (11.30 Fri and Sat) **Meals:** alc (main courses £8.50 to £13). Set L £8.95 to £13.95 (all 1 course) **Service:** 12.5% (optional), card slips closed **Cards:** Amex, Delta, Diners, Maestro, MasterCard, Visa **Details:** 80 seats. 8 seats outside. Vegetarian meals. No-smoking area. Music. Air-conditioned **Tube:** Knightsbridge

MAP 15

Hakkasan

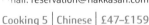

8 Hanway Place, W1T 1HD
Tel: (020) 7927 7000
Email: reservation@hakkasan.com

Cooking 5 | Chinese | £47–£159

Hakkasan is tucked away at the end of a tiny alleyway just off Tottenham Court Road, giving a hint of the authentic Hong Kong experience in finding it. Once there, you descend to an unexpectedly opulent basement space, past banks of chrysanthemums and a smell of incense, into a room hung with birdcages, where low-slung lights hover just above the tables. Both the ambience and the menu are similar to what is on offer at the younger sibling, Yauatcha (see entry), the expansive menu choice taking in some bold, experimental dishes as well as familiar Chinese favourites and Western desserts.

Tong Chee Hwee appears to take all this in his stride, producing fabulously rich clay-pot-braised aubergine with morinaga tofu, the egg-based bean curd for once absorbing its surrounding flavours, including some mushrooms, superbly, as well as oddball dim sum items like shumai of prawns, water chestnuts and white mushroom that also contains a lychee. Delicately gelatinous fried turnip cake with Chinese chive buds is an essay in classic slippery texture, while another cake of lotus root, cuttlefish and dried shrimp benefits from its vinegar dip. Braised pork belly with cloud ears is a star turn, delivering meltingly soft meat, and authentically retaining plenty of fat – 'stunning in its old-fashioned pork taste'. With a range of green teas and eye-catching cocktails on offer too, you might almost overlook the wine list, but there are plenty of good things to be had, albeit at screaming West End mark-ups. Glass prices go from £6 for a dry Greek white.

Chef: Tong Chee Hwee **Proprietor:** Alan Yau **Open:** all week 12 to 3 (4 Sat and Sun), 6 to 11.30 (12.30 Thur to Sat) **Closed:** 24 and 25 Dec, L 26 Dec, L 1 Jan **Meals:** alc (main courses £8 to £48). Set L £30 to £50, Set D £50 to £100 **Service:** 13% **Cards:** Amex, Delta, Maestro, MasterCard, Visa **Details:** 200 seats. Private parties: 160 main room, 50 to 100 private rooms. Vegetarian meals. No cigars in dining room. Wheelchair access (also WC). Music. Air-conditioned **Tube:** Tottenham Court Road

To submit a report on any restaurant, please visit *www.which.co.uk/gfgfeedback.*

MAP 12

Havelock Tavern

AR

57 Masbro Road W14 0LS
Tel: (020) 7603 5374

Coming up to its tenth anniversary as a destination for great food, this corner boozer is still very much a pub. Standing at the bar watching the plates of food going by it is hard to resist. Start with fennel and parsley soup (£4) or dive straight into roast chicken breast with couscous, spiced aubergine, baby gems and tzatziki (£11), or skate cheeks wrapped in Parma ham with rocket and salsa verde. The cooking is straightforward but careful, and the quality of the ingredients impresses. The atmosphere is appropriately lively, wine prices start at £10.50, and note cards are not accepted. Open all week.

MAP 13

The House

63–69 Canonbury Road, N1 2DG
Tel: (020) 7704 7410
Website: www.inthehouse.biz

Cooking 2 | Modern European | £29–£61

'A packed room on a bitterly cold night' testifies to the success of this lively gastro-pub just off the Islington main drag. Crowds drink and mingle in the bar and courtyard, while appreciative diners populate the simple, dimly lit restaurant. The attraction is upbeat food with French and Italian overtones: deep-fried courgette and aubergine fritters with aged balsamic and tomato vinaigrette opened one meal in style, before a contemporary take on veal Holstein and a generous slab of pan-fried cod with baby spinach, cherry tomatoes and almonds. Desserts revert to tradition: hot Valrhona chocolate pudding with home-made vanilla ice cream, for example. 'Express lunches' are served during the week, and brunch is the main event at weekends. The idiosyncratic wine list brings together a bunch of eminently drinkable bottles with prices from £12.50. The team have opened a second pub: The Bull, 13 North Hill, Highgate.

Chef: Robert Arnott **Proprietor:** Barnaby Meredith **Open:** Tue to Sun L 12 to 2.30 (3.30 Sat and Sun), all week D 6 to 10.30 (6.30 to 10.30 Sat, 6.30 to 9.30 Sun) **Closed:** 24 to 26 Dec **Meals:** alc (main courses £9.50 to £22.50). Set L Tue to Fri £14.95 (2 courses) to £17.95 **Service:** 12.5% (optional), card slips closed **Cards:** Delta, Maestro, MasterCard, Visa **Details:** 100 seats. 80 seats outside. Private parties: 200 main room. Vegetarian meals. Children's helpings. No smoking in 1 dining room. Wheelchair access (also WC). No music **Tube:** Highbury and Islington

MAP 14

Hunan

NEW ENTRY

51 Pimlico Road, SW1
Tel: (020) 7730 5712
Email: hunan.peng@btopenworld.com

Cooking 3 | Chinese | £45–£93

The deal in this modestly appointed Pimlico Chinese is to go with the flow and forget any notions of a conventional menu. Instead, allow chef/proprietor Michael Peng to entertain you with a seemingly endless cavalcade of dishes based on his interpretations of Hunan, Taiwanese, Sichuan and Cantonese cuisine. Meals trundle on relentlessly, from little palate awakeners like cucumber in sweet vinaigrette right through to 'very Chinese' almond jelly with pancakes. In between, there might be pig's ear with spicy 'drunken' chicken topped with 'vicious' chilli oil, and belly pork served cold with pungent garlicky vinaigrette – although the star turn for one party was spectacularly sweet scallops with morning glory in a sauce that 'looks like nothing and tastes like heaven'. Vegetables add variety and texture in the shape of, say, deep-fried green beans with chilli, and there is less emphasis on starchy staples such as rice and noodles. The wine list seems 'quite remarkable for a Chinese restaurant', offering classy drinking at far-from-greedy prices, starting at £12.

Chef/Proprietor: Michael Peng **Open:** Mon to Sat 12.30 to 2, 6.30 to 11 **Closed:** 25 Dec, 1 Jan, Easter, and bank hol Mons **Meals:** alc (main courses £8 to £35). Set L £28.80, Set D £32.80. Cover 80p **Service:** 12.5% (optional), card slips closed **Cards:** Amex, Delta, Diners, Maestro, MasterCard, Visa **Details:** 44 seats. Private parties: 20 main room. Vegetarian meals. No smoking. No music. Air-conditioned **Tube:** Sloane Square

MAP 13

Huong Viet

An-Viet House, 12-14 Englefield Road, N1 4LS
Tel: (020) 7249 0877

Cooking 1 | Vietnamese | £24–£40

A canteen housed in the local Vietnamese Community Centre sounds an unlikely prospect, but this place is a real eye-opener, bustling with life and offering genuine food at bargain-basement prices. Where else in the capital could you feast on a whole steamed sea bass for around £7? The all-embracing menu has its quota of traditional canh and pho soups, wood-charcoal BBQ dishes such as tuna wrapped in a banana leaf and a strong showing of noodles, plus other specialities such as claypot chicken or tofu with green leaves and garlic. Desserts range from pineapple leaf cake to French cream caramel. Drink Vietnamese beer or house wine at around £7.50. The restaurant did not return our questionnaire, so some of the information below may not be up to date.

Chef: Thanh Vu **Proprietor:** Huong-Viet Ltd **Open:** Mon to Sat 12 to 3.30, 5.30 to 11 **Meals:** alc (main courses £4.70 to £6.90). Set L £6, Set D £13 **Service:** 10%, card slips closed **Cards:** Maestro, MasterCard, Visa **Details:** 70 seats. 8 seats outside. Private parties: 25 private room. Vegetarian meals. Wheelchair access (also WC). Occasional music **Tube:** Angel, Liverpool Street

MAP 15

Ikkyu

AR

67A Tottenham Court Road, W1P 9PA
Tel: (020) 7636 9280

Great-value Japanese food in a basement café moments from Goodge Street station. Set lunches from £6.50 are based around grilled fish or deep-fried pork, while the comprehensive menu takes in sushi, sashimi, yakitori, and a vast array of dishes, with English translations to make it all manageable for the uninitiated. Maybe try nameko oro (Japanese mushroom with grated white radish; £3.75) or ika natto (cuttlefish with fermented soya beans; £6.50). Closed Sat and Sun L.

MAP 15

Incognico

117 Shaftesbury Avenue, WC2H 8AD
Tel: (020) 7836 8866
Website: www.incognicorestaurant.com

Cooking 4 | French-Plus | £42–£73

Beyond the rather anonymous entrance, a dining room of character, with dark wood, high ceilings and tall windows, has a brasserie look that fits the menu to a T. The kitchen starts with sound ingredients and balances their flavours with judgement, thanks in part to some tried and tested combinations, from Bayonne ham with celeriac rémoulade to honey-roast duck breast with fondant potato. Well-executed dishes range from salt cod in batter with aïoli ('very light indeed'), via a generous portion of roast salmon with spinach and tarragon sauce, to a 'melting to eat' rack of lamb with herbs and pommes purée. Additional side orders include French beans and a few ways with the potato. Puddings run to chocolate mousse, 'light and delicate' sticky toffee pudding, or lime mousse with raspberries. The roving wine list offers but little under £20, including house Syrah and Terret/Sauvignon from Languedoc at £16.50 (£4.50 a glass).

Chef: Jeremy Brown **Proprietor:** Chez Nico Restaurants Ltd **Open:** Mon to Sat 12 to 3, 5.30 to 11 **Closed:** Christmas, New Year, bank hols **Meals:** alc (main courses £12.50 to £17.50) **Service:** 12.5% (optional), card slips closed **Cards:** Amex, Diners, Maestro, MasterCard, Visa **Details:** 75 seats. Private parties: 120 main room, 10 to 32 private rooms. Vegetarian meals. Children's helpings. No smoking. Music. Air-conditioned **Tube:** Leicester Square

MAP 15

Inn the Park

St James's Park, SW1A 2BJ
Tel: (020) 7451 9999
Website: www.innthepark.com

Cooking 2 | Modern British | £36–£81

In the north-east of St James's Park the turf roof of Oliver Peyton's well-named contemporary eatery swells up out of the landscape. From breakfast to dinner both 'grab-and-go' and sit-down eaters get simply prepared, fresh British food: from boiled eggs and soldiers to a Ploughman's or smoked salmon finger sandwiches. Try king scallops with pumpkin purée and capers, then roast sucking pig with champ and apple sauce, and steamed treacle sponge with custard, or English cheeses. A no-nonsense, single-page wine list has some half-dozen bottles under £20 and opens at £12.50. Sit outside on the light-wood covered terrace (with overhead heaters), or watch park life from inside through a glass wall. Chairs are chrome, tables smallish, service youthful and sometimes inconsistent, but the atmosphere is friendly and informal.

Chef: Mark Bradbury **Proprietor:** Oliver Peyton and Gruppo Ltd **Open:** all week L 12 to 2.45 (3.45 Sat/Sun), Mon to Sat D 6 to 9 (10.45 in summer) **Meals:** alc (main courses £10.50 to £25). Self-service menu available 8 to 6 **Service:** not inc, 12.5% for table of 8 or more **Cards:** Amex, Delta, Maestro, MasterCard, Visa **Details:** 70 seats. 50 seats outside. Vegetarian meals. Children's helpings. No smoking. Wheelchair access (also WC). Music. Air-conditioned **Tube:** St James's Park

MAP 12

Inside

19 Greenwich South Street, Greenwich, SE10 8NW
Tel: (020) 8265 5060
Website: www.insiderestaurant.co.uk

Cooking 1 | Modern British | £28–£52

A godsend for Greenwich, this jolly, good-natured venue does sterling service to the community providing relaxed bistro food, cut-price menus for theatre-goers and Saturday brunch (handy for visitors to the market). Food is cosmopolitan, and ingredients jostle on the plate: grilled stuffed baby squid comes with crispy potatoes, black pudding and warm mustard dressing, while Welsh lamb chump is complemented by Puy lentils, Savoy cabbage, roast root vegetables and rosemary jus. Vegetarians are well looked after, and desserts might include cardamom crème brûlée with ginger flapjack. The respectable, French-biased list opens with house wines from £10.95.

Chefs: Guy Awford and Brian Sargeant **Proprietors:** Guy Awford, Brian Sargeant and Pavlin Petrov **Open:** Wed to Fri and Sun L 12 (11 Sat) to 2.30 (3 Sun), Tue to Sat D 6.30 to 11 **Meals:** alc (not Sat L; main courses £11 to £16). Set L £15.95 (2 courses) to £18.95, Set D 6.30 to 8 £15.95 (2 courses) to £18.95. Sat brunch menu available **Service:** not inc **Cards:** Delta, Maestro, MasterCard, Visa **Details:** 38 seats. Private parties: 40 main room. Vegetarian meals. Children's helpings. No-smoking area. Wheelchair access (also WC). Music. Air-conditioned **Tube:** Greenwich DLR

MAP 12

Istanbul Iskembecisi AR

9 Stoke Newington Road, N16 8BH
Tel: (020) 7254 7291

Classic Turkish menu to eat in or take away from this good-value institution. Open with a selection of meze and move on to kebabs and grills or dishes such as kuzu firin (lamb in a tomato and vegetable sauce; £7). For authenticity's sake, add in traditional soups, including the eponymous iskembe (tripe soup) or dil paça (lamb's tongue soup). Vegetarians get a look-in with various falafel dishes or güveç türlü (£6.50), an aubergine bake. Drink Buzbag for £8.50. Open all week.

MAPS 14 AND 15

Itsu

118 Draycott Avenue, SW3 3AE
Tel: (020) 7590 2400
103 Wardour Street, W1F 0UQ
Tel: (020) 7479 4790
Website: www.itsu.co.uk

Cooking 2 | Japanese | £19–£49

Itsu now flourishes in six prime sites across the capital (our rating applies principally to the branches in Soho and Chelsea), and all make the most of their location. Cool but functional modern design with flashes of colour is the perfect backdrop for top-of-the-range sushi and more besides: anyone who is unfamiliar with the style of food or the niceties of conveyor belt (kaiten) grazing can rely on 'user-friendly service from a multinational team' (press the buzzer to gain attention). Benchmark freshness is the key to Itsu's success, whether it's eel sushi ('don't leave without eating this,' insists a connoisseur) or prawn tempura with salmon hand-roll. Sashimi is impressively good, and the kitchen also ventures beyond Japan for 'nouvelle' chilli salmon with oba leaf, seared tuna salad, and duck crystal roll with hoisin sauce. Green tea and Asahi beer suit the food, and there's a modest selection of wines from £14. Further branches are at Vogue House, 1 Hanover Square, W1, and at Cabot Place East, Jubilee Place Mall, and Canada Place Mall, all three in Canary Wharf, E14; see website for details.

Chef: Angela Baird **Proprietors:** Julian Metcalfe and Clive Schlee **Open:** Mon to Sat 12 to 11 (12 Fri and Sat), Sun 1 to 10 **Closed:** D 24 Dec, 25 Dec **Meals:** alc (main courses £3.50 to £20) **Service:** not inc **Cards:** Amex, Delta, Maestro, MasterCard, Visa **Details:** 80 seats. Private parties: 100 main room. Vegetarian meals. No smoking. Wheelchair access (also WC). Music. Air-conditioned **Tube:** Piccadilly Circus (Soho), South Kensington (Chelsea)

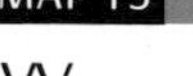

MAP 15

Ivy

1–5 West Street, WC2H 9NQ
Tel: (020) 7836 4751

Cooking 4 | Modern British | £37–£87

A perennial favourite of celebrities, from pop stars to politicians, the Ivy is undoubtedly one of Britain's most famous restaurants, prompting one visitor to remark: 'I have never visited before, yet I somehow feel familiar with it.' The lively, happy atmosphere puts diners at their ease, and no matter if you missed the A-list, all-comers are accorded an unstuffy welcome. The menu is a remarkable blend of the contemporary and the deeply old-fashioned. No current culinary trend is unrepresented – for example, a starter of mixed sashimi with hot soy and ginger dressing, or a main course of grilled surf and razor clams with lemon and steamed samphire – and yet there are also dishes that would seem odd in most other contexts: Scotch woodcock, kedgeree or eggs Florentine. Between the extremes fall offerings like wild rabbit salad, chicken and pearl barley broth, caviar, lobster and chips, pumpkin and ricotta tortelloni, or Goosnargh duck with blood oranges. Vegetables are extra. Desserts such as sticky toffee pudding with vanilla ice cream, or wobbly pannacotta with rhubarb compote provide a comforting finish. France dominates the wine list, with prices starting at £16 for a Syrah or £15 for a Chilean Sauvignon Blanc.

Chef: Alan Bird **Proprietor:** Caprice Holdings Ltd **Open:** all week 12 to 3 (3.30 Sun), 5.30 to 12 **Meals:** alc (main courses £10 to £25). Set L Sat/Sun £21.50. Cover £2 **Service:** not inc **Cards:** Amex, Delta, Diners, Maestro, MasterCard, Visa **Details:** 100 seats. Private parties: 25 to 60 private rooms. Vegetarian meals. Children's helpings. Wheelchair access (not WC). No music. No mobile phones. Air-conditioned **Tube:** Leicester Square

MAP 13

Iznik

19 Highbury Park, N5 1QJ
Tel: (020) 7704 8099

Cooking 2 | Turkish | £21–£34

'Iznik' is carved into the wooden chairs at this atmospheric restaurant, which is adorned with all manner of hanging lamps, candles, decorative tiles and glazed plates. It's a place that drips with TLC. The menu covers all the traditional Turkish bases, with no real surprises but plenty of upfront flavour and authenticity. Meze are the main attraction: from the varied list choose, say, patlican tava (fried aubergines with yoghurt and garlic dressing), patates koftesi (Turkish-style potato croquettes) or arnavut cigeri (diced liver fried with paprika and olive oil). Main courses are dominated by substantial helpings of grilled and skewered meat, supplemented by alternatives like kuzu firin (oven-baked lamb). A better-than-average bunch of desserts includes bramble mousse and sutlac (rice pudding with poached quince). Turkish house wines are £9.95.

Chef: Adem Oner **Proprietors:** Adem and Pirlanta Oner **Open:** all week 10am to 11pm **Closed:** 25 Dec **Meals:** alc (main courses £6.50 to £8.50) **Service:** 10%, card slips closed **Cards:** Delta, Maestro, MasterCard, Visa **Details:** 78 seats. Private parties: 78 main room. Vegetarian meals. No-smoking area. Music **Tube:** Highbury & Islington

MAP 15

J. Sheekey

28–32 St Martin's Court, WC2N 4AL
Tel: (020) 7240 2565
Email: reservations@j-sheekey.co.uk

Cooking 4 | British Seafood | £35–£92

This venerable seafood restaurant is the sort of place where the congenial atmosphere and well-practised menu soothe with a combination of familiar combinations (potted shrimps with wholemeal toast) and luxuries: egg Benedict royale with sevruga caviar, or lobster mayonnaise. The panelled interior hung with modern artworks shows an easy mix of old and new. Main courses offer plenty of choice, from the well-reported fish pie (stuffed with smoked haddock, cod, salmon, smoked salmon 'and a few prawns'), and fried fillet of haddock with mushy peas and chips – which also gets a thumbs-up – to fillet of pollack with langoustine and sea purslane risotto. Puds like spotted dick with butter and golden syrup sauce, or baked rice pudding with raspberry jam will arouse nostalgia in some. Slight mistiming occasionally unsettles, but the performance is usually sound. Wines can help to bump up the bill; prices start at £16 although most bottles are over £25, and there are 14 by the glass from £4.50.

Chef: Martin Dickenson **Proprietor:** Caprice Holdings Ltd **Open:** all week 12 to 3 (3.30 Sun), 5.30 (6 Sun) to 12 **Closed:** 26 and 27 Dec, 28 Aug **Meals:** alc (main courses £11 to £30). Set L Mon to Fri £21.50 **Service:** not inc **Cards:** Amex, Delta, Diners, Maestro, MasterCard, Visa **Details:** 90 seats. Vegetarian meals. Children's helpings. No cigars/pipes. Wheelchair access (not WC). No music. No mobile phones. Air-conditioned **Tube:** Leicester Square

(£)	This symbol means that it is possible to have a three-course meal, including coffee, half a bottle of house wine and service, at all sessions for £30 or less per person.

MAP 13

K10

20 Copthall Avenue, EC2R 7DN
Tel: (020) 7562 8510
Website: www.K10.com

Cooking 2 | Japanese | £21–£53

Join the queue on the stairs if you want to be part of the action in this frantically busy basement sushi joint – and arrive early to beat the influx of City slickers. The self-named kaiten (conveyor belt) 'slowly snakes along a complexly cornered course like the Brands Hatch circuit', bearing items on colour-coded plates. Reporters have singled out thinly sliced fatty tuna sashimi, but the range encompasses all manner of nigiri and maki rolls. Cooked dishes have impressed less, but it's worth hanging on for the glut of minuscule desserts: green tea mousses in tiny cups, mini knickerbocker glories, crème brûlée with raspberries. Drink tea, saké or beer; otherwise, opt for house wine (£12.95).

Chef: J.T. Mohamed **Proprietor:** K10 Ltd **Open:** Mon to Fri L only 11 to 3 **Meals:** plate prices £1.25 to £5.50 **Service:** not inc **Cards:** Amex, Delta, Diners, Maestro, MasterCard, Visa **Details:** 70 seats. Private parties: 80 main room. Vegetarian meals. No smoking. Music. Air-conditioned **Tube:** Moorgate, Liverpool Street

MAP 12

Kastoori

188 Upper Tooting Road, SW17 7EJ
Tel: (020) 8767 7027

Cooking 3 | Gujarati Vegetarian | £22–£33

Dinesh and Manoj Thanki set up shop here in 1987, and their version of Indian vegetarian cuisine is a family tradition rooted in 'tomato-based recipes' from the temperate Katia Wahd region of Gujarat. The Thankis also spent many years in Uganda, and their cooking is tempered with ideas from Africa (sweetcorn in coconut milk with peanut sauce, for example). Home-made chutneys have been described as 'superb', and regulars have also endorsed staples such as bhel puri, masala dosa, and bhatura bread. Elsewhere, the menu reads like an inventory of exotic vegetables, with kontola, karela, and mustard leaves all on show alongside a 'euroveg' extravaganza involving leeks, spring onion, aubergine, spinach and even rhubarb. Drink Kingfisher beer or dip into the helpfully annotated wine list. House French is £8.95.

Chef: Manoj Thanki **Proprietor:** Dinesh Thanki **Open:** Wed to Sun L 12.30 to 2.30, all week D 6 to 10.30 **Closed:** 25 and 26 Dec **Meals:** alc (main courses £4.50 to £6.50) **Service:** not inc, card slips closed **Cards:** MasterCard, Visa **Details:** 82 seats. Private parties: 15 main room. Vegetarian meals. Children's helpings. Wheelchair access (not WC). Music. Air-conditioned **Tube:** Tooting Broadway

MAP 13

Kasturi

AR

57 Aldgate High Street, EC3N 1AL
Tel: (020) 7480 7402

Keenly priced Indian food in smart surroundings hard by Aldgate's big-city institutions. Dhansak and other curry-house stalwarts are eclipsed by a range of regional specialities including nalli gosht (lamb shank with coriander and red chillies; £9), king prawns Malabar with coconut milk and fennel seeds (£13), and chicken Hyderabadi (£8). Starters favour the tandoor for things like peshwari lamb tikka (£6); vegetables include aloo annardhana (baby potatoes with pomegranate seeds; £3.50). Thalis from £15.95, house wines from £13.95. Open all week.

MAP 13

Kensington Place

201–209 Kensington Church Street, W8 7LX
Tel: (020) 7727 3184
Website: www.egami.co.uk

Cooking 5 | Modern British | £31–£78

Rowley Leigh's brand of straightforward cooking based on good seasonal produce has proved a winning formula here for nearly twenty years, and has not wavered in terms of quality in all that time. The room has not changed either, the large, booming space filled with close-packed tables, and large plate-glass windows overlooking Kensington Church Street add to the hard-edged effect. Simplicity is evident in omelette fines herbes, or grilled polenta with roast peppers and rocket – but all this indicates that attention is focused where it should be: raw materials are of good quality, techniques are sound, and tastes and textures are properly considered. Despite some contemporary crossover dishes (such as steamed sea bass with ginger and spring onions), Rowley Leigh's heart is seemingly in the Mediterranean, in treviso and cuttlefish salad with chilli, orange and mint, for example, or roast chicken with flageolet beans and garlic.

It is worth remembering the good-value set-price meals. Lunch might consist of raw tuna with mango and chillies, followed by rabbit stew with button onions and wild garlic, then kiwi salad with chilli syrup and vanilla ice cream, while the carte offers a generous choice from grilled wild boar chop with sage and lemon to roast John Dory with blood oranges and balsamic. The close-printed wine list is packed with quality bottles grouped into loose categories along the lines of 'chardonnay and similar'. Wines by the glass are a speciality with 15 options from around the globe (£5 to £8.75) in addition to the four house options (£4; £14 a bottle) and a range of sherries.

Chef: Rowley Leigh **Proprietor:** Place Restaurants Ltd **Open:** all week 12 to 3.30, 6.30 to 11.45 (10.15 Sun) **Closed:** 24 to 26 Dec **Meals:** alc (main courses £13.50 to £21.50). Set L Mon to Sat £18.50, Set L Sun £21.50, Set D £24.50 **Service:** 12.5% (optional), card slips closed **Cards:** Amex, Delta, Diners, Maestro, MasterCard, Visa **Details:** 140 seats. Private parties: 45 private room. Vegetarian meals. Children's helpings. Wheelchair access (also WC). No music. Air-conditioned **Tube:** Notting Hill Gate

MAP 15

Kiku

17 Half Moon Street, W1J 7BE
Tel: (020) 7499 4208

Cooking 4 | Japanese | £26–£94

Having occupied its swish Mayfair site for more than 20 years, Kiku is now one of the few remaining 'traditional' Japanese restaurants in the capital. The name means 'chrysanthemum', and the delightful interior evokes oriental calm with its clean lines, stone floor, and bamboo blinds. All the major components of the cuisine are represented, and the kitchen delivers the goods with 'confidence and accuracy'. Recent successes have included agedashi tofu (deep-fried bean curd), yakinasu (grilled aubergine topped with fish flakes and grated ginger), and some 'sparklingly fresh' sushi. For the full experience, kaiseki dinners are also recommended: here you can work your way through appetisers like cold grilled cod, clear soups served in dobin pots, and sashimi of 'transfixing quality'; the encyclopaedic tour continues with a centrepiece such as traditional peasant-style shabu-shabu (a 'fondue-style' hot-pot based around sliced Aberdeen Angus beef), and fresh fruit makes a suitably cleansing finale. The short wine list is not cheap (prices start at £14.50); stick to tea and beer.

Chef: H. Hattori **Proprietors:** Hisashi and Mariko Taoka **Open:** Mon to Sat L 12 to 2.30, all week D 6 (5 Sun and bank hols) to 10.15 **Closed:** 25 and 26 Dec, 1 Jan **Meals:** alc (main courses £5 to £30). Set L £13 to £23, Set D £42 to £60 **Service:** 12.5% (optional), card slips closed **Cards:** Amex, Delta, Diners, Maestro, MasterCard, Visa **Details:** 95 seats. Private parties: 10 private room. Vegetarian meals. Wheelchair access (also WC). Music. Air-conditioned **Tube:** Green Park

MAP 15

Kulu Kulu Sushi

76 Brewer Street, W1F 9TX
Tel: (020) 7734 7316

Cooking 2 | Japanese | £21–£38

At peak times, customers have just 45 minutes to peruse and polish off what they desire from the conveyor belt in this Soho sushi joint. The busy pint-sized room may seem a touch makeshift, and there's no standing on ceremony, but this old warhorse still delivers a wealth of alluring Japanese morsels at bargain-basement prices. Pick from an array of nigiri including horse mackerel, scallop and eel, explore the choice of hand rolls (salmon skin or prawn tempura, for example) or opt for one of the mixed plates if you are bewildered. Drink free tea, beer, saké or house wine at £12. There are branches at 39 Thurloe Place, SW7, tel: (020) 7589 2225, and 51–53 Shelton Street, WC2, tel: (020) 7240 5687.

Chef/Proprietor: Kenji Toyama **Open:** Mon to Sat 12 to 2.30 (3.30 Sat), 5 to 10 **Closed:** bank hols **Meals:** alc (main courses £8.50 to £13) **Service:** not inc **Cards:** Delta, Maestro, MasterCard, Visa **Details:** 30 seats. No smoking. Music. Air-conditioned **Tube:** Piccadilly Circus

MAP 13

Lahore Kebab House

2–4 Umberston Street, E1 1PY
Tel: (020) 7488 2551

Cooking 1 | Punjabi | £15–£22

For more than three decades, this Punjabi eating house has been a neon-lit beacon just off Commercial Road. It's down to earth and free from restaurant paraphernalia (don't expect knives or tablecloths here), but the food is what counts. It is also extraordinarily cheap: prices range from 75p for samosas and seekh kebab to a princely £6.50 for grilled lamb chops and chicken biryani. In between, the kitchen delivers a selection of unadorned curries including karahi chicken and masala fish and meatless items like aloo sag. Desserts are confined to kheer – an authentically milky Asian rice pudding. Drink lassi or BYO wine. There are branches at King's Cross Holiday Inn, 56 Calthorpe Street, WC1, tel: (020) 7833 9787, and 148–150 Brent Street, NW4, tel: (020) 8203 6904.

Chefs: Mohammad Azeem and Naeem Hussain **Proprietor:** Mohammad Siddique **Open:** all week 12 to 11.45 **Meals:** alc (main courses £5 to £6.50). Set L and D £12 (2 courses) **Service:** not inc, card slips closed **Cards:** MasterCard, Visa **Details:** 140 seats. Vegetarian meals. Wheelchair access (also WC). Occasional music. Air-conditioned **Tube:** Aldgate East, Whitechapel

MAP 13

Lansdowne

90 Gloucester Avenue, NW1 8HX
Tel: (020) 7483 0409

Cooking 2 | Modern British | £30–£49

Enter through the lively ground-floor pub before ascending to the restaurant. The dining room is a 'classy place – not posh but distinctly cool' with high ceilings, terracotta walls and well-spaced tables with white linen. The food is unfussy, and much of it is Mediterranean-influenced, say buffalo mozzarella teamed with roast pumpkin and a mustard fruits marmalade or 'flavourful' seared scallops and braised chicory with a blob of sweet tomato chutney. Comforting main courses have included ribeye steak with spinach, creamy mash and a rich gravy, and sea bass with fennel, caper and parsley salad and crème fraîche new potatoes. Finish with generous desserts like 'really good' chocolate and Amaretti cheesecake, or baked plums with honey and mascarpone. Service is pretty laid back, while the appealing wine list offers house bottles at £12.90 (£3.30 a glass).

Chef: Isabel Davies **Proprietor:** Amanda Pritchett **Open:** Tue to Sun L 12.30 to 3, Mon to Sat D 7 to 10.30 **Meals:** alc (main courses £10 to £14.50). Set L Tues to Fri £5 (1 course). Bar snacks available **Service:** 12.5% (optional), card slips closed **Cards:** Delta, Maestro, MasterCard, Visa **Details:** 120 seats. 25 seats outside. Private parties: 55 main room. Vegetarian meals. Occasional music. No mobile phones **Tube:** Chalk Farm

MAP 14

Launceston Place

1A Launceston Place, W8 5RL
Tel: (020) 7937 6912
Website: www.egami.co.uk

Cooking 2 | Modern British | £33–£66

Away from the city's bustle, this venue makes the most of its civilised, almost rural situation in a leafy part of South Kensington. The interior is formal but not overdone, and tables are discreetly well spaced: 'one feels obliged to dress up a bit,' thought one visitor appreciatively. Twice-baked goats' cheese soufflé is a regularly endorsed starter, and the kitchen likes to assemble vibrant ideas on the plate: tuna carpaccio with wasabi mayonnaise, or Asian spiced duck breast with buckwheat noodle salad, say. Main courses tend towards orthodox renditions of modern classics like pan-fried sea bass with aubergine caviar and lemon butter (varying textures making it 'a continually surprising joy to eat'), or calf's liver with devils on horseback. Desserts like pavlova with kiwi and mango are capably handled. The 70-bin wine list presents an engaging mix of classic France and fresh international flavours, with bottles from £16 and seven by the glass.

Chef: Philip Reed **Proprietor:** Image Restaurants Plc **Open:** Sun to Fri L 12.30 to 2.30, all week D 7 to 11.30 (10.30 Sun) **Closed:** 24 to 27 Dec, 1 to 4 Jan **Meals:** alc (not Sun L; main courses £16.50 to £18.50). Set L £15.50 (2 courses) to £18.50. Set L Sun £22.50 **Service:** 12.5% (optional), card slips closed **Cards:** Amex, Delta, Diners, Maestro, MasterCard, Visa **Details:** 80 seats. Private parties: 80 main room, 2 to 13 private rooms. Vegetarian meals. No music. Air-conditioned **Tube:** Gloucester Road

MAP 13

Ledbury

NEW ENTRY

127 Ledbury Road, W11 2AQ
Tel: (020) 7792 9090
Website: www.theledbury.com

Cooking 7 | Modern European | £41–£90

Opening in spring 2005, the Ledbury is a new venture from Nigel Platts-Martin, he of the Square and Chez Bruce (see entries). It occupies a large Notting Hill corner site and is painted black. Inside, long black gathered drapes risk a gently sombre note, but the square room is otherwise bright white, with mirrors reflecting the French windows to enlarge the space. Black teardrops hang from an elegant chandelier, and the faintly pensive tone appears to have been picked up by certain of the staff (though not the excellent sommelier).

Chef Brett Graham hails from Sydney but is no stranger to the Platts-Martin stable, having previously worked at the Square under Philip Howard. With a pedigree like that, one would expect a certain level of high-gloss proficiency, and indeed it is not lacking. Home-made pasta sets the pace, appearing as a single raviolo filled with mixed shellfish, in a boldly creamy, dark shellfish sauce based on champagne, a 'world-class' dish of classic refinement. Even more astonishing is a first-course lasagne of rabbit and morels with thyme velouté, in which the 'membranous texture of the pasta was out of this world', and the balance and seasoning of the dish make the most of exemplary mushrooms and tender, flavourful meat.

Some of the trademark complexity of the Square's style has been imported here, as is evidenced by a main course of roast sea bass, which appears with creamed potato and an effective vinaigrette of raisins, pine nuts and cockles. Great intensity and depth result from dishes that have clearly been extensively worked on, so that even a straightforward red wine sauce with beef fillet is 'close to breathtaking', and the accompanying croustillant of snails, oxtail and celeriac adds satisfying weight to the dish. Bresse pigeon is served in its own madeira-laced consommé and partnered by more of that flawless pasta in the form of foie gras tortellini.

At dessert stage, a wafer-thin piece of pineapple is fashioned into a parcel to contain passion-fruit sorbet, and sits in a tropical fruit soup seasoned with lemongrass and lime. Chicory is the flavour note in a crème brûlée teamed with coffee ice cream and a chocolate madeleine, while chocolate soufflé is a technical *tour de force*, the mixture lifted with pieces of banana and the top sprinkled with honeycomb fragments. 'The dining-room may be muted,' concluded an inspector, 'but the cooking is spectacular. Brett Graham is going to be a star.'

The 'engaging' sommelier is on hand to discuss the top-class wine list, where anyone on a budget will have to take heart from the range by the glass and half-bottle. Burgundy is a clear strength, with Australia and California well worth exploring. Prices start at £17.50.

Chef: Brett Graham **Proprietors:** Nigel Platts-Martin and Philip Howard **Open:** all week 12 to 2.30 (2.45 Sat and Sun), 6.30 to 10.45 (10.30 Sun) **Closed:** 24 to 26 Dec **Meals:** Set L £19.50 (2 courses) to £55, Set D £39.50 to £55 **Service:** 12.5% (optional), card slips closed **Cards:** Amex, Delta, Maestro, MasterCard, Visa **Details:** 64 seats. 32 seats outside. Vegetarian meals. Children's helpings. No smoking. Wheelchair access (also WC). No music. No mobile phones. Air-conditioned **Tube:** Westbourne Park

MAP 13

Lemonia

AR

89 Regent's Park Road, NW1 8UY
Tel: (020) 7586 7454

The Evangelous' authentic taverna has been a crowd-pleaser in Primrose Hill since 1979. Ultra-cheap weekday lunches (three courses £8.50) hit the button, but the full menu is an equally affordable prospect. Meze (from £3.50 per item) cover a lot of familiar ground; elsewhere, the kitchen moves confidently from afelia (£9.50) and tsipoura (grilled sea bream; £13.50) to more unusual specials. Conclude with baklava or yoghurt with honey and nuts. Drinkable Greek and Cypriot wines, plus house French at £14 a litre. Closed Sat L and Sun D.

MAP 13

Lightship

5A St Katharine's Way, E1W 1LP
Tel: (020) 7481 3123

Modern European cooking on the oldest lightship in the world (circa 1877). Drink at the open-air bar or sit below decks in one of the dining rooms. A few tame Scandinavian intruders (from the 'herrings/meatballs' school) appear alongside the likes of guinea fowl and apricot terrine (£6.75), salmon fillet with prawn risotto and lobster emulsion (£13.75), and desserts such as crème brûlée. Uneven results, but the setting is fun. House Italian £12.50. Open Tue to Fri L and Mon to Sat D.

MAP 12

Light House Restaurant

75–77 Ridgway, Wimbledon, SW19 4ST
Tel: (020) 8944 6338
Email: lightrest@aol.com

Cooking 3 | Modern European | £28–£72

This unpretentious neighbourhood restaurant offers modern brasserie dishes evolved out of Mediterranean traditions at reasonable prices. Informal, helpful service contributes to a laid-back feel that seems to suit the sunny food. There's a strong Italian influence, not least in the four-course menu structure, starting with antipasti – perhaps a charcuterie plate with hummus, guindilla chillies and olives – succeeded by tagliatelle with wild mushrooms, or chargrilled quail with saffron risotto, rocket and chilli oil, before mains of braised lamb shank with spinach, tomato and chickpea stew, or maybe sea bass with shichimi-roast butternut squash and peanut and black bean salsa. Besides the predictable tiramisù, and cantucci with a glass of vin santo, desserts might subsume chocolate, hazelnut and caramel tart, and banana mess. Hefty mark-ups undermine value on the globe trotting wine list; prices start at £12.50 and quickly escalate, but there are 12 by the glass (£3.25–£6.75).

Chef: David Winton **Proprietors:** Ian Taylor and Bob Finch **Open:** all week L 12 to 2.30, Mon to Sat D 6.30 to 10.30 **Closed:** three days at Christmas, two days at Easter **Meals:** alc (main courses £11 to £21). Set L £14 (2 courses) to £16.50 **Service:** 12.5% (optional), card slips closed **Cards:** Amex, Delta, Maestro, MasterCard, Visa **Details:** 80 seats. 10 seats outside. Private parties: 80 main room. Vegetarian meals. Children's helpings. No pipes/cigars. Wheelchair access (also WC). Occasional music **Tube:** Wimbledon

MAP 15

Lindsay House

21 Romilly Street, W1D 5AF
Tel: (020) 7439 0450
Website: www.lindsayhouse.co.uk

Cooking 6 | Modern British | £46–£101

The restaurant is in a converted Georgian town house, and, amid the razzle-dazzle of Soho, it comes as some surprise to be ringing a front-door bell to gain entry, and then stepping into a domestic hallway. Large paintings depicting sons of the soil dominate the dining rooms, where rugs are thrown over the bare-boarded floor in a rough approximation of rusticity.

Richard Corrigan's several years here have allowed him to hone his culinary style, which is all about arraying humble ingredients in the same kind of finery that other places reserve for luxuries. Gooey-textured crubeen (trotter) crops up in a coat of breadcrumbs among the appetisers, and not many kitchens would think of pairing prawns with chickpeas in a starter to produce revelatory textural contrasts, the whole accented with forthright cumin seasoning. Pig dishes usually score highly, as was the case with an inspector's main course of cheek and belly, appositely offset by pickled endive and pineapple, the textures again fascinating, ranging from gelatinous to crunchy. Crab tortellini with coriander oil has been an excellent first course, but a main course of leg and breast of duck with turnips and haricots blancs was less impressive. Pre-desserts have crept in here as elsewhere, but the puddings themselves have been uneven. An apple and prune tart has had lacklustre, over-buttered pastry, but coconut and lime sorbet accompanying an airy lime soufflé has been a masterpiece. Service has been found a little absent-minded on more than one occasion. The wine list, ably promoted by the 'enthusiastic' sommelier, casts interesting small French producers against legends such as Romanée-Conti and Latour. Otherwise, California is the strongest suit in the astute global selection. House bottles are a steep £22, but there are satisfying options by the glass.

Chef/Proprietor: Richard Corrigan **Open:** Mon to Fri L 12 to 2.30, Mon to Sat D 6 to 11 **Closed:** 1 week at Christmas, 2 weeks Aug **Meals:** alc (main courses £26). Set L £25 to £59, Set D £48 to £59, Pre-theatre Set D £25 (3 courses). **Service:** 12.5% (optional), card slips closed **Cards:** Amex, Delta, Diners, Maestro, MasterCard, Visa **Details:** 80 seats. Private parties: 34 main room, 4 to 24 private rooms. Vegetarian meals. Children's helpings. No music. No mobile phones. Air-conditioned **Tube:** Leicester Square

MAP 13

Little Bay

AR

171 Farringdon Road, EC1R 3AL
Tel: (020) 7278 1234

One of a mini-chain of casual restaurants famed for their bargain-basement prices: starters £2, mains £6, desserts £2 (add £1 in the evening for starters and puddings, £2 for main courses). The modern European menu runs to chicken livers with mushrooms and spinach, haddock with mash, green beans and sorrel velouté, and chocolate cheesecake. Two dozen affordable wines from £10.90. Open all week. Branches at 228 Belsize Road, NW6, tel: (020) 7372 4699; 228 York Road, SW11, tel: (020) 7223 4080; and 32 Selsdon Road, Croydon, tel: (020) 8649 9544.

MAP 13

Lobster Pot

AR

3 Kennington Lane, SE11 4RG
Tel: (020) 7582 5556

Still going strong after 14 years, Hervé Régent continues to serve textbook French dishes such as one might eat over the Channel. Fish soup (£6.50), bouillabaisse (£16.50), and wild sea bass cooked in sea salt match the extravagant nautical setting with sound effects of seagulls and breaking waves. There are meaty offerings too – perhaps chicken fillet with Dijon mustard sauce (£14.50), or duck confit – and a popular eight-course surprise menu (£39.50). Compact, all-French wine list from £11.50. Closed Sun and Mon.

MAP 15

Locanda Locatelli

8 Seymour Street, W1H 7JZ
Tel: (020) 7935 9088
Website: www.locandalocatelli.com

Cooking 6 | Italian | £40–£88

'Urban chic without being too scary' is how one regular summed up Giorgio Locatelli's restaurant just north of Oxford Street. The colours are chosen from the fashionable natural template – tan, cream, white and brown (don't say beige!) – and comfort levels are high. Banquette seating flows through the centre of the room, creating semicircular booths, and etched-glass screens provide a bit of discrete separation. Service is 'superb, knowledgeable' for some, although others find that the influence of nearby Mayfair pervades a touch too much over any natural Italian effusiveness.

Bread – perhaps focaccia, ciabatta and grissini – is always well reported, providing stimulation while perusing the traditionally laid-out menu (antipasti, pasta, carne and so on). Quail risotto with grana padano makes an impressive first course, with a leg and breast perfectly cooked atop the rice, and chargrilled cuttlefish salad ably demonstrates the virtue of simplicity. Roast sea bream comes with fennel and anchovy sauce as a main course, and pan-fried calves' kidneys with potato purée and lentils. 'Outstanding' chargrilled eel in a herb crust served with baby vine tomatoes and a rocket salad in a 'divine' dressing was the stellar dish for one inspector. Keep your eyes open for the tart of the day if the chocolate and liquorice version, of 'wonderfully, soothingly subtle flavour', served with chocolate ice cream is anything to go by. As the Guide went to press, the restaurant was considering opening for lunch and dinner on Sundays.

The regionally focused wine list has Tuscany and Piedmont as the undoubted stars. Fancy Barolo? Choose from a mesmerising list. Bottle prices start at £12, and around ten are available by the glass.

Chef: Giorgio Locatelli **Proprietors:** Giorgio and Plaxy Locatelli **Open:** Mon to Sat 12 to 3, 6.45 to 11 (11.30 Fri and Sat) **Closed:** bank hols **Meals:** alc (main courses £14 to £29) **Service:** not inc **Cards:** Amex, Delta, Maestro, MasterCard, Visa **Details:** 80 seats. Vegetarian meals. Children's helpings. No cigars/pipes in dining room. Wheelchair access (also WC). Music. Air-conditioned **Tube:** Marble Arch

MAP 13

Lola's

The Mall, 359 Upper Street, N1 0PD
Tel: (020) 7359 1932
Website: www.lolas.co.uk

Cooking 4 | Modern European | £33–£75

After an absence of some years, Juliet Peston (last listed here in 2000) takes up the cudgels once again at Lola's, long the jewel in Upper Street's gastronomic crown. A large, light loft space of a dining room on the first floor of a former tram shed, the venue is nicely eccentric, and preserves the feel of a sympathetic neighbourhood restaurant rather than aiming for West End anonymity.

The cooking has stayed true to its peasanty European roots, combining vivid flavours and forthright seasoning with carefully crafted presentations. There wasn't much wrong with a seasonal serving of grilled asparagus that started a June meal, especially not as it had lightly dressed white crab spooned over it. Goats' cheese and melted onion tart is a competently rendered contemporary favourite, and risotto is an object lesson, the generous main course of a primavera version with added morels the star dish at inspection. Broad beans, Jersey Royals and a butter sauce pairing shrimps and cucumber were the accompaniments to a dish of properly cooked organic salmon, or there might be lamb chump with Puy lentils, spring vegetables and mustard sauce. 'Lost bread' is a powerfully convincing rendition of classic pain perdu, served with vanilla ice cream and caramelised apple, while pannacotta has the right fragility of texture, and a spot-on accompaniment of strawberries delicately pickled in aged balsamic.

'Who could ask for more?' commented one reporter on a no-nonsense international wine list that offers good choices at all price levels (from £14.25) and an interesting range by the glass, including sherries.

Chef: Juliet Peston **Proprietor:** Morfudd Richards **Open:** all week L 12 to 2.30 (3 Sat and Sun), Mon to Sat D 6 to 11 **Meals:** alc (main courses £13 to £24). Set L £12.75 (2 courses) to £28.50 (inc wine). Set D Mon to Wed 6 to 11, Thur to Sat 6 to 7 £15.75 (2 courses) to £31.50 (inc wine). Cover £1.50 **Service:** not inc, 12.5% for parties of 5 or more **Cards:** Amex, Delta, Diners, Maestro, MasterCard, Visa **Details:** 80 seats. Private parties: 80 main room, 6 to 16 private rooms. Vegetarian meals. Children's helpings. Occasional music. Air-conditioned **Tube:** Angel

MAP 13

Lou Pescadou

241 Old Brompton Road, SW5 9HP
Tel: (020) 7370 1057

Cooking 3 | Seafood | £21–£55

'A sea-fresh holiday feel' permeates this long-running French seafood restaurant pitched only a few minutes from Earls Court. Shades of blue and a famous 'porthole' window catch the eye, and the interior is bedecked with framed wooden hulls of boats and naïve paintings depicting French scenes. 'Les plateaux de fruits de mer' are the stars of the show, but the menu embraces all things piscine from clams, oysters and winkles *au naturel* to 'deep earthy red' fish soup ladled from a tureen, crab ravioli in a powerful langoustine sauce and seared swordfish with a pepper concassé. Meat eaters might enjoy steak or spatchcocked 'poulet jaune' spiked with lemon, while ice creams and sorbets are the pick of the desserts. Fish-friendly Gallic whites (from £11.80) dominate the well-constructed wine list.

Chef: Laurent David **Proprietors:** Daniel Chobert and Laurent David **Open:** all week 12 to 3, 7 to 12 (6.30 to 12 Sat and Sun) **Closed:** Christmas **Meals:** alc (main courses £8 to £16.50). Set L £10.90, Set D Sat and Sun £14.50. **Service:** 15% (optional), card slips closed **Cards:** Amex, Delta, Diners, Maestro, MasterCard, Visa **Details:** 61 seats. 22 seats outside. Private parties: 61 main room, 10 to 48 private rooms. Vegetarian meals. Children's helpings. Wheelchair access (not WC). No music. Air-conditioned **Tube:** Earls Court

MAP 14

Lundum's

119 Old Brompton Road, SW7 3RN
Tel: (020) 7373 7774
Website: www.lundums.com

Cooking 3 | Danish | £29–£73

Deep blue ceilings with sunken spotlights and splendid Danish seascapes on the walls make a dramatic backdrop for Lundum's two-pronged operation. Lunches provide the traditional fare of Denmark, such as marinated herrings and open sandwiches, while evenings showcase the new Danish cuisine, which has more than a hint of contemporary French fashion to it. Reporters have enjoyed ravioli filled with monkfish and halibut and served with truffle beurre blanc, seared scallops with mango-chilli compote, and main courses like pork fillet wrapped in tissue-thin Danish ham with a dainty courgette timbale and sage-seasoned pommes Anna. Desserts might include chocolate in three colours – white mousse, milk ice cream and a tart of the dark stuff – or old-fashioned Danish apple cake with whipped cream. An extensive, deeply classical wine list includes fine Italians alongside French treasures, and even the odd English wine. House red and white from the Languedoc are £14.

Chef/Proprietor: Kay Lundum **Open:** all week L 12 to 4, Mon to Sat D 6 to 11 **Closed:** 22 Dec to 4 Jan **Meals:** alc (not Sun L; main courses L £9 to £14.50, D £12.50 to £23). Set L Mon to Sat £13.50 (2 courses) to £16.50, Sun buffet brunch £19.50, Set D £17.25 (2 courses) to £21.50 **Service:** 13.5% (optional), card slips closed **Cards:** Amex, Delta, Diners, Maestro, MasterCard, Visa **Details:** 86 seats. 20 seats outside. Private parties: 18 private room. Vegetarian meals. No cigars. Wheelchair access (also WC). Music. Air-conditioned **Tube:** Gloucester Road, South Kensington

MAP 13

Mandarin Kitchen

14–16 Queensway, W2 3RX
Tel: (020) 7727 9012

Cooking 1 | Chinese | £26–£63

A collage of 'partially identifiable sea creatures' filling one window of this long-running Queensway Chinese reminds visitors that fish is the kitchen's speciality. Most people come here for plates of lobster and noodles, but the range of seafood impresses across the board: 'superlatively fresh' steamed scallops and razor clams (with an accompanying bowl of warm soy and coriander dipping sauce) and pearly-white stewed king prawns (with not-quite-crisp squid) won over an inspector. The menu takes note of regional traditions, offering familiar items like deep-fried shredded smoked chicken and barbecued pork as well as a few unexpected ideas such as stir-fried asparagus ('asparagus giganticus' indeed!) in a limpid consommé: 'I spooned up the soup voraciously,' noted an enthusiast. Service is hands-on. House wine is £12.50.

Chef: K.W. Man **Proprietor:** Steven Cheung **Open:** all week 12 to 11.30 **Meals:** alc (main courses £6 to £18). Set L and D £10.90 (2 courses) to £20 **Service:** not inc, card slips closed **Cards:** Amex, Delta, Diners, Maestro, MasterCard, Visa **Details:** 100 seats. Private parties: 100 main room. Vegetarian meals. Wheelchair access (not WC). No music. Air-conditioned **Tube:** Queensway

MAP 14

Mandarin Oriental Hyde Park, Foliage

66 Knightsbridge, SW1X 7LA
Tel: (020) 7235 2000
Website: www.mandarinoriental.com/london

Cooking 6 | Modern European | £63–£106

The entrance beneath fluttering flags up a steep flight of steps opposite Harvey Nics may make you feel as if you are entering a particularly chic mausoleum, but the décor within gleams with global opulence. A serious attempt has been made in the Foliage restaurant to remind you that you are only a hair's breadth away from Hyde Park, with real leaves beneath the plates gathered daily from the park, and an abundance of white silk foliage caught in the glass wall panels, which change colour with the seasons.

You might think Chris Staines had his work cut out to match the cooking to these rarefied surroundings, but reporters remain convinced that there is much more than just surface lustre. There is real invention, for one thing: successful dishes have included roast scallops with a caramelised cauliflower beignet, pan-fried turbot with a fricassee of peas, and herb-crusted cannon of lamb with cannelloni of sweetbreads and morels. A finger is kept firmly on the pulse of today's taste for robust combinations, extending to the fashionable incorporation of savoury elements into the desserts, so that tonka beans appear as a soufflé, pearl barley makes a sorbet to go with hot chocolate fondant, and an ice cream of salted caramel comes with banana tart. Service is flawlessly professional, and friendly with it. The star-studded wine list shines brightest in France and California. Prices (from £18.50) are often steep, but you can find Dei's Vino Nobile and other reliably stylish bottles for under £30, and there are good options by the glass and half-bottle.

Chef: Chris Staines **Proprietor:** Mandarin Oriental Hotel Group **Open:** all week 12 to 2.30, 7 to 10 **Meals:** Set L £25 to £47.50, Set D £50 to £70 **Service:** 12.5% (optional), card slips closed **Cards:** Amex, Delta, Diners, Maestro, MasterCard, Visa **Details:** 42 seats. Private parties: 150 to 250 private rooms. Vegetarian meals. No cigars/pipes in dining room. Wheelchair access (also WC). No music. No mobile phones. Air-conditioned **Accommodation:** 200 rooms, all with bath/shower. TV. Phone. Room only £345 to £4,500. Rooms for disabled. Baby facilities **Tube:** Knightsbridge

MAP 14

Mango Tree

AR

46 Grosvenor Place, SW1X 7EQ
Tel: (020) 7823 1888

On the ground floor of an office block in an upper-crust location behind Buckingham Palace, this Thai restaurant offers a spacious, clean-cut, minimalist décor. The extensive menu takes in appetisers such as yum talay (mixed seafood salad; £7.50) and tod mun pla (spicy fishcakes) as well as curries such as green curry with monkfish and scallops (£14.50), grills, and stir-fries like minced chicken with chilli and basil (£12.75). There's a good vegetarian choice. The food is not cheap, and the wine list opens at £19 and climbs steeply thereafter. Open all week.

MAP 13

Manna

AR

4 Erskine Road, NW3 3AJ
Tel: (020) 7722 8028

This vegetarian favourite has been satisfying the denizens of Primrose Hill and beyond for ten years in 2005. The white-painted frontage heralds a simple interior, where Matthew Kay's menu takes inspiration from the global larder. Start with green chilli tempura (£6.50) or sweet potato and coriander roulade (£6.50), before something like pho, a Vietnamese rice noodle soup with marinated tofu and baby vegetables (£10.95). Europe is represented by cannelloni, filled with slow-roasted tomatoes, wild garlic leaves and ricotta (£12.50). Finish with baked rhubarb with hazelnut meringue and pomegranate cream (£6.50). Wines start at £10.50. Open Sun L and all week D.

MAP 15

Manzi's

AR

1–2 Leicester Street, WC2H 7BL
Tel: (020) 7734 0224

Venerable family-run institution that has been a West End landmark since 1928. Expect classic fish cookery of the old school: grilled Dover sole is a favourite; otherwise plump for grilled sardines (£4) or jellied eels (£9) before poached skate with beurre noisette (£15.50 'for two pieces') or plaice and chips. Ribeye steak for meat eaters, and retro desserts like crème caramel and profiteroles (£4.50). Convenient for theatreland and the West End nightspots. Accommodation available. House wine from £11.95. Closed Sun.

MAP 15

Masala Zone

AR

9 Marshall Street W1F 7ER
Tel: (020) 7287 9966

Senior member of a group of canteen-style Indian brasseries. Options range from street snacks like sev puris (£3.50 upwards), masala burgers, and noodle bowls to composite curry and rice plates (from £6), including lamb vindaloo and mushroom kofta. Alternatively, plump for one of the varied thalis (£6.50 to £11.50). Drinks include lassi, Indian lemonade and a handful of international wines from £10. Open all week. Branches at 80 Upper Street, N1, tel: (020) 7359 3399, and 147 Earls Court Road, SW5, tel: (020) 7373 0220.

MAP 15

Mash

19–21 Great Portland Street, W1W 8QB
Tel: (020) 7637 5555
Website: www.mashbarandrestaurant.co.uk

Cooking 2 | Modern European | £35–£60

'Mash' as in 'mash tun', as this is a place that doubles as a microbrewery and restaurant, with the tuns on display behind glass panels. Downstairs, the bright, buzzy bar/café contrasts with the upper-floor restaurant's green décor and relaxed atmosphere. Effort goes into sourcing good ingredients: buffalo mozzarella salad with properly ripe tomatoes and decent olive oil, for example, and Cornish crab with a salad of apple, coriander and lime. Ribeye steak, from Ireland, is full flavoured and accompanied by green beans and wild mushroom sauce, while West Country chicken breast comes with a chorizo and chestnut sauce. Puddings such as bourbon and vanilla ice cream with hot chocolate sauce, or mixed berry crème brûlée with a topping 'that cracked like ice' confirm the commitment to simple, well-executed basics laced with imaginative innovation. Service combines slickness with cheery knowledge. Around a third of the wines on the 30-bottle list (from £14) are served by the glass (£4.50 to £7.80) – and there are the beers too, of course.

Chef: Simon Wadham **Proprietors:** Gruppo Ltd **Open:** Mon to Fri L 12 to 3, Mon to Sat D 6 to 11 **Meals:** alc (main courses £11 to £18.50). Bar menu available **Service:** 12.5% (optional), card slips closed **Cards:** Amex, Delta, Maestro, MasterCard, Visa **Details:** 120 seats. Private parties: 120 main room, 28 private room. Vegetarian meals. No-smoking area. Wheelchair access (also WC). Music. Air-conditioned **Tube:** Oxford Circus

MAP 13

Matsuri High Holborn

Mid City Place, 71 High Holborn, WC1V 6EA
Tel: (020) 7430 1970
Website: www.matsuri-restaurant.com

Cooking 3 | Japanese | £39–£116

'Matsuri really does brighten up this most dull street,' writes one London-based reporter. It is located on the ground floor of an office block and inside is a contemporary, high-ceilinged room with a state-of-the-art sushi counter and a teppanyaki area in the basement. The kitchen focuses on classic Japanese cuisine without veering off into the fusion fancies of some other places. Appetisers range from edamame and soft-shell crabs to grilled ox tongue and salmon tataki, and the repertoire encompasses salads and soups, breadcrumbed kushiage dishes, tempura and the like. A few details, such as 'chewy' beef teriyaki, have let the side down, but this remains a most convivial restaurant, with 'particularly genteel' service. Hot and cold sakés, beers and cocktails bolster the international wine list, where prices start at £16. The original Matsuri is at 15 Bury Street, SW1, tel: (020) 7839 1101.

Chef: Hiroshi Sudo **Proprietor:** JRK (UK) **Open:** Mon to Sat 12 to 2.30, 6 to 10 **Closed:** bank hols **Meals:** alc (main courses L £12 to £28, D £15 to £35). Set L £8.50 (2 courses) to £22, Set D £35 to £60 **Service:** 12.5% (optional) **Cards:** Amex, Delta, Diners, Maestro, MasterCard, Visa **Details:** 117 seats. Private parties: 100 main room, 2 to 10 private rooms. Vegetarian meals. No smoking in 1 dining room at L. Wheelchair access (also WC). Music. Air-conditioned **Tube:** Holborn

🍷	This symbol means that the wine list is well above the average.
🍾	This symbol means that the restaurant has a truly outstanding wine cellar.

MAP 15

Maze

NEW ENTRY

10–13 Grosvenor Square, W1K 6JP
Tel: (020) 7107 0000
Website: www.gordonramsay.com

Cooking 5 | Modern French | £44–£63

Can central London dining get more glamorous? Just when you thought there might be a sufficiency of Gordon Ramsay restaurants in the capital, along comes another. This one shares a square with the US Embassy and has been designed in classically unadorned, monochrome minimal fashion by David Rockwell, who did the makeover of New York's Grand Central Station. Chef Jason Atherton arrived here from the proprietor's Dubai venture, Verre, as well as Spain's premier address, El Bulli. The crockery is Limoges, the glassware Riedel, and one reporter found himself sitting quite near Lord Lloyd-Webber. Phew.

The culinary idiom is essentially modern French with Asian undertones, but the USP here is the serving of dishes in tapas-sized portions, the recommendation being for around six to eight per head. Highlights at inspection were a creamy, well-timed risotto of peas, broad beans and wood sorrel; honey- and soy-roast quail with foie gras and a chutney of peach and saffron; a pair of Orkney scallops with peppered raisin purée; and a fairly traditional shellfish bisque scented with star anise and enriched with puréed sweetcorn on a croûton.

If a succession of small dishes (for which the same cutlery is retained) doesn't appeal, there is also a carte with larger versions as starters, and main courses such as squab roast in a wood-fired oven served with spiced celeriac, cabbage purée and dates wrapped in bacon, or roast sea bass with asparagus, a nage of tomato and lemongrass, some candied aubergine and a wee dollop of oscietra caviar. For dessert, the wilder shores are explored. A peanut butter and cherry jam sandwich might evoke memories of midnight feasts in the dorm for a certain constituency. Sea salt and almond ice cream is the accompaniment to a runny Valrhona chocolate fondant. More mainstream is rhubarb and passion-fruit trifle topped with fine lemon granita and served with luscious vanilla madeleines.

The wine list offers a decent range by the glass, and 'Wines by Flight', where three glass follow a theme: 1997 Bordeaux, perhaps, or Riesling, or New Zealand Pinot Noir. The champagne list runs and runs, and both Burgundy and Bordeaux are among the main attractions in the Old World. Bottle prices start at £16.

Chef: Jason Atherton **Proprietor:** Gordon Ramsay Holdings Ltd **Open:** all week 12 to 3, 6 to 11 **Meals:** alc (main courses £11.50 to £16) **Service:** 12.5% (optional), card slips closed **Cards:** Amex, Delta, Maestro, MasterCard, Visa **Details:** 90 seats. Private parties: 90 main room, 8 to 10 private rooms. Vegetarian meals. Children's helpings. No smoking. Wheelchair access (also WC). Music. Air-conditioned **Tube:** Bond Street

MAP 13

Medcalf

NEW ENTRY

40 Exmouth Market, EC1R 4QE
Tel: (020) 7833 3533
Website: www.medcalfbar.co.uk

Cooking 4 | Modern British | £27–£52

'Very sophisticated shabby-chic décor,' noted a reporter who relished Medcalf's laid-back vibe, friendly, obliging service and full-blooded food. A scuffed, painted metal garden table looked 'as though it had been pulled off a skip', chairs are rickety, floors are plain wood, and the place doubles as a bar – there's no mistaking that this is a lively venue for the young (and young at heart). The kitchen pumps out classic British dishes with the odd nod towards France and Italy. Welsh rarebit and potted shrimps share the stage with sautéed squid and risotto nero, or spatchcocked poussin with marrow provençale, and the roll-call of dishes reporters recommend include sparkling-fresh rock oysters, crab risotto, and chargrilled bavette steak with horseradish cream and 'enormous chunky chips'. Skate wing with brown butter, capers and spinach is an outright winner, while desserts range from lemon tart via pannacotta with grappa and raspberries to chocolate brownie ice cream. The food represents good value for money – and so do the wines, which start with house Spanish at £12.

Chefs: Tim Wilson and Andy Hogg **Proprietors:** Justin Unsworth and Simon Lee **Open:** all week L 12 to 3, Mon to Thur and Sat D 6 to 10 **Closed:** bank hol Mon **Meals:** alc (main courses £8 to £14.50) **Service:** not inc, 12.5% for parties of 5 or more **Cards:** Maestro, MasterCard, Visa **Details:** 65 seats. 30 seats outside. Vegetarian meals. Children's helpings. No cigars in dining room. Wheelchair access (also WC). Music **Tube:** Farringdon

MAP 13

Mehek

45 London Wall, EC2M 5TE
Tel: (020) 7588 5043

Stylish contemporary décor – complete with wooden floors, yellow walls and antique panels – sets the mood in this City Indian. The menu is a familiar run through onion bhajias (£3), chicken tikka masala (£8.50) and king prawn bhuna, bolstered by a few more promising dishes such as Goan fish curry (made with halibut) and raan-e-mehek (marinated roast leg of lamb). Decent choice of vegetables (from £3.75), rice and breads. Well-chosen wines from £12.50. Open Mon to Fri.

MAP 15

Mela

152–156 Shaftesbury Avenue, WC2H 8HL
Tel: (020) 7836 8635

Vibrantly colourful and contemporary restaurant dealing in a wide-ranging repertoire of dishes from the Subcontinent. 'Indian cuisine – country style' is the kitchen's motto, which translates into starters like Goan mackerel fritada (£4), tandooris, including duck and salmon, plus various curries and stir-fries like achari champen (marinated lamb cooked in pickling spices with stuffed chillies; £10.25). 'Paratha Pavilion' snacks at lunchtime. House wines from £10.95. Open all week. Related to Chowki (see entry).

MAP 13

Metrogusto

13 Theberton Street, N1 0QY
Tel: (020) 7226 9400
Website: www.metrogusto.co.uk

Cooking 3 | Modern Italian | £37–£58

Regional Italian food in a self-styled 'art tabernacle' is the deal at this useful 'upper-middle-range' Islington restaurant. The welcome is friendly, service attentive, and the décor 'agreeably unusual', with many interesting works of art on display. Sicilian influences show up on the menu, which is laid out in traditional style with pasta and risottos following starters like a salad of grilled pears, rucola and Pecorino, or swordfish carpaccio with myrtle and pomegranate. Main courses range from pan-fried duck breast with saffron sauce and potato tart to fillet of sea bass with oregano pesto and aubergine pie, while desserts fly the tricolore with citrus sorbet soaked in limoncello and caramelised chestnut cheesecake served in a glass. Wines stick to Italy but represent all parts from north to south, with smart names aplenty. Bottles start at £17.50, and ten come by the glass.

Chef: Antonio Di Salvo **Proprietors:** Ambro and Susi Ianeselli **Open:** Fri and Sat L 12 to 2.30, Mon to Sat D 6.15 to 11 **Closed:** bank hols **Meals:** alc D (main courses £11 to £17.50). Set L £16.50 (2 courses) to £21.50 **Service:** 12.5% (optional), card slips closed **Cards:** Amex, Delta, Maestro, MasterCard, Visa **Details:** 60 seats. 10 seats outside. Private parties: 50 main room, 20 to 30 private rooms. Vegetarian meals. No children under 1 at D. No smoking in 1 dining room; entirely non-smoking at weekends. Wheelchair access (not WC). Music. Air-conditioned **Tube:** Angel, Highbury and Islington

MAP 13

Mezzanine

AR

National Theatre, SE1 9PX
Tel: (020) 7452 3600

Arrive early if you want a table with a view of the river from this buzzy theatre venue. Pre-show set deals are good value (£19.50/£21.50) while the post-show carte offers similar dishes along the lines of spring vegetable risotto (£6.50), battered cod loin stuffed with caper butter, and French pork and garlic sausages with pulses, roasted garlic and port (£13.25), while cinnamon crème brûlée (£5) might provide a happy ending. Open Mon to Sat D (and occasional matinees).

MAP 14

Millennium Knightsbridge, Mju

17 Sloane Street, SW1 9NU
Tel: (020) 7201 6330
Website: www.millenniumhotels.com

Cooking 5 | Modern Euro-Plus | £40–£134

Hidden away on the first floor of the Millennium Hotel, Mju may well prove a handy pit stop for tired shoppers, sandwiched as it is between Gucci and Fendi, with Cartier beaming back from across the road. The spacious atrium dining room is a little foyer-like, with its low ceiling and several pillars, but the romantic lighting should obviate any sense of just passing through.

Tom Thomsen, Danish by birth, has brought a new European focus back to the menus, where the prevailing tone was once Pacific Rim. The pace of service is slow, and the helplessly uncoordinated performance at inspection is a worry at these prices. Fortunately, the cooking inspired greater confidence. Highlights from the gastronomic menu in February included: tartare of langoustine with avocado bavarois dressed with oscietra caviar and served in a martini glass; perfectly timed Bresse quail with a poached egg, wild mushrooms, foie gras and truffle; and a dessert of chocolate fondant with 'earthily pungent' white truffle ice cream and mocha anglaise. In among the European luxuries, the menu finds space for one outstanding pan-Asian dish in thin-sliced Japanese Kobe beef with spring onions, mint and a few spears of Thai asparagus, served with a Vietnamese-style pho broth. Extras might include oysters dressed in passion fruit on ice in a clear glass bowl, and a selection of farmhouse cheeses. Despite the changed allegiances of the menu, the wine list remains particularly strong in Australia. If it's a lunchtime stop, the 15 or so options by the glass should more than satisfy.

Chef: Tom Thomsen **Proprietor:** Millennium Hotels **Open:** Mon to Fri L 12 to 2.30, Mon to Sat D 6 to 10.30 **Closed:** bank hols **Meals:** alc (main courses L £18 to £22, D £23 to £29). Set L £17.50 (2 courses) to £19.50, Set D £48 to £68 **Service:** 12.5% (optional), card slips closed **Cards:** Amex, Delta, Diners, Maestro, MasterCard, Visa **Details:** 110 seats. Private parties: 100 main room. Car park. Vegetarian meals. Children's helpings. No smoking. Wheelchair access (also WC). Music. Air-conditioned **Accommodation:** 222 rooms, all with bath/shower. TV. Phone. Room only £270 to £552. Rooms for disabled. Baby facilities **Tube:** Knightsbridge

MAP 15

Mint Leaf

NEW ENTRY

Suffolk Place, SW1Y 4HX
Tel: (020) 7930 9020
Website: www.mintleafrestaurant.com

Cooking 3 | Indian | £47–£99

Occupying several thousand square feet of floor space in London's 'theatre wonderland', this basement venue manages to be both extravagant and intimate, thanks to inspired contemporary design and superb lighting. The kitchen delivers a razor-sharp, modern interpretation of classic Indian cuisine, as in 'dazzling' methi murgh (fenugreek-spiked chicken pieces arranged around a compote of onions with mint sauce), or fanned wild duck breast in a pool of tamarind sauce alongside a cylinder of pea pilau. Other options might include tandoori minced rabbit rolls, and sea bass wrapped in a banana leaf with seafood biryani. Vegetables are noteworthy, and desserts are well above the Indian norm: halva served in a filo case with ginger ice cream, for example. Like the menu, the wine list comes with a hefty price tag: house selections open the bidding at £18.

Chef: K.K. Anand **Propriotor:** Dinesh Bhattessa **Open:** Mon to Fri L 12 to 3, all week D 5.30 to 11 **Closed:** bank hols **Meals:** alc (main courses £10 to £28.50). Set L £15 (2 courses), Set D £35 to £45 (min 10). Bar menu available **Service:** 12.5% (optional) **Cards:** Amex, Delta, Diners, Maestro, MasterCard, Visa **Details:** 144 seats. Private parties: 500 main room, 60 to 100 private rooms. Vegetarian meals. Wheelchair access (also WC). Music. Air-conditioned **Tube:** Charing Cross

MAP 15

Mirabelle

56 Curzon Street, W1J 8PA
Tel: (020) 7499 4636
Website: www.whitestarline.org.uk

NEW CHEF | French | £38–£92

Past the doorman at the anonymous entrance, down the stairs, and once you've checked in with the receptionist and walked through to the bar, the décor hits you – ocean liner circa 1920, chic, plush and classy. There's a sense of space and airiness too – you may enter a basement, but it is the ground floor at the back, and skylights and French doors on to a small terrace let the light flood in.

The appeal of the long and relatively unchanging menu (much of it written in gastronomic franglais) is not hard to find, delivering good renditions of dishes that soothe rather than challenge, and the arrival of a new head chef is unlikely to result in a change in direction. The straightforwardness of the cooking is another confidence-booster, as the repertoire runs from dressed crab with mayonnaise, via omelette Arnold Bennett, to grilled lobster with béarnaise sauce. Another element at work is the comfort factor, which produces foie gras in a couple of guises (parfait en gelée, for example) and classics like caramelised skate wing with winkles, beurre noisette and jus à la parisienne, and daube of beef, followed by lemon tart. Service is generally well drilled, but watch out for time limits on tables.

The wine list is a mere two pages, but the print is fine and the selection impeccable – and there is an 'extensive' separate list for fine wines. The bias is appropriately French but New World countries and modern styles are well represented. Bottles start at £18 and an excellent dozen come by the glass.

Chef: Igor Timshincin **Proprietors:** Marco Pierre White and Jimmy Lahoud **Open:** all week 12 to 2.30, 6 to 11.30 **Closed:** 26 Dec, 1 Jan **Meals:** alc (main courses £15 to £27). Set L £17.50 (2 courses) to £21, Set L Sun £22 **Service:** 12.5% (optional), card slips closed **Cards:** Amex, Delta, Diners, Maestro, MasterCard, Visa **Details:** 120 seats. Private parties: 120 main room, 12 to 48 private rooms. Children's helpings. Music. Air-conditioned **Tube:** Green Park

MAP 12

Mirch Masala

AR

1416 London Road, SW16 4BZ
Tel: (020) 8679 1828

Founder member of a mini chain of bargain-basement Indian canteens. Kick off with 'warmers' (starters £1.50 to £8) like chilli bhajias, jeera chicken wings, or grilled lamb chops before checking out the big contingent of meat and vegetarian dishes, which range from karahi methi gosht (£5.50) to masala baigan. BYO wine or stick with lassi. Open all week, noon to midnight. Branches at 213 Upper Tooting Road, SW17, tel: (020) 8672 7500, and 171–173 The Broadway, Southall, tel: (020) 8867 9222, plus a new outlet on Commercial Road.

MAP 15

Miyama

38 Clarges Street, W1Y 7PJ
Tel: (020) 7499 2443

Mr Miyama's eponymous restaurant has been a feature of the Mayfair scene since 1982 and continues to deal in traditional Japanese food at far-from-W1 prices. The menu ploughs a stoically classic furrow, opening with appetisers like kaisou (seaweed salad; £5) and chicken yakitori, before sushi, sashimi and cooked dishes ranging from sake shioyaki (grilled salmon with salt; £10) to fillet of beef teriyaki and deep-fried pork tonkatsu. Set meals from £28. House wines from £12.50 Closed Sat L and Sun L.

AR	Not a full entry but provisionally recommended (known as 'round-ups' in previous editions, these 'also recommended' establishments are now integrated throughout the book).

MAP 15

Mr Kong

21 Lisle Street, WC2H 7BA
Tel: (020) 7437 7341

Cooking 2 | Chinese | £24–£51

Over the years, Mr Kong and family have turned this Lisle Street address into a bastion of reliable Cantonese cooking in ever-changing Chinatown. The kitchen makes the most of the maritime harvest: not only lobster, squid and king prawns, but also razor clams, turbot and eels (perhaps braised with whole garlic and roast pork). A long list of chef's specials and 'manager's recommendations' is peppered with esoteric delicacies: for example, stuffed fish maw with baby clams and prawn paste, deep-fried stuffed pig's intestine, and sautéed 'dragon's whiskers' (aka pea shoots) with dried scallops. In more familiar vein you might also notice stewed chicken in black-bean sauce, sliced beef with ginger and spring onions, and some promising vegetarian options like bean curd and asparagus with fresh mango. House French is £8.50.

Chefs: K. Kong and Y.W. Lo **Proprietor:** Mr Kong Chinese Restaurant Ltd **Open:** all week 12 to 2.45am (1.45am Sun) **Meals:** alc (main courses £6 to £16). Set L and D £9.30 (2 courses) to £22 (all min 2 to 8) **Service:** 10% **Cards:** Amex, Delta, Diners, Maestro, MasterCard, Visa **Details:** 110 seats. Private parties: 25 to 35 private rooms. Vegetarian meals. No cigars/pipes in dining room. Occasional music. Air-conditioned **Tube:** Leicester Square

MAP 15

Momo

AR

25 Heddon Street, W1R 7LG
Tel: (020) 7434 4040

Once inside, it is difficult to imagine you are in the heart of London. The atmosphere created by the Moroccan décor really invokes North Africa, and carved wooden screens and shutters, ornate plasterwork, and low tables lit by candles in metal lanterns are complemented by a menu strong on couscous and tagines, backed up by harira soup (£6.50) and roast quail with a crispy tapioca galette (£18.50), with riz au lait pastilla (£6.50) among desserts. The wide-ranging wine list includes a handful of Moroccan reds; prices from £18. Closed Sun L.

MAP 15

Mon Plaisir

19–21 Monmouth Street, WC2H 9dd
Tel: (020) 7836 7243

Bastion of unreservedly bourgeois French cooking for more than three decades, conjuring up the Parisian brasserie world of cassolette d'escargots (£6), boeuf bourguignonne, and coq au vin (£14.50) – although the kitchen also makes a few detours for a 'compression' of beef tomato and seared tuna, and chicken breast with roast peanut sauce and beans. Desserts are things like chestnut tart and îles flottantes. Two-course theatre deals £12.50. Totally Gallic wines from £11.50. Closed Sat L and Sun.

MAP 15

Montcalm Hotel, Crescent Restaurant

34–40 Great Cumberland Place, W1H 7TW
Tel: (020) 7402 4288
Website: www.montcalm.co.uk

Cooking 2 | Modern British | £31–£58

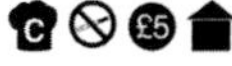

Décor is upmarket, tall windows 'extravagantly swagged and pelmeted' and well-spaced tables dressed with white linen, but the fixed-price menus offer 'one of the best bargains in town'. Well-reported dishes are a tasting of breast, rillettes and foie gras of duck; ginger-scented butternut squash soup with four fat deep-fried prawns; and fillet steak with wild mushroom and black truffle ragoût, roast root vegetables and béarnaise. At inspection poor timing let down a main-course bream fillet with wilted spinach on champ, though poached and roasted chicken breast with dauphinoise potatoes and thyme jus hit the spot. 'Positive, refreshing' green apple mousse and Granny Smith sorbet, and chocolate brownie with pecan ice cream and Valrhona milkshake have made convincing endings. Wines, mostly but not exclusively French, start at £20.

Chef: Tristan Kenworthy **Proprietor:** Nikko Hotels (UK) Ltd **Open:** Mon to Fri L 12.30 to 2.30, all week D 6.30 to 10.30 **Meals:** Set L (inc ½-bottle wine) £20 (2 courses) to £25, Set D (inc ½-bottle wine) £22.50 (2 courses) to £27.50. Bar/lounge menu available **Service:** not inc **Cards:** Amex, Delta, Maestro, MasterCard, Visa **Details:** 60 seats. Private parties: 60 main room, 20 to 60 private rooms. Vegetarian meals. Children's helpings. No smoking. Wheelchair access (also WC). Music. No mobile phones. Air-conditioned **Accommodation:** 120 rooms, all with bath/shower. TV. Phone. Room only £150 to £250. Rooms for disabled. Baby facilities **Tube:** Marble Arch

MAP 13

Morgan M

489 Liverpool Road, N7 8NS
Tel: (020) 7609 3560
Website: www.morganm.com

Cooking 5 | Modern French | £38–£77

Behind a dark-green frontage and potted bay trees in gentrifying Holloway, Morgan Meunier's French establishment has helped to set the local eating scene alight. Apple green and white are the colours *du jour* inside, and the place is generously hung about with the proprietor's own artworks.

A variety of formulas is on offer: there are seasonal and vegetarian menus of six courses each, or you might just stick with three courses from the main carte. The cooking essays a high degree of experimentation. Lobster and ricotta cannelloni with creamy shellfish cappuccino was right on the money at inspection, with plenty of lobster meat packed into the silky pasta roll, and more served on the half-shell. South-west French-style bean soup gained punch from its little splodges of lemon confit and pesto. Roasted veal fillet with sweetbreads, braised cabbage, Jerusalem artichoke and a velouté of morels and vin jaune is a star main course, the meat showing plenty of positive flavour. French cheeses are good, but carry the usual inexplicable supplement on the menu price. Desserts include pineapple soufflé with coconut sorbet, or apple mille-feuille with cinnamon tuile and Granny Smith sorbet. Service at inspection was led in a rather hectoring style. The wine list is almost entirely French, and while there is a handful under £20, prices are mostly stiff. Wines by the small glass start at £4.50.

Chefs: Morgan Meunier and Sylvain Soulard **Proprietor:** Morgan Meunier **Open:** Wed to Fri and Sun L 12 to 2.15, Tue to Sat D 7 to 10.30 **Closed:** 24 to 30 Dec **Meals:** Set L £19.50 (2 courses) to £39, Set D £30 to £39 **Service:** 12.5% (optional), card slips closed **Cards:** Delta, Diners, Maestro, MasterCard, Visa **Details:** 48 seats. Private parties: 48 main room, 12 to 14 private rooms. Vegetarian meals. No smoking. Wheelchair access (not WC). No music. No mobile phones. Air-conditioned **Tube:** Highbury & Islington

MAP 13

Moro

34–36 Exmouth Market, EC1R 4QE
Tel: (020) 7833 8336
Website: www.moro.co.uk

Cooking 5 | Spanish/North African | £33–£54

'Wow, is this place buzzing,' exclaimed a reporter. That Moro is still full of noise and clamour almost 10 years on is testimony to the 'simple food done well' that draws inspiration from all over the southern Mediterranean. The décor gives a kind of canteen charm, and the bar and the open-to-view kitchen add to the sense of 'heart-on-sleeve straightforwardness'. The cooking is built on admirable principles, both in sourcing materials from specialists, and in the execution – a wood-burning oven and a charcoal grill are preferred methods. Squid as a first course arrives cooked perfectly and accompanied by a dollop of 'fantastic' harissa, and a soup of chestnuts, white bean and jamón is judged to be 'thick and earthy'.

The simple and uncluttered presentation of dishes highlights the care and precision of the cooking. 'Fresh-tasting' mackerel, for example, is simply grilled and served with nothing more than a romescu sauce 'crunchy with nuts and sweet with peppers', while pan-fried calves' sweetbreads are beautifully cooked with cardamom and set off well by a salad of preserved lemon and artichoke hearts. Among desserts, chocolate and apricot tart has found favour, as has a rather alcoholic Málaga and raisin ice cream. Good sourdough bread has come in for praise too, and 'attentive, responsive but unobtrusive' describes the service. A mostly Spanish wine list opens with nine sherries by the glass. House red and white wines are £12.50.

Chefs: Sam and Sam Clark **Proprietors:** Mark Sainsbury, and Sam and Sam Clark **Open:** Mon to Fri L 12.30 to 2.30, Mon to Sat D 7 to 10.30 **Closed:** Christmas to New Year, bank hols **Meals:** alc (main courses £13 to £16.50). Tapas menu available **Service:** not inc, 12.5% for parties of 6 or more **Cards:** Amex, Delta, Diners, Maestro, MasterCard, Visa **Details:** 85 seats. 15 seats outside. Private parties: 80 main room, 12 to 14 private rooms. Vegetarian meals. Children's helpings. No cigars/pipes in dining room. Wheelchair access (also WC). No music. Air-conditioned **Tube:** Farringdon

	This symbol means that smoking is not permitted.
	This symbol means that there are some restrictions on smoking though it may be allowed in some eating areas.

MAP 12

Mosaica @ the factory

Chocolate Factory, Clarendon Road, N22 6XJ
Tel: (020) 8889 2400
Website: www.mosaicarestaurants.com

Cooking 3 | Modern European | £26–£53

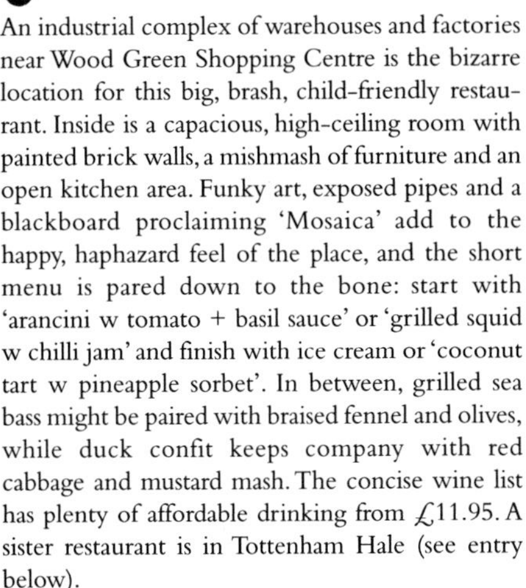

£5

An industrial complex of warehouses and factories near Wood Green Shopping Centre is the bizarre location for this big, brash, child-friendly restaurant. Inside is a capacious, high-ceiling room with painted brick walls, a mishmash of furniture and an open kitchen area. Funky art, exposed pipes and a blackboard proclaiming 'Mosaica' add to the happy, haphazard feel of the place, and the short menu is pared down to the bone: start with 'arancini w tomato + basil sauce' or 'grilled squid w chilli jam' and finish with ice cream or 'coconut tart w pineapple sorbet'. In between, grilled sea bass might be paired with braised fennel and olives, while duck confit keeps company with red cabbage and mustard mash. The concise wine list has plenty of affordable drinking from £11.95. A sister restaurant is in Tottenham Hale (see entry below).

Chef/Proprietor: John Mountain **Open:** Tue to Fri and Sun L 12 to 2.30, Tue to Sat D 7 to 9.30 **Meals:** alc (main courses L £6 to £16, D £12 to £16) **Service:** not inc, 10% for parties of 6 or more **Cards:** Amex, Delta, Maestro, MasterCard, Visa **Details:** 100 seats. Private parties: 150 main room. Car park. Vegetarian meals. Children's helpings. Wheelchair access (also WC). Music. Air-conditioned **Tube:** Wood Green

MAP 12

Mosaica @ the lock

Heron House, Ferry Lane, N17 9NF
Tel: (020) 8801 4433
Website: www.mosaicarestaurants.com

Cooking 3 | Modern European | £28–£54

£5

Beside 'Tottenham Lock 17', this Mosaica occupies the ground floor of a building that also houses the College of North-East London. Like its elder brother in the Wood Green chocolate factory (see above), it emphasises eclectic modern food with a cosmopolitan edge, served in good humoured, offbeat surroundings. The short daily menu might open with grilled squid, chilli jam and leaves, or foie gras with toast and pickles, before main courses of pink salmon with wild garlic and caper risotto, or pork belly with mustard mash and red cabbage. Vegetarians are looked after, although meatless dishes may not always appear on the menu. Rounding things off are desserts such as rose crème brûlée, or almond and blueberry tart with raspberry ice cream. The short, catholic wine list has some gluggable stuff from £13.90.

Chefs: John Mountain and Josh Gale **Proprietor:** John Mountain **Open:** Tue to Fri and Sun L 12 to 2.30, Tue to Sat D 7 to 9.30 (10 Sat) **Meals:** alc (main courses: L £6 to £16, D £12.50 to £16) **Service:** not inc **Cards:** Amex, Delta, Maestro, MasterCard, Visa **Details:** 70 seats. 20 seats outside. Private parties: 50 main room. Car park. Vegetarian meals. Children's helpings. Wheelchair access (also WC). Music **Tube:** Tottenham Hale

MAP 13

Moshi Moshi Sushi AR

Unit 24, Liverpool Street Station, Broadgate, EC2M 7QH
Tel: (020) 7247 3227

The original kaiten restaurant in the UK is still going strong, and the views across the station still make an impressive backdrop. A laudable environmental consciousness has resulted in the dropping of the endangered bluefin tuna from the menu. The conveyor belt snakes its way around the room delivering coloured plates (prices from £1.20 to £3.50): choose from a range of nigiri sushi, maki, and sashimi. Plus there is a range of bento and donburi boxes, and excellent tempura. There is another branch in Brighton (see entry), and the following addresses in London: 7–8 Limeburner Lane, EC4, tel: (020) 7248 1808; Waitrose, Canada Place, E14, tel: (020) 7512 9201; Kiosk 2B, Central Square, Broadgate, EC2, tel: (020) 7920 0077.

MAP12

MVH

5 White Hart Lane, SW13 0PX
Tel: (020) 8392 1111

Cooking 4 | Eclectic | £39–£59

Michael Von Hruschka's restaurant is pure theatre from start to finish. Space is limited, whether upstairs in the bar stuffed with weird artefacts and decorative objects or in the downstairs restaurant, where the décor is 'less obtrusive' and easier on the eye. The kitchen goes out of its way to source unfamiliar ingredients, but the ways in which they are combined are intelligent, with appetisers giving due notice of the style: at inspection, three test tubes containing a 'deliciously refreshing' blend of cucumber, ginger, lime and mint. Materials have included soft-shell crabs given a Japanese twist, seared white albacore tuna 'oozing delicious flavour' teamed with parsley mash and seaweed tartare, and 'sensitively handled' blackened cod in sweet miso with lime risottini. There are, predictably, some failures among the whirl of innovation, notably roast smoked chicken breast with colcannon and pâte brique, but the meal was put back on course by kalamanci – an 'impressive' lime crème brûlée – and a 'fascinating' upside-down spiced cake served with a scoop of intensely flavoured pistachio ice cream. Not surprisingly, the wine list is equally globetrotting, starting in Italy at £20.

Chef/Proprietor: Michael Von Hruschka **Open:** Thur to Sun L 12 to 2.30, all week D 6 to 10.30 **Meals:** Set L £19 (2 courses) to £22, Set D £26 (2 courses) to £29 **Service:** 12.5% (optional), card slips closed **Cards:** Amex, Delta, Diners, Maestro, MasterCard, Visa **Details:** 32 seats. Private parties: 40 main room, 10 to 20 private rooms. Children's helpings. No-smoking area. Music. No mobile phones. Air-conditioned

MAP 14

Nahm

Halkin Hotel, 5 Halkin Street, SW1X 7DJ
Tel: (020) 7333 1234
Website: www.nahm.como.bz

Cooking 3 | Thai | £50–£88

The dining room of the swish, cosmopolitan Halkin Hotel is all stylistic simplicity, with honey, russet and teak tones forming a backdrop to David Thompson's Thai-inspired cooking. For those not familiar with the cuisine, a team of well-drilled waiters is on hand to dispense advice in a friendly and non-patronising manner. The format seems straightforward enough: either choose from the carte or go for the Nahm Arharn eight-dish four-course tasting menu, which is arranged so that you balance curries (shredded oxtail with coconut milk and potato) with salads (lemongrass with prawns, squid, shredded chicken, peanuts and mint) and stir-fries (Appleton belly pork with shrimp paste, kaffir lime leaves and chillies). Although not all dishes are equally thrilling, desserts are wonderful concoctions, playing with sweet, sour and salt sensations in black sticky rice with caramelised coconut, or balancing sweet and sour in a fermented rice custard coupled with steamed coconut pudding. The wine list is aimed squarely at high rollers, with the entry fee over £20.

Chefs: David Thompson and Matthew Albert **Proprietor:** Como Hotels & Resorts **Open:** Mon to Fri L 12 to 2.30, all week D 7 to 10.30 (10 Sun) **Closed:** bank hols **Meals:** alc (main courses £11 to £16). Set L £26, Set D £47 **Service:** 12.5% (optional) **Cards:** Amex, Delta, Diners, Maestro, MasterCard, Visa **Details:** 78 seats. Private parties: 60 main room, 15 to 30 private rooms. Vegetarian meals. Children's helpings. No-smoking area. Wheelchair access (also WC). Music. Air-conditioned **Accommodation:** 41 rooms, all with bath/shower. TV. Phone. Room only £310 to £1,100. Rooms for disabled. Baby facilities **Tube:** Hyde Park Corner

MAP 15

National Gallery, Crivelli's Garden

AR

Trafalgar Square, WC2N 5DN
Tel: (020) 7747 2869

'Exactly right for a public art gallery,' noted a visitor to this restaurant with a view on the first floor of the Sainsbury Wing. Choose anything from a sandwich to more substantial dishes like grilled aubergine filled with mozzarella, asparagus and basil dressing (£7), various pastas, and grilled corn-fed chicken breast with spinach and pickled vegetables (£13), followed by desserts such as tiramisù (£5). Short Italian wine list with prices from £11.95. Open all week L and Wed D.

MAP 15

Neal Street Restaurant

26 Neal Street, WC2H 9QW
Tel: (020) 7836 8368
Website: www.carluccios.com

NEW CHEF | Italian | £41–£97

Antonio Carluccio's Covent Garden temple to fungal gastronomy took on a new head chef in the shape of Maurilio Molteni just as we were going to press. However, it can confidently be expected that the style of straightforward Italian cooking with fine ingredients will continue. Mixed sautéed mushrooms with wild garlic and chilli are the must-have way to start, and may be followed by a pasta or gnocchi dish (perhaps truffle-buttered tagliolini), and then main courses of halibut with asparagus and hollandaise, or rabbit baked with black olives and cherry tomatoes and served with a potato cake. Finish with orange brûlée, or panna-cotta with mixed berries. Wines are predominantly Italian and predominantly expensive, although there is a good selection of by-the-glass offerings from £4.75.

Chef: Maurilio Molteni **Proprietors:** Antonio and Priscilla Carluccio **Open:** Mon to Sat 12 to 2.30, 6 to 11 **Closed:** from 23 Dec to 2 Jan, bank hols **Meals:** alc (main courses £14 to £28). Set L £21 (2 courses) to £25, Set D 6 to 7 and 10 to 11 £21 (2 courses) to £25 **Service:** 12.5% (optional) **Cards:** Amex, Delta, Diners, Maestro, MasterCard, Visa **Details:** 70 seats. Private parties: 10 main room, 10 to 24 private rooms. Vegetarian meals. No children under 8. No-smoking area. Wheelchair access (not WC). No music. No mobile phones. Air-conditioned **Tube:** Covent Garden

MAP 15

New World

AR

1 Gerrard Place, W1D 5PA
Tel: (020) 7434 2508

Cantonese 700-seater providing unbeatable value and great entertainment in Chinatown. Go for the dim sum, which are dispensed from a flotilla of heated trolleys propelled incessantly around the room. All the favourites (and a few curiosities) are here, from steamed dumplings (under £3), deep-fried morsels, roast meats and bowls of soup noodles to custard tarts. The full menu is a massive tome spanning everything from deep-fried soft-shell crab (£4.75) to crispy shredded chilli beef (£8). House wine £10.50. Open all week.

MAP 15

Nicole's

158 New Bond Street, W1Y 9PA
Tel: (020) 7499 8408
Email: nicoles@frenchconnection.com

Cooking 3 | Modern European | £47–£75

Bond Street retail therapy patients, ladies who lunch and others in the know pack the basement of the Nicole Farhi store for daytime refuelling in classy 1930s-style surroundings that might have been lifted from the set of *Poirot*. The all-day bar menu tilts towards healthy-sounding salads (roast duck with oyster mushroom, frisée and orange), while the main carte starts with things like smoked haddock chowder, or ricotta ravioli with roast fennel, semi-sun-dried tomato and rocket, then moves on to modish ensembles like grilled scallops with lentils, pancetta and gremolata, or calf's liver saltimbocca with crispy potatoes and green beans. Desserts may take the form of honey-roast figs with cinnamon shortbread, or fruit crumble and cream. Once the shopping throngs have dispersed, there is much more elbow room at dinner. Most wines on the lively list are over £20, but there's a generous assortment by the glass.

Chef: Annie Wayte **Proprietor:** Stephen Marks **Open:** Mon to Sat L 11.30 to 5.30, Mon to Fri D 6 to 9 **Closed:** bank hols **Meals:** alc (main courses £18 to £23.50). Bar L menu available. Cover £1 **Service:** 15% (optional), card slips closed **Cards:** Amex, Delta, Diners, Maestro, MasterCard, Visa **Details:** 80 seats. Private parties: 80 main room. Vegetarian meals. Children's helpings. No smoking in 1 dining room. Wheelchair access (also WC). Music. Air-conditioned **Tube:** Green Park

MAP 15

Noble Rot

3–5 Mill Street, W1S 2AU
Tel: (020) 7629 8877
Website: www.noblerot.com

Cooking 5 | Modern European | £37–£86

In a fashionable Mayfair location just off Regent and Conduit Streets, Noble Rot is as well turned out as its chic clientele. On the ground floor is a cool, stylish L-shaped dining room with floor-to-ceiling windows hung with dark-wood Venetian blinds and stone floors softened by large antique rugs. Dark walls carry black-and-white photos of the famous, and candles and modern spotlighting illuminate white-clothed tables. It's buzzy and high-volume and as vibrant and slick as the ambitious cooking, but the young, black-clad staff are suitably friendly and professional.

Julian Owen-Mold's modern European repertoire fits in perfectly, underpinned by classical themes and well-sourced produce. Menus are liberally sprinkled with luxury items, and adventurous ideas are enhanced on the plate by skilful cooking, fine presentation and interesting variations of flavour, temperature and texture. For example, an opener of hot and cold foie gras juxtaposes a foie gras and smoked eel parfait with seared foie gras with fig sherbet, while tournedos of beef could come with a Pyefleet oyster, roast shallots and forest mushrooms. Desserts shine too, perhaps via a pear trio, or a classic prune and Armagnac soufflé with praline ice cream.

Though sweet wines are not the major focus that the establishment's name suggests, they take in Yquem, Patrick Baudouin's Layon and some century-old Tokaji. A glitzy international range of dry wines is mostly pitched at budgets of £30 upwards. Guigal's red Côtes du Rhône (£20) looks the best of the budget options.

Chef: Julian Owen-Mold **Proprietor:** Soren Jessen **Open:** Mon to Sat 12 to 3.30, 5.30 to 11 **Closed:** 25and 26 Dec, 1 Jan, bank hols **Meals:** alc (main courses £17 to £25). Set L £18 (2 courses) to £22.50, Set D £30. **Service:** 12.5% (optional), card slips closed **Cards:** Amex, Delta, Diners, Maestro, MasterCard, Visa **Details:** 65 seats. 20 seats outside. Private parties: 80 main room, 12 to 55 private rooms. Vegetarian meals. Children's helpings. No-smoking area. Music. Air-conditioned **Tube:** Oxford Circus

MAP 15

Nobu

19 Old Park Lane, W1Y 4LB
Tel: (020) 7447 4747
Website: www.noburestaurants.com

Cooking 5 | Modern Japanese | £54–£146

Ascend the white staircase to the hustle-bustle of this first-floor venue in the hub of London, where staff cry greetings in Japanese as you sashay to your table. The décor is Tokyo-plain, with white walls, bare tables and small chairs. At inspection, Japanese patrons were all sitting up at the teppanyaki-style counter, watching the chefs at work. A little Latin American fire in the form of anti-cucho Peruvian-style spicy dishes (of salmon, chicken or ribeye) adds cultural variation to the slick modern Japanese fulcrum of the lengthy menu. Lobster ceviche contains tomato and shiso leaf and a world of citric sourness. 'New-style sashimi' of oysters comprises five oysters sharing their shells with spring onions, shoyu, sesame seeds and ginger. The chef's specials are where the main action is, with harumaki rolls of soft-shell crab in puddles of creamed wasabi and balsamic, and gyoza dumplings composed of wagyu beef and foie gras among the inspection highlights. Standard side orders such as sushi rolls, vegetables in salty tempura batter and fish roes all come up to snuff, and, if the strictly applied time limit allows (don't be startled to be told verbatim 'your time is up'), the desserts are worth a punt as well: a dish of daisy-fresh apricot purée gains extraordinary depth from the chunks of salty peanut brittle submerged in it.

Prices generally reflect the five-star West End context, with wines contributing energetically to the cost, along with the 15% service charge. As well as a grand spread of Western grape wines, there are sakés with tasting-note pointers to consider too, and a range of appealing cocktails. Wines by the glass start at £5.50, by the bottle at £26. As the Guide went to press a third London branch opened at 15 Berkeley Street, W1; tel: (020) 7290 9222. See entry for Ubon bu Nobu for the second of the trio.

Chef: Mark Edwards **Proprietor:** Nobu Matsuhisa **Open:** Mon to Fri 12 to 2.15, 6 to 10.15, Sat 12.30 to 2.30, 6 to 11.15, Sun 12.30 to 2.30, 6 to 9.45 **Meals:** alc (main courses £5 to £29.50). Set L £25 to £50, Set D £70 to £90 **Service:** 15% (optional) **Cards:** Amex, Diners, Maestro, MasterCard, Visa **Details:** 150 seats. Private parties: 12 main room, 14 to 40 private rooms. Vegetarian meals. No-smoking area. Wheelchair access (not WC). No music. Air-conditioned **Tube:** Hyde Park Corner

MAP 13

Notting Hill Brasserie

92 Kensington Park Road, W11 2PN
Tel: (020) 7229 4481
Email: enquiries@nottinghillbrasserie.com

Cooking 4 | Modern European | £33–£78

This restaurant in three converted houses still impresses with its mix of period detail and stylish good looks, while live music in the bar and 'efficient and friendly' service put diners at ease. The cooking is contemporary and Mediterranean-influenced. Fish, like a starter of John Dory served with delicate gnocchi and red wine sauce, figures largely, but roast and marinated red pepper with goats' cheese and rocket may be an equally contemporary alternative. Well-timed wild sea bass, a main course, has come with provençale vegetables, pesto and 'very good spiced aubergine', or there could be venison with braised red cabbage and 'intense' parsnip purée. Vegetables are extra. For dessert, try home-made vanilla yoghurt with rhubarb compote, or farmhouse cheeses. Incidentals like good bread and 'super chunky chips' have been praised, and a neat, concise wine selection opens with house French at £14 but hits its stride above £20.

Chef: Mark Jankel **Proprietor:** Carlo Spetale **Open:** all week L 12 to 2.45, Mon to Sat D 7 to 11 **Closed:** Dec 24 to 27 **Meals:** alc D (main courses £19 to £23.50). Set L £14.50 (2 courses) to £19.50, Set L Sun £25 (2 courses) to £30. Bar menu available **Service:** 12.5% (optional), card slips closed **Cards:** Amex, Delta, Maestro, MasterCard, Visa **Details:** 110 seats. Private parties: 12 main room, 4 to 44 private rooms. Vegetarian meals. No cigars/pipes. No-smoking area. Wheelchair access (not WC). Music. Air-conditioned **Tube:** Notting Hill Gate

MAP 13

Noura Brasserie

16 Hobart Place, SW1W 0HH
Tel: (020) 7235 9444
Website: www.noura-brasseries.co.uk

Cooking 3 | Lebanese | £39–£76

The Bou-Antoun brothers scored a hit in Paris with their mini-chain of stylish Lebanese brasseries and are now making an impact in central London. The Hobart Place original oozes minimalist elegance and offers a vast selection of meze to suit all dietary persuasions: expect anything from bastorma (thinly sliced smoked beef) to batinjan makdous (pickled baby aubergines stuffed with walnut and garlic) and mana'eesh (thyme and sesame-seed pizzas). Main courses rely on the chargrill, with a couple of baked kebbeh specialities (minced lamb with cracked wheat) for good measure. To finish, home-made ice creams have been more enjoyable than sweet pastries. Big French names and Lebanese bottles dominate the wine list; house recommendations start at £18. Other branches are Noura Mayfair, 16 Curzon Street, W1, tel: (020) 7495 1050; Noura Central, 122 Jermyn Street, SW1, tel: (020) 7839 2020; and a Delicatessen Café at 12 William Street, SW1, tel: (020) 7235 5900.

Chef: Badih Asmar **Proprietor:** Nader Bou-Antoun **Open:** all week 11.30 to 11.45 **Meals:** alc (main courses £10 to £19). Set L £14.50 (2 courses), Set D £25 to £34 (all min 2). Cover £2. Bar menu available **Service:** not inc **Cards:** Amex, Delta, Diners, Maestro, MasterCard, Visa **Details:** 125 seats. Private parties: 125 main room. Vegetarian meals. Wheelchair access (also WC). Music. Air-conditioned **Tube:** Victoria

MAP 15

No. 6 George Street

6 George Street, W1U 3QX
Tel: (020) 7935 1910

Cooking 2 | Modern British | £32–£54

Emma Miller's shop sells quality produce to the denizens of Marylebone, while the back of the premises plays host to a little gem of a restaurant. From noon to teatime, the simple, rustic space is filled with a cheerful buzz. Simplicity prevails on the daily-changing menu as well, with red lentil, carrot and cumin soup exemplifying the approach. Duck livers are pan-fried with bacon and come with green beans and balsamic roasted onions as a starter, while smoked haddock fish cakes are paired with baby spinach and a lemon butter sauce as a main course. Dishes can be as refreshingly simple as herb omelette with salad, and desserts run to pear and prune tart, or lemon polenta cake with blood orange compote. There is a minimum charge of £14 per head, and wines start at £14.50.

Chef: Emma Miller **Proprietors:** the Miller family **Open:** Mon to Fri L 12 to 3 **Closed:** bank hols, 2 weeks Aug **Meals:** alc L (main courses £10.50 to £16.50) **Service:** not inc **Cards:** Maestro, MasterCard, Visa **Details:** 32 seats. Private parties: 32 main room. Vegetarian meals. Children's helpings. No smoking. No music. Air-conditioned **Tube:** Bond Street

MAP 12

Numidie

48 Westow Hill, SE19 1RX
Tel: (020) 8766 6166
Website: www.numidie.co.uk

Cooking 2 | North African | £16–£48

Numidie's ethnic style and identity lend a laid-back, Bohemian edge to the Crystal Palace scene, and you can soak up the mood in the subdued basement wine bar or the simply set-out ground-floor dining room. The core of the menu doesn't change, but daily specials keep regular customers interested: the theme is North Africa in the shape of couscous, tagines served with rechetta (home-made Algerian pasta steamed with cinnamon), and some pleasant options for vegetarians (globe artichoke and broad bean risotto, for example). The kitchen also puts on its European hat for, say, duck breast with pear and orange flower sauce, or beef fillet with truffle jus, potato gratin and chicory. Wines are a bit different, and prices (from £9.50) are fair. As the Guide went to press the owners were planning to open all day.

Chef: Serge Ismail **Proprietors:** Serge Ismail and Ashleigh Hope **Open:** all week 10 to 2, 6 to 10.30 **Meals:** alc (main courses L £6 to £12, D £8.50 to £15.50). Set L £8.95 **Service:** not inc, card slips closed **Cards:** Delta, Maestro, MasterCard, Visa **Details:** 50 seats. Private parties: 50 main room. Vegetarian meals. Children's helpings. No smoking. Wheelchair access (not WC). Music. Air-conditioned

This symbol means that the restaurant has elected to participate in *The Good Food Guide's* £5 voucher scheme (see 'How to Use the Guide' for details).

MAP 13

Nyonya

2A Kensington Park Road, W11 3BU
Tel: (020) 7243 1800
Website: www.nyonya.co.uk

Cooking 2 | Malay/Chinese | £18–£50

'Nyonya' refers to the hybrid culinary offspring of the Malay/Chinese community and also to the women from that culture. Appropriately, the lady of the house cooks in this unusual half-moon-shaped dining room, with its clean lines, sparse décor and curved tables. The food is 'as authentically gutsy as you're likely to find in any of London's Malaysian joints', and flavours are subtly intricate: witness textbook chicken satay and 'lobak' (deep-fried rolls of roughly chopped pork marinated with five-spice and wrapped in bean curd). Composite platefuls such as nasi lemak ('a bonanza of flavours') fit the bill for lunch; otherwise, you might choose stir-fried beef with French beans, or sambal brinjal (slithery aubergines topped with pungent shrimp paste). To finish, don't miss the dainty assortments of traditional 'kuih' cakes. Drink jasmine tea, Asian beer or house wine (£13.50).

Chef: Mary Chong **Proprietor:** Nyonya Ltd **Open:** all week 11.30 to 2.45, 6 to 10.30 **Meals:** alc (main courses £6.50 to £8.50). Set L £8 **Service:** not inc, card slips closed **Cards:** Amex, Delta, Diners, Maestro, MasterCard, Visa **Details:** 55 seats. Private parties: 55 main room. Vegetarian meals. No smoking. Music. Air-conditioned **Tube:** Notting Hill Gate

MAP 13

Odette's

130 Regents Park Road, NW1 8XL
Tel: (020) 7586 5486
Email: odettesrestaurant@yahoo.co.uk

Cooking 2 | Modern British | £32–£79

Odette's dark emerald green canopy is still a landmark on Primrose Hill's main shopping street. Inside the Victorian house has three dining rooms, each differently decorated, with a wine bar in the basement. A broadly contemporary menu offers well-reported jumbo snails poached in Chablis and baked in garlic butter, alongside velouté of celeriac and aged Parmesan with a 'lovely smooth texture'. Among meat main courses an excellent piece of griddled foie gras has partnered an under-flavoured Barbury duckling, and a typical fish dish is wild sea bass with ratte potatoes, mussels, scallops, carrot puree, and shiraz sauce. Hot chocolate fondant with black cherry compote and praline ice cream has made a happy ending. The 'tidy' wine list offers some decent drinking under £25; house wine from £14.

Chef: Simon Bradley **Proprietor:** Artisan Restaurants Ltd **Open:** Sun to Fri L 12 to 2.30, Mon to Sat D 7 to 11 **Meals:** alc (main courses £18 to £28). Set L £16.50 (2 courses) to £18 **Service:** 12.5% (optional), card slips closed **Cards:** Amex, Delta, Maestro, MasterCard, Visa **Details:** 61 seats. 10 seats outside. Private parties: 28 main room, 6 to 10 private rooms. Vegetarian meals. No pipes/cigars. Wheelchair access (not WC). No music. No mobile phones **Tube:** Chalk Farm

MAP 13

Old Delhi

AR

48 Kendal Street, W2 2BP
Tel: (020) 7723 3335

Despite its emphatically Subcontinental name, this smart restaurant receives most plaudits for its 'must-try' Persian dishes. Look for appetisers like mirza-ghasemi (mashed aubergines and eggs with garlic and spices; £5.50) and minced lamb kufteh as well as main courses ranging from kebabs to fesenjune (roast duck with sweet-and-sour pomegranate and walnut sauce; £13.75). A more conventional Indian repertoire encompasses everything from rogan josh (£10.25) to king prawn masala. House wine £12.80. Harpist Wed and Sat evenings. Open all week.

MAP 13

Olivo

21 Eccleston Street, SW1W 9LX
Tel: (020) 7730 2505
Email: maurosanna@oliveto.fsnet.co.uk

Cooking 2 | Italian/Sardinian | £32–£57

Invariably crowded, bustling and cheery, Olivo, with its Mediterranean atmosphere, tightly packed tables and high decibels, can be counted on to produce convincingly 'rustic but well-prepared' Sardinian-orientated food. Wooden floors, walls plastered in ochre and blue, and a lack of napery help crank up the volume and lend an informal air to proceedings. There are plenty of interesting Sardinian specialities with an emphasis on fish and seafood; think traditional Sardinian pasta with clams, chargrilled cuttlefish or fresh sardines, plus seasonal Italian classics like risotto with asparagus and grilled porcini with truffle oil. Pasta comes in starter and main-course portions, while desserts follow the standard Italian repertoire of tiramisù, semi-freddo or perhaps pannacotta, and there are Sardinian cheeses too. The patriotic, concise, all-Italian wine list includes a good selection of Sardinian bottles, with two house Sardinians kicking things off at £14.50 (£3.50 by the glass).

Chef: Marco Melis **Proprietor:** Mauro Sanna **Open:** Mon to Fri L 12 to 2.30, all week D 7 to 11 (10 Sun) **Closed:** bank hols **Meals:** alc (main courses £14.50 to £16). Set L £16.50 (2 courses) to £18.50. Cover £1.50 **Service:** not inc **Cards:** Amex, Diners, Maestro, MasterCard, Visa **Details:** 40 seats. Vegetarian meals. No music. Air-conditioned **Tube:** Victoria

MAP 12

Olé

AR

Broadway Chambers, Fulham Broadway, SW6 1EP
Tel: (020) 7610 2010

Tapas joint serving the real thing in minimalist surroundings. The menu is a long run from cold 'frias' like marinated anchovies (£4.25), through various ensaladas to myriad hot 'calientes' ranging from chorizo cooked in white wine to solomillo de cerdo (fillet of pork with vegetables and mustard essence; £5.25). To finish, 'postres' include coconut cream caramel on spicy rice pudding (£4). Good selection of Spanish wines from £11.50. Closed Sun to Thur L.

MAP 13

One Aldwych, Axis

Aldwych, WC2B 4RH
Tel: (020)7300 0300
Website: www.onealdwych.com

Cooking 3 | Modern European | £35–£79

The 'multi-level, subterranean space' of the Axis restaurant beneath the One Aldwych Hotel reminded one visitor of the dining room of an ocean liner, perhaps one coming up for a refit. The service is friendly and attentive, and the cooking is bright, modern and not liable to startle. Crispy duck noodle salad, offering a pleasant range of tastes and textures, was 'fun to eat'; a generous starter of organic smoked salmon with a warm blini and crème fraîche has won approval, as have mains of accurately timed sea bass with egg noodles and Chinese spinach, and hay-baked leg of lamb with colcannon potatoes and carrots. Puddings may be rather less reliable, though, and wines under £20 a bottle are few, though there's a good selection by the glass. House French is £19.95.

The hotel's above-ground restaurant, Indigo, opens from breakfast to post-theatre time for dishes like smoked bacon and rosemary risotto, and grilled chicken breast with roast squash and fennel sauce.

Chef: Mark Gregory **Proprietor:** Gordon Campbell Gray **Open:** Mon to Fri L 12 to 2.45, Mon to Sat D 5.45 to 10.45 (11.30 Sat) **Closed:** 24 Dec to 6 Jan, Easter, bank hols **Meals:** alc (main courses £14 to £28). Set L £16.75 (2 courses) to £19.75, Set D 5.45 to 7.15 and 10.15 to 10.45 £16.75 to £19.75 **Service:** 12.5% (optional), card slips closed **Cards:** Amex, Delta, Diners, Maestro, MasterCard, Visa **Details:** 120 seats. Private parties: 120 main room. Vegetarian meals. Children's helpings. No cigars/pipes. Wheelchair access (also WC). Occasional music. Air-conditioned **Accommodation:** 105 rooms, all with bath/shower. TV. Phone. Room only £179 to £405 plus VAT. Rooms for disabled. Baby facilities. Swimming pool **Tube:** Covent Garden

MAP 13

1 Lombard Street

1 Lombard Street, EC3V 9AA
Tel: (020) 7929 6611
Website: www.1lombardstreet.com

Cooking 6 | Modern European | £54–£96

Right opposite the Bank of England, 1 Lombard Street has one of the most enviable locations in the City. The discreet but expensive decorative trimmings suit the well-dressed, well-heeled customers, who stop at the brasserie for comfort food like coq au vin and braised lamb shank, or continue on to the formal dining room if something more luxurious is called for. A bevy of staff helps to maintain a high degree of efficiency.

Under the guidance of Herbert Berger, the kitchen applies classic French techniques to modern ideas, and each dish has something distinctive to say for itself. The menus typically combine the heartiness of, say, rib of beef with shallot confit, claret sauce, and roast marrowbones with the sunny outlook of sea bass with fennel seeds and provençale vegetables, while the immediacy of a salad of artichokes, wild mushrooms and French beans (with pumpkin seed oil and balsamic vinegar) is balanced against a more studied feuilleté of smoked finnan haddock with quail's eggs and English mustard sauce. Above all, it is the combination of technical skill and assertive flavours that gives the cooking its imprimatur. Produce is of the highest quality, and appropriate treatment is the order of the day: cream of morels in vin jaune for a breast and fricassee of black-leg chicken, or a Pinot Noir jus and lobster essence for roast turbot. Among desserts, bitter Ecuadorean chocolate pyramid with almond milk gratinée is as modish as they come, but there may also be figs poached in mulled wine with spiced orange sorbet and chocolate sauce, or a daily soufflé. The wine list tours the world for a snappy mix of everyday and better bottles (from £17.50), with starry names and rarities for those who can afford them.

Chef: Herbert Berger **Proprietor:** Soren Jessen **Open:** Mon to Fri 12 to 2.30, 6 to 10 **Closed:** D 24 Dec, bank hols **Meals:** alc (main courses £28.50 to £29.50). Set L £39, Set D £36 **Service:** 12.5% (optional), card slips closed **Cards:** Amex, Delta, Diners, Maestro, MasterCard, Visa **Details:** 40 seats. No smoking. Wheelchair access (also WC). Occasional music. Air-conditioned **Tube:** Bank

MAP 14

One-O-One

101 Knightsbridge, SW1X 7RN
Tel: (020) 7290 7101
Website: www.oneoonerestaurant.co.uk

Cooking 4 | Seafood | £46–£127

Occupying a smart address (part of the Sheraton Park Tower Hotel) and a big chunk of expensive pavement, One-O-One is a spacious, civilised, light-coloured ground-floor dining room. Pascal Proyart hails from Brittany, specialises in fish cookery, and offers menus covering a good range of appealing-sounding dishes, with a liberal sprinkling of luxury ingredients. Accompanying pan-fried langoustine may be squid a la plancha, or braised pork belly, while red tuna carpaccio may come with pan-fried duck foie gras. One reporter enjoyed whole wild sea bass baked with a sea salt crust, or there could be roast brill served with sauce Choron, candied tomato and pont-neuf potatoes. There are a few meat dishes too, including slow-braised lamb shank, and pavé of beef béarnaise, and desserts run to warm chocolate fondant with orange mascarpone ice cream, or variations on a theme (apple walnut Tatin with crottin de Chavignol ice cream and red port caramel). Excellent staff 'have a sense of humour'. The wine list drips class and is particularly strong in France, but mark-ups are high and options severely restricted below £30.

Chef: Pascal Proyart **Proprietor:** Starwood Hotels and Resorts **Open:** all week 12 to 2.30, 7 to 10.30 **Meals:** alc (main courses £22 to £28). Set L £21 (2 courses) to £25, Set D (7 to 9 or 9.30, whole table only) £48 to £79 **Service:** not inc **Cards:** Amex, Delta, Diners, Maestro, MasterCard, Visa **Details:** 60 seats. Private parties: 100 main room, 10 to 20 private rooms. Children's helpings. Wheelchair access (also WC). Music. Air-conditioned **Accommodation:** 280 rooms, all with bath/shower. TV. Phone. Room only £299 to £3,000. Rooms for disabled. Baby facilities **Tube:** Knightsbridge

MAP 15

Orrery

55 Marylebone High Street, W1M 3AE
Tel: (020) 7616 8000
Website: www.orrery.co.uk

Cooking 6 | French | £41–£126

The area on which the Marylebone outpost of the Conran group stands was once the site of the local manor house when Marylebone was no more than a village. Henry VIII transformed it into a hunting lodge, although only the stable block survived the eighteenth-century wrecking crew. The present-day restaurant occupies a long, narrow, first-floor dining room, with an angled mirror allowing diners facing away from the windows to keep an eye on what's going on outside. André Garrett keeps things light and modern, with one eye firmly fixed on contemporary fashion. Scallops with cauliflower is a tried and true combination, the vegetable presented as beignets and purée, with slivers of sherry jelly, the modest brace of shellfish succulently wrapped in ventrêche. Main courses try out new juxtapositions, as when two fillets of John Dory come with sweetcorn ravioli and caramelised endive, along with capers and raisins, in a meaty jus, and Denham Estate venison (braised shoulder and roast saddle) with spiced pears and sauce grand veneur has been pronounced excellent. An under-concentrated red wine sauce rather let down a generous piece of good beef fillet at inspection. End on a high note with fine, ripe cheeses from Vernier, or highly accomplished desserts such as an expertly rendered, feather-light prune and Armagnac soufflé with vanilla ice cream.

The wine list is a roll-call of the finest names, with real depth throughout France and international bottles of repute that aren't often seen on these shores, such as Jean Daneel's Chenins from South Africa. Reporters' palates have consistently been satisfied, but mark-ups have raised more than eyebrows. House bottles are £15, and wines by the glass run from £3.75 to some very smart kit at £14.50.

Chef: André Garrett **Proprietor:** Conran Restaurants **Open:** all week 12 to 3, 7 to 11 (10.30 Sun) **Closed:** 24 to 26 Dec, 1 Jan, Good Fri, Aug bank hol **Meals:** alc (main courses £17.50 to £30). Set L £25 to £90 (inc wine), Set D Mon to Sat £55 to £90 (inc wine), Set D Sun £30 to £90 (inc wine). Bar menu available **Service:** 12.5% (optional), card slips closed **Cards:** Amex, Delta, Diners, Maestro, MasterCard, Visa **Details:** 75 seats. Vegetarian meals. Children's helpings. No-smoking area. Wheelchair access (also WC). No music. Air-conditioned **Tube:** Baker Street, Regent's Park

MAP 13

Ottolenghi

NEW ENTRY

287 Upper Street, N1 2TZ
Tel: (020) 7288 1454
Website: www.ottolenghi.co.uk

Cooking 2 | Global | £28–£50

At the heart of Islington, close enough to the Almeida Theatre to catch the ravenous late crowd, Ottolenghi is one of those places that has creatively redefined what we expect of eating out. Two long refectory-style tables with modern plastic chairs dominate the bright white room. In the morning, toasters are set up for self-service, lunches are served from a deli counter, and in the evening an ever-so-slightly more formal air reigns for dinner. The cooking is Middle Eastern, Southern European, North African, East Asian – that sort of thing. The dinner menu is composed of starter-sized dishes, of which three are reckoned to add up to the complete experience. Rare beef fillet with soy, garlic, chilli and ginger offers tender and tasty organic Scottish meat, and a vegetable dish of roast butternut squash with feta, nigella seeds and parsley is nicely oily, cheesy and generous. Red mullet broth contains a lot of food too, but has been a little heavy on the saffron, while braised Portobello mushrooms with leek fondue ('a rich, creamy gunge') on grilled sourdough bread brings whole new meaning to the toasted sandwich concept. A 15-minute dessert wait may be rewarded by highly accomplished apple and raspberry pan pudding. Wacky ice creams are also available: black sesame brittle, or star anise and coffee. A tiny, Italian-orientated wine list starts at £13.50. A sister establishment is at 63 Ledbury Road, W11, tel: (020) 7727 1121, but it doesn't do dinner.

Chef: James Webb **Proprietors:** Yotam Ottolenghi and Noam Bar **Open:** all week 12 to 4, 6 to 10.45 **Meals:** alc (main courses L £7.50 to £12.50, D £4.50 to £8.50) **Service:** not inc **Cards:** Delta, Maestro, MasterCard, Visa **Details:** 52 seats. 4 seats outside. Private parties: 44 main room. Vegetarian meals. No smoking. Wheelchair access (not WC). Music. Air-conditioned **Tube:** Angel, Highbury & Islington

MAP 13

Oxo Tower

Oxo Tower Wharf, Barge House Street, SE1 9PH
Tel: (020) 7803 3888

Cooking 4 | Modern British | £44–£96

At night the tower shines out like a beacon, its red-neon lettering calling the faithful to dinner. Conveyed swiftly to the eighth floor, you may feel, as did one, that you have arrived in an airport terminal building, except that the lighting is sexily muted and the pigeon's-eye view over London is a treat. The drill is simpler than you may expect, with no canapés, appetisers or pre-desserts, which means that the focus remains sharply on Jeremy Bloor's imaginative dishes. These may well take an eclectic approach, with a variety of elements appearing separately on rectangular plates. A starter might comprise salmon rillettes in a smoked salmon topcoat with a caviar-garnished leek terrine holding the line between the fish and a citrus vanilla cream, to be followed by a main course in which a fillet of wild sea bass with mash is attended by a brochette of oysters and artichoke barigoule on fennel purée. Techniques are as varied as the style mandates: a starter of lobster in fine tempura batter comes with daikon and wasabi dressing, while main-course Barbary duck has truffled cabbage purée, foie gras and apple for company. Desserts such as walnut tart with honey and whisky ice cream are the alternatives to fine British and Irish cheeses.

'House wines' means a bistro-style page listing around 40 bottles, starting at £14.50 and including some of the more affordable options from top producers like Pipers Brook and Torbreck. The bluntly named 'Big Wine List' is packed with the stuff of dreams as well as fleshing out the canny modern selection. Prices seem good value to some, over the top to others, but there's plenty of action under £25.

Chef: Jeremy Bloor **Proprietor:** Harvey Nichols **Open:** all week 12 to 3, 6 to 11.30 (10.30 Sun and bank hols) **Meals:** alc D (main courses £18 to £31). Set L £29.50 **Service:** 12.5% (optional), card slips closed **Cards:** Amex, Delta, Diners, Maestro, MasterCard, Visa **Details:** 120 seats. 80 seats outside. Private parties: 150 main room. Vegetarian meals. Wheelchair access (also WC). No music. Air-conditioned **Tube:** Blackfriars, Waterloo

MAP 13

The Painted Heron

112 Cheyne Walk, SW10 0DJ
Tel: (020) 7351 5232
Website: www.thepaintedheron.com

Cooking 3 | Modern Indian | £39–£62

A modern makeover helped to set the tone for this new-wave curry house when it opened opposite the houseboats near Battersea Bridge. The menu continues to eschew Indian dish names in favour of concise English descriptions: a typical springtime line-up might begin with conventional tandoori lamb chops with mint alongside herrings in Keralan chilli paste, while main courses maintain the eclectic momentum with, say, veal topside in a South Indian stew with spring vegetables, guinea fowl with spinach, and stir-fried cod with okra, spices and 'dry' limes. Vegetables are a bit different (English asparagus and sugar snaps in tomato chutney, for example), breads include naan with chilli and rosemary, and you could finish in style with carrot halwa in tamarind chutney pancake with rose petal sauce. The wine list is 'well chosen and good value'. There's a second branch at 205-209 Kennington Lane, SE11, tel: (020) 7793 8313. The restaurant did not return our questionnaire, so some of the information below may be out-of-date.

Chef: Yogesh Datta **Proprietor:** Charles Hill **Open:** Sun to Fri L 12.30 to 2.45, all week D 7 to 10.45 **Closed:** Dec 25 **Meals:** alc (main courses £11.50 to £18). Set L £9 to £12 **Service:** 12.5% (optional), card slips closed **Cards:** Amex, Delta, Maestro, MasterCard, Visa **Details:** 70 seats. 25 seats outside. Private parties: 30 main room. Vegetarian meals. Children's helpings. Wheelchair access (1 step; not WC). No music. Air-conditioned **Tube:** Gloucester Road

MAP 12

Parsee

34 Highgate Hill, N19 5NL
Tel: (020) 7272 9091
Website: www.theparsee.co.uk

Cooking 1 | Parsee | £36–£53

Established by Cyrus Todiwala as an informal alternative to Café Spice Namaste (see entry), this is a showcase for Parsee cooking. There's a subtlety about the cuisine which sets the place apart from most of its (Indian) rivals, with vegetable platters and grills of interesting marinated meats and fish forming the basis of starters, with Goan-style pork vindaloo, classic dhansak, and shank of lamb marinated in garlic, cumin and green chillies among main courses. Papeta purr eeda – thick slices of potato with cumin seeds, green chilli and coriander, topped with an egg – is a must-try side dish, and chapatis make a good accompaniment. Drink one of twenty decent wines costing between around £12 and £23.

Chef/Proprietor: Cyrus Todiwala **Open:** Mon to Sat D only 6 to 10.30 **Closed:** 25 Dec to 1 Jan, bank hols **Meals:** alc (main courses £11 to £13). Set D £25 **Service:** 10% (optional), card slips closed **Cards:** Amex, Delta, Diners, Maestro, MasterCard, Visa **Details:** 48 seats. Private parties: 40 main room. Vegetarian meals. No-smoking area. Wheelchair access (not WC). Music. Air-conditioned **Tube:** Archway

MAP 15

Passione

10 Charlotte Street, W1T 2LT
Tel: (020) 7636 2833
Website: www.passione.co.uk

Cooking 4 | Modern Italian | £41–£70

Before the narrow frontage a small, slightly raised terrace area flanked by potted bay trees sets the tone for this, agreeably appointed regional Italian restaurant. If the cooking style it specialises in has become increasingly familiar of late, it's worth coming to see what a southern Italian native makes of it. Some wonder whether the cooking's earthy straightforwardness quite justifies the West End prices, but Gennaro Contaldo has a sureness of touch with richer dishes that coaxes astonishing depth of flavour out of game-stuffed pasta with a winey, truffle-scented sauce, or highly salted rabbit with rosemary and garlic. Simpler domestic dishes, such as risotto with wild sorrel, or bresaola with plenty of goats' cheese, are capably rendered, and vegetarians might appreciate the main-course potato and artichoke bake. Tiramisù has proved a good choice among desserts. The Italian wine list lets one romp through Fiano and Aglianico territory, instead of sticking with Chardonnay and Merlot. Prices start at £13.50 for Sicilian house wines.

Chefs: Gennaro Contaldo and Margherita Capuozzo **Proprietors:** Gennaro Contaldo, Gennaro D'Urso and Liz Przybylski **Open:** Mon to Fri L 12.30 to 2.15, Mon to Sat D 7 to 10.15 **Meals:** alc (main courses £11.50 to £22.50) **Service:** 12.5% (optional), card slips closed **Cards:** Amex, Delta, Diners, Maestro, MasterCard, Visa **Details:** 40 seats. 6 seats outside. Private parties: 40 main room, 12 to 20 private rooms. Vegetarian meals. No pipes/cigars. Wheelchair access (not WC). No music **Tube:** Goodge Street

MAP 15

Patara

NEW ENTRY

15 Greek Street, W1D 4DP
Tel: (020) 7437 1071

Cooking 3 | Thai | £37–£60

There are branches of this Thai restaurant dotted all over the world, including Bangkok, Singapore, and a few addresses in London (see below). The Soho branch is a smart and striking venue, with good use of ambient lighting, including candles along the back wall, and Thai figurines inlaid with glass mosaic tiles. The whole effect is contemporary, not cliché. The kitchen displays a high level of ambition. Tom yum goong is a fine version of this classic soup, with tender prawns and a 'delicious, spicy broth'. Angus beef – pink in the middle – comes with a green curry sauce, and mango salad is topped with two deep-fried soft shell crabs. Pad Thai noodles are another hit, although desserts have impressed less. Service has been 'superb', and wines start at £13.50. There are other branches in South Kensington, Knightsbridge and Oxford Circus.

Proprietor: S & P Restaurants Ltd **Open:** Mon to Sat L 12.30 to 2.30, all week D 6.30 to 10.30 **Closed:** 25 Dec **Meals:** alc (main courses £13.95 to £19.95). Set L £11.95 to £14.95 **Service:** 12.5% **Cards:** Amex, Delta, Diners, Maestro, MasterCard, Visa **Details:** 110 seats. Private parties: 50 main room. Vegetarian meals. No smoking in dining room. Wheelchair access (also WC). Music. Air-conditioned **Tube:** Tottenham Court Road

MAP 15

Patterson's

4 Mill Street, W1S 2AX
Tel: (020) 7499 1308
Website: www.pattersonsrestaurant.com

Cooking 4 | Modern French | £35–£70

The low-key entrance is easy to miss, and you may find the dining room equally discreet – white walls, high-backed brown-leather dining chairs and light wood floor – but it is certainly comfortable. The short carte delivers some luxury items: soups take in cauliflower velouté with truffle oil, foie gras comes in a mosaic with chicken and ceps and also as a glaze for breast of black-leg chicken, and a set lunch menu is devoted to langoustines. Seared Atlantic salmon might come with black pudding, caramelised apple and a hollandaise emulsion, a main-course roast halibut is served with brown, red and white onions, broad beans and sauce du pain, and Parmentier of oxtail comes with roast asparagus, Parmesan, bone marrow and a beef and olive jus. Desserts are variations on popular themes: perhaps chocolate fondant with malted milk ice cream, or white grape crème brûlée with grape sorbet. French wines dominate a list that offers little under £20, although seven house wines range from £15 to £24.50.

Chefs/Proprietors: Raymond and Thomas Patterson **Open:** Mon to Fri L 12 to 3, Mon to Sat D 6 to 11 **Closed:** bank hols **Meals:** alc (main courses £13 to £17). Set L £15 (2 courses) to £22 **Service:** 12.5% (optional) **Cards:** Amex, Delta, Maestro, MasterCard, Visa **Details:** 90 seats. Private parties: 60 main room, 10 to 30 private rooms. Vegetarian meals. Children's helpings. No-smoking area. Music. Air-conditioned **Tube:** Oxford Circus

MAP 13

The Perseverance

AR

63 Lamb's Conduit Street, WC1N 3NB
Tel: (020) 7405 8278

The ground floor of this pub oozes character, with echoes of its Victorian past hanging heavily in the air. The tapas menu is a reminder that this is the 21st century. The dining room is up a narrow staircase on the first floor, a small room with just a few tables, and casement windows looking onto the street below. Here the menu might kick off with watermelon and tomato gazpacho (£5) or cockles, crab, crème fraîche and parsley risotto (£6.95/£11.50), before roasted pork belly with braised red cabbage and dauphinoise (£10.50), or roasted organic salmon with salad niçoise (£12.95). Appealing desserts include orange and vanilla rice pudding with vanilla ice cream (£5.50). Closed Sun D.

MAP 13

Pearl

252 High Holborn, WC1V 7EN
Tel: (020) 7829 7000
Website: www.pearl-restaurant.com

Cooking 5 | Modern French | £41–£97

Occupying a magnificent marble hall in the one-time Pearl Assurance building (now the Chancery Court Hotel), this is a truly glamorous backdrop for food that is improving by leaps and bounds. Jun Tanaka's cooking has come of age: he trusts his

judgement, lets ingredients speak for themselves and allows global influences to impinge freely on classic French ideas. Saucing, texture and balance are spot-on, witness a warm salad of peppered venison, red cabbage coleslaw and redcurrant jus with 'exquisite layers of flavour' or herb-crusted rack of Pyrenean lamb with a fricassee of baby Mediterranean vegetables and asparagus purée. As for fish, you might expect seared yellowfin tuna with pissaladière and tapenade dressing or line-caught sea bass en papillote with fennel and tomato confit, clam and olive broth and a salad of crisp fennel. A 'shot' glass of home-made vanilla yoghurt with strawberry granita could precede triumphant orange and almond cake with revelatory candied fennel and vanilla and mascarpone sorbet. Staff are impressively good at their job, and the wine list is a wide-ranging (but painfully priced) slate starting at £18.

Chef: Jun Tanaka **Proprietor:** Hotel Property Investors **Open:** Mon to Fri L 12 to 2.30, Mon to Sat D 6 to 10 **Closed:** Christmas to New Year, Easter, last 2 weeks Aug **Meals:** Set L £21.50 (2 courses) to £24.50, Set D £39.50 (2 courses) to £42.50 **Service:** 12.5% (optional) **Cards:** Amex, Delta, Diners, Maestro, MasterCard, Visa **Details:** 70 seats. Private parties: 6 main room, 1 to 12 private rooms. Vegetarian meals. No smoking. Wheelchair access (also WC). Music. No mobile phones. Air-conditioned **Accommodation:** 356 rooms, all with bath/shower. TV. Phone. Room only £225 to £275. Rooms for disabled. Baby facilities **Tube:** Holborn

MAP 14

Pengelley's

NEW ENTRY

164 Sloane Street, SW1X 9QB
Tel: (020) 7750 5000
Website: www.pengelleys.com

Cooking 2 | Pacific Rim | £31–£80

Opened in February 2005, this venture is the brainchild of Ian Pengelley, who lived for many years in Hong Kong and now realises a desire to bring the pick of East Asian cooking to an affluent quarter of London. A corpulent figure of the Buddha greets you on arrival at the first-floor dining room, which is a wood-dominated space with colourful panel paintings depicting sections of naked torso.

Early performances reported to us have been hit-and-miss, but there is the distinct impression that, with greater consistency, the kitchen should be able to aim high. Thick-sliced yellowtail hamachi is the hot tip among the appetisers, while commendable main courses have included well-balanced halibut with black bean and chilli, and wasabi soy-coated beef fillet served on a tiny plate garnished with salsify. Picking your way through the rest of the menu offers a choice of inventive dim sum, various tempura, sushi rolls, and curries such as lamb-shank mussaman. A confection of dark chocolate, nuts and caramel looks like a good way to finish. Service is all willingness, and the varietally identified wines have a sizeable clutch of impressive growers, but prices quickly ascend from their base of £16. A slate of fine wines encompasses Romanée-Conti, Mouton and others of the usual suspects.

Chef/Proprietor: Ian Pengelley **Open:** all week 12 to 3, 6 to 11 **Closed:** 2 weeks at Christmas **Meals:** alc (main courses £7.50 to £23). Set L £15 **Service:** 12.5% (optional), card slips closed **Cards:** Amex, Delta, Maestro, MasterCard, Visa **Details:** 80 seats. Private parties: 80 main room. Vegetarian meals. Children's helpings. No smoking. Wheelchair access (also WC). Music. Air-conditioned **Tube:** Knightsbridge, Sloane Square

MAP 12

Le Petit Max

AR

Riverside Plaza, Chatfield Road, SW11 3SE
Tel: (020) 7223 0999

Inspirational Max Renzland has moved on, and the new team are still finding their feet, but this remains a pleasant neighbourhood eating place. The location by the Thames Path is a plus-point, and the kitchen continues to serve no-nonsense French bistro food: braised Pyrenean lamb is a speciality; otherwise, the menu moves from pork and duck rillettes (£6), via grilled sea bass fillets with beurre blanc (£17.50) to tarte Tatin (£6). France dominates the short wine list (from £12.50). Closed Sun D.

MAP 14

Pétrus

The Berkeley, Wilton Place, Knightsbridge, SW1X 7RL
Tel: (020) 7235 1200
Website: www.marcuswareing.com

Cooking 8 | Modern French | £48–£123

On entering the marble lobby of the Berkeley from Wilton Place, bear right through the clubby, leather-upholstered bar and towards the restaurant's double doors. It's a large room, the colours all sober, masculine tones of mahogany brown and

Pétrus red, dominated at one end by a decorative feature that looks like a giant abacus, with glowing glass beads on silver wires. Service is both copious and flawless, matching the tenor of the approach to each table, precision-formal here, amiably chatty there.

Marcus Wareing has overseen a steady lift in the already formidable pace he had set before the move here from St James's a few years ago. Not only has the skill of the kitchen's output been elevated to a rarefied level, but the conception of dishes is constantly surprising and novel. These are not new takes on classic cuisine; they are often entirely new dishes. So much food comes your way, one way and another, what with canapés, appetisers, pre-desserts, breads and petits fours, that the unwary might easily over-face themselves. That said, the balance of the menu dishes is not in question. Take a first course of turbot ceviche, a mass of wafer-cut slices of sashimi-fresh fish, fringed about with slices of Périgord winter truffle, kitted out with a trio of cold, soft-fried quail's eggs, all adding up to a bracing, appetising, well-weighted starter. Pressed terrine of tête de veau is hugely enhanced by being served slightly warm, its underlay of pickled gherkin further deepening the rustic savour of the dish. The choice of ingredients and techniques among main courses is broad, each presenting an array of contrasting flavours. Dazzling details have included the Croesus-rich crustacean sauce anointing a raviolo of salmon and lobster, accompanying a pairing of lobster sections and lightly seared scallops, and the tawny, hazelnut veal jus poured over fried sweetbread, that latter served with a bowl of deep-fried shallot rings dusted in smoked paprika. Ripe French cheeses in tiptop condition are a possible prelude to ingenious desserts such as a mango-filled white chocolate mousse teamed with passion-fruit sorbet. Then, before coffee, the bonbon trolley glides forth.

The 'intimidating tome' of a wine list in fact caters for all tastes and budgets, from £17 house Bordeaux Blanc to a magnum of the eponymous château's 1961 at £22,500. It's expansive in France, polished in Italy and Spain, and succinct in the New World. Prices are generally high, but quality is a given wherever you look.

Chef/Proprietor: Marcus Wareing **Open:** Mon to Fri L 12 to 2.30, Mon to Sat D 6 to 11 **Closed:** 1 week at Christmas **Meals:** Set L £30 to £80, Set D £60 to £80 **Service:** not inc **Cards:** Amex, Delta, Diners, Maestro, MasterCard, Visa **Details:** 70 seats. Private parties: 70 main room, 12 to 16 private rooms. Vegetarian meals. Children's helpings. No smoking. Wheelchair access (not WC). No music. No mobile phones. Air-conditioned

MAP 13

Philpott's Mezzaluna

424 Finchley Road, NW2 2HY
Tel: (020) 7794 0455
Website: www.philpotts-mezzaluna.com

Cooking 3 | Italian | £32–£53

David Philpott and Alex Ross recently celebrated five years at Childs Hill, and their popular Italian still puts the emphasis firmly on robust bourgeois cuisine. No wonder it has a devoted local following. All-year supplies of truffles and other luxury ingredients impinge on their regularly changing, four-course menus: lobster and chickpea ravioli has been 'splendid in texture'. Simplicity rules when it comes to main courses like Philpott's signature dish of ribeye steak with crushed Gorgonzola potatoes and Barolo, braised guinea fowl with a herb- and lime-spiked jus, or grilled tuna steak with courgettes and sun-dried tomatoes. To finish, chocolate terrine with iced nutty torrone and berry salsa has proved more successful that pannacotta with rhubarb. The wine list is global, but enthusiasts should look to Italy, where there are some splendid bottles with unscary mark-ups. Prices start at £13.

Chef: David Philpott **Proprietors:** David Philpott and Alex Ross **Open:** Tue to Fri and Sun L 12 to 2.30 (3 Sun), Tue to Sun D 7 to 11 **Closed:** 25, 26 and 31 Dec **Meals:** Set L £15 (2 courses) to £19, Set D £22 (2 courses) to £30 **Service:** 12.5% (optional), card slips closed **Cards:** Delta, Maestro, MasterCard, Visa **Details:** 60 seats. 12 seats outside. Private parties: 60 main room. Vegetarian meals. Children's helpings. No cigars/pipes in dining room. Wheelchair access (not WC). Occasional music. Air-conditioned

MAP 12

Phoenix

162–164 Lower Richmond Road, SW15 1LY
Tel: (020) 8780 3131
Website: www.sonnys.co.uk

Cooking 4 | Italian | £26–£63

Phoenix is a gem of a local restaurant and, although many places aspire to Italian ways of cooking, this one really was a little piece of home transplanted to South-west London for one Italian visitor. Neatly dressed tables, a feeling of comfort and space, and on-the-ball waiting staff set the tone for such dishes as vincisgrassi molisani – a kind of lasagne – and delicate gnocchi with broad beans, or a main-course serving of rotolo di pasta filled not only with grilled pumpkin but also peppers, mushrooms, aubergine, onion and olives.

Roger Brook worked at the Walnut Tree Inn (see entry, Wales) with Franco Taruschio – who is a consultant here – and he coaxes bold flavours from his ingredients. Rack of lamb with grilled vegetables and vibrantly flavoured oils, garnished with deep-fried thyme, made an excellent main course for one reporter, who finished with a generous selection of Italian cheeses, including pecorino di fossa – a hard ewes' cheese. For those with a sweet tooth, there's vanilla pannacotta (with rhubarb), or panettone bread-and-butter pudding, as well as perfectly executed treacle tart. Espresso is excellent, and the wines from Italy, France, Spain and the New World are reasonably priced. House wine is £11.95.

Chef: Roger Brook **Proprietors:** Rebecca Mascarenhas and James Harris **Open:** Sun to Fri L 12.30 to 2.30 (3 Sun), all week D 7 to 11 (11.30 Fri and Sat, 10 Sun) **Closed:** bank hols **Meals:** alc (main courses £9.50 to £19). Set L Mon to Fri £13.50 (2 courses) to £15.50, Set L Sun £19.50, Set D Sun to Thur £15.50 (2 courses) to £17.50 **Service:** 12.5% (optional), card slips closed **Cards:** Amex, Delta, Maestro, MasterCard, Visa **Details:** 90 seats. 40 seats outside. Private parties: 60 main room. Vegetarian meals. Children's helpings. No smoking in 1 dining room. Wheelchair access (also WC). Music. Air-conditioned **Tube:** Putney Bridge

MAP 13

Phoenix Palace

3–5 Glentworth Street, NW1 5PG
Tel: (020) 7486 3515

Cooking 2 | Chinese | £25–£78

'Feels genuinely Hong Kong without showing off,' runs a report on this sprawling Chinese restaurant beneath a vast apartment block just off Baker Street. Dim sum have wowed visitors with their 'freshness and clarity': the range encompasses not only steamed crab and coriander dumplings and prawn cheung fun but also some oriental interlopers like Vietnamese spring rolls and surf clam sashimi. Stuffed courgette with black-bean sauce is a neat take on the more usual aubergines, steamed glutinous rice is a 'prime version', and it's worth checking the lunchtime one-plate dishes (morning glory with squid and noodles, for example). The full 200-dish menu leapfrogs the regions for pork trotters with vinaigrette, steamed turbot with Tientsin cabbage, and unusual vegetables like 'loganberry on pea shoot'. 'The waitresses are a delight.' House wine is £9.80.

Chef: Master Lee **Proprietor:** K. Lee **Open:** all week 12 to 11.30 **Meals:** alc (main courses £6 to £25). Set D £13.80 (2 courses) to £19.80 **Service:** 12.5%, card slips closed **Cards:** Amex, Delta, Maestro, MasterCard, Visa **Details:** 250 seats. Private parties: 270 main room, 10 to 30 private rooms. Vegetarian meals. No smoking in 1 dining room. Music. Air-conditioned **Tube:** Baker Street

MAP 15

Pied-à-Terre

34 Charlotte Street, W1T 2NH
Tel: (020) 7636 1178
Website: www.pied-a-terre.co.uk

Cooking 8 | French | £44–£107

In autumn 2004 a fire at 34 Charlotte Street wrought terrible damage on Pied-à-Terre, with water rather than flames wreaking most havoc, and initially the stability of the terrace in which it stands was put into question. Many months later the restaurant remains closed, but David Moore and Shane Osborn's restaurant is set to rise from the ashes, so to speak, before the Guide is published.

We have yet to see the results of the refurbishment, so can't comment on the new look, and Osborn has a new kitchen from which to deliver his brand of intelligent, confident cooking. We are told that the number of covers is due to be reduced slightly, and a new first-floor bar is planned. Just before the fire, a reporter began an autumn dinner with an amuse-bouche of two fine slivers of delicate, crisp pastry with smears of foie gras terrine, before a starter of three first-rate scallops with Jerusalem artichoke purée and asparagus vinaigrette, pea shoots and pea jelly. Flavours are balanced and timing just so: witness main-course venison – 'extremely tender' – on a bed of caramelised onions with creamed celeriac, a potato galette and a pear and thyme jus. Among other main courses, red mullet comes with pickled mackerel tarte fine, black olive purée and escabèche, and pan-fried veal sweetbreads with fennel salad, pickled baby carrots and carrot sauce. Desserts keep pace with a bittersweet chocolate tart with stout ice cream, or roast baby banana with praline mousse and butterscotch ice cream.

Bread is a highlight – bacon rolls, perhaps, or walnut and raisin – and coffee is 'excellent'. Service, led by David Moore, is courteous and professional. The wine list has previously inspired readers and inspectors alike, with France the clear focus, and the good news is the bulk of the wines remain undamaged. Some of the details below may change; reports, please.

Chef: Shane Osborn **Proprietors:** David Moore and Shane Osborn **Open:** Mon to Fri L 12.15 to 2.30, Mon to Sat D 6.30 to 11 **Closed:** last week Dec, first week Jan **Meals:** Set L £26.50 to £70, Set D £54.50 to £70 **Service:** 12.5% (optional), card slips closed **Cards:** Amex, Delta, Maestro, MasterCard, Visa **Details:** 45 seats. Private parties: 7 main room, 6 to 12 private rooms. Vegetarian meals. No smoking in 1 dining room. Wheelchair access (not WC). Occasional music. Air-conditioned **Tube:** Goodge Street

MAP 12

Plateau

Canada Place, Canary Wharf, E14 5ER
Tel: (020) 7715 7100
Website: www.conran.com/eat

Cooking 3 | Modern French | £40–£88

Tricky to find it may be, but this fourth-floor Conran restaurant looking over Canada Square is a striking oasis amid the copious amounts of steel and glass viewed through the floor-to-ceiling windows. It comes in two parts: on one side a bar and grill, on the other, divided by a semi-open kitchen, the smart dining room. A Mediterranean perspective is evident in pumpkin risotto with mascarpone and marjoram, and while a few luxury ingredients are perhaps to be expected – champagne in the vinaigrette for prawn salad, black truffle with the tart of fontina cheese – success does not depend on them. There are roasts of monkfish and pheasant, comfort food in the shape of fillet of lamb with belly confit and choucroute, and English-with-attitude desserts of rice pudding with exotic fruit foam mixed in with the tarte Tatin and chocolate fondant. The wines are a cosmopolitan collection of old and new styles – a fair selection at pocket-friendly prices. A dozen wines by the glass begin at £4.

Chef: Tim Tolley **Proprietor:** Conran Restaurants **Open:** Mon to Fri L 12 to 3, Mon to Sat D 6 to 10.30 **Closed:** bank hols (phone to confirm) **Meals:** alc (main courses £14.50 to £27). Set D £24.75 to £48. Bar and Grill menus available **Service:** 12.5% (optional), card slips closed **Cards:** Amex, Delta, Diners, Maestro, MasterCard, Visa **Details:** 124 seats. 28 seats outside. Private parties: 124 main room, 24 private room. Vegetarian meals. Wheelchair access (also WC). No music. Air-conditioned **Tube:** Canary Wharf

MAP 13

Le Pont de la Tour

36D Shad Thames, SE1 2YE
Tel: (020) 7403 8403
Website: www.conran.com

Cooking 3 | Modern European | £45–£108

At this vibrant South Bank Conran flagship, mirrored walls help even those not facing the windows to enjoy the jaw-dropping views over the restaurant's namesake Tower Bridge and the Thames. The terrace is the place for fair-weather al fresco dining, and there's also a more informal, bustling Bar & Grill, plus food store, wine shop and coffee kiosk. But the restaurant proper is a long low-ceilinged room with tables smartly set with white napery. There's no doubting the quality of the 'well-sourced' ingredients, with luxury produce (including oodles of crustaceans) fairly peppering a repertoire of slick, straightforward, modern cooking in a French-inspired, classically influenced style. A mille-feuille of 'very fresh' Devon crab comes with cucumber and sevruga caviar beurre blanc, then a whole Dover sole (served on the bone) comes simply garnished with watercress, or a tranche of calf's liver has pommes ecrasées and sauce normande for company. 'The star' of one reviewer's evening was a 'sharp, zingy' lemon tart with lime syrup, selected from classics like crème brûlée or petit pot au chocolat. Service, from a smart and smiling team, can occasionally miss a beat.

The impressive range of wines by the glass (£5.25 to £14.50) and in the themed 'sommelier's selection' come with detailed tasting notes. Otherwise pick from 50 pages of mostly premium bottles centred on classic French regions, but don't waste time sniffing for bargains.

Chef: James Walker **Proprietor:** Conran Restaurants **Open:** all week 12 to 3, 6 to 11 **Meals:** alc D (main courses £12.50 to £35.50). Set L £29.50. Bar/grill L menu available **Service:** 12.5% (optional), card slips closed **Cards:** Amex, Delta, Diners, Maestro, MasterCard, Visa **Details:** 100 seats. 50 seats outside. Private parties: 10 to 20 private rooms. Vegetarian meals. Children's helpings. Wheelchair access (not WC). Music **Tube:** Tower Hill, London Bridge

	This symbol means that smoking is not permitted.
	This symbol means that there are some restrictions on smoking though it may be allowed in some eating areas.

MAP 12

Popeseye

108 Blythe Road, W14 0HD
Tel: (020) 7610 4578

Cooking 1 | Steaks | £24–£83

If you like grilled steak and decent claret in unfussy surroundings, this is one of the best deals in town. There are no starters, and main dishes consist entirely of top-of-the-range, grass-fed Aberdeen Angus steaks – sirloin, fillet and the eponymous popeseye (Scots for rump) – served with chips (and salad if you fancy it). Deliveries arrive daily from the Highlands, and the meat is hung for at least a fortnight: choose any weight from a dainty 6-ouncer to a 30oz Goliath. Home-made puds and farmhouse cheeses complete the picture. The red-blooded wine list ranges from quaffable house recommendations (£11.50) up to *deuxièmes crus*. There's another branch at 277 Upper Richmond Road, SW15, tel: (020) 8788 7733.

Chef/Proprietor: Ian Hutchison **Open:** Mon to Sat D only 6.45 to 10.30 **Meals:** alc (main courses £10 to £45.50) **Service:** 12.5% (optional) **Cards:** none **Details:** 34 seats. Private parties: 34 main room. No cigars. Wheelchair access (not WC). Occasional music **Tube:** Olympia

MAP 13

Porte des Indes

AR

32 Bryanston Street W1H 7EG
Tel: (020) 7224 0055

Grandiose Indian with echoes of Bollywood and Disney World in its giant palms, cascading waterfall and paintings. Conventional dishes like spinach pakoras, crab Malabar (£8.50), tandooris and pork vindaloo (£13) share the billing with a sizeable contingent from 'Les Indes Françaises', including cassoulet de fruit de mer and magret de canard pulivaar. Finish with kulfi (£5.50) or mousse au chocolat. Extravagant thalis (from £20) are served on gold platters. Cocktails in the Jungle Bar; 100-plus global wines from £16. Closed Sat L.

This symbol means that the restaurant has elected to participate in *The Good Food Guide's* £5 voucher scheme (see 'How to Use the Guide' for details).

MAP 15

Portrait Restaurant

National Portrait Gallery, Orange Street,
St Martin's Place, WC2H 0HE
Tel: (020) 7312 2490
Website: www.searcys.co.uk

Cooking 2 | Modern British | £38–£68

'The real stimulus comes from the view towards the river and the London Eye ... worth asking for a window seat', advised a reporter who felt this L-shaped dining room's minimal decoration was down to the wealth of pictures in the National Portrait Gallery below. If food and service haven't always matched the view, the cuisine is contemporary without being too fashionable. Starters include goats' cheese fritter with marinated plum tomato salad, and Cumbrian air-dried ham accompanied by Swiss cheese and pineapple chutney. Reporters have enjoyed tagliatelle with spring vegetables, baked cod fillet with chorizo sausage and piquillo pepper broth, and shoulder of lamb with mashed potato; finish with British cheeses or straightforward sticky toffee pudding. House French is £15.

Chef: Brendan Fyldes **Proprietor:** Searcy Tansley & Co. Ltd **Open:** all week L 11.45 to 2.45 (3 Sat/Sun), Thur and Fri D 5.30 to 8.30 **Closed:** 24–26 Dec, Good Friday **Meals:** alc (main courses £12 to £24). Light L, brunch and pre-theatre (Thur and Fri 5.30 to 6.30) menus available. **Service:** 12.5% (optional), card slips closed **Cards:** Amex, Delta, Maestro, MasterCard, Visa **Details:** 120 seats. Private parties: 120 main room. Vegetarian meals. Children's helpings. No smoking in 1 dining room. Wheelchair access (also WC). Occasional music. Air-conditioned **Tube:** Leicester Square, Charing Cross

MAP 13

Potemkin

144 Clerkenwell Road, EC1R 5DP
Tel: (020) 7278 6661
Website: www.potemkin.co.uk

Cooking 3 | Russian | £24–£57

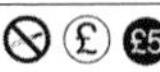

Beneath the eponymous vodka bar, this Clerkenwell basement restaurant serves a range of rustic Russian dishes and traditional staples from various parts of the former Soviet Union, in a comfortable and strikingly decorated space. It's often packed with boisterous Russian expats and locals. Pickles and bread – indispensable to the Russian table – are outstanding, and the cooking is generally of a decent standard, although occasional disappointments have been noted and there is scant regard for seasonality. Herring cake, sturgeon solyanka, and golubtsy (pork- and chicken-stuffed cabbage leaves) impressed at inspection, and beef stroganoff, pancakes, and pelmeni dumplings are reasonably authentic. Wash all this down with a few of the hundred-odd vodkas, starting with the excellent house Cristall at £2.50. A modest selection of international wines, priced from £12, is enlivened by a couple of unusual Georgian bottles.

Chef: Elena Makuseyeva **Proprietor:** Irina Omelkova **Open:** Mon to Fri L 12 to 3, Mon to Sat D 6 to 10.30 **Meals:** alc (main courses L £4.50 to £10, D £9.50 to £16). Set L £10 (2 courses) **Service:** 12.5% (optional) **Cards:** Amex, Diners, Maestro, MasterCard, Visa **Details:** 40 seats. Private parties: 40 main room. Vegetarian meals. No children under 14. No smoking. Occasional music. Air-conditioned

MAP 14

La Poule au Pot

231 Ebury Street, SW1W 8UT
Tel: (020) 7730 7763

Cooking 2 | French | £29–£66

Fashions come and go, but the irresistibly charming Poule au Pot endures, evoking the spirit of old-world Parisian brasseries. Everything about it is 'classic', from the 'truly French clutter' of bric-à-brac, birdcages ('thankfully empty') and chandeliers to cheekily Gallic waiters and the entrenched, utterly bourgeois menu. The kitchen revels in the earthy glories of tarte à l'oignon, cassoulet and (of course) the eponymous poule au pot, but it also cooks scallops with butter and lemon juice, and tackles that Roux brothers' paupiette of smoked salmon stuffed with crab. There are no surprises – though plenty of skill – when it comes to desserts such as crème brûlée, and it's worth exploring the tray of patriotically Gallic cheeses. The wine list stays loyal to the French regions, with prices from £13.

Chefs: Francisco Reis-Vilela and Krystof Golebiowski **Proprietor:** Peter Frankel **Open:** all week 12.30 to 2.30 (3.30 Sun), 7 to 11 (10 Sun) **Meals:** alc (main courses £14 to £20). Set L £15.50 (2 courses) to £17.50 **Service:** 12.5% (optional), card slips closed **Cards:** Amex, Delta, Diners, Maestro, MasterCard, Visa **Details:** 70 seats. 40 seats outside. Private parties: 20 main room, 16 to 20 private rooms. Vegetarian meals. No music. Air-conditioned **Tube:** Sloane Square

MAP 15

Providores

109 Marylebone High Street, W1U 4RX
Tel: (020) 7935 6175
Website: www.theprovidores.co.uk

Cooking 5 | Fusion | £45–£74

Peter Gordon still pretty much has the market cornered in this part of town for the kind of food that draws attention to itself through its sheer recherché novelty. 'Do nothing ordinary' was the motto suggested by one reporter. The house take on brunch might involve French toast stuffed with ricotta and cinnamon, alongside baked peaches and crisp bacon in vanilla sauce, to be followed by a glass of bitter coffee topped with an ice cream float served with hot lemon cheese puffs.

The upstairs restaurant is often found more convivial than the ground-floor Tapa Room, but both are lively, animated spaces. Tapa dishes will take a lot of perusing, as ingredients multiply almost to excess. A salad of tea-smoked salmon comes with mango, spiced candied pecans, avocado, green peppercorns and baby gem, with orange-pumpernickel labneh and Manuka honey and yuzu dressing. The main menu might take you from Thai-style seared venison salad with coriander, caramelised peanuts, lime and chilli with a black sesame rice fritter to crab-crusted halibut on roast sweet potato, shiitake and bok choy with red lentil coconut sauce and curry leaves. See a meal out with lime-leaf-poached pear with guava sorbet ripple and black cardamom syrup, or a couple of cheeses with oatcakes. Wines are a buzzy selection from New Zealand, with an efficient round-up of 'other world' offerings that also make sense with the food. House Aotea is £17.50, and 17 come by the glass.

Chefs: Peter Gordon and Anna Hansen **Proprietors:** Peter Gordon, Michael McGrath, Anna Hansen and Jeremy Leeming **Open:** all week 12 to 2.45, 6 to 10.30 (10 Sun) **Meals:** alc (main courses £16.50 to £23) **Service:** 12.5% (optional), card slips closed **Cards:** Amex, Delta, Maestro, MasterCard, Visa **Details:** 38 seats. 6 seats outside. Private parties: 38 main room. Vegetarian meals. No smoking in 1 dining room. Wheelchair access (also WC). Music. Air-conditioned **Tube:** Baker Street, Bond Street

To submit a report on any restaurant, please visit *www.which.co.uk/gfgfeedback*.

MAP 15

Quo Vadis

26–29 Dean Street, W1D 3LL
Tel: (020) 7437 9585
Website: www.whitestarline.org.uk

Cooking 4 | Italian/Mediterranean | £35–£70

Artworks made of animal skeletons may contribute to the feeling of eating in a zoological museum, but, from the moment Marco Pierre White's group acquired it in the 1990s, Quo Vadis has always aimed to make a singular impression. The menu these days is modern Italian, written in English and Italian and cooked by a new Italian chef, Fernando Coradazzi.

Ideas can be head-turning: lobster ravioli in vanilla sauce topped with segments of mandarin orange were a hit at an inspection dinner, and a similarly engaging pasta dish combined duck cappelletti with lentils and pomegranate in a dressing of thyme oil. Main courses demonstrate skilful timing of both fish and meat, and an understanding of complementary flavours, so that John Dory is intelligently partnered with artichoke confit and a pepper and Parmesan broth, while guinea fowl appears as a delicate roulade with peppers, courgettes and asparagus. Ice creams, such as a nougat version to accompany a vanilla macaroon with ultra-sweet dried fruit marmalade, are as good as they should be from an Italian chef. House vins de pays are £15, but most wines, led by Italy and France, are painfully high-priced, although 18 by the glass from £4.50 give some relief.

Chef: Fernando Coradazzi **Proprietors:** Marco Pierre White and Jimmy Lahoud **Open:** Mon to Fri L 12 to 3, Mon to Sat D 5.30 to 11.30 (10.30 bank hols) **Closed:** 25 and 26 Dec, 1 and 2 Jan **Meals:** alc (main courses £10 to £19.50). Set L £14.95 (2 courses) to £19.95, Set D 5.30 to 6.30 £14.95 (2 courses) to £19.95 **Service:** 12.5% (optional) **Cards:** Amex, Delta, Diners, Maestro, MasterCard, Visa **Details:** 90 seats. Private parties: 8 main room, 2 to 90 private rooms. No cigars. Wheelchair access (not WC). No music. Air-conditioned **Tube:** Tottenham Court Road

This symbol means that the chef has changed since last year's entry, and the Editor has judged that the change is of sufficient interest to merit the reader's attention.

MAP 14

Racine

239 Brompton Road, SW3 2EP
Tel: (020) 7584 4477

Cooking 4 | Rustic French | £30–£67

When the French president upset Anglo sensibilities in 2005 by declaring the UK to have the second-worst food in Europe he must have forgotten momentarily about restaurants like Racine. This is a defiantly, flag-wavingly French operation, 'civilised yet relaxed, casual yet serious', with food that is 'as comforting or challenging as you dare to be'.

Herring roes and sorrel on toast offered four lightly cooked pieces of roe of demonstrable freshness, the sorrel leaves mixed into a seafood bisque that soaked the toast with 'beautiful fishy flavour'. Deep-fried artichokes with chickpea purée was another well-wrought starter dish that delivered layers of deep flavour. The generous breadth of choice is such that main courses might embrace everything from a whole roast plaice with leeks and Gewürztraminer sauce, to lean venison loin in its own cooking juices with roasted chestnuts and red-cabbage pickle, to deep-fried lamb's testicles with béarnaise and watercress. Simple one-veg garnishing might put white beans with grilled poussin, or a bundle of their green cousins with rabbit and smoked bacon in mustard sauce. Desserts are straight out of the bistro cookbook, encompassing vanilla cream with chopped prunes, tarte fine aux pommes, and a crème caramel that receives rave notices. 'Charming, friendly and relaxed' service enhances the experience, which is completed by an exclusively French wine list that begins with 13 by the glass from £3.65, and ends up among the rarefied peaks of *cru classé* Bordeaux.

Chefs: Henry Harris and Chris Handley **Proprietors:** Eric Garnier, Henry Harris and James Lee **Open:** all week 12 to 3 (3.30 Sat and Sun), 6 to 10.30 (10 Sun) **Closed:** 25 Dec **Meals:** alc (main courses £12.50 to £20). Set L £15.50 (2 courses) to £17.50, Set D (6 to 7.30) £15.50 to £17.50 **Service:** 14.5% (optional), card slips closed **Cards:** Amex, Diners, Maestro, MasterCard, Visa **Details:** 65 seats. Private parties: 8 to 12 private rooms. Vegetarian meals. Children's helpings. No smoking in 1 dining room. No music. Air-conditioned **Tube:** Knightsbridge/South Kensington

MAP 12

Radha Krishna Bhavan

86 Tooting High Street, SW17 0RN
Tel: (020) 8682 0969
Website: www.mcdosa.com

Cooking 1 | South Indian | £15–£37

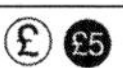

The Haridas family proudly acclaim that their neighbourhood restaurant evokes 'the soul of Kerala in the heart of Tooting'. Top billing on their menu goes to the sizeable contingent of South Indian snacks and starters, including several kinds of dosa, idli (steamed rice and black gram cakes) and puri masala (fried puffed bread with spiced potato masala). Beetroot thoran and carrot poriyal liven up the choice of vegetables, although most meat and seafood dishes are more predictable curry-house stalwarts such as chicken dopiaza and king prawn korma. Thalis are the main attraction on Sunday lunchtimes. Lassi and beer suit the food; house wine is £8.

Chefs: Mr T. Ali and Mr Yusuf **Proprietors:** T. Haridas and family **Open:** all week 12 to 3, 6 to 11 (12 Fri and Sat) **Closed:** 25 and 26 Dec **Meals:** alc (main courses £2.50 to £8) **Service:** 10% **Cards:** Amex, Delta, Diners, Maestro, MasterCard, Visa **Details:** 50 seats. Private parties: 60 main room. Vegetarian meals. Children's helpings. No-smoking area. Wheelchair access (not WC). Occasional music. Air-conditioned **Tube:** Tooting Broadway

MAP 15

Randall & Aubin

AR

14–16 Brewer Street, W1R 3FS
Tel: (020) 7287 4447

White tiles and hooks hanging from the ceiling are reminders that this trendy Soho deli-cum-canteen was once a butcher's shop. Displays of seafood fill the window and the rôtisserie turns out spit roasts (£10.50), although you can order anything from a hot chicken baguette with frites (£8) or a plate of oysters to sausages and butter-bean mash or whole grilled lobster with garlic butter (£28). Wines from £12.50. Open all week. There's a branch at 329–331 Fulham Road, SW10, tel: (020) 7823 3515.

Not a full entry but provisionally recommended (known as 'round-ups' in previous editions, these 'also recommended' establishments are now integrated throughout the book).

MAP 12

Rani

7 Long Lane, N3 2PR
Tel: (020) 8349 4386

Modish Finchley venue that has been flying the flag for Indian vegetarian food since 1984. The Pattni family produce vivid regional Gujarati dishes, and their menus cover a lot of ground, from hot and cold starters like aloo papri chat (£3.50) to slow-cooked curries, including lilotri sak (Kenyan aubergines with broad beans, peas and potatoes; £5) and chola (spiced blackeye beans). Interesting breads, home-made chutneys and traditional desserts such as shrikand (£3). Drink lassi, falooda or wine from £9.70. Open Sun L and all week D.

MAP 12

Ransome's Dock

35–37 Parkgate Road, SW11 4NP
Tel: (020) 7223 1611
Website: www.ransomesdock.co.uk

Cooking 4 | Modern European | £32–£68

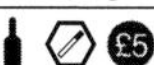

Eager reporters testify to the ongoing popularity of Ransome's Dock – a canalside restaurant equidistant between Albert and Battersea bridges – where Martin and Vanessa Lam have been plying their trade since 1992. The range is wide and the choice generous; there is certainly no question of the kitchen taking things easy. The style is broadly European, mixing 'old favourites' – Morecambe Bay potted shrimps, sirloin steak and chips with green peppercorn sauce – with lively additions. The kitchen stands by the quality of the output: a sense of balance characterises grey-legged partridge (served with sarladaise potatoes and 'a sticky, meaty port sauce'), and the cooking typically has an appealing straightforwardness, expressed, for example, in griddled saddle of wild rabbit with cabbage stuffed with bacon, mustard sauce and mashed potato. The upbeat style continues into desserts of honey and yogurt pannacotta with plums poached in a lemon thyme syrup, or try more homely warm chocolate and hazelnut pudding, or pears poached in sweet wine. The long wine list – 'as ever wonderful' – works its magic at all price levels and bottles are knowledgeably 'served just right'. Organisation is by grape variety or style, whichever suits, fronted by a range of sherries and a stimulating house selection from

£13.50. A few more than the two whites, two reds by the glass wouldn't hurt, though.

Chefs/Proprietors: Martin and Vanessa Lam **Open:** all week L 12 to 5 (3.30 Sun), Mon to Sat D 6 to 11 **Closed:** Christmas, Aug bank hol **Meals:** alc (exc Sat and Sun L; main courses £9 to £21.50). Set L £14.75 (2 courses). Brunch menu available Sat and Sun L **Service:** 12.5% (optional), card slips closed **Cards:** Amex, Delta, Diners, MasterCard, Maestro, Visa **Details:** 56 seats. 24 seats outside. Private parties: 40 main room. Car park (evenings and weekends only). Vegetarian meals. No smoking in 1 dining room. Wheelchair access (also WC). Music. No mobile phones **Tube:** Sloane Square

MAP 12

Rasa

55 Stoke Newington Church Street, N16 0AR
Tel: (020) 7249 0344
Website: www.rasarestaurants.com

Cooking 2 | Indian Vegetarian | £22–£35

Das Sreedharan has been instrumental in putting Keralan cuisine on London's gastronomic map, through his group of restaurants and 'express take-aways'. Unlike its offspring, the Stoke Newington original has a totally vegetarian menu that opens on a high note with superlative home-made pickles and chutneys plus crisp, crunchy snacks. Beyond the nibbles, there are starters like steamed idli (black lentil cakes) and deep-fried slices of plantain in batter with peanut and ginger sauce, plus several kinds of dosa and a healthy line-up of vegetable curries and specialities including stir-fried cabbage thoran, dry-roasted tindori (a kind of squash) with cashews and coconut, and a Keralan salad of guava, avocado and shallots. House wine is £9.95. See below for some of the other restaurants in the group.

Chef: Rajan Karattil **Proprietor:** Das Sreedharan **Open:** Sat and Sun L 12 to 3, all week D 6 to 10.45 (11.45 Fri/Sat) **Closed:** 24 to 26 Dec, 1 Jan **Meals:** alc (main courses £3 to £3.95). Set L and D £16 **Service:** 12.5% (optional), card slips closed **Cards:** Amex, Diners, Maestro, MasterCard, Visa **Details:** 64 seats. Private parties: 26 main room. Vegetarian meals. No smoking. Wheelchair access (not WC). No music. Air-conditioned **Tube:** Finsbury Park

 This symbol means that smoking is not permitted.

MAP 15

Rasa Samudra

5 Charlotte Street, W1T 1RE
Tel: (020) 7637 0222
Website: www.rasarestaurants.co.uk

Cooking 4 | Indian Seafood/Vegetarian | £34–£54

Decked out in the same vivid colours as its relatives (see entries above and below), Rasa Samudra makes an impact by focusing on the seafood cuisine of Kerala as well as its better-known vegetarian traditions. As ever, meals open on a high note with an assortment of poppadoms and other crunchy nibbles with blisteringly good home-made pickles and chutneys. The menu covers a lot of ground, and recent piscine stars have included kappayum meenum (kingfish in a tangy sauce served with steamed cassava) and crab varuthathu (stir-fried with ginger, curry leaves, chilli, and mustard seeds). On the vegetarian front, look for crisp cabbage thoran with lentils, and thakkali pal (a tangy curry of tomatoes and coconut milk). Incidentals such as tamarind rice and parathas have been spot-on, and desserts include tiny banana pancakes spiked with cardamom, and three kinds of home-made kulfi. House wine from £11.95.

Chef: Prasad Mahadevan **Proprietor:** Das Sreedharan **Open:** Mon to Sat L 12 to 2.30, all week D 6 to 10.30 **Closed:** 24 Dec to 2 Jan **Meals:** alc (main courses £6.50 to £13). Set L and D £22.50 to £30 **Service:** 12.5% (optional), card slips closed **Cards:** Amex, Delta, Maestro, MasterCard, Visa **Details:** 99 seats. Private parties: 30 main room, 10 to 30 private rooms. Vegetarian meals. No smoking in 1 dining room. Wheelchair access (not WC). Music. Air-conditioned **Tube:** Tottenham Court Road, Goodge Street

MAP 12

Rasa Travancore

56 Stoke Newington Church Street, N16 0NB
Tel: (020) 7249 1346

An offshoot of the original Rasa (see entry, above), on the opposite side of the road, Travancore sports the same pink fascia and clattering canteen atmosphere but takes its cue from the non-vegetarian Syrian Christian tradition of Kerala, enthusiastically mythologised throughout the menu. Seafood is much used, as in meen charu (black pomfret with fish tamarind; £6.50) or konju thenga (£7.25), a mild prawn curry. Start with sagara rasam (seafood soup) or spiced lamb in puff pastry (£4) and make room for authentic breads and tamarind rice. Drink Indian beer or wine from £9.95. Open Sun L and all week D.

MAP 15

Rasa W1

AR

6 Dering Street, W1T 1RE
Tel: (020) 7629 1346

Central London outpost of a mini group that has made its name by promoting the delights of Keralan cuisine. Like its siblings (see entries above), it is famed for its crunchy pre-meal snacks and home-made pickles as well as authentic vegetarian dishes ranging from medhu vadai dumplings (£4.25) to chilli onion rava dosai. Meat and seafood dominate most main dishes. Around 20 wines from £11.50. Closed Sun.

MAP 14

Rasoi Vineet Bhatia

10 Lincoln Street, SW3 2TS
Tel: (020) 7225 1881
Website: www.vineetbhatia.com

Cooking 5 | Modern Indian | £42–£110

Ring the doorbell of this Victorian Chelsea town house to gain admittance to Vineet Bhatia's 'rasoi' (kitchen). Inside, all is exotic and intimate: Kashmiri rugs, hand-carved religious statues and artefacts fill the space, a dazzling assortment of tribal face masks gaze down, and wedding saris are draped over the walls.

Vineet's cooking balances up-to-the-minute sophistication with a respect for deep-rooted regional traditions. This is the world of tamarind- and cumin-glazed quails, wild sea bass with asparagus and pea upma, and smoked tandoori rump of lamb. Starters tend to be clusters – perhaps a trio consisting of a crispy chicken roll filled with masala cheese and roast sesame seeds plus two kinds of tikka (one infused with saffron, the other with green herbs). Main courses veer between classic Kashmiri rogan josh prepared with lamb shank and ginger, and chilli lobster with spiced lobster jus, broccoli, sour spices and cocoa. Desserts are lavishly westernised: for example, crispy marbled chocolate and almond samosas with caramelised nuts, and silky chocolate torte with Indian tea ice cream. The upmarket wine list is replete with fine Rieslings, which may well be the best match for many of the dishes, but serious reds feature too, including a page of classic Bordeaux. There are no house wines as such, but prices start at £18 and a good number come by the glass.

Chef: Vineet Bhatia **Proprietors:** Vineet and Rashima Bhatia **Open:** Mon to Fri L 12 to 2.30, Mon to Sat D 6.30 to 10.30 **Closed:** Christmas, New Year, bank hols **Meals:** alc (main courses £18 to £34). Set L £19 (2 courses) to £24, Set D £55 to £65 **Service:** 12.5% (optional), card slips closed **Cards:** Amex, Delta, Diners, Maestro, MasterCard, Visa **Details:** 54 seats. Private parties: 24 main room, 8 to 16 private rooms. Vegetarian meals. No smoking. No music. Air-conditioned **Tube:** Sloane Square

MAP 13

Real Greek

15 Hoxton Market, N1 6HG
Tel: (020) 7739 8212
Website: www.therealgreek.com

Cooking 4 | Greek | £26–£59

(£) £5

The name is no idle boast, since this ultra-fashionable Hoxton rendezvous delivers a cutting-edge version of genuine metropolitan Greek food without clichés or compromise. Meze set the tone, moving quickly from stuffed vine leaves and tsatsiki to, say, gigandes giahni (slow-roast giant Kastorian beans with fennel, onion, tomatoes, and orange peel); authentic regional flavours also point up dishes like salt-cod casseroled with chickpeas and Santorinian capers, and duck stuffed with sage and walnuts served with Cretan gamopilafo (a 'wedding pilaff'). Steamed fish comes with pickled vegetables, milk-fed kid is casseroled and served with seasonal wild leaves and celeriac, and desserts could take in things like Greek coffee ice cream parfait, and baked manouri (a Greek ewe's milk cheese) cheesecake. Indigenous wines are imported direct from Greece, with prices starting at £12.50. Next door is Mezedopolio, a casual alternative serving meze, with the same opening hours as the restaurant.

Chefs: Theodore Kyriakou and Alisdair Fraser **Proprietor:** Clapham House Group **Open:** Mon to Sat 12 to 10.30 **Closed:** bank hols **Meals:** alc (main courses £8.50 to £17.50) **Service:** 12.5% (optional), card slips closed **Cards:** Delta, Maestro, MasterCard, Visa **Details:** 72 seats. 20 seats outside. Private parties: 80 main room, 4 to 20 private rooms. Vegetarian meals. Wheelchair access (also WC). Music **Tube:** Old Street

MAP 13

Real Greek Souvlaki and Bar

140–142 St John Street, EC1V 4UA
Tel: (020) 7253 7234
Website: www.therealgreek.co.uk

Cooking 2 | Greek | £24–£44

The streetwise younger brother of the Real Greek (see above) struts its stuff in an increasingly trendy part of town. Don't expect the sounds of rembetika (Greek urban folk music) or much in the way of Hellenic décor: instead, this 'one-off', industrial-chic venue concentrates all its energies on what one fan called 'Greek mainland taverna food with no concessions to English preconceptions'. Perch on a high stool or grab a table and enjoy seasonal variations on souvlaki with superb bread; also check out the vigorously spiced Armenian sausages and intriguing meze before finishing with ice creams, baklava or loukoumia (Greek mastic sweets from Syros). The 100 per cent Greek wine list offers palatable drinking at realistic prices from £11.75. A second branch is at Riverside House, 2A Southwark Bridge Road, SE1, tel: (020) 7620 0162.

Chef: George Logothetis **Proprietor:** Clapham House Group **Open:** Mon to Sat 12 to 11 **Closed:** 24 Dec, bank hols **Meals:** alc (main courses £6 to £8.50) **Service:** 12.5% (optional), card slips closed **Cards:** Delta, Maestro, MasterCard, Visa **Details:** 80 seats. 16 seats outside. Private parties: 80 main room, 10 to 50 private rooms. Vegetarian meals. Children's helpings. Wheelchair access (also WC). Music **Tube:** Farringdon

MAP 12

Rebato's AR

169 South Lambeth Road, SW8 1XW
Tel: (020) 7735 6388

Split personality is no problem for this Spanish old-timer. In the dimly lit dark wood and tiled front bar, graze your way through the tapas menu – albóndigas (meatballs), grilled sardines, kidneys in sherry, and octopus – or make your way to the light-filled formal dining room and feast on gazpacho (£4.75) and duck breast with olives, roast peppers and sherry (£12). Wherever you are, start with a sherry, then get stuck into the Riojas, and appreciate the cheerful, professional service and good value. Closed Sat L and all Sun.

MAP 15

Red Fort

77 Dean Street, W1D 3SH
Tel: (020) 7437 2525
Website: www.redfort.co.uk

Cooking 3 | Modern Indian | £33–£88

At this engaging and stylish West End Indian 'the whole style concept seems to merge Asian with French', and the menu aims to highlight the regional cooking of Lucknow and Hyderabad. Fish is a strong point (especially star-quality salmon tikka seared with ginger and garlic), and there are other intriguing ideas, like tarbooji (diced water melon and squid). Ingredients are generally well sourced: Welsh lamb shanks are cooked with garlic, saffron, almond and mace, although 'corn-fed' chicken has proved flavourless. Rice, breads and chutneys hit the target, and desserts are show-stoppers: fruity raspberry shrikand is a new take on a classic, and one reporter's mango kulfi was beyond compare. Set lunches are a 'fine tasting bargain'. The wine list is a class act, although prices (from £19) can seem painful towards the top end.

Chef: Iqbal Ahmed **Proprietor:** Amin Ali **Open:** Mon to Fri (exc bank hols) L 12 to 2.30, all week D 5.45 to 11.15 **Meals:** alc (main courses £12 to £29.50). Set L £12 (2 courses), pre-theatre D 5.45 to 7 £16 (2 courses) **Service:** 12.5% (optional), card slips closed **Cards:** Amex, Delta, Maestro, MasterCard, Visa **Details:** 77 seats. Vegetarian meals. No-smoking area. Wheelchair access (also WC). Music. Air-conditioned **Tube:** Tottenham Court Road

MAP 12

Redmond's

170 Upper Richmond Road West, SW14 8AW
Tel: (020) 8878 1922
Website: www.redmonds.org.uk

Cooking 5 | Modern British | £28–£55

With its low-key décor, interesting modern paintings and decently spaced tables, Redmond's presents a cool, mature setting for some attractively understated cooking. Redmond Hayward deals in simple, straightforward ideas, yet with an intelligent streak of novelty: perhaps brandade of home-salted cod with smoked salmon and a lemon dressing, or duck hors d'oeuvres – 'small but satisfying samples of smoked breast, smooth pâté, terrine of confit leg, and fried liver with a salad featuring finely diced beetroot'. Chargrilled ribeye steak is paired with garlic purée, wild mushrooms and parsley sauce, while vegetarian options are as enticing as anything else: for example, imam bayaldi served with bulgur wheat, Greek yoghurt with ginger, parsley and garlic, and tomato sauce. Classical elements figure in desserts too, as in tarte Tatin with vanilla ice cream, or chestnut and orange tart with prune and Armagnac parfait. And if there is one niggle from readers, it is that the menu doesn't change frequently enough. Wines are an engaging mix from all over, chosen with imagination and a good palate. Bottles start at £14.95, and a polished line-up of halves rounds things off. There's a sister restaurant in Chiswick; see entry for the Burlington.

Chef: Redmond Hayward **Proprietors:** Redmond and Pippa Hayward **Open:** Sun L 12 to 2.30, Mon to Sat D 6.30 (7 Fri and Sat) to 10 **Meals:** Set L £18.50 (2 courses) to £23, Set D Mon to Thur 6.30 to 7.45 £12.50 (2 courses) to £15.50, Set D Mon to Sat £27.50 (2 courses) to £32 **Service:** not inc, 10% for parties of 6 or more **Cards:** Delta, Maestro, MasterCard, Visa **Details:** 45 seats. Private parties: 45 main room. Vegetarian meals. Children's helpings. No smoking. Wheelchair access (not WC). Occasional music. Air-conditioned

MAP 13

Refettorio

Crowne Plaza – the City, 19 New Bridge Street, EC4V 6DB
Tel: (020) 7438 8052
Website: www.tableinthecity.com

NEW CHEF | Italian | £49–£102

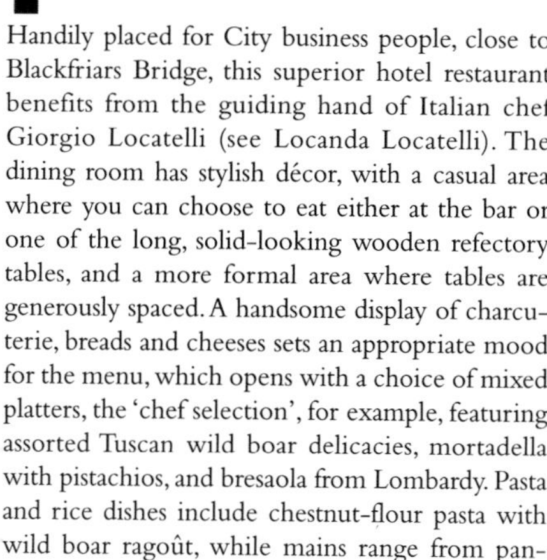

Handily placed for City business people, close to Blackfriars Bridge, this superior hotel restaurant benefits from the guiding hand of Italian chef Giorgio Locatelli (see Locanda Locatelli). The dining room has stylish décor, with a casual area where you can choose to eat either at the bar or one of the long, solid-looking wooden refectory tables, and a more formal area where tables are generously spaced. A handsome display of charcuterie, breads and cheeses sets an appropriate mood for the menu, which opens with a choice of mixed platters, the 'chef selection', for example, featuring assorted Tuscan wild boar delicacies, mortadella with pistachios, and bresaola from Lombardy. Pasta and rice dishes include chestnut-flour pasta with wild boar ragoût, while mains range from pan-fried veal T-bone to skate wing with capers and black olives. Prices on the exclusively Italian wine list start at £15. A chef change occurred as we went to press; reports, please.

Chef: Mattia Camorani **Proprietor:** Crowne Plaza Hotels **Open:** Mon to Sat L 12 to 2.30, Mon to Fri D 6.30 to 10.30 **Closed:** bank hols **Meals:** alc (main courses £16 to £22). Set L and D £40 to £65 **Service:** 12.5% (optional) **Cards:** Amex, Delta, Diners, Maestro, MasterCard, Visa **Details:** 100 seats. Private parties: 100 main room, 12 to 30 private rooms. Vegetarian meals. No cigars. Wheelchair access (also WC). Music. Air-conditioned **Accommodation:** 203 rooms, all with bath/shower. TV. Phone. Room only £109 to £305. Rooms for disabled. Baby facilities **Tube:** Blackfriars

MAP 13

Rhodes Twenty Four

Tower 42, 25 Old Broad Street, EC2N 1HQ
Tel: (020) 7877 7703
Website: www.rhodes24.co.uk

Cooking 5 | British | £42–£80

Perched high above the City, with the Swiss Re building for immediate company, this must be one of the most dramatically sited of all London restaurants. The views from both bar and restaurant are breathtaking, and quite worth all the ground-floor security hassle that such a location inevitably entails.

Gary Rhodes and head chef Adam Gray aim for an almost defiantly understated culinary style in these high-flying surroundings, with the English demotic mode that Rhodes has long advocated given a subtle haute-cuisine gloss. Welsh rarebit with smoked haddock and a tomato cake, or a Cheddar cheese omelette with added lobster, might set the ball rolling. Main courses rifle the heritage cookbook, coming up with mutton suet pudding with buttered cabbage and carrots, or roast partridge on game toast with wild mushroom gravy, but can also strike a more obviously contemporary note, as in skate wing served with langoustines, leeks and ham. A slate of sweet wines accompanies desserts like lemon meringue pie with matching sorbet and blackberries, or caramelised poached pear with chocolate nut mousse and vanilla ice cream. Immaculate service adds to the allure, and wines by the glass from £5.50 head a list full of both imagination and scary City mark-ups. As the guide went to press Gary Rhodes opened Rhodes W1 (a brasserie and separate fine dining restaurant) at the newly refurbished, and now ultra-modern, Cumberland

Hotel, Great Cumberland Place, W1, tel: (020) 7479 3838.

Chefs: Gary Rhodes and Adam Gray **Proprietor:** Restaurant Associates – Compass Group **Open:** Mon to Fri 12 to 2.30, 6 to 9 **Closed:** 25 Dec, 1 Jan, bank hols **Meals:** alc (main courses £12 to £23) **Service:** 12.5% (optional) **Cards:** Maestro, MasterCard, Visa **Details:** 76 seats. Private parties: 80 main room. Vegetarian meals. Wheelchair access (also WC). Music. Air-conditioned

MAP 12

River Café

Thames Wharf Studios, Rainville Road, W6 9HA
Tel: (020) 7386 4200
Website: www.rivercafe.co.uk

Cooking 6 | Italian | £55–£82

Fast approaching 20 years of service, Rose Gray and Ruth Rogers' new-wave Italian restaurant by the river still runs to the formula that it always did, and time hasn't dimmed its huge appeal. With television appearances and a number of cookbooks under their belts, the publicity machine occasionally hits overdrive, and yet regulars remain convinced both by the freshness and the beauteous simplicity of the food here. As the menu changes twice daily, there is also a sense of spontaneity to the cooking. It takes guts to serve a hunk of buffalo mozzarella only marinated in crème fraîche, lemon and herbs, but when you can stand by the irreproachable quality of the ingredients the result may well be found 'so simple and so incredibly delicious'. Chargrilling is well judged, either for a starter of squid with red chilli and rocket, or for main-course leg of lamb with slow-cooked fennel, spinach and salsa verde. The wood-fired oven is the centrepiece of all the endeavour here, put to telling use in roasting a whole grey partridge wrapped in pancetta, accompanied by 'smashed celeriac' and watercress and sauced with Chianti Classico.

There are readers who wonder at the cost of it all – 'my monkfish was a splendid piece of fish, beautifully moist and fresh', but the recipient questioned the £27 price tag. One can only return to the sheer quality of the materials and the unwavering concentration with which they are prepared. Pannacotta is copybook, texturally spot-on, perhaps anointed with grappa and pomegranate, the lemon tart evokes gasps of admiration, or take a glance at the listing of impeccably served Italian cheeses. Despite the time limit on tables, service is 'relaxed, assured and efficient'. House wines are just £10.50 on a list that mixes good-value and special bottles from all over Italy with aplomb, including a dozen charmers by the glass and a selection of Tuscan wines from the outstanding 1997 vintage.

Chefs: Rose Gray, Ruth Rogers and Theo Randall **Proprietors:** Rose Gray and Ruth Rogers **Open:** all week L 12.30 to 3, Mon to Sat D 7 to 9.30 **Meals:** alc (main courses £25 to £31) **Service:** 12.5% (optional), card slips closed **Cards:** Amex, Delta, Diners, Maestro, MasterCard, Visa **Details:** 105 seats. 70 seats outside. Car park (D and weekends only). Children's helpings. No smoking. Wheelchair access (also WC). No music **Tube:** Hammersmith

MAP 13

Rivington Bar and Grill

NEW ENTRY

28–30 Rivington Street, EC2A 3DZ
Tel: (020) 7729 7053
Website: www.rivingtongrill.co.uk

Cooking 3 | British | £33–£81

Set in a warren of narrow streets, this corner-sited, warehouse-style brick building hits all the right notes, blending character with modern vogue. Tall doors open on to an L-shaped bar with a sofa and easy chairs, while the dining area comes decked out with school-style wooden chairs and white-clothed tables. It's simple but stylish, like the appealing seasonal British repertoire that focuses on high-quality regional ingredients and blends classics (eggs Benedict, Barnsley lamb chop with bubble and squeak, oxtail braised in ale, and a 'refreshingly light' rhubarb cobbler with custard) with a few more modish ideas (think baby squid with a fried egg and bacon, or beetroot salad with smoked anchovies among starters). Young waiting staff are pleasant and helpful, and the compact, fashionable wine list offers a decent choice by the glass (from £3.75), with bottle prices from £14.50. The adjacent deli (eat in or take away) has a separate entrance. Note that parking in the area is restricted until 11pm.

Chef: Sami Talberg **Proprietor:** Clive Gregory **Open:** all week 12 to 3, 6.30 to 11 **Closed:** 25 and 26 Dec, 1 Jan **Meals:** alc (main courses £9.50 to £24.50). Set L and D Sun £22.50. Bar menu available **Service:** 12.5% (optional), card slips closed **Cards:** Amex, Delta, Diners, Maestro, MasterCard, Visa **Details:** 85 seats. Private parties: 10 to 25 private rooms. Vegetarian meals. Wheelchair access (not WC). Music. Air-conditioned

MAP 15

Roka

NEW ENTRY

37 Charlotte Street, W1T 1RR
Tel: (020) 7580 6464

Cooking 5 | Japanese-Plus | £30–£138

Under the same ownership as Zuma in SW7 (see entry), Roka opened in 2004 and added to the embarrassment of gastronomic riches on lucky Charlotte Street. The orientation is again new-wave Japanese with pan-Asian inflections, and one reporter could have sworn she had wandered on to the set of *Lost in Translation*, so opulent, glitzy and dazzling is the design, with a high quotient of professionally beautiful people among the clientele, and acres of steel and wood on show through the expansive glass frontage.

Gold screens seal off an inner sanctum, but dominating the whole place is the central cooking area, where smoke rises dramatically into the extractor, surrounded by ice-lined glass cases crammed with everything from sashimi to sour little umeboshi plums. The chefs are in high-collared Mao jackets with martial-arts headbands, and are under the supervision of Nicholas Watt, who isn't Japanese but knows how to call out 'Onegai shimasu!' when dishes are ready.

An inspection visit hit repeated highs. Rolled sushi of soft-shell crab, cucumber, kim-chee and chilli mayonnaise was salty, crunchy and seductive, with a hot chilli kick following each bite. Salmon cured in brown miso and baked in a hoba leaf was seasoned with yuzu, and was immaculately soft and tender. Charred skewered chicken was accompanied by baby leek, and brushed with yakitori sauce for an attractively bitter edge. Others have enjoyed 'stunningly good' tuna sashimi, delicately battered vegetable tempura, skewered field mushrooms and garlic, tender quail marinated in plum wine and red miso, and Korean-spiced lamb cutlets, the last two sizzled on the grill. Desserts include aromatic baked green tea cream, with caramelised banana and tonka-bean ice cream, as well as ginger and honey chawan mushi with nashi pear, passion fruit and banana. A switched-on, glossy little list of wines from £16 is squeezed in between the sake and cocktails.

Chef: Nicholas Watt **Proprietors:** Arjon Waney and Rainer Becker **Open:** Mon to Sat L 12 to 2.30, all week D 5.30 to 11.15 **Closed:** 24 to 26 Dec **Meals:** alc (main courses £4 to £55). Set L £50, Set D £20 (5.30 to 6.30) to £50 (all min 2). Bar menu available **Service:** 12.5% (optional) **Cards:** Amex, Diners, Maestro, MasterCard, Visa **Details:** 90 seats. 20 seats outside. Vegetarian meals. Under 12s must be accompanied by an adult at bar. No smoking. Wheelchair access (also WC). No music. Air-conditioned **Tube:** Goodge Street

MAP 14

Roussillon

16 St Barnabas Street, SW1W 8PE
Tel: (020) 7730 5550
Website: www.roussillon.co.uk

Cooking 5 | Modern French | £44–£100

A two-roomed, bow-fronted restaurant in a quiet Pimlico side street is home to this smart French restaurant. Soft, mellow colours create a soothing interior, and the unobtrusive attentions of the staff go a long way to ensuring enjoyment. Those who know their French geography will be unsurprised to learn that chef Alexis Gauthier hails from southern France, and his menus have a pleasingly seasonal bent to them, with much use of regional ingredients.

The menu structure is quite complex, with multi-course tasting options being joined by themed sections (Garden, River and Sea, Land), from which one may mix and match. Our inspector was mightily impressed by the intense, 'dreamily smooth' simplicity of cauliflower soup, and also by a preliminary dish of foie gras terrine and orange compote with artichoke brioche, the boldness of which reminds us that foie gras is more of a rustic product in southern France than it is in London restaurants. A dish of truffle risotto could have done with a couple more minutes' softening, but wild sea bass was well timed, complete with a tiny square of crisped skin and accompanied by new season's leeks. Roasted Highland venison came with a truffled purée of celeriac and a small piece of poached pear, both of which complemented the meat eloquently. Among well-reported desserts have been soufflé Grand Marnier – 'a masterpiece in miniature' – and a tube of wafer-thin pineapple wrapped around its own sorbet and garnished with lemon balm.

Praise has been heaped upon sommelier Roberto della Pietra for his surefooted guidance. From a strong base in southern France, including the dessert wines, his list turns up interesting bottles from all corners of the world and attends well to both under-£25 and sky's-the-limit budgets. A strong selection by the glass helps keep pace with the wide range of flavours in a typical meal. House Côtes du Roussillon is £13.50.

Chef: Alexis Gauthier **Proprietors:** James and Andrew Palmer, and Alexis Gauthier **Open:** Wed to Fri L 12 to 2.30, Mon to Sat D 6.30 to 11 **Closed:** Christmas, bank hols, last 2 weeks Aug **Meals:** Set L £30, Set D £45 to £65 **Service:** 12.5% (optional), card slips closed **Cards:** Amex, Delta, Maestro, MasterCard, Visa **Details:** 42 seats. Private parties: 60 main room, 4 to 28 private rooms. Vegetarian meals. No children under 12. No smoking. Wheelchair access (not WC). No music. Air-conditioned **Tube:** Sloane Square

MAPS 12,13,15

Royal China

24–26 Baker Street, W1N 7AJ
Tel: (020) 7487 4688
68 Queen's Grove, NW8 6ER
Tel: (020) 7586 4280
13 Queensway, W2 4QJ
Tel: (020) 7221 2535
30 West Ferry Circus, E14 8RR
Tel: (020) 7719 0888
Website: www.royalchinagroup.co.uk

Cooking 3 | Chinese | £38–£93

The Royal China brand straddles the capital from W1 to E14, and trademark design features including 'surreal 1970s panelled screens' define each of its four branches. Dim sum are reckoned to be among the best of their kind in the capital: char siu buns, steamed prawn and chive dumplings, and a variation involving scallops and Chinese greens have all been applauded. As ever, there are some discrepancies, with Baker Street and Queensway finding more favour than St John's Wood and Canary Wharf. The full menu embraces the Cantonese tradition, as in steamed sea bass, or crabmeat fin dumpling floating in a bowl of earthy broth 'like something from a science fiction movie', although specials pull in influences from elsewhere. Everyone agrees that vivid green gai lan (Chinese broccoli) with oyster sauce is a benchmark dish, and few would dispute the quality of the Singapore noodles. Service ranges from 'hyper-efficient' to 'genteel'. House wine is £15.

Chef: Man Yuk Leung (executive chef) **Proprietor:** Royal China Restaurant Group **Open:** all week 12 (11 Sun) to 10.45 (11.15 Fri and Sat, 9.45 Sun) **Meals:** alc (main courses £7 to £24). Set D £28 to £36 (all min 2) **Service:** 12.5% (optional) **Cards:** Amex, Delta, Maestro, MasterCard, Visa **Details:** (for Baker Street; may vary at other branches) 180 seats. Private parties: 10 to 36 private rooms. Vegetarian meals. No-smoking area. Wheelchair access (also WC). Music. Air-conditioned **Tube:** Baker Street, St John's Wood, Bayswater/Queensway, Westferry DLR

	This symbol means that the wine list is well above the average.
	This symbol means that the restaurant has a truly outstanding wine cellar.

MAP 13

RSJ

33 Coin Street, SE1 9NR
Tel: (020) 7928 4554
Website: www.rsj.uk.com

Cooking 3 | Modern French | £31–£58

RSJ continues to impress, clocking up over 25 years on the same site. The appeal is the list of wonderful Loire wines and a sensibly modern menu that pays as much attention to fish and vegetable main courses as it does to meat dishes. Warm tartlet of caramelised red onions and freshwater crayfish with a hollandaise glaze, or foie gras parfait with fig chutney and home-made soda bread, might precede crispy-skinned sea bass on a soft herb risotto with braised fennel and tarragon juices, or a roast Mediterranean vegetable lasagne. Meat main courses are rich and filling, dressing grilled fillet of beef with wild mushrooms and a rich port sauce. Look forward to versions of old favourites at the dessert stage, from sticky date pudding with treacle-toffee sauce to chocolate brownie with ice cream and hot chocolate sauce.

The wine list gives a quick intro to Loire grapes and vintages for the uninitiated before proceeding with a hand-picked selection from some fine producers, including Huet, Philippe Alliet and Yannick Amirault. Prices start at £14.95, with lots of good drinking below £20, and ten come by the glass. Sweet wines are a treat.

Chef: Ian Stabler **Proprietor:** Nigel Wilkinson **Open:** Mon to Fri L 12 to 2.30, Mon to Sat D 5.30 to 11 **Meals:** alc (main courses £13 to £18). Set L and D £15.95 (2 courses) to £17.95 **Service:** 12.5% (optional), card slips closed **Cards:** Amex, Delta, Diners, MasterCard, Maestro, Visa **Details:** 90 seats. 10 seats outside. Private parties: 12 to 45 private rooms. Vegetarian meals. Children's helpings. No-smoking area. No music. Air-conditioned **Tube:** Waterloo

MAP 15

Rules

NEW ENTRY

35 Maiden Lane, WC2E 7LB
Tel: (020) 7836 5314
Website: www.rules.co.uk

Cooking 3 | British | £45–£68

'I was sitting right underneath a huge mural of ar armoured Mrs Thatcher looking like she wa accompanying George against the dragon, observed one first-time visitor to this bastion o

patriotic Englishness. London's oldest restaurant purrs along like a Bentley, thanks to outstandingly polite staff who are helpful but never simpering. Chef David Chambers has been replaced by Richard Sawyer, although the menu is as traditional as ever: this is the world of Pimms No.1, roast grouse and lemon posset. Everything depends on first-rate supplies, whether it's sea-fresh Cuan rock oysters or roast squab with truffles, foie gras, white onions and red wine. Occasionally there are detours for, say, grilled wild sea bass with pearl barley and summer herb risotto, but it's back home for queen of puddings with apricot sauce. The conservative wine list offers fair value from £15.95.

Chef: Richard Sawyer **Proprietor:** John Mayhew **Open:** all week 12 to 11.45 (10.45 Sun) **Closed:** 24 to 27 Dec **Meals:** alc (main courses £16 to £20). Set D Mon to Thur 10 to 11.45 £18.95 (2 courses) **Service:** 12.5% (optional), card slips closed **Cards:** Amex, Delta, Diners, Maestro, MasterCard, Visa **Details:** 94 seats. Private parties: 6 main room, 10 to 20 private rooms. Vegetarian meals. Children's helpings. No smoking. Wheelchair access (not WC). No music. No mobile phones. Air-conditioned **Tube:** Covent Garden

MAP 12

Sabras

263 High Road, Willesden Green, NW10 2RX
Tel: (020) 8459 0340

Cooking 4 | Indian Vegetarian | £23–£35

After more than 30 years at the helm, Hemant Desai 'continues to reign supreme as the pre-eminent Gujarati chef in the UK'. So writes a long-time devotee of this unassuming and colourful little café by Willesden bus garage. From these unlikely surroundings the kitchen consistently delivers dishes that entirely elude grander places devoted to Indian vegetarian cooking. A lot of time and effort is involved here, witness patra (stuffed yam leaves that are rolled up and steamed, then cut into slices and fried) and specials such as potatoes cooked with green peppers, mustard seeds and ginger. Deluxe sev puris ('an explosion of taste') and fascinating regional variations on the dosa theme continue to impress, while black 'udad' dhal is in a class of its own. To finish, try creamy basudi (a cooked milk dessert pepped up with pistachios and cardamom) or 'divine' alphonso mango pulp. The wine list (from £10) is rudimentary, but Indian beers and six versions of 'soothing' lassi are the drinks of choice.

Chef: Nalinee Desai **Proprietor:** Hemant Desai **Open:** Tue to Sun D only 6.45 to 10.30 **Meals:** alc (main courses £4.50 to £7.50). Set D 6.45 to 8 £6.50 to £13.50 **Service:** 12.5%, card slips closed **Cards:** Delta, Maestro, MasterCard, Visa **Details:** 32 seats. Private parties: 36 main room. Vegetarian meals. No smoking. Wheelchair access (not WC). Music. No mobile phones **Tube:** Dollis Hill

MAP 13

St John

26 St John Street, EC1M 4AY
Tel: (020) 7251 0848
Website: www.stjohnrestaurant.com

Cooking 5 | British | £36–£63

A cavernous former warehouse has been made over to provide the functional backdrop for this singular and enthusiastically supported enterprise. The focus is earthy regional British food, laudably making full use of the animal to create dishes reminiscent of the days when the British happily sat down with a will to foods such as rolled pig spleen and bacon, or ox kidney with swede. And GFG readers and inspectors can't get enough of this sort of thing, judging by reports. A thin broth containing pig cheek and some texturally spot-on butter beans made a good lunch opener on a chilly November day. Large pies for two are generally well-reported main courses, the beef and kidney version offering substantial satisfaction, not least on account of its deeply flavourful unthickened cooking juice. Most dishes come with one vegetable – viz. tripe and fennel, or mallard and radishes – but there are side-dishes such as potatoes or 'squeakily fresh' buttered greens for those who want them. Finish with rhubarb jelly, custard tart or, if you're a bit of a fancypants, blood orange sorbet slicked with vodka.

The entirely French wine list might raise eyebrows these days – but then, what could be more British? A spare £575 will buy you a bottle of La Tâche, or you might settle for the Languedoc Syrah at £13.50.

Chefs: Fergus Henderson and Chris Gillard **Proprietors:** Fergus Henderson and Trevor Gulliver **Open:** Mon to Fri L 12 to 3, Mon to Sat D 6 to 11 **Closed:** Christmas, Easter and bank hol weekends **Meals:** alc (main courses £13.50 to £20) **Service:** not inc, 12.5% for parties of 6 or over **Cards:** Amex, Delta, Diners, Maestro, MasterCard, Visa **Details:** 100 seats. Private parties: 110 main room, 6 to 18 private rooms. Vegetarian meals. No-smoking area. No music. No mobile phones. Air-conditioned **Tube:** Farringdon

MAP 13

St John Bread & Wine

94–96 Commercial Street, E1 6LZ
Tel: (020) 7247 8724
Website: www.stjohnbreadandwine.com

Cooking 3 | British | £36–£63

A pared-down version of the Clerkenwell original (see above), this 'bakery, restaurant, bar and wine shop' deals in 'technically fantastic', no-frills food sourced mainly from small British producers. Humble ingredients like crispy pig's skin with chicory and aïoli, and smoked sprats and horseradish appear on a thrifty menu that also takes in stuffed lamb's heart and bacon, pigeon and red cabbage, and steak and kidney pie. There's no demarcation between courses, and the plates are small to encourage sharing. To finish, there may be British classics like rhubarb crumble, and spotted dick and custard, or British farmhouse cheeses. Note, however, that – such is the commitment to fresh, daily supplies – those with late evening bookings may find the already limited menu further reduced as popular dishes sell out. Wines, like the bread, are available retail; for on-sales, prices start at £15 for house vins de pays.

Chefs: Karl Goward and Justin Gellatly **Proprietors:** Fergus Henderson and Trevor Gulliver **Open:** all week noon to 10.30 Sun 12 to 4.45 **Closed:** 24 Dec to 2 Jan, bank hols **Meals:** alc (main courses £11 to £16) **Service:** not inc, 12.5% (optional) for parties of 6 or more **Cards:** Amex, Delta, Diners, Maestro, MasterCard, Visa **Details:** 60 seats. Private parties: 70 main room. Vegetarian meals. Wheelchair access (not WC). No music. Air-conditioned **Tube:** Liverpool Street

MAP 12

Salisbury Tavern

21 Sherbrooke Road, SW6 7HX
Tel: (020) 7381 4005
Website: www.thesalisbury.co.uk

Cooking 3 | Modern European | £37–£55

A smart neighbourhood pub, despite the TV screens in the bar (showing occasional big sporting events) and the, at times, smoky atmosphere. The Salisbury Tavern is in the same ownership as the Admiral Codrington (see entry), so expect food in the modern pub fashion – cosmopolitan and earthy. The less pubby dining room is the setting for crispy fried baby squid with lemon mayonnaise, roast rump of veal with wild mushroom and madeira jus, and chargrilled loin of bluefin tuna with Welsh marsh samphire. There are classics too, like potted crab or eggs Benedict to start, then fish pie or ribeye burger with a green tomato relish, while roast beef with Yorkshire pudding keeps Sunday traditional. A short list of upbeat wines are all available by the glass (from £3.30); house wine is £12.

Chef: Darius Endriukaitis **Proprietor:** Longshot plc **Open:** all week 12 to 2.30 (3.30 Sat, 4 Sun), 7 to 11 (10 Sun) **Closed:** 24 to 26 Dec **Meals:** alc (main courses £7 to £13.50). Cover 50p at D. Bar snacks available **Service:** 12.5% (optional), card slips closed **Cards:** Amex, Delta, Maestro, MasterCard, Visa **Details:** 110 seats. Private parties: 100 main room. Vegetarian meals. Children's helpings. Wheelchair access (also WC). Music. Air-conditioned **Tube:** Fulham Broadway, Parsons Green

MAP 14

Salloos

62–64 Kinnerton Street, SW1X 8ER
Tel: (020) 7235 4444
Website: www.salloos.co.uk

Cooking 3 | Pakistani | £33–£60

Tucked away in Knightsbridge, Salloos has been feeding the local community and a discerning, well-heeled crowd since 1976. Its aim has always been to serve the kind of authentic dishes that might be eaten in Pakistani homes: many recipes have been handed down through generations of the Salahuddin family and the kitchen bypasses fashion in favour of proven tradition. Chef Abdul Aziz has been at the stoves since the start and he uses the charcoal-fired tandoor to good effect for shish kebabs, chicken tikka, lamb chops and so forth, while the remainder of the refreshingly short menu is taken up with curry-house favourites (murgh korma, prawn biryani) and less familiar specialities such as haleem akbari (shredded lamb with wheatgerm and lentils). The Corney & Barrow wine list opens with house selections at £12.50.

Chef: Abdul Aziz **Proprietor:** Muhammad Salahuddin **Open:** Mon to Sat 12 to 2.15, 7 to 11 **Closed:** 25 and 26 Dec **Meals:** alc (main courses £11 to £15). Set L £16 (2 courses) to £21. Cover £1.50 **Service:** 12.5% (optional), card slips closed **Cards:** Amex, Delta, Diners, Maestro, MasterCard, Visa **Details:** 65 seats. Private parties: 65 main room. Vegetarian meals. No children under 8. No cigars/pipes. No music. Air-conditioned **Tube:** Knightsbridge

MAP 13

Salusbury

50–52 Salusbury Road, Queens Park, NW6 6NN
Tel: (020) 7328 3286
Email: info@thesalusbury.com

NEW CHEF | Italian | £29–£47

'The Salusbury Pub and Dining Room' is just that: a Kilburn watering hole equally favouring drinkers and those wanting to indulge in a spot of gastro-pub dining. New chef Germano Novati arrived in 2005, but the menu still inhabits the Italian world of octopus salad with red onion and chickpeas, pasta (pappardelle with broad-bean pesto and Parma ham), and organic corn-fed chicken breast stuffed with Taleggio and Swiss chard. Roast English asparagus with poached eggs and hollandaise flies a different flag, and desserts range from peach tarte Tatin to Tia Maria and mascarpone semi-freddo with Amaretto and chocolate sauce. Italian wines sit happily with bottles from the world's vineyards; prices start at £11.

Chef: Germano Novati **Proprietors:** Nicholas Mash and Robert Claassen **Open:** Tue to Sun L 12.30 to 3.30, all week D 7 to 10.15 (10 Sun) **Closed:** 25 and 26 Dec, 1 Jan **Meals:** alc (main courses £11 to £16.50) **Service:** 12.5% (optional) **Cards:** Delta, Maestro, MasterCard, Visa **Details:** 50 seats. 20 seats outside. Vegetarian meals. No children under 9 at D. Wheelchair access (not WC). Music **Tube:** Queens Park

MAP 15

Sardo

45 Grafton Way, W1T 5DQ
Tel: (020) 7387 2521
Website: www.sardo-restaurant.com

Cooking 4 | Sardinian | £35–£58

For seven years Romolo Mudu has sought to spread the fame of Sardinian cuisine in a place that combines elegant minimalism with flourishes of the classical. Essential simplicity, based on excellent ingredients laced with elements of gustatory surprise, characterises chef Roberto Sardu's food. Dishes such as tartare of fresh tuna with caramelised red onions and balsamic vinegar, or wild-boar prosciutto teamed with pear and pecorino cheese set tradition alongside more modern twists. In parallel, overtly regional dishes such as spaghetti bottariga and culurgiones (cheese-and-potato-filled ravioli sauced with tomato and mint) may represent the intermediate pasta course. Mains might bring herb-coated veal chop with spinach and sauté potatoes, or a risotto-like fregola with prawns, mussels and sea asparagus. Puddings are straightforwardly, typically Italian and might include tiramisù, pannacotta or mousse al caffè.

Sardinian wines, accounting for almost half the list's 80-odd bins, start at £14 and are complemented by an encouraging romp around the rest of Italy at a range of prices to satisfy both the extravagant and the more frugal. Sardo Canale (see below) is run by Signor Mudu's daughter Bianca.

Chef: Roberto Sardu **Proprietor:** Romolo Mudu **Open:** Mon to Fri L 12 to 3, Mon to Sat D 6 to 11 **Closed:** Christmas, bank hols **Meals:** alc (main courses £9 to £18) **Service:** 12.5% (optional), card slips closed **Cards:** Amex, Delta, Diners, Maestro, MasterCard, Visa **Details:** 55 seats. 9 seats outside. Private parties: 55 main room, 20 to 30 private rooms. Vegetarian meals. No smoking in 1 dining room. Wheelchair access (not WC). Music. Air-conditioned **Tube:** Warren Street

MAP 13

Sardo Canale

NEW ENTRY

42 Gloucester Avenue, NW1 8JD
Tel: (020) 7722 2800
Website: www.sardocanale.com

Cooking 4 | Sardinian | £38–£63

Related to Sardo (see entry above), Sardo Canale – on the Regent's Canal (hence the name) – has been making waves of its own since it opened in May 2004. The large dining room is divided into four eating areas (one a conservatory), and there's a courtyard for those hot summer days. Each room is different but equally stylish, with brown-painted or brick walls, cobbled or tiled floors, and an abundance of glass, mosaic inlays and contemporary lighting. It's informal, popular and high on decibels, but service is 'first-rate', and the authentic Sardinian food is sophisticated and carefully prepared from quality ingredients; daily specials take advantage of seasonal produce. Among main courses, linguine comes with a sauce of crabmeat, extra-virgin olive oil, parsley and chillies, and grilled swordfish in an orange-infused oil served with asparagus, and steak pan-fried in apple-infused vinegar accompanied by spinach and potatoes. Proceedings might open with antipasti along the lines of carpaccio or bresaola and finish with tiramisù, pannacotta, or a selection of Sardinian cheeses. Around 40 Sardinian wines are matched by a similar number from mainland Italy, with prices starting at £14.

Chefs: Roberto Sardu and Massimo Sodduù **Proprietors:** Romolo and Bianca Mudu **Open:** Tue to Sun L 12 to 3, all week D 6 to 10 **Meals:** alc (main courses £12 to £17.50). Set L £13 (2 courses). Cover £1.50 **Service:** 12.5% (optional), card slips closed **Cards:** Amex, Delta, Maestro, MasterCard, Visa **Details:** 100 seats. 25 seats outside. Private parties: 15 to 60 private rooms. Vegetarian meals. Children's helpings. No smoking in 1 dining room. Wheelchair access (also WC). Music. Air-conditioned **Tube:** Camden Town, Chalk Farm

MAP 12

Sarkhel's

199 Replingham Road, SW18 5LY
Tel: (020) 8870 1483
Website: www.sarkhels.com

Cooking 3 | Indian | £19–£48

Sarkhel's has established itself as a jewel in the environs of suburban SW18, and it's just the kind of Indian you might wish for at the end of your road. Service is well above the norm, and the menu is a fascinating jaunt around the regions of the Subcontinent, stopping off for shingara chaat (Bengali shortcrust samosas with spiced chickpeas), kolmi nu patia (Parsee-style tiger prawns with aubergines and red pumpkin), and – from Goa – galinha cafreal (chicken marinated in a green masala paste). Interesting breads include onion kulcha, while desserts are limited to payesh (Bengali rice pudding) and carrot and sweet potato halva. Express lunches, Sunday buffets and thalis are decent value. Drink lassi, beer, or wine from £10.90. A second branch is now open at 119 Upper Richmond Road West, SW14, tel: (020) 8876 6220, although at an early visit it did not match up to the original.

Chef: Udit Sarkhel **Proprietors:** Udit and Veronica Sarkhel **Open:** Tue to Sun 12 to 2.30, 6 to 10.30 (11 Fri and Sat) **Meals:** alc (main courses £7.50 to £10). Set L Tue to Sat £5 (2 courses), Set L Sun £9.95, Set D 6 to 8 £9.95 **Service:** not inc **Cards:** Maestro, MasterCard, Visa **Details:** 88 seats. Private parties: 110 main room. Vegetarian meals. No smoking in 1 dining room. Wheelchair access (also WC). Music. Air-conditioned **Tube:** Southfields

This symbol means that there are some restrictions on smoking though it may be allowed in some eating areas.

MAP 13

Savoy Grill

The Strand, WC2R 0EU
Tel: 020 7592 1600
Website: www.marcuswareing.com

Cooking 6 | Modern French-Plus | £43–£115

Grandeur often manifests itself in surreal ways. Happening in at the Savoy one Thursday evening, a reporter noticed a pianist tinkling away in the riverside restaurant all by himself, 'a vast carpeted acreage of central London with absolutely nothing going on'. It subsequently closed. There is considerably more going on in the Grill Room since the Marcus Wareing/Gordon Ramsay group took it over in 2003. The makeover feels cool and smooth, with distressed mirror-pillars helping to soften the lighting tones, and black Venetian blinds partially obscuring the view of turning taxis outside.

Josh Emett has risen with distinction to the occasion since being installed here, doing ample justice to first-class materials such as seafood and meats, and bringing a sound sense of timing to dishes that manage to retain an air of simplicity, even within the context of a seven-course tasting menu. Terrine of foie gras and smoked goose breast is appealingly paired with a salad of thin-sliced, briefly blanched charlotte potato and spring onion; spanking-fresh scallops are boldly salted and accompanied by sweet, fresh pea purée; sea bass and smoked eel turn out to be a clever combination; and rack of Cornish lamb is sleek and lean, teamed with a confit of the shoulder and some brightly flavoured celery-leaf gnocchi. Also deceptively simple was another reporter's leg of organic chicken roasted with lemon and thyme, served with parsnip cubes and mushrooms, an 'uplifting and delightful' assemblage. Enterprising desserts such as Earl Grey parfait with almond ice cream, or poached pear with prune sorbet, round things off in style, while the charming, even witty service is just as it should be at this level. The hefty wine list concentrates on prestigious French wines, with a scattering of stars from most other regions. Expect to pay £30 upwards, although there is a handful of cheaper bottles.

The Banquette is Marcus Wareing's take on an American diner. This forty-seater venue above the Grill room runs the gamut from beef fillet burger (with caramelised onion and Gruyère) to linguine with smoked salmon and asparagus.

Chef: Josh Emett **Proprietor:** Marcus Wareing and Gordon Ramsay Group **Open:** all week 12 to 3, 5.45 to 11 (Sun 12 to 4, 7 to 11) **Meals:** Set L £30 to £55, Set L Sun £18 (2 courses) to £25, Set D £55 to £65 **Service:** not inc **Cards:** Amex, Delta, Maestro, MasterCard, Visa **Details:** 100 seats. Private parties: 100 main room, 16 to 60 private rooms. Vegetarian meals. Children's helpings. No smoking. Wheelchair access (not WC). No music. Air-conditioned **Tube:** Charing Cross, Covent Garden, Embankment

MAP 13

Searcy's

Level 2, Barbican Centre, Silk Street, EC2Y 8DS
Tel: (020) 7588 3008
Website: www.barbican.org.uk

Cooking 2 | Modern British | £35–£47

The long, narrow dining room overlooking St Giles Cripplegate church from Level 2 of the Barbican is a useful adjunct to the Centre's cultural offerings. New chef Jane Collins offers a short, varied contemporary carte prepared with skill and care. An inspector commended the freshness of a tian of Devon crab with avocado and wild bay sorrel, and sea bream on a bed of ratte potatoes with Jerusalem artichoke fricassée and romescu sauce (meat-eaters might fancy braised Pyrenean lamb with coco beans, spinach and roast garlic). Poached rhubarb, biscotti and Greek yoghurt ice cream and a chocolate assiette have both impressed, and wines on a short but pricey list open at £17.50.

Chef: Jane Collins **Proprietors:** Nigel and Richard Goodhew **Open:** Mon to Fri L 12 to 2.30, Mon to Sat D 5 to 10.30 **Closed:** 25 and 26 Dec, some bank hols **Meals:** Set L £22.50 (2 courses) to £26.50, Set D £22.50 (2 courses) to £26.50. Bar snack menu available **Service:** 12.5% (optional), card slips closed **Cards:** Amex, Delta, Diners, Maestro, MasterCard, Visa **Details:** 100 seats. Private parties: 140 main room. Vegetarian meals. No children under 5. No-smoking area. Wheelchair access (also WC). Music. Air-conditioned **Tube:** Barbican, Moorgate

MAP 13

Singapore Garden

83–83A Fairfax Road, NW6 4DY
Tel: (020) 7328 5314

Cooking 2 | Singaporean | £20–£66

Singapore Garden shines like a colourful beacon in the backwaters of Swiss Cottage, and it remains the very model of a family-run neighbourhood restaurant. Classic specialities from Singapore and Malaysia form the backbone of the menu, ingredients are the real thing and flavours pack a punch. Noodles and curries are bolstered by more esoteric specials that broaden the pan-Asian theme: teochew braised pigs' trotters and spicy okra with blachan (preserved shrimp paste) rub shoulders with crispy-fried pomfret with lemon and chillies, and prawns in wasabi mayonnaise. Elsewhere, China has its say with barbecued pork and lemongrass chicken. Drink Tiger beer or tap into the 40-strong wine list, which embraces affordable bottles from £13.50 and some wallet-emptying vintage clarets.

Chef: Mrs S. Lim **Proprietors:** the Lim family **Open:** all week 12 to 2.45, 6 to 10.45 (11.15 Fri and Sat) **Closed:** 4 days at Christmas **Meals:** alc (main courses £6.50 to £32). Set L £7.50 (2 courses) to £9, Set D £22 to £35 **Service:** 12.5% (optional), card slips closed **Cards:** Amex, Delta, Diners, Maestro, MasterCard, Visa **Details:** 100 seats. 12 seats outside. Private parties: 50 main room, 6 private room. Vegetarian meals. No cigars in dining room. Music. Air-conditioned **Tube:** Swiss Cottage

MAP 15

Sketch, Gallery

NEW ENTRY

9 Conduit Street, W1S 2XG
Tel: (0870) 777 4488
Website: www.sketch.uk.com

Cooking 5 | Modern French | £43–£116

This is the place to eat more economically (if that is the word) within the Sketch phenomenon. The décor is as eye-popping as the upstairs Lecture Room and Library (see entry below), a riot of screens stuck with appliquéd stingrays, snails and sequins, sepulchrally dim angled lighting, and a backing of modern dance music. 'We don't let just anyone into Sketch, you know,' the receptionist advised our inspector when booking. You have been warned.

If you can get past all that, the simpler style of upmarket brasserie cooking the Gallery offers is the reward. Pierre Gagnaire has devised dishes that use the minimum of heavy carbohydrates and dairy fats so as to aid digestion, a considerate approach that results in dishes such as superb tempura-battered prawns with foie gras croquettes, dried vegetables and 'sketchup' sauce, a reduced tomato potion laced with spices. Meat and fish combinations being *de rigueur* now, here is an odd but contented marriage of duck magret and bluefin tuna, the latter raw and glazed in miso, the former cooked pink in an infusion of green cardamom, coriander and Szechuan pepper. Cornish Dover sole is fresh, flavourful and properly timed, with a mash of Paris mushrooms, green pepper and Indian spices supporting it well. A side order of impeccable steamed vegetables is worth the extra outlay. Dessert might come in a cocktail glass and consist of three items separated by daylight: a chocolate tuile, a quantity of ganache, and a praline. Service makes things happen in the right order, with even a visit to the lavatory, where an attendant is on hand to seal you into a large white egg, an adventure. The wine list offers very little under £40.

Chefs: Pierre Gagnaire and Grégoire Sein **Proprietors:** Mourad Mazouz and Pierre Gagnaire **Open:** Mon to Sat D only 7 to 10.30 **Closed:** Christmas, bank hols **Meals:** alc (main courses £11.50 to £36). Set D £42 (2 courses) to £45 **Service:** 12.5% (optional), card slips closed **Cards:** Amex, Delta, Diners, Maestro, MasterCard, Visa **Details:** 150 seats. Private parties: 130 main room, 24 to 74 private rooms. Vegetarian meals. Music. Air-conditioned **Tube:** Oxford Circus

MAP 15

Sketch, Lecture Room and Library

9 Conduit Street, W1S 2XG
Tel: (0870) 777 4488
Website: www.sketch.uk.com

Cooking 6 | Modern French | £56–£217

Approaching its third birthday, Sketch is settling into the London scene, although it always seems likely to remain full of surprises. The Gallery (see above) has found its feet as a (relatively!) lower-cost way in which to get the Sketch experience, while the upstairs Lecture Room and Library remains the setting for the fine dining experience, as seen through the eyes of co-owner Mourad Mazouz, executive chef Pierre Gagnaire – 'one of the most original and creative chefs on earth' – and head chef Pascal Sanchez.

The disarmingly discreet frontage does not prepare visitors for what lies within. The presence of doormen, however, might give a clue. A glimpse of a private party in one room was a window into another world for one reader, when confronted by angelic supermodel-like waitresses in diaphanous smock dresses gliding in and out bearing trays of drinks. A marble staircase leads the way into the Lecture Room and Library, two parts of the same space and providing strong visual impact. Ceilings are high, and the colours and textures unashamedly ostentatious, while tables are well spaced and smartly set.

The £35 set-price lunch is a bargain in a world where a starter of mousseline of scallops with black truffle and Limousin beef from the carte costs £59. One spring luncher began with a subtle pumpkin Chantilly 'that would not look out of place in a painting by Matisse' and went on to a main course of 'sublime' leg of lamb with roast leeks and wild mushrooms on top of a 'sensational' risotto Vialone N'ano and Parmesan mousse. Desserts arrived in three mini waves, including a classic raspberry tart with white chocolate mousse of 'outstanding quality', and quetsche (an Alsatian plum) with blackcurrant mousse and marzipan ravioli.

There is a tasting menu at £90 for six courses, and a vegetarian version for £65, alongside the carte, whose highly creative constructions might take you from foie gras with rock oysters, via Scottish blue lobster to a treatise on lemon (cream, jelly, sorbet and meringue). As one philosophical reader put it: 'not everything worked, but it's worth living for the dishes that do.' Service is mostly good-natured. The wine list sets the ball rolling at £21, but we weren't sent a copy so can't comment in depth.

Chefs: Pierre Gagnaire and Pascal Sanchez **Proprietors:** Mourad Mazouz and Pierre Gagnaire **Open:** Tue to Fri L 12 to 2.30, Tue to Sat D 7 to 10.30 **Closed:** Christmas, bank hols **Meals:** alc (main courses £35 to £59). Set L £35 to £90, Set D £65 to £90 **Service:** 12.5% (optional), card slips closed **Cards:** Amex, Delta, Diners, Maestro, MasterCard, Visa **Details:** 40 seats. Private parties: 74 main room, 37 to 130 private rooms. Vegetarian meals. No smoking in 1 dining room. Music. Air-conditioned **Tube:** Oxford Circus

MAP 13

Smiths of Smithfield, Top Floor

67–77 Charterhouse Street, EC1M 6HJ
Tel: (020) 7251 7950
Website: www.smithsofsmithfield.co.uk

Cooking 4 | Modern European | £40–£91

The long, window-lined rooftop Top Floor restaurant is the fine-dining arm at SOS – a four-floor converted warehouse complex – and eclipses the bustling bar, cocktail bar and informal Dining Room on the levels below. One attraction is its cracking City views (there's a decked terrace too), while blond-wood floors, tightly-packed tables and plain white walls add a modern, minimalist, hard edge that allows those rooftop panoramas centre stage. As the building is smack opposite

Smithfield meat market, it's no surprise that the centrepiece of the menu echoes this, with signature well-hung steaks from named farms, served grilled or fried with béarnaise, red wine butter, or creamed horseradish. But the modern-focused menu has lots more besides, from Irish rock oysters to beluga caviar, or foie gras terrine with baby globe artichokes. Mains might include well-timed fried sea bass on saffron linguine with mussels and chilli, or slices of Old Spot pork loin with young carrots, leeks, turnips and fennel, plus salsa verde. To finish, perhaps a fine Worcestershire apple and Conference pear tart with cream. Though prices are high and results sometimes inconsistent, dishes are well conceived, and produce is tiptop.

The international wine list features plenty of sturdy reds to wash down the steaks, with a good balance of affordable (if not budget) and serious bottles from £15.50 and loads by the glass.

Chef: John Torode, Tony Moyse, Ashley Shergold and Sarah Briegal **Proprietor:** John Torode **Open:** Sun to Fri L 12 to 2.30, all week D 6.30 to 10.30 **Closed:** 25 and 26 Dec, 1 Jan **Meals:** alc (not Sun L; main courses £15 to £35). Set L Sun £25 **Service:** 12.5% (optional) **Cards:** Amex, Delta, Diners, Maestro, MasterCard, Visa **Details:** 70 seats. 48 seats outside. Private parties: 100 main room. Vegetarian meals. Children's helpings. Wheelchair access (also WC). No music. Air-conditioned **Tube:** Farringdon

MAP 12

Snows on the Green

166 Shepherd's Bush Road, W6 7PB
Tel: (020) 7603 2142
Website: www.snowsonthegreen.co.uk

Cooking 4 | Modern British | £30–£56

Sebastian Snow points out that he must have had a Guide entry longer than any other chef-patron in west London. His first entry, in 1993, noted that he was 'bringing metropolitan chic to the benighted villages of Shepherd's Bush and Hammersmith', and since then he has maintained a formidably consistent standard in comfortable, high-ceilinged premises that are now done in a mixture of woodland shades. The Mediterranean explosion of the nineties still inspires menus that range from chargrilled focaccia with grilled vegetables and anchovies, and starter portions of cassoulet, via spaghettini genovese, to osso bucco with milanese risotto, or spiedini of monkfish cheeks and prawns with peperonata. Dishes impress for their freshness and the broad spectrum of technical skills applied to them, as well as for their delicate flavours. Finish with espresso crème brûlée, baked Venetian-style cheesecake with blood orange compote, or fine unpasteurised cheeses with toasted walnut bread and pickled grapes. A wide-ranging modern wine list favours the New World and keeps prices within reason, opening with French country wines at £11.95; for the curious, there are a couple from Moldova.

Chef/Proprietor: Sebastian Snow **Open:** Mon to Fri L 12 to 3, Mon to Sat D 6 to 11 **Closed:** 24 to 28 Dec, bank hols **Meals:** alc (main courses £13 to £16). Set L and D £13.50 (2 courses) to £17.50. Cover 95p **Service:** not inc, 12.5% for parties of 6 or more **Cards:** Amex, Delta, Diners, Maestro, MasterCard, Visa **Details:** 80 seats. 10 seats outside. Private parties: 28 main room, 10 to 18 private rooms. Vegetarian meals. Children's helpings. No smoking in 1 dining room. Wheelchair access (not WC). Occasional music. No mobile phones. Air-conditioned **Tube:** Hammersmith Broadway

MAP 13

The Social

AR

33 Linton Street, N1 7DU
Tel: (020) 7354 5809

Aptly named, convivial hostelry with an upstairs bar for lounging and pool, as well as a good line in food. The short menu mixes pub classics with a few more upbeat ideas: start with chicory, Stilton, pear and walnut salad (£5.50), then move on to lamb burger with aubergine and pine-nut chutney (£8.50) or smoked haddock and prawn pie with mash. Desserts could include chocolate brownie with crème fraîche. Short wine list from £13. Closed Mon to Fri L.

MAP 15

Sofra

AR

36 Tavistock Street, WC2E 7PB
Tel: (020) 7240 3773

In its twenty-fifth year, this Turkish stalwart (part of an above-average mini chain) is still chargrilling chicken, beef and lamb with skill. There's something for everyone, especially on the line-up of some 20 or so hot and cold meze (£3.50), ranging from hummus and baba ganoush (smoked aubergine) to grilled garlic sausage and börek (a filo parcel of cheese, spinach and herbs). Good value extends to main courses of grilled fillets of mackerel (£9) and mixed grill (£11). Wines from £11.95. Open all week. Other branches with the same menu are at 18 Shepherd Market, tel: (020) 7493 3320, and 1 St Christopher Place, tel: (020) 7224 4080, both in W1.

MAP 12

Sonny's

94 Church Road, SW13 0DQ
Tel: (020) 8748 0393
Website: www.sonnys.co.uk

NEW CHEF | Modern European | £27–£60

In a parade of shops at a busy Hammersmith junction, Sonny's aims to deliver brasserie cooking in an idiosyncratic setting. Internal dividing walls of opaque glass bricks, coupled with very dim lighting in the evenings, set the tone. A change of chef occurred as we went to press. David Massey's menu kicks off with ham hock terrine with home-made piccalilli, or linguine with langoustines, mussels and shellfish butter, before main courses like fillet of wild halibut with sweet potato purée, samphire and chive beurre blanc. Finish with three home-made sorbets, or a French cheese selection. Service gets rather a pasting in some reports, but was reasonably efficient at inspection. A succinct wine list begins with fifteen by the glass from £3.50 to £8.75 before two closely typed pages of contemporary stars with a dusting of classics.

Chef: David Massey **Proprietor:** Rebecca Mascarenhas and James Harris **Open:** all week L 12.30 to 2.30 (3 Sat/Sun), Mon to Sat D 7.30 to 11 **Closed:** bank hols **Meals:** alc (main courses £11 to £18). Set L Mon to Sat £13.50 (2 courses) to £16.50, Set D Mon to Thur £17.50 (2 courses) to £19.50. Café L menu available **Service:** 12.5% (optional), card slips closed **Cards:** Amex, Delta, Maestro, MasterCard, Visa **Details:** 100 seats. Private parties: 80 main room, 12 to 26 private rooms. Vegetarian meals. Children's helpings. No-smoking area. Music. Air-conditioned **Tube:** Hammersmith

MAP 13

South Restaurant

128 Curtain Road, EC2A 3AQ
Tel: (020) 7729 4452
Email: southrestaurant@aol.com

Cooking 2 | French | £24–£56

South brings a refreshing taste of Provence to Hoxton. Simple, honest French cooking – accessible to both palate and wallet – combines with a light, modern but unpretentious interior to evoke southern warmth. Plain cream walls, windows on to the street, blond-wood floorboards and trendy chairs create a sunny mood, while the open kitchen (along one side of the small room) and relaxed but attentive and polite service add further atmosphere. The daily carte delivers light, fresh, colourful, well-balanced and authentic dishes built from quality ingredients, perhaps a simple partnership of Bayonne ham and celeriac rémoulade to start, then fried fillet of wild sea bass with a mussel broth, or confit duck leg with rosemary and garlic potato purée. Desserts take in a gâteau of chocolate and nuts and a selection of French cheeses. There's a value, no-choice prix-fixe menu too, and a short, all-French wine list offers house at £12.90.

Chef: Cathy Bolton **Proprietors:** Cathy Bolton and Jonathan Mortimer **Open:** Mon to Sat 12 to 3, 6 to 10.30 **Closed:** 10 days at Christmas, bank hols **Meals:** alc (main courses £9.50 to £18). Set L and D 6 to 7.30 £12.95 **Service:** 12.5% (optional), card slips closed **Cards:** Delta, Diners, Maestro, MasterCard, Visa **Details:** 50 seats. Private parties: 50 main room. Vegetarian meals. Children's helpings. Wheelchair access (also WC). Music **Tube:** Old Street, Liverpool Street

MAP 15

Square

6–10 Bruton Street, W1J 6PU
Tel: (020) 7495 7100
Website: www.squarerestaurant.com

Cooking 8 | Modern French | £46–£139

The prime site, on a street connecting Berkeley Square and Bond Street, is London at its most comfortably well-heeled. Behind a long, frosted-glass frontage, the atmosphere inside is more laid back than at many of London's premier eateries, with parquet flooring and buff-coloured walls enlivened by some large, bright abstract paintings. Service proceeds like clockwork, drilled to almost military precision, with dishes arriving on colossal trays borne by strong-armed understrappers, who slink invisibly away when the dishes are transferred to table. Even this is not intimidating but serves to ensure a reliable pace, so that everybody feels properly attended to.

Our postbag bulges at the seams most years with overwhelmingly rapturous write-ups of Philip Howard's food. In an era when restless exploration of the outer limits of culinary possibility is the norm, the cooking here is at once gently reassuring and yet powerful in its appeal. Here is a first course comprising three plump, juicy langoustine tails, mounted on gnocchi, topped with shaved truffle actually tasting of truffle and adorned with chanterelles, shallots and spoonfuls of truffle butter sauce. Due care and attention are evident in a main course of Bresse pigeon, pink and flavourful, resting on sweet butternut squash, with a wafer-thin raviolo of wild mushrooms, chestnuts and a madeira-based demi-glace sauce, where the flavours resound in three dimensions. Other enjoyable dishes have been crab lasagne, its white and brown meat packed between loose-leafed circles of spinach pasta, accompanied by rich, basilled shellfish cappuccino, a lunch main course of plainly roast Dover sole, and the opulent desserts. These last have included well-risen prune and Armagnac soufflé with a cone of vanilla ice cream, and an assiette of chocolate that comes not just in three different colours but in three different temperatures too. And don't miss out on coffee, which comes with high-class petits fours.

Nigel Platts-Martin is 'nuts about wine', according to a reporter, and his monumental global list comes in for high praise, even from diners with a budget in the £20s rather than the £200s, who do not feel in the least slighted despite the preponderance of premium bottles. Prices start at £16, and a fabulous range by the glass broadens the scope.

Chef: Philip Howard **Proprietors:** Philip Howard and Nigel Platts-Martin **Open:** Mon to Fri L 12 to 3, all week D 6.30 to 10.45 (9.45 Sun) **Closed:** 24 to 26 Dec, L bank hols **Meals:** Set L £25 (2 courses) to £60, Set D £60 to £75 **Service:** 12.5% (optional), card slips closed **Cards:** Amex, Delta, Diners, Maestro, MasterCard, Visa **Details:** 90 seats. Private parties: 6 main room, 8 to 18 private rooms. Vegetarian meals. Children's helpings. No smoking. Wheelchair access (also WC). No music. No mobile phones. Air-conditioned **Tube:** Green Park

MAP 15

Sumosan

26 Albemarle Street, W1S 4HY
Tel: (020) 7495 5999
Website: www.sumosan.com

Cooking 4 | Modern Japanese | £34–£150

A flashy entrance marked by a blue-tinted glass step sets the tone in this unashamedly fashionable hang-out, where elegance, style and stunning presentation are part of the package. Here, everything makes a full-on visual impact. Iconic dishes from the modern Japanese repertoire such as black cod in miso and rock shrimp tempura with spicy cream sauce predictably find their way onto the menu, which takes an expansive view of things. High-quality sushi and sashimi include not only squid, scallops and sea bass, but also goose liver, Peking duck and 'T & T' (tuna and truffle rolls). Elsewhere, traditional appetisers like tuna tataki and oysters with ponzu dressing sit alongside beef tartare with nashi pear, while salads include a version with avocado, prawns, kamchatka crab and kiwi dressing. Soups, udon noodles and dishes like yellowtail teriyaki are in classic vein, but fusion rules when it comes to meat specialities such as teppanyaki duck breast with buckwheat risotto. Prices on the worldwide wine list zoom skywards from £15.

Chef: Bubker Belkhit **Proprietor:** Janina Wolkow **Open:** Mon to Fri L 12 to 2.45, all week D 6 to 11.30 (10.30 Sun) **Closed:** Dec 25 and 26, bank hols **Meals:** alc (main courses £12.50 to £55). Set L £19.50 to £45, Set D £27.50 to £65 **Service:** 12.5% (optional) **Cards:** Amex, Delta, Diners, Maestro, MasterCard, Visa **Details:** 140 seats. Private parties: 160 main room, 30 private room. Vegetarian meals. Wheelchair access (also WC). Music. Air-conditioned **Tube:** Green Park

MAP 12

Sushi-Hiro

1 Station Parade, Uxbridge Road, W5 3LD
Tel: (020) 8896 3175

Cooking 2 | Japanese | £13–£35

'Little plastic models of the food on offer' provided an authentic reminder of Tokyo for one couple who trekked out of town to this utilitarian Japanese joint. Sushi plain and simple is the deal here – no appetisers, other dishes or desserts – and you tick what you want on the menu. Organic salmon sushi has been approved, but the choice extends to sea urchin, turbot and chilli cod roe. There are also a few maki rolls, including the unusual 'futomaki' version – a large specimen with a filling of egg, prawn, cucumber, inoki mushrooms and plum. Accompanying miso soup – fleshed out with some clams in their shells – is a pleasant brew. Prices are extremely modest, but note that payment is by cash only. Drinks are limited to saké, plum wine, beers and soft options. Our questionnaire was not returned, so some of the information below may have changed.

Chef/Proprietor: H. Shimakage **Open:** Tue to Sun 11 to 1.30, 4.30 to 9 **Meals:** alc (main courses £1.50 to £9). Set L and D £5 to £14 **Service:** not inc **Cards:** none **Details:** 21 seats. Music. Air-conditioned **Tube:** Ealing Common

This symbol means that the restaurant has elected to participate in *The Good Food Guide's* £5 voucher scheme (see 'How to Use the Guide' for details).

MAP 12

Sushi-Say

33B Walm Lane, NW2 5SH
Tel: (020) 8459 2971 and 7512

Cooking 3 | Japanese | £25–£78

'Sincere hospitality' is just one of the endearing qualities of this neat-and-tidy, family-run Japanese in the outer reaches of Willesden. Mr Shimizu has been a sushi chef for some forty years and his repertoire is extensive, taking in everything from red clams and flying-fish roe to marinated mackerel with kelp. Elsewhere, earthy rusticity is the key to dishes like succulent buta kakuni (diced belly pork in a special sauce), and daily specials are well worth considering: steamed pumpkin in a 'traditional Japanese way' has passed muster, likewise hotate (perfectly deep-fried king scallops). Tempura are some of the best around, miso soup is comfortingly restorative and ice creams appear with all manner of flavourings (the sesame version is recommended). The wine list (from £10) is a modest affair; alternatively, check out the choice of sakés.

Chef: Katsuharu Shimizu **Proprietors:** Katsuharu and Yuko Shimizu **Open:** Sat and Sun L 1 to 3.15, Tue to Fri D 6.30 to 10.30, Sat D 6 to 11, Sun D 6 to 10 **Closed:** 25 and 26 Dec, 1 Jan, 1 week Aug **Meals:** alc (main courses £6.50 to £20). Set L £8.70 to £12.30 (all 1 or 2 courses), Set D £19.20 to £29.70 **Service:** not inc **Cards:** Amex, Delta, Maestro, MasterCard, Visa **Details:** 36 seats. Private parties: 20 main room. Vegetarian meals. No smoking. Wheelchair access (also WC). No music. Air-conditioned **Tube:** Willesden Green

MAP 14

Swag & Tails AR

10–11 Fairholt Street, SW7 1EG
Tel: (020) 7584 6926

Just two minutes from Harrods, this civilised little pub bills itself as a neighbourhood restaurant-cum-bar, attracting local business people and residents rather than passing trade. On the international menu, starters have included 'chandoori' chicken with cucumber salad (£7.75) and hummus, while main courses run to burger with shoestring fries (£10.25), quesadillas with guacamole, sour cream and salsa, and braised lamb shank with leek and rosemary mash (£13.75). The global wine list starts at £11.95. Closed Sat and Sun.

MAP 13

Swissôtel The Howard, Jaan

Temple Place, WC2R 2PR
Tel: (020) 7300 1700
Email: jaan.london@swissotel.com

Cooking 3 | French/S-E Asian | £62–£82

The Howard may be a 'less-than-handsome' hotel on the outside, but the plush reception area, courteous welcome, and bright, spacious, hotel-style dining room leading on to a courtyard make it an agreeable place. Styling itself 'modern French cuisine with Asian touches', the cooking runs to pan-fried veal sweetbreads coated in Japanese breadcrumbs (served with braised chicory, sautéed ceps, and sliced truffle with teriyaki and honeycomb), and nage of seafood flavoured with coriander and laksa. Results do not always match ambition (an inspection meal found the cooking uneven), but among the more successful dishes have been scallop and duck two ways – sashimi of scallop with ponzu dressing and tobiko, duck consommé, and a seared scallop atop confit of duck leg – and high-quality seared cod on brandade with vanilla-infused osso buco and a courgette flower. The wine list, mainly French, with some nods abroad, carries prices unfriendly to modest budgets. Only one bottle is under £20, and just a handful under £30.

Chef: Paul Peters **Proprietor:** Samosir Ltd **Open:** Mon to Fri L 12 to 2.30, all week D 5.45 to 10.30 **Meals:** Set L £25 (2 courses) to £41, Set D £41 to £48 **Service:** 12.5% (optional), card slips closed **Cards:** Amex, Delta, Diners, Maestro, MasterCard, Visa **Details:** 50 seats. 30 seats outside. Private parties: 100 main room. Car park. Vegetarian meals. Children's helpings. No cigars/pipes in dining room. Wheelchair access (also WC). Music. Air-conditioned **Accommodation:** 189 rooms, all with bath/shower. TV. Phone. Room only £299. Rooms for disabled. Baby facilities **Tube:** Temple

MAP 15

Tamarind

20 Queen Street, W1J 5PR
Tel: (020) 7629 3561
Website: www.tamarindrestaurant.com

Cooking 4 | Modern Indian | £34–£99

Classy transcontinental Indian food can be expected in this smartly decorated basement dining room. First, there is the output of the

tandoor, which is used creatively for 'piquant' broccoli, marinated monkfish, and mixed mushrooms with pickled onions in a curry-leaf dressing. Westernised touches occasionally raise an eyebrow (salmon and potato cakes sit on a blob of raspberry coulis), but dishes have clear flavours, and there's a 'honest feel' to the cooking. Game features in season, and the regularly changing menu might also offer lasooni macchi (sea bass on crisp spinach with a garlicky sauce) and tari ghost (slow-cooked chunks of lamb shank on the bone). Incidentals such as dhal, rice and chutneys have been applauded and, to finish, kulfi may rub shoulders with earthily flavoured beetroot halwa. Service is sharp, attentive and well paced (so the two-hour time limit on tables shouldn't pose a problem). The wine list is a lengthy international slate, with prices escalating from house selections at £16.50.

Chef: Alfred Prasad **Proprietor:** Indian Cuisine Ltd **Open:** Sun to Fri L 12 to 2.45, all week D 6 to 11.15 (10.30 Sun) **Closed:** 25 and 26 Dec, 1 Jan **Meals:** alc (main courses £13 to £22). Set L £16.95 (2 courses) to £18.95, Set D £48 to £65 **Service:** 12.5% (optional), card slips closed **Cards:** Amex, Delta, Diners, Maestro, MasterCard, Visa **Details:** 90 seats. Private parties: 90 main room. Vegetarian meals. No children under 8. Music. Air-conditioned **Tube:** Green Park

MAP 12

Tandoor

232 Kingsbury Road, NW9 0BH
Tel: (020) 8205 1450
Email: tandoorlondon@aol.com

Cooking 2 | Indian | £25–£57

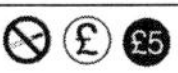

A 'brilliant Indian gastro-pub' in the outer reaches of NW9 seems an unlikely prospect, but fans are happy to make the journey because the food here is spot on. Tandooris are the stars – not only the usual tikkas and prawns, but also an Afghan variation involving cauliflower. Delicately spiced awadhi seekh kebab is a good starter, fish amritsari (deep-fried fillets) has been applauded, while authentic biryanis and even chicken tikka masala ('best I've had') continue to win votes. Among vegetables look for dum aloo kashmiri (baby potatoes simmered in yoghurt with fennel) and peas cooked to creaminess with fenugreek leaves. Romali roti remains the pick of the breads. Dishes are cooked to order, so be prepared to wait. Beer suits the food, otherwise there are everyday wines from £10.95.

Chef: Raman Sharda **Proprietor:** Nitu Khurana **Open:** all week 12 to 3, 6 to 11.30 (Fri to Sun open all day) **Meals:** alc (main courses £6 to £14.50) **Service:** not inc **Cards:** Amex, Diners, Maestro, MasterCard, Visa **Details:** 80 seats. Private parties: 100 main room, 20 to 50 private rooms. Car park. Vegetarian meals. No smoking. Wheelchair access (also WC). Music **Tube:** Kingsbury

MAP 13

Tas

33 The Cut, SE1 8LF
Tel: (020) 7928 1444
Website: www.tasrestaurant.com

Cooking 2 | Turkish | £27–£47

'Bustling, noisy and energetic' captures the mood in this upmarket Turkish brasserie, which is handily placed for the Old Vic and the Festival Hall. Authentic meze are a big draw, and the range extends from patlican salatasi (grilled aubergine purée) to fried squid with walnut sauce. Following on, a meaty mixed grill on tomato couscous has provided carnivorous satisfaction, and casseroles include tavuklu ispanak (chicken with spinach). Chocolate cake makes a suitably sweet finale. Turkish house wines are £11.95. Tas is a burgeoning chain (see the website for all the current addresses).

Chef/Proprietor: Onder Sahan **Open:** all week 12 to 11.30 **Closed:** 25 Dec **Meals:** alc (main courses £6 to £14.50). Set L and D £8.25 (2 courses) to £18.50 **Service:** 12.5%, card slips closed **Cards:** Amex, Delta, Maestro, MasterCard, Visa **Details:** 125 seats. 10 seats outside. Private parties: 55 main room. Vegetarian meals. No smoking in 1 dining room. No cigars/pipes. Wheelchair access (also WC). Occasional music. Air-conditioned **Tube:** Southwark

MAP 13

Tate Britain Restaurant

Millbank, SW1P 4RG
Tel: (020) 7887 8825
Website: www.tate.org.uk

Cooking 3 | Modern British | £40–£59

'It's a fabulous way to spend a day – strolling in the galleries then lunching in this heavenly place,' enthuses a reporter. The basement restaurant's murals attract almost as many comments as its food – which is not to disparage the well-sourced and

highly seasonal fare. A finnan haddock and colcannon cake has pleased, served with a duck's egg and grain mustard hollandaise, while roast Loch Duart salmon might come with a lemon and herb risotto and prawn bisque. Start with an 'exquisite' tartlet of lambs' sweetbreads with beans and girolles, followed by thyme-roast chicken breast accompanied by salsify, chestnuts and 'excellent' gravy. Fittingly, perhaps, the apples in one diner's tarte Tatin were of an old English 'heritage' variety.

The wine list itself is a powerful draw – Eurocentric, for sure, but with ample scope for New World wine aficionados. Several reporters have vowed a return visit to explore its pages more fully. One was enraptured with a JJ Prum 2000 Wehlener Sonnehuhr Kabinett, 'especially at the bargain price of £13 for a half-bottle'.

Chef: Andy Barber **Proprietor:** Tate Catering **Open:** all week L only 11.30 to 3, plus D first Fri of month 6.45 to 8.45 **Closed:** 24 to 26 Dec **Meals:** alc (main courses) £14.50 to £17.50) **Service:** 12.5% (optional), card slips closed **Cards:** Amex, Delta, Diners, Maestro, MasterCard, Visa **Details:** 90 seats. 20 seats outside. Vegetarian meals. Children's helpings. No smoking. Wheelchair access (also WC). No music. Air-conditioned **Tube:** Pimlico

MAP 13

Tentazioni

2 Mill Street, SE1 2BD
Tel: (020) 7237 1100
Website: www.tentazioni.co.uk

Cooking 3 | Modern Italian | £41–£61

Round the corner from the riverfront and lively Butler's Wharf, tucked away in an alleyway amid the old stevedore warehouses, this jolly, very friendly Italian has a strong local following. The long, narrow dining room, with tables ranked either side of the main gangway, has 'an overall arty red effect' and walls hung with modern artworks on the theme of the restaurant's name (which translates as 'temptation'). A 'truly delicious' basket of breads delivers just such enticement from the off and heightens anticipation, while the main repertoire offers a contemporary take on traditional Italian cuisine. Think thyme-seasoned pork fillet with a pea sauce, prawns in black ravioli and cured wild boar ham, for instance, or perhaps a martini tiramisù. There's also a five-course *degustazione* option, a vegetarian offering, and, recommended by one reporter, a monthly-changing set three-course 'traditional menu' that showcases the cooking of one region: the Lombardy menu, for example, delivering fritters of buckwheat flour with Bitto cheese, juniper-flavoured venison navarin with spätzli, and warm pear and ricotta strudel. Prices on the short but appealingly patriotic all-Italian wine list open at £15.

Chef: Riccardo Giacomini **Proprietors:** Anna Perra and Riccardo Giacomini **Open:** Tue to Fri L 12 to 3, Mon to Sat D 6.30 to 10.45 **Closed:** 24 Dec to 2 Jan **Meals:** alc (main courses £17 to £19). Set L and D £28 to £38 **Service:** 12.5%, card slips closed **Cards:** Amex, Delta, Maestro, MasterCard, Visa **Details:** 60 seats. Private parties: 40 main room, 10 to 25 private rooms. Vegetarian meals. No-smoking area. Wheelchair access (not WC). Music **Tube:** London Bridge

MAP 12

Thai Bistro

AR

99 Chiswick High Road, W4 2ED
Tel: (020) 8995 5774

Friendly service and good cooking are the watchwords at this small, informal and long-running Chiswick restaurant. For one satisfied customer, papaya salad (£6) was 'particularly good', and spicy prawns (£7) are carefully cooked with a coconut-influenced curry sauce. Hot-and-sour prawns with lemongrass soup (£5) and pad thai noodles also get the thumbs-up. The short wine list suits the style of the food, with prices from £11.50. Closed Tue L and Thur L.

MAP 12

Thai Garden

AR

249 Globe Road, E2 0JD
Tel: (020) 8981 5748

Seafood and vegetarian specialities are the twin attractions at this functional Thai café/restaurant that now has doors opening on to the street in fine weather. Prawn satay (with wholemeal bread, peanut sauce and pickle; £6), and fried pomfret with red curry sauce (£8) share the bill with deep-fried yellow bean curd with hot-and-sour sauce, and pahd ma kua (fried aubergine with chilli, basil and black-bean sauce). Genuine flavours, bargain-basement prices. Drink beer, tea or house wine (£8.50). Closed Sat L and Sun L.

AR	Not a full entry but provisionally recommended (known as 'round-ups' in previous editions, these 'also recommended' establishments are now integrated throughout the book).

MAP 13

Timo

343 Kensington High Street, W8 6NW
Tel: (020) 7603 3888

Cooking 3 | Italian | £35–£66

'The chance to visit a good Italian restaurant is something we in the provinces generally miss out on unless we make it to the capital' observed one who sought out Timo and was not disappointed. The buzzy, convivial ambience generates the perfect atmosphere for the contemporary Italian cooking. A concise set-price menu lists four courses, with pasta for the second, and juxtaposes classics like vitello tonnato with trendier offerings including squid with baby spinach and paprika mayo. Home-made tortelloni with red mullet and crispy artichoke sauce could follow, then roast quail with thyme sauce and Colfiorito lentils. Service is good, but 'at times almost over-attentive'. The all-Italian wine list begins at £15, but prices climb steeply thereafter; around ten, in a variety of styles, come by the glass from £4.

Chefs: Samuele Pacini and Marco Squillace **Proprietor:** Piero Amodio **Open:** all week 12 to 2.30, 7 to 11 **Closed:** 23 Dec to 5 Jan, 14 to 16 April **Meals:** Set L £18.50 (2 courses) to £24.50, Set D £24.50 (2 courses) to £32.50 **Service:** 12.5% (optional), card slips closed **Cards:** Amex, Delta, Maestro, MasterCard, Visa **Details:** 58 seats. Private parties: 12 to 21 private rooms. Vegetarian meals. Occasional music. Air-conditioned **Tube:** High Street Kensington

MAP 15

Tokyo Diner

AR

2 Newport Place, WC2H 7JJ
Tel: (020) 7287 8777

This corner-sited, Soho-based, Tokyo-inspired eating house offers good value throughout the day and late into the night. Basic Japanese-style curries, bento boxes comprising rice, sunomono, salmon sashimi, pickles and a main item such as chicken teriyaki (£11.50), and single-course 'donburi' boxes. Lunch specials are served until 6.30pm, and there's a short, easy-on-the-pocket midnight menu served from 11.30pm. No booking, no tipping, and house wine is £6.90. Open all week noon to midnight.

MAP 14

Tom Aikens

43 Elystan Street, SW3 3NT
Tel: (020) 7584 2003
Website: www.tomaikens.co.uk

Cooking 8 | Modern French | £42–£112

The volume of correspondence the Guide has again received for Tom Aikens's acclaimed Chelsea restaurant suggests that this is one of the most admired of London's handful of top kitchens. The superlatives flow forth: 'simply one of the finest lunches any of us have had', 'my best meal ever'. It's an understated setting, black-fronted corner premises on a largely residential side street, the inside screened from view by dark wooden blinds. The interior has a Japanese feel, with black paintwork, a dark wooden floor, and louvred screens randomly breaking up the space. There are mixed accounts of service, which can struggle with its English, but the tone is generally one of courteous professionalism.

In keeping with the minimal surroundings, the menus are written in Terse, that contemporary lingua franca of ambitious kitchens. Each dish is noted by its headline protein – PHEASANT, for example – above an explanatory subtitle ('boudin of pheasant and lentils with truffle, Sauternes foam' in that instance). There is a clearly personal style in the food too, with notable favouring of certain ingredients and techniques. Boudins and jellies loom large, as do purées and little pasta constructions, while an entire new culinary vocabulary has been coaxed out of the humble lemon. Presentations have readers reaching for aesthetic comparisons: a study in peas that involves whole pods, shoots, a minted mousse and a lake of soup (as well as a couple of slices of rabbit boudin), distantly suggesting an Arcimboldo composition, while Pollock seems the reference point for battered snails with chervil mousse, sorrel and roast leeks. There are luxuries here too, of course – foie gras crops up reliably throughout the menu – but what fascinates more is the degree of depth evoked from more everyday ingredients, such as carrots or beetroot.

Main courses get even cleverer: thick slices of roast rib of piglet are exactly matched for texture as well as flavour with various presentations of squid, the batter on one whole creature matching the sage-scented crackling of the meat. Another 'arrestingly presented' dish teams one large slice of roast lamb with its sweetbreads, black olive mash, figs and goats' cheese, everything pulling together in harmony. Occasionally, impact is lessened, as when fillets of John Dory appear submerged in a soup plate of creamy sauce with celeriac and a foie gras boudin, but then desserts turn up to astonish and delight. Coffee is the theme of a plate containing a nutty cake, mousse and parfait, while a study in lemon takes in mousse, sorbet, pannacotta and an exquisite rice pudding, the whole 'carpet-bombed' with tongue-tingling lemon intensity. For the less sweet (and sour) of tooth, the cheese trolley of largely French items is not only utterly superb but is served with consummately knowledgeable aplomb, 'the best cheese service I have ever encountered in this country'.

The assured wine list continues to grow, with southern hemisphere stars such as Cullen's Diana Madeleine Cabernet/Merlot (£75) measuring up to the best from Europe. Prices are undeniably high, but the few wines below £25 (try southern France or South Africa) are worthwhile options – and hats off to a sommelier who can point diners to a better and cheaper bottle than their first choice. Thirty wines are promised by the glass.

Chef/Proprietor: Tom Aikens **Open:** Mon to Fri 12 to 2.30, 7 to 11 **Closed:** Christmas and New Year, last 2 weeks Aug, bank hols **Meals:** Set L £29, Set D £60 to £75 **Service:** 12.5% (optional), card slips closed **Cards:** Amex, Delta, Maestro, MasterCard, Visa **Details:** 60 seats. No smoking. Wheelchair access (also WC). No music. No mobile phones. Air-conditioned **Tube:** South Kensington

MAP 13

Les Trois Garçons

1 Club Row, E1 6JX
Tel: (020) 7613 1924
Website: www.lestroisgarcons.com

NEW CHEF | Modern French | £43–£86

Inside this former pub on an unremarkable corner in the City is an architectural and decorative hotchpotch of high camp glamour and gothic shadows – where coronets and goblets decorate tables and chandeliers drip from the ceiling. We were told of the new chef's arrival too late for us to assess his work (so, reports, please), but the French-inspired carte continues, with the trademark luxuries of foie gras, truffles and caviar, alongside starters such as tartare of tuna with coconut, grapefruit and soy beans, and oyster beignets on potato blinis with liquorice crème fraîche and pickled celery. Mains pair monkfish with duck breast and accompany them with baby spinach, vegetable julienne and veal jus, or there could be a straightforward fillet of beef with fondant potatoes, madeira jus and ceps; vegetables are extra. Calvados-flamed tarte Tatin with cinnamon ice cream makes an interesting finish. Wine mark-ups are what one might expect in the City, but the list opens at £19 and provides plenty of interest – most of the action tends to centre on France.

Chef: Daniel Phippard **Proprietors:** Michel Lasserre, Stefan Karlson and Hassan Abdullah **Open:** Mon to Sat D only 7 to 10.30 **Meals:** alc (main courses £15 to £26). Set D Mon to Wed £22 (2 courses) to £26 **Service:** 12.5% (optional), card slips closed **Cards:** Amex, Delta, Diners, Maestro, MasterCard, Visa **Details:** 75 seats. Private parties: 75 main room, 6 to 12 private rooms. Vegetarian meals. Wheelchair access (not WC). Music. Air-conditioned **Tube:** Liverpool Street

MAP 12

La Trompette

5–7 Devonshire Road, W4 2EU
Tel: (020) 8747 1836
Website: www.latrompette.co.uk

Cooking 6 | French | £39–£80

A hop and skip from the hustle and bustle of Chiswick High Street, La Trompette sits a little ostentatiously among bathroom-fitting and curio shops, its double front 'spilling out on to the pavement with a certain sense of style', thought one reporter. Nonetheless, it is very much a neighbourhood restaurant, and a smartly appointed one at that, with leather-panelled columns and large displays of lilies. Here is no hushed reverence, though, but a lively and informal environment dedicated to good eating.

Subtle changes of emphasis in the culinary orientation were noted when James Bennington replaced his French predecessor in April 2005, but essentially the theme and intent are similar – which is to say, expect finely wrought renditions of modern French cooking. New season's garlic soup was 'meticulously judged', avoiding harshness and acridity, and was garnished with a pair of filo pastillas containing an 'other-worldly' mushroom filling, while red mullet fillets are topped with sectioned squid, partnered with a battered courgette-flower fritter, diced ratatouille and an ink sauce. Rustic French cuts such as côte de boeuf, veal cheek en blanquette and rump of lamb are the main-course meat offerings, that veal 'meltingly soft' but stunningly concentrated in flavour, served with the crisped sweetbreads, spring vegetables and mash, the braising juices a 'laid-back' background note to the dish. Desserts bring on Valrhona chocolate variations, as well as straightforward lemon tart and crème brûlée, but also a more diverting basil granita with pineapple and fromage blanc sorbet. Service has personality and charm, and takes things easy, so don't be in a hurry.

Wines are a star turn. Every region is plundered with enthusiasm to deliver a thrilling report of the global state of play, from a precision selection of vintage Bordeaux to fashionable New Zealand Syrah, loads from Australia and the estates *du jour* of regional France. House bottles are £16, and 14 come by the glass.

Chef: James Bennington **Proprietors:** Nigel Platts-Martin and Bruce Poole **Open:** all week 12 to 2.45, 6.30 to 10.45 (Sun 12.30 to 3, 7 to 10) **Meals:** Set L £23.50, Set D £32.50 **Service:** 12.5% (optional), card slips closed **Cards:** Amex, Delta, Maestro, MasterCard, Visa **Details:** 75 seats. 16 seats outside. Vegetarian meals. Children's helpings. No smoking. Wheelchair access (also WC). No music. No mobile phones. Air-conditioned **Tube:** Turnham Green

MAP 15

La Trouvaille AR

12A Newburgh Street, W1F 7RR
Tel: (020) 7287 8488

Unconventional French regional cooking in bistro surroundings just off Carnaby Street. Expect dishes like pumpkin velouté with crunchy palm hearts, thyme and Cantal cheese, grilled Saddleback pork with oyster mushrooms and Chinese artichokes sautéed in a coconut milk emulsion, and gurnard fillets with curry zabaglione. Desserts are novelties like fruit minestrone with spicy winter coulis or chocolate and violet fondant with Armagnac ice cream. Pre-theatre menus £15.50/£18.75. Unusual wines from southern France, with prices from £13. Closed Sun.

MAP 12

Tsunami

5–7 Voltaire Road, SW4 6DQ
Tel: (020) 7978 1610
Website: www.tsunamijapaneserestaurant.co.uk

Cooking 3 | Japanese | £31–£73

A healthy buzz pervades this agreeable Japanese restaurant in the unlikely setting of Clapham's railway sidings. 'Tsunami dishes are best enjoyed by sharing,' states the menu, and the long list of appetisers encourages grazing with its array of grilled scallops with smelt eggs and creamy spiced sauce, chicken yakitori, tuna tataki and nasu goma (grilled aubergine with sesame sauce). Also look for toban hotpots and crossover specials such as prime fillet of beef with sea urchin and foie gras butter served with wasabi pepper sauce and baby leaf salad. The range of sushi and sashimi, traditionally listed at the end of the menu, encompasses everything from eel and turbot to yellowtail and scallion roll. Cocktails, beers and saké are alternatives to the short wine list, which kicks off with house French at £12.

Chef/Proprietor: Ken Sam **Open:** Mon to Fri 6 to 11.30, Sat 12.30 to 11.30 **Meals:** alc (main courses £6.50 to £21) **Service:** 12.5% (optional), card slips closed **Cards:** Amex, Delta, Maestro, MasterCard, Visa **Details:** 100 seats. 12 seats outside. Vegetarian meals. Children's helpings. No-smoking area. Music. Air-conditioned **Tube:** Clapham North

MAP 12

Two Brothers

297-303 Regents Park Road, N3 1DP
Tel: (020) 8346 0469

Cooking 1 | Fish and Chips | £21–£52

(£)

Early-evening queues outside Leon and Tony Manzi's place testify to the fact that standards rarely falter in this gem of a chippie/restaurant. All the staples of the fish-fryer's repertoire are to be found here, from haddock and plaice to rock eel and halibut – not to mention grilled whole sea bream and specials like monkfish in mushroom sauce. Try some jellied eels or a plate of rock oysters to start, and finish off with, say, banana fritters and whipped cream, or iced yoghurt with honey and nuts. By all accounts, the house white (£10.35) from the owners' own vines in the Côtes de Duras 'goes excellently with the fish'.

Chef/Proprietor: Leon and Tony Manzi **Open:** Tue to Sat; 12 to 2.30, 5.30 to 10.15 **Closed:** bank hol Mons and succeeding Tues, 2 weeks Aug **Meals:** alc (main courses £8.50 to £18.50) **Service:** not inc, card slips closed **Cards:** Amex, Delta, Maestro, MasterCard, Visa **Details:** 90 seats. Children's helpings. No smoking in evenings. Occasional music. Air-conditioned **Tube:** Finchley Central

(£)	This symbol means that it is possible to have a three-course meal, including coffee, half a bottle of house wine and service, at all sessions for £30 or less per person.

MAP 12

Ubon by Nobu

34 Westferry Circus, Canary Wharf, E14 8RR
Tel: (020) 7719 7800
Website: www.noburestaurants.com

Cooking 5 | Japanese | £49–£147

Allow time to find it if you haven't been before. The journey is an extended pilgrimage through the labyrinth of Canary Wharf, broken by valet parking and the ringing of a bell to gain admittance to the grounds of the Four Seasons Hotel. A further odyssey through landscaped gardens leads to an entrance lobby and a lift. Ubon is on the fourth floor, a dramatic designscape of singular brilliance that comes into its own after dark, when the threaded amber-coloured stones that trickle down the windows and cascade from the light fittings create a theatrical backdrop. The food's quite good too.

Veterans of the partner restaurant Nobu at Hyde Park Corner (see entry) will recognise the weird, but weirdly successful, symbiosis of Japanese and South American styles that prevails at both venues. Signature dishes do not disappoint: both the yellowtail sashimi with jalapeño and ponzu sauce, and the fabled chunky-flaked black cod with sticky-sweet miso hit the spot at inspection. Newer dishes have fared less well, although, that said, the quality of the fresh fish itself is not in doubt. Desserts close things on a high note, with the chocolate bento box and its bitter green tea ice cream a dazzling alternative to an equally accomplished, straightforward mango soufflé with passion-fruit sauce. The fact that house wines from Sicily are £28 give a fair indication of the pricing structure on the rest of the undoubtedly quality-conscious list.

Chef: Mark Edwards **Proprietor:** Nobuyuki Matsuhisa **Open:** Mon to Fri L 12 to 2.15, Mon to Sat D 6 to 10.15 **Closed:** bank hols **Meals:** alc (main courses £5.50 to £29.50). Set L £45 to £50, Set D £70 to £90 **Service:** 15% (optional) **Cards:** Amex, Delta, Diners, Maestro, MasterCard, Visa **Details:** 120 seats. Private parties: 150 main room. Car park. Vegetarian meals. No smoking. Wheelchair access (also WC). Music. Air-conditioned **Tube:** Canary Wharf DLR, Westferry DLR

NEW ENTRY	This appears after the restaurant's name if the establishment was not a main entry in last year's Guide, although it may have been a 'round-up/also recommended' in previous editions.

MAP 15

Umu

NEW ENTRY

14–16 Bruton Place, W1J 6LX
Tel: (020) 7499 8881
Website: www.umurestaurant.com

Cooking 5 | Japanese | £46–£341

Classy Japanese restaurants often don't make much of an exterior show of themselves, and this one – despite making a splash on its opening in September 2004 – is about as anonymous as they get. Tucked down a quiet Mayfair side street, it has a palm-operated security pad entry system that left our inspector momentarily flummoxed. Persistence pays off. The interior, by Taiwanese-born New Yorker Tony Chi, is muted, pared-down, softly lit, and divided into a private eating area and the surprisingly small main dining room. Lush black velvet banquettes are the last word in comfort, and the lighting is provided by handsome tubes of Murano glass. The wooden floor and hand-crafted pottery hark back to more traditional modes.

This is Britain's first Kyoto-style restaurant, inspired by a city that has its own venerable culinary traditions. Chef Ichiro Kubota has been prised out of Kyoto in order to come and cook here, and a stream of authentic Japanese ingredients has followed him. The best things in life ain't free, of course, and the fixed-price menus here are beyond expensive, rising to the full imperial majesty of the special Kyoto sushi kaiseki menu, with matching sakés or wines, at £250. Dishes that have impressed include the curtain-raising sweet shrimp with saké jelly, 'a ravishing initiation', deep-fried langoustine yuba roll, a delicately textured cylinder of soya milk encasing translucent shellfish, and compellingly fresh deep-fried prawns with sweet potato. The Kyoto kaiseki menu at £130 ascends through several more gears to take in 'splendidly grassy' green tea tofu with a sea urchin, a daisy-fresh deep-fried oyster with lemon vinaigrette and caviar, fabulous sashimi of yellowtail tuna, and vermicelli-spiked lobster yuba roll with yuzu salt.

There are blander dishes that fail to strike with convincing impact and, while they may be genuine enough, are not guaranteed to impress at these prices. Soya milk pudding (think Japanese pannacotta) is the trad way to finish; it comes with Williams pear, green tea ice cream and red bean sauce. Supercilious service hasn't impressed, for all that you are rubbing shoulders with the 'über-rich and super-cool'. Saké is naturally a speciality, but there is also a long French-centred wine list. Bottles start at £25, and over a dozen come by the glass.

Chef: Ichiro Kubota **Proprietor:** Marc Ltd **Open:** Mon to Sat 12 to 2.30, 6 to 11 **Closed:** Christmas, Easter, bank hols **Meals:** alc (main courses £10 to £45). Set L £22 (2 courses) to £44, Set D £60 to £250 (inc wine) **Service:** 12.5% (optional), card slips closed **Cards:** Amex, Delta, Diners, Maestro, MasterCard, Visa **Details:** 60 seats. Private parties: 60 main room, 1 to 12 private rooms. Vegetarian meals. No smoking. Wheelchair access (also WC). Music. Air-conditioned

MAP 12

Le Vacherin

NEW ENTRY

76–77 South Parade, W4 5LF
Tel: (020) 8742 2121
Website: www.levacherin.co.uk

Cooking 4 | Modern French | £28–£64

The large picture windows look out on to a quiet, leafy road in the environs of Chiswick and Turnham Green. A pair of expansive rooms is decorated in the uncomplicated modern style, with rust-coloured tiles on the floors, fairly uncommunicative pictures on the walls, and simple napery and glassware on the tables. Barely had Malcolm and Donna John's latest addition to West London gastronomy opened in 2004 than reporters began writing in to praise the venture.

The menus deal in considered French brasserie cooking, with results on the plate repeatedly achieving the 'gosh' factor. Textures and flavours work seamlessly together to produce dishes of great harmony. Crisply seared duck liver is cooked pink and balanced by chunks of sharply flavoured beetroot and well-dressed leaves. Another salad is comprised of plump scallops on an open-textured mash of blood pudding and strips of Alsace bacon. Fish is impeccably fresh, as was witnessed by an inspector's main course of succulent halibut topped with a mound of briskly seasoned white crabmeat, on a supporting structure of baby leeks, while côte de boeuf is the real thing – a huge piece of tender beef on the bone, cooked blue, as requested, and served with sweetly buttery béarnaise. Good side dishes include exemplary, crisp, salty frites, and puddings will tempt with the likes of apple chausson (turnover) with goats' cheese ice cream, or ambrosial chocolate fondant with Amaretto ice. The signature dish, although available only in its season, of course (November to February), is the soft mountain cheese after which the place is named, perhaps baked with truffles and almonds. Service bustles along but manages to remain attentive. Entirely French wine lists are a rarity nowadays, but this one is full of interesting choices, with many from outside the traditional regions, and contains plenty of choice below £25. House wines, from the South-west, are £13.40, or £3.50 a glass.

Chef: Malcolm John **Proprietors:** Malcolm and Donna John **Open:** Tue to Sun L 12 to 3, all week D 6 to 10.30 **Closed:** 25 Dec **Meals:** alc D (main courses £12 to £17.50). Set L £12.95 (2 courses) to £15.95 **Service:** 12.5% (optional), card slips closed **Cards:** Delta, Maestro, MasterCard, Visa **Details:** 72 seats. 10 seats outside. Private parties: 60 main room, 10 to 40 private rooms. Vegetarian meals. Children's helpings. No smoking. No music. No mobile phones **Tube:** Chiswick Park

MAP 13

Vama

438 King's Road, SW10 0LJ
Tel: (020) 7565 8500

'Untamed North-west Frontier cuisine' is the promise at this glitzy King's Road 'Indian Room' (the name means 'essence of woman'). Tandooris of every description top the bill, from monkfish and lobster to smoked minced lamb (£10). Starters include pudina aloo tikka (mint and potato fritters with chickpeas; £8.50), while curries run to crab and vegetable kofta (£14), chicken tikka masala, and sag gosht. Paper-thin zeera roomali (£3) is an unusual bread. Short wine list from £15. Open all week.

MAP 15

Vasco & Piero's Pavilion

AR

15 Poland Street, W1F 8QE
Tel: (020) 7437 8774

Long-serving, family-run Italian and a veteran of the West End gastro-scene. Menus change twice daily, and the kitchen delivers forthright regional dishes including hand-made aubergine tortelloni with tomato and rosemary, sea bass fillet wrapped in zucchini with cannellini beans, and calf's liver with onions and cauliflower. Desserts follow suit with coffee pannacotta and robiola cheesecake. Lunch is a carte (main courses around £14.50), dinner set price (£22/£26). Predominantly Italian wines from £13. Closed Sat L and Sun.

MAP 15

Veeraswamy

AR

99–101 Regent Street, W1R 8RS
Tel: (020) 7734 1401

Born in 1926, 'Britain's oldest Indian restaurant' is under the same ownership as Amaya, Chutney Mary, and Masala Zone (see entries). The kitchen's repertoire is broad, ranging from chicken samosas (£6.50) and spiced crab cake with plum chutney to Kerala-style marinated lamb chops with parsnip mash (£18). Intriguing desserts include bibinca (Goan coconut cake with cracked peppercorn ice cream; £5.75). Set-price lunch and theatre menus; help-yourself Sunday buffets. Well-chosen wines with Mayfair prices from £16.25. A 'sumptuous' makeover is promised as we go to press. Open all week.

MAP 12

Victoria

10 West Temple Sheen, SW14 7RT
Tel: (020) 8876 4238
Website: www.thevictoria.net

Cooking 2 | Modern European | £28–£60

'Delightful, cool and airy' sums up this gastropub/restaurant-with-rooms in the suburban reaches of Richmond. A sleek new Danish wood-fired stove provides welcome warmth in the split-level conservatory, and there is now more space in the relocated bar. Spanish influences are noticeable among the starters, which range from extremely generous tapas to Serrano ham with grilled chicory and sherry vinegar dressing, while main courses are beefed up with animal protein: steaks from pure-bred Charolais, roast rump of lamb with pumpkin and chickpea salad, and seasonal specials like traditional roast mallard with all the trimmings. Desserts embrace Yorkshire rhubarb trifle as well as tarte Tatin. Coffee comes in mugs, and the wide-ranging wine list is bolstered by a few special bottles. Prices start at £12.95.

Chef: Darren Archer **Proprietors:** Mark Chester, Rex Chester and Darren Archer **Open:** all week 12 to 2.30 (3 Sat, 4 Sun), 7 to 10 (9 Sun) **Closed:** 25 and 26 Dec **Meals:** alc (main courses £8 to £20) **Service:** 12.5% (optional), card slips closed **Cards:** Amex, Delta, Maestro, MasterCard, Visa **Details:** 70 seats. 40 seats outside. Private parties: 45 main room. Car park. Vegetarian meals. Children's helpings. No-smoking area. Wheelchair access (not WC). No music **Accommodation:** 7 rooms, all with bath/shower. TV. Phone. B&B £98.50 (double room). Baby facilities

MAP 15

Villandry

170 Great Portland Street, W1W 5QB
Tel: (020) 7631 3131
Website: www.villandry.com

Cooking 2 | Modern European | £30–£64

Nothing could whet the appetite more than taking a leisurely browse through this foodie paradisus terrestris. You might opt for breakfast (from 8am), graze on charcuterie and cheeses in the café bar or choose something more substantial in the utilitarian dining room at the back – not forgetting tables on the pavement. The daily-changing menu follows the market and many of its components are likely to be on sale in the deli. Tease your palate with seared scallops and tabbouleh salsa or warm wild mushroom salad on toasted brioche with fried duck egg, before considering soy-braised belly pork, shredded vegetables, pak choi and noodles or pan-fried salmon fillet with baby organic leeks and tarragon dressing. Finish with summer pudding with clotted cream or moist chocolate cake with crème Chantilly. Forthright tasting notes help with wine choices from the wide-ranging list, with bottles from £13.50 and up to ten by the glass.

Chef: Steve Evenett-Watts **Proprietor:** Martha Greene **Open:** all week L 12 to 3, Mon to Sat D 6 to 10.30 **Closed:** Christmas, bank hols **Meals:** alc (main courses £11.50 to £20). Set D Mon to Fri 6 to 7 £15.50 (2 courses) to £17.50. Bar menu available **Service:** 12.5% (optional), card slips closed **Cards:** Amex, Maestro, MasterCard, Visa **Details:** 100 seats. Private parties: 94 main room. Vegetarian meals. Children's helpings. No smoking. Wheelchair access (not WC). No music. Air-conditioned **Tube:** Great Portland Street

MAP 13

Vivat Bacchus

47 Farringdon Street, EC4A 4LL
Tel: (020) 7353 2648

A tour of the cheese storage room and the 6,000-bin wine cellars is part of the package on offer at this idiosyncratic basement near Smithfield Market. The modern seasonal menus promise dishes like seared scallops with spiced Puy lentils and lime crème fraîche (£9.50), marinated pork brochette with clams, garam masala and shallot vinaigrette (£14.50), and warm berry and Shiraz crumble tart with clotted cream (£5.50). Wine prices start at £13.95. Closed Sat and Sun.

MAP 12

Wapping Food

Wapping Hydraulic Power Station, Wapping Wall, E1W 3ST
Tel: (020) 7680 2080
Website: www.thewappingproject.com

Cooking 3 | Modern European | £36–£60

'Come for the cocktails, the brunch, the papers to read, the sense of escape from industrial alienation,' enthused one correspondent. There's clearly more to this huge eating arena than the food itself, but the results on the plate seldom disappoint. Sunday lunch highlights the kitchen's cosmopolitan approach and commitment to good shopping and sourcing: begin with a plate of charcuterie or buffalo Mozzarella salad, then try sea bass fillet with parsley mash and a citrus, buttery reduction, or roast lamb accompanied by roasted beetroot and sprouting broccoli. At other times, the repertoire includes steamed palourdes with lime, coriander and coconut, and it would be sinful to miss 'lovingly made' desserts like ultra-sticky toffee pudding. Aussie wine fans can rejoice: the entire list is from down-under, with loads of up-front drinking from £16.

Chef: James Robson **Proprietor:** Wapping Restaurants Ltd **Open:** all week L 12 (1 Sat/Sun) to 3.30, Mon to Sat D 6.30 to 11 **Meals:** alc (main courses £11 to £17.50). Brunch menu available Sat and Sun 10 to 12.30 **Service:** 12.5% (optional), card slips closed **Cards:** Amex, Delta, Diners, Maestro, MasterCard, Visa **Details:** 110 seats. 60 seats outside. Private parties: 150 main room, 100 to 300 private rooms. Car park. Children's helpings. No cigars. Wheelchair access (also WC). Occasional music **Tube:** Wapping

MAP 12

Wells

30 Well Walk, NW3 1BX
Tel: (020) 7794 3785
Website: www.thewellshampstead.co.uk

NEW CHEF | French | £26–£52

In the middle of posh, residential Hampstead and close to the Heath, this classic Georgian corner building cuts a sophisticated gastro-pub edge these days. Downstairs there's a chic, contemporary bar, while upstairs a stylish, more formal restaurant is spread over a trio of dramatic, yet understated dining rooms. Standing on polished-wood flooring, white-clothed tables come flooded by natural light from large windows, and, in the evenings, subtle contemporary lighting. Under chef Ian Sutton, a student of Marco Pierre White and veteran of both The Dorchester and The Savoy, and who arrived in 2005, a more compact menu now offers fixed-price options for two and three courses. The quality of ingredients takes centre stage, with simple, skilfully cooked, modern-focused dishes with a classic accent; take a foie gras terrine served with rosemary toast and sauce gribiche, for instance, and perhaps a fillet of steak with pomme purée, buttered spinach and red-wine sauce, while a glazed rhubarb and custard tart might head up desserts. A shorter, simpler menu is offered in the bar. Wines are a well-chosen international mix from £13.50, with ten by the glass.

Chef: Ian Sutton **Proprietor:** Beth Coventry **Open:** Sun L 12 to 3, Tue to Sun D 7 to 10 (10.30 Sat) **Closed:** 24 and 25 Dec **Meals:** Set L Sun £12.95 (2 courses) to £13.95, Set D £24.50 (2 courses) to £29.50. Bar menu available **Service:** 12.5% (optional), card slips closed **Cards:** Delta, Maestro, MasterCard, Visa **Details:** 105 seats. 50 seats outside. Private parties: 22 main room, 8 to 12 private rooms. Vegetarian meals. No smoking. Occasional music. Air-conditioned **Tube:** Hampstead

MAP 13

White Swan

NEW ENTRY

108 Fetter Lane, EC4A 1ES
Tel: (020) 7242 9696
Website: www.thewhiteswanlondon.com

Cooking 3 | Modern British | £35–£62

The refurbished White Swan re-launched itself at the end of 2003 in fairy-tale fashion as a serious contender in the gastro-pub stakes. Beyond the buzzy, upmarket bar, with its gigantic wall mirror (something of a theme here), a staircase (mirror-lined) leads up to the more formal Dining Room. Closely packed, white-clothed tables are reflected back from a mirrored ceiling – 'it's small but beautifully formed' – and the friendly, attentive French staff add charm to the experience. Jason Scrimshaw's appealing, crowd-pleasing modern menus come bolstered by daily specials and combine classics (tuna niçoise, 'excellent' crisp-battered haddock and chips, and sticky toffee pudding with chocolate ice cream) with more avant-garde offerings (deep-fried calves' brains with a Thai dipping sauce to start, for instance, or a main course of organic salmon with sesame, pak choi and coconut broth). The fashionable, French-led wine list fits the bill too. Although few bottles are under £20, it has a good range of halves and a decent choice by the glass, with house selections opening the account at £12.50.

Chef: Jason Scrimshaw **Proprietors:** Tom and Ed Martin **Open:** Mon to Fri 12 to 3, 6 to 10 **Closed:** bank hols **Meals:** alc D (main courses £13.50 to £16.50). Set L 12 to 1 £15 (2 courses), Set L 12 to 3 £24 (2 courses). Bar menu available **Service:** 12.5% (optional) **Cards:** Amex, Delta, Maestro, MasterCard, Visa **Details:** 40 seats. Private parties: 120 main room, 40 private room. Vegetarian meals. Children's helpings. Music. Air-conditioned **Tube:** Chancery Lane

MAP 12

William IV

AR

786 Harrow Road, NW10 5JX
Tel: (020) 8969 5944

Tapas are now the main theme at this jolly gastro-pub on the Harrow Road. The ambitious line-up divides into vegetarian, meat and fish, taking in warm pumpkin and chickpea salad with tahini (£5), tocino (confit of belly pork with caramelised onions), and grilled swordfish with green tomato chutney (£6.25). Finish with a slice of almond and strawberry tart. Sunday lunches (two courses £15) return home for traditional roasts. Wines with a European bias from £12.25. Open all week.

MAP 15

Wiltons

55 Jermyn Street, SW1Y 6LX
Tel: (020) 7629 9955
Website: www.wiltons.co.uk

Cooking 4 | Traditional English | £61–£138

Wiltons is a restaurant of the old school: 'within seconds of entering, we were relieved of our coats and hats by a man with the uniform and manner of a butler.' It's a long, thin room decorated in a 'gentleman's club' style that 'nods towards the less garish end of contemporary design' and has immaculately set tables. The menu follows suit – conservative to its fingertips, with no compromise to fashion – this is the place to come to for such British classics as avocado pear with white crabmeat, potted shrimps, mixed grill, and lobster four ways. At its best, the kitchen can hit the high spots with, for example, an impressive dish of goose foie gras with brioche, or a 'superbly prepared' apple crumble, and buying is evidently good, producing 'fresh and in tiptop condition' roast veal with vegetables and potatoes on the side ('at extra cost, of course'). France is at the heart of the wine list, but it's hard to drink well under £50. House white is £25, red £29.

Chef: Jerome Ponchelle **Proprietors:** the Hambro family **Open:** Mon to Fri 12 to 2.30, 6 to 10.30 **Closed:** 23 Dec to 2 Jan, bank hols **Meals:** alc (main courses £20 to £45) **Service:** 12.5% (optional) **Cards:** Amex, Delta, Diners, Maestro, MasterCard, Visa **Details:** 90 seats. Private parties: 4 to 18 private rooms. Jacket and tie. No-smoking area. Wheelchair access (also WC). No music. No mobile phones. Air-conditioned **Tube:** Green Park

MAP 15

Wolseley

160 Piccadilly, W1J 9EB
Tel: (020) 7499 6996
Website: www.thewolseley.com

NEW CHEF | International | £33–£91

This former car showroom is a hive of activity and endeavour from 7am until midnight, offering a range of menus so extensive that they need an index (all-day menu, page six; afternoon tea, page ten; cocktails, page eleven). Number 160 Piccadilly is a grand building on an illustrious street, and it takes vision and enterprise to fill this imposing and handsome venue; Chris Corbin and Jeremy King have certainly brought life and vibrancy to the space.

A comprehensive breakfast menu starts the ball rolling – how about fried duck eggs with Ayrshire bacon, or a grilled Manx kipper with mustard butter? – and the all-day menu kicks in at 11.30am with something as comforting as chicken soup with dumplings, or spinach and Parmesan tart. The carte runs to usual lunch and dinner timings, and gives a substantial choice from crab hash with lemon aïoli to black pudding and oxtail Parmentier, via lobster bisque or soufflé Suisse. Wind up with cherry clafoutis with almond milk ice cream, or St-Marcellin with walnut bread. The £2 cover charge continues, and service is up and down. Half a dozen or so wines are under £20, starting at £14.75, and everything apart from the reserve collection is available by the glass.

Chefs: Cyrus Cato and Ed Wilson **Proprietors:** Chris Corbin and Jeremy King **Open:** all week 12 to 2.30, 5.30 to 12 (11 Sun) **Meals:** alc (main courses £9.50 to £27.50). Cover £2 **Service:** not inc **Cards:** Amex, Delta, Diners, Maestro, MasterCard, Visa **Details:** 150 seats. Vegetarian meals. Children's helpings. No smoking in 1 dining room. Wheelchair access (also WC). No music. Air-conditioned **Tube:** Green Park

MAP 15

W'Sens

NEW ENTRY

12 Waterloo Place, SW1Y 4AU
Tel: (020) 7484 1355
Website: www.wsens.co.uk

Cooking 4 | Mediterranean-Plus | £37–£86

The unpronounceable name indicates that this new venture, that opened just before Christmas 2004, is the latest offspring of the highly acclaimed Le Jardin des Sens in Montpellier, owned by the Pourcel brothers, Jacques and Laurent. (The W here stands for the street name, apparently.) With décor in mid-brown woody tones by Algerian-born Imaad Rahmouni, the feeling is hard-edged and contemporary, with no coverings of any sort on either floor or tables.

Chef Christophe Langree sold up a restaurant in Bourges to come and run the Pourcels' London arm, and cooks a menu that is finely attuned to their culinary orientation of southern Mediterranean, shot through with a swatch of East Indies spice. Start with a quartet of tempura prawns with thin plantain chips, served alongside a glass of sweet chilli and coriander dip, the shellfish excellent and cooked *à point*. Scallops might be topped with creamy aïoli, and accompanied by strips of tasty tomato confit and a trio of well-made garlic croquettes. Main courses mix it up: roast lamb cutlets appear with a spiced samosa of the meat, sea bass is served meunière with a shellfish ragoût and basil, and a pairing of sliced tuna and foie gras in red-wine sauce comes with a blob of technically impressive wasabi cream. The French cheeses arrived fridge-cold at inspection, but Caribbean chocolate fondant restored faith, with its perfect molten centre and a chocolate sorbet of flawless texture and intense flavour.

The wine list is not as new-fangled as the cooking, and accords pride of place to the French regions, but there are a few from the southern hemisphere to bring things up to date. Prices open at £15, and quickly ascend.

Chef: Christophe Langree **Proprietors:** Jacques and Laurent Pourcel and Olivier Chateau **Open:** Mon to Fri L 12 to 2.30, Mon to Sat D 5.30 to 11 **Meals:** alc (main courses £11.50 to £31). Set L £20 (2 courses) to £25, Set D £25 (2 courses) to £30. Bar menu available **Service:** 12.5% (optional), card slips closed **Cards:** Amex, Delta, Maestro, MasterCard, Visa **Details:** 130 seats. Private parties: 130 main room. No-smoking area. Wheelchair access (also WC). Music. Air-conditioned **Tube:** Piccadilly Circus

MAP 15

Yatra

AR

34 Dover Street, W1S 4NF
Tel: (020) 7493 0200

Revamped décor, a new chef and a simplified fixed-price menu (£21.50/£24.50) are the latest developments in this unusual, urbane Mayfair Indian. Staples like chutneys and thick dhal are well up to scratch; otherwise, expect regional ideas, modish presentation and dishes such as Burmese minced lamb kebabs, freshwater shrimp curry, and dum ki nalli (braised lamb shank in a tomato-based sauce with curry leaf mash and slow-roast vegetables). Buffet lunches £9.95; house wine £14. Closed Sat L and Sun.

MAP 15

Yauatcha

15–17 Broadwick Street, W1F 0DL
Tel: (020) 7494 8888
Email: mail@yauatcha.com

Cooking 4 | Chinese | £44–£124

A tea house, pastry shop, all-day dim sum restaurant and sexy evening venue are all combined in one two-storeyed package in this sibling to Hakkasan (see entry). There is a neat combination of experimentation and familiarity on the lengthy menus, with one confirmed regular reporting that the dim sum are 'as good as any in London'. Char siu buns are reliably superb, as is lightly stir-fried, tender young gai lan with ginger. Newer dishes have pleased unequivocally too. Prawn and cuttlefish dumplings impress because the latter component avoids rubberiness, while 'meltingly delicate' roast silver cod with lily flower, red dates and rice wine has been a triumph. Venison puffs, as at Hakkasan, are something of a signature, and Singapore noodles are commendably light in texture. Western desserts may seem beside the point but maintain the creative pace, with a mousse of marc de champagne accompanied by a lemon macaroon and mango 'carpaccio'. Wines vie for attention with tea smoothies and cocktails on the cosmopolitan drinks list. The eclectic mix, arranged by style, is well suited to the food, with most attention paid to pink champagne and aromatic whites. Prices start at £17 in Italy and France.

> **Chef:** Soon Wah Cheong **Proprietor:** Alan Yau **Open:** Mon to Fri 12 to 11, Sat and Sun 11 to 10.30 **Meals:** alc (main courses £4.50 to £38) **Service:** 12.5% **Cards:** Amex, Delta, Diners, Maestro, MasterCard, Visa **Details:** 100 seats. Private parties: 120 main room. Vegetarian meals. No smoking. Wheelchair access (also WC). Music. Air-conditioned **Tube:** Tottenham Court Road

MAP 15

Yoshino

AR

3 Piccadilly Place, W1V 0DB
Tel: (020) 7287 6622

Useful unadorned Japanese 'within a spit and a hop of Piccadilly'. Bento boxes (£5.80 to £19.80) are the kitchen's stock-in-trade, and there's also a good showing of sushi and sashimi (from £2.50) – including 'perkily fresh' brill. 'Silky, seductive' home-made bean curd features, and the kitchen also handles familiar cooked dishes, including tempura and teriyaki. Finish with moreish bean curd ice cream (£3.80). Drink beer, saké or something from the minimal wine list. Closed Sun.

MAP 14

Zafferano

15 Lowndes Street, SW1X 9EY
Tel: (020) 7235 5800
Website: www.zafferanorestaurant.co.uk

Cooking 6 | Italian | £44–£87

Given the Knightsbridge location, readers are surprised to note the distinctly ordinary look of the place, with plants in tubs out front, suburban-style. An expansion in 2005 into the adjacent property has eased the previously close packing of tables, and the atmosphere remains relaxed and easy-going, the staff being communicative and helpful rather than city-slick.

The largely traditional Italian seasonal cooking, executed by Andy Needham with uncommon panache for a non-native, elicits copious praise from readers. A starter of shaved fennel and radish in anchovy-rich bagna cauda sauce with red chicory is noteworthy for its 'bright, unadulterated flavours'. Pasta is as good as it should be, its faultless texture enhancing anything from a simple dish of tagliatelle with porcini and spinach to tortellini of crab and courgette enlivened with a suggestion of chilli. Main courses are memorable for the opulent quality of ingredients, many of which are brought in from Italy. Tender veal is grilled on the bone, and served on a mound of buttery spinach in a light veal jus, while halibut is moist and fresh-tasting, coming with slices of sautéed potatoes, chopped tomato and more of that impeccable spinach. Similarly, the most straightforward desserts inspire the most contented sighs: a pairing of chocolate and passion-fruit sorbets of unearthly concentration, or properly rich tiramisù.

An extremely fine list of Italian wines, supplemented by a few French things, will provide a world of choice for the amply resourced, with runs of Barolo and Barbaresco, and successive vintages of the best super-Tuscans. Dotted here and there are a few served in the parsimonious 125ml glass, starting at £3.50.

> **Chef:** Andy Needham **Proprietor:** London and Henley Restaurants Seven Ltd **Open:** all week 12 to 2.15 (12.30 to 3 Sat and Sun), 7 to 11 **Closed:** Christmas, bank hols **Meals:** Set L £25.50 (2 courses) to £34.50, Set D £29.50 (2 courses) to £45 **Service:** 12.5% (optional) **Cards:** Amex, Delta, Diners, Maestro, MasterCard, Visa **Details:** 62 seats. Private parties: 12 private room. Vegetarian meals. No smoking in 1 dining room. Wheelchair access (not WC). Music. Air-conditioned **Tube:** Knightsbridge

MAP 13

Zaika

1 Kensington High Street, W8 5NP
Tel: (020) 7795 6533
Website: www.zaika-restaurant.co.uk

Cooking 3 | Modern Indian | £33–£84

A glamorous venue in a former bank building in trendy Kensington, Zaika is copiously adorned with Indian fabrics and artefacts, including statuettes of Hindu deities. Inveigling Western ingredients such as truffles, asparagus and foie gras into an Indian template, Sanjay Dwivedi offers a vivid and convincing take on the now-familiar Europe-meets-Asia theme. Tandoori-spiced smoked salmon kebab is served with good raita, while lamb tikka comes with a khurchan of artichoke and broccoli. Proceed from there to monkfish and cauliflower risotto with spiced lobster jus, sour spices and cocoa, or to more traditional butter chicken if you will. With vegetarian options and a tasting menu, most bases are covered, and there is proper kulfi to finish, as well as the likes of reshmi mithai – pine-nut, cashew and pistachio brittle with silky chocolate mousse and pistachio ice cream.

The monumental wine list looks first to Europe, tackling France and Italy with panache. New World countries are not far behind and the overall feel is of a switched-on contemporary mix plumped up with classic bottles. Bottles start at £19 and the 15 by the glass look tempting.

Chef: Sanjay Dwivedi **Proprietor:** Cuisine Collection **Open:** Sun to Fri L 12 to 2.45, all week D 6 to 10.45 (9.45 Sun) **Closed:** bank hols L **Meals:** alc (main courses £12.50 to £18.50). Set L £15 (2 courses) to £19, Set D £38 to £87 (inc wine) Pre-theatre D £15 (2 courses) to £19. **Service:** 12.5% (optional), card slips closed **Cards:** Amex, Delta, Diners, Maestro, MasterCard, Visa **Details:** 82 seats. Private parties: 100 main room. Vegetarian meals. Children's helpings. No cigars/pipes. Wheelchair access (not WC). Music. No mobile phones. Air-conditioned **Tube:** South Kensington

MAP 14

Zuma

5 Raphael Street, SW7 1DL
Tel: (020) 7584 1010
Website: www.zumarestaurant.com

Cooking 5 | Modern Japanese | £41–£146

In a wilderness of office blocks not far from Harrods, Zuma is a big, inviting barn of a place, all open-plan and hard surfaces, with marble pillars, a granite-tiled floor and a decorative theme of rough-hewn wood emphasising the informality of it all. It looks built to last, which is some sort of statement of faith in London's well-honed latter-day love affair with Japanese food (see entry for the sister restaurant, Roka). The multi-sectioned menu is comprised of sushi, sashimi, maki, robata grills, tempura and various specials, with a far broader range of choice than would be available at the home-grown izakaya eateries on which it is modelled.

The raw marinated items shine out like beacons of quality: eight thin slices of sea bass in emulsified yuzu and truffle oil with salmon roe was a pungently sweet delight on a winter's evening. Sautéed organic mushrooms intriguingly combine chewy and juicy textures and are seasoned with soy, yuzu and mustard seeds, with salsify and leek adding variety. Dishes arrive as they are finished, so the order of eating may not always seem logical to Western palates, and some dishes – such as aubergine and miso – are much more powerfully seasoned than others. Desserts cater to occidental tastes, with banana gâteau a good, moist mouthful, served with coconut ice cream and peanut toffee sauce. An aficionado's range of saké is matched by a varietally arranged wine list (from £19) chosen with exquisite taste but at stiff mark-ups. Around ten come by the glass.

Chefs: Colin Clague and Rainer Becker **Proprietors:** Rainer Becker and Arjun Waney **Open:** all week 12 to 2.30 (12.30 to 3.30 Sat and Sun), 6 to 10.30 **Closed:** 25 and 26 Dec, 1 Jan **Meals:** alc (main courses £4.50 to £30). Set L £10.80 to £14.80 (2 courses), Set D £96 (min 2) **Service:** 13.5% (optional), card slips closed **Cards:** Amex, Delta, Diners, Maestro, MasterCard, Visa **Details:** 147 seats. 20 seats outside. Private parties: 10 main room, 6 to 14 private rooms. Vegetarian meals. No smoking. Wheelchair access (also WC). Music. Air-conditioned **Tube:** Knightsbridge

To submit a report on any restaurant, please visit *www.which.co.uk/gfgfeedback*.

MAP 3 **Abinger Common** SURREY

Stephan Langton Inn

Friday Street, Abinger Common RH5 6JR
Tel: (01306) 730775

Cooking 3 | Modern British | £33–£43

The dining room at this red-brick and timbered pub-cum-restaurant is off to one side of the rustic, no-frills bar. And finding the place is quite an adventure, too; it's tucked away down winding country lanes in a wooded valley with a few cottages and a pond for company – and, as you were wondering, it's named after the archbishop who drew up the Magna Carta (he lived nearby apparently). Stripped floorboards, beams, dark-wood tables and cottagey chairs create a relaxed and unstuffy restaurant atmosphere. Sunshine yellow walls make a sunny Mediterranean complement to chef-patron Jonathan Coomb's robust cooking, with its generous portions, clear flavours and sound-quality ingredients. Take goats' cheese fritters with roast peppers and rocket to start, or chestnut mushrooms and snails on toast, then roast cod, mash and salsa verde, or perhaps poached ham hock, ox tongue and cotechino with lentils and mustard fruits. Finish with buttermilk pudding and spiced apricots. Lunches are simpler and pubbier, ice creams and breads come home-made, and the compact, globe-trotting wine list has plenty under £20, with house from £10.95.

Chef: Jonathan Coomb **Proprietors:** Jonathan Coomb and Cynthia Rajabally **Open:** Tue to Sat D only 7 to 10 **Meals:** alc (main courses £12 to £13.50). Bar L menu available Tue to Sun 12.30 to 2.30 **Service:** not inc, card slips closed **Cards:** Delta, Maestro, MasterCard, Visa **Details:** 45 seats. 60 seats outside. Private parties: 45 main room. Car park. Children's helpings. No smoking. No music

MAP 3 **Abinger Hammer** SURREY

Drakes on the Pond

Dorking Road, Abinger Hammer RH5 6SA
Tel: (01306) 731174
Website: www.drakesonthepond.com

Cooking 5 | Modern European | £39–£82

Against a background of gently rising hillside, Drakes looks like a little farmhouse, and indeed shares its entrance with a trout farm. A long, narrow dining room has picture windows looking on to the rural A25, and all is kitted out in bright primrose.

The owners appointed a new head chef in 2005. First impressions are that the cooking looks set to continue in the same ambitious vein for which this venue has always been renowned. Extras include an appetiser and pre-dessert, and there is a palpable level of achievement in a main course of well-flavoured roasted Gressingham duck breast, halved and set on a 'cassoulet' of white beans and Alsace bacon, served with a sweet, strong madeira sauce. Current fashions are noted in the shape of scallops with cauliflower purée and truffle dressing among the starters, and a main-course assembly of marinated Balmoral venison with chorizo, Clonakilty black pudding, braised salsify and asparagus. Finish with raspberry and white chocolate soufflé with praline ice cream, or well-conceived slow-roasted pineapple with two coconut biscuits sandwiching a slab of ginger parfait. Wines kick off with nine house selections from £17.50 (£3.85 a glass), before heading off around the world.

Chef: Jonathan Clarke **Proprietors:** John Morris and Tracey Honeysett **Open:** Tue to Fri L 12 to 1.30, Tue to Sat D 7 to 9.30 **Meals:** alc D (main courses £21 to £25). Set L £18.50 (2 courses) to £23.50 **Service:** not inc **Cards:** MasterCard, Maestro, Visa **Details:** 32 seats. Private parties: 32 main room. Car park. Vegetarian meals. No children under 10. No smoking. Wheelchair access (not WC). No music. Air-conditioned

MAP 8 Addingham WEST YORKSHIRE

Fleece

154 Main Street, Addingham LS29 OLY
Tel: (01943) 830491

Cooking 3 | Modern British | £23–£48

Still resolutely a village pub, complete with a drinkers' bar and a roaring fire in winter, this low-ceilinged inn also serves as a busy venue for generous food with a North Country accent. Menus are on blackboards and you can mix and match between pub grub, like rich meat and potato pie with mushy peas, and more ambitious restaurant-style dishes. Owner Chris Monkman is proud of his suppliers, citing steaks from Bolton Abbey, creel-caught langoustines from Redcar, Manx queenie scallops (served with spinach and Gruyère) and abundant game, including roast woodcock or pheasant pie. Vegetables are true to the season (baked Jerusalem artichokes in January), and desserts are straightforward ideas like vanilla crème brûlée. Twenty house wines run from £11.50 to £17.50, and there's plenty of quaffable stuff among the seventy-some bins of the main list.

Chefs: Matthew Brown and Andrew Wilkinson **Proprietor:** Chris Monkman **Open:** all week 12 to 2.15, 6 to 9.15 (Sun 12 to 8) **Meals:** alc (main courses £6 to £15) **Service:** not inc, card slips closed **Cards:** Delta, Maestro, MasterCard, Visa **Details:** 70 seats. 70 seats outside. Private parties: 30 main room, 15 to 30 private rooms. Car park. Vegetarian meals. Children's helpings. Wheelchair access (also men's WC). No music

MAP 6 Aldeburgh SUFFOLK

Lighthouse

77 High Street, Aldeburgh IP15 5AU
Tel: (01728) 453377
Website: www.lighthouserestaurant.co.uk

Cooking 3 | Modern British-Plus | £26–£47

This two-storey, bistro-style restaurant has a penchant for seafood and a straightforward style that lets fresh ingredients shine. Think potted shrimps with toast and lemon, or crayfish cocktail, then perhaps haddock in beer batter with hand-cut chips, crushed peas and tartare sauce, or sea bass fillet on a red pepper salsa with spinach and new potatoes. But there's meat too – lamb chump on rosemary bean ragout with broccoli, or duck confit on red cabbage – and vegetarians might try the olive and sun-dried tomato pasta. Finish yourself and the meal with bread-and-butter pudding wickedly served with a shot of Scotch and double cream. There's the odd delay when the place is packed, but service is friendly. A well-rounded wine list has nine by glass and bottles from £11.75.

Chefs: Sara Fox, Guy Welsh and Leon Manthorpe **Proprietors:** Sara Fox and Peter Hill **Open:** all week 12 to 2 (2.30 Sat/Sun), 6.30 to 10 **Closed:** 1 week Oct, 2 weeks Jan **Meals:** alc (main courses £8 to £15). Set L and D £13.25 (2 courses) to £16.50. Light L menu available Mon to Sat **Service:** not inc, card slips closed **Cards:** Amex, Delta, Maestro, MasterCard, Visa **Details:** 95 seats. 20 seats outside. Private parties: 43 main room, 14 to 25 private rooms. Vegetarian meals. No smoking. Wheelchair access (also WC). No music. No mobile phones. Air-conditioned

152 Aldeburgh

152 High Street, Aldeburgh IP15 5AX
Tel: (01728) 454594
Website: www.152aldeburgh.co.uk

Cooking 3 | Modern European | £26–£55

The laid-back style and informality of this open-plan brasserie suits Aldeburgh's seaside location to a T. Situated a stroll from the beach, it entices the crowds with its robust, straightforward cooking: call in for a light snack or a plate of fish and chips. Local seafood also fares well in the guise of, say, fish soup with rouille, and roast cod with watercress royale, saffron mash and red-pepper pesto. Elsewhere, there are signs of proficient meat cookery in juicy lamb shank on a bed of ratatouille with young spring greens, and high-quality ribeye steak served the classic way with tomatoes, mushrooms and chips. Desserts such as iced rhubarb parfait provide a light finale. The all-round wine list is from Adnams of Southwold; prices start at £11.75.

Chef: Garry Cook **Proprietors:** 152 Restaurants Ltd **Open:** all week 12 to 3, 6 to 10 **Meals:** alc (main courses £10.50 to £18.50). Set L and D £13 (2 courses) to £16 **Service:** not inc **Cards:** Amex, Delta, MasterCard, Maestro, Visa **Details:** 56 seats. 24 seats outside. Private parties: 60 main room. Vegetarian meals. No smoking. Wheelchair access (not WC). Music. No mobile phones

MAP 8 **Alrincham** GREATER MANCHESTER

Juniper

21 The Downs, Altrincham WA14 2QD
Tel: (0161) 929 4008
Website: www.juniper-restaurant.co.uk

Cooking 6 | Modern French | £34–£95

Paul Kitching clocked up ten years in Altrincham in 2005, a location which doubtless has not seen such innovation and boldness since the days of the Industrial Revolution. At the end of the metro line from central Manchester, this culinary wizard offers something that can't be matched in the nearby metropolis.

The Downs is like an appendix dangling off Altrincham's main drag, with the unassuming frontage of Juniper giving nothing away. The greeting is warm and enthusiastic, and the basement bar is a comfortable space in which to peruse the menus. The ground-floor dining room is dominated by the imposing Rout of San Romano by Uccello, contrasting with calming green and natural colours and smartly set, well-spaced tables. The menu descriptions have seen a welcome simplification of late, with many of the more ethereal references replaced by a more contemporary listings style, although the pairings of ingredients and constructions still catch the eye: trout fillet, caviar, lentils, chocolate, or maybe beef fillet, white asparagus, fried apricot eggs, sultana noodles. At inspection, a starter of butter-baked rabbit was overly mild and lacking the textural pleasures of this meat, with the accompanying thin slices of boudin noir left to raise the flavour quotient, while the lamb's kidney accompanying best end of lamb was decidedly undercooked. Ingredients are of top quality, though, such as beef, rich and well hung, and scallops, served in a main course alongside turbot, olives and pimento butter, with thin slices of dried banana successfully partnering the gently cooked, translucent shellfish. Colours are vibrant and bold, with vivid greens a favourite, as in an inter-course soup of leek and potato with pineapple and hazelnuts. The chef's sense of fun is evident as the meal progresses: witness the 'four beverage-based desserts' that include a light and frothy tiramisù, served in a plastic cup, and a collection of shot glasses, among them a crème brûlée. Front-of-house is professional and friendly, and Juniper remains a destination restaurant.

The wine list concentrates on Bordeaux and Burgundy, offering fair value on high-end bottles. Elsewhere, short selections cover the field from fruity Sicilian Nero d'Avola by Mandrarossa (£18) to Australia's refined Petaluma Chardonnay (£40). Only two wines come by the glass, but there are plenty of half-bottles.

Chef/Proprietor: Paul Kitching **Open:** Tue to Fri L 12 to 2, Tue to Sat D 7 to 10 **Meals:** alc (main courses £16 to £24). Set L £17.50 (2 courses) to £45, Set D £65 **Service:** not inc, card slips closed **Cards:** Amex, Delta, Maestro, MasterCard, Visa **Details:** 36 seats. Private parties: 32 main room. No smoking. Music. Air-conditioned

MAP 8 **Ambleside** CUMBRIA

Drunken Duck Inn

NEW ENTRY

Barngates, Ambleside LA22 0NG
Tel: (015394) 36347
Website: www.drunkenduckinn.co.uk

Cooking 3 | Modern British | £32–£67

The Drunken Duck represents some kind of departure among Lakeland establishments, nailing its colours neither to the 'layers of chintz' nor the 'cheerily homespun' masts. Indeed, it feels positively city slick, thought a visitor. On a steep crag in its own 60 acres high above Windermere, the cream-coloured inn certainly looks the part, and the imaginative décor inside extends to a wooden-floored sleek bar area and retro scenes of country fairs gone by on the dining room walls. Nick Foster runs a vibrant, thoroughly contemporary kitchen, with plenty to fire the imagination. Tempura-fried okra with lime, orange and cardamom marmalade is full of sharp flavour contrasts, and has preceded a main course of soft-battered cod with chunky chips and salt and vinegar butter sauce, all artfully constructed into a tower. On another occasion, a starter of gamey, pink, liquorice-marinated pigeon with prune and Parmesan risotto went before noisettes of Herdwick shearling (which is a little older than traditional lamb), sparsely sauced with watercress cream and accompanied by potato galette, red pepper and leek purée. The provenance of materials is proudly trumpeted, and the inventive impulse continues through to desserts such as maple-syruped waffles with an ice cream flavoured with both vanilla and Tag Lag beer, this last ingredient provided by the on-site Barngates brewery. The enterprising, carefully chosen wine list has useful notes and a strong listing of wines by the glass from £2.95. Bottle prices open at £11.95.

Chef: Nick Foster **Proprietors:** Stephanie Barton, Paul Spencer and Peter Barton **Open:** all week 12 to 2.30, 6 to 9 **Closed:** 25 Dec **Meals:** alc (main courses £9.50 to £23). Bar L menu available **Service:** not inc, card slips closed **Cards:** Amex, Delta, Maestro, MasterCard, Visa **Details:** 60 seats. Private parties: 20 main room. Car park. Vegetarian meals. Children's helpings. No smoking. Wheelchair access (also WC). No music **Accommodation:** 16 rooms, all with bath/shower. TV. Phone. B&B £75 to £210. Rooms for disabled. Fishing

Rothay Manor

Rothay Bridge, Ambleside LA22 0EH
Tel: (015394) 33605
Website: www.rothaymanor.co.uk

Cooking 3 | Modern British | £29–£58

Since the late 1960s this listed Georgian residence has made its mark as one of the most personable country houses in the Lake District. Thanks to 'Nixon family solidarity', it has become a truly approachable small hotel 'without delusions of grandeur'. Lunch is particularly good value: a professionally made game terrine with Cumberland sauce, followed by escalopes of pork fillet with sautéed leeks and bacon, and mustard and dill sauce impressed one visitor. Dinner can run to five courses, and the kitchen makes the most of fine raw materials for dishes with bags of old-fashioned vigour: roast Cartmel Valley pheasant is paired with damson compote, rack of fell-bred lamb is served medium-rare on couscous, and grilled lemon sole fillet is accompanied by lemongrass and coriander butter. The tradition of Lakeland desserts flourishes here with the likes of sticky toffee pudding, and blueberry brûlée with Grasmere gingerbread. An unpretentious wine list mixes everyday bottles with more serious options, all at good prices (from £14). Alsace and the Rhône sparkle in France, with Australia and New Zealand taking the southern hemisphere honours. As well as five basics by the glass, most bottles can be split if you want only half.

Chefs: Jane Binns and Colette Nixon **Proprietors:** Nigel and Stephen Nixon **Open:** all week 12.30 to 1.45, 7.15 to 9 **Closed:** 3 to 27 Jan **Meals:** alc L exc Sun (main courses £10). Set L Sun £19.50, Set D £33 to £37. Light L menu available **Service:** not inc **Cards:** Amex, Delta, Diners, Maestro, MasterCard, Visa **Details:** 65 seats. Private parties: 34 main room. Car park. Vegetarian meals. Children's helpings. No children under 7 at D. No smoking. Wheelchair access (also WC). No music. Air-conditioned **Accommodation:** 19 rooms, all with bath/shower. TV. Phone. B&B £65 to £185. Rooms for disabled. Baby facilities. Fishing

MAP 3 **Amersham**
BUCKINGHAMSHIRE

Artichoke

9 Market Square, Amersham HP7 0DF
Tel: (01494) 726611
Website: www.theartichokerestaurant.co.uk

Cooking 4 | Modern French | £39–£66

Tailor-made for the gentrified affluence of Old Amersham, this smart conversion of a sixteenth-century listed house is intimate, serene and tasteful almost to a fault. The kitchen delivers modern European food with a strong French bias and a feel for seasonal ingredients. Fish is from Devon, and resulting dishes could include poached turbot fillet with fine green beans, cockle and grain-mustard broth and creamed celeriac, or roast monkfish paired with crisp belly pork, cauliflower purée and red wine jus. Meaty alternatives are in the same mould: duck breast comes with a confit of leg, quince and rhubarb compote and purple sprouting broccoli, while Aberdeen Angus fillet is embellished with seared foie gras, sautéed ceps, trompettes and girolles and dauphinois potatoes. The Anglo-French cheeseboard is impressive and desserts have featured warm dark-chocolate fondant with Seville orange confit and orange Cointreau jelly. The wine cellar has been beefed up (especially in the Burgundy section) and there's plenty of choice beyond France; prices start at £15.

Chef: Laurie Gear **Proprietors:** Laurie Gear and Jacqueline Dare **Open:** Tue to Sat 12 to 2, 6.30 to 9.15 (9.45 Fri and Sat) **Meals:** alc L (main courses £12 to £20). Set L £23.50 (2 courses) to £29.50, Set D £27 (2 courses) to £50 (whole table). **Service:** 12.5% (optional), card slips closed **Cards:** Delta, MasterCard, Maestro, Visa **Details:** 24 seats. 4 seats outside. Private parties: 26 main room. Vegetarian meals. Children's helpings. No smoking. Music

Gilbey's

1 Market Square, Amersham HP7 0DF
Tel: (01494) 727242

'It has consistently been a pleasant local restaurant,' is one verdict on this wine bar/bistro in a former seventeenth-century grammar school, now jazzed up with vibrant landscapes and foodie watercolours. It offers good-value set lunches – tuna with rösti, confit tomatoes and salsa verde, and herb-crusted cod fillet with provençale linguine (£11.75 for two courses), as well as an eclectic carte where all tastes are indulged, be it for fillet steak, or barramundi with mussels, pak choi, vermicelli and curried coconut sauce (£17). Homemade ice creams and sorbets figure among desserts along with rhubarb crumble (£5). Open all week.

MAP 10 **Applethwaite** CUMBRIA

Underscar Manor

Applethwaite CA12 4PH
Tel: (01768) 775000

Cooking 5 | Anglo-French | £41–£72

From the conservatory dining room of this ornate, Italianate Victorian house sweeping views down to Derwentwater provide all the visual drama Lakeland is famous for. The cooking's country-house opulence ranges from starters like a duo of fried calf's liver and duck foie gras, to mains such as saddle of local venison with lentil and game hotpot, red cabbage and wild mushrooms. Honey-glazed Barbary duck breast with a crispy duck pancake, oriental sauce and deep-fried leek makes an impressive starter, and a crisp-skinned sea bass fillet with crunchy baby asparagus and 'subtle saucing' was one diner's 'best dish of the evening', although frozen Café de Paris butter didn't enhance an otherwise perfectly cooked ribeye steak. Well-tried desserts include warm banana and butterscotch tart served with rum and raisin ice cream and Bailey's crème anglaise, and an iced apple parfait topped with hazelnut crumble accompanying hot apple fritters and raspberry sauce. Breads are good, and service can be highly professional. France heads the international wine list, which begins with house wines at £18, and rises gently thereafter.

Chef: Robert Thornton **Proprietors:** Pauline and Derek Harrison and Gordon Evans **Open:** all week 12 to 1, 7 to 8.30 (9 Sat) **Closed:** 2 or 3 days after New Year **Meals:** alc (main courses, L £15, D £21). Set L £28, Set D £38 **Service:** not inc, card slips closed **Cards:** Amex, Delta, Maestro, MasterCard, Visa **Details:** 50 seats. 12 seats outside. Private parties: 30 main room, 20 to 25 private rooms. Car park. Vegetarian meals. No children under 12. Jacket. No smoking. Occasional music. No mobile phones **Accommodation:** 11 rooms, all with bath/shower. TV. Phone. D,B&B £110 to £275. No children under 12. Swimming pool

MAP 2 **Ardington** OXFORDSHIRE

Boar's Head

Church Street, Ardington OX12 8QA
Tel: (01235) 833254
Website: www.boarsheadardington.co.uk

Cooking 4 | Modern European | £31–£60

The Boar's Head looks every inch the village pub with its black-and-white façade, simple, uncluttered interior and open fire; its easy-going approach is just the ticket, too, allowing options of just drinking, or snacking, or eating a meal in the restaurant. Bruce Buchan's food responds to the seasons and sourcing is a strength – poultry, game and vegetables all come from within a five-mile radius, while fish is delivered daily from Newlyn – and the kitchen takes a lively approach to whatever comes its way. This could include a starter of sole cannelloni with crab stuffing and mussel stew, or main courses of flash-roast partridge with red cabbage, seared foie gras and shallots in red wine, and seared cod with chorizo, caramelised sweetbreads and shiraz sauce. Although European-based, the kitchen takes naturally to some lively Eastern flavourings, including crispy duck and five-spice salad. Farmhouse cheeses are served with sticky malt bread, and desserts have included Paris-Brest with praline cream and chocolate sorbet, and pink grapefruit gratin with passion-fruit sorbet. The wine list's heart lies in France, but there's a brief global roundup, and prices open at £11.

Chef: Bruce Buchan **Proprietors:** Bruce Buchan, Terry Chipperfield and Richard Douglas **Open:** all week 12 to 2.15, 7 to 9.30 (10 Fri and Sat) **Closed:** 3 to 4 days Christmas and New Year **Meals:** alc (not Sun L; main courses £14 to £19.50). Set L Sun £20. Bar menu also available **Service:** not inc, card slips closed **Cards:** Amex, Delta, MasterCard, Maestro, Visa **Details:** 40 seats. 20 seats outside. Private parties: 26 main room, 10 to 16 private rooms. Car park. Children's helpings. No smoking in 1 dining room. Music. No mobile phones **Accommodation:** 3 rooms, all with bath/shower. TV. Phone. B&B £75 to £130. Baby facilities

AR	Not a full entry but provisionally recommended (known as 'round-ups' in previous editions, these 'also recommended' establishments are now integrated throughout the book).

MAP 2 **Arlingham** GLOUCESTERSHIRE

Old Passage Inn

Passage Road, Arlingham GL2 7JR
Tel: (01452) 740547
Website: www.fishattheoldpassageinn.co.uk

Cooking 3 | Seafood | £33–£93

Stunning isolation (beyond Arlingham village), where the lowest ferry over the Severn once plied its trade, is part of the allure of this civilised, brasserie-style inn overlooking the river and the Forest of Dean. There's now a second dining room-with-views alongside the first, otherwise it's business as usual. The inn's reputation hinges on its seafood (most from 'sustainable stocks in the South-west', according to owner and fish maestro Somerset Moore). Oysters, lobsters and fruits de mer are all on the menu, but it also runs to scallops thermidor, roasted whole dab with bacon lardons, clams and other molluscs in parsley sauce, and poached turbot with hollandaise. Meat-eaters could opt for Severn Vale sirloin steak, while desserts range from passion-fruit crème brûlée to poached rhubarb with set vanilla cream. The broadly based, knowledgably sourced wine list is arranged by price, from £11.20 upwards.

Chefs: Patrick Le Mesurier and Raoul Moore **Proprietors:** the Moore family **Open:** Tue to Sun L 12 to 2, Tue to Sat D 6.30 to 9 **Meals:** alc (main courses £11.50 to £37.50) **Service:** not inc **Cards:** Amex, Delta, Maestro, MasterCard, Visa **Details:** 60 seats. 20 seats outside. Private parties: 50 main room, 8 to 14 private rooms. Car park. Children's helpings. No smoking. Wheelchair access (also WC). Occasional music. No mobile phones. Air-conditioned **Accommodation:** 3 rooms, all with bath/shower. TV. Phone. B&B £50 to £95

MAP 8 **Arncliffe** NORTH YORKSHIRE

Amerdale House

Arncliffe, Littondale BD23 5QE
Tel: (01756) 770250
Website: www.amerdalehouse.co.uk

Cooking 4 | Modern European | £45–£54

More like a carefully tended family home than a country hotel, Amerdale House remains a delightful place to visit, tucked away from it all in a quiet corner of the Dales. Having a high-class butcher close by is a blessing for chef/proprietor Nigel Crapper, who serves loin of Dales lamb on minted couscous with a port and redcurrant jus, and pairs Gloucester Old Spot pork with caramelised apples and red wine gravy. Fish also appears, in the guise of, say, roast fillets of sea bass with cherry tomatoes and warm pesto dressing. Dinner is a four-course affair, with starters like herb omelette with tomato and basil followed by an intermediate course (perhaps asparagus with hollandaise), while the choice of desserts could range from chocolate marquise with minted cream and raspberries to steamed syrup sponge with custard. France and the New World occupy the lion's share of the varied wine list. House selections start at £13.50.

Chef: Nigel Crapper **Proprietors:** Paula and Nigel Crapper **Open:** all week D only 7.30 to 8.30 **Closed:** mid-Nov to mid-Mar **Meals:** Set D £34.50 **Service:** not inc, card slips closed **Cards:** Maestro, MasterCard, Visa **Details:** 24 seats. Car park. No smoking. No music **Accommodation:** 11 rooms, all with bath/shower. TV. Phone. D,B&B £101 to £176. Baby facilities

MAP 3 **Arundel** WEST SUSSEX

Arundel House

NEW ENTRY

11 High Street, Arundel BN18 9AD
Tel: (01903) 882136
Website: www.arundelhouseonline.com

Cooking 3 | Modern British | £39–£59

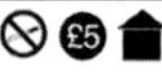

This bow-windowed former B&B sits at the bottom of the High Street hill, just a stroll from the castle. A pair of dining rooms is simply kitted out in bold primary colours, the congenial atmosphere only slightly undermined by piped pop music, and the seasonal menu revolves around solid, classic preparations. Dish of the day at inspection was a starter of creamy scrambled pheasant egg, served with prawns and smoked salmon. A fondness for working two main ingredients together might involve interlacing pork rillettes with duck confit, or painstakingly plaiting together salmon and halibut fillets. Meats are sensitively handled, whether Scotch beef fillet with celeriac rösti and a well-judged Stilton sauce, or juicy, sweet lamb loin with a sausage of the kidney and a satisfying red wine reduction. Desserts have included chocolate Amaretto torte with vanilla cream, or orange pannacotta topped with caramelised zest and accompanied by honeyed figs. Co-owner Billy Lewis-Bowker leads the front-of-house with enormous enthusiasm. His well-thought, French-led wine list opens with a page of glass selections from £3.50, but prices look reasonable throughout. Bottles start at £14.

Chefs: Luke Hackman and Johnathon May **Proprietors:** Billy Lewis-Bowker and Luke Hackman **Open:** Mon to Sat 12 to 2, 7 to 10. Reservations only **Closed:** 25 and 26 Dec, 15 to 28 Feb **Meals:** alc (main courses L £12, D £18) **Service:** not inc, 10% for parties of 8 or more **Cards:** Amex, Delta, Maestro, MasterCard, Visa **Details:** 34 seats. Private parties: 16 main room. Vegetarian meals. No children under 12. No smoking. Music **Accommodation:** 5 rooms, all with bath/shower. TV. Phone. B&B £65 to £140. No children under 12.

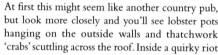

MAP 9 **Asenby** NORTH YORKSHIRE

Crab & Lobster

Dishforth Road, Asenby YO7 3QL
Tel: (01845) 577286
Website: www.crabandlobster.com

Cooking 3 | Fish/Modern European | £31–£66

At first this might seem like another country pub, but look more closely and you'll see lobster pots hanging on the outside walls and thatchwork 'crabs' scuttling across the roof. Inside a quirky riot of curios and memorabilia (a suspended bass drum here, fishermen's nets there) give the place an OTT bohemian uniqueness. Fish is the big thing here: lobster thermidor has been praised, but the kitchen turns its hand to everything from seared king scallops with sweet paprika, chorizo and white bean croûte to cured haddock with cheese and onion mash and poached egg. Meat eaters are also well accommodated with, perhaps, braised lamb shank with 'hotpot' potatoes and home-pickled cabbage, while desserts range from plum and apple crumble to tarte Tatin of local rhubarb. Breads are excellent, and the wine list has plenty of vigorous drinking from £16. The accommodation is in nearby Crab Manor.

Chef: Steve Dean **Proprietor:** Paul Mackings **Open:** all week 12 to 2.30, 7 to 9 (6.30 to 9.30 Sat) **Meals:** alc (main courses £10 to £19.50). Set L £14.50 (2 courses) to £17.50, Set D £29.50. Afternoon menu available 3 to 6 **Service:** not inc, card slips closed **Cards:** Amex, Delta, Maestro, MasterCard, Visa **Details:** 140 seats. 70 seats outside. Private parties: 110 main room, 5 to 110 private rooms. Car park. Vegetarian meals. Children's helpings. No smoking. Wheelchair access (also WC). Music. No mobile phones. Air-conditioned **Accommodation:** 14 rooms, all with bath/shower. TV. Phone. B&B £90 to £200. Rooms for disabled. Baby facilities

MAP 5 **Ashbourne** DERBYSHIRE

Callow Hall

Mappleton Road, Ashbourne DE6 2AA
Tel: (01335) 300900
Website: www.callowhall.co.uk

Cooking 3 | Modern British-Plus | £38–£62

The Spencer family have been at this Victorian pile set in 44 acres since 1984. Nobody succeeds for this length of time without adapting to change, and the Spencers embrace variety with a will. The kitchen smokes, butchers, makes its own sausages, bakes bread and pastries, and takes full advantage of local produce. It hits all the fashionable buttons with sweet-and-sour red onions (accompanying asparagus spears and toasted goats' cheese), Thai-style crushed sweet potato (with confit of duck), and mustard mash (teamed with wild halibut steak and leek fumé), but can also turn out a straightforward roast loin and rack of lamb with lamb and leek sausages and rosemary and honey glaze. It all hangs together because the well-balanced four-course format – not cheap, but you get a lot for your money – has realistic aims that are consistently achieved. The trolley is wheeled out for dessert with British and French cheeses in good condition as an alternative.

From affordable clarets through to sound Argentinian bottles from Norton, the wine list offers consistent interest and value, with prices from £11.95, and there are good options by the glass and half-bottle. Fine wines are admirably international.

Chefs: Anthony and David Spencer **Proprietors:** David, Dorothy, Anthony and Emma Spencer **Open:** Sun L 12.30 to 1.30, Mon to Sat D 7.30 to 9 **Closed:** 25 and 26 Dec **Meals:** alc (main courses £16.50 to £19.50). Set L Sun £23.50, Set D £39.50 **Service:** not inc **Cards:** Amex, Delta, Diners, MasterCard, Maestro, Visa **Details:** 80 seats. Private parties: 40 main room, 25 to 30 private rooms. Car park. Vegetarian meals. Children's helpings. No smoking. Wheelchair access (not WC). No music. No mobile phones **Accommodation:** 16 rooms, all with bath/shower. TV. Phone. B&B £90 to £175. Rooms for disabled. Baby facilities. Fishing

The Dining Room

33 St John Street, Ashbourne DE6 1GP
Tel: (01335) 300666
Website: www.thediningroomashbourne.co.uk

Cooking 4 | Modern British-Plus | £36–£65

Peter and Laura Dale's sixteenth-century restaurant scores heavily with its attentive, knowledgeable

service and modern furnishings that blend well with low beams and an old kitchen range. Peter's cooking is infused with fashionable round-the-world treatments, from langoustine and bacon served with shellfish bisque pannacotta, oxtail rösti, passion fruit, green lemon oil and sesame biscuit, to home-smoked salmon with horseradish foam, caperberries, olive oil and cucumber dressing with brown bread, caviar and lemon and lime jelly. Scallops appear to be a staple on the menu, according to one regular, who was equally impressed by the use of less commonly seen cuts of meat, among them 'succulent' pig's cheek and saddle, faggots and a tiny rack of hare in a chocolate and blood sauce. The food's strongly seasonal feel extends to desserts like a winter-menu apple and sweet-potato bread-and-butter pudding served with five-spice and orange biscuit, honeycomb ice cream and English custard foam. The all-British cheeseboard continues to elicit praise, and well-chosen wines are very fairly priced, starting with house French at £15.95.

Chef: Peter Dale **Proprietors:** Peter and Laura Dale **Open:** Tue to Sat 12 to 1.30, 7 to 8.30 **Closed:** 2 weeks from Christmas, 1 week Mar, 1 week Sept **Meals:** alc (main courses L £13, D £20). Set L £22.50. Set D (tasting menu; needs pre-booking) £40 **Service:** not inc, card slips closed **Cards:** Delta, MasterCard, Maestro, Visa **Details:** 16 seats. Private parties: 16 main room. No children under 12. No smoking. Wheelchair access (also WC). No music. No mobile phones

MAP 1 **Ashburton** DEVON

Agaric

30 North Street, Ashburton TQ13 7QD
Tel: (01364) 654478
Website: www.agaricrestaurant.co.uk

Cooking 4 | Modern British-Plus | £36–£63

'What a really smashing little restaurant,' enthused a visitor who left this unprepossessing gem with a big smile on his face. There's not a trace of stuffy formality here, but bags of good humour and evidence of serious domestic enterprise on every shelf. Nick Coiley is a food crusader, championing Devon produce, harvesting from his kitchen garden and producing everything from focaccia to pungent home-cured ham (used as a wrapping for baked asparagus spears and goats' cheese). The result is genuine, unaffected natural cooking. Pan-fried scallops with smoked bacon and a pool of buttery juices is typical of his unadorned approach, while fragrant five-spice duck breast, with a steamed and crispy leg and rhubarb sauce, is all about 'great flavours, immediacy and subtlety'. Vegetables are vibrantly fresh, and desserts highlight the virtues of simplicity in the shape of, say, warm lemon tart with 'just the right citrus edge'. The wine list does its job, with a good range and fair prices from £13.

Chef: Nick Coiley **Proprietors:** Nick and Sophie Coiley **Open:** Wed to Fri L 12 to 2, Wed to Sat D 7 to 9; also open for L first and last Sun in month **Closed:** 2 weeks at Christmas, last 2 weeks Aug **Meals:** alc (main courses £15 to £17.50). Set L Wed to Fri £12.95 (2 courses) **Service:** not inc, card slips closed **Cards:** Delta, Maestro, MasterCard, Visa **Details:** 28 seats. 20 seats outside. Private parties: 30 main room. Vegetarian meals. Children's helpings. No smoking. Wheelchair access (also WC). No music. No mobile phones **Accommodation:** 6 rooms, all with bath/shower. B&B £40 to £140. Rooms for disabled. Baby facilities

MAP 9 **Ashford** DERBYSHIRE

Riverside House

Ashford in the Water DE45 1QF
Tel: (01629) 814275
Website: www.riversidehousehotel.co.uk

Cooking 4 | French-Plus | £53–£64

Owned by one of the Thorntons Chocolates dynasty, this highly attractive Georgian house looks out on to immaculately maintained gardens by the banks of the River Wye. Inside, the whole place is imbued with a sense of gracious living and elegant sophistication, although the atmosphere can sometimes seem a touch 'precious'.

John Whelan's assured cooking owes much to France, as evidenced by a cleverly fashioned terrine of pressed confit of corn-fed chicken, foie gras and girolles, with a beautiful marbled effect, and fillet of Derbyshire-reared beef with shallots, mushrooms and parsley aïoli, but other influences are also at work: 'glistening' seared Cornish scallops with sweet tomatoes, red onions and air-dried ham are topped with deep-fried basil leaves, while 'snowy white' fillet of brill (also from Cornwall) sits on a cushion of colcannon with slivers of chorizo and aubergine purée. Desserts include 'a small battalion of doll's-house-sized dishes' comprising a citrus compote, jelly and mousse, or a savoury like warm apple and Stilton crumble, plus an excellent international array of cheeses. The ringbound wine 'directory' offers a well-balanced international selection and affable commentaries with house bottles from £16.95.

Chef: John Whelan **Proprietor:** Penelope Thornton **Open:** all week 12 to 2, 6 to 9.30 **Meals:** alc L (main courses £9 to £16), Set D £44.95 **Service:** not inc **Cards:** Amex, Delta, Diners, MasterCard, Maestro, Visa **Details:** 55 seats. 20 seats outside. Private parties: 55 main room, 15 to 30 private rooms. Car park. Vegetarian meals. No children under 12. No smoking. Wheelchair access (also WC). No music. No mobile phones **Accommodation:** 14 rooms, all with bath/shower. TV. Phone. B&B £100 to £220. Rooms for disabled. No children under 12

MAP 1 **Ashwater** DEVON

Blagdon Manor

Ashwater EX21 5DF
Tel: (01409) 211224
Website: www.blagdon.com

Cooking 2 | English/Mediterranean | £30–£54

Genuine family hospitality sets the tone in Steve and Liz Morey's intimate hideaway on the Devon–Cornwall border. Blagdon was listed in the Domesday Book, although the current building (and most of its original features) dates from the seventeenth century. Steve produces 'an interesting, modern but sensible menu', as one reporter put it, built around well-sourced local ingredients: West Country scallops might be served on a niçoise salad with a red wine vinegar dressing (the same treatment is also applied to goats' cheese), while main courses have included a 'fun' version of fish and chips as well as roast haunch of venison with braised red cabbage and green peppercorn sauce. Hot banana soufflé with rum and raisin ice cream is a typical dessert. A good showing of half-bottles bolsters the well-spread wine list. House wine is £12.70.

Chef: Steve Morey **Proprietors:** Liz and Steve Morey **Open:** Wed to Sun L 12 to 2, Tue to Sat D 7 to 9 (residents only Sun D and Mon D) **Closed:** New Year, 2 weeks Jan to Feb, 2 weeks Oct to Nov **Meals:** Set L Wed to Sat £15 (2 courses) to £18, Set L Sun £21.50, Set D £28 (2 courses) to £32 **Service:** not inc **Cards:** Delta, Maestro, MasterCard, Visa **Details:** 30 seats. Private parties: 16 main room, 10 to 16 private rooms. Car park. No children under 12. No smoking. Wheelchair access (also WC). No music. No mobile phones **Accommodation:** 7 rooms, all with bath/shower. TV. Phone. B&B £80 to £110. No children under 12

This symbol means that the restaurant has elected to participate in *The Good Food Guide's* £5 voucher scheme (see 'How to Use the Guide' for details).

MAP 2 **Awre** GLOUCESTERSHIRE

Red Hart Inn

NEW ENTRY

Awre GL14 1EW
Tel: (01594) 510220

Cooking 2 | Modern British | £26–£48

Hidden away almost on the bank of the Severn, the tiny hamlet of Awre now sports a splendidly revitalised village pub – thanks to enthusiastic new licensees. They are making a real effort to get their hands on genuinely local raw materials: the Awre family butcher provides top-notch meat, green-stuff is grown nearby, cheeses are from Gloucestershire dairies, and even cider is brewed in the village. Simplicity and flavour win the day: witness a warm seafood salad with sun-blush tomatoes, or medallions of beef with beetroot and aubergine sauce accompanied by a harvest festival of 'out-of-this-world' vegetables. Pub favourites like Gloucester Old Spot sausages with bubble and squeak also feature, and desserts are straightforward ideas like warm pear and almond tart. House wine is £11.95.

Chefs: Andrew Palmer, Wayne Preece and Sam Buzzard **Proprietors:** Marcia Griffiths and Martin Coupe **Open:** all week 12 to 2.30, 6 to 9.30 (9 Sun) **Closed:** 23 Jan to 5 Feb **Meals:** alc (main courses £8 to £16). Light L menu available in summer **Service:** not inc, card slips closed **Cards:** Amex, Delta, Maestro, MasterCard, Visa **Details:** 60 seats. 40 seats outside. Private parties: 60 main room, 30 private room. Car park. Vegetarian meals. Children's helpings. No smoking. Wheelchair access (not WC). Music. No mobile phones **Accommodation:** 2 rooms, both with bath/shower. TV. B&B £50 to £80. Baby facilities

MAP 10 **Aycliffe** CO DURHAM

County

13 The Green, Aycliffe Village DL5 6LX
Tel: (01325) 312273
Website: www.the-county.co.uk

Cooking 3 | Modern European | £33–£54

Outside it looks like a regular village pub overlooking the green, and inside a bar dispenses hand-pumped ales. But pine tables and chairs in both rooms and a prominent blackboard menu emphasizes food's ascendancy. Mushroom soup with truffle oil started a spring bar lunch enjoyably; cod in beer batter with 'excellent' chips followed, and a 'refreshing and lively trio' of orange pannacotta, sorbet and jelly made a light ending. The evening carte runs from pressed terrine of smoked rabbit and leek, to sea bass fillet with olive oil new potatoes and grilled Mediterranean vegetables, or pan-roast duck breast with sweet carrot purée and poached fig with port sauce. Then there's local cheeses or bitter chocolate tart to finish. Service is unpretentious and friendly. House wines from £3.10 a glass, £11.95 a bottle, head a short, global and fairly priced list.

Chefs: Andrew Brown and John McCerery **Proprietors:** Andrew and Deborah Brown **Open:** Mon to Sat 12 to 2, 6 (Sat 6.45) to 9.15 **Closed:** 25 and 26 Dec, 1 Jan **Meals:** alc D (main courses £6.95 to £19.50). Bar menu available Mon to Sat L and Mon to Fri 6 to 7 **Service:** not inc, card slips closed **Cards:** Amex, Delta, Maestro, MasterCard, Visa **Details:** 90 seats. Car park. Children's helpings. No smoking. Occasional music

MAP 3 Aylesbury BUCKINGHAMSHIRE

Hartwell House

Oxford Road, Aylesbury HP17 8NL
Tel: (01296) 747444
Website: www.hartwell-house.com

Cooking 4 | Modern European | £31–£81

Stately homes don't come much more palatial than this grandiose mansion, with its extravagant Jacobean and Georgian features and vistas of parkland. It makes an aristocratic but unstuffy setting for precisely executed modern European food. Vale of Aylesbury lamb, organic vegetables from the hotel's garden, and other carefully sourced ingredients are deployed for fixed-price menus that steer clear of over-elaboration. Terrines are a favourite starter (a marbled triangle with foie gras, smoked duck, and baby leeks made a good impression), and the kitchen seems fond of fungi: 'forest' mushrooms in a risotto, morels with roast breast of Gressingham duck and Savoy cabbage, and a port and truffle sauce with 'exceedingly fresh' sea bass fillet, for example. Dishes can lack sparkle, but desserts are impeccably crafted: witness dark chocolate mousse with white chocolate and orange ice cream and orange syrup. Service is 'all very correct', but the mood never seems solemn. The monumental wine list has an immense range but aggressive mark-ups. Prices start at £17.50.

Chef: Daniel Richardson **Proprietor:** Historic House Hotels Ltd **Open:** all week 12.30 to 1.45, 7.30 to 9.45 **Meals:** Set L Mon to Sat £22 (2 courses) to £29, Set L Sun £22.50, Set D £46. Buttery L menu available **Service:** net prices, card slips closed **Cards:** Amex, Maestro, MasterCard, Visa **Details:** 60 seats. 25 seats outside. Private parties: 60 main room, 12 to 60 private rooms. Car park. Vegetarian meals. No children under 8. Jacket. No smoking. Wheelchair access (also WC). Occasional music. No mobile phones **Accommodation:** 46 rooms, all with bath/shower. TV. Phone. B&B £165 to £270. Rooms for disabled. No children under 8. Swimming pool. Fishing

MAP 3 Aylesford KENT

Hengist

NEW ENTRY

7–9 High Street, Aylesford ME20 7AX
Tel: (01622) 719273
Email: the.hengist@btconnect.com

Cooking 2 | Modern French | £23–£60

Aylesford is reputed to be one of the oldest village in England, but as far as Hengist is concerned y olde England stops at the door. What you get is strongly pared-back, minimalist look with lots c ancient wood and stone teamed with wack touches like bronze taffeta curtains and a chande lier encased in the glass reception desk. The con nection with Thackeray's (see entry, Tunbridg Wells) is easy to spot, and Kieren Steinborn-Busse former chef at Thackeray's, mans the stoves. Loc and regional materials play a role, and the style c cooking embraces duck foie gras with a poache egg and celeriac velouté infused with truffle, an pan-fried red mullet with basil linguine, blac olives, and pesto butter sauce. The highlight of a inspection meal was dessert: a trio of mini crèm brûlées – white chocolate, rhubarb, and lemor Bread is 'outstanding', service young, enthusiasti and prompt, and reasonable mark-ups characteriz the intelligently composed wine list, which star at £12.

Chefs: Richard Phillips and Kieren Steinborn-Busse **Proprietors:** Kevin James, Paul Smith and Richard Phillips **Open:** Tue to Sun L 12 to 2.30, Tue to Sat D 6.30 to 10.30 **Meals:** alc exc Sun L (main courses £12 to £17). Set L Tue to Sat £9.95 (2 courses) to £11.95, Set L Sun £16.50 (2 courses) to £18.50 **Service:** 12.5% (optional) **Cards:** Amex, Maestro, MasterCard, Visa **Details:** 70 seats. 20 seats outside. Private parties: 42 main room, 8 to 18 private rooms. Vegetarian meals. Children's helpings. No smoking. Wheelchair access (also WC). Music. Air-conditioned

MAP 8 **Bakewell** DERBYSHIRE

Renaissance

Bath Street, Bakewell DE45 1BX
Tel: (01629) 812687
Website: www.renaissance-restaurant.com

Cooking 3 | £23–£62

Housed in an architecturally attractive Derbyshire-stone building, the Piedaniels' welcoming restaurant does the local community proud. The cooking has its heart in the right place, looking to the owners' native France for much of its inspiration. 'Delightful' soufflés and mousses pop up all over the place and the cooking involves a good deal of artifice: slices of pink lamb fillet are supported by a twirl of pastry, topped with a spinach soufflé and served with tarragon and red wine sauce, while tournedos of Gressingham duck is set on a slice of peppery pineapple confit with lime sauce. Refreshing mid-course sorbets arrive unannounced, and desserts are pleasing creations like iced nougatine timbale wrapped in a honey biscuit. The fairly priced wine list flies the flag for France, although the rest of the world isn't excluded; house selections are £11.99.

Chefs: Eric Piedaniel and J. Gibbard **Proprietors:** Mr and Mrs Eric Piedaniel, and Mrs D. Béraud **Open:** Tue to Sun L 12 to 2, Tue to Sat D 7 to 9.30 **Closed:** 2 weeks Aug, 2 weeks Christmas **Meals:** Set L Tue to Thur £14.95, Set L Tue to Sat £27.95, Set L Sun £17.95 (3 courses), Set D Tue to Thur £14.95, Tue to Sun £27.95. Bistro menu also available. **Service:** not inc **Cards:** Amex, MasterCard, Maestro, Visa **Details:** 45 seats. Private parties: 70 main room, 27 private room. Vegetarian meals. Children's helpings. No smoking. Wheelchair access (not WC). Occasional music

MAP 2 **Barnsley** GLOUCESTERSHIRE

Barnsley House

NEW ENTRY

Barnsley GL7 5EE
Tel: (01285) 740000
Website: www.barnsleyhouse.com

Cooking 5 | Modern European | £45–£81

Easy to find on the main street, the large, Cotswold-stone house is under the same ownership as the Village Pub a few doors along. It sits in gorgeously appointed gardens, designed by the great Rosemary Verey, and the interiors have been refurbished with every conceivable modern amenity, from plasma-screen TVs in the guest rooms to suede-upholstered seating in the dining room. The chef is Graham Grafton, who arrived after stints at various London Guide listings. The centre of culinary gravity is Italian, with plenty of pasta, ingredients such as pancetta and artichokes, and a house speciality rendition of eastern Italy's vincisgrassi – an eighteenth-century baked pasta dish containing Parma ham, porcini and truffles, resembling nothing so much as 'the most sumptuous version of lasagne ever'. A fortifying slew of white haricots and potato cooked in tomato makes a cassoulet-like underlay for a pair of sautéed red mullet fillets, and an accurately timed piece of lean pork fillet, of good flavour, is accompanied by slices of apple and bitter chicory. These are refreshingly simple dishes that steer clear of over-elaboration.

A version of crème brûlée made with mascarpone gains density from the cheese and contrasting bite from a concealed layer of chopped rhubarb, or there are classics such as peach cooked in marsala with vanilla ice cream and shortbread. Front-of-house does a bang-up job of selling the recommended dishes as well as fielding all menu queries. The wine list opens each section with Italy but soon gets lost in France. Prices are uncomfortable, with even half-bottles looking very steep, although there is a monthly selection of ten wines by the glass from £5.75. A new chef arrived at the Village Pub as we went to press, so reports please.

Chef: Graham Grafton **Proprietors:** Tim Haigh and Rupert Pendered **Open:** all week 12 to 3, 7 to 10 **Meals:** Set L £19.50 (2 courses) to £26, Set D £39.50 to £46 **Service:** 12.5% (optional), card slips closed **Cards:** Delta, Maestro, MasterCard, Visa **Details:** 55 seats. 20 seats outside. Private parties: 58 main room, 12 private room. Car park. No children under 12 at D. No smoking. Wheelchair access (also WC). No music **Accommodation:** 10 rooms, all with bath/shower. TV. Phone. B&B £270 to £475. Rooms for disabled

MAP 2 **Barton on Sea** HAMPSHIRE

Pebble Beach

Marine Drive, Barton on Sea BH25 7DZ
Tel: (01425) 627777
Website: www.pebblebeach-uk.com

Cooking 3 | Modern European/Seafood | £32–£70

After many years in the cosseted, luxurious world of Chewton Glen (see entry, New Milton), Pierre Chevillard crossed to the other side of the A337 and now oversees the kitchen in this upmarket seafront café/brasserie with splendid views out

past the Needles. Chicken and foie gras terrine with pistachios and wild mushrooms recalls bygone country-house days, and foie gras turns up again as a topping for tuna tournedos with red wine and port sauce. Elsewhere, there's plenty to suit all palates, from smoked haddock with bubble and squeak and navarin of lamb to wild mushroom and spinach lasagne. Fish and chips and sausage with mustard mash are reckoned 'lighter options', along with linguine with crab and crayfish, while three-chocolate marquise with coffee anglaise is a typical dessert. France dominates the wine list; ten house selections are from £10.95.

Chef: Pierre Chevillard **Proprietor:** Mike Caddy **Open:** all week 12 to 2 (2.30 Sun), 6.30 to 9.30 (10 Fri/Sat) **Closed:** 25 Dec D, 1 Jan D **Meals:** alc (main courses £9 to £25) **Service:** not inc **Cards:** Amex, Delta, Maestro, MasterCard, Visa **Details:** 70 seats. 40 seats outside. Car park. Vegetarian meals. Children's helpings. No smoking. Wheelchair access (also WC). Music. No mobile phones. Air-conditioned **Accommodation:** 3 rooms, all with bath/shower. TV. B&B £44.95 to £69.95. Baby facilities

MAP 9 **Barton upon Humber** NORTH LINCOLNSHIRE

Elio's AR

11 Market Place, Barton upon Humber DN18 5DA
Tel: (01652) 635147

Elio Grossi's Italian trattoria has been satisfying the people of Humberside for over twenty years. Seafood is something of a speciality – look out for the daily specials. Grilled seabass might come in a lemon sauce (£15.95), and baby squid stuffed with seafood and braised (£14.55). The T-bone steak has been declared 'the best ever', and the list of pizzas (from £8.25) includes a seafood version. Open Mon to Sat D.

MAP 2 **Barwick** SOMERSET

Little Barwick House

Barwick BA22 9TD
Tel: (01935) 423902
Website: www.littlebarwickhouse.co.uk

Cooking 6 | Modern English | £32–£74

In a tranquil setting just outside the village, this elegant, white Georgian restaurant-with-rooms is in three and a half acres of well-maintained gardens. Inside, the small rooms are comfortably furnished and decorated in soothing tones that lend a distinctly English country-house air. Regulars will notice that the dining room has been redecorated, resplendent with natural-coloured, striped hand-painted wallpaper, its wooden floor-boards refurbished and new watercolours hung, giving the room a more elegant and lighter look. There are no changes in the kitchen, though, where Tim Ford works his culinary magic, while wife Emma leads front-of-house with self-assured professionalism. Prime produce from the abundant West Country larder are the raw materials for the imaginative modern cooking, the approach via daily-changing menus that come dotted with luxury items (and no supplements). Expect twice-baked cheese soufflé to feature among starters, perhaps served with fillets of Cornish red mullet and lobster, with main courses along the lines of roast rump of local lamb, maybe teamed with buttered baby spinach, asparagus and a rosemary jus, or grilled fillet of sea bream with sun-dried tomato risotto. Banana tarte Tatin with star anise ice cream is a speciality among appealing desserts.

An imaginative and well-priced range of wines is arranged by style. Closer inspection of the upper reaches of the reds reveals a wish list orientated around France, California and Australia, all with appropriate bottle age. Four house wines (from £13.95) and a number of dessert options come by the glass, and the list of halves runs to around 50 bins.

Chef: Tim Ford **Proprietors:** Tim and Emma Ford **Open:** Wed to Sun L 12 to 2, Tue to Sat D 7 to 9 (9.30 Fri and Sat) **Meals:** alc L (main courses £18.50 to £24). Set L Wed to Sat £16.95 (2 courses) to £18.95, Set L Sun £21.95, Set D £28.95 (2 courses) to £32.95 **Service:** not inc, card slips closed **Cards:** Delta, Maestro, MasterCard, Visa **Details:** 40 seats. 12 seats outside. Private parties: 56 main room, 1 to 18 private rooms. Car park. Vegetarian meals. Children's helpings. No children under 5. No smoking. No music. No mobile phones. Air-conditioned **Accommodation:** 6 rooms, all with bath/shower. TV. Phone. B&B £70 to £130. No children under 5

MAP 9 **Baslow** DERBYSHIRE

Gallery Restaurant

Cavendish Hotel, Baslow DE45 1SP
Tel: (01246) 582311
Website: www.cavendish-hotel.net

Cooking 3 | Modern English | £47–£69

The proprietor of this peaceful country hotel not far from Chatsworth has been running it for three decades with seemingly consummate ease. Of the two dining rooms, the Garden Room enjoys the

minimum formality that comes with an all-day menu and value-for-money pricing, while the Gallery Restaurant is grander in style, but not in approach. The menu descriptions show there's a lot going on in the Gallery dishes, but they make clear culinary sense – whether it's a first course of sweet crispy pork salad with Thai basil, roasted peanuts and sweet chilli dressing, or a tribute to Derbyshire beef consisting of steak-and-mushroom pie, beef-and-stout sausage and chargrilled calf's liver. On a simpler level, the Cavendish seafood mixed grill is a highly praised stalwart of the kitchen. Desserts extend from iced cappuccino parfait with warm sugared doughnuts to baby fig and mascarpone spring roll with a white chocolate and marsala sauce. House wines from France and Chile at £13.75 start a well-chosen list of forty-odd bins.

Chef: Chris Allison **Proprietor:** Eric Marsh **Open:** all week 12.30 to 2, 6.30 to 10 **Meals:** alc (main courses £16 to £20.50) **Service:** 5% **Cards:** Amex, Delta, Diners, Maestro, MasterCard, Visa **Details:** 45 seats. Private parties: 45 main room, 4 to 16 private rooms. Car park. Children's helpings. No smoking. Music. No mobile phones **Accommodation:** 24 rooms, all with bath/shower. TV. Phone. Room only £103 to £173. Rooms for disabled

Fischer's Baslow Hall

Calver Road, Baslow DE45 1RR
Tel: (01246) 583259
Website: www.fischers-baslowhall.co.uk

Cooking 7 | Modern European | £39–£96

Not far from the Chatsworth estate, a little outside the village, is this solid and attractive Edwardian manor house built of mellow Derbyshire stone and tucked into spacious gardens and woodlands. The Fischers have been running it as a hotel with great professionalism and panache since the late 1980s, and some of our correspondents come to stay here a couple of times a year.

What they return for, apart from the finely judged balance of formality and warmth that distinguishes the approach, is the consummately accomplished cooking from a kitchen headed by Rupert Rowley under the aegis of Max Fischer. While a deal of labour has clearly gone into each dish, nothing somehow seems overworked. A pair of John Dory fillets atop a plethora of spring vegetables as a May starter was accompanied by properly crimped tortellini, earthy morels and a herb-infused velouté, the whole dish achieving astonishing depth. On an autumn occasion, a perfectly constructed pie of pigeon and butternut squash, served with wild mushrooms, made a head-turning first course. Shellfish may well turn up alongside meat in main courses – langoustines with squab, or a single scallop on one end of a skewered rabbit sausage, the saddle roasted and matched with roast sweet potatoes. Flavours and seasonings are intense, despite the delicacy of presentation. Lighter dishes might include steamed sea bass on cucumber spaghetti in a champagne nage, while Sunday lunch brings on first-class renditions of more familiar offerings, including roast sirloin of local beef with Yorkshire pudding.

The fashion for desserts that explore one fruit item in a variety of guises is not overlooked here. A pyramid of apple and Calvados parfait of great concentration is partnered by apple soufflé baked in half a Braeburn, alongside a well-textured sorbet of Granny Smith. Summer pudding with crème fraîche and an additional garnish of berries proved a satisfying way to end an August lunch. Upmarket French bottles make up the meat of the wine list, with peers from Australia, California and Italy for company. But there are good affordable options too, starting with five tempting house bottles from £16.

Chefs: Max Fischer and Rupert Rowley **Proprietors:** Max and Susan Fischer **Open:** Tue to Sun L 12 to 1.30, Mon to Sat D 7 to 9.30 (residents only Sun D) **Closed:** 25 and 26 Dec **Meals:** Set L Tue to Sat £20 (2 courses) to £24, Set L Sun £35, Set D Mon to Fri £35 to £65, Set D Sat £60 to £65 **Service:** not inc, card slips closed **Cards:** Amex, Delta, Diners, Maestro, MasterCard, Visa **Details:** 70 seats. 10 seats outside. Private parties: 40 main room, 4 to 18 private rooms. Car park. Vegetarian meals. Children's helpings. No children under 12 after 7pm. No smoking. Wheelchair access (not WC). No music. No mobile phones **Accommodation:** 11 rooms, all with bath/shower. TV. Phone. B&B £100 to £180. Baby facilities

MAP 2 **Bath** BATH & N.E. SOMERSET

Bath Priory

Weston Road, Bath BA1 2XT
Tel: (01225) 331922
Website: www.thebathpriory.co.uk

NEW CHEF | Modern French | £41–£95

Rooms are 'a riot of Edwardiana', writes a visitor to this elegant Bath-stone priory set in one of the city's earliest suburbs and boasting well-tended 'rather romantic gardens' at the back. Chef Robert Clayton left in summer 2005 and his replacement, Chris Horridge, has a background that includes time as senior sous-chef at Le Manoir aux Quat' Saisons (see entry, Great Milton). The new man's menu pairs roasted scallops with broad beans and courgette and lemon purée among starters, and brochette of Gressingham duck with pickled figs and Calvados jus as a main course. Finish with warm Valrhona chocolate fondant with toasted almond ice cream. The wine list is as expensive as the rest of the place, although a few bottles are under £20, with house wines £16.50.

Chef: Chris Horridge **Proprietor:** Andrew Brownsword **Open:** all week 12 to 1.45, 7 to 9.30 (10 Sat) **Meals:** Set L Mon to Sat £20 (2 courses) to £25, Set L Sun £30, Set D £49.50 **Service:** not inc **Cards:** Amex, Delta, Diners, Maestro, MasterCard, Visa **Details:** 64 seats. Private parties: 64 main room, 10 to 64 private rooms. Car park. Vegetarian meals. Children's helpings. No children under 8. No smoking. Wheelchair access (also WC). No music. No mobile phones **Accommodation:** 31 rooms, all with bath/shower. TV. Phone. B&B £145 to £425. Rooms for disabled. Baby facilities. Swimming pool

Firehouse Rotisserie AR

2 John Street, Bath BA1 2JL
Tel: (01225) 482070

This lively joint delivers transatlantic cooking based around the rôtisserie and grill. Best end of lamb with herb-roast vegetables and mint and coriander gremolada (£14), and stone-baked fillets of sea bass with sesame, ginger and wilted Asian greens are typical; otherwise, there are 'small plates' (crayfish and rocket salad with lemon and tarragon dressing; £7), and pizzas from the brick-fired oven (from £10). House wine from £13. Closed Sun. There's a branch at Anchor Square, Bristol; tel: (0117) 915 7323.

FishWorks

6 Green Street, Bath BA1 2JY
Tel: (01225) 448707
Website: www.fishworks.co.uk

Cooking 2 | Seafood | £33–£85

Mitchell Tonks set out his stall in Bath before embarking on a piscine crusade to other locations (Bristol, Christchurch and London; see entries). A trademark bright blue façade and wet-fish display mark the spot, but you need to go upstairs to the main dining area. All branches share a menu comprising assorted crustacea on ice and classics like fish stew and roast skate with black butter and capers. Supplementing this is a more promising specials board based on daily deliveries: plainly grilled scallops with olive oil and lemon have been highly praised. The wine list (from £15.25) shuns the New World in favour of Europe.

Chef: Garry Rosser **Proprietor:** FishWorks plc **Open:** Tue to Sat 12 to 2.30, 6 to 10.30 **Closed:** 24 Dec to early Jan, Tue after bank hols **Meals:** alc (main courses £7 to £35) **Service:** not inc **Cards:** Amex, Delta, Maestro, MasterCard, Visa **Details:** 52 seats. 16 seats outside. Vegetarian meals. Children's helpings. No smoking. Wheelchair access (not WC). Music. Air-conditioned

Hole in the Wall

16–17 George Street, Bath BA1 2EN
Tel: (01225) 425242
Website: www.theholeinthewall.com

Cooking 2 | Modern British | £25–£52

The Hole in the Wall is a two-room restaurant below an elegant Bath-stone house. Modern red paintings add dashes of colour to the green and cream walls, a number of candles create an atmosphere of intimacy, and there's a large stone fireplace, a flagstone floor and banquettes. A fashionably modern British repertoire is on offer via a set-price format: perhaps a fillet of brill teamed with wilted spinach, poached lobster and a champagne velouté, or pork tenderloin with celeriac and thyme mash and caramelised plum chutney. Starters have ranged from an 'outstanding' duck breast marinated in ginger with rocket, to chicken, pigeon and cep terrine with a blackberry and balsamic dressing. Crème brûlée (vanilla and raspberry) or chocolate and pecan tart (with mixed berries) might head up familiar sounding desserts, while the wine list starts off with Chilean house at £11.95.

Chefs: Gerry Dowd and Marco Appel **Proprietors:** Guy Adams, Anthony Whitehouse and Gerry Dowd **Open:** Mon to Sat L 12 to 2.30, all week D 5 (6.30 Sun) to 10 (10.30 Sat, 9.30 Sun) **Meals:** Set L and D 5 to 6.30 £9.95 (2 courses) to £14.95, Set D £19.95 (2 courses) to £24.95 **Service:** not inc **Cards:** Amex, Delta, Diners, Maestro, MasterCard, Visa **Details:** 74 seats. Private parties: 120 main room. Vegetarian meals. No smoking. Wheelchair access (also women's WC). Music. Air-conditioned

King William NEW ENTRY

36 Thomas Street, Bath BA1 5NN
Tel: (01225) 428096
Website: www.kingwilliampub.com

Cooking 2 | English | £25–£40

The Digneys have brought a cheerful passion for food to this pub in an up-and-coming area. Menus are seasonal and kept sensibly short, while West

Country ingredients are handled 'with respect and sensibility'. Commitment to good value and a tribute to English tradition bring bar snacks such as salt-beef sandwich and Welsh rarebit and main courses of oxtail in ale, or a succulent, flavoursome pork chop with apples and pears. At inspection, a carefully constructed terrine of sweetbreads impressed with its delicate creaminess, and rhubarb crumble came with a light and sweet topping contrasting perfectly with the tang of the fruit. Decent bread, butter and coffee show reassuring and comprehensive attention to detail. 'Consistently interesting' beers sit alongside a wine list that starts at £11 and offers a good range by the glass.

Chef: Charlie Digney **Proprietors:** Charlie and Amanda Digney **Open:** Tue to Sun L 12 to 2.45, Wed to Sat D 6.30 to 10 **Meals:** alc L (main courses £7 to £12.50). Set D £17.50 (2 courses) to £20. Bar snack D menu available **Service:** not inc, card slips closed **Cards:** Amex, Delta, Diners, Maestro, MasterCard, Visa **Details:** 50 seats. Private parties: 20 main room, 8 to 24 private rooms. Vegetarian meals. No children in bar area. No smoking. Music

Queensberry Hotel, Olive Tree Restaurant

4–7 Russel Street, Bath BA1 2QF
Tel: (01225) 447928
Website: www.thequeensberry.co.uk

Cooking 3 | Modern British | £28–£69

The Olive Tree is in the basement of a hotel constructed of a row of knocked-together Georgian town houses on a steep hill. Golden-orange lamps and subtle lighting cast a warm glow over the informal ambience of wooden floor and simply laid tables. New chef Marc Salmon, taking over in February 2005, aims to continue the light, modern British style of his predecessor, with much use of seasonal and local produce. Caramelised Gressingham duck breast impressed at inspection, its skin crisp, the meat gaining from nicely tart apple mash, while a vertical tower of pork belly and pleasantly gelatinous cheek has been well supported by coarsely chopped peas with butter and nutmeg. Fish-based starters might include Cornish haddock pie with braised vine tomatoes under a puff pastry lid, while meals could end with nougatine parfait with honey-roast clementines and biscotti. Service needs better training. Wines are grouped into styles that sound good enough to eat – 'raspberries and strawberries', 'black fruits full of body' and so on – and the pin-sharp contemporary selection, including a dozen snappy house wines by glass or bottle (from £13.75), fulfils its promise.

Chef: Marc Salmon **Proprietors:** Helen and Laurence Beere **Open:** Tue to Sun L 12 to 2, all week D 7 to 10 **Meals:** alc (main courses £17 to £23). Set L £14.25 (2 courses) to £16, Set D £29.50 **Service:** not inc **Cards:** Amex, Delta, Maestro, MasterCard, Visa **Details:** 60 seats. Private parties: 70 main room, 12 to 30 private rooms. Vegetarian meals. Children's helpings. No smoking. Music. Air-conditioned **Accommodation:** 29 rooms, all with bath/shower. TV. Phone. Room only £105 to £295. Rooms for disabled. Baby facilities

Royal Crescent, Pimpernel's

16 Royal Crescent, Bath BA1 2LS
Tel: (01225) 823333
Website: www.royalcrescent.co.uk

Cooking 4 | Modern British | £43–£104

Pause at the pillared front entrance of the Royal Crescent Hotel to admire a fine view of Bath on the hillside dropping beyond the lawns to Royal Victoria Park. Pimpernel's is in a grey-stone building at the rear, separated by a 'small, immaculately tended' garden from the main hotel. Technical skills and quality raw materials are the kitchen's strongest suit.

For starters, smoked salmon is carved at the table, while a duo of tuna might come with couscous, white radish rémoulade, Bloody Mary sorbet and garlic cream. A starter of scallops on butternut squash purée with infused curry oil 'certainly had the courage of its minimalist convictions', the shellfish 'perfectly and evenly timed'. Slow-braised lamb shoulder with roast rump has made an impressive main course ('perfection from start to finish'), accompanied by aubergine purée and provençale vegetables, while Anjou squab pigeon has come on a bed of mung beans, wilted leaves and a soy and bacon dressing. Desserts, such as redcurrant baked Alaska with marinated grapefruit and a grenadine and thyme soup, have been rated 'exceptional' by reporters. Extras are bountiful, as are helpful and efficient staff. The wine list presents a worthy range of accompaniments – with bottles starting around the £20 mark.

Chef: Steven Blake **Proprietor:** Von Essen Hotels **Open:** all week 12.30 to 2, 7 to 10 **Meals:** Set L £18 (2 courses) to £25, Set D £55. Light L and bar menus available **Service:** not inc **Cards:** Delta, Diners, Maestro, MasterCard, Visa **Details:** 60 seats. 45 seats outside. Private parties: 40 main room, 40 to 100 private rooms. Car park. Vegetarian meals. Children's helpings. No smoking. Wheelchair access (not WC). Occasional music. Air-conditioned **Accommodation:** 45 rooms, all with bath/shower. TV. Phone. B&B £220 to £850. Rooms for disabled. Baby facilities. Swimming pool

Yak Yeti Yak

AR

12A Argyle Street, Bath BA2 4BQ
Tel: (01225) 442299

The name deserves a gong, and it gives a clue to the food in this cosy, stone-walled basement. Nepalese home cooking is the deal, and the kitchen conjures up flavours that are genuinely subtle, 'light and lovely'. Vegetarian dishes have been well reported, although there's more besides: earthy black-eyed beans and bamboo shoots, a stir-fry of spinach and mushrooms, and broad beans with mint and spring onions have been applauded. Thalis from £10.50. Service is 'charm personified'. Drink Gurkha beer. Open all week.

MAP 3 Battle EAST SUSSEX

Pilgrims

AR

1 High Street, Battle TN33 0AE
Tel: (01424) 772314

'Local produce restaurant' in a fifteenth-century, timber-framed Wealden hall house a stone's throw from Battle Abbey. A new chef was settling in as the Guide went to press, but visitors can expect European bistro-style dishes along the lines of chicken liver parfait with dried fruit compote (£6), fish cassoulet, and breast of duck with braised cabbage, bacon and fondant potato (£14.25), followed by local rhubarb oat crumble with crème anglaise (£5.25). Fixed-price deals (£14.95/ £19.95). Open all week. Reports please.

MAP 6 Bawburgh NORFOLK

Kings Head

AR

Harts Lane, Bawburgh NR9 3LS
Tel: (01603) 744977

This attractive pub by the village pond manages a successful balance of the old and the new. Fires burn in the distinctive inglenooks, beams are exposed, lighting is contemporary, and the whole effect is quite striking. Chef Brendan Ansbro used to work with Ruth Watson (see Crown and Castle, Orford), and his daily-changing menu contains much to catch the eye. Home-made sourdough bread makes a good first impression, followed by carpaccio with grilled artichokes and spiced aubergine (£8), and then a main course of crispy belly pork with chorizo, mussels, green beans, piquillo peppers, judion beans and rouille (£13.50). House wine is £13.50. Closed D Mon and Sun. Reports please.

MAP 11 Berwick-upon-Tweed NORTHUMBERLAND

No. 1 Sallyport

1 Sallyport, off Bridge Steet, Berwick-upon-Tweed TD15 1EZ
Tel: (01289) 308827

Essentially a smart B&B operation with a modern outlook (bare boards, DVDs and luxury showers), but weekend evenings bring on 'rustic French provençale suppers' (£29.50) served by arrangement around the large communal oak dining table. Hostess Elizabeth Middlemiss might offer home-cured gravad lax, followed by braised lamb shank with apricots, then Calvados apples with home-made caramel ice cream. Bring your own wine; £3 corkage per person. Open Fri to Sun D only.

MAP 3 Biddenden KENT

West House

28 High Street, Biddenden TN27 8AH
Tel: (01580) 291341

Cooking 5 | Modern British | £36–£51

On the main street of this exquisitely pretty village, in a terrace of houses hung with Kentish tiles, West House is a calm, relaxing place. The décor is fresh and simple: wooden floors, beams, slatted blinds, a roaring winter log-burner and a few simple food prints on plain cream walls. Graham Garrett's regularly changing, seasonal menus make the best use of high-quality produce, much of it local, although he uses ingredients from further afield if of outstanding quality. Cheeses are always British (from Neal's Yard, perhaps), with fish from the local coast. His menus are sensibly compact, crisply scripted and appealing, and he delivers confident, accomplished and well-executed dishes of intelligent simplicity and clear flavours.

Typical main courses might pair slow-cooked belly pork with black pudding and confit turnips, or a fillet of gurnard alongside saffron-braised fennel and lobster bisque. Proceedings might start with cream of chorizo soup of 'wonderful smoky flavour', or potted and pickled herring, and to finish an 'exceptional' chocolate fondant with a mandarin sorbet, or warm gingerbread with rhubarb and clotted cream. Good rolls, personable service from casually dressed staff, and an annotated, user-friendly global wine list – with house vins de pays £12.95, a handful of half-bottles and six by the glass from £3.50 – hit the mark too.

Chef: Graham Garrett **Proprietors:** Graham Garrett and Jackie Hewitt **Open:** Tue to Fri and Sun L 12 to 2, Tue to Sat D 7 to 9.30 **Closed:** Christmas to New Year, 2 weeks in summer **Meals:** Set L £21 (2 courses) to £24, Set D £29.50 **Service:** 10% (optional), card slips closed **Cards:** Delta, Maestro, MasterCard, Visa **Details:** 30 seats. Private parties: 26 main room. Car park. Children's helpings. No cigars/pipes in dining room. Wheelchair access (not WC). Music

MAP 1 **Bigbury-on-Sea** DEVON

Oyster Shack

AR

Milburn Orchard Farm, Stakes Hill,
Bigbury-on-Sea TQ7 4BE
Tel: (01548) 810876

Locally farmed oysters every which way (from £1 each) are naturally the stars at this enthusiastically run, laid-back 'al fresco eating place'. Other options include pan-fried sardines with provençale sauce (£4.25), potted shrimps, and baked John Dory with lime butter (£16). Lobsters and crabs are sold by weight, and you can even build your own seafood platter from a choice of 20 different items. House wine £9.95. Breakfast 9 to 11am. Open all week L and Sat D (booking essential).

MAP 5 **Birchover** DERBYSHIRE

Druid Inn

NEW ENTRY

Main Street, Birchover DE4 2BL
Tel: (01629) 650302
Website: www.thymeforfood.co.uk

Cooking 3 | Modern European | £27–£59

This tastefully modernised 200-year-old stone inn on a bend in the village centre is sister to Sheffield's highly regarded Richard Smith at Thyme (see entry), and, as one reporter remarked, is a 'place I'd definitely want to return to again and again'. Dining options include the bar and adjacent snug as well as a separate dining room with views over the valley. Menus are the same throughout, and the lengthy, crowd-pleasing, modern-focused repertoire delivers plenty of choice, backed up by good flavours from well-sourced local ingredients. 'Terrific' bread – huge squares of focaccia – gets things going, before perhaps an 'exceptionally good' terrine of hot oak-smoked salmon with prawns, artichoke hearts and citrus salad, or a platter of cured meats with dipping sauces, then monkfish with braised lentils, crushed potatoes and chorizo, or more traditional shepherd's pie. 'Very good' egg custard tart with Cassis sorbet makes an impressive finale. Service is 'relaxed, friendly and chatty'. A page of wines by the glass, from £3.75, opens the international wine list. House Hungarian Chardonnay and French Merlot are £13.

Chef: Michael Thompson **Proprietors:** Richard and Victoria Smith, Adrian Cooling and Michael Thompson **Open:** all week L 12 to 2.30 (3 Sun), Mon to Sat D 6 to 9.30 **Closed:** first 2 weeks Jan **Meals:** alc exc Sun L (main courses £8 to £17). Set L Mon to Fri and D 6 to 7 Mon to Fri £12 (2 courses) to £16 (3 courses) **Service:** not inc, card slips closed **Cards:** Maestro, MasterCard, Visa **Details:** 90 seats. 40 seats outside. Private parties: 40 main room, 6 to 24 private rooms. Car park. Vegetarian meals. Children's helpings. No smoking. Music

MAP 8 **Birch Vale** DERBYSHIRE

Waltzing Weasel

AR

New Mills Road, Birch Vale SK22 1BT
Tel: (01663) 743402

Stone-built pub/restaurant away from it all in the heart of the Peak District overlooking Kinder Scout. Ownership has changed since the last edition of the Guide, but the kitchen still produces hearty dishes based on local ingredients with a few Mediterranean leanings. Expect grilled sardines with tapenade (£5.75) and a 'Fantasia Italiana' mixed platter (£12) as well as roast leg of Kinder lamb and Moroccan vegetable casserole, followed by home-made puddings. House wine £13. Accommodation. Open all week.

NEW ENTRY	This appears after the restaurant's name if the establishment was not a main entry in last year's Guide, although it may have been a 'round-up/also recommended' in previous editions.

MAP 5 **Birmingham** WEST MIDLANDS

Bank

4 Brindley Place, Birmingham B1 2JB
Tel: (0121) 633 4466
Website: www.bankrestaurants.com

Cooking 2 | Modern European | £29–£85

Located in Brindley Place, this 'cavernous' restaurant is exactly what you would expect from the Midlands branch of this urban, modern-day brasserie group (see entry, London). The prices are fair, menus flexible enough to appeal to a wide range of people, and the kitchen aims for a recognisably contemporary style. A first-rate tian of crab and citrus salad takes its place among starters, while main courses might feature generously portioned scallops and black pudding with crushed peas and pommes mousseline, or chargrilled calf's liver with caramelised tomatoes, thyme, sweet and sour onions and crispy bacon. Round off with a 'feather-light' bread-and-butter pudding. Architecture and décor on a grand scale – a vast expanse of plate glass, bold colours and granite – help make the place 'stimulating with bundles of energy', alfresco posing is a warm-weather option, and service is 'engaging and hospitable'. Wines keep up the snappy pace, with lots of options by the glass, succinct notes for guidance, and something to suit all pockets and palates from £12.25 house vin de pays upwards.

Chef: Steve Woods **Proprietor:** Bank Restaurant Group **Open:** all week 12 to 2.45 (11.30 to 2.30 Sat and Sun), 5.30 to 11 (5 to 9.30 Sun) **Meals:** alc (main courses £9.50 to £32). Set L and D (exc 7 to 10pm) £12.50 (2 courses) to £15. Bar menu available **Service:** 12.5% (optional) **Cards:** Amex, Delta, Diners, MasterCard, Maestro, Visa **Details:** 150 seats. Private parties: 150 main room, 16 to 100 private rooms. Vegetarian meals. Children's helpings. No-smoking area. Wheelchair access (also WC). Music. Air-conditioned

Chung Ying Garden AR

17 Thorp Street, Birmingham B5 4AT
Tel: (0121) 666 6622

Big, brash, colourful venue close to the Hippodrome and the Chinese quarter. The menu is a 400-dish monster opening with scores of dim sum (from £2.50). Results have been mixed, although the kitchen gives the Cantonese repertoire a thorough work-out, tackling stir-fries, casseroles (eel with belly pork and garlic is a 'solid winter warming dish'), roast meats, noodles, and more. Listed specialities include shredded duck with jellyfish and celery (£9.50) and fillet of beef with ground walnuts. Service can be unwelcoming. House wine £10. Open all week.

Hotel du Vin & Bistro

25 Church Street, Birmingham B3 2NR
Tel: (0121) 200 0600
Website: www.hotelduvin.com

Cooking 3 | Modern European | £33–£55

The Hotel du Vin chain was sold by its founder Robin Hutson in October 2004, but the group that now owns it has wisely decided to preserve its successful formula of modern brasserie food served alongside a supersonic wine list. 'Simple Classics' and vegetarian listings – perhaps whole grilled trout with almond beurre noisette and new potatoes, or cep and artichoke risotto respectively – bulk out the starters and main courses. A meal might open with scallop and prawn brochette with pineapple salsa, before following on with confit duck leg with braised red cabbage and mash. Gâteau opéra, a chocolate and coffee creation, is one way to finish, a warm broth of figs and port, served with mascarpone ice cream, another. The wine list builds up to speed with the whites before really letting rip with page after page of fine, rare, offbeat and affordable reds from all points of the compass. Prices start quietly at around the £12 mark, but classical France and California bring on the sonic booms.

Chef: Nick Turner **Proprietor:** MWB Group plc **Open:** all week 12 to 1.45, 7 to 10 **Meals:** alc exc Sun L (main courses £14.50 to £17.50). Set L Sun £24.50 **Service:** not inc **Cards:** Amex, Delta, Diners, Maestro, MasterCard, Visa **Details:** 85 seats. Private parties: 120 main room. Vegetarian meals. Children's helpings. No smoking. Wheelchair access (also WC). No music **Accommodation:** 66 rooms, all with bath/shower. TV. Phone. Room only £125 to £350. Baby facilities

⊘	This symbol means that smoking is banned in all restaurants.
⊘	This symbol means that there are some restrictions on smoking though it may be allowed in some eating areas.

Jessica's

1 Montague Road, Edgbaston,
Birmingham B16 9HN
Tel: (0121) 455 0999
Website: www.jessicasrestaurant.co.uk

Cooking 5 | Anglo-French | £35–£64

The back half of a private house in comfortable Edgbaston has been remade into this ambitious and high-achieving restaurant. One dining room is inside the original building, the other in a pleasant conservatory extension, looking out on to a courtyard garden. Pale wood flooring and hanging baskets lend the place a bright, modern feel, and Glynn Purnell, now into his third year here, is cooking with great verve. The influence of his time at Hibiscus (see entry, Ludlow) lingers on in dishes such as a croustillant of poached egg with lentil salad, Jerusalem artichoke purée and matching foam, and the serving of corn-fed chicken in two courses – the breast first up, cooked in hay with quince purée, dates, sweetcorn and thyme, and then a leg with a salad of endive, pistachios and sultanas. A starter of confit of skate wing is an acclaimed dish, appearing not with the usual brown butter but with lemon béchamel, and hazelnuts rather than capers. Main-course fish might be poached brill with puréed avocado and black olives, and the fashion for serving meat in more than one guise shows up not just in that two-tiered chicken dish, but in saddle of lamb with braised tongue, or pork belly with trotter in ravioli.

Desserts are paired with suggested wines, tempting you to match a glass of Muscat de Frontignan at £3.95 to passion-fruit délice with bitter chocolate sorbet. French and English cheeses come with walnut and apricot bread. Nine house wines from £15.95, most available by the glass (from £4.75), introduce a developing list.

Chef: Glynn Purnell **Proprietors:** Keith and Diane Stevenson and Glynn Purnell **Open:** Tue to Fri L 12.30 to 2, Mon to Sat D 7 to 10 **Closed:** 1 week at Christmas, 1 week at Easter, last 2 weeks July **Meals:** Set L £15 (2 courses) to £21.50, Set D £29.95 to £42.50 **Service:** 12.5% (optional), card slips closed **Cards:** Delta, MasterCard, Maestro, Visa **Details:** 36 seats. Private parties: 18 main room. Vegetarian meals. No smoking. Wheelchair access (not WC). Music. No mobile phones. Air-conditioned

Lasan

3–4 Dakota Buildings, James Street,
Birmingham B3 1SD
Tel: (0121) 212 3664

Sophisticated minimalist Indian restaurant over three floors offering a modish alternative to the city's myriad balti houses. Chicken tikka is garnished with bhindi and mango coulis (£5), lamb shank is cooked with fenugreek (£10), and breast of duck is served on a curry of fine green beans (£13). Favourites like chicken dopiaza and bhuna gosht also have their say, and East/West desserts (£5) include saffron bread-and-butter pudding, and raspberry shrikand. Short, modern wine list from £16.95. Open Mon to Sat D only.

Le Petit Blanc

9 Brindley Place, Birmingham B1 2HS
Tel: (0121) 633 7333

A new-look Parisian-style interior complete with a long pewter-topped bar marks the re-launch of this flexible brasserie. Like other branches (see entries in Cheltenham, Manchester, Oxford and Tunbridge Wells), it provides everything from daily fixed-price menus (two courses £12) and food for children to distinctive dishes like chargrilled asparagus with sauce gribiche (£7), grilled haddock with warm potato salad and a soft-boiled egg (£13.50), and poached pear with almond shortbread and butterscotch sauce (£5.50). Vins de pays £12.95. Open all week.

Metro Bar & Grill

73 Cornwall Street, Birmingham B3 2DF
Tel: (0121) 200 1911
Website: www.metrobarandgrill.co.uk

Cooking 2 | Modern European | £30–£58

The combination of a pulsating, heavily populated bar and a slightly less frenetic, split-level dining room ensure a buzz in this cosmopolitan brasserie at the heart of the city's commercial district. Menus follow the classic formula of salads, pasta and rice dishes (maybe roast butternut squash and sage risotto), seafood (fishcakes with wilted spinach and beurre blanc), grills and mains (spit-roast chicken with parsnip dauphinoise, or confit duck leg with corned beef and onion hash).

Starters range from duck liver and cherry parfait with walnut and watercress salad to marsala squid with mango and avocado guacamole; additional fish specials are on a board, and desserts have included simple things like rice pudding. Sandwiches and 'light plates' are available from noon to 10pm. The short, fashionable wine list is topped up with ten champagnes; house vin de pays is £11.95.

Chef: Matthew Knight **Proprietors:** Chris Kelly and David Cappendell **Open:** Mon to Fri L 12 to 2.30, Mon to Sat D 6 to 10 **Closed:** 25 Dec, bank hols **Meals:** alc (main courses £10 to £18). Bar menu available **Service:** not inc, 10% (optional) for parties of 6 or more **Cards:** Amex, Maestro, MasterCard, Visa **Details:** 120 seats. Private parties: 100 main room. Vegetarian meals. Wheelchair access (also WC). Music. Air-conditioned

Paris

109–111 Wharfside, The Mailbox,
Birmingham B1 1RF
Tel: (0121) 632 1488
Website: www.restaurantparis.co.uk

Cooking 5 | Modern French | £39–£92

Shades of coffee, chocolate and cream plus a sense of spaciousness give a very contemporary look to Pat McDonald's restaurant in the Mailbox shopping mall. The kitchen is run by Richard Turner, and ambition (and Francophilia) come across clearly in combinations like seared scallops with boudin noir, pommes mousseline and truffled chicken jus. The menus (carte, fixed-price lunch, and tasting menu) take in their stride a range of different and sometimes complex dishes, from loin of venison with mulled pear, celeriac and bitter chocolate sauce, to confit pork belly with buttered cabbage, parsnip purée and prune and marjoram jus. A lighter note is apparent in fish dishes, such as tranche of sea bass with aubergine caviar and baby fennel, or an unusual fillet of turbot with baby gem fondue, oyster raviolo and shellfish nage.

The carte prices are on the high side (the fixed-price lunch has been recommended), but quality is evident throughout with starters such as pressed terrine of overcoat duck and foie gras with toasted pain Poilâne, and perhaps hazelnut and caramel parfait with pink grapefruit and passion-fruit coulis to finish. An extensive wine list starts at £17, though prices are mostly more London than Birmingham.

Chef: Richard Turner **Proprietor:** Pat McDonald **Open:** Tue to Sat 12 to 2.15, 7 to 9.30 (10 Sat) **Closed:** 1 week Christmas, 1 week Easter, 2 weeks Aug **Meals:** alc (main courses £19.50 to £26.50). Set L £16.50 (2 courses) to £21.50, Set D £55 (whole table only) **Service:** 12.5% (optional), card slips closed **Cards:** Amex, Delta, Maestro, MasterCard, Visa **Details:** 42 seats. Private parties: 42 main room, 6 to 12 private rooms. Vegetarian meals. Children's helpings. No smoking. Wheelchair access (also WC). Music. No mobile phones. Air-conditioned

San Carlo

AR

4 Temple Street, Birmingham B2 5BN
Tel: (0121) 633 0251

The founder member of a group of stylish Italian restaurants/pizzerias with younger siblings in Bristol, Leicester and Manchester. Pizzas and pastas of every description (from £6.50) take up a lot of space on the menu, along with trattoria stalwarts such as bresaola with rocket salad (£6.75), fegato alla veneziana (£13) and fillet steak with Barolo sauce. Also check the blackboard of fish specials like salmon in lobster sauce. Predominantly Italian wines from £15.45. Open all week. Handy city-centre location close to New Street station.

Simpsons

NEW ENTRY

20 Highfield Road, Edgbaston,
Birmingham B15 3DU
Tel: (0121) 454 3434
Website: www.simpsonsrestaurant.co.uk

Cooking 6 | Modern French | £38–£70

Having earned his reputation – and long-standing Guide recognition – in Kenilworth, Andreas Antona set his sights on Birmingham in the autumn of 2004. His destination was a classically proportioned Georgian mansion in the leafy suburb of Edgbaston that was ripe for transformation into a boutique hotel with a 'class-act' restaurant and an orangery for pre-prandial drinks.

Aspirations are high, and the kitchen's attributes are many, from near-faultless ingredients to fine technique and sensitivity. The main event is a six-course menu surprise (less elaborate set menus are also available), which shows the kitchen at full stretch. Classical ideas are often tempered by exotic flavours: seared scallops coated in Indian spices come with caramelised cauliflower purée, sultanas and curry oil, while seared duck foie gras is turned into a 'rather seductive dish' with the addition of roast banana, pain d'épice and banana purée. By contrast, roast loin of Finnebrogue venison is handled in time-honoured fashion with 'wonderfully pungent' haggis and a host of other components including glazed fig, turnip fondant, Savoy cabbage, fig marmalade and juniper sauce, while desserts are immaculately crafted creations like warm Valrhona chocolate croquants with orange salad and star-anise ice cream. Then, as if to break the mould, the kitchen may deliver 'a playful set of lollipops masquerading as petits fours'. Service from young, well-drilled staff is suitably formal and enthusiastic. From an insightful French list, Burgundy starts with real-world bottles like Ambroise's gutsy Pinot Noir (£24) before flourishing the star names. Other countries show less ambition. Bottles start at £15 and 20 by the glass span the range.

Chefs: Andreas Antona and Luke Tipping **Proprietors:** Andreas and Alison Antona **Open:** all week 12.30 to 2, 7 to 9.30 (10 Fri and Sat) **Meals:** alc (main courses £19 to £21.50). Set L £20 (2 courses) to £25, Set D £30 **Service:** 10% (optional), card slips closed **Cards:** Amex, MasterCard, Maestro, Visa **Details:** 70 seats. Private parties: 10 to 18 private rooms. Car park. Vegetarian meals. Children's helpings. No smoking. Wheelchair access (also WC). No music. No mobile phones. Air-conditioned **Accommodation:** 4 rooms, all with bath/shower. TV. Phone. B&B £100 to £190

La Toque d'Or

27 Warstone Lane, Hockley,
Birmingham B18 6JQ
Tel: (0121) 233 3655
Website: www.latoquedor.co.uk

Cooking 4 | French | £32–£57

Set like a solitaire among jewellery shops, the Toque d'Or is a French restaurant that aims to meld classical technique with modern idioms in an ambience of wooden and metal beams and bare brick walls. The printed fixed-price menus are supported by blackboard specials, generally seasonal dishes that carry supplements to the main menu tariff. A pair of reporters emerged thoroughly satisfied after a dinner that took in copybook pâté de foie gras, cod cooked in Mediterranean style, expertly rendered pheasant breast on lentils with a sparse jus, and richly memorable toffee soufflé with ice cream. Vegetarians might be catered for with roasted polenta served with seasonal mushrooms and a sherry cream sauce, and other dessert options have included mango soup with marinated pineapple, fromage blanc sorbet and gingerbread crumble. The French-led wine list is shortish but to the point; most bottles are north of £20, but there are a fair few half-bottles, and house wines from £12.90.

Chef: Didier Philipot **Proprietor:** SSPG Consulting Ltd **Open:** Tue to Fri L 12.30 to 1.30, Tue to Sat D 7 to 9.30 **Closed:** 1 week Christmas, 1 week Easter, 2 weeks summer **Meals:** Set L £16.50 (2 courses) to £19.50, Set D £24.50 **Service:** not inc **Cards:** Delta, Maestro, MasterCard, Visa **Details:** 30 seats. Private parties: 30 main room. Vegetarian meals. Children's helpings. Smoking at the bar. Wheelchair access (also WC). Music. Air-conditioned

MAP 8 **Birtle** GREATER MANCHESTER

Waggon

131 Bury and Rochdale Old Road, Birtle BL9 6UE
Tel: (01706) 622955
Website: www.thewaggonatbirtle.com

Cooking 3 | Modern British | £22–£51

Set right on the B6222, this is a converted village pub that now puts food top of the agenda. It has a light, up-to-date style but hasn't forsaken its roots or its local customers, and there's plenty of Lancastrian chatter echoing around. Choose between the fixed-price 'market menu' and the full-blown carte: black pudding from Chadwick's of Bury is given the tempura treatment, then served with Lancashire cheese, bacon and apple salad, while main courses range from saddle of venison and hare with raspberry vinegar and chocolate sauce to seafood stew with garlic croûtons and rouille. Bringing up the rear are desserts like prune, almond and apricot tart, or chocolate and cherry terrine with cherry and Kirsch ice cream. Three dozen well-spread wines offer plenty of affordable drinking; house selections are £10.95 (£2.75 a glass).

Chef: David Watson **Proprietors:** Lorraine and David Watson **Open:** Wed to Fri and Sun L 12 to 2, Wed to Sat D 6 to 9.30 **Closed:** 1 to 7 Jan, 1 to 17 Aug **Meals:** alc (main courses £8.50 to £16). Set L and D Wed to Fri £12.50 (2 courses) to £14.50 **Service:** not inc, card slips closed **Cards:** Amex, Delta, Maestro, MasterCard, Visa **Details:** 70 seats. Private parties: 50 main room, 8 to 30 private rooms. Car park. Vegetarian meals. Children's helpings. No smoking in dining room. Wheelchair access (also WC). Music

MAP 3 Bishop's Stortford HERTFORDSHIRE

Lemon Tree AR

14–16 Water Lane, Bishop's Stortford
CM23 2JZ
Tel: (01279) 757788

Now licensed for civil weddings, this convivial restaurant is handily placed in a Georgian terrace near the centre of town. Menus ring the changes with the likes of steamed mussels and pumpkin-seed pesto (£6.50), and loin of veal with roast parsnips, carrots, and peppercorn sauce (£14), followed by vanilla and stem ginger crème brûlée (£4.50). Great-value one-course lunches £8.50 (including a drink); fixed-price menus £20.50–£25. House wines from £10.50. Closed Sun D and Mon.

MAP 5 Bishop's Tackbrook WARWICKSHIRE

Mallory Court

Harbury Lane, Bishop's Tachbrook CV33 9QB
Tel: (01926) 330214
Website: www.mallory.co.uk

Cooking 3 | Modern British | £42–£89

Designed in an Arts-and-Crafts influenced 1920s manorial style, and surrounded by ten-acre grounds, Mallory Court is a country-house hotel with all appropriate frills and furbelows. The cooking fits the same mould; luxury ingredients don't dominate, but they are present – as, for example, in tian of tomato, roast langoustine tails and pineapple salsa, or croustade of wild mushrooms, wood pigeon and pan-fried foie gras. Ideas tend to have a classical foundation, and fish shares equal billing with meat, as, for example, in a winter menu offering a duo of roast beef fillet and braised oxtail served with vanilla lime mash and also a fried fillet of brill with dressed crab and saffron sauce. Presentation is a strong point, not least among desserts, which might feature glazed lemon tartlet, Fosse Way honey ice cream and autumnal fruits. The extensive wine list has hardly anything under £20.

Chef: Simon Haigh **Proprietor:** Sir Peter Rigby **Open:** all week 12 to 2, 7 to 9.30 **Meals:** alc D (main courses £22 to £28). Set L £19.50 (2 courses) to £25, Set D £39.50 **Service:** not inc **Cards:** Amex, Delta, Diners, Maestro, MasterCard, Visa **Details:** 54 seats. 30 seats outside. Private parties: 54 main room, 4 to 150 private rooms. Car park. Vegetarian meals. Children's helpings. No smoking. Wheelchair access (also WC). Occasional music. No mobile phones **Accommodation:** 29 rooms, all with bath/shower. TV. Phone. B&B £125 to £340. Rooms for disabled. Swimming pool

MAP 8 Bispham Green LANCASHIRE

Eagle & Child AR

Malt Kiln Lane, Bispham Green L40 3SG
Tel: (01257) 462297

Combining the virtues of an old-fashioned country inn and restaurant, this charming country pub stands in an attractive part of Lancashire. Reliable hands in the kitchen conjure up robust, full-flavoured dishes like Bury black pudding with mash and gravy (£5), roast duck breast with wild berry sauce (£12) and Cajun steak kebab (£11), in addition to bar snacks such as steak and ale pie (£8) and substantial sandwiches served with chips. Open all week.

MAP 8 Blackpool LANCASHIRE

Kwizeen

47–49 King Street, Blackpool FY1 3EJ
Tel: (01253) 290045
Website: www.kwizeen.co.uk

Cooking 2 | Modern European | £24–£45

Hidden away in a maze of narrow streets between the parish church and the bus station, Kwizeen adds colour to a rather drab part of town. Marco Calle-Calatayud delivers the goods with 'real style and expertise', although his cooking can sometimes become unfocused. Lunches are unbeatable value and the main menu steps up a gear for a jazzy line-up that puts sweet chilli beef casserole with liquorice sauce alongside local ham hock and Lancashire sausage terrine, and offers fillet of sea bass with oriental stir-fry and ginger soy sauce as well as loin of veal with caramelised onions and béarnaise sauce. Hot mango pancake with Malibu ice cream is a typically lively dessert and the concise, bistro-style wine list opens with house French at £9.95.

Chef/Proprietor: Marco Calle-Calatayud **Open:** Mon to Fri L 12 to 1.30, Mon to Sat D 6 to 9 **Meals:** alc (main courses £11 to £20). Set L £5.95 (2 courses) **Service:** not inc **Cards:** Delta, MasterCard, Maestro, Visa **Details:** 40 seats. Private parties: 40 main room. No-smoking area. No music. No mobile phones

MAP 6 **Blakeney** NORFOLK

White Horse Hotel

4 High Street, Blakeney NR25 7AL
Tel: (01263) 740574
Website: www.blakeneywhitehorse.co.uk

Cooking 1 | Modern British-Plus | £32–£53

Local supply lines define the food in this brick-and-flint pub/restaurant up the hill from Blakeney quay. Morston mussels, crabs and lobsters, produce from Wiveton Hall Fruit Farm and Norfolk game all appear on the seasonal restaurant menus, which might begin with goats' cheese salad with griddled pear and rocket, before sea bass fillet in Goan curry paste, or Moroccan-spiced maize-fed chicken breast with pickled lemon and couscous. Finish with iced chocolate and praline parfait or sticky orange and almond cake. Chef Chris Hyde also runs the separate bar kitchen, which feeds visitors with dishes like cockle chowder and Norfolk lamb hotpot. The fairly priced Adnams wine list opens with vins de pays at £10.95.

Chef: Chris Hyde **Proprietors:** Dan Goff and Martin Painter **Open:** all week D only 7 to 9 **Closed:** second week Jan **Meals:** alc (main courses £11 to £19). Bar menu available **Service:** not inc **Cards:** Delta, Maestro, MasterCard, Visa **Details:** 34 seats. Private parties: 34 main room. Car park. Vegetarian meals. Children's helpings. No smoking. No music. No mobile phones **Accommodation:** 9 rooms, all with bath/shower. TV. Phone. B&B £50 to £120

This symbol means that it is possible to have a three-course meal, including coffee, half a bottle of house wine and service, at all sessions for £30 or less per person.

MAP 3 **Bodiam** EAST SUSSEX

Curlew

Junction Road, Bodiam TN32 5UY
Tel: (01580) 861394
Website: www.thecurlewatbodiam.co.uk

Cooking 2 | Modern European | £35–£76

Set in quintessential 'Garden of England' countryside on the Kent/Sussex border, this white-painted clapboard hostelry now plies its trade as a casual pub/restaurant. There has been a change of ownership since the last edition of the Guide, although the original chefs have been retained. Menus follow the seasons, and Mediterranean influences come through strongly. A Spanish-style 'plato de carne' and pigeon breast with sun-dried tomato and beetroot risotto are offered as starters, and the kitchen also tackles everything from seared tuna (cooked 'pink') with crispy pasta and sunflower and saffron pesto to 'various varieties' of skilfully cooked steaks. Exotically boozy desserts like caramelised ginger and saké rice pudding with chocolate and wasabi ice cream round things off. Prices on the wine list escalate from £12.95.

Chefs: Robert Leeper and Tom Clarke **Proprietors:** Roger Chaudra and Simon Lazenby **Open:** Mon to Sat L 12 to 2, Tue to Sun D 7 to 9 **Meals:** alc (not Sun; main courses £15 to £21). Set L and D Tue to Fri £18.95 (2 courses) to £22.95. Light L menu available Tue to Sat. Set L Sun £13.95 to £17.95 **Service:** not inc, 10% for parties of 8 or more **Cards:** Amex, Delta, Diners, MasterCard, Maestro, Visa **Details:** 80 seats. 20 seats outside. Private parties: 40 main room. Car park. Vegetarian meals. No smoking in 1 dining room. Music. No mobile phones. Air-conditioned

MAP 3 **Bodsham** KENT

Froggies at the Timber Batts

AR

School Lane, Bodsham TN25 5JQ
Tel: (01233) 750237

'Traditional English with a very French edge' sums up this fifteenth-century freehouse run by an eager Gallic team. Blackboards in French advertise foie gras de canard (£8.50), noisette d'agneau, and nougat glacé alongside 'giant' seared scallops with sauce vierge (£9.50), grilled fillet of beef with Roquefort sauce (£19), and other desserts including a gratin of fruits with sabayon (£5.50). Bar snacks are served at lunchtime, real ales are on tap, and the modest, mainly French wine list opens at £12. Closed Sun D and all day Mon.

MAP 9 **Bolton Abbey** NORTH YORKSHIRE

Devonshire Arms, Burlington Restaurant

Bolton Abbey BD23 6AJ
Tel: (01756) 710441
Website: www.devonshirehotels.co.uk

Cooking 5 | Modern British | £45–£172

With an enviable location and views towards the moors of Wharfedale, the Devonshire Arms makes a favourable impression on visitors. Several luxurious lounges are filled with furnishings, antiques and paintings from Chatsworth, and the Burlington Restaurant has highly polished antique tables, silver-capped wine decanters, an abundance of sketches and architectural designs, and a recently extended conservatory. At dinner, nibbles arrive with the four-course menu, which, for those used to the country-house norm, holds a few surprises. Michael Wignall's dishes are described simply and are marked by a high degree of technical accomplishment – even the extras, of which there are quite a few in a dish. Output is founded on high-quality and sometimes luxurious raw materials, ranging from foie gras (with caramelised pear and carpaccio of squab pigeon) to red mullet (teamed with lobster pannacotta and a confit terrine of plum tomatoes and crab). Pasta also makes its presence felt, perhaps in ravioli of smoked haddock with hand-dived scallops. Artful main-course compositions have included a dual lamb presentation, with a cannon and braised shoulder teamed with oxtail, tomato vinaigrette and wild mushrooms. Desserts continue the line of studied understatement – crème brûlée with caramelised puff pastry and poached pear, or chocolate marquise with rhubarb parfait and a vanilla tuile.

The wine list is a monumental achievement, bringing together many of the world's greatest and rarest wines in numerous vintages. There's day-to-day realism too, with a serviceable line-up of house bottles from £14.25 to £40-plus and a quality slate by the glass. Sniffing about between these edited highlights and the big names can yield good-value bottles such as Minervois Les Plots by Coupe-Roses for £19.50.

Chefs: Michael Wignall and Philip Phillips **Proprietors:** The Duke and Duchess of Devonshire **Open:** Sun L 12 to 2, Tue to Sun D 6.30 to 9 **Meals:** Set L £33.50, Set D Tue to Thur and Sun £60, Set D Fri and Sat £60 to £130 (inc wine). Brasserie menu available **Service:** not inc, card slips closed **Cards:** Amex, Delta, Diners, Maestro, MasterCard, Visa **Details:** 76 seats. Private parties: 30 main room, 2 to 22 private rooms. Car park. Vegetarian meals. Children's helpings. No smoking. Wheelchair access (also WC). Occasional music **Accommodation:** 40 rooms, all with bath/shower. TV. Phone. B&B £165 to £380. Rooms for disabled. Baby facilities. Swimming pool. Fishing

MAP 3 **Bonchurch** ISLE OF WIGHT

Pond Café

Bonchurch Village Road, Bonchurch PO38 1RG
Tel: (01983) 855666
Website: www.pondcafe.com

Cooking 4 | Modern Anglo-French | £26–£66

David Thomson's restaurant is idyllically situated in a 'hidden away' village and does indeed overlook the eponymous pond. A few outside tables make much of the vista, while those eating inside get a smart and contemporary space. Daily specials bolster the Sunday lunch menu, perhaps warm foie gras with a candied pear salad, or rack of lamb with sweet pepper and basil. The restaurant didn't furnish us with menus or a wine list, but previous dinner menus show Mediterranean leanings. Start with a light salad of asparagus with mushrooms and butternut squash with ruby chard and a French dressing, followed by oven-baked salmon with a tian of baby prawns, herb aïoli and new island potatoes. Wind up with an assiette of chocolate with strawberry sorbet.

Chef/Proprietor: David Thomson **Open:** all week 12 to 3, 6 to 10 **Closed:** Mon and Sun Nov to end Mar (ring to check) **Meals:** alc (main courses £14 to £20). Set L £15.50 (2 courses), £20 (3 courses) **Service:** not inc **Cards:** Amex, Delta, MasterCard, Switch, Visa **Details:** 30 seats. 16 seats outside. Private parties: 30 main room, 6 to 12 private rooms. Vegetarian meals. Children's helpings. Wheelchair access (not WC). Music.

🍷	This symbol means that the wine list is well above the average.
	This symbol means that the restaurant has a truly outstanding wine cellar.

MAP 9 **Boroughbridge** NORTH YORKSHIRE

Dining Room

20 St James's Square, Boroughbridge YO51 9AR
Tel: (01423) 326426

Cooking 4 | Modern British | £34–£48

In a terrace in the main square, the Dining Room has a first-floor lounge for aperitifs, but the eponymous scene of eating is on the ground floor. A white-painted room with beams and smartly attired tables is the setting for chef/proprietor Christopher Astley's well-wrought cooking. The menu keeps things within sensible bounds and is built around carefully considered combinations such as Thai-style crab cake with chilli mayonnaise, or a textbook pairing of Parma ham and Parmesan. Corn-fed chicken and black pudding make congenial partners for a main course, sauced with white wine and tarragon cream, or there may be sea bass and king prawns in a double act with a sauce of coconut and coriander. Finish with blueberry frangipane tart with vanilla ice cream, or champagne jelly with raspberry coulis. Service is friendly and efficient, and a well-rounded wine list from £13.50 is pitched to satisfy rather than impress.

Chef: Christopher Astley **Proprietors:** Christopher and Lisa Astley **Open:** Sun L 12 to 2, Tue to Sat D 7 to 9.30 **Closed:** 25 and 26 Dec **Meals:** alc L (main courses £11.50 to £16). Set D £20.95 (2 courses) to £24.95 **Service:** not inc, card slips closed **Cards:** Delta, Maestro, MasterCard, Visa **Details:** 32 seats. Private parties: 36 main room. Car park. Vegetarian meals. Children's helpings. No children under 3. No smoking. Wheelchair access (not WC). Music. No mobile phones

MAP 2 **Bournemouth** DORSET

Chef Hong Kong AR

150 Old Christchurch Road, Bournemouth BH1 1NL
Tel: (01202) 316996

The unassuming frontage may not catch the eye of those passing by, but this is a useful address in the bustling seaside town of Bournemouth. The décor is basic, the service friendly and helpful, with the food the star of the show. The long menu contains many familiar favourites – chicken with ginger and spring onions (£5.25), for example – but also runs to good dim sum, crab meat and shark's fin soup (£5.75) and stir-fried sea spicy duck (£6.25). The cooking is careful and the quality of ingredients notably above the norm. Open all week.

Westbeach AR

Pier Approach, Bournemouth BH2 5AA
Tel: (01202) 587785

This glass-fronted slice of minimalism with some Art Deco touches and a beach-front deck is just a stone's throw from the pier. Seafood is a strong hand, with daily specials to complement the menu. Lunchtimes see light bistro dishes like crab cakes (£10), with swordfish brochette for heartier appetites (£16.50), while dinner is a step up: maybe carpaccio with figs (£7), followed by grilled fillet of gilthead bream with mussels infused with Asian flavours (£15) and rounded off with lemon syllabub. Alternatively, splash out on caviar or snack on tapas. Around 50 wines from £13.50. Open all week.

MAP 2 **Bourton-on-the-Water** GLOUCESTERSHIRE

Dial House AR

High Street, Bourton-on-the-Water GL54 2AN
Tel: (01451) 822244

A Cotswold-stone house with an ancient sundial above the entrance and period features aplenty. The kitchen is firmly in tune with the present, offering luxurious modern dishes along the lines of carpaccio of tuna with a salt-cod beignet and herb salad (£9), and roast loin of venison with parsnip purée, red onion tarte Tatin and juniper jus (£19) before – say – plum and brandy mousse with a plum and blackberry milkshake (£8). House wine £12.95. Open all week.

MAP 3 **Bovingdon Green** BUCKINGHAMSHIRE

Royal Oak AR

Frieth Road, Bovingdon Green SL7 2JF
Tel: (01628) 488611

One of a group of Home Counties gastro-pubs with a flexible attitude. The lengthy menu opens with 'small plates' like Cornish Yarg and sage brûlée (£5.75), while 'main meals' range from grilled lemon sole with samphire and black pepper butter (£15.75) to seared local pigeon breast with black pudding and swede mash. Bringing up the rear are desserts such as poached pear and pistachio crumble (£4.75). Twenty-five quaffable wines from £11.25. Open all week.

MAP 8 **Bowness-on-Windermere** CUMBRIA

Linthwaite House

Crook Road, Bowness-on-Windermere LA23 3JA
Tel: (015394) 88600
Website: www.linthwaite.com

Cooking 4 | Modern British | £26–£78

Great views of Lake Windermere and the fells are ever present from this 1900 black and white house, which cleverly blends formal sumptuousness with casual cheerfulness. Simon Bolsover, who took over the kitchen in autumn 2004, buys locally sourced ingredients like Lune valley lamb and Holker Hall venison and has the technical skills to deliver consistently unfussy cooking. The daily-changing dinner menu offers a choice of six dishes at each course. Home-baked bread gets things off to a good start, as does a first course of a terrine of chicken, pork and black pudding with fig chutney. Accurately cooked Goosnargh duck breast with rich red cabbage and a subtle port sauce, or pink and tender slices of roast beef with a well-reduced red wine jus and Yorkshire pudding might make appearances among main courses. Puddings command most praise: 'wobbly, intense' passion-fruit pannacotta with a matching sorbet and caramelised pineapple, for instance, and crème caramel with a scoop of 'delicious' orange sorbet. A choice of British and Irish cheeses makes a fine alternative. A contemporary, international collection of wines is arranged by style and bursts with good names, particularly from South Africa, where Jordan, Warwick and Glen Carlou all feature. Prices start at £16, and the bulk of the list is under £30.

Chef: Simon Bolsover **Proprietor:** Mike Bevans **Open:** all week 12.30 to 1.30, 7 to 9 **Meals:** alc L (main courses £7.50 to £15). Set L Mon to Sat £13.95, Set L Sun £17.95, Set D £44. Bar menu available **Service:** not inc, card slips closed **Cards:** Amex, Delta, Diners, Maestro, MasterCard, Visa **Details:** 60 seats. 20 seats outside. Private parties: 40 main room, 16 to 40 private rooms. Car park. Vegetarian meals. Children's helpings. No children under 7 at D. No smoking. Wheelchair access (also WC). Music. No mobile phones **Accommodation:** 27 rooms, all with bath/shower. TV. Phone. B&B £120 to £280. Rooms for disabled. Baby facilities. Fishing

MAP 8 **Bradford** WEST YORKSHIRE

Mumtaz

386–400 Great Horton Road, Bradford BD7 3HS
Tel: (01274) 571861
Website: www.mumtaz.co.uk

Cooking 1 | Kashmiri | £26–£53

Mumtaz Khan's vast, ultra-modern conversion of a stone terrace not far from the city centre can feed 500 in a plush setting of marble floors and contemporary paintings. Excellent home-made pickles are an indicator of things to come, and the menu shows off its Kashmiri credentials with chargrilled appetisers like skewered chicken boti followed by a big choice of karahi dishes ranging from keema mattar (minced lamb with peas) to king prawn makhani. Vegetarian options are many and varied, including paneer shahi (cheese with tomatoes, mustard seeds and creamed cashews). No alcohol is allowed on the premises, but lassi and freshly squeezed juices should quench the thirst.

Proprietor Mumtaz Khan **Open:** all week 11 to 12 (1am Fri and Sat) **Meals:** alc (main courses £6.50 to £14.50) **Service:** not inc **Cards:** Amex, Delta, Diners, Maestro, MasterCard, Visa **Details:** 500 seats. Private parties: 200 main room, 10 to 150 private rooms. Car park. Children's helpings. No-smoking area. Wheelchair access (also WC). Music. Air-conditioned

MAP 6 **Bramfield** SUFFOLK

Queen's Head AR

The Street, Bramfield IP19 9HT
Tel: (01986) 784214

Local ingredients get top billing at this Suffolk-pink village pub/restaurant by Bramfield's distinctive thatched church. The menu and specials board advertise grilled goats' cheese and smoked duck salad (£5), Longwood organic chicken braised in red wine with garlic and mushrooms (£13), and whole sea bass wrapped in bacon, before desserts like chocolate fudge cake with Village Farm Jersey cream (£4.50). Child-friendly garden. Real ales and a well-spread wine list (from £11.50) from Adnams. Open all week.

MAP 6 **Brampton** CAMBRIDGESHIRE

Grange Hotel

115 High Street, Brampton PE28 4RA
Tel: (01480) 459516
Website: www.grangehotelbrampton.com

Cooking 2 | Modern European | £30–£58

Today's incarnation of this comfortably appointed red-brick Georgian residence is as an affable hotel/restaurant and bar dedicated to satisfying the appetites of food-lovers and oenophiles alike. Nick Steiger's regular 'classics' menu concentrates on tried-and-tested ideas like warm salad of Parma ham with pear and Stilton, and deep-fried haddock with hand-cut chips, while the monthly carte has more to offer. Expect modern European dishes along the lines of chicken liver parfait with saffron brioche and celeriac rémoulade, and roast fillet of sea bream with baby aubergines, pan-fried potatoes, roast cherry tomatoes and tapenade dressing, followed by hot praline soufflé. Both menus (plus blackboard specials) are available in the bar and restaurant.

Intense, ripe St-Véran from la Croix Senaillet at £20 is typical of the good value on a wine list whose compiler has a nose for quality. The international mix, priced from £11.50, is loosely arranged by grape variety, with 16 by the glass.

Chef: Nick Steiger **Proprietor:** Steiger Partnership **Open:** all week L 12 to 2 (2.30 Sun), Mon to Sat D 6.30 to 9.30 **Closed:** 26 to 28 Dec, 1 to 4 Jan **Meals:** alc (main courses £9 to £20) **Service:** not inc **Cards:** Amex, Delta, Maestro, MasterCard, Visa **Details:** 40 seats. Private parties: 40 main room, 6 to 16 private rooms. Car park. Vegetarian meals. Children's helpings. No smoking. Wheelchair access (also WC). No music **Accommodation:** 7 rooms, all with bath/shower. TV. Phone. B&B £70 to £90. Baby facilities

MAP 10 **Brampton** CUMBRIA

Farlam Hall

Brampton CA8 2NG
Tel: (016977) 46234
Website: www.farlamhall.co.uk

Cooking 3 | Modern English | £52–£62

The sixteenth-century manorial house only began to be seriously extended in the Victorian era, and it is to that period that the interior décor still alludes, with busily patterned wallpapers and silver cockerel table decorations. Service by dignified ladies in long skirts also seems in keeping with the overall tone. Doing its best to keep things on an admirable regional leash, the kitchen team works with Gressingham duck, Lancashire guinea fowl and local beef, and tacks to a Lakeland formula of five courses, with a sorbet after the starter and cheeses following dessert. A soup of watercress and pear was a great hit as an opener at inspection, and was well succeeded by sautéed king scallops in saffron oil with sharp-tasting peperonata, and a chicken and smoked bacon risotto. Battalions of vegetables accompany main courses, and desserts such as chocolate-topped rum mousse pie in a biscuit crust will fill any remaining vacant corners. That said, it would be a pity to miss the fine English cheeses. Two red and four white house wines, mostly from the southern hemisphere, come in at £19.95, and there are some good growers on the main list.

Chefs: Barry Quinion and Martin Langford **Proprietors:** the Quinion and Stevenson families **Open:** all week D only 8 to 8.30 **Closed:** 25 to 30 Dec **Meals:** Set D £36 **Service:** not inc, card slips closed **Cards:** Amex, Maestro, MasterCard, Visa **Details:** 45 seats. Private parties: 24 main room, 2 to 24 private rooms. Car park. No children under 5. No smoking. Wheelchair access (also men's WC). No music. No mobile phones **Accommodation:** 12 rooms, all with bath/shower. TV. Phone. D,B&B £140 to £300. No children under 5

MAP 3 **Bray** BERKSHIRE

Fat Duck

1 High Street, Bray SL6 2AQ
Tel: (01628) 580333
Website: www.fatduck.co.uk

Cooking 9 | Modern European | £66–£229

In the course of the last ten years the Fat Duck has gone from a quirky village pub conversion with an outside loo and fabulous French-inspired food to a shrine to cutting edge gastronomy. On day one back in 1995, Heston Blumenthal manned the stoves by himself, and now, at the last count, there are some 22 souls producing food of supreme technical virtuosity.

With the purchase of the Hinds Head (see entry below) in 2004, the Blumenthal empire is continuing to grow within Bray. There's a new development kitchen, too, across the road from the restaurant, which is home to the centrifuge and distillation unit so essential to the work of a molecular gastronomist. A fresh logo – an elegant design morphing duck appendages into cutlery – now swings from the board above the door and is embossed on to the new menus. This Duck was never likely to stand still.

The low-ceilinged dining room is charming and unaffected, with modern art on the walls, and the staff continue to impress ('a jovial bunch'). At lunchtime there is a menu du jour – start with pumpkin risotto with hazelnuts and rosemary, before 'sublime' braised belly pork with Savoy cabbage infused with the smokiness of lardo from Colonnato, and finish with carrot toffee with butternut ice cream and pumpkin seed oil. The carte and tasting menus are available at both lunchtime and in the evening.

Look to the tasting menu if you want all the bells and whistles; it is ideal for the uninitiated and those in search of the classic Blumenthal experience, assuming you have £97.50 to spare. There is the nitro-green tea and lime mousse to cleanse the palate, and the Pommery grain mustard ice cream with its 'beautifully distilled and pungent' red cabbage gazpacho among the tasters. Then on through eight courses, including snail porridge with jabugo ham, sardine on toast sorbet with a ballottine of mackerel, and smoked bacon and egg ice cream with pain perdu and tea jelly.

The carte contains old favourites alongside some new dishes and is likely to bear the fruits of the new development kitchen. Here we can expect to see the kitchen's interpretation of classic dishes such as sole véronique, and lasagne of langoustine, pig's trotter and truffle with 'glorious pasta made by angels with cold hands', a heaven-sent combination of flavours. Not everyone reports with enthusiasm on the slow-cooking technique frequently favoured for meats, with confit lamb shoulder as unctuous as you would expect, while the fat on the starring best end of lamb remained too solid at an inspection meal; the accompanying jellied lamb consommé was considered perfect at preparing the palate for the lamb flavours to follow. There is no let-up in the innovation at dessert stage. The recipient of tarte Tatin receives a Granny Smith green apple juice with a foaming top, the smell alone reminiscent of 'freshly mown grass in an apple orchard', and is left to wonder how such intensity of flavour was conjured up.

Alongside a fine collection of wines from all around France, including unusually good lists of Loire and Alsace whites, exclusive New World producers abound – the likes of Greenock Creek and Torbreck in Australia, Eben Sadie in South Africa, Araujo in California. The list doesn't tarry long on the nursery slopes and barring the odd basic Corbières there is little to be had for under £30. A wonderful range of around 30 wines come by the glass from £5.50 to £18.

Chef/Proprietor: Heston Blumenthal **Open:** Tue to Sun L 12 to 2 (3 Sun), Tue to Sat D 7 to 9.30 (10 Fri and Sat) **Closed:** Christmas to 7 Jan **Meals:** Set L £37.50 (exc Sun) to £97.50, Set D £67.50 to £97.50 **Service:** 12.5% (optional), card slips closed **Cards:** Amex, Delta, Maestro, MasterCard, Visa **Details:** 46 seats. Private parties: 46 main room. Children's helpings. No smoking. No music. No mobile phones. Air-conditioned

Hinds Head Hotel **NEW ENTRY**

High Street, Bray SL6 2AB
Tel: (01628) 626151

Cooking 3 | British | £32–£60

Veterans of gastronomic pilgrimages to Bray will recognise the Hinds Head as the old, rambling pub in whose shadow the Fat Duck (see entry above) stands. The Duke of Edinburgh apparently held his stag night here before marrying Princess Elizabeth in 1947, and it is an instantly likeable place, with floors on different levels, a multitude of alcoves and leather-upholstered chairs riveted with brass studs.

In August 2004 it became assimilated into the Fat Duck family when Heston Blumenthal bought it. The intention has not been to extend scientific gastronomy here, though, but to re-create traditional British tavern cuisine that reflects the building's heritage. Thus do oxtail and kidney pudding, Lancashire hotpot, treacle tart and Eton Mess find their way on to the menus. A seasonal serving of English asparagus with a perfect poached egg and lemon butter sauce was a winner at inspection, as was the pair of soused herring fillets with a pile of vinegared onions, beetroot and mild horseradish dressing. Chargrilled steak with marrowbone and chips offers a good piece of well-aged meat and smoky marrow, and oxtail and kidney pudding is rich and unctuous, served with lightly cooked cabbage spiked with bacon.

The must-have dessert may well be the evocatively named Quaking Pudding. Otherwise, there is sweet, sherry trifle, or British cheeses with quince paste. Service gets a little absent-minded when the place is busy. There is nothing olde worlde about the wine pricing, which is pure modern Berkshire, but a good selection by the glass opens at £3.25, or £13 a bottle.

Chef: Heston Blumenthal **Proprietor:** Fat Duck Restaurants Ltd **Open:** all week L 12 to 2.30 (4 Sun), Mon to Sat D 6.30 to 9.30 **Service:** not inc, card slips closed, 10% for group bookings **Cards:** Amex, Delta, Maestro, MasterCard, Visa **Details:** 200 seats. Private parties: 60 main room, 20 to 60 private rooms. Children's helpings. No smoking. No music

Riverside Brasserie

Bray Marina, Monkey Island Lane, Bray SL6 2EB
Tel: (01628) 780553
Website: www.riversidebrasserie.co.uk

Cooking 3 | Modern European | £41–£59

A couple of miles from Bray, in the Marina complex, this small, no-frills eatery has a great riverside position and a straightforward café-style menu. Heston Blumenthal sold his share in 2004, but the informal tone continues, with buzzy music, wobbly tables and open-plan kitchen. Start with oysters in shallot vinaigrette, or open tartine of artichokes and goats' cheese with balsamic-dressed rocket, then try slow-cooked, tender pork belly in a rich dark sauce with black pudding and chorizo. Poached salmon was over-salted at inspection, with classic skate wing with capers and beurre noisette a potential alternative. Portions are light, and extra vegetables – perhaps broccoli cooked with chilli, garlic and olive oil – could be needed. Lavender pannacotta makes a good light finish, banana Eton Mess a fuller one. Service is attentive. The short, snappy wine list starts at £15 and has flair; among global contenders are tastes of regional France like Berthoumieu's Madiran (£20) and Clos Lapeyre Jurançon Sec (£26).

Chef: Garrey Dawson **Proprietors:** Garrey Dawson, Lee Dixon and Alfie Hitchcock **Open:** Tue to Sun L 12 to 2.30, Tue to Sat D 6.30 to 9.30 **Meals:** alc (main courses £13 to £15). **Service:** 12.5% (optional), card slips closed **Cards:** Amex, Delta, Maestro, MasterCard, Visa **Details:** 35 seats. 50 seats outside. Private parties: 30 main room. Car park. Children's helpings. No-smoking area. Music

Waterside Inn

Ferry Road, Bray SL6 2AT
Tel: (01628) 620691
Website: www.waterside-inn.co.uk

Cooking 8 | French | £57–£199

The setting is indeed idyllic, a whitewashed former pub with windows open to a river view where one half-expects to find Mole and Ratty disporting themselves, and where waterborne arrivals may moor their craft. Within, all is placidly dated and chintzy, although the sense of relaxation certainly doesn't infect the service, which is a model of watchfulness and impeccable civility. 'You can count on one hand the number of restaurants in this country capable of reaching this level of graciousness and hospitality' – not to mention the charioteering skills that make the serving of digestifs and cheeses resemble a more decorous version of *Ben Hur*.

The Roux *père et fils* kitchen team – Michel and Alain, the former serenely into his fourth decade here – is a formidable one, producing an ultra-refined style of French haute cuisine that was once the preserve of London hotel dining rooms. Bilingual menus deal in descriptions that don't feel they need to justify every penny of the asking price but rely on a certain level of trust and confidence in the knowing customer. Lobster poached in bouillon and served with an emulsion scented with lemongrass and thyme sounds straightforward enough, and costs £52. The cooking is capable of stratospheric achievement: escalopes of sautéed foie gras are thoughtfully partnered with soft white beans and wild mushrooms, the whole assemblage pointed up with a well-balanced citrus sauce; deeply coloured langoustine consommé of majestic clarity of flavour; roast leg and best end of milk-fed lamb, 'moist, tender and blissful', adorned with fresh spring vegetables and gently supported by minted hollandaise.

If duck magret served with asparagus and marjoram jus from the lunch menu seemed rather ordinary one April day, a nigh-on-perfect first course of sautéed lobster medallions, the meat 'supple and translucent', with julienne of carrot, leek and ginger root and an astonishing, high-octane sauce of white port, is what lingers in the memory. The French and English cheeses are stunning, and desserts impress with the mainstream likes of delicately spiced caramel and chocolate mousses, or a whole 'decadently sweet' pear tarte Tatin.

The wine list offers assured, encyclopedic coverage of France and feels no obligation to venture further afield. Budget options are hardly to be expected – the baseline is a reliable Muscadet at £22 – but there is no chaff and the very best bottles abound. Top-notch halves start at £11.

Chefs/Proprietors: Michel and Alain Roux **Open:** Wed to Sun 12 to 2 (2.30 Sun), 7 to 10; also Tue D 1 June to 31 Aug **Closed:** 26 Dec to 26 Jan **Meals:** alc (main courses £36 to £52). Set L Wed to Sat £40 to £87.50, Set L Sun £56 to £87.50, Set D £87.50 **Service:** 12.5% (optional), card slips closed **Cards:** Amex, Delta, Diners, Maestro, MasterCard, Visa **Details:** 75 seats. Private parties: 80 main room, 6 to 10 private rooms. Car park. Vegetarian meals. No children under 12. No cigars in dining room. Wheelchair access (not WC). No music. No mobile phones **Accommodation:** 9 rooms, all with bath/shower. TV. Phone. B&B £165 to £340. No children under 12

MAP 12 Brentford GREATER LONDON

Pappadums

AR

Ferry Quays, Ferry Lane, Brentford TW8 0BT
Tel: (020) 8847 1123

Stylish modern Indian in a riverside development by the historical Thames River Crossing. Plain wood and primary colours set the tone, and the menu has a familiar northern regional bias as well as making a few detours for, say, masala dosai and hakka noodles. Tandoori king prawns (£14) and authentic chicken biryani have passed muster, aloo gobi (£4.75) is a textbook version and it's worth checking the weekly chef's specials (salmon and dill tikka, for example). House wine £11.50. Open all week.

MAP 3 Bridge KENT

White Horse Inn

53 High Street, Bridge CT4 5LA
Tel: (01227) 830249
Website: www.whitehorsebridge.co.uk

Cooking 4 | Modern British | £31–£55

You can't miss the White Horse, a substantial inn painted a pale custard colour and decked out with hanging baskets. The setting may be a pub (a non-smoking one at that), but the large, open space is plain and uncluttered, with old beams and deep leather sofas in the bar area, while the restaurant has a brighter, airier feel and operates on more formal lines. Proprietor Alan Walton is 'committed, polite and unpretentiously friendly' at front-of-house, and, while son Ben's cooking style focuses on the modern, it concentrates on using well-sourced, good-quality, seasonal produce from the abundant local larder – a page of the menu is devoted to listing the main suppliers. Flavours are 'robust and clear' and portions generous; witness a main-course peppered ribeye served with a fricassee of smoked bacon, baby Jersey Royals, leeks and green beans with an 'impressive' onion pithiviers and red-wine jus. Do find room for the 'very professional' in-house breads and the desserts, perhaps a lemon tart with raspberry coulis and rhubarb sorbet. Like the food, the wine list aims at good value and includes a page of Kentish wines, with house opening at £12.50.

Chef: Ben Walton **Proprietor:** Alan Walton **Open:** Tue to Sun L 12 to 2, Tue to Sat D 7 to 9.30 **Meals:** alc (main courses £8.95 to £19.75) **Service:** not inc, card slips closed **Cards:** Delta, MasterCard, Maestro, Visa **Details:** 35 seats. 40 seats outside. Private parties: 35 main room. Car park. Vegetarian meals. Children's helpings. No smoking. No music. No mobile phones

MAP 2 Bridport DORSET

Chez Cuddy

AR

47 East Street, Bridport DT6 3JX
Tel: (01308) 458770

Stylish, spruce and minimalist venue that aims to brighten up the Bridport scene. Co-owner Badir Hadj-Aissa has taken over the culinary reins, and the emphasis is now primarily on morning coffee and light lunches (Caesar salad; £5.50), with evening meals limited to Saturday. The dinner menu could feature home-cured gravlax with celeriac rémoulade (£6), duck breast with pak choi, egg-fried rice and plum sauce (£11.50), and sticky date pudding (£4.50). Twenty wines from £11.50. Open Tue to Sat L and Sat D.

MAP 3 Brighton EAST SUSSEX

Due South

AR

139 Kings Road Arches, Brighton BN1 2FN
Tel: (01273) 821218

Right on the seafront, and located in the arches formerly used by fisherman, Due South has an enviable position, and possesses excellent views out to sea (due south, of course) from windows at the front, and from the terrace. The menu focuses on local ingredients, with 80% of the produce coming from a 20 mile radius of the restaurant. Start, perhaps, with Sussex High Weald organic ricotta, spinach and chard dumplings with a sage and hazelnut pesto (£6.95), followed by navarin of local Court Garden lamb (£12.95), or grilled fish of the day. Finish with warm chocolate fondant cakes with vanilla ice cream. Open all week.

This symbol means that accommodation is available at this establishment.

La Fourchette

105 Western Road, Brighton BN1 2AA
Tel: (01273) 722556
Website: www.lafourchette.co.uk

Cooking 2 | French | £23–£47

La Fourchette makes the best of its location: a corner site, glass-fronted on two sides, looking onto a main shopping street linking Brighton to Hove. Everything is reassuringly straightforward – décor, food, service – and has the easy self-confidence of an operation that knows its craft and its limitations. This is 'decent' bourgeois French cooking, dealing in starters like crispy duck rillettes with lentils and sauce vierge, or fish soup, then gilthead bream ballottine with coriander butter, or côte du boeuf with béarnaise sauce. The set-price lunch looks a bargain, 'hardly surprising they were busy' when you consider potato and cauliflower soup and venison casserole with red cabbage for £10. An appropriately French-dominated wine list starts at £12 and offers good choice under £20.

Chef: Pascal Benamari **Proprietor:** Pascal Madjoudj **Open:** all week L 12 to 2.30, Mon to Sat D 7 to 10.30 **Meals:** alc D (main courses £16). Set L £10 (2 courses) to £13 Mon to Sat, £14 to £18 Sun **Service:** 10%, card slips closed **Cards:** Amex, Delta, Diners, Maestro, MasterCard, Visa **Details:** 70 seats. Private parties: 35 main room. Vegetarian meals. Children's helpings. No smoking in 1 dining room. Wheelchair access (also WC). Music

Gingerman

21A Norfolk Square, Brighton BN1 3BG
Tel: (01273) 326688
Website: www.gingermanrestaurants.com

Cooking 3 | Modern European | £25–£55

'Food people want to eat, rather than what chefs want to cook' is the motto here, which explains why it is always hard to get a table without booking well ahead. It's a compact place, with rather monochrome décor, in a street off the seafront, but the cooking is assured. Lightly pickled trout fillet with horseradish potato salad is one way to start, then perhaps slow-roasted lamb shoulder with rosemary jus, or braised duck leg with celeriac purée, port and redcurrants. It offers impeccable value (especially at lunch). Finish with pear tatin and vanilla ice cream, or hot chocolate fondant with blood orange sorbet. House wines at £12.50 head a list with attractive bottles from around the world, including Australia's exciting Suckfizzle Cabernet Sauvignon at £37.

Chef: David Keates **Proprietors:** Ben and Pamela McKellar **Open:** Mon to Sat 12.30 to 2, 7 to 10 **Closed:** 2 weeks Christmas **Meals:** Set L £12.95 (2 courses) to £14.95, Set D £22 (2 courses) to £25 **Service:** not inc **Cards:** Amex, Delta, Maestro, MasterCard, Visa **Details:** 32 seats. Private parties: 32 main room. Vegetarian meals. Children's helpings. No smoking until 10pm. Music. Air-conditioned

Gingerman at Drakes

NEW ENTRY

44 Marine Parade, Brighton BN2 1PE
Tel: (01273) 696934
Website: www.gingermanrestaurants.com

Cooking 5 | Modern European | £29–£66

This restored, double-bow-fronted, seafront building has become a modern, stylish hotel, the basement given over to the latest incarnation of Ben McKellar's popular Gingerman (see entry above). The restaurant has a low-lit, hushed tone and certainly provides high-end dining – plus exemplary value to boot.

McKellar has moved up a gear and, one feels, shows his true paces here. Apple- and beech-smoked eel fillets are topped with fried beetroot, and a spoonful of horseradish cream (still on the spoon) laid across the plate. Three aubergine tortellini, garlicky filling impressively resonant, are crowned with a poached scallop apiece and sauced with a grainy, roast garlic and cream reduction. Meat is notably tender and flavoursome – even veal haunch with thinly sliced potatoes wrapped in bacon – while venison of such rare depth as barely to need its crusting of hazelnuts comes with chopped red cabbage and a red wine jus. Fish from the local catch might include lemon sole with saffron tagliatelle and brown shrimps. A hit at inspection was a fig tart Tatin, the fruit lightly caramelized, ably supported by cinnamon ice cream and a fruity red wine syrup; there are also simple crowd-pleasers like spotted dick with custard. Service is slick and fairly familiar; the wine list (the same as the original Gingerman's) starts at £12.50.

Chefs: Ben McKellar and Andy McKenzie **Proprietors:** Ben and Pamela McKellar **Open:** all week 12.30 to 2.30, 7 (8 Sat/Sun) to 10 **Meals:** Set L £12 (1 course) to £18, Set D £25 (2 courses) to £30 **Service:** not inc **Cards:** Amex, Delta, Diners, Maestro, MasterCard, Visa **Details:** 55 seats. Private parties: 30 main room, 6 to 12 private rooms. No smoking before 10pm. Music. Air-conditioned **Accommodation:** 20 rooms, all with bath/shower. TV. Phone. B&B £80 to £295. Rooms for disabled

Hotel du Vin & Bistro

2–6 Ship Street, Brighton BN1 1AD
Tel: (01273) 718588
Website: www.hotelduvin.com

Cooking 2 | Modern European | £33–£60

The Brighton branch of this hotel chain follows the group's winning formula: a 'cool' bar with low-lying leather sofas and chairs, and a loosely themed French-style restaurant that gives a nod to the style of food served. Here, crowd-pleasers like French onion soup and ribeye steak with béarnaise share the stage with more cosmopolitan ideas like crab, leek and clotted cream quiche, and sea bass with pipérade and balsamic. Successful dishes have included roast veal sweetbreads with celeriac fondant and wholegrain mustard sauce as a starter, and a main course of roast cod with Salamanca lentils, chorizo and salsa verde. Service is smart and friendly.

A dozen options by the glass kick off the wine list, a heavyweight for sure but not the all-round powerhouse one might expect. French reds in particular look uneven – how come there are only three from the Rhône? – but Italy, Australia and California all come up with the goods. Prices start at £13.

Chef: Robert Carr **Proprietor:** MWB Group plc **Open:** all week 12 (12.30 Sat and Sun) to 1.45, 6.30 (7 Sat and Sun) to 9.45 **Meals:** alc exc Sun L (main courses £14.50 to £18). Set L Sun £23.50 **Service:** not inc **Cards:** Amex, Delta, Diners, Maestro, MasterCard, Visa **Details:** 85 seats. Private parties: 14 to 36 private rooms. Vegetarian meals. Children's helpings. No smoking. Wheelchair access (also WC). No music **Accommodation:** 37 rooms, all with bath/shower. TV. Phone. Room only £120 to £365. Rooms for disabled. Baby facilities

La Marinade

77 St George's Road, Kemp Town,
Brighton BN2 1EF
Tel: (01273) 600992
Website: www.lamarinade.co.uk

Cooking 1 | Modern European | £26–£59

Nick Lang cooks with confidence and verve in this small-scale neighbourhood restaurant, with its close-packed tables and great-value menus. His carte and competitive fixed-priced deals make the most of enthusiastically garnered, worldwide ingredients: pan-fried chicken livers might be served on red onions with crème de cassis compote and sherry jus, sea bass fillet comes with roasted tomatoes, tapenade and aubergine 'caviar' while his rendition of cassoulet is loaded with goodies including duck confit, pork belly, Toulouse sausage and chickpeas. To finish, the kitchen has produced a fine crème brûlée as well a mango, apple and rhubarb crumble. The 'sensible' wide-ranging wine list keeps prices in check house Chilean is £11.75.

Chef/Proprietor: Nick Lang **Open:** Thur to Sat L 12 to 2.30, Tue to Sat D 6 to 9.30 (10 Sat) **Meals:** alc (main courses £14.50 to £19.50). Set L £15 Thur to Sat **Service:** 12.5% for parties of 6 or more, and for Set L **Cards:** MasterCard, Maestro, Visa **Details:** 40 seats. No cigars/pipes. No smoking in 1 dining room. Music. Air-conditioned

Momma Cherri's

11 Little East Street, Brighton BN1 1HT
Tel: (01273) 774545

'Bringing the soul to Brighton' exclaims Charit Jones (Momma Cherri herself) about he American soul food restaurant just back from th seafront. This small, homely place is where to go t get the best ribs in town, jerk chicken and classi jambalaya. 'Soul in a bowl' is a good way to sampl smaller portions of a number of dishes, and at £1 per person is great value. Brunch (Sat and Su only) has impressed, and service is always friendl Closed Mon.

Moshi Moshi Sushi

AR

Bartholomew Square, Brighton BN1 1JS
Tel: (01273) 719195

Take a seat alongside the kaiten (conveyor belt) a it snakes around the room and grab whateve catches your eye. Colour-coded plates (price from £1.20 to £3.50) pass by with nigiri, mak and sashimi as the main contenders. There are sush sets like the 'Stamina' (£8.50) and bento boxe perhaps Loch Duart salmon teriyaki (£8), and selection of hot and cold Japanese tapas. Drin beer, saké or wine (from £11.50). Closed Mon.

This symbol means that the chef has changed since last year's entry, and the Editor has judged that the change is of sufficient interest to merit the reader's attention.

One Paston Place

Paston Place, Brighton BN2 1HA
Tel: (01273) 606933
Website: www.onepastonplace.co.uk

Cooking 5 | Modern European | £33–£71

The elegant dining room on a side street off the eafront on the Kemptown side of Brighton volves apace. A pastoral mural that dominated ne wall under the previous owners has been rased and replaced by more of the gilt-framed nirrors that hang elsewhere, and front-of-house is ow run with high polish by a French maître d' nd Italian sommelier who, between them, conrive to make everyone feel like a privileged guest.

Francesco Furriello made great waves when he ook over Paston Place in 2004, and the cooking ooked ready to reach for the stars. Inspection visits his year have revealed a distinct reorientation in avour of exquisitely presented minimalism, lthough there are still great dishes to be had. moked eel is wrapped in carrot and micro-sliced, ccompanied by slightly under-seasoned prawn nd clam cannelloni and a foam dressing of eaweed, and makes a largely successful first course, ut three servings of lamb, though imaginative and icluding a hazelnut-crusted, foie gras-filled utlet, lose impact through tiny portions, and the eat itself (bemusingly hailed as 'free-range') is not f extravagant quality for the price. Veal noisettes ith foie gras praline, accompanied by a potato violo containing a quail's egg was a fine main ish on another occasion, and seared halibut on a bster and zucchini tortello with Sauternes sauce a starter has wowed some (but left others doubtl).

The Italian accent is stressed for a plate of varizioni di cioccolato, and produces spectacular sults in a dessert that matches a glossy pear 'chartte', the sponge replaced with slivers of poached ear, with intensely rich orange chocolate fondant. Vines are gradually shifting away from French assics and in the direction of new-wave Italians, hich can only be all to the good. House selecons are £16 and £17.

Chef: Francesco Furriello **Proprietor:** Gusto Ltd **Open:** Tue to Sat 12 to 2, 7 to 10 **Meals:** Set L £16.50 (2 courses) to £19, Set D £32.50 (2 courses) to £39 **Service:** not inc **Cards:** Amex, Delta, Maestro, MasterCard, Visa **Details:** 42 seats. Private parties: 50 main room. Children's helpings. No children under 7. No smoking. Wheelchair access (not WC). Music. No mobile phones. Air-conditioned

Sevendials

1 Buckingham Place, Brighton BN1 3TD
Tel: (01273) 885555
Website: www.sevendialsrestaurant.co.uk

Cooking 3 | Modern European | £25–£51

Sevendials, on a seven-pronged intersection a short uphill canter from the railway station, is the four-year-old brainchild of London escapee Sam Metcalfe. The informal ambience of varnished wood floor and undressed tables is in keeping with his modern brasserie cooking. Dishes are ingredient-laden, so that a soup of curry-spiced smoked haddock and leek contains a poached egg, while a serving of local scallops is grilled, served on sweet potato champ and finished off with toasted hazelnuts and coriander butter. A fish main course might pair sea bass and lemon sole in puff pastry with currants and ginger, its hollandaise sauce spiked up with Pernod. Slow-cooked local pork belly comes more straightforwardly with grain mustard mash, cabbage and a sauce of cider and apple. Sides – which you may not need – are extra, and meals end with the likes of poached pear with star-anise parfait, or lemon and blueberry cheesecake with raspberry coulis. The wine list is noticeably weightier in reds than whites, with six house wines from £12.

Chef/Proprietor: Sam Metcalfe **Open:** Tue to Sun 12 to 3, 7 to 10.30 (9.30 Sun) **Closed:** 1 week Christmas, bank hols (exc Easter weekend) **Meals:** Set L £10 (2 courses) to £26.50 (3 courses) Mon to Sat, Set Sun L £16.50 to £19.50 Set D £21.50 (2 courses) to £26.50 **Service:** 12% (optional), card slips closed **Cards:** Amex, Delta, Diners, Maestro, MasterCard, Visa **Details:** 75 seats. 50 seats outside. Private parties: 55 main room, 1 to 20 private rooms. Vegetarian meals. No children after 6.00pm. No-smoking area. Wheelchair access (also WC). Music

Terre à Terre

71 East Street, Brighton BN1 1HQ
Tel: (01273) 729051
Website: www.terreaterre.co.uk

Cooking 3 | Global Vegetarian | £38–£52

A bright light in the trendy centre of town for more than a decade, this 'extraordinary place' continues as a standard-bearer for inventive vegetarian food. Flavours are global, ingredients can be bewildering (but staff know their stuff), and dish names are deliberately wacky (black-bean cellophane frisbee, for example). New chef Glen Lester is proving his worth, and while some declare the food too clever for its own good, others find the labour-intensity of it all highly effective. Components often gel impressively, as in cannelloni stuffed with pumpkin and Beenleigh Blue alongside a blob of pickled walnut ice cream on a disc of Gewürztraminer jelly. Elsewhere you might encounter 'Fundamentally Fungus' soufflé (a mushroom bonanza), plus Sussex cheeses, sweet 'tapas', and puddings like 'Sticky Blackstrap' (stem ginger and molasses gingerbread with spiced pears, jerky caramel sauce and crème fraîche). Wines are 100 per cent organic or biodynamic, with prices from £15.75.

Chef: Glen Lester **Proprietors:** Philip Taylor and Amanda Powley **Open:** Wed to Fri L 12 to 3.30, Tue to Fri D 6.30 to 10.30, Sat and Sun 12 to 10.30 **Closed:** 25 and 26 Dec, 1 Jan, Easter Mon **Meals:** alc (main courses £12.25 to £13.25) **Service:** not inc **Cards:** Amex, Delta, Diners, Maestro, MasterCard, Visa **Details:** 100 seats. 12 seats outside. Private parties: 20 main room. Vegetarian meals. No smoking. Wheelchair access (also WC). Music. Air-conditioned

MAP 5 Brimfield HEREFORDSHIRE

Roebuck Inn

Brimfield SY8 4NE
Tel: (01584) 711230
Website: www.theroebuckinn.com

Cooking 3 | Modern British | £27–£56

Set in a tiny village on a lane paralleling the A49, this bow-windowed, fifteenth-century inn focuses on its conservatory-styled restaurant extension. New owners David and Jackie Ward have made improvements, particularly to the bar, but long-standing chef Jonnie Waters still heads a sound kitchen that mixes old favourites with more modern ideas, emphasizing quality, locally sourced produce wherever possible. So expect steamed steak and mushroom pudding (rich ale gravy, suet pastry) with creamy mash and steamed vegetables, and bread-and-butter pudding (this version made with brioche, croissant and apricot preserve) competing for attention against lemon-spiced gravad lax, or a fillet of venison with crushed new potatoes and damson gin and bay sauce, and a tropical-inspired coconut pannacotta served with fresh pineapple compote. The sympathetically priced global wine list kicks off with house bottles at £11.50.

Chef: Jonnie Waters **Proprietors:** David and Jackie Ward **Open:** all week 12 to 2.30, 6.30 to 9 **Meals:** alc (main courses £11 to £19). Set L £11.50 (2 courses) to £15.50. Light L menu available **Service:** not inc, card slips closed **Cards:** Maestro, MasterCard, Visa **Details:** 60 seats. Private parties: 36 main room, 20 private room. Car park. Vegetarian meals. No children under 10 on Fri/Sat. No smoking. Wheelchair access (not WC). No music **Accommodation:** 3 rooms, all with bath/shower. TV. Phone. B&B £50 to £80

MAP 2 Bristol BRISTOL

Bell's Diner

1–3 York Road, Montpelier, Bristol BS6 5QB
Tel: (0117) 924 0357
Website: www.bellsdiner.com

Cooking 5 | Modern European-Plus | £39–£71

Bell's Diner looks low-key from the outside, wit half-blinds obscuring much of what is happenin inside, while white-clothed tables in the intimat setting of a former grocery store might lull cus tomers into thinking this is an ordinary restauran Christopher Wicks, however, is noted for innova tive ideas and adventurous flavour combination Though many of the combinations seem darin they are well thought out and executed with degree of restraint. At inspection, seared foie gr with blood-orange lozenge, black treacle jus an pain d'épice espuma provided 'stunning combina tions', and roast wood pigeon with chocolate sauc and chestnut risotto also impressed. Some dish are variations on familiar themes, such as the com bination of 'tender, juicy and mildly gamey' who partridge with Savoy cabbage, carrots, leeks, wint chanterelles and truffle oil, and the inten Mediterranean flavours of red mullet with fenne tapenade, orange reduction and crab biscui Techniques are impeccable, flavours spot-on rig through to desserts, be it a silky orange pannacot teamed with a carrot sorbet, a soufflé streaked wi red plum, the mulled wine used for cooking th plums appearing as a sorbet of 'intense flavour an spiciness', or chocolate fondant and blood-orang coulis with harissa ice cream. Service is intelliger and moves at a gentle, leisurely pace.

The wine list concentrates on France but countries turn out a slate of well-reviewed bottl at fair prices (from £12). Look out for Anjo Blanc from Domaine Pithon (£22.50), or for special occasion explore the nine vintages Domaine de Trévallon.

Chef/Proprietor: Christopher Wicks **Open:** Tue to Fri L 12 to 2.30, Mon to Sat D 7 to 10 **Closed:** 24 to 30 Dec, bank hols exc Good Friday **Meals:** alc (main courses £14.50 to £18.50). Set D £45 (Mon to Thur, whole table only, max 6) **Service:** 10% (optional), card slips closed **Cards:** Amex, Delta, MasterCard, Maestro, Visa **Details:** 60 seats. Private parties: 25 main room. Children's helpings. No smoking. Music. No mobile phones

Culinaria

1 Chandos Road, Bristol BS6 6PG
Tel: (0117) 973 7999
Website: www.culinariabristol.co.uk

Cooking 3 | Bistro | £33–£47

Bright and relaxed, with a simple menu and a deli/takeaway as part of the operation, Culinaria is a great neighbourhood asset in Bristol's Redlands area – 'a bistro with a touch of class'. Stephen Markwick's menu changes weekly, with the focus generally on effective treatment of unshowy ingredients, say house terrine with celeriac rémoulade, or boeuf bourguignon, and it's all typically straightforward with just four choices per course. But the kitchen is not above turning out petits fondues à la bourgogne with beetroot and walnut salad, or breast of duck with purple sprouting broccoli, while a panaché of market fish might get the leek and saffron sauce treatment. Finish with bread-and-butter pudding or chocolate brownies. It's a package that appeals, from simple food at realistic prices to smooth service led by Judy Markwick, and a succinct, worldwide list of modern wines from £11.25.

Chef: Stephen Markwick **Proprietors:** Stephen and Judy Markwick **Open:** Fri and Sat L 12 to 2, Wed to Sat D 6.30 to 9.30 **Closed:** Christmas/New Year, 1 week June, 1 week Oct **Meals:** alc (main courses £11.50 to £14.50) **Service:** not inc **Cards:** Delta, Maestro, MasterCard, Visa **Details:** 30 seats. Vegetarian meals. Children's helpings. No smoking. Wheelchair access (also WC). No music

FishWorks

128 Whiteladies Road, Clifton, Bristol BS8 2RS
Tel: (0117) 974 4433
Website: www.fishworks.co.uk

Cooking 2 | Seafood | £33–£85

Like its relatives, this branch of Mitchell Tonks's burgeoning seafood chain (see entries in Bath, Christchurch and London) combines the virtues of fishmonger and informal fish restaurant under one roof – in this case a converted corner shop with an open-to-view kitchen. Fish is delivered daily, and the range is extensive: a regular menu of 'classics' like Dartmouth crab salad, haddock in breadcrumbs, spaghetti with clams and chilli, and various crustacea on ice are bolstered by a daily specials board depending on the catch (gurnard fillet with roast tomatoes and thyme, for example). Desserts such as sticky toffee sponge are an afterthought. Fish-friendly European whites (from £15.25) hold pride of place on the short, well-chosen wine list.

Chef: Romero Costa **Proprietor:** FishWorks plc **Open:** Tue to Sat 12 to 2.30, 6 to 10.30 **Closed:** 24 Dec to early Jan, Tue after bank hols **Meals:** alc (main courses £7 to £35) **Service:** not inc **Cards:** Amex, Delta, Maestro, MasterCard, Visa **Details:** 54 seats. Vegetarian meals. Children's helpings. No smoking. Wheelchair access (not WC). Music. Air-conditioned

Hotel du Vin & Bistro

The Sugar House, Narrow Lewins Mead, Bristol BS1 2NU
Tel: (0117) 925 5577
Website: www.hotelduvin.com

Cooking 3 | Modern European | £41–£61

This Hotel du Vin outpost (see also entries Birmingham, Brighton, Harrogate, Henley-on-Thames, Tunbridge Wells, Winchester) occupies a listed eighteenth-century sugar warehouse that has had a sympathetic contemporary makeover. The menu will appeal to hankerers after the true flavours of French brasserie cooking (with occasional Italian influences tossed in for luck): under 'Simple Classics' you find bouillabaisse, coq au vin, and smoked haddock with poached egg and mustard beurre blanc. Other options might include fried scallops with rocket and aïoli, and breast of duck with braised endive and cocotte potatoes, or baked flat mushrooms with Roquefort and walnuts for vegetarians; then it's back to the comfort zone for desserts like apple crumble with cinnamon ice cream and sticky toffee pudding, as well as roast plums with toasted panettone and mascarpone ice cream. The wine list remains as impressive as ever, starting with a dizzyingly long list of champagne, and delving deep into regional France. The regional split continues into the new world – New Zealand North and South

Island, for example, and a hefty choice of Californian reds.

Chef: Marcus Lang **Proprietor:** MWB Group Plc **Open:** all week 12 to 2, 6 to 10 **Meals:** alc (not Sun L; main courses £12.50 to £14.50). Set L Sun £24.50 **Service:** not inc **Cards:** Amex, Delta, Diners, Maestro, MasterCard, Visa **Details:** 85 seats. Private parties: 72 main room, 10 to 30 private rooms. Car park. Vegetarian meals. Children's helpings. No smoking. Wheelchair access (also WC). No music **Accommodation:** 40 rooms, all with bath/shower. TV. Phone. Room only £130 to £395. Rooms for disabled. Baby facilities

Michael Caines at the Bristol Marriott Royal

College Green, Bristol BS1 5TA
Tel: (0117) 910 5309
Email: tablesbristol@michaelcaines.com

Cooking 4 | Modern European | £37–£87

In the heart of the city, next to the cathedral, this reborn Victorian hotel has really gone for it. The dining room, in what was the lobby, is a vast space surmounted by a stained-glass atrium, endowed with Bath stone pillars, Romanesque statues and balconies. Shane Goodway is the executive chef's vicar on earth here, and he interprets the Caines style with vigour and accuracy. A tian of aubergine, peppers and tomato, served with roast langoustines, ratatouille and basil vinaigrette, was a vibrant inspection starter, while two cuts of lamb – best end and shoulder – were seasoned with mustard and cumin and attractively partnered with celeriac fondant in a cumin-spiked jus. Sea bass has been less well judged, with sage-dominated gnocchi, a rich madeira sauce and a lot of garlic defeating the fish, but desserts are good. Fine pastry work distinguishes classic tarte Tatin with Calvados ice cream, and a traditional gaufrette is cleverly balanced with caramelised banana and caramel ice cream, the whole managing somehow to avoid over-sweetness. Youthful service tries hard, and the varietal wine list stays mostly proud of £25, although there are half a dozen house selections at £16.50, or £3.95 a glass.

Chef: Shane Goodway **Proprietor:** Marriott Hotels **Open:** Tue to Fri L 12 to 2.15, Mon to Sat D 7 to 9.45 **Closed:** bank hols **Meals:** alc (main courses £18.50 to £26.50). Set L £17.50 (2 courses) to £21.50, Set D (whole table only) £57.50 **Service:** not inc **Cards:** Amex, Diners, Maestro, MasterCard, Visa **Details:** 76 seats. Private parties: 80 main room. Children's helpings. No smoking. Wheelchair access (not WC). Music. No mobile phones. Air-conditioned **Accommodation:** 242 rooms, all with bath/shower. TV. Phone. Room only £149 to £340. Rooms for disabled. Swimming pool

One30

130–132 Cheltenham Road, Bristol BS6 5RW
Tel: 0117 944 2442
Website: www.one30.com

Cooking 2 | Modern European/Tapas | £39–£58

This cavernous, hard-edged restaurant is an offshoot of Bell's Diner (see entry above), and offers lively, Spanish-tinged modern European cooking. Arroz negro of Calasparra rice with squid, ink and red peppers, or a main course of slow-cooked belly pork with butter beans, paprika, tomatoes and thyme, typify the style. Ribeye steak may come with salsa picante or béarnaise sauce, there's a selection of good-sized tapas (try Moorish spiced chickpeas with spinach and baked egg, or clams with jamón), and desserts include crème Catalan and prune ice cream with Pedro Ximenez. Reports comment on slow service, but it remains 'polite and accurate'. The compact list of good-value wines from Spain and Portugal starts at £12.

Chefs: Johnny Evans and Christopher Wicks **Proprietor:** Freerange Restaurant Ltd **Open:** all week L 12 to 2.30, Mon to Sat D 6.30 to 10.45 **Closed:** 25 and 26 Dec, 1 Jan, bank hol Mons **Meals:** alc (main courses £13.50 to £16). Breakfast and tapas menus available **Service:** not inc **Cards:** Amex, Delta, Maestro, MasterCard, Visa **Details:** 70 seats. 25 seats outside. Private parties: 130 main room. Vegetarian meals. No-smoking area. Wheelchair access (also WC). Music. Air-conditioned

Quartier Vert

85 Whiteladies Road, Bristol BS8 2NT
Tel: (0117) 973 4482
Website: www.quartiervert.co.uk

Cooking 4 | Mediterranean | £30–£62

Barny Haughton's commitment to organic produce burns brightly at this simply decorated and unpretentious restaurant in the smart Clifton district. With a fortnightly delivery from the market in Milan supplementing the more local supplies, the culinary orientation is towards provincial European traditions. Start with classic provençale fish soup with Gruyère, rouille and croûtons, or roasted scallops with balsamic red-onion compote and wild garlic pesto, before proceeding to red mullet served with linguine, fennel, chilli and lemon, or a meat dish such as Barrow Gurney spring lamb with Sicilian cherry tomatoes, aubergine and salsa verde. Everything has a refreshingly simple air to it, a style enhanced by the café servings of small tapas-like dishes all day from noon. A typical pudding might be passion-fruit and raspberry tart with raspberry sorbet, or there are fine farmhouse cheeses. Sherries and a host of wines by the glass kick off a sound Europhile selection from £12.95.

Chefs: Barny Haughton and Connemara Coombes **Proprietor:** Barny Haughton **Open:** all week L 12 to 3, Mon to Sat D 6 to 10.30 **Closed:** 3 to 7 days at Christmas **Meals:** alc (main courses L £10.50 to £18.50, D £11.50 to £20.50). Set L £16.50 (2 courses) to £19.50, Set D (exc Fri and Sat) £19.50. Bar tapas menu available **Service:** 10% (optional) **Cards:** Delta, MasterCard, Maestro, Visa **Details:** 70 seats. 25 seats outside. Private parties: 70 main room, 10 to 20 private rooms. Vegetarian meals. No smoking. Music

riverstation

The Grove, Bristol BS1 4RB
Tel: (0117) 914 4434
Website: www.riverstation.co.uk

Cooking 3 | Modern British-Plus | £24–£60

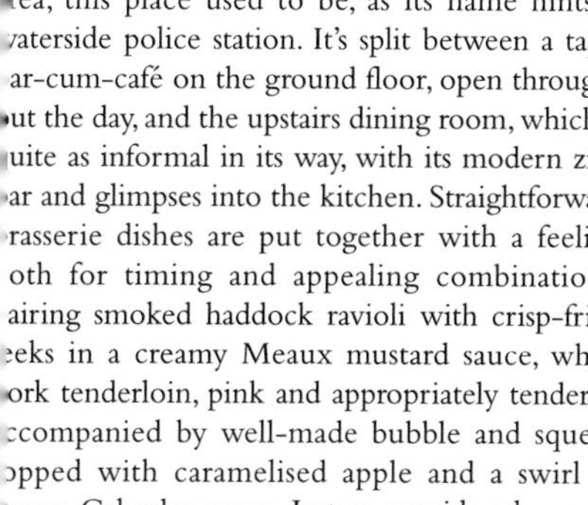

Right on the water in Bristol's revitalised harbour area, this place used to be, as its name hints, a waterside police station. It's split between a tapas bar-cum-café on the ground floor, open throughout the day, and the upstairs dining room, which is quite as informal in its way, with its modern zinc bar and glimpses into the kitchen. Straightforward brasserie dishes are put together with a feeling both for timing and appealing combinations, pairing smoked haddock ravioli with crisp-fried leeks in a creamy Meaux mustard sauce, while pork tenderloin, pink and appropriately tender, is accompanied by well-made bubble and squeak topped with caramelised apple and a swirl of strong Calvados sauce. Just as considered was an inspector's main course of roast halibut, the fish retaining moistness and bounce, served with endive, celeriac crisps and beurre blanc flavoured with orange. End with 'frangipane' tart made with pistachios. The globally-inspired wine list kicks off at £13.50.

Chefs: Peter Taylor and Ross Wills **Proprietors:** John Payne and Peter Taylor **Open:** Mon to Fri 12 to 2.30, 6 to 10.30 (11 Fri), Sat 10.30 to 2.30, 6 to 11, Sun 12 to 3, 6 to 9 **Closed:** 24 to 26 Dec, 1 Jan **Meals:** alc (main courses £11 to £17). Set L Mon to Fri £11.50 (2 courses) to £13.75, Set L Sun £15 (2 courses) to £17.50. Bar and Sat brunch menus available **Service:** not inc **Cards:** Delta, Diners, Maestro, MasterCard, Visa **Details:** 100 seats. 28 seats outside. Private parties: 100 main room. Vegetarian meals. Children's helpings. No smoking. No music

MAP 2 **Britwell Salome**
OXFORDSHIRE

The Goose

Britwell Salome OX49 5LG
Tel: (01491) 612304

Cooking 5 | Modern European | £29–£64

Three years on, there's a lot to be said for The Goose under its chef-proprietor Michael North. All is neat, uncluttered and unshowy, with plain wooden chairs and white linen the backdrop to a seasonal menu built around excellent raw materials from leading local suppliers, and the young team – both in the kitchen and front-of-house – are 'committed, enthusiastic and industrious'. The menu offers an intriguing array of dishes, from savoury pithiviers with truffle jus, via country terrine of pork with pistachio, to 'impeccably fresh' grilled diver-caught scallops with roasted tomato salad. There's some fine and original cooking in main courses, too, with a proper appreciation of the importance of flavour: the combination of chicory tart, 'Irish' cabbage and beetroot jus, for example, went perfectly with a flavourful breast of Gressingham duck tried at inspection. Desserts, no less inventive, have a habit of introducing unexpected items, adding a liquorice stick to a rhubarb dessert (served with its own ice cream and mint syrup). Own-baked bread and an amuse-bouche of wild mushroom soup with truffle oil have been praised, as have bar lunches, which offer 'lots of interesting sandwiches' as well as the likes of chicken-liver parfait and lamb stew with vegetables and potato purée. Some 100 wines are a cogent mix of styles and prices, starting with 17 by the glass from £3.25. Bottle prices start at £10.50.

Chef: Michael North **Proprietor:** The Goose Restaurant Ltd **Open:** all week L 12 to 2.30 (3 Sun), Mon to Sat D 7 to 9 **Meals:** alc (main courses £16 to £22). Set L Mon to Fri £15 (2 courses) to £18, Set D Mon to Thur £15 (2 courses) to £18. Bar menu available **Service:** not inc **Cards:** Amex, Delta, MasterCard, Maestro, Visa **Details:** 50 seats. 40 seats outside. Private parties: 30 main room, 10 to 30 private rooms. Car park. Vegetarian meals. Children's helpings. No smoking. Wheelchair access (not WC). Music. Air-conditioned

To submit a report on any restaurant, please visit *www.which.co.uk/gfgfeedback*.

MAP 1 **Brixham** DEVON

Pilgrims Restaurant AR

64B Fore Street, Brixham TQ5 8EF
Tel: (01803) 853983

Family-run, seaside-town restaurant decked out to look like the cabin of the *Mayflower*. Fish is from local boats: Brixham lobster risotto (£8.50), and baked fillet of bream with lime and tomato salsa (£15.50), for example. Devon-reared meat provides alternatives in the shape of, say, loin of pork with apple, cider and mustard, while desserts could include prune, almond and Armagnac tart with crème anglaise (£5.25). Around 35 good-value wines from £10.75. Open Thur to Sat L and Tue to Sat D.

MAP 2 **Broadhembury** DEVON

Drewe Arms

Broadhembury EX14 3NF
Tel: (01404) 841267

Cooking 3 | Seafood | £36–£51

West Country fish and seafood cooked simply and quickly is the lodestar of this charming thatched pub in a picture-postcard Devon village. Two blackboards in different rooms may well have different dishes on them, so move about and get your bearings before ordering. Reports of good things have included light, fresh crab soup ('better than any I have tasted in Brittany'), the rightly famed gravad lax, and main courses that manage to make fish such as Dover sole and turbot 'taste as though they had just been pulled from the sea'. Nor are preparations always the most obvious: inventive treatments might mean serving grated horseradish with halibut, or red pepper chutney with red mullet. If you aren't piscatorially inclined, try rack of lamb with onion marmalade. Simple desserts take in lemon posset and hazelnut parfait as well as rhubarb soup with stem ginger ice cream. The whites-led wine list offers an array of Sauvignons and Chardonnays, with the odd Viognier and Riesling thrown in for variety. Côtes du Roussillon house wines in both colours are £12.85.

Chefs: Andrew and Nigel Burge **Proprietor:** Andrew Burge **Open:** all week L 12 to 2, Mon to Sat D 7 to 9.15 **Closed:** 25 Dec, L 31 Dec **Meals:** alc (main courses £14.50 to £18). Bar menu available **Service:** not inc **Cards:** Delta, Maestro, MasterCard, Visa **Details:** 50 seats. 50 seats outside. Private parties: 24 main room. Car park. Vegetarian meals. Children's helpings. No smoking in 1 dining room. Wheelchair access (also WC). No music

MAP 5 **Broadway** WORCESTERSHIRE

Dormy House

Willersey Hill, Broadway WR12 7LF
Tel: (01386) 852711
Website: www.dormyhouse.co.uk

Cooking 3 | Modern European-Plus | £31–£62

The view over the Vale of Evesham is arresting by any standards. This former farmhouse provides modern hotel comforts, although oak beams and mellow stone walls show its seventeenth-century origins, and a large tapestry gives the dining room its name. Alan Cutler's cooking starts in unabashed country-house mode – prime cuts of meat and fillets of fish are the main commodities – then a luxury touch is added with purées, roulades and truffles; the only offal in evidence may be foie gras. Truffled tartare, for example, may be teamed with girolles, radish salad and watercress dressing, or baked fillet of sea bass with a sweet potato galette and crisp marsh samphire. Finish with orange and marshmallow jaffa cake with orange sauce, or rose petal iced parfait. The wine list covers the world but favours classical France; prices start at £12.75 a bottle, and there's a range of halves.

Chef: Alan Cutler **Proprietor:** Mrs I.P. Sørensen **Open:** Sun L 12 to 2, all week D 7 to 9.30 (9 Sun) **Closed:** 25 to 27 Dec **Meals:** alc D (main courses £15.50 to £23). Set L Sun £20.50, Set D £25 to £33.50 (July and Aug only). Bar L and D menu available all week **Service:** not inc **Cards:** Amex, Delta, Maestro, MasterCard, Visa **Details:** 80 seats. 30 seats outside. Private parties: 170 main room, 10 to 170 private rooms. Car park. Vegetarian meals. No children under 16 at D. Children's helpings. Jacket and tie. No smoking. Wheelchair access (also WC). No music. Air-conditioned **Accommodation:** 47 rooms, all with bath/shower. TV. Phone. B&B £120 to £210. Rooms for disabled. Baby facilities

Lygon Arms

Broadway WR12 7DU
Tel: (01386) 852255
Website: www.thelygonarms.co.uk

Cooking 5 | French/East European | £36–£130

The Lygon Arms has had 500 years' practice as a hostelry of one sort or another. During the Civil War it hedged its bets, hosting both Charles I and Oliver Cromwell, though presumably not simultaneously. It retains an air of unruffled venerability with a variety of rooms for lounging in, much

polished panelling, and a Great Hall replete with heraldic friezes and a minstrels' gallery. Martin Blunos, who arrived here in 2003, has a cooking style of some ostentation, pyrotechnics even (as witness the witty pre-dessert of a boiled egg, fashioned of crème Chantilly and mango purée), and there is naturally a multi-course tasting menu to go at as well as the richly impressive carte. Caramelised, salt-sprinkled foie gras terrine with pain d'épice and Tokaji jelly, garnished with a few green beans, is the kind of first course you might expect to come across in these surroundings, with a gratin of crayfish and asparagus a less obvious one.

The menu appears to develop slowly, with some dishes continuing from one year to the next, but there is a sense of things being worked to a high pitch of precision. Good meat cookery at inspection turned up roast breast of tenderly gamey guinea fowl with celeriac mash, garlic fritters and tarragon cream, and loin of well-hung venison with haggis raviolo on finely shredded Savoy cabbage and a sauce of port and juniper. Desserts tone things down with classic selections such as peach melba or raspberry croustillant. Overeager topping up of glasses slightly tips the balance of service that is otherwise 'natural and friendly'. A French-led wine list has many fine bottles at prices that, while high, are not unforgivable in the context. House French is £16.25.

Chef: Martin Blunos **Proprietor:** Furlong Hotels **Open:** all week 12 to 2.30, 7.30 to 9.30 **Meals:** alc (main courses L £13 to £14.50, D £19.50 to £26.50). Set L £26.50, Set D Sun to Wed £39.50, Thur to Sat £39.50 to £90 (inc wine) **Service:** not inc **Cards:** Amex, Delta, Diners, Maestro, MasterCard, Visa **Details:** 90 seats. 24 seats outside. Private parties: 100 main room, 4 to 100 private rooms. Car park. Vegetarian meals. Children's helpings. No children under 12 in Great Hall. No smoking. Wheelchair access (also WC). No music. Air-conditioned **Accommodation:** 69 rooms, 66 with bath/shower. TV. Phone. B&B £119 to £545. Rooms for disabled. Swimming pool

MAP 2 **Brockenhurst** HAMPSHIRE

Le Poussin at Whitley Ridge

Beaulieu Road, Brockenhurst SO42 7QL
Tel: (01590) 622354
Website: www.lepoussin.co.uk

Cooking 6 | Modern British | £34–£87

The Aitkens have not forsaken their old home at Parkhill in Lyndhurst but have moved a few miles up the road to this country hotel for a couple of years while the old place is refurbished and extended. For the time being, Whitley Ridge will do nicely, if idiosyncratically, with its vista of stretching parkland, ornate ceiling friezes and outsize Brueghel reproductions dominating the dining room.

Alex Aitken's cooking continues to develop in its diverting, experimental vein, the new dishes including a quail puff pie with foie gras and morel mousse in the centre, or skewers of sticky belly pork and prawns served with texturally contrasting sauces of ginger foam and lime syrup. Venison, a signature dish, showed up well at inspection, the saddle roasted rare, a magnificent chunk of fillet wrapped in Parma ham, with a selection of organs – a small slice each of liver, kidney and heart – and 'the best haggis ever', the whole tricked out with baby vegetables, Savoy cabbage and caramelised walnuts. Halibut might be poached in aromatic milk and served with a kind of pasty of duxelles and saffron potatoes. The same level of complexity is maintained for desserts that might include a whole roast clementine with mandarin sorbet, Seville orange curd and a mini crêpe suzette, or a riff on passion-fruit involving a hot soufflé with coordinated sorbet, curd and sauce. Thankfully the wine cellar also made the move from Lyndhurst. It starts with a house selection of organic Chilean bottles at £15.50 and then shifts into gear with a sublime classical collection, and features some of the best New World estates.

Chefs: Alex Aitken and Shane Hughes **Proprietors:** Alex and Caroline Aitken **Open:** all week 12.30 to 2, 6.30 to 9.30 **Meals:** alc (main courses £21 to £25.50). Set L £15 (2 courses) to £25, Set D £35 to £55 **Service:** 10% (optional), card slips closed **Cards:** Amex, Delta, Maestro, MasterCard, Visa **Details:** 40 seats. 15 seats outside. Private parties: 48 main room, 6 to 25 private rooms. Car park. Children's helpings. No smoking. Wheelchair access (not WC). No music. No mobile phones **Accommodation:** 18 rooms, all with bath/shower. TV. B&B £70 to £200. Rooms for disabled. Baby facilities

Simply Poussin

The Courtyard, Brookley Road, Brockenhurst SO42 7RB
Tel: (01590) 623063
Website: www.lepoussin.co.uk

Cooking 3 | Modern British | £26–£50

The smaller sibling of Le Poussin (see entry above) offers informal eating in a slate-floored dining-room festooned with cartoons, with the further option, weather permitting, of eating in what the owner describes as a 'cute mews courtyard'.

Cooking follows unfussy brasserie lines, with starters such as wild mushroom risotto accompanied by a herb salad dressed with truffle oil, and mains like fried red mullet and tagliatelle, or casseroled pigeon served in its cooking juices. Dishes deliver positive flavour and accurate seasonings, with the same quality of raw materials for which the more illustrious stablemate is renowned. Meals end on a high note with honey and hazelnut parfait with fruit syrup, or hot chocolate fondant with white chocolate ice cream. The short wine list opens at £14.50 for a fruity Chilean Malbec.

Chefs: Alex Aitken and Ian Comerford **Proprietor:** Alex Aitken **Open:** Tue to Sat 12 to 2, 6.45 to 9.45 **Meals:** alc (main courses £12 to £16). Set L £10 (2 courses) to £15, Set D Tue to Fri £10 (2 courses) **Service:** 10% (optional) **Cards:** Amex, Maestro, MasterCard, Visa **Details:** 30 seats. 12 seats outside. Private parties: 30 main room. No smoking. Music

MAP 5 Bromsgrove WORCESTERSHIRE

Grafton Manor

Grafton Lane, Bromsgrove B61 7HA
Tel: (01527) 579007
Website: www.graftonmanorhotel.co.uk

Cooking 3 | Modern Indian/European | £29–£53

The Morrises have been here since 1980 and continue to nurture the baronial feel of this ancient redbrick pile. Englishness rules. By contrast, the food intermittently espouses the spicy flavours of the Indian Subcontinent, when Simon Morris lets rip with dishes like Goan crab cakes on egg, chickpea and peanut salad, and 'First Class Railway Lamb' infused with coconut milk. Such dishes are interspersed among more conventional modern European ideas like steamed lemon sole fillet with a courgette pudding, Parmesan and lemon oil, and loin of lamb with fennel and morel emulsion, as well as a full-on vegetarian repertoire. India may resurface among the desserts, although the emphasis is on things like white chocolate parfait with coffee jelly. The wine list (from £10.25) is predominantly French, with a nod to the New World, and has a fair few halves.

Chef: Simon Morris **Proprietors:** the Morris family **Open:** all week 12 to 1.30, 7 to 9 **Closed:** bank hols **Meals:** Set L £18.50 to £20.50, Set D £27.85 to £32.50 **Service:** not inc, card slips closed **Cards:** Amex, Diners, Maestro, MasterCard, Visa **Details:** 60 seats. Private parties: 60 main room. Car park. Vegetarian meals. Children's helpings. No smoking. Wheelchair access (also WC). No music. No mobile phones **Accommodation:** 9 rooms, all with bath/shower. TV. Phone. B&B £85 to £150. Rooms for disabled

MAP 2 Bruton SOMERSET

Bruton House

NEW ENTRY

2–4 High Street, Bruton BA10 0AA
Tel: (01749) 813395
Website: www.brutonhouse.co.uk

Cooking 6 | British | £32–£58

At the top of the steep hill that runs through Bruton, this bright blue, architecturally complicated restaurant-with-rooms was re-launched at the end of 2004 with a chef from Hambleton Hall (see entry, Hambleton). A trio of rooms has been knocked through to create one narrow space, decorated in muted tones, and with fine, floor-length linen on the tables. Clunky Muzak rather spoils the intended effect of gracious country elegance.

The kitchen runs on ecologically sound principles, ensuring that most of its raw materials don't have to travel too far to reach it. What exceptions there are, such as game from the Clarendon Estate near Salisbury or fish from Cornwall, clearly earn their places. A refreshing lack of undue fuss characterises dishes such as a pair of corpulent scallops on thin, smooth Jerusalem artichoke purée, with orange oil dressing, or a main course of well-seared Dorset Down lamb chump with a spring bouquet of greens, broad beans and peas. Flower Marie, a soft Sussex sheep's cheese, might be baked as a starter and served with endive, pear and walnuts, while brill is braised to make an earthy main course with a risotto of cockles and wild garlic. Mainstream desserts such as tarte Tatin with vanilla ice cream, or passion-fruit soufflé with matching sorbet, round things off gently. Staff aim to please, although wine service is a bit variable. A short wine list keeps prices mostly in check, and opens at £13.50 for Argentinian white, or £14 for French red.

Chefs: Scott Eggleton and James Andrews **Proprietor:** Christie-Miller Andrews Ltd **Open:** Tue to Sun L 12 to 2, Tue to Sat D 7 to 9.30 **Meals:** Set L £28 (2 courses) to £35 (3 courses), Set Sun L £18.50 to £35 (3 courses), Set D £28 (2 courses) to £35 **Service:** not inc, card slips closed, 10% for parties of 8 or more **Cards:** Amex, Delta, MasterCard, Maestro, Visa **Details:** 30 seats. Private parties: 40 main room. Vegetarian meals. No smoking in 1 dining room. Music. No mobile phones **Accommodation:** 3 rooms, 2 with bath/shower. TV. B&B £25 to £50

MAP 2 **Buckland** OXFORDSHIRE

Lamb at Buckland

Lamb Lane, Buckland SN7 8QN
Tel: (01367) 870484
Email: enquiries@thelambatbuckland.co.uk

Cooking 1 | Modern British | £26–£64

For all that the village itself is tiny, this country pub hides itself well: look for the signposts. Taped golden oldies play in the dining room, and tables are all fanned napkins, posies and candles. The nice, old-fashioned, friendly family atmosphere is enhanced by cooking that eschews pretension in favour of the simple likes of roast rack of English lamb (naturally) with a sauce of lamb stock, mint and sorrel, the meat copious with both fat and flavour. Seafood, chalked on the blackboard, appears in starters such as a warm scallop mousse with asparagus and chive butter. Plentiful vegetables in side dishes are all of a piece with the pub ambience, but rather heavy sticky toffee and date pudding let the side down at inspection. Peta Barnard runs the front-of-house with eagle-eyed proficiency. An imaginative and fairly priced wine selection starts in Chile at £14.95.

Chef: Paul Barnard **Proprietor:** Lamb at Buckland Ltd **Open:** Tue to Sun L 12 to 2 (2.30 Sun), Tue to Sat D 7 to 9.30 (10 Sat) **Closed:** 24 Dec to 7 Jan **Meals:** alc (main courses £11.50 to £24). Set L £10 (2 courses) to £13.50, Set D Tue to Fri £15 (2 courses) to £18.50 **Service:** not inc **Cards:** Delta, Maestro, MasterCard, Visa **Details:** 60 seats. 30 seats outside. Private parties: 45 main room, 10 to 18 private rooms. Car park. Vegetarian meals. Children's helpings. No smoking. Wheelchair access (not WC). Music **Accommodation:** 1 room, with bath/shower. TV. Phone. B&B £75 to £145. Baby facilities

MAP 2 **Bucklers Hard** HAMPSHIRE

Master Builder's House Hotel, Riverview Restaurant

Bucklers Hard SO42 7XB
Tel: (01590) 616253
Website: www.themasterbuilders.co.uk

Cooking 3 | Modern European | £35–£60

The master builder in question was in shipping, and his former house has a 'great feel to it', making the most of its 'lazy, hazy days of summer' setting on the banks of the Beaulieu River. Serious eating takes place in the Riverside Restaurant, where the kitchen's approach is to perk up interest using excellent-quality raw materials, although menus play a fairly safe modern European tune. Simplicity seems to be the key to the operation, with a repertoire that ranges from crab ravioli with red-pepper sauce to whole Dover sole with lemon. Otherwise, tagliatelle with wild mushroom sauce might precede ribeye steak with pommes, Pont-neuf, mushroom and tomato burger and Café de Paris butter, or duck with a duck cassoulet. To finish there could be ginger and honey nougat glace, or chocolate marquise with coffee sauce. Staff are very welcoming, and the French-dominated global list organises wines by price, starting with 13 house choices at £14.

Chef: Denis Rhoden **Proprietors:** John Illsley and Jeremy Willcock **Open:** all week 12 to 3, 7 to 10 **Meals:** alc (main courses £13 to £18). Set L £16.50 (2 courses) to £19.95, Set D £29.50. Bar menu available **Service:** not inc, card slips closed **Cards:** Amex, MasterCard, Maestro, Visa **Details:** 70 seats. 70 seats outside. Private parties: 40 main room, 10 to 40 private rooms. Car park. Vegetarian meals. Children's helpings **Accommodation:** 25 rooms, all with bath/shower. TV. Phone. B&B £135 to £245

NEW ENTRY	This appears after the restaurant's name if the establishment was not a main entry in last year's Guide, although it may have been a 'round-up/also recommended' in previous editions.

MAP 5 Buckminster LEICESTERSHIRE

Tollemache Arms NEW ENTRY

48 Main Street, Buckminster NG33 5SA
Tel: (01476) 860007
Website: www.thetollemachearms.com

Cooking 4 | Modern British | £24–£62

Highly polished wooden floors, oatmeal-coloured walls and a welcome lack of clutter produce a 'modern, minimalist' feel to this impressive stone-built inn. Well-spaced tables, high-backed leatherette chairs and gentle lighting create a calm environment in which to study Mark Gough's menus, which have some appealing ideas: foie gras ballottine with parsnip chutney and white truffle dressing, for example, or a main course of roast guinea fowl with pasta rösti and a lime and madeira jus. First-class materials underpin the operation, and reporters have enjoyed pan-fried pigeon breasts with onion marmalade and red wine sauce, Jerusalem artichoke soup, grilled scallops with smoked bacon and truffle mash, and wild sea bass with basil mash and baby chorizo sausages. It there were any doubt about mastery of technical skills, it would be dispelled by desserts such as a 'first-class' rhubarb tart. Good producers feature on the sharply chosen wine list. Prices start helpfully at £12.95 but climb quite steeply for the style of restaurant.

Chef/Proprietor: Mark Gough **Open:** Tue to Sun L 12 to 2 (2.30 Sun), Tue to Sat D 7 to 9.30 **Meals:** alc (main courses £9.50 to £18). Set L Tue to Sat £11 (2 courses) to £15, Set L Sun £14.50 (2 courses) to £18.50, Set D £14 (2 courses) to £18.50. Bar menu available **Service:** not inc **Cards:** Amex, Delta, Maestro, MasterCard, Visa **Details:** 60 seats. 20 seats outside. Private parties: 40 main room, 10 to 20 private rooms. Car park. Vegetarian meals. Children's helpings. No smoking. Occasional music **Accommodation:** 5 rooms, all with bath/shower. TV. Room only £45 to £60

	This symbol means that smoking is not permitted.
	This symbol means that there are some restrictions on smoking though it may be allowed in some eating areas.

MAP 6 Burnham Market NORFOLK

Fishes

Market Place, Burnham Market PE31 8HE
Tel: (01328) 738588
Website: www.fishesrestaurant.co.uk

Cooking 4 | Seafood | £31–£75

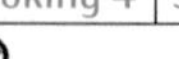

Name and north Norfolk location make it no surprise that this relaxed restaurant in the heart of Burnham Market deals in the bounty of the sea. Matthew Owsley-Brown's menu may start with Norfolk smoked eel teamed with terrine of foie gras and piquillo and chilli salt, followed by bourride of sea bass, lemon sole, squid and langoustine, with dark chocolate fondant and candied orange ice cream to round things off. Variety extends to roast cod rubbed with smoked paprika and served with braised Puy lentils and salsa verde, while a tandoori oven delivers spicier dishes, from roast butterfish kebab with hummus, chilli sauce, tsatsiki and flat bread to tandoori monkfish with pilau rice, kachumba and raita. Meat-eaters and vegetarians are catered for, given notification when booking. The cooking can be undermined by variable service. Whites predominate on the wine list, of course, though revellers in red are not neglected; prices start at £14.

Chef: Matthew Owsley-Brown **Proprietors:** Matthew and Caroline Owsley-Brown **Open:** Tue to Sun L 12 to 2, Tue to Sat D 7 to 9 **Meals:** alc (main courses £10.50 to £18). Set L £16.50 (2 courses) to £19.50, Set D £28.50 (2 courses) to £33.50 **Service:** not inc, card slips closed **Cards:** Delta, Maestro, MasterCard, Visa **Details:** 42 seats. Private parties: 10 main room, 10 to 16 private rooms. Car park. Children's helpings No children after 8.30pm. No smoking. Wheelchair access (not WC). Music. No mobile phones

Hoste Arms

The Green, Burnham Market PE31 8HD
Tel: (01328) 738777
Website: www.hostearms.co.uk

Cooking 2 | Modern British | £29–£64

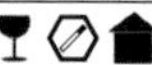

This substantial Georgian coaching inn on the village green 'combines the best of all worlds'. At the front is a large public bar with a 'great atmosphere, good conversation and well-kept beer', while a modern conservatory extension provides a lounge full of comfortable settees. Then there is the informal brasserie and a dining room. Here a ong and imaginatively varied menu offers starters ranging from duck and beetroot broth with uniper oil to tiger prawn and cockle pizza with rocket and saffron syrup, and mains encompassing pan-fried sea bass with sweet potato, courgette and pak choi with chilli butter, alongside honey-glazed ham hock with apple mash and cider sauce. Execution is generally successful, portions are 'more than ample', and service is 'professional' though at times overstretched – notably when the place is busy, which is more often than not. The impressive wine list kicks off at £11.50, and mark-ups are commendably kept in check.

Chef: Andrew McPherson **Proprietor:** Paul Whittome **Open:** all week 12 to 2, 7 to 9 **Meals:** alc (main courses £9.50 to £17.50) **Service:** not inc, card slips closed **Cards:** Delta, Maestro, MasterCard, Visa **Details:** 140 seats. 80 seats outside. Private parties: 80 main room, 16 to 24 private rooms. Car park. Vegetarian meals. No smoking in 1 dining room. Occasional music. Air-conditioned **Accommodation:** 36 rooms, all with bath/shower. TV. Phone. B&B £82 to £248. Rooms for disabled. Baby facilities

MAP 8 **Burnsall** NORTH YORKSHIRE

Devonshire Fell

Burnsall BD23 6BT
Tel: (01756) 729000

NEW CHEF | Modern British | £32–£47

Originally 'a club for gentlemen mill owners', this old Dales pub has been catapulted into the twenty-first century by its current proprietor. The views over the River Wharfe remain as stunning as ever, but the exterior has been touched up with landscaped gardens, sweeping steps and a contemporary railing depicting birds in flight. Inside, all is thoroughly contemporary. A new chef and manager arrived during 2005, but the style of food remains intact. Locally sourced ingredients are deployed for a short brasserie menu that skips through pigeon terrine and red wine fig salad, fillet of red mullet with a fricassee of olives, tomatoes and parisienne potatoes, then blueberry and almond tart with caramel sauce. The extensive wine list is catalogued by price, with house selections £11.95.

Chef: Mehdi Boukemach **Proprietor:** the Duke of Devonshire **Open:** all week 11.30 to 2.30 (3 Sun), 6.30 to 9.30 **Meals:** alc (main courses £12 to £16.50). Bar menu available **Service:** not inc, card slips closed **Cards:** Amex, Delta, Diners, Maestro, MasterCard, Visa **Details:** 50 seats. 18 seats outside. Private parties: 70 main room. Car park. Vegetarian meals. Children's helpings. No smoking. Wheelchair access (also WC). Music **Accommodation:** 12 rooms, all with bath/shower. TV. Phone. B&B £75 to £190. Baby facilities

MAP 5 **Burton on the Wolds** LEICESTERSHIRE

Langs

Horse Leys Farm, 147 Melton Road, Burton on the Wolds LE12 5TQ
Tel: (01509) 880980
Website: www.langsrestaurant.co.uk

Cooking 3 | Modern European | £26–£52

This farmhouse was declared an oasis in the desert by one visitor. In its L-shaped, split level dining room, juxtaposing wood-strip floors, metal-framed chairs with low beams and upholstered rattan chairs, local meats contribute to short lunch and longer dinner menus. These might start with chicken, bacon and walnut terrine, or smoked haddock tortilla with tomato and coriander salsa. Duck with lentils and accompanying vegetables has been praised, or try lamb's liver, kidneys, smoked bacon and shallot Tatin. Other sound combinations involve tomato and basil salad with Halloumi cheese and pesto, grilled red mullet with provençale vegetables, and apple and Calvados parfait with wild cherries and Kirsch. 'Very good' service enhances the sense of well-being, and wines are chosen for both interest and value; six house wines start at £13.25 (£3.15 a glass).

Chefs: Gordon Lang and John Duffin **Proprietors:** Gordon and June Lang **Open:** Tue to Sat L 12 to 2.15 (3 Sun), Tue to Sat D 7 to 9.45 (6 to 10 Sat) **Meals:** alc (main courses £12 to £17). Set L £10.50 (2 courses) to £15.50, Set D £17 **Service:** not inc, card slips closed **Cards:** Delta, Maestro, MasterCard, Visa **Details:** 48 seats. 10 seats outside. Private parties: 10 to 70 private rooms. Car park. Vegetarian meals. Children's helpings. No smoking. Wheelchair access (also WC). Occasional music. No mobile phones

MAP 6 Bury St Edmunds SUFFOLK

Angel Hotel

AR

3 Angel Hill, Bury St Edmunds IP33 1LT
Tel: (01284) 714000

Imposing, fifteenth-century, creeper-covered hotel run by the same family for over 30 years. Menus in the formal Abbeygate Restaurant are in the modern mould of warm pigeon and rabbit salad with quince jelly and quail's eggs (£6.75), sea bass fillet on crushed new potatoes with tomato and basil (£15), and caramelised lemon tart. Good-value lunches (two courses £10.50) and an all-day brasserie menu in the lounge, bar and subterranean Vaults. International wines from £12.95, including plenty by the glass. Open all week.

Maison Bleue

30–31 Churchgate Street,
Bury St Edmunds IP33 1RG
Tel: (01284) 760623
Website: www.maisonbleue.co.uk

Cooking 2 | Seafood | £25–£67

There's a traditional look to the menu at this agreeable French seafood restaurant (with a couple of meat options for those who must). The classic approach brings whitebait, perhaps, or an 'impeccably timed' lemon sole stuffed with cod and basil mousse served with an asparagus sauce. There are some foreign forays, too, like spicy Thai-style smoked haddock and coriander fishcakes with a rice vinegar sauce, or pan-fried fillet of sea bass with sautéed turnips, sesame seeds and honey sauce. But it's home to France for desserts: one reporter's crème brûlée with rosemary was 'spot on', and there's pain perdu as well, and crêpes suzette. Cheeses too are Gallic, and service young and efficient. On the lengthy wine list France looms large, *bien sûr*, but there's plenty of sound drinking from elsewhere; house wines start at £10.50.

Chef: Pascal Canevet **Proprietor:** Régis Crépy **Open:** Tue to Sat 12 to 2.30, 7 to 9.30 (10 Fri and Sat) **Closed:** 3 weeks Jan, 1 week end-Aug **Meals:** alc (main courses £9 to £29). Set L £10.95 (2 courses) to £15.95, Set D £23.95 **Service:** not inc **Cards:** Amex, Delta, Maestro, MasterCard, Visa **Details:** 65 seats. Private parties: 36 main room, 14 to 22 private rooms. Vegetarian meals. Children's helpings. No smoking. Wheelchair access (not WC). Music

MAP 3 Bushey HERTFORDSHIRE

St James

30 High Street, Bushey WD23 3HL
Tel: (020) 8950 2480

Cooking 3 | Modern British | £31–£59

Taking the name of the church opposite, this smar suburban restaurant is unpretentious and has warm, friendly bistro-esque atmosphere. Bar brick walls and wooden floorboards give a slightly rustic feel, and tightly packed tables add to th buzz. A dozen starters take in asparagus and roas plum tomato salad with sauté wild mushrooms alongside corned beef paté with home-made pic calilli, or crab and avocado salad with Parmesa tuile, lobster and roast pepper dressing. The doze mains divide into meat – say, pork fillet wrapped i smoked bacon with mushroom farce, potato rösti a sage jus and apple sauce – and fish, perhap including fennel-crusted sea bass fillet with tomato butter sauce, or traditional Dover sol meunière. Toblerone cheesecake with crèm Chantilly to finish should tempt the sweet toothed. House wines are £13.

Chef: Simon Trussel **Proprietors:** Simon Trussel and Alfonso La Cava **Open:** Mon to Sat 12 to 2, 6.30 to 9.30 **Closed:** 25 Dec, bank hols **Meals:** alc (main courses £15 to £20). Set L £13.95 (2 courses), Set D £14.95 (2 courses) **Service:** 12.5%, card slips closed **Cards:** Maestro, MasterCard, Visa **Details:** 80 seats. Private parties: 66 main room, 35 to 44 private rooms. Vegetarian meals. No smoking. Wheelchair access (also WC). Occasional music. No mobile phones. Air-conditioned

MAP 9 Buxton DERBYSHIRE

Columbine

7 Hall Bank, Buxton SK17 6EW
Tel: (01298) 78752
Website: www.buxtononline.net/columbine

Cooking 2 | Modern British | £25–£39

Handily located a few minutes' downhill wa from Buxton's theatre and gardens, Columbi does a good line in pre- and post-show suppe (booking essential): the atmosphere is leisurel service is 'well-paced' and prices are fair, accordi to satisfied customers who have taken advantage the deals on offer. Regular dinner menus focus o lishes like warm French onion tart, and sauté nedallions of monkfish and tiger prawns with ıerbs and lemon, followed by a blackboard of lesserts such as brandy-snap basket filled with resh raspberries. There are also daily specials like oraised local pheasant with red cabbage and port gravy, plus a menu for vegetarians. Columbine bills tself as a 'restaurant with cellars', and the wine list s a reasonably priced slate including house Duboeuf at £8.95.

Chef: Steve McNally **Proprietors:** Kim and Steve McNally **Open:** Wed to Sat and Mon (May to Oct: Mon to Sat) D only 7 to 9.30 **Closed:** 24 Dec to 1st week Jan, Feb half term **Meals:** alc D (not July; main courses £10.95 to £14). Set D July only £17.50 (2 courses) to £20.50 **Service:** not inc, card slips closed **Cards:** Delta, Maestro, MasterCard, Visa **Details:** 45 seats. Private parties: 18 main room, 10 to 18 private rooms. Vegetarian meals. Children's helpings. No smoking in 1 dining room. Music

MAP 3 Camber EAST SUSSEX

The Place

AR

New Lydd Road, Camber TN31 7RB
Tel: (01797) 225057

Holidaying families and the business conference rowd mix happily in this lively venue across the oad from Camber Sands. Local and organic ingreients – including fish from 'non-threatened pecies' – appear on the menu in the shape of teamed Rye Bay scallops with chilli, ginger and oy (£6.25), chump of Romney Marsh lamb with vild garlic mash (£14.75), and pot-roast wild abbit with mustard sauce (£11.75). Treacle tart £5) is a renowned dessert. Two dozen wines from £11.95. Accommodation available. Open all veek.

MAP 6 Cambridge CAMBRIDGESHIRE

Hotel Felix

Whitehouse Lane, Huntingdon Road, Cambridge CB3 0LX
Tel: (01223) 277977
Website: www.hotelfelix.co.uk

Cooking 2 | Mediterranean | £27–£74

The hotel comprises a dramatically refurbished nd enlarged Victorian mansion with a courtyard at the back and ample parking in the grounds (a rarity in Cambridge). At its heart is the Graffiti restaurant – a stylish, minimalist venue offering brasserie-style food with modern Mediterranean influences and a smattering of upmarket luxuries. Ingredients are carefully chosen, presentation is chic and the results are satisfying. Impressive starters range from vegetable boudin with lentil salsa and herb vinaigrette to seared scallops with slow-baked plum tomato and basil ice cream. Braised belly of Denham rare-breed pork ('full of flavour') with sautéed purple sprouting broccoli, tarragon fondant potatoes and apple crisps has been devoured with gusto, and to finish there are attractive desserts like chocolate mousse cake with balsamic strawberries. House wines from £12 kick off the affordable, accurately described list.

Chef: Stuart Conibear **Proprietor:** Jeremy Cassel **Open:** all week 12 to 2, 6.30 to 10 (10.30 Fri and Sat, 9.30 Sun) **Meals:** alc D (main courses £13 to £24). Set L £12.50 (2 courses) to £16.50. Bar menu available **Service:** not inc **Cards:** Amex, Delta, Diners, MasterCard, Maestro, Visa **Details:** 45 seats. 60 seats outside. Private parties: 60 main room, 6 to 45 private rooms. Car park. Vegetarian meals. Children's helpings. No smoking. Wheelchair access (also WC). Music **Accommodation:** 52 rooms, all with bath/shower. TV. Phone. B&B £132 to £270. Rooms for disabled. Baby facilities

Midsummer House

CAMBRIDGESHIRE RESTAURANT OF THE YEAR

Midsummer Common, Cambridge CB4 1HA
Tel: (01223) 369299
Website: www.midsummerhouse.co.uk

Cooking 6 | Modern French | £45–£98

On the bank of the Cam, overlooking the common, Midsummer House is a well-maintained Victorian villa with three areas for eating: a conservatory, a small ground-floor dining room, and the Blue Room, which has views of the river. When the sun obliges, it's even possible to eat outside in the kitchen's herb garden. It's all highly relaxing, and if service would just do the same all would be right with the world.

Chef/proprietor Daniel Clifford has a restless imagination and is one of that elite band of British chefs who has pushed back the boundaries of French-centred haute cuisine. A first course might well be a grouping of strange bedfellows, fashionably of meat and shellfish perhaps, in a successful assortment of braised belly pork, salt-cod brandade, crisp Parma ham and langoustines, each with its own little dressing – a bit of foamy seafood broth here, a swirl of apple purée there. Poached veal fillet (another starter) is garnished with oscietra caviar and accompanied by tuna mayonnaise, capers and celery. The tone thus set, main courses raise the stakes even higher, perhaps teaming braised monkfish with parsnip and cumin risotto, parsnip purée, a pastilla of oxtail, buttered spinach and a meaty jus. For those not quite prepared to venture forth as boldly as this, there is evidence of more mainstream thinking in a rewarding dish of slow-roast beef fillet with shallot marmalade, celeriac purée, a bonbon of foie gras, and a carefully reduced, not overpowering, sauce of port.

Desserts are divided into hot and cold options, with the former producing exciting contrasts of texture and temperature in the likes of caramel and lime soufflé with ginger and lemongrass ice cream, or Valrhona chocolate and pistachio fondant with liquorice ice cream. The wine list is a high-class heavyweight with prices to match.

Chef: Daniel Clifford **Proprietor:** Crown Group **Open:** Tue to Sat 12 to 2, 7 to 9.30 **Meals:** Set L £20 (2 courses) to £26, Set D £48.50 to £60 **Service:** not inc **Cards:** Amex, Delta, Maestro, MasterCard, Visa **Details:** 40 seats. 20 seats outside. Private parties: 40 main room, 20 private room. Vegetarian meals. No smoking. Wheelchair access (not WC). No music

Restaurant 22

22 Chesterton Road, Cambridge CB4 3AX
Tel: (01223) 351880
Website: www.restaurant22.co.uk

Cooking 2 | Modern European | £38–£61

The small Victorian house is domestic in scale and even ambience but this is backed by professionalism where it counts. David Carter's formula has served his customers well for 14 years – value for money and variety provided via a monthly changing fixed-price menu – and the kitchen confidently keeps combinations fairly simple, timing accurate, and interweaves subtle flavours and stronger ones. An inspector's roast venison loin married 'dark, velvety' redcurrant and chocolate jus and red cabbage with moist, tender meat. Corn-fed chicken with root vegetables and tarragon and white wine sauce was similarly a success. Starters may include the brochette of monkfish and chorizo with tomato and butter bean salad that reporters have praised, or ham hock with celeriac rémoulade, and puddings perhaps Armagnac parfait with prunes in Earl Grey syrup. The good-value wine list focuses on classic France, but nods other sources from old world and new; house wines from £12.50 (£3.50 a glass).

Chefs: Martin Cullum and Seb Mansfield **Proprietor:** David Carter **Open:** Tue to Sat D only 7 to 9.45 **Closed:** 1 week Christmas/New Year **Meals:** Set D £24.95 to £36.95 **Service:** not inc **Cards:** Amex, Delta, Diners, Maestro, MasterCard, Visa **Details:** 40 seats. Private parties: 28 main room, 7 to 12 private rooms. Vegetarian meals. No children under 10. No smoking. Occasional music. No mobile phones. Air-conditioned

The Volunteer

60 Trumpington Road, Cambridge CB2 2EX
Tel: (01223) 841675
Website: www.volunteerrestaurant.com

Cooking 4 | Modern European | £38–£58

The transformation here from town pub to convivial restaurant has been an unqualified success. The décor may be plain, but visitors have found the new Volunteer 'quite delightful' and much appreciated its friendly unpretentiousness. 'This is a place to taste real food', says one, and the fare is generally straightforward and honest, from pea and ham soup to bread-and-butter pudding; nonetheless there are some original ideas adding zest to the menu: seared scallops on spiced carrot fritters with sweet chilli jam and crème fraîche continue to impress, and the kitchen also tackles roast rack of lamb with a brochette of lamb saddle and kidney with a sherry vinegar sauce. In simpler vein, expect smoked duck breast with celeriac salad, and ragoût of corn-fed chicken with wild mushroom sauce, followed by desserts such as orange and passion fruit tart with orange sorbet. The creditable, all-round wine list has been expanded, and more are now available by the glass; house selections start at £12.50. The car park is a godsend.

Chef: David Rideout **Proprietors:** Nick and Vanessa Cross **Open:** Tues to Sat L 12 to 2, Mon to Sat D 7 to 9.30 **Closed:** bank hols **Meals:** alc (main courses £14.50 to £20). Light L menu also available **Service:** not inc, card slips closed **Cards:** Delta, Maestro, MasterCard, Visa **Details:** 58 seats. 20 seats outside. Private parties: 58 main room. Car park. Vegetarian meals. Children's helpings. No children under 8 at D. Wheelchair access (not WC). Music

This symbol means that the restaurant has elected to participate in *The Good Food Guide's* £5 voucher scheme (see 'How to Use the Guide' for details).

MAP 3 **Canterbury** KENT

Goods Shed

Station Road West, Canterbury CT2 8AN
Tel: (01227) 459153

Cooking 2 | Modern British | £27–£50

Kentish foodies making a beeline for the all week farmers' market also get the benefit of this on-site, cavernous restaurant. The industrial look of this former railway building – large windows, wooden floors and chunky undressed tables – is the ideal setting for some robust cooking: purple sprouting broccoli and bacon soup to start, perhaps, followed by organic pot roast chicken with wild garlic, or a fillet of ling with home-made black pudding. Not surprisingly proper attention is paid to produce, whether 'extremely tender' roast baby pig, or a bowl of fresh mussels with cider, cream and garlic. Finish with crème brûlée or a selection of cheeses with quince jelly. House wines start at £13.

Chefs Rafael Lopez, Nick Packer and Robin Walker **Proprietor** Susanna Atkins **Open:** Tue to Sun L 12 to 2.30 (3 Sat and Sun), Tue to Sat D 6 to 9.30 **Meals:** alc (main courses £9.50 to £16.50). **Service:** not inc, card slips closed **Cards:** Delta, Diners, MasterCard, Switch, Visa **Details:** 75 seats. Car park. Vegetarian meals. Children's helpings. No-smoking area. Wheelchair access (also WC). No music

MAP 10 **Carlisle** CUMBRIA

Number 10

10 Eden Mount, Stanwix, Carlisle CA3 9LY
Tel: (01228) 524183

Cooking 2 | Modern British | £32–£49

A mood of bonhomie prevails at Geoff and Isabel Ferguson's homely restaurant in a converted Carlisle townhouse. He cooks, while she takes care of business out front. Local produce is used to good effect on their regularly changing dinner menus: shallow-fried Croglin ewes' milk cheese with pear and date chutney is a typical starter, or you might choose pork and duck rillettes with apple and herb jelly. Alongside bacon- and mushroom-stuffed chicken breast with wine and cream sauce, main courses might develop an international theme with spicy Moroccan-style casseroled lamb and couscous, or prawn kebabs marinated in chilli oil served on an orange and sultana risotto; vegetarians might relish shallow-fried nutcakes: creamy cashew and roast hazelnut. Homespun desserts could include baked almond cheesecake with butterscotch sauce. House wines from £11.75 kick off the modest list.

Chef: Geoff Ferguson **Proprietors:** Geoff and Isabel Ferguson **Open:** Tue to Sat D 7 to 9.30, booking recommended **Closed:** Feb, last week Oct **Meals:** alc (main courses £12.50 to £18) **Service:** not inc, card slips closed **Cards:** Amex, Delta, Maestro, MasterCard, Visa **Details:** 24 seats. Private parties: 24 main room. Vegetarian meals. Smoking only after all diners have finished. Wheelchair access (not WC). Music

MAP 8 **Cartmel** CUMBRIA

L'Enclume

Cavendish Street, Cartmel LA11 6PZ
Tel: (015395) 36362
Website: www.lenclume.co.uk

Cooking 7 | Modern European | £42–£144

On passing through the plate-glass doors, you will come immediately upon a hooping wheel, where blacksmiths used to fashion metal wheel rims. L'Enclume was once a smithy (the name means 'anvil') and is now the location of one of the most avant-garde culinary operations in the country. In open-plan dining areas that are light and airy, with rough-plastered walls and flagstone floors, a balance of tone is struck between the seriousness appropriate to a temple of gastronomy and the wit and enjoyment to be had from food designed to jolt the sensibilities of even the most confirmed epicurean.

A range of fixed menus is offered, from relatively straightforward three-course lunches to Taste and Texture options in three tiers. Are you at Introduction, Intermediate or Gourmand level? (There is also a carte for those who want to hold on to their bearings.) Menu descriptions make the dishes sound like conceptual artworks. 'Cubism in foie gras, two cold, one hot, cantaloupe, fragrant myrrh, almond cake' might just turn out to be an art-school arrangement on the plate, but the result is more Damien Hirst: smooth and silky pâté, salted foie gras sorbet, a sliver of warm foie gras that seeps out of a tiny box, a minuscule almond tart, cantaloupe coulis, a dribble of perfumed syrup made from myrrh (sweet cicely), and a couple of wafers of toasted brioche. This was preceded by two chips made of polenta and Gorgonzola, with an accompanying glass of frothy broth composed of apple with a finishing hint of lovage.

Despite such raising of the gastronomic stakes, and the widely noted intimation that there doesn't necessarily seem to be any continuity between or within dishes, the cooking tends to win people over. Course after course at inspection produced delight, from a scallop with battered cauliflower, passion-fruit cream and hibiscus coulis to an almost mainstream serving of loin of lamb, cooked pink, strewn with grains of paradise and teamed with aubergine caviar, confit of butternut squash and cumin-scented stock.

After a selection of mostly immaculate French cheeses, one girds one's loins once again for the dessert performances, which might begin with 'Slammer all in one' – lemon jelly topped with tequila, cream and salt – and proceed to the multifarious 'Chocolate mayhem, no more voices' before an army of petits fours – too many and too rich by now, perhaps – arrives with cafetière coffee. Service ensures that the whole procession runs as smoothly as it needs to, with explanations readily forthcoming as each new composition appears. The wine list is a traditional heavyweight focused on France and with solid names elsewhere, which seems a little at odds with the restless imagination of the cooking. Nonetheless, there are many fine bottles to be had from £18.

Chef: Simon Rogan **Proprietors:** Simon Rogan and Penny Tapsell **Open:** Wed to Sun 12 to 1.45, 7 to 9.30 **Meals:** alc (main courses £23 to £27). Set L £25, Set D £50 to £95 **Service:** not inc, card slips closed **Cards:** Amex, Delta, Diners, Maestro, MasterCard, Visa **Details:** 40 seats. Private parties: 20 main room. Car park. Vegetarian meals. No smoking. Wheelchair access (also women's WC). No music. No mobile phones **Accommodation:** 7 rooms, all with bath/shower. TV. Phone. B&B £110 to £200. Baby facilities

Uplands

Haggs Lane, Cartmel LA11 6HD
Tel: (015395) 36248
Website: www.uplands.uk.com

Cooking 4 | British | £28–£53

'Pretty well unchangeable' is one regular's fond verdict on this enduring stalwart of the Lakeland restaurant scene. Tom and Diana Peter are not about to rock an exceedingly steady ship, and their food remains true to the spirit of generosity, wholesome flavour and comfort. Sound raw materials are the bedrock of their menus and dinner begins, as always, with a little appetiser (perhaps pork, game and herb terrine with Cumberland air-dried ham and damson relish). Next comes a tureen of soup with a 'trademark' whole loaf of hot wholemeal bread before a choice of three mains such as turbot with Morecambe Bay shrimp and parsley sauce or roast loin of local saltmarsh spring lamb with redcurrant and caper sauce. Vegetable (a set of five) are abundant, and desserts conform t the Lakeland tradition of old-school 'sweetness an light': chocolate and Grand Marnier mousse, o warm poached rhubarb with ginger and crèm fraîche, for example. The short wine list has plent of decent, carefully selected bottles at realisti prices from £14.90.

Chef: Tom Peter **Proprietors:** Tom and Diana Peter **Open:** Fri and Sun L 12.30 for 1 (1 sitting), Tue to Sun D 7.30 for 8 (1 sitting) **Closed:** Jan, Feb, 3 days mid-May **Meals:** Set L £17.50, Set D £32.50 **Service:** not inc, card slips closed **Cards:** Amex, Delta, MasterCard, Maestro, Visa **Details:** 24 seats. Private parties: 28 main room. Car park. Vegetarian meals. Children's helpings; no children under 8. No smoking. No music **Accommodation:** 5 rooms, all with bath/shower. TV. Phone. D,B&B £86 to £172. No children under 8

MAP 2 Castle Combe WILTSHIRE

Manor House, Bybrook Restaurant

Castle Combe SN14 7HR
Tel: (01249) 784803
Website: www.exclusivehotels.co.uk

Cooking 3 | English | £39–£75

Italian gardens, a 'Peter Allis-designed golf course and lawns sweeping down to the River Bybroo set the tone in this ancient manor house surrounded by 365 acres of parkland. It's an apt backdrop for posh country-house dishes served on art plates. Home-baked breads and pre-starter (perhaps a little lobster soup) have been applaude likewise clever desserts such as clear-flavoured ice candied ginger parfait with warm rhubar crumble and rhubarb sorbet. Starters and main can seem a touch 'fiddly' – for example, orange dusted diver scallops with crushed minted pe ('full of the joys of spring'), pancetta and warn tomato, fennel and lobster vinaigrette, or roast fille of Marsh Farm beef with creamed Savoy cabbage confit button onions and Puy lentils in red-win jus. Service has failed to deliver 'when it comes t the nitty-gritty'. The lengthy international win list offers nothing below £20.

Chef: David Campbell **Proprietor:** Exclusive Hotels **Open:** all week 12 to 2, 7 to 10 **Meals:** Set L £16.95 (2 courses) to £18.95, Set D £45. Bar menu available **Service:** not inc **Cards:** Amex, Delta, Diners, MasterCard, Maestro, Visa **Details:** 120 seats. 40 seats outside. Private parties: 120 main room, 2 to 120 private rooms. Car park. Vegetarian meals. Children's helpings. No smoking. Wheelchair access (not WC). Occasional music. No mobile phones **Accommodation:** 48 rooms, all with bath/shower. TV. Phone. B&B £150 to£600. Rooms for disabled. Baby facilities. Swimming pool. Fishing

MAP 5 **Caunton** NOTTINGHAMSHIRE

Caunton Beck

Main Street, Caunton NG23 6AB
Tel: (01636) 636793

Cooking 2 | Modern European | £23–£54

Like its parent, the Wig & Mitre (see entry, Lincoln), this self-styled, all-day 'meeting house, reading room, watering hole and restaurant' is big on hospitality. The setting is a revamped Tudor cottage by a 'beck' that gives the place its name, and there's a terrace for al fresco meals. Breakfast starts the day, otherwise order from a menu that promises a mixed bag of contemporary European ideas: confit of belly pork or sardines with pancetta and toasted pine nuts could precede rack of lamb with anchovies and a confit of aubergine and mint or veal schnitzel with baby potatoes, spring onion salad, capers and chives, while desserts might feature honeycomb and caramel brûlée. The diverse wine list provides good-value drinking from £12.45.

Chefs: Andrew Pickstock and Katie Crewe **Proprietor:** Wig & Mitre **Open:** all week 8 to 11 **Meals:** alc (main courses £9.50 to £19). Set L Mon to Sat £11 (2 courses) to £13.95, Set D Sun to Fri £11 (2 courses) to £13.95 **Service:** not inc **Cards:** Amex, Delta, Diners, MasterCard, Maestro, Visa **Details:** 90 seats. 40 seats outside. Private parties: 55 main room. Car park. Vegetarian meals. Children's helpings. No smoking in 1 dining room. Wheelchair access (also WC). No music

MAP 5 **Chaddesley Corbett** WORCESTERSHIRE

Brockencote Hall

Chaddesley Corbett DY10 4PY
Tel: (01562) 777876
Website: www.brockencotehall.com

Cooking 4 | Modern French | £34–£73

Return visitors will find themselves impressed anew by this pristine house set in 70 acres of parkland. It is divided into a number of comfortable drawing and dining rooms, decorated in traditional country-house style. The food echoes some of the luxurious notes, too, in a croustillant of foie gras with duck leg confit, and a partnership of wood pigeon and wild mushroom ballottine with truffle, quail's egg and smoked oil. However, a range of menu options and prices reflects the choice of ingredients as much as Jérôme Barbançon's workmanship: a duo of pollack and mackerel with caramelised chicory on the table d'hôte, for example, and tournedos of veal with honey-roast lamb sweetbreads, girolles and port reduction on the carte. Contemporary techniques and ingredients abound, from cockles and mussels saffron risotto with red pepper coulis to a 'trilogy of Normandy rabbit': stuffed saddle, leg with mustard, croustade of bolognaise with madeira and mustard jus. Desserts, such as caramelised pineapple, ginger and apple raviolini with black treacle ice cream, follow suit. The majority of the wines on the list derive from France, although there is a sprinkling from elsewhere. House wine is from £15.50.

Chef: Jérôme Barbançon **Proprietors:** Alison and Joseph Petitjean **Open:** Sun to Fri L 12.30 to 1.30, all week D 7 to 9.30 **Closed:** first 10 days of Jan **Meals:** alc (main courses £14.50 to £22.50). Set L Mon to Fri £13 (two courses) to £20.20, Set L Sun £24.50, Set D £48 to £70 **Service:** not inc, card slips closed **Cards:** Amex, Delta, Diners, MasterCard, Maestro, Visa **Details:** 50 seats. Private parties: 50 main room, 10 to 30 private rooms. Car park. Vegetarian meals. Children's helpings. No smoking. Wheelchair access (also WC). Music. No mobile phones **Accommodation:** 17 rooms, all with bath/shower. TV. Phone. B&B £85 to £180. Rooms for disabled. Baby facilities. Fishing

	This symbol means that smoking is not permitted.
	This symbol means that there are some restrictions on smoking though it may be allowed in some eating areas.

MAP 1 **Chagford** DEVON

Gidleigh Park

Chagford TQ13 8HH
Tel: (01647) 432367
Website: www.gidleigh.com

Cooking 7 | Modern European | £58–£123

Driving along the mile and a half of cul-de-sac to find Gidleigh Park is a bucolic treat indeed. There are beech trees and a stream, rough-stone walls covered in moss and ferns, flowery hedgerows and a couple of wooden bridges. It's another half a mile or so once you enter the private drive, but eventually a sprawling, half-timbered building rises before you. In March 2005 it was acquired from long-standing owners Paul and Kay Henderson by Andrew Brownsword, proprietor also of the Bath Priory (see entry, Bath). Michael Caines, who has been cooking here for over a decade, has been retained, and the air of professional, if unduly hushed, formality is preserved, especially in the dining room.

Reported highlights this year have been: a trio of seared scallops on discs of deep-fried celeriac, with a little warm, intense purée of the root and a well-balanced vinaigrette; exemplary John Dory, immaculately timed and served with tender langoustines, asparagus tips and new potatoes crushed with olives; pedigree British cheeses in flawless condition; and a textbook soufflé of prunes and Armagnac with a matching ice cream. However, performance can be patchy, fish can occasionally be mistimed, and the incidentals have been below par on some occasions.

There was little wrong with an inspector's main course of accurately cooked beef fillet topped with shallot and horseradish cream, accompanied by sublime truffled mash. A dessert of passion-fruit mousse with rice pudding ice cream was well rendered, for all that the textures of the two components were arguably too similar, but the garnish of micro-diced pineapple, mango and papaya and a soft coconut tuile were apposite enough. Not everybody is happy with being told what order to eat the cheeses in, but the selection – which might include Timsbury goat, Quick's Cheddar and Cornish Blue – is as sound as a bell.

Around £50 seems a fair price for wine to some reporters, and it will buy a smart village Burgundy such as the Vosne-Romanée from René Engel, mature Priorat Clos de l'Obac from Spain or a stellar Turley Zinfandel from California – all fair value for the quality. But excellent bottles from less prestigious addresses on the global list can be had for half the price too.

Chef: Michael Caines **Proprietor:** Andrew Brownsword **Open:** all week 12.30 to 2, 7 to 9 **Meals:** Set L Mon to Thur £27 (2 courses) to £35, Set L Fri to Sun and bank hols £33 (2 courses) to £41, Set D £75 to £80 **Service:** not inc, card slips closed **Cards:** Amex, Delta, Diners, Maestro, MasterCard, Visa **Details:** 35 seats. Private parties: 22 main room. Car park. Vegetarian meals. No children under 7. No smoking. Wheelchair access (also men's WC). No music. No mobile phones **Accommodation:** 15 rooms, all with bath/shower. TV. Phone. D,B&B £275 to £600. Baby facilities

22 Mill Street

22 Mill Street, Chagford TQ13 8AW
Tel: (01647) 432244

Cooking 5 | Modern European | £34–£54

The narrow-fronted restaurant has a tiny courtyar at the back overlooked by the small lounge. Larg oils depict hunting with hounds, and a terracott colour scheme prevails. Duncan Walker oversee with great aplomb, happy to socialise with cus tomers to the extent that during our inspectio visit he popped into the kitchen for only a coupl of minutes at a time. The pace of the operation is be it noted, extremely relaxed, which for some wi translate as plain slow but for others means onl that there's more time to soak up that sociabl atmosphere.

Reporters have emerged full of praise for accu rately cooked John Dory, turbot, and guinea fow with foie gras, and raw materials are from the to drawer. Duck breast is Gressingham and may com with a mille-feuille of figs, while roast rack o Dartmoor lamb has spiced aubergine and roas garlic. At inspection a grilled fillet of sea bass as starter didn't impress, while sautéed calf's liver an sweetbreads as a main course with oxtail tortellini red wine and capers was overwhelmingly rich an crowned with a pile of excessively salted onio rings. Finish with warm pear and almond tart wit cinnamon ice cream, or crème brûlée accompa nied by raspberries marinated in port and balsami vinegar. The wine list darts hither and yon, no according precedence to any one country, with quartet of house wines starting at £17.80.

Chefs: Duncan Walker, Dexter Fuller and Raphael Rabiller **Proprietor:** Duncan Walker **Open:** Wed to Sat L 12.30 to 1.45, Mon to Sat D 7.30 to 9 **Closed:** bank hol Mon (but open bank hol Sun) **Meals:** Set L £21 (2 courses) to £26, Set D £29.50 (2 courses) to £38 **Service:** net prices, card slips closed **Cards:** Delta, Maestro, MasterCard, Visa **Details:** 22 seats. No smoking. Occasional music. No mobile phones **Accommodation:** 2 rooms, both with bath/shower. TV. B&B £45 to £75

MAP 3 **Chandler's Cross**
HERTFORDSHIRE

The Grove, Colette's

Chandler's Cross WD3 4TG
Tel: (01923) 807807
Website: www.thegrove.co.uk

Cooking 6 | Modern European | £53–£110

A country house fit for royalty on the outskirts of Watford – Queen Victoria dined here with the Earl of Clarendon (some time ago, admittedly). Colette's, the smartest of three restaurants at this upmarket hotel, makes good use of light and space and is assuredly civilised, with white-clad tables and appealing contemporary food. Meals are sumptuous, and luxury materials are the order of the day (with prices to match), from langoustines to Dover sole. All the same, the scope of the culinary thinking is broad, so the alternative to a starter of cured duck with duck confit beignet, foie gras mousse and Cabernet Sauvignon jelly might be native oysters with pickled watermelon, vodka and wasabi cream.

Dishes often show a degree of complexity, as in halibut with butternut squash purée and parsley oil with roast ceps and salsify and a pancetta crisp, or roast best end and braised shoulder of lamb in a smoked garlic and olive sauce with fennel and aubergine purées. To finish there may be chocolate mille-feuille with Seville orange and marshmallow, or a plate of fine British and French cheeses. Staff are agreeable and ready to help, and the wine list has loads of interesting bottles, but mark-ups are steep and only a handful are under £25; ten come by the glass (£7 to £17).

Chef: Christopher Harrod **Proprietor:** Ralph Trustees Ltd **Open:** Sun L 12.30 to 2.30, Mon to Sat D 7 to 10.30 **Meals:** alc D (main courses £24 to £32). Set L Sun £35 to £50, Set D £65 (whole table only) **Service:** not inc **Cards:** Amex, Delta, Diners, Maestro, MasterCard, Visa **Details:** 60 seats. Private parties: 30 main room, 12 to 20 private rooms. Car park. Vegetarian meals. Children's helpings. No smoking. Wheelchair access (also WC). Music. Air-conditioned **Accommodation:** 227 rooms, all with bath/shower. TV. Phone. Room only £190 to £900. Rooms for disabled. Baby facilities. Swimming pool. Fishing

This symbol means that accommodation is available at this establishment.

MAP 5 **Cheltenham**
GLOUCESTERSHIRE

Le Champignon Sauvage

24–26 Suffolk Road, Cheltenham GL50 2AQ
Tel: (01242) 573449
Website: www.lechampignonsauvage.co.uk

Cooking 8 | French | £37–£84

It is as well to allow a little time to find somewhere to park if you're coming by car to the Champignon, but any stress in the effort will soon be smoothed away as you step through the door. A tiny bar/lounge and the small dining room comprise the front-of-house, the latter 'pleasantly exuberant', with bright yellow walls, blue-upholstered chairs, and colourful modern paintings. The tone throughout, even when full, is calm and assured, effortlessly charming, and there is often an interesting social mix of clientele. David Everitt-Matthias has always favoured a contemporary French style, with ancillary ingredients such as snails, clams, liquorice, cockscombs and burdock root taking their places alongside the star players of scallops, foie gras, pigeon and Cinderford lamb. There is a richness about it all, but also evidence of great culinary intelligence. After appetisers and first-rate breads, it's down to the main business. An inspection dinner began with a fillet of cod served with snail and pig's trotter risotto and chestnut velouté, a prime example of how components of a dish are worked hard so that they may not necessarily be individually recognisable in the finished result but still make for enjoyable eating as a 'total flavour experience'.

Meat dishes achieve great profundity of impact. Roast pigeon is the whole deal, the pink breast meat accompanied by the kidneys and heart, together with wild mushrooms, whole roast garlic cloves and (just tipping the balance slightly) a rich, sticky sauce. Another intense, dark sauce – this time shot through with liquorice – supports a pavé of lamb served on crushed Jerusalem artichokes and baby leeks. Any hint of slumberous satisfaction may be banished at this stage by the arrival of a pre-dessert involving a floral-scented crème brûlée alive with popping candy, while the dessert itself could well be chicory cheesecake with chicory ripple ice cream, a hugely clever construction of gentle bitterness and caramel sweetness, avoiding any clagginess of texture, or a frozen mousse of prunes and burdock root, served with an ice cream of toasted almonds. Cheeses are also very fine. Wines, mostly French, are good value, from the

£11 house bottles upwards. A quality supporting cast encompasses Australia, New Zealand and Clos du Val in California.

Chef: David Everitt-Matthias **Proprietors:** David and Helen Everitt-Matthias **Open:** Tue to Sat 12.30 to 1.30, 7.30 to 9 **Closed:** 10 days at Christmas, 3 weeks June **Meals:** Set L £20 (2 courses) to £44, Set D Tue to Fri £20 (2 courses) to £50, Set D Sat £36 (2 courses) to £50 **Service:** not inc **Cards:** Amex, Diners, Maestro, MasterCard, Visa **Details:** 28 seats. Private parties: 22 main room. No smoking before 10pm at D. Wheelchair access (not WC). No music. No mobile phones

Daffodil

18–20 Suffolk Parade, Montpellier, Cheltenham GL50 2AE
Tel: (01242) 700055
Website: www.thedaffodil.com

Cooking 3 | Modern European | £25–£61

Black and white photographs of old movie stars, a sweeping staircase and a predominance of Art Deco green and cream give clues to the building's earlier use: the last films were shown here in the 1960s. There is nothing nostalgic about the cooking, however, with decent, robust versions of thoroughly modern dishes: a warm salad of pancetta, black pudding and rösti topped with a poached egg, for instance, or a main course of olive-crusted cod fillet on a risotto of sun-dried tomatoes and mange-tout with asparagus velouté. At lunchtime, expect a 'first-rate', moist fishcake of smoked haddock and parsley on a bed of wilted spinach with fine hollandaise, or perfectly timed chicken breast in a carefully spiced marinade, each dish characterised by an essentially simple approach and a good sense of flavouring. Puddings like pistachio crème brûlée and a slightly under-powered lemon tart generally lack the verve of the savoury department. A sensible wine list brings bottles starting at £12.90, with most under £25 and eight by the glass.

Chef: Mark Davidson **Proprietor:** Marcel Frichot **Open:** Mon to Sat 12 to 2, 6.30 to 9.30 (10 Sat) **Meals:** alc D (main courses £13 to £20). Set L £12 (2 courses) to £14.50 **Service:** not inc, 10% for parties of 6 or more **Cards:** Amex, Delta, Maestro, MasterCard, Visa **Details:** 140 seats. Private parties: 140 main room. Vegetarian meals. Children's helpings. No smoking in 1 dining room. Wheelchair access (also WC). Music

Lumière

Clarence Parade, Cheltenham GL50 3PA
Tel: (01242) 222200
Website: www.lumiere.cc

Cooking 5 | Global | £51–£73

The Chapmans' compact, evenings-only restaurant is to be found in a small Regency terrace just off the Promenade in the centre of town. Deep red and creamy grey are the predominant tones, with low lighting and tables set with fine crockery and Riedel glassware creating a pleasingly refined mood. Dishes bear evidence of serious culinary thought, with flair and originality running strongly through the menu. Materials are sourced with the greatest of care, reaching the plate in the form, perhaps, of a warm salad of grilled quail with smoked bacon and a dressing of cider and shallots, or pepper-roasted salmon with truffled mayonnaise, oyster mushroom pasta and dill cream. Roasting is used in the modern way to point up the flavours of accompanying ingredients, such as field mushrooms with chargrilled springbok fillet (and there isn't much of that about in Gloucestershire), or red peppers to go with highly recommended braised monkfish, served with rice embedded with smoked salmon and basil. Desserts aim to bring the palate down gently with chocolate and vanilla, or there may be a pair of sorbets (mango and coconut) with passion-fruit butter sauce, or then again just the satisfying simplicity of 'one perfect cheese'.

The wine list is a highly personal collection of quality bottles, peppered with feisty tasting notes. The line-up is fluid but usually features a strong showing from the US, with prices running from around £20.

Chef: Geoff Chapman **Proprietors:** Lin and Geoff Chapman **Open:** Tue to Sat D 7 to 8.30 **Closed:** first 2 weeks Jan, 2 weeks late summer **Meals:** Set D £29 (2 courses) to £35 **Service:** not inc **Cards:** MasterCard, Maestro, Visa **Details:** 28 seats. Private parties: 32 main room. Unsuitable for very small children. No smoking. No music. No mobile phones. Air-conditioned

 This symbol means that the wine list is well above the average.

MAP 5 **Cheltenham** GLOUCESTERSHIRE

Mayflower

AR

32–34 Clarence Street, Cheltenham GL50 3NX
Tel: (01242) 522426

Ever-popular family-run Chinese restaurant with mother and son at the stoves. Their strength is a mainstream menu done well, with crispy duck a notable recent success. Carefully planned set menus for two upwards are a good deal, or you can splash out on a whole imperial Peking duck (£38 with 24 hours' notice) or lobster. Global wine list from £12.95, with some classy fine wines too. Open all week.

Le Petit Blanc

AR

The Queens Hotel, Cheltenham GL50 1NN
Tel: (01242) 266800

Buzzy brasserie handily placed opposite Montpelier in the former ballroom of the Queens Hotel. Like other members of the chain (see entries in Birmingham, Manchester, Oxford and Tunbridge Wells), it follows a flexible formula with attractive fixed-price deals and an enticing menu ranging from well-liked beetroot risotto and pappardelle with prawns and chilli (£6.50) to braised French corn-fed chicken with morels, leeks and white wine (£14.50) and summer berry pavlova (£5.50). Wines with a French accent from £12.95. Open all week.

MAP 7 **Chester** CHESHIRE

Brasserie 10/16

AR

Brookdale Place, Chester CH1 3DY
Tel: (01244) 322288

Lively modern venue that makes a handy addition to the Chester scene. Menus scan the global brasserie repertoire, homing in on dishes like Louisiana prawn rémoulade with Cajun tomato sauce (£4.25), tapas, and grilled salmon with Greek salad (£8.75) before heading home for Cumberland sausage with mash, and desserts such as sticky toffee pudding with toffee sauce (£3.50). 'Lite' lunch dishes from £3; house wines from £9.95. Open all week. Related to the Brasserie, Hawarden (see entry, Wales).

Chester Grosvenor, Arkle Restaurant

CHESHIRE RESTAURANT OF THE YEAR

Eastgate, Chester CH1 1LT
Tel: (01244) 324024
Website: www.chestergrosvenor.com

Cooking 7 | European | £75–£104

No country cousin floating adrift in the rolling shires, the Grosvenor is smack in the middle of Chester, ensconced in a shopping centre indeed. It sits at one end of a picturesque and largely pedestrianised area with two ancient tiers of arcades. Inside, a vaguely raffish, other-worldly ambience predominates, with the dining room a model of burnished elegance, gleaming varnished tabletops and high-backed chairs, with equine pictures for backdrop.

The kitchen appears to live up to these surroundings with deceptive effortlessness, producing dishes of high gloss. Classical French techniques are the bedrock, but with the freedom to try out productive modern riffs around them. A pressed terrine of rabbit cleverly involves both hot and cold meat, as well as the obligatory foie gras, along with artichokes and leeks, dressed in a vinaigrette fortified with Banyuls. Fish and meat pairings might result in oxtail and langoustines turning up on the same plate, with a sauce based thriftily on celery leaves, while a main course of turbot is given the bourguignonne treatment, with ceps, smoked bacon and red wine. Aberdeen beef fillet comes with its sticky short rib and an 'ox and truffle pudding', while Limousin veal, accompanied by its sweetbreads and a kidney, appears in Kashmiri guise, with golden raisins, almonds and basmati rice. Suggested sweet wines are noted with the dessert options, in case you feel like trying a spot of Recioto di Soave to go with a confection made up of warm banana génoise with liquid Valrhona chocolate and white rum. The wine list centres on fine wines in mature vintages at prices to match, with a particular focus on Opus One. More affordable options crop up around the edges from Italy to South Africa, and these too have plenty of bottle age. House wines are £17.

As well as the main restaurant, there is also La Brasserie, made over in quasi-Montparnasse style, all brass rails and large mirrors with tile surrounds under a big glass cupola. Here, glazed Parmesan risotto with scallop carpaccio, seared tuna with a crab sausage and cannellini beans, or great cod and chips with mushy peas are the norm, with nutmegged custard tart, or Granny Smith charlotte to finish. A compacted version of the wine list is offered.

Chef: Simon Radley **Proprietor:** Duke of Westminster Estate **Open:** Tue to Sat D only 7 to 9.30 **Closed:** 24 Dec to 20 Jan, 22 to 30 Aug **Meals:** Set D £55 to £65 **Service:** 12.5% **Cards:** Amex, Delta, Diners, Maestro, MasterCard, Visa **Details:** 55 seats. Private parties: 55 main room. Vegetarian meals. No children under 12. Jacket and tie. No smoking. Wheelchair access (also WC). Occasional music. No mobile phones. Air-conditioned **Accommodation:** 80 rooms, all with bath/shower. TV. Phone. B&B £180 to £750. Rooms for disabled

MAP 9 Chesterfield DERBYSHIRE

Old Post Restaurant AR

43 Holywell Street, Chesterfield S41 7SH
Tel: (01246) 279479

Intimate restaurant in a converted fifteenth-century building close to Chesterfield's famous church with a bent spire. Hugh Cocker's cooking is ambitious, and he delivers dishes like seared peppered tuna with asparagus mousse Nantua topped with a poached egg (£6.25) and roast Derbyshire beef fillet served with daube of ox cheek ravioli and ceps (£19.50), followed by mille-feuille of rhubarb and Muscatel with toffee-apple ice cream and vanilla sabayon (£5.50). Moderately priced wines from £11.95. Closed Sat L, Sun D and Mon.

MAP 2 Chettle DORSET

Castleman Hotel

Chettle DT11 8DB
Tel: (01258) 830096
Website: www.castlemanhotel.co.uk

Cooking 2 | Modern British | £25–£45

Edward Bourke, master of all he surveys, owns this hotel (formerly the dower house to the local manor) and the entire tiny village too. Any expectation of grandiosity is soon dispelled by the down-to-earth, informal approach at the Castleman, where children are enthusiastically welcomed and Barbara Garnsworthy cooks some pleasingly straightforward food. In the dining room overlooking a hay meadow Loch Fyne smoked salmon with dill mustard sauce makes a satisfying starter, as might a soup of leek, cannellini beans and ham with cheese straws. Main courses embrace peppered fillet steak and a vegetarian Wellington that includes mushrooms, pine nuts and Brie, while sea bass may be dressed in balsamic and served with roast vegetables. End on a high note with dark chocolate and brandy pots with pecan cookies. Wines are a lively international mix and very good value, with prices starting at £10. Half-bottles keep up the good work, and a handful of fine wines polish things off.

Chefs: Barbara Garnsworthy and Richard Morris **Proprietors:** Edward Bourke and Barbara Garnsworthy **Open:** Sun L 12 to 2, all week D 7 to 9.30 **Closed:** 25 and 26 Dec, Feb **Meals:** alc D (main courses £9 to £16.50). Set L Sun £19 **Service:** not inc, card slips closed **Cards:** Maestro, MasterCard, Visa **Details:** 40 seats. Private parties: 40 main room. Car park. Vegetarian meals. Children's helpings. No smoking. Wheelchair access (also WC). No music **Accommodation:** 8 rooms, all with bath/shower. TV. Phone. B&B £50 to £85. Baby facilities

MAP 2 Chichester WEST SUSSEX

Comme Ça AR

67 Broyle Road, Chichester PO19 6BD
Tel: (01243) 788724

'Gutsy' French family lunches (£18.95/£21.95) attract Sunday crowds to this staunchly Gallic venue convenient for the theatre. Asparagus, then beef with red wine sauce, followed by crème caramel might be the order of the day. At other times the kitchen delivers sautéed duck livers with onion confit (£6) and roast cannon of thyme-scented lamb with a brioche herb crust and madeira jus (£14), plus assorted desserts 'du moment' (£6). Wine prices start at £14.50. Open Wed to Sun L and Tue to Sat D.

MAP 3 Chieveley BERKSHIRE

Crab at Chieveley

Wantage Road, Chieveley RG20 8UE
Tel: (01635) 247550
Website: www.crabatchieveley.com

Cooking 2 | Seafood | £32–£104

The Crab, on a quiet country road near M4 junction 13, is fish bar, restaurant and inn all in one. The Barnards used to own the Crab & Lobster, Asenby (see entry), so quality fish delivered daily from Cornwall is no surprise: expect 'very fresh' mackerel salad with Parma ham and feta parcels on the set-lunch menu, for example, or linguine of crab, dill, rocket and lobster oil on the extensive carte. Other classical touches are fish soup with aïoli; smoked salmon terrine and caper butter; and celeriac purée and asparagus accompanying our inspector's roast sea bream. Rare meaty choices include mango and crispy duck salad, or roast saltmarsh lamb with sweet potato gratin and garlic. Desserts are straightforward, perhaps blackcurrant délice or espresso crème brûlée. House wine starts at £15.50 (£3.75 a glass).

Chef: David Horridge **Proprietors:** David and Jacqueline Barnard **Open:** all week 12 to 2.30, 6 to 10 **Meals:** alc L and D (main courses £14 to £37.50). Set L Mon to Sat £16.50 (2 courses) to £19.50, Sun £18.50 to £22.50 **Service:** not inc **Cards:** Amex, Delta, Maestro, MasterCard, Visa **Details:** 100 seats. 80 seats outside. Private parties: 60 main room, 20 to 30 private rooms. Car park. Vegetarian meals. Children's helpings. No smoking. No music. Air-conditioned **Accommodation:** 10 rooms, all with bath/shower. TV. Phone. B&B £110 to £170. Rooms for disabled

MAP 3 **Chigwell** ESSEX

Bluebell

117 High Road, Chigwell IG7 6QQ
Tel: (020) 8500 6282
Website: www.thebluebellrestaurant.co.uk

Cooking 3 | Modern European | £30–£66

Tucked away in a tiny antique enclave of old Chigwell village, this 'ramifying' cottage restaurant is a 'fantastic resource' for the local community. The décor creates a festive feel, and the kitchen impresses with its vibrant modern cooking. Set lunches bring on dishes like braised aromatic lamb with vegetable couscous, but the main action takes place in the evening. Lots of influences are at work: crab cakes are served with coriander and leek crisps and sweet-and-sour sauce, butternut squash and sage raviolo arrives with cumin and tomato sauce, rocket and Parmesan, while roast Gressingham duck breast is accompanied by wilted pak choi, sesame-roast carrots and oriental dressing. To finish, apple tart with apple sorbet is the real McCoy. The wine list covers most bases quite affordably, with prices from £11.95.

Chef: Paul Korten **Proprietor:** Gregory Molen **Open:** Tue to Fri and Sun L 12 to 2, Tue to Sat D 6.45 to 10 **Closed:** bank hols **Meals:** alc D (main courses £15 to £20). Set L Tue to Fri £12.95 (2 courses), Set L Sun £19.95 **Service:** not inc, card slips closed **Cards:** Amex, Delta, Diners, Maestro, MasterCard, Visa **Details:** 95 seats. Vegetarian meals. Children's helpings. No cigars/pipes in dining room. Occasional music. Air-conditioned

MAP 3 **Chilgrove** WEST SUSSEX

White Horse

Chilgrove PO18 9HX
Tel: (01243) 535219
Website: www.whitehorsechilgrove.co.uk

Cooking 3 | Modern British | £37–£63

Wisteria grows in swags over the front of this low-slung, whitewashed inn, and the interior is easy on the eye too, with white-clothed tables and pine floorboards creating a breezy, modern feel. Juan Otero brings touches of the Mediterranean to menus that offer fine fresh seafood, either in fish soup with pesto, or as a stuffing for sweet red peppers with a rich tomato sauce. Properly choosy buying of main-course meats brings Gloucester Old Spot cutlet with sherry gravy, and half a Gressingham duck classically sauced with orange and Grand Marnier. The vegetarian choice could be risotto with a stroganoff of wild mushrooms in paprika mustard cream. Finish with Valrhona chocolate 'diablo', or biscuit-based lemon soufflé with clotted cream. All dishes come with a wine suggestion from the standard list, but lovers of classic wines should make time for a thorough read of the 'indulgence' list, which contains such good-value offerings as Château de Pez 1995 at £35. House wines are £14.

Chef: Juan Otero **Proprietor:** Charles Burton **Open:** Tue to Sun L 12 to 2, Tue to Sat D 7 to 10 **Meals:** alc (main courses £14 to £18). Set L and D Oct to Apr only £24.50. Open sandwich menu available May to Sept **Service:** 10% (optional), card slips closed **Cards:** Delta, Maestro, MasterCard, Visa **Details:** 60 seats. 60 seats outside. Private parties: 60 main room. Car park. Vegetarian meals. No smoking. Music. Occasional music. No mobile phones. Air-conditioned **Accommodation:** 8 rooms, all with bath/shower. TV. Phone. B&B £65 to £120. Rooms for disabled

MAP 2 **Chinnor** OXFORDSHIRE

Sir Charles Napier

OXFORDSHIRE RESTAURANT OF THE YEAR

Sprigg's Alley, Chinnor OX39 4BX
Tel: (01494) 483011
Website: www.sircharlesnapier.co.uk

Cooking 4 | Modern European | £36–£67

'Joyous, seductive, romantic, addictive!' Superlatives come easily when talking about this instantly alluring gem high on a hill overlooking the Chiltern

beechwoods. Everywhere there are sculptures – a black female nude reclines on the lawn, pigs and other animals inhabit the dining room – and the garden is a delight. Julie Griffiths runs the show with supreme style and good humour.

Not surprisingly, the food here is meant for pleasurable enjoyment, not critical analysis, although the kitchen is sure-handed when it comes to technique, timing and seasoning. Seasonal flavours hit the senses head on: vibrant scallops are served with Jersey Royals, shaved asparagus, truffle oil and crisp Parma ham ('a real song of summer'), while four rack chops of 'decadently luscious' new season's lamb arrive with cauliflower purée, broad beans, capers and mint. Ingredients are brought together with wit and wisdom – breast of duck, cut into thick wedges with Jerusalem artichokes and morel fritters, for example. Desserts also show a touch of class: perfectly risen raspberry soufflé with 'heavenly' basil ice cream or warm vanilla rice pudding served with a dollop of chunky mango and passion-fruit coulis are both winners.

A passion for wine shows in winning short selections from all regions, and suitable for all pockets, including some mature bottles. France, Australia and California lead the way. The changing house line-up of ten wines by glass or bottle (from £14.95) offers good value, and there are plenty of interesting half-bottles.

Chef: Richard Burkert **Proprietor:** Julie Griffiths **Open:** Tue to Sun L 12 to 2.30 (3.30 Sun), Tue to Sat D 6.30 to 10 **Closed:** 3 days at Christmas, bank hols **Meals:** alc (main courses £12.50 to £19.50). Set L Tue to Sat £15.50 (2 courses), Set D Tue to Fri £16.50 (2 courses) **Service:** 12.5% (optional), card slips closed **Cards:** Amex, Delta, Diners, Maestro, MasterCard, Visa **Details:** 70 seats. 70 seats outside. Private parties: 45 main room, 10 to 45 private rooms. Car park. Vegetarian meals. Children's helpings. No children under 6 at D. No smoking in 1 dining room. Wheelchair access (not WC). Music. No mobile phones. Air-conditioned

MAP 5 **Chipping Campden** GLOUCESTERSHIRE

Cotswold House, Juliana's Restaurant

The Square, Chipping Campden GL55 6AN
Tel: (01386) 840330
Website: www.cotswoldhouse.com

Cooking 5 | Modern British | £38–£78

Once through the front door of this Georgian-fronted Cotswold-stone hotel, perched at a corner of the town square, you find a smart urban makeover plus a handful of modern artworks. Dark wood dominates the restaurant, where there are the lavish trappings of starched tablecloths, appetisers, and several different kinds of silver-served bread. The food does not aim to be cutting edge; rather, it soothes, with the likes of ravioli of Port Ellen scallops with vegetable butter sauce, woodland mushroom risotto, and Highland beef with an oxtail faggot and grand-mère sauce, as well as a few luxuries such as truffles, foie gras, turbot, and seasonal game like venison with sauce périgourdine.

The highlight of an inspection meal was cannon of local Lighthorne lamb served with a small version of shepherd's pie, grain mustard purée and ratatouille topped by a piece of sweetbread. Technical wizardry seems to reach its peak when it comes to dessert: for example, an assiette au pomme delivered a fine tarte Tatin, 'delightfully creamy' bavarois, and 'impressive' Calvados ice cream and apple sorbet. Prestigious bottles pepper the wine list, and prices are not friendly. Ordinary folk can glug the house wine for £17, but otherwise the entry fee is £20.

Chef: Jamie Foreman **Proprietors:** Christa and Ian Taylor **Open:** Sun L 12 to 2.30, all week D 7 to 9.30 **Meals:** Set L £27.50, Set D £35 (2 courses) to £45. Brasserie menu available **Service:** not inc **Cards:** Amex, Delta, Maestro, MasterCard, Visa **Details:** 40 seats. 30 seats outside. Private parties: 80 main room. Car park. Vegetarian meals. Children's helpings. No smoking. No music. No mobile phones. Air-conditioned **Accommodation:** 29 rooms, all with bath/shower. TV. Phone. B&B £130 to £450. Rooms for disabled. Baby facilities

MAP 2 **Christchurch** DORSET

FishWorks

10 Church Street, Christchurch BH23 1BW
Tel: (01202) 487000
Website: www.fishworks.co.uk

Cooking 3 | Seafood | £33–£85

After launching his 'fishmonger's with tables' concept in Bath, Mitchell Tonks set up shop in these pretty premises on a cobbled street next to Christchurch Priory. Deliveries arrive daily, and it pays to check out what's on the specials board – although there are also some decent dishes on the static menu that is common to all branches (see entries in Bath, Bristol and London). Simply prepared shellfish and crustacea are a good bet, with steamed River Fowey mussels given the classic marinière treatment, and other options range from skate with black butter and capers to whole sea bream baked in sea salt. Desserts like lemon tart can seem 'ordinary'. The wine list is an interesting assemblage of fish-friendly offerings from European sources. Prices start at £15.25.

Chef: Nick Davies **Proprietor:** FishWorks plc **Open:** Tue to Sat 12 to 2.30, 6 to 10.30 **Closed:** 24 Dec to early Jan, Tue after bank hols **Meals:** alc (main courses £7 to £35) **Service:** not inc **Cards:** Amex, Delta, Maestro, MasterCard, Visa **Details:** 44 seats. Vegetarian meals. Children's helpings. No smoking. Wheelchair access (not WC). Music. Air-conditioned

MAP 7 Church Stretton SHROPSHIRE

The Studio AR

59 High Street, Church Stretton SY6 6BY
Tel: (01694) 722672

'Very homely' little neighbourhood restaurant in a one-time artist's studio. Chef/proprietor Tony Martland's dinner menus offer substantial bistro-style dishes, kicking off with pork, bacon and wild mushroom terrine with beetroot and ginger relish (£5.25) before pan-fried fillets of sea bass with watercress velouté (£14.50). Desserts like passion-fruit and mango mousse (£4.50) and a trio of cheeses complete the picture. House wines £11.95. Open Tue to Sat D; also L first and third Sun each month.

MAP 5 Clifford's Mesne GLOUCESTERSHIRE

Yew Tree Inn

Clifford's Mesne GL18 1JS
Tel: (01531) 820719

Cooking 3 | Modern European | £31–£58

This country pub in a well-wooded part of the Forest of Dean is run with panache and good cheer by the Hacketts. Dogs are a decorative theme, whether in cast-iron or cuddly toy format. Paul Hackett sources his materials conscientiously from within a reassuringly small radius of the place, with fish making a longer journey. That might be Brixham cod, a large fillet sauced with champagne, sun-dried tomatoes and mussels, the fish sitting on well-made buttery mash, and everything accurately timed. Meats include Gloucester Old Spot pork and local chicken, the latter perhaps sautéed and sauced with Burgundy and wild mushrooms. An old-fashioned, well-constructed terrine at inspection was composed of duck, pigeon and hazelnuts and came with a marmalade of red cabbage and onion, and meals end with the likes of pear poached in red wine with rice pudding and wafer-thin pear crisps. The wine list offers a good selection by the glass, and plenty of choice around the £20 mark.

Chef: Paul Hackett **Proprietors:** Paul and Anna Hackett **Open:** Tue to Sun L 12 to 2, Tue to Sat D 7 to 9 **Closed:** Jan **Meals:** Set L Sun £15.75 (2 courses) to £18.75, Set D £23.75 (2 courses) to £28.50 **Service:** not inc, card slips closed **Cards:** Delta, Diners, Maestro, MasterCard, Visa **Details:** 40 seats. 36 seats outside. Private parties: 70 main room. Car park. Children's helpings. No smoking. Wheelchair access (also WC). No music **Accommodation:** 2 rooms, both with bath/shower. TV. B&B £55 to £70

MAP 6 Clipsham RUTLAND

Olive Branch

Main Street, Clipsham LE15 7SH
Tel: (01780) 410355
Website: www.theolivebranchpub.com

Cooking 3 | Modern British | £25–£57

Rescued from extinction in 1999 by three friends and lots of local goodwill, the Olive Branch is now a fully-grown pub success story. Whether you are taking advantage of the garden or sitting inside amid hop-garlanded beams, all is busy, convivial and unreservedly good-natured. As a curtain-raiser, each table gets a hunk of fresh brown bread (plus knife for slicing) on a board with a pot of olive-flavoured butter. The kitchen works in tandem with regional producers but inspiration comes from near and far: homespun English diehards (pork and Stilton pie with home-made piccalilli) sit happily beside classic European ideas (stuffed leg of guinea fowl, Savoy cabbage, sweet potato mash and madeira sauce) and occasional forays to the Orient (tandoori baked halibut with Bombay potato and mint yoghurt). Desserts like chocolate meringue marquise with raspberry sorbet close proceedings. A wide range of enticing

 This symbol means that there are some restrictions on smoking though it may be allowed in some eating areas.

bin-ends complements a short printed list of wines, plenty of them under £15.

Chef: Sean Hope **Proprietors:** Ben Jones, Sean Hope and Marcus Welford **Open:** all week 12 to 2 (3 Sun), 7 to 9.30 (9 Sun) **Closed:** 26 Dec, 1 Jan **Meals:** alc L and D (main courses £8 to £19). Set L £12.50 (2 courses) to £15, Set L Sun £16.50 **Service:** not inc, card slips closed **Cards:** Delta, Maestro, MasterCard, Visa **Details:** 45 seats. 30 seats outside. Private parties: 20 main room. Car park. Vegetarian meals. Children's helpings. No smoking in 1 dining room. Wheelchair access (not WC). Music

MAP 10 **Cockermouth** CUMBRIA

Quince & Medlar

11–13 Castlegate, Cockermouth CA13 9EU
Tel: (01900) 823579

Cooking 2 | Vegetarian | £32–£44

After some eight autumn pilgrimages to the Lakes, one couple found this vegetarian oasis unchanged, with its 'discreet eighteenth-century exterior and Laura Ashley waitresses impeccably spoken and mannered'. Others continue to applaud 'the originality of the use of ingredients' that can result in a polyglot of dishes vigorously eschewing the usual hackneyed vegetarian gestures. Ginger-poached pear with a caper filling and pickled walnuts is a typically inventive starter, while main courses could range from wild and button mushrooms cooked in red wine and tamari sauce on a polenta crust to spinach, cream cheese and Wensleydale gâteau. To finish, consider the day's 'hot pudding' or opt for something cold (Glayva parfait, for example). The wine list is totally organic and prices (from £11.30) are eminently affordable.

Chefs/Proprietors: Colin and Louisa Le Voi **Open:** Tue to Sat D only 7 to 9.30 **Closed:** 24 to 26 Dec, 1 Jan, 1 week mid-Feb **Meals:** alc (main courses £13 to £14) **Service:** not inc, card slips closed **Cards:** MasterCard, Maestro **Details:** 26 seats. Private parties: 14 main room. No children under 5. No smoking. Music

AR Not a full entry but provisionally recommended (known as 'round-ups' in previous editions, these 'also recommended' establishments are now integrated throughout the book).

MAP 2 **Codford St Peter** WILTSHIRE

George Hotel

High Street, Codford St Peter
BA12 0NG
Tel: (01985) 850270

Cooking 4 | Modern British | £26–£56

Once an A-road hotel in the now bypassed village centre, the George remains a pub that attracts the locals but has also become a restaurant that is a destination for people who care about food. It has a bright and warm modern feel, tempered by touches like an open fire in winter, and is run with aplomb and well-honed professionalism. The kitchen demonstrates sound talent, avoiding complication and concentrating attention on the main ingredients. Delicate flavours in a rillette of guinea fowl and green beans complemented by a quince chutney, outstandingly fresh brill, and 'proper' chips accompanying chargrilled sirloin epitomise careful buying and an unfussy approach. Clear and imaginative flavours, as in pannacotta scented with rosemary and bourbon and topped with a mango coulis, nevertheless indicate a willingness to depart from normal practice. The sensibly brief wine list offers a surprisingly wide span of choice; starting at £11.60 there is a smattering of halves but no desire to impress with posh bottles.

Chef: Boyd McIntosh **Proprietors:** Boyd McIntosh and Joanne Fryer **Open:** Wed to Mon L 12 to 2, Mon and Wed to Sat D 7 to 9 **Meals:** alc (main courses L £8 to £15, D £8 to £19) **Service:** not inc, card slips closed **Cards:** Delta, MasterCard, Maestro, Visa **Details:** 50 seats. 28 seats outside. Private parties: 30 main room. Car park. Children's helpings. No-smoking area. Music **Accommodation:** 4 rooms, 2 with bath/shower. TV. B&B £45 to £65

MAP 2 **Colerne** WILTSHIRE

Lucknam Park

Colerne SN14 8AZ
Tel: (01225) 742777
Website: www.lucknampark.co.uk

Cooking 6 | Modern European | £48–£90

Five hundred acres of parkland surround an immaculately preserved Palladian mansion that is geared towards the corporate end of the market, with conference and leisure facilities among its attractions. Chandeliers and heavily swagged curtains feature in a dining room 'the size of a ballroom', but if you are expecting gentle country-house cooking, prepare to be startled. Hywel Jones took up the cleavers in the kitchen at the beginning of 2004.

His menu combines classic European ideas with some innovative flavours, especially when it comes to seafood: grilled baby mullet with a ballottine of bluefin tuna, aubergine caviar and tomato and basil coulis, for instance, or pan-roast scallops teamed with a fricassee of snails and ceps, turnip purée and creamed parsley. Materials are first-rate, and the food combines a few earthy touches such as pot-roast Roundway Hill pork with more luxurious items like pan-fried foie gras (and caramelised apples, baby leeks, girolles and sauce aux épices), or saddle of Wiltshire rabbit roasted in Carmarthen ham and served with asparagus cannelloni and sweetcorn purée. Novel touches at dessert stage have included whisky ice cream with hot chocolate fondant, and mint ice cream with a salad of summer berries and a macaroon. The cellar's traditional French backbone is fleshed out by bottles from elsewhere, but prices are stiff, with not much below £20, starting at £17.50.

Chef: Hywel Jones **Proprietor:** Lucknam Park Hotels Ltd **Open:** Sun L 12.30 to 2.30, all week D 7 to 10 **Meals:** Set L £30, Set D £55. Light menu available **Service:** not inc, card slips closed **Cards:** Amex, Delta, Diners, Maestro, MasterCard, Visa **Details:** 80 seats. Private parties: 80 main room, 10 to 30 private rooms. Car park. Vegetarian meals. Children's helpings. No children under 8 at D. Jacket and tie. No smoking. Wheelchair access (also WC). Occasional music. No mobile phones **Accommodation:** 41 rooms, all with bath/shower. TV. Phone. Room only £225 to £770. Rooms for disabled. Baby facilities. Swimming pool

MAP 5 Colwall Stone HEREFORDSHIRE

Colwall Park AR

Walwyn Road, Colwall Stone WR13 6QG
Tel: (01684) 540000

A favourite stop of one regular business traveller for its 'warm welcome and first-class food', this smartly presented mock-Tudor hotel offers a modern take on a traditional British menu. Chef James Garth draws on local suppliers for the likes of pan-seared scallops with cauliflower purée and sherry caramel (£8), followed by fillet of Hereford organic pork with cabbage and bacon, apple fondant and sage juices (£17.25), then apricot-glazed bread-and-butter pudding (£6.50). Three course set lunch £17.95 (reservations only), and bar menu available. Strong wine list from £13.50. Open all week.

MAP 1 Constantine CORNWALL

Trengilly Wartha AR

Nancenoy TR11 5RP
Tel: (01326) 340332

Get directions to locate this multi-purpose pub, restaurant, hotel and wine merchant's deep in a remote wooded valley. 'Pub grub' and full menus (£23/£29) highlight local produce in the guise of asparagus and Cornish new potato salad with poached free-range egg, marinated ribeye steak with twice-baked aubergine and blue cheese soufflé, all sorts of fish and desserts like green apple sorbet with lavender shortbread. Drinks aplenty, from beers and ciders to a classy wine list (prices from £10.50). Accommodation. Open all week.

MAP 3 Cookham BERKSHIRE

Manzano's

19–21 Station Hill Parade, Cookham SL6 9BR
Tel: (01628) 525775

Cooking 3 | Spanish/Mediterranean | £43–£52

A white awning and glass frontage pick out this friendly and unpretentious Cookham Spanish from the crowd in its rather ordinary parade of shops by the station. There's real homely appeal, just what you'd expect of a small neighbourhood restaurant, with warm smiles for all-comers and hugs and kisses for regulars. Proprietors Richard and Deena Manzano are guided by the philosophy that the place is 'run by the proprietors for the customers', and, as one reporter echoed in agreement, service exceeds 'all expectations'. The authentic cooking, like the hospitality, is honest, generous and unfussy, its robust flavours awash with the taste and colours of Spain. Take a 'big-flavoured dish' of slow-roasted roulade of suckling pig with chorizo sausage and Serrano ham, or perhaps traditional Castilian lamb, slow roasted in a wood-fired oven with roasted vegetables. Save room for the likes of Galician pancakes in a buttery pool of orange sauce perfumed with brandy and Grand Marnier, and indulge in the well-chosen wine list, which showcases a decent selection of patriotic Spanish bottles, a quartet of house from £13.95 and plenty of drinking under the £20 threshold.

Chef: Richard Manzano **Proprietors:** Richard and Deena Manzano **Open:** Mon to Fri L 12.30 to 2, Mon to Sat D 7 to 10 **Closed:** 2 weeks Aug, bank hols **Meals:** Set L £13.50 (2 courses), Set D £24.50 (2 courses) to £28.50. Tapas menu available Mon to Fri L and Mon to Thur D **Service:** 12.5%, card slips closed **Cards:** Amex, MasterCard, Maestro, Visa **Details:** 36 seats. 12 seats outside. Private parties: 38 main room. Car park. Vegetarian meals. Children's helpings. Wheelchair access (not WC). Occasional music. Air-conditioned

MAP 3 **Cookham Dean** BERKSHIRE

Inn on the Green

The Old Cricket Common,
Cookham Dean SL6 9NZ
Tel: (01628) 482638
Website: www.theinnonthegreen.com

Cooking 4 | Modern British | £31–£81

Once through the front door of this erstwhile mock-Tudor inn tucked down the side of the old cricket green, you'll find decor that goes from 'log cabin' wood-planked walls to rich shades of colour, with burgundy predominating – 'it's certainly different,' concluded one visitor. Ceilings are painted silver (in between the wooden beams), leather chesterfields give the lounge a clubby feel, and in the three interconnecting dining rooms linen-clad tables sport sparkling wine glasses. In keeping with the rustic-chic surroundings, the food is British done in a modern style, and while much is made of Garry Hollihead's name, his ideas are interpreted by a well-drilled brigade. An inspector was impressed by a starter of ham hock and foie gras terrine, which came with port jelly and caramelised brioche and delivered 'clean, clear flavours', while a well-timed roast fillet of cod was of cracking quality and accompanied by a clam chowder that made the dish 'sing'. For dessert, peach and passion-fruit soufflé teamed with champagne sorbet was an 'assured, accomplished delivery of a classic'. Presentation skills are high, with sauces and ingredients arranged artistically, and staff are generally attentive and professional. On the wine list prices start at £14.50 but move up quickly.

Chef: Garry Hollihead **Proprietors:** Garry Hollihead, Mark Fuller and Andy Taylor **Open:** Sun L 12 to 4, Tue to Sat D 7 to 10 **Meals:** alc D (main courses £15 to £24). Set L Sun £17.50, Set D £17.95 **Service:** 12.5% (optional), card slips closed **Cards:** Amex, Delta, MasterCard, Maestro, Visa **Details:** 76 seats. 100 seats outside. Private parties: 100 main room, 10 to 40 private rooms. Car park. Vegetarian meals. Children's helpings. No-smoking area. Wheelchair access (also WC). Occasional music. No mobile phones. Air-conditioned **Accommodation:** 9 rooms, all with bath/shower. TV. Phone. B&B £90 to £195. Rooms for disabled. Baby facilities

MAP 10 **Corbridge** NORTHUMBERLAND

Angel of Corbridge NEW ENTRY

Main Street, Corbridge NE45 5LA
Tel: (01434) 632119
Website: www.theangelofcorbridge.co.uk

Cooking 2 | Modern European | £30–£57

Reputedly the oldest pub in Corbridge – as well as the largest – this impressive-looking town-centre inn makes a big impression with its leather chesterfields and grand piano gracing the entrance. Dinner is the main event, served in a smart, split-level restaurant with purple carpets and grey walls. The menu has a modern European flavour, opening with, say, twice-baked slow-roast tomato soufflé or pan-fried salmon niçoise salad before main courses including a near-faultless piece of roast North Sea halibut on a bed of al dente tagliatelle with asparagus velouté or breast of Gressingham duck with crushed peppercorns and honey. Vegetarians have their own menu, and traditional desserts have featured cherry tart with home-made ice cream as well as lemon syllabub. House wine is £11.

Chef: Alan O'Kane **Proprietors:** Peter and Alan O'Kane **Open:** all week L 12 to 2.30, Mon to Sat D 6.30 to 9.30 **Meals:** alc (main courses £10 to £20). Set L £13.50 (2 courses), Set D Mon to Thur £20 (2 courses) **Service:** not inc **Cards:** Amex, Delta, Maestro, MasterCard, Visa **Details:** 60 seats. 20 seats outside. Private parties: 60 main room, 25 to 60 private rooms. Car park. Vegetarian meals. Children's helpings. No smoking in 1 dining room. Occasional music **Accommodation:** 5 rooms, all with bath/shower. TV. Phone. B&B £55 to £99

MAP 2 Corscombe DORSET

Fox Inn

AR

Corscombe DT2 0NS
Tel: (01935) 891330

Archetypal thatched Dorset inn with a 'hot house' conservatory, lots of rustic memorabilia and a liking for fish. The regular menu is bolstered by blackboard specials ranging from gratin of crab, salmon and scallops and sea bass fillets with wild mushrooms and asparagus to chorizo sausages with orange chutney and pork tenderloin with apricots and roasted garlic. Real ales and an eclectic wine list. Accommodation. Open all week. New chef: reports please.

MAP 5 Corse Lawn GLOUCESTERSHIRE

Corse Lawn House

Corse Lawn GL19 4LZ
Tel: (01452) 780771
Website: www.corselawn.com

Cooking 3 | Anglo-French | £32–£75

Since 1978 the Hine family has fostered a decidedly gentrified and endearingly old-fashioned Englishness in their listed Queen Anne residence. Polite, formally dressed staff oversee the sedate dining room, and the lengthy carte ploughs a well-tried Anglo-French furrow. The food relies on careful and conscientious sourcing, and the owners have made an ecological stand by banishing all 'endangered species' of fish from their menus. Of course, there's still plenty to choose from: witness a spot-on starter of grilled sea bream fillets with tapenade toast and tomato dressing. Other ingredients are equally well handled: 'hugely enjoyable' saddle of venison has been served with port sauce, creamed cabbage and chestnuts, while pork fillet might be partnered by grilled apple, curly kale and coriander sauce. The 'pleasing consistency' also applies to desserts like hot passion-fruit soufflé with a matching sorbet. Similar dishes are available in the casual bistro. The wine list concentrates on quality without showiness or fanfares. France is its central passion, picked with total assurance and an eye for value in even the most prestigious appellations. Shorter selections from elsewhere are no less acute, and an exceptional list of half-bottles runs to over 60. Very reasonable prices start at £12.50.

Chefs: Baba Hine and Andrew Poole **Proprietors:** the Hine family **Open:** all week 12 to 2, 7 (7.30 Sun) to 9.30 **Closed:** 24 to 26 Dec **Meals:** alc (main courses £13 to £28.50). Set L £19.50 (2 courses) to £22.50, Set D £29.50. Bistro menu available **Service:** not inc, card slips closed **Cards:** Amex, Delta, Diners, Maestro, MasterCard, Visa **Details:** 80 seats. 30 seats outside. Private parties: 80 main room, 6 to 40 private rooms. Car park. Vegetarian meals. Children's helpings. No smoking. Wheelchair access (not WC). No music. No mobile phones **Accommodation:** 19 rooms, all with bath/shower. TV. Phone. B&B £87.50 to £170. Rooms for disabled. Baby facilities. Swimming pool

MAP 7 Cranbrook KENT

Apicius

NEW ENTRY

23 Stone Street, Cranbrook TN17 3HE
Tel: (01580) 714666

Cooking 4 | Modern European | £32–£44

Reporters have been quick to spot this small, shopfronted restaurant that opened in December 2004 and to praise Tim Johnson's classically based modern cooking. Local produce is a mainstay of the short, good-value set-price menus, seen in starters such as a ballottine of guinea fowl and pheasant with celeriac rémoulade and Cumberland sauce, or asparagus with black truffle dressing, followed perhaps by boneless osso buco with 'fantastic potato purée which mopped up some wonderful rich cooking juices', or a fillet of John Dory with confit garlic, girolles and thyme oil. Other reference points have included a main-course vegetarian option of a duo of light, full-flavoured goats' cheese soufflés accompanied by buttered spinach and tomato jus, and indulgences such as a powerfully flavoured iced hazelnut mousse with winter fruits, or a delicate, wobbly crème caramel. Faith Hawkins runs front-of-house with unpretentious hospitality. The short but thoughtfully compiled wine list opens with South African white at £14 and Spanish red at £16.

Chef: Tim Johnson **Proprietors:** Tim Johnson and Faith Hawkins **Open:** Wed to Sun L 12 to 2, Tue to Sat D 6.45 to 9 **Meals:** Set L £15.50 (2 courses) to £19.50, Set D £19.50 (2 courses) to £23.50 **Service:** not inc, card slips closed **Cards:** Delta, Maestro, MasterCard, Visa **Details:** 24 seats. Private parties: 12 main room. Vegetarian meals. No children under 8. No smoking. Wheelchair access (also WC). No music. No mobile phones

MAP 9 **Crayke** NORTH YORKSHIRE

Durham Ox

Westway, Crayke, nr Easingwold YO61 4TE
Tel: (01347) 821506
Website: www.thedurhamox.com

NEW CHEF | Modern European | £34–£60

'A wonderful place to get away from it all and be really well fed,' enthused a couple after staying over at this exceedingly friendly, 300-year-old pub on the fringes of the Vale of York. New chef Rick Blake arrived in 2005, and it seems likely that he will keep local produce on the top of his shopping list. Previously the kitchen has delivered game and winter vegetable terrine with salsa verde before baked salmon on home-made fettucine with wild mushroom velouté, or prime Yorkshire beef from the grill. Desserts have tended towards classics like lemon meringue pie with raspberry coulis. The wine list has plenty of decent workaday bottles (from £13.50), plus a smattering of 'great' vintages. Reports please.

Chef: Rick Blake **Proprietor:** Michael Ibbotson **Open:** all week 12 to 2.30 (3 Sun), 6 to 9.30 (10 Sat, 8.30 Sun) **Closed:** 25 Dec (drinks only) **Meals:** alc (main courses £12.50 to £19). Light L menu available Mon to Sat **Service:** not inc, card slips closed, 10% for parties of 10 or more **Cards:** Amex, Delta, Maestro, MasterCard, Visa **Details:** 100 seats. 30 seats outside. Private parties: 35 main room, 18 to 80 private rooms. Car park. Vegetarian meals. Children's helpings. No young children in dining room. No smoking. Occasional music **Accommodation:** 5 rooms, all with bath/shower. TV. B&B £60 to £120. Rooms for disabled. Baby facilities

MAP 2 **Cray's Pond** BERKSHIRE

White Lion

Goring Road, Goring Heath, Cray's Pond RG8 7SH
Tel: (01491) 680471
Website: www.innastew.com

Cooking 3 | Global | £28–£51

This small corner pub admirably combines the role of a traditional local with a 'real dining experience'; tongue-and-groove walls and ceilings and parquet flooring give it a rural feel. Beyond the compact public bar are the dining areas; a lounge bar/restaurant with a prodigiously low, dark-maroon ceiling, high dado and plain wood tables and, beyond that, a much lighter garden room extension. The crowd-pleasing, fashionable menus change twice daily – driven by seasonal local produce and fresh fish arriving from Brixham – and offer plenty of interest at reasonable prices for generous portions. Simple classics like pork and leek sausages (with mash and onion gravy) or salmon fishcakes (with chive butter sauce, spinach and new potatoes) vie with more Mediterranean dishes. Take warm fig, Serrano ham and mozzarella with tomato, black olives and rocket to start, then perhaps a mixed seafood laksa with bean shoots, coconut and lime, or shoulder of lamb with tomato and olive and oregano polenta to follow. The cheeseboard 'is a delight', while the compact wine list similarly travels the globe for inspiration; helpfully laid out by style, it offers plenty of drinking under £20 and a ten-strong house selection from £10.95 (£3.25 a glass).

Chef: Andrew Hill **Proprietors:** Stuart and Caroline Pierrepont **Open:** Tue to Sun L 12 to 2, Tue to Sat D 6 to 9.30 **Closed:** 25 and 26 Dec, 1 Jan **Meals:** alc (not Sun L; main courses £9.50 to £14.50). Set L Sun £13.95 (2 courses). Set D Tue to Thur £13.95 (2 courses) **Service:** not inc **Cards:** Delta, Maestro, MasterCard, Visa **Details:** 50 seats. 40 seats outside. Private parties: 30 main room. Car park. Vegetarian meals. Children's helpings. No smoking. Music

MAP 2 **Crockerton** WILTSHIRE

Bath Arms

NEW ENTRY

Crockerton BA12 8AJ
Tel: (01985) 212262

Cooking 3 | Modern British | £28–£44

Dean Carr tells us he spent 17 years working the stoves in London hot spots like the Ivy (see entry) but now wants to 'bring a little bit of West End style to the West Country'. The chosen spot for his mission is a prosperous-looking pub with mullioned windows and an ancient sundial on the façade. Inside, it looks, feels and sounds like a local boozer, but there is serious work going on in the kitchen. Bypass the pub clichés in favour of the full menu, which shows a laudable commitment to top-class raw materials. Chunky pheasant and venison terrine comes with chutney and toast, and slow-cooked 'sticky beef' is served with braised red cabbage. Fish also gets the thumbs up in the shape of seared salmon on pesto, while desserts have included chocolate brownie with home-made hazelnut ice cream. House wine is £10.50.

Chef/Proprietor: Dean Carr **Open:** all week 12 to 2, 6.30 to 9 **Closed:** D 25 Dec, D 26 Dec, D 1 Jan **Meals:** alc (main courses £9.50 to £15). Bar menu available **Service:** not inc, card slips closed **Cards:** Delta, Maestro, MasterCard, Visa **Details:** 60 seats. 100 seats outside. Private parties: 12 main room, 24 to 40 private rooms. Car park. Children's helpings. No smoking. Wheelchair access (also WC). Music. No mobile phones

MAP 2 Crudwell WILTSHIRE

Rectory

Crudwell SN16 9EP
Tel: (01666) 577194
Website: www.oldrectorycrudwell.co.uk

Cooking 3 | Modern British | £45–£60

New owner Robert Standing dropped the 'Old' from the name of this modestly proportioned Georgian hotel when he acquired it in the summer of 2005, although the place, with its period flagstoned hallway and oak-panelled dining room, thankfully hasn't got any newer. Peter Fairclough continues at the stoves, too, producing a style of food that is classic British gastro-pub with a few modern twists and turns. Expect Cornish crab risotto or duck terrine with French bean salad to start, followed by seared sea bass with spinach and sauce vierge, or braised Welsh lamb shank with basil mash and an olive and tomato jus. Vegetables are extra and might include bubble and squeak, and meals are rounded off with the likes of passion-fruit jelly with raspberry sorbet, or poached peaches and thyme ice cream, served with suggested dessert wines. The main wine list opens with a fine selection by the glass from £3.25 before exploring France in some detail, while the rest of the world includes a stopover in Uruguay.

Chef: Peter Fairclough **Proprietor:** Robert Standing **Open:** all week 12 to 2, 7 to 9 (9.30 Fri and Sat) **Meals:** alc (main courses £15.50 to £18.50) **Service:** not inc **Cards:** Delta, MasterCard, Maestro, Visa **Details:** 60 seats. 24 seats outside. Private parties: 40 main room, 2 to 60 private rooms. Car park. Vegetarian meals. Children's helpings. No smoking. Wheelchair access (also WC). Occasional music. No mobile phones **Accommodation:** 12 rooms, all with bath/shower. TV. Phone. B&B £88 to £145. Baby facilities. Swimming pool

This symbol means that the restaurant has elected to participate in *The Good Food Guide's* £5 voucher scheme (see 'How to Use the Guide' for details).

MAP 3 Cuckfield WEST SUSSEX

Mansfields

1 Broad Street, Cuckfield RH17 5LJ
Tel: (01444) 410222

Cooking 2 | Modern European | £29–£51

There's a sense of true dedication about this family-run restaurant in a prosperous part of Sussex. It is a very personal operation, with attentive service from Patricia Schlender, who overseas the three small dining rooms with intelligence and warmth. Husband Günther's food appeals for well-executed straightforwardness: butternut squash and parsnip soup, medallions of scallops and crispy bacon, or best end of English lamb with ratatouille, rosemary and thyme jus. Even more exotic and imaginative dishes, like saddle of local venison with creamed oyster, shiitake and button mushrooms, are similarly sure-footed. Vegetables are extra. To finish there may be Belgian chocolate crème brûlée, or sticky toffee pudding with butterscotch sauce. It's all 'great value' according to one visitor, and 'portions are good'. House French is £11.95, and there's a decent selection under £20.

Chefs: Günther and Marc Schlender **Proprietors:** Günther and Patricia Schlender **Open:** Tue to Sat D 7 to 10 **Closed:** 23 Dec to 4 Jan **Meals:** alc D (main courses £10 to £16) **Service:** not inc, 10% for parties of 6 or more, card slips closed **Cards:** Amex, Delta, Maestro, MasterCard, Visa **Details:** 32 seats. Private parties: 12 main room, 10 to 15 private rooms. Vegetarian meals. No smoking. Music

Ockenden Manor

Ockenden Lane, Cuckfield RH17 5LD
Tel: (01444) 416111
Website: www.hshotels.co.uk

Cooking 5 | Modern French | £43–£91

This substantial building, added to and adapted from the sixteenth century onwards, sits secluded behind tall trees and high walls, with nine acres of gardens at the back. The tone of service is good-humoured, and the main dining room, with its dark oak panelling, has human proportions that make the place feel much less daunting than many country houses.

Steve Crane makes a virtue of simplicity, and the composition and presentation of his dishes always seem to make perfect sense. But that doesn't preclude a certain creativity: sautéed langoustines are made into a mille-feuille with baby spinach and celeriac, while good Brixham crab appears as a lasagne. Local ingredients might include pheasant from nearby Balcombe, the breast honey-roasted, the leg meat prepared as confit. Flavours accompanying fish are just as robust as those with red meat (roast cod comes with buttered cabbage, smoked salmon and crisp potato, while horseradish mash and a peppercorn sauce enhance grilled beef fillet). Interesting dessert ideas have taken in warm cinnamon doughnuts served with yoghurt ice cream and apple sauce. A resourceful wine list covers ten countries, opening with a dozen house selections at £17.50 a bottle (£3.95 a glass). For those with ample pockets, the clarets look especially tempting.

Chef: Steve Crane **Proprietors:** The Goodman and Carminger families **Open:** all week 12.30 to 2, 7 to 9.30 (7.15 to 9 Sun) **Meals:** alc (main courses £39 to £48). Set L £13.95 (2 courses) to £46, set L Sat £15.50 (2 courses) to £46, set L Sun £26.95 to £46. Tasting and bar menus also available **Service:** not inc **Cards:** Amex, Delta, Diners, Maestro, MasterCard, Visa **Details:** 45 seats. 20 seats outside. Private parties: 75 main room, 8 to 16 private rooms. Car park. Vegetarian meals. Children's helpings. No smoking. Wheelchair access (also WC). Occasional music. No mobile phones **Accommodation:** 22 rooms, all with bath/shower. TV. Phone. B&B £108 to £325

MAP 3 Dargate KENT

Dove

Plum Pudding Lane, Dargate ME13 9HB
Tel: (01227) 751360

Cooking 3 | French | £37–£58

Woods and apple orchards form the backdrop to this quintessential sturdy Kentish pub on quaintly named Plum Pudding Lane. Inside, it looks the rustic part, with pine panelling, bare boards and scrubbed tables in a network of knocked-through rooms. Nigel Morris keeps his customers satisfied with uncluttered modern dishes and plenty of fish in the guise of, say, grilled sardines with garlic and olive oil, or pan-fried whole local plaice with a caper, shallot and herb butter. Alternatively, you might begin with Bayonne ham and oyster mushroom tart before roast duck breast on crushed new potatoes flavoured with tapenade, or chump of English lamb with roast cherry tomatoes. Desserts have included passion-fruit brûlée. Prices on the concise, reasonably priced wine list start at £16.50.

Chef: Nigel Morris **Proprietors:** Nigel and Bridget Morris **Open:** Tue to Sun L 12 to 2, Wed to Sat D 7 to 9 **Meals:** alc (main courses £14 to £20). Bar snack menu available **Service:** not inc, card slips closed **Cards:** Delta, Maestro, MasterCard, Visa **Details:** 20 seats. 20 seats outside. Car park. Vegetarian meals. Music

MAP 1 Dartmouth DEVON

New Angel

2 South Embankment, Dartmouth TQ6 9BH
Tel: (01803) 839425
Website: www.thenewangel.co.uk

Cooking 5 | Modern Anglo-French | £39–£74

Followers of TV gastronomy can't have missed the ongoing saga of John Burton-Race's adventures in setting up this place, long a stalwart of the Guide when it was run by Joyce Molyneux as the Carved Angel. Diners in the summer of 2004 may well have subsequently found themselves on camera. There are two levels, both with fine views over the Dart, the lower a mixture of wooden floors and antique chandeliers, against the backdrop of an open-plan kitchen, the upper intended as a more 'intimate and romantic' venue.

When Burton-Race is around, things proceed at a rarefied level. A 1980s signature dish of a courgette flower stuffed with lobster mousse is brought off with persuasive aplomb, while summer main courses that pleased one group included pot-roast duck breast, and lamb fillet with crab mousse. French and English cheeses are served in peak condition, and meals might end with a slice of 'superb' lemon tart, or 'sublime' chocolate fondant with pistachio ice cream. Other experiences have been less happy, with over-salted mash spoiling a black pudding starter, and suspect timing of roast wild duck. Only the reliable lemon tart redeemed that disappointing lunch. Wines are an appealing mix from recent vintages. France leads the way, with Italy and Australia providing most of the back-up. Bottle prices kick off at £12, and a dozen come by the glass.

Chefs: John Burton-Race, Nigel Marriage and Robin Zavou **Proprietor:** John Burton-Race **Open:** Tue to Sun L 12 to 2.30, Tue to Sat D 6.30 to 10.30; also open for brunch 9 (8.30 summer) to 11 **Meals:** alc (main courses £14.50 to £25) **Service:** not inc, 10% for parties of 8 or more **Cards:** Amex, Delta, Maestro, MasterCard, Visa **Details:** 80 seats. Private parties: 55 main room. Vegetarian meals. Children's helpings. No smoking. Wheelchair access (not WC). Music. Air-conditioned

MAP 6 **Dedham** ESSEX

milsoms

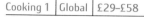

Stratford Road, Dedham CO7 6HW
Tel: (01206) 322795
Website: www.milsomhotels.com

Cooking 1 | Global | £29–£58

The formal exterior of this Georgian country house contrasts dramatically with the 'striking and bold' lively bistro within. Smart and friendly young staff help to create a relaxed ambience, and the informal atmosphere extends to a no-booking policy and writing your own food order on a notepad provided at each table, then taking it to the bar. The cold assemblages that make up most of the starters – say, mixed Italian cured meats with charred artichoke and pepper salad, or pumpkin, blue cheese and tomato croûton salad – are made with well-chosen, quality ingredients, and main courses, while equally unfussy, offer a good choice with something to please both conservative and more adventurous palates. Shepherd's pie made with roast Suffolk mutton is never off the menu, but there's also pavé of cod on cockle, crab and pea risotto, bang-bang chicken, and aromatic duck breast with noodles and Asian greens. Strawberry and chocolate fondue with home-made marsh-mallow is a fun way to finish. House wine is £12.45.

Chef: Stas Anastasiades **Proprietor:** Paul Milsom **Open:** all week 12 to 2.15, 6 to 9.30 (10 Fri and Sat) **Meals:** alc (main courses £8.50 to £20) **Service:** not inc **Cards:** Amex, Delta, Diners, Maestro, MasterCard, Visa **Details:** 80 seats. 80 seats outside. Private parties: 8 to 16 private rooms. Car park. Vegetarian meals. Children's helpings. No-smoking area. Wheelchair access (also WC). Music. Air-conditioned **Accommodation:** 15 rooms, all with bath/shower. TV. Phone. Room only £75 to £135. Rooms for disabled. Baby facilities

Sun Inn

High Street, Dedham CO7 6DF
Tel: (01206) 323351
Website: www.thesuninndedham.com

Cooking 2 | Mediterranean | £26–£41

This fifteenth-century inn works comfortably as a village pub – complete with real fires, real ales, and timbers – as a place to eat, and to sleep. Its main business is undoubtedly food, robustly flavoured cooking with the splash of the Mediterranean never far away, which combines seasonal supplies of vegetables, leaves, and herbs with meat from local farms (some of it from rare breeds), and takes care in both composition and presentation. Roast butternut squash and red onion salad is accompanied by goats' cheese, toasted walnuts and aged balsamic, and among other starters is a short list of tapas to share: red pepper and thyme frittata, say. For main courses there could be Gloucester Old Spot pork and bean stew with pancetta, chorizo, black pudding, tomatoes and paprika, or roast fillet of cod with salsa verde. Desserts include lemon and lime tart, and rhubarb fool. House wines, from Sicily, are £10.50.

Chefs: Piers Baker and Kathleen McDonnell **Proprietor:** Piers Baker **Open:** all week L 12 to 2.30 (3 Sat and Sun), Mon to Sat D 6.30 to 9.30 (10 Sat and Sun) **Closed:** Christmas, 31 Dec **Meals:** alc (main courses £7.50 to £13.50) **Service:** not inc, card slips closed **Cards:** Maestro, MasterCard, Visa **Details:** 120 seats. 200 seats outside. Private parties: 20 main room. Car park. Vegetarian meals. Children's helpings. No smoking in 1 dining room. Music **Accommodation:** 4 rooms, all with bath/shower. TV. B&B £55 to £120

MAP 7 **Derby** DERBYSHIRE

Darleys

Darley Abbey Mills, Haslams Lane, Darley Abbey, Derby DE22 1DZ
Tel: (01332) 364987
Website: www.darleys.com

Cooking 4 | Modern British | £27–£57

The Hobsons' restaurant is divertingly sited in an old cotton mill on the Derwent. In a relaxed and warmly friendly atmosphere, a seasonally changing menu based on local supplies manages to push most of the right buttons. To begin with, vegetarians have their own menu, which might proceed in fine style from terrine of roast aubergine and sweet potato with sticky red onion compote to cauliflower and creamed leek spring roll with Pommery mustard velouté. Others will find sturdy comfort food on offer: perhaps a pairing of beef fillet and ox cheek boudin with wild mushrooms, cabbage and horseradish, or poached skate wing on crushed potatoes with beurre noisette spiked with lemon and anchovy. Desserts come with appropriate ice cream garnishes: espresso with coffee and mascarpone mousse, Kirsch with cherry and almond parfait. A short, serviceable wine list opens with 'personal recommendations' from £14 a bottle, £3.50 a glass.

Chefs: Jonathan Hobson and Kevin Stone **Proprietors:** Jonathan and Kathryn Hobson **Open:** all week L 12 to 2, Mon to Sat D 7 to 10 **Closed:** bank hols **Meals:** alc D (main courses £16.50 to £20). Set L £13.95 (2 courses) to £15.95 **Service:** not inc **Cards:** Delta, Maestro, MasterCard, Visa **Details:** 70 seats. 16 seats outside. Private parties: 70 main room. Car park. Vegetarian meals. No smoking. Wheelchair access (not WC). Music. No mobile phones. Air-conditioned

MAP 2 Didmarton GLOUCESTERSHIRE

Kings Arms Inn

AR

The Street, Didmarton GL9 1DT
Tel: (01454) 238245

A converted seventeenth-century coaching inn originally leased from the Beauforts of Badminton. The Estate provides game, which figures prominently in the shape of rabbit, pheasants and rooks (served in a pie at the renowned Rook Supper Night). Otherwise, expect smoked mackerel and trout terrine with celeriac and apple rémoulade (£6), and guinea fowl with garlic confit and basil risotto (£14) before vanilla and caramel custard tart with caramel poached pear (£5.25). Local real ales and reasonably priced wines from £10.95. Accommodation. Open all week.

MAP 3 Dinton BUCKINGHAMSHIRE

La Chouette

Westlington Green, Dinton HP17 8UW
Tel: (01296) 747422

Cooking 4 | Belgian | £25–£64

It may have regulation beams, a wooden floor and open fire, but the cooking at this former pub overlooking the village green is more sophisticated than the country-casual interior suggests. Frederic Desmette runs the place with vigour and character (too much for some), a passion for wildlife photography, and owls (chouettes) in particular, in evidence on the walls, and his Belgian origins shape the cooking with dishes like fillet of brill served with a sauce made with Belgian beer. Among other dishes visitors are likely to encounter are a salad of chicken livers, veal chop with its cooking juice, and duck breast in a green peppercorn sauce. Seafood is a feature; what's available depends on daily deliveries but might include coquilles St Jacques in a chicory sauce, and fillet of sea bass with chive sauce. The French wine list (has anyone ever dared order the sole Italian offering?) probes both classic and less-travelled regions, with multiple vintages from some celebrated domaines, especially in the Loire (Dagueneau, Foucault) and the Rhône (Clape, Rostaing). Most bottles are a big step up from the £13.50 house red and white.

Chef/Proprietor: Frederic Desmette **Open:** Mon to Fri L 12 to 2, Mon to Sat D 7 to 9 **Meals:** alc (main courses £14 to £17). Set L £13.50 to £36.50, Set D £29.50 to £36.50 **Service:** 12.5% (optional), card slips closed **Cards:** Delta, Maestro, MasterCard, Visa **Details:** 35 seats. Private parties: 45 main room. Car park. Children's helpings. No smoking in 1 dining room. Occasional music. No mobile phones

MAP 6 Diss NORFOLK

Weavers Wine Bar

AR

Market Hill, Diss IP22 4JZ
Tel: (01379) 642411

Reliable neighbourhood 'eating house' in a timbered fifteenth-century building that was once a chapel. Good-value set menus and a flexible range of all-round dishes span everything from lemon sole in parsley butter (£16.75) to roast duck breast with a 'spring roll of vegetable risotto' and sweet-and-sour sauce. Start with sautéed chicken livers in madeira and cream (£4.75) and conclude with amaretti and chocolate chip trifle (£4.50). Extensive, well-considered wine list from £11.95. Open Tue to Fri L and Mon to Sat D.

MAP 1 Doddiscombsleigh DEVON

Nobody Inn

AR

Doddiscombsleigh EX6 7PS
Tel: (01647) 252394

An awesome collection of more than 50 West Country cheeses and a monumental, 800-strong wine list (including at least 20 by the glass) are star turns in this thatched fifteenth-century inn. Restaurant menus feature the likes of warm goats' cheese and cherry tomato confit (£5), sliced beef fillet with creamy tarragon sauce (£12.75), and desserts such as vanilla parfait with warm cherries and Kirsch (£4.50). Similar dishes are served more cheaply in the bar. Wonderfully peaceful setting; accommodation available. Restaurant open Tue to Sat D; bar food served L and D all week.

MAP 2 **Donhead St Andrew** WILTSHIRE

Forester AR

Lower Street, Donhead St Andrew SP7 9EE
Tel: (01747) 828038

This immaculate stone-built thatched inn is reached after driving along lovely country lanes. But this is no unchanging olde-worlde venue, with the talented Tom Shaw cooking the likes of sautéed breast of wood pigeon with a tart of caramelised red onions and chicory (£6.50), followed by pan-seared tuna with noodles, crispy won tons and chilli jam (£14.50). Desserts run to blackcurrant and white chocolate marbled soufflé (£7), and sticky toffee pudding with clotted cream (£5). French-focused wine list from £11.95. Accommodation. Open all week.

MAP 2 **Dorchester** DORSET

Sienna AR

36 High West Street, Dorchester DT1 1UP
Tel: (01305) 250022

Diminutive modern restaurant run by Russell and Eléna Brown. Menus change on a 'rolling basis' and ingredients are regional, so expect contemporary dishes like Cornish king scallops with wilted wild garlic leaves and ratatouille sauce, followed by braised and roast local rare-breed pork belly with buttered Savoy cabbage and cider sauce, before exotic finales such as pineapple tarte Tatin with coconut ice cream. Lunch £14.50/£17.50; dinner £25.50/£31. Around three dozen wines from £12. Closed Sun and Mon.

MAP 5 **Dorridge** WEST MIDLANDS

The Forest

25 Station Approach, Dorridge B93 8JA
Tel: (01564) 772120
Website: www.forest-hotel.com

Cooking 4 | Modern French | £22–£49

Just across the road from the railway station, the Forest started life in the nineteenth century as a railway hotel. Nowadays it is handy for the M42 and the NEC as well, so, moving with the times, it boasts a modern extension housing a busy bar with 'vaguely oriental décor' and an up-to-date, mirrored dining room with laminate floors and bare tables. The brasserie-look is matched by a repertoire of dishes including deep-fried goats' cheese with tapenade, green bean salad and red pepper reduction, coq au vin, and fillet of cod with linguine, spinach, dill and Avruga caviar cream. Desserts are a suitably varied bunch, taking in anything from apple and blackberry 'flapjack' crumble to pineapple tarte Tatin with spiced ice cream and caramel sauce. Staff are 'obliging and pleasant', and judging by reports, the restaurant performs well during the week, but can lapse under weekend pressures. The wine list is categorised by style; nine are offered by the glass, and prices move gently upwards from £11.95. The Monday/Tuesday set dinners include a glass of house.

Chef: James Pye **Proprietors:** Gary and Tracy Perkins **Open:** all week L 12 to 2.30 (3 Sun), Mon to Sat D 6.30 to 10 **Closed:** 25 Dec **Meals:** alc (not Sun L; main courses £9.50 to £17). Set L £10 (2 courses) to £13, Set L Sun £14.50 (2 courses) to £17.95, Set D Mon and Tue £12.50 (2 courses) to £17.50 **Service:** not inc **Cards:** Amex, Delta, Maestro, MasterCard, Visa **Details:** 70 seats. 70 seats outside. Private parties: 70 main room, 10 to 150 private rooms. Car park. Vegetarian meals. Children's helpings. No smoking. Wheelchair access (also WC). Music. Air-conditioned **Accommodation:** 12 rooms, all with bath/shower. TV. Phone. B&B £92.50 to £112.50. Baby facilities

MAP 5 **Dunhampton** WORCESTERSHIRE

Epic Bar Brasserie AR

Ombersley Road, Dunhampton DY13 9SW
Tel: (01905) 620000

'Lifestyle eating and drinking' is the mantra behind Patrick McDonald's group of contemporary Midlands brasseries. This outlet spreads the word with an eclectic menu of French fish soup with rouille and croûtons (£4.75), chorizo, Parma ham and red onion pizza (£8.75), grills, and desserts such as warm prune and almond tart (£5). Reasonably priced global wines from £11.75. Open Tue to Sat. Branches at Hanbury Road, Stoke Prior, Bromsgrove, tel: (01527) 871929, and 15A Reindeer Court, New Street, Worcester, tel: (01905) 745625.

 This symbol means that smoking is not permitted.

MAP 10 Durham CO DURHAM

Almshouses

AR

Palace Green, Durham DH1 3RL
Tel: (0191) 3861054

Facing the wide expanse of the green and overlooked by the majestic cathedral, this café is housed in an ancient stone building. Once inside, however, things become much more 21st century. The menu, on blackboards, runs to red lentil and oregano soup, salads, filled rolls (Craster crab with lemon and chive, for example), and 'wonderful' home-made cakes and puddings. Hot dishes might include pork and leek sausages with sweet peppers in a tomato sauce. Open all week 9am to 5pm (8pm June–Aug).

Bistro 21

Aykley Heads House, Aykley Heads,
Durham DH1 5TS
Tel: (0191) 384 4354

Cooking 4 | Mediterranean | £26–£56

Terry Laybourne's welcoming bistro is still drawing the crowds ten years on (see Newcastle for the other remaining member of his '21' stable). The feel is relaxed and unpretentious, and menus of a sensible length keep things simple but maintain interest, focusing on showing off good raw materials. A spring inspection meal produced fresh local asparagus 'perfectly al dente' with a good hollandaise sauce, and a successful partnership of new season's saddle of lamb ('cooked pink, melted in the mouth') with wild garlic, wilted wild spinach and mint-flavoured gravy. That meal finished in style with bitter chocolate mousse with a passion fruit mousse at its centre – a perfect foil to the bitterness of the chocolate. Winter brings local game and hearty modern classics like slow-cooked shoulder of pork with braised cabbage, black pudding mash and crackling. Wines are a decent selection at fair mark-ups, opening with house French at £12.50.

Chef: Paul O'Hara **Proprietor:** Terence Laybourne **Open:** Mon to Sat 12 to 2, 7 (6 Sat) to 10.30 **Closed:** 25 Dec, bank hols **Meals:** alc (main courses £11 to £20). Set L £13 (2 courses) to £15.50 **Service:** not inc **Cards:** Amex, Delta, Maestro, MasterCard, Visa **Details:** 55 seats. 24 seats outside. Private parties: 55 main room, 5 to 30 private rooms. Car park. Vegetarian meals. No smoking. Wheelchair access (also WC). Music. No mobile phones

Pump House

AR

Farm Road, Durham DH1 3PJ
Tel: (0191) 386 9189

Once the Durham City Waterworks, this Victorian pump house now functions as a seafood and steak restaurant. Fish lovers might choose seared scallops with Asian mango salad, then steamed rock lobster with a coriander potato cake, while meat eaters could opt for Stornoway black pudding with apple and foie gras sauce (£7) before grilled sirloin of mature Northumbrian beef (£17.50). Finish with, say, mascarpone, Amaretto and mixed berry brûlée (£5). International wines from £13.50. Open all week.

MAP 3 Eastbourne EAST SUSSEX

Grand Hotel, Mirabelle

King Edwards Parade, Eastbourne BN21 4EQ
Tel: (01323) 412345
Website: www.grandeastbourne.com

Cooking 5 | Modern European | £28–£101

At the quieter, western end of the seafront, the Grand Hotel lives up to the billing – think big – with neoclassical touches and handsome, well-tended grounds to the front. If there are no parking spaces left along the sweeping driveway, the seafront should be able to oblige. The Mirabelle has a separate entrance to the eastern side of the hotel, with a suitably grand lobby. It is hardly surprising that the restaurant is a little old-fashioned, as this is an old-school hotel dining room...in Eastbourne. Large windows overlook the gardens and across the road to the sea, and pillars, so large as to be seemingly supporting the whole building, pepper the room. Tables are smartly set, linen suitably stiff, and chairs comfortably cushioned; a pianist was capably running through his repertoire at inspection. The style of service may be formal, but staff are warm and relaxed.

The kitchen's good sense of timing is demonstrated in a starter of warm squab pigeon topped with a perfectly seared piece of foie gras and supported by Puy lentils with just the right amount of bite. Main courses arrive with a dome-lifting flourish: perhaps artfully presented black bream with chorizo, the pieces of sausage sitting on towers of spinach, or honey-glazed duck breast with tarte Tatin. Desserts continue to draw praise, including liquid-centred Valrhona chocolate soufflé, its sweetness perfectly judged, partnered by 'wonderful' ruby orange sorbet.

Detailed tasting notes point the way on a wine list that is strong on grand bottles. Forays into the New World turn up familiar names and a few unusual finds like Longview in the cool-climate Adelaide Hills. House selections start at £17.50.

Chefs: Keith Mitchell and Gerald Röser **Proprietor:** Elite Hotels **Open:** Tue to Sat 12.30 to 2, 7 to 10 **Closed:** first 2 weeks Jan **Meals:** Set L £16.50 (2 courses) to £19, Set D £35 to £55 **Service:** net prices, card slips closed **Cards:** Amex, Delta, Diners, Maestro, MasterCard, Visa **Details:** 48 seats. Private parties: 60 main room. Car park. Vegetarian meals. Children's helpings. Jacket and tie. No smoking. Wheelchair access (also WC). Music. No mobile phones **Accommodation:** 152 rooms, all with bath/shower. TV. Phone. B&B £135 to £450. Rooms for disabled. Baby facilities. Swimming pool

MAP 3 East Chiltington EAST SUSSEX

Jolly Sportsman

Chapel Lane, East Chiltington BN7 3BA
Tel: (01273) 890400
Website: www.thejollysportsman.com

Cooking 3 | Modern European | £26–£60

The narrow lanes and backdrop of the South Downs add to the rural impression of a visit to this pub-cum-restaurant, where the denizens of Lewes and Brighton vie with locals for the outside tables in summer. Although still a pub in name, especially when the sun shines and the garden comes into its own, the bar counter is small and eager diners fill the copious tables inside and on the attractive terrace. When bar nibbles include boquerones and pickled Cornish mussels it is clear that food is taken seriously. Ingredients are well sourced, with a Mediterranean flavour to much of the menu: ribollita is a hearty Italian soup, and there might be butternut squash risotto among the starters. Crispy duck confit with plum and ginger compote is a long-running main course, and local Ditchling lamb has come with an aubergine stew. Desserts shout 'restaurant' rather than 'pub', with frozen orange and ginger parfait alongside mango tarte Tatin with coconut ice cream. The wine list kicks off with house French at £11.85, has plenty of half-bottles, and shows strength in Italy, Bordeaux and Burgundy, although the ever-changing real ales in casks behind the bar are an alternative.

Chef: Richard Willis **Proprietors:** Bruce and Gwyneth Wass **Open:** Tue to Sun L 12.30 to 2 (3 Sun), Tue to Sat D 7 to 9 (10 Fri and Sat) **Closed:** 4 days Christmas **Meals:** alc (main courses £9 to £19.50). Set L Tue to Sat £12 (2 courses) to £15.75 **Service:** 10% (optional), card slips closed **Cards:** Delta, MasterCard, Maestro, Visa **Details:** 80 seats. 40 seats outside. Private parties: 60 main room, 10 to 20 private rooms. Car park. Vegetarian meals. Children's helpings. No smoking. Wheelchair access (also WC). No music. Air-conditioned

MAP 2 East Coker SOMERSET

Helyar Arms

NEW ENTRY

Moor Lane, East Coker BA22 9JR
Tel: (01935) 862332
Website: www.helyar-arms.co.uk

Cooking 1 | Modern European | £26–£54

This fifteenth-century inn with heavily mullioned windows 'has all the relaxed and friendly unpretentiousness that one hopes for in a pub'. The cooking, more modern than you would expect from the traditional surroundings, has an emphatic commitment to local, seasonal produce, such as a pheasant, venison and rabbit terrine, or a generous, well-flavoured plate of home-cured gravad lax. Main courses might include coq au vin, or char-grilled lamb leg steak with garlic and rosemary potatoes (rather heavily peppered for one diner), and there's coffee mousse, or hot Valrhona chocolate fondant pudding afterwards. Value for money is extremely good, not least in the short, lively list of wines, all offered by the glass or bottle. House wines are £11.50, and there's plenty under £20.

Chefs: Mathieu Eke and Tyrone Knight **Proprietor:** Ian McKerracher **Open:** all week 12 to 2.30 (4.30 Sun), all week (Jan to Easter Tue to Sat) 6.30 to 9.30 **Closed:** 25 Dec **Meals:** alc (main dishes £8 to £18). Bar menu available **Service:** not inc, card slips closed **Cards:** Amex, Delta, Maestro, MasterCard, Visa **Details:** 95 seats. 40 seats outside. Private parties: 55 main room, 10 to 38 private rooms. Car park. Vegetarian meals. Children's helpings. No smoking in 1 dining room. Wheelchair access (not WC). Music **Accommodation:** 6 rooms, all with bath/shower. TV. Phone. B&B £59 to £70. Baby facilities

To submit a report on any restaurant, please visit *www.which.co.uk/gfgfeedback*.

MAP 3 East Grinstead WEST SUSSEX

Gravetye Manor

Vowels Lane, East Grinstead RH19 4LJ
Tel: (01342) 810567
Website: www.gravetyemanor.co.uk

Cooking 6 | Modern British/French | £40–£83

An Elizabethan stone mansion on the Surrey–Sussex border, Gravetye was once a haven for smugglers plying the southern route into the country. Its own intrinsic splendour – all is dark oak panelling and gilt-framed mirrors within – is more than matched by the extravagant thousand or so acres in which it sits, one-thousandth of which is constituted by a walled kitchen garden supplying Mark Raffan with all the bounty of the seasons.

Other ingredients come from far and wide and are treated to lavish country-house gilding. Hebridean scallops are roasted and served with coriander purée, caramelised garlic and a port and sesame reduction, while Angus beef fillet is topped with a mousseline of Roquefort and accompanied by crisp-fried onions, braised celery and a rich red wine sauce. Autumn game showed up well at a November dinner, with both cabbage-wrapped partridge breast and loin of venison getting the nod, while fish cookery might be as simple as Dover sole dressed in herb butter or as ambitious as sea bass served with a tempura-battered soft-shell crab and sweet chilli dressing. A hot soufflé of prunes and Armagnac with mulled winter fruits is a neat idea at the chilly end of the year. Service is generally expertly coordinated and, even though some have found the genteel hush of the dining room a little stifling, there is no doubting the professionalism.

The vast, majestic wine list is a match for the surroundings, with a depth that offers real fascination for lovers of classic appellations, yet it stands up very well as a showcase for global pretenders too. Prices start at £17 (including service), and a handful of imaginative house suggestions from £20 offer a short-cut for anyone who feels overfaced.

Chef: Mark Raffan **Proprietors:** Andrew Russell and Mark Raffan **Open:** all week 12.30 to 1.45, 7.30 to 9.30 **Meals:** Set L £27 to £52, Set D £37 to £52 **Service:** net prices, card slips closed **Cards:** Amex, Delta, Maestro, MasterCard, Visa **Details:** 45 seats. Private parties: 9 to 20 private rooms. Car park. Vegetarian meals. No children under 8. Jacket and tie. No smoking. No music. No mobile phones **Accommodation:** 18 rooms, all with bath/shower. TV. Phone. Room only £100 to £325. No children under 8. Fishing

MAP 3 East Lavant WEST SUSSEX

Royal Oak

NEW ENTRY

Pook Lane, East Lavant PO18 0AX
Tel: (01243) 527434
Website: www.thesussexpub.co.uk

Cooking 3 | Modern British | £31–£60

Once the local watering hole in an off-the-beaten-track Downland village close to Goodwood, the Royal Oak has been teleported into the gastro-pub age without losing any of its original bonhomie. The menu keeps faith with tradition by offering high-class renditions of pub classics plus specials with a more modern accent. Whitebait with caper mayonnaise could open proceedings alongside seared scallops with black pudding and creamed Savoy cabbage, while main courses such as warm roast gammon with a fried egg, 'punchy' garlic mash and herb butter rub shoulders with fillets of local sea bass stacked on ratte potatoes with fine beans, lemongrass, shallots and chives. There's also skill in the dessert department, judging by home-made mango sorbet ('a master of the type') and vanilla and white chocolate brûlée with marinated strawberries. The wine list offers tantalising drinking at very 'ungreedy' prices from £11.50.

Chefs: Malcolm Goble and Oz Whatson **Proprietors:** Nick and Lisa Sutherland **Open:** all week 12 to 2.30, 6 to 9.30 **Closed:** 31 Dec **Meals:** alc (main courses £11 to £19) **Service:** not inc **Cards:** Amex, Diners, Maestro, MasterCard, Visa **Details:** 60 seats. 32 seats outside. Car park. Vegetarian meals. Children's helpings. No smoking. Wheelchair access (also WC). Music. No mobile phones **Accommodation:** 6 rooms, all with bath/shower. TV. Phone. B&B £55 to £130

MAP 2 Easton Grey WILTSHIRE

Whatley Manor

Easton Grey SN16 0RB
Tel: (01666) 822888
Website: www.whatleymanor.com

Cooking 7 | Modern European | £76–£111

There are enough facilities at Whatley Manor for the well-heeled to get bedded in against a threatened siege. As well as a spa and hydrotherapy pool, there is a 'wave dream sensory room', not to mention a 'camomile steam grotto', and fine gardens to wander through once you've been suitably cleansed.

Also on hand is Martin Burge, who has been running the kitchens since 2003, and offers contemporary French cuisine overlaid with his own tirelessly inventive personal touches. Snails might appear set in garlic mousse, topped with a red wine sauce infused with kidney, accompanied by parsley purée and garlic croutons, as one way to start. Another might involve partnering caramelised langoustines with smoked ham ravioli, and adding some braised celery and a sauce of pork juices with cider. The menu descriptions are lengthy, but crisply and precisely written, so you know what to expect. A vegetarian main course might be a pithiviers of roasted ceps with puréed butternut squash and a salad of almonds and leaves. For the rest, it isn't all familiar prime cuts, as witness a dish of stuffed trotter with mash and a deep-fried pig's ear, while fish could well be smoked cod with cockles, a caramelised scallop and chicken jus. Ring the changes at dessert stage with a 'taste of coffee and chocolate', or light out for the wilder shores with a poached pear that comes with a parfait of white chocolate and blue cheese, and further garnishes of truffle honey and candied walnuts. The wine list traverses the wine producing globe, with a good selection from Bordeaux and Italy. Prices start around £20.

There is also a less formal brasserie venue served by the same kitchen, called Le Mazot. Here, you can feast more cheaply, but no less imaginatively, on the likes of curry-buttered smoked salmon terrine with raita dressing, corn-fed chicken on creamed leeks, with wild mushrooms and a hazelnut turkey jus, and fig tart in red wine with pistachio ice cream.

Chef: Martin Burge **Proprietor:** Mr C Landolt **Open:** Wed to Sun D only 7 to 10 **Meals:** Set D £60 to £75 **Service:** 10% **Cards:** Amex, Diners, Maestro, MasterCard, Visa **Details:** 40 seats. 20 seats outside. Private parties: 30 main room. Car park. Vegetarian meals. No children under 12. Wheelchair access (also WC). Occasional music. No mobile phones **Accommodation:** 23 rooms, all with bath/shower. TV. Phone. B&B £275 to £850. Rooms for disabled. No children under 12. Swimming pool

NEW ENTRY	This appears after the restaurant's name if the establishment was not a main entry in last year's Guide, although it may have been a 'round-up/also recommended' in previous editions.

MAP 8 **East Witton** NORTH YORKSHIRE

Blue Lion

East Witton DL8 4SN
Tel: (01969) 624273
Website: www.thebluelion.co.uk

Cooking 3 | Modern British | £30–£58

Built some 200 years ago as a coaching inn and stopover for travellers on their way through Wensleydale, this stone-built watering hole still plays its part as a busy local pub – complete with flagstone floors and real ales. These days, however, it's better known for the food served in the cosy bar and the more formal candlelit restaurant. The kitchen keeps up with the times by offering Whitby crab and beetroot salad with curried lemon dressing or sautéed breast of wood pigeon with roast fig and quince chutney, before full-bodied main courses like slow-braised leg of veal with sautéed spätzli or beef and onion suet pudding with dark onion sauce. Vegetarians have their own menu and desserts could range from raspberry crème brûlée to dark chocolate and orange tart. House wine is £11.95.

Chef: John Dalby **Proprietors:** Paul and Helen Klein **Open:** Sun L 12 to 2, all week D 7 to 9 **Closed:** 25 Dec **Meals:** alc D (main courses £10 to £19). Set L Sun £18.95 **Service:** not inc **Cards:** Delta, MasterCard, Maestro, Visa **Details:** 80 seats. 30 seats outside. Private parties: 40 main room. Car park. Vegetarian meals. Children's helpings. No smoking in 1 dining room. Wheelchair access (also WC). No music **Accommodation:** 12 rooms, all with bath/shower. TV. Phone. B&B £53.50 to £99. Rooms for disabled

MAP 8 **Elland** WEST YORKSHIRE

La Cachette

31 Huddersfield Road, Elland HX5 9AW
Tel: (01422) 378833

Cooking 3 | Modern European | £23–£54

This well-established French-styled bistro/brasserie and wine bar is no longer any secret; it's become known for its bustling, friendly atmosphere, attentive service and appealing, value-for-money repertoire. Light, bright and airy, the large room has a central bar and walls hung with posters and modern art, with the emphasis on informality.

The fashionable bistro-style dishes offer something for everyone, with flexible carte and fixed-price menus. Salads, pastas and risottos vie for attention alongside mains like bacon-wrapped king scallops with sticky rice and a garlic and white wine dressing, or breast of Gressingham duck with fondant potato, chorizo and a borlotti bean sauce, or maybe plainly grilled steaks with creamed black pepper or béarnaise sauces. Desserts include old favourites like banoffi cheesecake and sticky toffee pudding. The wine list gives an equal shout to France, other European countries and the New World, and provides a mix of good-value, well-chosen bottles, including interesting finds like Châteauneuf-du-Pape from Château Maucoil (£24.90). House wines from £10.95 are listed by flavour.

Chef: Jonathan Nichols **Proprietor:** CGL Partnership **Open:** Mon to Sat 12 to 2.30, 6 to 9.30 (10 Fri/Sat) **Closed:** 26 Dec to 5 Jan, last 2 weeks Aug, bank hol Mons **Meals:** alc (main courses £8 to £17). Set L £9.95 (2 courses), Set D Mon to Thur and 6 to 7 Fri/Sat £16.95 **Service:** not inc **Cards:** Delta, Maestro, MasterCard, Visa **Details:** 85 seats. Vegetarian meals. Children's helpings. Wheelchair access (not WC). Music. Air-conditioned

MAP 6 **Ely** CAMBRIDGESHIRE

Old Fire Engine House

25 St Mary's Street, Ely CB7 4ER
Tel: (01353) 662582
Website: www.theoldfireenginehouse.co.uk

Cooking 1 | Traditional English | £35–£51

Ann Ford set up shop here in 1968 and, since then, she and Michael Jarman have run the place as an art gallery and genuine English country restaurant, offering the kind of traditional dishes that seldom surface elsewhere nowadays. The setting is a handsome eighteenth-century building close to the cathedral, and it's nothing if not informal: have a drink at the bar before wandering through the kitchen to reach your table. You might begin with mitton of pork and red onion relish or celery and Stilton soup before tackling beef and shallots braised in Adnams ale or black bream with dill and cream sauce. Portions are ample, seconds are offered and freshly cooked vegetables are appreciated. Finish off with apple pie or sherry trifle – if you can find room. The wine list kicks off with a good selection by the glass and half-bottle, and descriptions are detailed and inspiring. Prices start at £10.

Chef Terri Baker **Proprietors:** Ann Ford and Michael Jarman **Open:** all week L 12.15 to 2, Mon to Sat D 7.15 to 9.15 **Closed:** 24 Dec to 7 Jan, bank hols **Meals:** alc (main courses £15.50 to £17) **Service:** not inc **Cards:** Delta, Maestro, MasterCard, Visa **Details:** 56 seats. 20 seats outside. Private parties: 22 main room, 12 private room. Car park. Vegetarian meals. Children's helpings. No smoking. No music

MAP 3 **Emsworth** HAMPSHIRE

Fat Olives

30 South Street, Emsworth PO10 7EH
Tel: (01243) 377914
Website: www.fatolives.co.uk

Cooking 3 | Modern British | £25–£53

Bowls of truly fat green olives do indeed start the ball rolling in Lawrence and Julia Murphy's converted seventeenth-century stone cottage a short stroll from the harbour. Theirs is an enthusiastic double act: she greets, takes orders and delivers; he holds sway in the kitchen, building his menus from a bedrock of local supplies. Influences are plucked from far and wide: pigeon breast is served as a starter with roast beetroot and black treacle dressing, while seared scallops come with pea and ham fritters. Moving on, you might find star anise fish stew, braised rabbit with crosnes (Chinese artichokes) and grain mustard sauce, or brill, prawn and tarragon risotto. Desserts conjure up some exotic flavours, as in coconut bavarois with pineapple sorbet and pineapple crisps. Chilean house wines at £11.95 open the short, wide-ranging list.

Chef: Lawrence Murphy **Proprietors:** Lawrence and Julia Murphy **Open:** Tue to Sat 12 to 1.45, 7 to 9.30 **Closed:** 2 weeks at Christmas, 1 week Oct **Meals:** alc exc Sat L (main courses £12 to £18.50). Set L £15 (2 courses) to £17 **Service:** not inc, card slips closed **Cards:** Maestro, MasterCard, Visa **Details:** 28 seats. 10 seats outside. Private parties: 24 main room. Vegetarian meals. No children under 8. No smoking. Wheelchair access (not WC). Music

36 on the Quay

47 South Street, Emsworth PO10 7EG
Tel: (01243) 375592
Website: www.36onthequay.co.uk

Cooking 6 | Modern European | £38–£84

Ramon and Karen Farthing are approaching thei tenth year at this restaurant-with-rooms by th

The Which? Good Food Guide 2006 voucher £5

The Which? Good Food Guide 2006 voucher £5

The Which? Good Food Guide 2006 voucher £5

The Which? Good Food Guide 2006 voucher £5

The Which? Good Food Guide 2006 voucher £5

The Which? Good Food Guide 2006 voucher £5

The Which? Good Food Guide 2006 voucher £5

The Which? Good Food Guide 2006 voucher £5

The Which? Good Food Guide 2006 voucher £5

The Which? Good Food Guide 2006 voucher £5

The Which? Good Food Guide 2006 voucher scheme

Terms and Conditions

This voucher can only be used in participating restaurants, highlighted by the £5 symbol. It is redeemable against a pre-booked meal for a minimum of two people, provided the customer highlights the intention to use the voucher at the time of booking. Only one voucher may be used per table booked. This voucher may not be used in conjunction with any other scheme.

Offer valid from 01/11/05 to 31/10/06. For additional terms and conditions see below.

Terms and Conditions

This voucher can only be used in participating restaurants, highlighted by the £5 symbol. It is redeemable against a pre-booked meal for a minimum of two people, provided the customer highlights the intention to use the voucher at the time of booking. Only one voucher may be used per table booked. This voucher may not be used in conjunction with any other scheme.

Offer valid from 01/11/05 to 31/10/06. For additional terms and conditions see below.

Terms and Conditions

This voucher can only be used in participating restaurants, highlighted by the £5 symbol. It is redeemable against a pre-booked meal for a minimum of two people, provided the customer highlights the intention to use the voucher at the time of booking. Only one voucher may be used per table booked. This voucher may not be used in conjunction with any other scheme.

Offer valid from 01/11/05 to 31/10/06. For additional terms and conditions see below.

Terms and Conditions

This voucher can only be used in participating restaurants, highlighted by the £5 symbol. It is redeemable against a pre-booked meal for a minimum of two people, provided the customer highlights the intention to use the voucher at the time of booking. Only one voucher may be used per table booked. This voucher may not be used in conjunction with any other scheme.

Offer valid from 01/11/05 to 31/10/06. For additional terms and conditions see below.

Terms and Conditions

This voucher can only be used in participating restaurants, highlighted by the £5 symbol. It is redeemable against a pre-booked meal for a minimum of two people, provided the customer highlights the intention to use the voucher at the time of booking. Only one voucher may be used per table booked. This voucher may not be used in conjunction with any other scheme.

Offer valid from 01/11/05 to 31/10/06. For additional terms and conditions see below.

Terms and Conditions

This voucher can only be used in participating restaurants, highlighted by the £5 symbol. It is redeemable against a pre-booked meal for a minimum of two people, provided the customer highlights the intention to use the voucher at the time of booking. Only one voucher may be used per table booked. This voucher may not be used in conjunction with any other scheme.

Offer valid from 01/11/05 to 31/10/06. For additional terms and conditions see below.

Terms and Conditions

This voucher can only be used in participating restaurants, highlighted by the £5 symbol. It is redeemable against a pre-booked meal for a minimum of two people, provided the customer highlights the intention to use the voucher at the time of booking. Only one voucher may be used per table booked. This voucher may not be used in conjunction with any other scheme.

Offer valid from 01/11/05 to 31/10/06. For additional terms and conditions see below.

Terms and Conditions

This voucher can only be used in participating restaurants, highlighted by the £5 symbol. It is redeemable against a pre-booked meal for a minimum of two people, provided the customer highlights the intention to use the voucher at the time of booking. Only one voucher may be used per table booked. This voucher may not be used in conjunction with any other scheme.

Offer valid from 01/11/05 to 31/10/06. For additional terms and conditions see below.

Terms and Conditions

This voucher can only be used in participating restaurants, highlighted by the £5 symbol. It is redeemable against a pre-booked meal for a minimum of two people, provided the customer highlights the intention to use the voucher at the time of booking. Only one voucher may be used per table booked. This voucher may not be used in conjunction with any other scheme.

Offer valid from 01/11/05 to 31/10/06. For additional terms and conditions see below.

Terms and Conditions

This voucher can only be used in participating restaurants, highlighted by the £5 symbol. It is redeemable against a pre-booked meal for a minimum of two people, provided the customer highlights the intention to use the voucher at the time of booking. Only one voucher may be used per table booked. This voucher may not be used in conjunction with any other scheme.

Offer valid from 01/11/05 to 31/10/06. For additional terms and conditions see below.

Vouchers are valid from 1st November 2005 to 31st October 2006. Only one £5 voucher can be used per table booked (for a minimum of 2 people). No photocopies or any other kind of reproduction of vouchers will be accepted. Some participating establishments may exclude certain times, certain days or certain menus from the scheme so long as they a) advise customers of the restrictions at the time of booking and b) accept the vouchers at a minimum of 70% of sessions when the restaurant is open. Please note that the number of participating restaurants may vary from time to time.

harbour. Consistency is the name of the game here, from the output of the kitchen to the relaxed and professional ambience. The dining room eschews contemporary contrivances and goes in for traditional comfort and makes much of the antiquity of the 17th century building. Tables are well spaced, chairs cushioned, and brightly coloured prints adorn the wall.

Dinner starts with an appetizer, perhaps cream of asparagus soup, before Anjou pigeon breast, 'pink and full of flavour', with a virtuoso pigeon and foie gras sausage, some warm plum chutney, and a lightly spiced white game sauce. With the water visible through the bow windows, thoughts turn to seafood: John Dory, perhaps, with steamed little gems and a cannelloni filled with bacon and vegetables, langoustines, and a fennel-flavoured chowder. Poached fillet of brill is topped with a crab and lime beignet, and comes with braised celery hearts, cocotte potatoes, baby leeks and a smooth leek velouté.

Another freebie follows main courses: passion-fruit cream with raspberry jelly was a perfectly balanced taster, and set up the recipient for a complex dessert of poached peaches with moist almond sponge and praline mascarpone with a cinnamon sauce and spiced biscuits. Fruits are certainly favoured at dessert stage: hot rhubarb soufflé with rich vanilla custard and rhubarb sorbet another enticing seasonal choice. The wine list doesn't have much to offer under £20, but there are plenty of half bottles and wines by the glass. France is the focus, although the New World is more than just name-checked.

Chef: Ramon Farthing **Proprietors:** Ramon and Karen Farthing **Open:** Tue to Fri L 12 to 1.45, Mon to Sat D 6.45 to 10 **Closed:** bank hols **Meals:** Set L £17.95 (2 courses) to £21.95, Set D £42.95 to £55 **Service:** not inc **Cards:** Amex, Delta, Diners, MasterCard, Switch, Visa **Details:** 45 seats. 10 seats outside. Private parties: 45 main room, 8 to 12 private rooms. Car park. Children's helpings. No smoking. Wheelchair access (not WC). Occasional music **Accommodation:** 4 rooms, all with bath/shower. TV. B&B £65 to £115. Baby facilities

MAP 3 **Epping** ESSEX

Clocktower AR

4 Station Road, Epping CM16 4HA
Tel: (01992) 575707

Unpretentious all-day bistro food in a buzzy town-centre restaurant/bar. The menu takes in goats' cheese and red onion tart (£4.75), assorted salads (smoked duck and chicken with fig compote, for example), and plenty of big-bodied main courses like braised lamb shank, and roast cod on Mediterranean vegetables with basil dressing (£9.25). Desserts (£3.50) are things like lemon tart with raspberry coulis. House wine £11.50. Open all week 'from 11 to late'. The restaurant's elder brother is at Budworth Hall, Chipping Ongar.

MAP 1 **Ermington** DEVON

Plantation House, Matisse

Totnes Road, Ermington PL21 9NS
Tel: (01548) 831100
Email: helencoby@aol.com

Cooking 1 | Modern European | £32–£68

The Georgian severity of this former rectory's façade has been somewhat relieved by a coat of primrose paint. Facing the steeply rising hillside of the Erme valley, it boasts a rather good Adam fireplace within, with pine chairs and contemporary chandeliers bringing an up-to-date feel to the dining room. Matisse is the presiding spirit, as might be guessed, and the walls are alive with the colours of his paintings in reproduction. Start, perhaps, with a trio of strongly flavoured tartares – salmon, scallop and tuna – served in a pool of orange oil dressing. Main courses present meats in a variety of ways, Crediton free-range duck appearing as the breast meat, with some longer-cooked meat served on a little tart with plum compote. Finish with pedigree Montgomery Cheddar with apple chutney, or warm chocolate tart with shortbread and orange cream. House wines from France, Chile, Argentina and Australia, all at £14.95, head up a short, international list.

Chefs: Alan Coby and Daniel Gillard **Proprietors:** Helen and Alan Coby **Open:** Tue to Sun L 12 to 2, Mon to Sat D 7 to 9 **Closed:** 25 Dec **Meals:** alc (main courses L £10 to £16, D £17 to £22). Set D £29.95 **Service:** not inc, card slips closed **Cards:** Amex, Maestro, MasterCard, Visa **Details:** 36 seats. 20 seats outside. Private parties: 40 main room, 12 private room. Car park. Vegetarian meals. Children's helpings. No smoking. Music **Accommodation:** 10 rooms, all with bath/shower. TV. Phone. B&B £50 to £119

MAP 2 **Eton** BERKSHIRE

Gilbey's

82–83 High Street, Eton SL4 6AF
Tel: (01753) 855182

Gilbey's is a wine merchants who import direct from France – so expect decent drinking at keen prices (from £10.65). Menus promise modern dishes including chicken and pistachio terrine with date chutney (£6.50), seared scallops with crab and rocket risotto (£18), and lemon tart with mixed berry compote (£5). Two-course lunches £11.75. Close to the Thames, between Eton College and Windsor Castle. Open all week.

MAP 5 **Evesham** WORCESTERSHIRE

Evesham Hotel

AR

Cooper's Lane, Evesham WR11 1DA
Tel: (01386) 765566

The Jenkinsons have been in residence at this delightfully quirky Cotswolds hotel for 30 years and thankfully show no signs of calling it a day. Weekly menus read like jottings from a cook's tour complete with wacky comments: 'air, land and sea' salad (£6), poached sea bass Andrea (in a crust of pine nuts and basil; £14.25), roast cushion of venison, and Turkish flan (a type of egg custard; £4.75) are typical. The monumental wine list has grown to 'just under 1,000 bins', housed in four photograph albums; prices from £14.50. Open all week.

MAP 1 **Exeter** DEVON

Brazz

10–12 Palace Gate, Exeter EX1 1JA
Tel: (01392) 252525
Website: www.brazz.co.uk

Cooking 2 | Modern Brasserie | £25–£54

A circular aquarium and a blue domed ceiling catch the eye in this hip brasserie laid out on two floors linked by a winding staircase. There has been a change of chef since the last edition of the Guide, but the original menu remains: graze on nibbles, choose a 'light bite' such as oak-smoked salmon with soda bread or go for the full works. Salads, eggs and pasta share the billing with seafood (roast sea bass with Pink Fir potatoes and spring greens), grills and dishes like pan-fried duck breast with red cabbage. Desserts range from poached pear with creamed rice pudding to home-made ice creams. Service can be off the ball. The succinct modern wine list starts at £11.95. There are branches in Taunton and Cardiff.

Chef: Mark Pulman **Proprietor:** Brazz plc **Open:** all week 12 to 3, 6 to 10.30 (11 Fri and Sat) **Closed:** 25 Dec **Meals:** alc (main courses £6.50 to £17) **Service:** 10% (optional), card slips closed **Cards:** Amex, Delta, Maestro, MasterCard, Visa **Details:** 150 seats. Private parties: 150 main room. Car park. Vegetarian meals. Children's helpings. No smoking. Wheelchair access (also WC). Music. Air-conditioned

The Royal Clarence Hotel, Michael Caines Restaurant

Cathedral Yard, Exeter EX1 1HD
Tel: (01392) 310031
Website: www.michaelcaines.com

Cooking 5 | French | £35–£91

This place makes a feature of its proximity to the cathedral, with diverting artworks and photographs depicting its stonework in various lights deployed throughout. A spacious Champagne Bar sets the opulent tone, while the main dining room is discreetly spotlit, with elegant classical table settings.

Michael Caines, master-chef of Gidleigh Park (see entry, Chagford), is expanding his empire into boutique hotels, with locations in Canterbury and Glasgow due to join the Royal Clarence in the new ABode group. Refurbishment of the rooms and public areas is underway here in Exeter as we go to press. Continuity remains in the kitchen, though, with Simon Dow in charge day to day, where a modern repertoire with the accent on balance makes excellent use of West Country produce. Start with tian of crab and tomato with avocado mousse and Sevruga, or try veal sweetbreads with shallot and mustard confit and sherry sauce. Fine raw materials might include Devon Ruby Red beef Rossini-style, garnished with celeriac and a madeira sauce, or roast sea bass on crushed olive potatoes with saffron onions and bouillabaisse sauce; vegetables are extra. Sophisticated desserts have included poached fig in spiced red wine with chestnut parfait and orange nougatine. Vegetarian menus offer good choice, and staff are amiable and professionally attentive. If you make it past the slate of Dom Pérignon vintages, financial relief comes in the form of seven red and white house wines at £16.50 (£3.95 per standard glass).

Chef: Simon Dow **Proprietor:** Michael Caines **Open:** Mon to Sat 12 to 2.30, 7 to 10 **Meals:** alc (main courses £18 to £25). Set L £17.50 (2 courses) to £21.50, Set D £58 **Service:** not inc, 12.5% (optional) for parties of 10 or more **Cards:** Amex, Delta, Diners, Maestro, MasterCard, Visa **Details:** 65 seats. Private parties: 80 main room, 10 to 30 private rooms. Vegetarian meals. Children's helpings. No smoking. Wheelchair access (also WC). No music. No mobile phones. Air-conditioned **Accommodation:** 53 rooms, all with bath/shower. TV. Phone. B&B £85 to £180. Rooms for disabled. Baby facilities

St Olaves Hotel

Mary Arches Street, Exeter EX4 3AZ
Tel: (01392) 217736

A new regime is making its mark at this intimate hotel in a listed building close to the city centre. The Treasury Restaurant offers fixed-price menus (dinner £27.50/£31.95) along the lines of smoked salmon on potato and spring onion rösti with mustard leaf salad, then spiced Gressingham duck breast with honey and a roast peach on braised chicory and melon jus, before desserts like espresso semifreddo with cinnamon doughnuts. Lighter daytime dishes also available. Open all week.

Thai Orchid

Three Gables, 5 Cathedral Yard, Exeter EX1 1HJ
Tel: (01392) 214215

Thai food in a sixteenth-century stonemason's cottage by the cathedral. Expansion was imminent and new chefs were expected as the Guide went to press, but expect a long menu covering all the staples of the cuisine. Look for sesame-coated minced pork toasts, hot and spicy squid salad (£5.50), stir-fries including crab with roast chillies (£9) and curries such as chicken with roast peanuts and sweet potato. Nine accessible set menus (from £18.50) and Guayteaw noodle lunches (from £7.50). House wine £12.50. Closed Sat L and all Sun.

MAP 5 **Fairford** GLOUCESTERSHIRE

Allium

1 London Street, Fairford GL7 4AH
Tel: (01285) 712200
Website: www.allium.uk.net

Cooking 6 | Modern European | £30–£82

'Allium is a secret I wish I could keep,' writes a reporter, 'but I think I've pointed half of Gloucestershire in the Fairford direction since eating here.' The Grahams opened here in spring 2004, in a pair of ancient houses at one end of the market square. The combination of Cotswold stone and an interior vision of mellow pastels and crisp linen is always likely to prove an irresistible one, the more so when the cooking combines great technical aplomb with a real sense of value for money.

Dishes aim to entice rather than to baffle, with fine renditions of lobster bisque, langoustine ravioli, and rich, warming daube of beef, a winter dish that centred on 'perfectly matured and precisely seasoned' meat. A summer main course that combined crisply seared halibut with warm potato and bacon salad and a smoothly intense purée of ceps impressed for its technical polish. A nice balance of the straightforward and the complex on the menus results in salmon with asparagus and peas being offered alongside a dish of veal sweetbreads wrapped in Parma ham served with a Tatin of red onions, carrot purée and a foaming sauce lit up with roast garlic. Presentation is a strength, witness a dessert of a whole poached peach with a spoonful of basil cream where the stone once was, almond ice cream on a biscuit base, and a row of raspberry jelly cubes. Desserts all come with their own suggested wine matches.

France is the first love of the wine list and dessert wines are a speciality, but the list globetrots from England to India via all the more familiar sources, giving a thorough account of the state of play at every stop, with contemporary names like Planeta and Heartland to the fore. Around 20 options come by the glass or carafe, and bottles start at £16.

Chef: James Graham **Proprietors:** James and Erica Graham, and Nick Bartimote **Open:** Wed to Sun 12 to 2, 7 to 9 **Meals:** Set L £15 (2 courses) to £17.50, Set D Wed and Thur £20 to £50, Set D Fri and Sat £28.50 (2 courses) to £50, Set D Sun £20 to £32.50 **Service:** not inc, card slips closed **Cards:** Delta, Maestro, MasterCard, Visa **Details:** 34 seats. Private parties: 30 main room, 8 to 10 private rooms. Vegetarian meals. Children's helpings. No smoking in 1 dining room. Occasional music. No mobile phones

MAP 1 Falmouth CORNWALL

Three Mackerel

Swanpool Beach, Falmouth TR11 5BG
Tel: (01326) 311886

Bright white weatherboarded café perched above Swanpool Beach, with stunning views and 'jazzy décor'. Cornwall's renowned iridescent fish naturally puts in an appearance, and the maritime contingent extends to seared scallops and black pudding salad (£7). Meat also gets a fair outing in the shape of roast rack of lamb with provençale vegetables (£14) and fillet of beef on tarragon and horseradish mash. Tapas are also available, and desserts have included treacle and toasted almond tart (£4). House wine £10.95. Open all week.

MAP 3 Farnborough KENT

Chapter One

Farnborough Common, Locksbottom,
Farnborough BR6 8NF
Tel: (01689) 854848
Website: www.chaptersrestaurants.co.uk

Cooking 5 | Modern European | £30–£50

Contrary to the implication in last year's Guide entry, Chapter One has never been a pub. What its mock-Tudor magnificence has been, since 2000, is home to Andrew McLeish's justly acclaimed cooking, which uses prime ingredients in novel and purposeful ways. Lobster ravioli with a cognac-laced sauce might be unexpectedly paired with cauliflower purée, while a boudin of sweetbreads and ham hock comes with raspberry and walnut salad. The range of choice among main-course meats and fish is cheering indeed: a winter menu ran from black bream with braised beans, pancetta and cep dressing to a poached and roasted saddle of rabbit with confit leg, glazed salsify and a sauce of Gewürztraminer. Desserts are no less creative, with blood orange trifle, chocolate marquise with Kirsched cherries, or caramel and sea salt parfait with toasted marshmallows. The French-led wine list boasts some pedigree bottles and punctiliously notes those New World wines that have been sealed under screwcaps; prices start from £13.95. There is also a brasserie on the site, and a sister restaurant, Chapter Two, in Blackheath (see entry, London).

Chef: Andrew McLeish **Proprietor:** Selective Restaurants Group **Open:** all week 12 to 2.30 (2.45 Sun), 6.30 to 10 (9 Sun) **Closed:** 2 to 6 Jan **Meals:** Set L £16.50 (2 courses) to £19.95 Set L Sun £16.95, Set D £26.95, Set D Sun £22.95; brasserie menu available Mon to Sat 12 to 3 **Service:** 12.5% (optional), card slips closed **Cards:** Amex, Delta, Diners, Maestro, MasterCard, Visa **Details:** 120 seats. Private parties: 20 to 55 private rooms. Car park. Vegetarian meals. Children's helpings. No smoking. Wheelchair access (not WC). Music. Air-conditioned

MAP 2 Farnham DORSET

Museum Inn

Farnham DT11 8DE
Tel: (01725) 516261
Website: www.museuminn.co.uk

Cooking 5 | Modern European | £34–£55

In a hamlet of thatched houses, the tall, red-brick inn stands out. It was built by Augustus Pitt-Rivers, the progenitor of modern archaeology, who set up a museum nearby to house his collections, and retains its seventeenth-century integrity in the form of flagged floors, an inglenook and a bread oven.

Mark Treasure's cooking is a nice mix of English domestic and Mediterranean ways, with yellow split-pea soup and streaky bacon cropping up among the likes of mozzarella risotto with pine nuts and Parmesan, or blue cheese fettuccine with zucchini and pesto. The place's identity as an inn is expressed in simply prepared main courses like plaice in beer batter with mushy peas and chips, or ribeye steak with horseradish butter, but there are usually one or two more obvious restaurant dishes, like the slow-roast belly pork with creamed Savoy cabbage in a sauce of garlic, parsley and madeira that appeared on a winter menu. Treats to finish include Granny Smith and black treacle tart dolloped with whipped cream, or tiramisù lit up with Amaretto. A dozen house wines start at £12, but the rest of the enterprising list has plenty to offer below £25.

Chef: Mark Treasure **Proprietors:** Mark Stephenson and Vicky Elliot **Open:** all week 12 to 2 (3 Sun), 7 to 9.30 **Closed:** 25 Dec, 26 Dec D, 31 Dec D **Meals:** alc (main courses £13.50 to £22.50) **Service:** not inc **Cards:** Delta, Maestro, MasterCard, Visa **Details:** 90 seats. 40 seats outside. Private parties: 40 main room. Car park. Vegetarian meals. No children under 5. No smoking in dining room. Wheelchair access (also WC). No music. No mobile phones **Accommodation:** 8 rooms, all with bath/shower. TV. Phone. B&B £75 to £140. Rooms for disabled. No children under 5

MAP 3 **Farnham Royal** BUCKINGHAMSHIRE

King of Prussia

NEW ENTRY

Blackpond Lane, Farnham Royal SL2 3EG
Tel: (01753) 643006
Website: www.thekingofprussia.com

Cooking 2 | British | £32–£62

One glance will tell you that the King of Prussia is 'no ordinary boozer': in leafy Farnham Royal, it has been given a polished new look by celeb chef Phil Vickery and a couple of local residents. The kitchen deals in trencherman helpings of pub dishes with a pronounced retro feel: mighty chargrilled Barnsley chop, burger with red onion jam, and chicken, leek and pea pie, for example. Twice-baked blue cheese soufflé is a good version, and the kitchen goes to town with desserts such as baked egg custard tart with green apple crumble ice cream and 'Phil's favourite pudding' (Carnation condensed milk rocky road marshmallow brownies with vanilla crème fraîche dip and raspberry beer). Cheery, well-informed staff deserve a round of applause. The wine list is a balanced, international spread with prices from around £13.

Chef: Andy Knight **Proprietors:** Phil Vickery, David Gibbs and Chris Boot **Open:** all week L 12 to 2, Mon to Sat D 6.30 to 9.15 **Meals:** alc (main courses £9 to £20) **Service:** not inc **Cards:** Amex, Delta, Maestro, MasterCard, Visa **Details:** 75 seats. 50 seats outside. Private parties: 45 main room. Car park. Vegetarian meals. Children's helpings. No smoking. Wheelchair access (not WC). Music

MAP 3 **Faversham** KENT

Read's

Macknade Manor, Canterbury Road, Faversham ME13 8XE
Tel: (01795) 535344
Website: www.reads.com

Cooking 6 | Modern British | £35–£95

The elegant Georgian house, fronted by lawns and mature trees, has an interior that is agreeable without appearing to contribute to the cost of a meal. Tables are well spaced and impeccably set, and visitors who stay over report back with tales of comfort and tranquillity. David Pitchford's cooking stands out from the crowd not least because he starts with high-quality raw materials, and he takes seasonality and local ingredients seriously. Dishes are frequently complex but never fussy, and flavours are fine-tuned so that they balance rather than compete with each other: for example, in a starter of grilled fillets of red mullet in a bouillabaisse sauce, served with a salad of fennel with rouille and croûtons. Contrasts are well handled: duckling comes as confit of leg teamed with red cabbage, the breast sliced on Puy lentils, and accompanied by a tarte Tatin of turnips with foie gras. The kitchen garden's contribution has included quince (as a purée with roast loin of organic pork), while home-made tomato ketchup (with salmon fishcakes) and piccalilli (with a chicken terrine) are just part of the output of this industrious kitchen. Desserts shine too, in the forms of warm parkin with new season's champagne rhubarb and rhubarb ripple ice cream, or caramelised mille-feuille of bitter chocolate and poached pears with orange cream and pistachios. Lunch is a simpler affair, and service, led by Rona Pitchford, is 'friendly and knowledgeable'.

Choose from a 'best buys' section of the wine list if you are on a budget (prices range from £16 to £28), although pricing remains restrained for the many fine French wines on the full selection, which also sees a good contribution from Australia and shorter round-ups elsewhere.

Chef: David Pitchford **Proprietors:** Rona and David Pitchford **Open:** Tue to Sat 12 to 2, 7 to 9.30 **Closed:** 25 and 26 Dec, 1 Jan **Meals:** Set L £21, Set D £45 to £69 (inc wine) **Service:** not inc, card slips closed **Cards:** Amex, Delta, Diners, Maestro, MasterCard, Visa **Details:** 40 seats. 18 seats outside. Private parties: 60 main room, 12 to 32 private rooms. Car park. Children's helpings. No-smoking area. Wheelchair access (also WC). No music. No mobile phones **Accommodation:** 6 rooms, all with bath/shower. TV. Phone. B&B £120 to £170

MAP 5 **Fawsley** NORTHAMPTONSHIRE

Fawsley Hall, Knightley Restaurant

Fawsley NN11 3BA
Tel: (01327) 892000
Website: www.fawsleyhall.com

Cooking 5 | Modern European | £41–£80

A little way south of Daventry, this ravishing Tudor edifice makes the most of its historical venerability. Although there are possibly a few too many reproduction portraits of Henry VIII's wives hung about, it manages not to feel like a Tudor theme park. The open fires, mullioned windows and well-set-up dining room combine to make a pretty spectacular effect. Great British ingredients form the foundation of Philip Dixon's cooking, which brings in influences from the favoured corners of Europe in a style that shows a pleasing degree of refinement. Poached baby Rocha pear with Beenleigh Blue and walnut foam is a nice new spin on the old Roquefort, walnut and pear idea, while a terrine of Blythburgh estate free-range pork with pear chutney has the earthy authenticity of French country cooking.

Some of the elements in dishes will raise eyebrows, as when scallops appear with white chocolate and caviar, or Angus beef with orange-flavoured mash, but the ideas seem to work. Finish with dandelion and burdock soufflé with lemon sorbet, or a high-intensity Calvados savarin with cider sorbet. The main wine list is arranged by style and runs from appealing basics to some smart bottles, while a section optimistically entitled 'Affordable Excess' steps up to another level. Ten house options under £20 also come by the glass.

Chef: Philip Dixon **Proprietor:** Simon Lowe **Open:** all week 12 to 2.30, 7 to 9.30 **Meals:** alc (main courses L £14 to £16, D £18 to £25.50). Set D £35 to £49.50 **Service:** 12.5% (optional) **Cards:** Amex, Delta, Maestro, MasterCard, Visa **Details:** 70 seats. 30 seats outside. Private parties: 70 main room, 8 to 150 private rooms. Car park. Vegetarian meals. Children's helpings. No smoking. Wheelchair access (also WC). Music. No mobile phones **Accommodation:** 43 rooms, all with bath/shower. TV. Phone. B&B £145 to £425. Rooms for disabled

MAP 3 **Fernhurst** SURREY

King's Arms

Midhurst Road, Fernhurst GU27 3HA
Tel: (01428) 652005
Website: www.kingsarmsfernhurst.com

Cooking 2 | Modern British | £29–£52

Set in pretty countryside near Haslemere, the King's Arms is an attractive, unspoilt, unpretentious stone-built pub with low beams and tightly packed tables. A long blackboard menu offers plenty of choice, starters ranging from simple asparagus hollandaise to field mushrooms with Stilton and bacon, or a warm salad of crispy duck with honey and soy, while mains take in everything from devilled kidneys, or beer-battered cod and chips, to crisp pork belly with black pudding and mustard mash, or roast goose with roast potatoes. An inspection meal found all dishes well executed, with consistently high-quality ingredients and robust flavours, rounding off with a satisfyingly rich melt-in-the-mouth chocolate cheesecake. Service is friendly, efficient and knowledgeable and wines are a reasonably priced bunch, starting at £12.

Chef: Michael Hirst **Proprietors:** Michael and Annabel Hirst **Open:** all week L 12 to 2.30, Mon to Sat D 7 to 9.30 **Closed:** 25 Dec **Meals:** alc (main courses £9 to £18) **Service:** not inc **Cards:** Delta, MasterCard, Maestro, Visa **Details:** 45 seats. 60 seats outside. Private parties: 28 main room, up to 12 private rooms. Car park. Vegetarian meals. Children's helpings; no children under 14 at D. No smoking in 1 dining room. Wheelchair access (not WC). No music

MAP 9 **Ferrensby** NORTH YORKSHIRE

General Tarleton

Boroughbridge Road, Ferrensby HG5 0PZ
Tel: (01423) 340284
Website: www.generaltarleton.co.uk

Cooking 4 | Modern British | £28–£48

Known affectionately as 'The GT', this civilised inn not far from the A1 runs smoothly in the capable hands of chef/proprietor and 'local boy' John Topham. Seasonal Yorkshire produce is at the heart of his business: 'our goal is to try and ensure that 80% of our food is grown/reared within a 20-mile radius,' he writes. Sweet Yorkshire ham knuckle and foie gras terrine with Cumberland sauce, and a duo of Dales lamb with baby vegetables, garlic and thyme jus, or maybe butter-roast cod fillet with prawn and chive beurre blanc, typify the dinner menu in the beamy, low-ceilinged restaurant. Desserts could feature chocolate torte with orange crème fraîche, or a rhubarb trio of crème brûlée, crumble and compote. The wine list is serious and helpfully annotated, with plenty of variety and prices that won't intimidate the enthusiastic drinker; ten house wines start at £12.95.

Lighter dishes appear on the bar/brasserie menu, which is supplemented by a board of daily fish specials like roast cod with creamed butter beans, egg and aïoli, or grilled grey mullet with herb risotto and salsa verde.

 This symbol means that accommodation is available at this establishment.

Chef: John Topham **Proprietors:** John and Claire Topham **Open:** Sun L 12 to 2.15, Mon to Sat D 6 to 9.30. **Meals:** Set L Sun £18.95, Set D £29.95. Bar/brasserie alc menu available all week L, Mon to Sat D **Service:** not inc **Cards:** Amex, Delta, Maestro, MasterCard, Visa **Details:** 70 seats. 40 seats outside. Private parties: 36 main room, 2 to 40 private rooms. Car park. Vegetarian meals. Children's helpings. No smoking. Wheelchair access (not WC). No music **Accommodation:** 14 rooms, all with bath/shower. TV. Phone. B&B £85 to £120

MAP 3 **Fletching** EAST SUSSEX

Griffin Inn

Fletching TN22 3SS
Tel: (01825) 722890
Website: www.thegriffininn.co.uk

Cooking 2 | Modern European | £32–£58

The sixteenth-century Griffin is, in every way, a very English inn, and it maintains a home-from-home atmosphere. The kitchen cares about the provenance of its supplies, and the owners now run their own market garden. Mediterranean influences loom large on the daily-changing menus, as in a neat starter of seared scallops with pea purée, crispy Parma ham and parsley oil. The quality also shows in dishes like organic veal chop with potato and parsnip purée and capers, and Somerset beef fillet with a cube of gratin dauphinois, braised endive and an 'honestly made' thyme and red wine jus. To finish, there are desserts like cherry and almond tart. Some dishes cross over on to the separate bar menu, which also features superior versions of pub classics. The wine list runs from an overachieving pub dozen by the bottle (from £10.80) or glass (from £2.90) to a handful of knockout fine wines. The middle ground is occupied by well-reviewed bottles from around the world at fair prices.

Chefs: Andrew Billings and Amanda Mott **Proprietors:** Bridget and Nigel Pullan **Open:** all week L 12 to 2.30, Mon to Sat D 7 to 9.30 **Closed:** 25 Dec, D 1 Jan **Meals:** alc exc Sun L (main courses £10.50 to £20). Set L Mon to Fri Jan to Mar £12.50 (2 courses), Set L Sun £25. Bar menu available **Service:** not inc **Cards:** Amex, Delta, Diners, Maestro, MasterCard, Visa **Details:** 60 seats. 30 seats outside. Private parties: 30 main room. Car park. Vegetarian meals. Children's helpings. No smoking. Wheelchair access (also WC). Occasional music. No mobile phones **Accommodation:** 8 rooms, all with bath/shower. TV. B&B £60 to £130. Rooms for disabled. Baby facilities

MAP 8 **Forton** LANCASHIRE

Bay Horse Inn

Bay Horse, Forton LA2 0HR
Tel: (01524) 791204
Website: www.bayhorseinn.com

Cooking 3 | Modern British | £28–£55

In a tiny hamlet only minutes from the M6, the Bay Horse is a respectable and immaculately maintained gastro-pub. It literally feeds off its location, for one look at the menu tells you that the kitchen is proud of Lancastrian and North Country produce: fillet of Lytham sea bass is served with potato purée, grilled asparagus, saffron and truffle dressing, while roast Goosnargh chicken breast comes with fondant potato, buttered spinach and tarragon cream, and the list extends to Morecambe Bay shrimps, Lune Valley venison and Cumbrian fell-bred beef. Craig Wilkinson is also going 'back to basics' with traditional recipes like Lancashire hot pot and potted Morecambe Bay shrimps supercharged with brandy and chives. Plentiful desserts range from set vanilla yoghurt with honey and Sauternes jelly to warm treacle and walnut tart. The wine list provides fair back-up at prices starting from £11.95.

Chefs: Craig Wilkinson and Matthew Illingworth **Proprietors:** Brian, Mae and Craig Wilkinson **Open:** Tue to Sun L 12 to 1.45, Tue to Sat D 7 to 9.15 **Meals:** alc (not Sun L; main courses L £10 to £13, D £14 to £18.95), set L £18.50, Sun £13.95 to £17.90. Light L menu available **Service:** not inc, 10% for parties of 8 or more, card slips closed **Cards:** Amex, Delta, Maestro, MasterCard, Visa **Details:** 50 seats. 26 seats outside. Private parties: 26 main room, 10 to 26 private rooms. Car park. Vegetarian meals. No smoking. No children in bar. Wheelchair access (not WC). Occasional music

MAP 6 **Fotheringhay** NORTHAMPTONSHIRE

Falcon

Fotheringhay PE8 5HZ
Tel: (01832) 226254
Website: www.huntsbridge.com

Cooking 3 | Modern European | £29–£56

After his trips to the Piedmont and Tuscany, chef and co-patron Ray Smikle's Mediterranean cooking has a more Italian slant. The 'eat what you like – no minimum orders' approach certainly

helps, as does the choice of where to eat: dining room, sunny conservatory extension, bar or garden. Generous, unpretentious, colourful cooking is the Smikle style, enhanced by that Italianate touch; take risotto of salmon, cockles, clams, peas, tarragon, crème fraîche and prosecco for openers, and move on to chargrilled beef liver and Parmesan polenta with grilled asparagus and sage butter, or whole roast sea bass complemented by lemon-roast Jersey Royals and braised spinach. Desserts continue the sunny theme, perhaps vanilla pannacotta with strawberries and grappa.

'Please experiment,' instructs the wine list, and few would demur, given the imaginative slate by the glass and inspiring mix of stars, newcomers and curiosities, split into under-£20 and 'top-class' selections.

Chef: Ray Smikle **Proprietors:** John Hoskins and Ray Smikle **Open:** all week 12 to 2, 6.30 to 9.30 **Meals:** alc (main courses £10 to £19). Set L Mon to Sat £12.50 (2 courses). Snack menu available **Service:** not inc **Cards:** Amex, Diners, Maestro, MasterCard, Visa **Details:** 70 seats. 30 seats outside. Private parties: 50 main room, 30 private room. Car park. Vegetarian meals. Children's helpings. No smoking. No music. No mobile phones

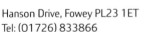

MAP 1 **Fowey** CORNWALL

Fowey Hall Hotel & Restaurant AR

Hanson Drive, Fowey PL23 1ET
Tel: (01726) 833866

Luxury hotel high above the village with views over the estuary and beyond. New chef Glynn Wellington sticks to the established set dinner at £32.50 based around local ingredients from both land and sea, with a number of choices at each course: perhaps Fowey River mussels, followed by Cornish beef fillet with parsnip purée, wild mushrooms and roast garlic, then pannacotta with local rhubarb. Lunch brings on lighter dishes and sandwiches. Ambitious wine list from £16. Open all week.

Marina Hotel, Waterside

17 Esplanade, Fowey PL23 1HY
Tel: (01726) 833315
Website: www.themarinahotel.co.uk

Cooking 3 | Seafood | £37–£89

The Esplanade address may give first-timers the wrong impression about the hotel's setting on the narrowest of back streets, but the Marina's crowning glory is its spectacular views over the estuary from the dining room at the back. There's a compact bar and equally small nautical-themed lounge, while the dining room has window tables on two sides (try to bag one when reserving) offering those 'absolutely lovely' vistas. Any décor would be no match (here they've gone for neutral tones), while a trompe l'oeil mural on one wall helps to compensate those not on a window table. Chris Eden heads the kitchen and, considering the location, the menu not unsurprisingly comes awash with the freshest of seafood (though there are non-fish options too). Perfectly timed pan-fried sea bass comes on a bed of fennel and dill and topped by a prawn raviolo, garnished with carrot purée and watercress velouté, while meat might be represented among main courses by fillet of beef in a red wine jus with rosemary-infused potatoes and truffle butter. Starters range from crab and basil cannelloni to a 'fussy' dish of saddle of rabbit with olives, red peppers, peas and bacon, while 'St Endillion' lemon cheesecake with lemon beignets and yoghurt sorbet might head up desserts. Service is 'very pleasant', and the French-led, globetrotting wine list offers around a dozen by the glass and bottle prices from £16.50, although most are on the wrong side of £20.

Chef: Chris Eden **Proprietor:** S. Westwell **Open:** all week 12 to 2.30, 6.30 to 10 **Meals:** Set L £24.95, Set D £32 to £38.95 **Service:** not inc, card slips closed **Cards:** Amex, Maestro, MasterCard, Visa **Details:** 40 seats. 16 seats outside. Private parties: 40 main room. Children's helpings. Music. No mobile phones **Accommodation:** 18 rooms, all with bath/shower. TV. Phone. B&B £72 to £188. Fishing

AR	Not a full entry but provisionally recommended (known as 'round-ups' in previous editions, these 'also recommended' establishments are now integrated throughout the book).

Old Quay House **NEW ENTRY**

28 Fore Street, Fowey PL23 1AQ
Tel: (01726) 833302
Website: www.theoldquayhouse.com

Cooking 2 | Modern British | £40–£70

The restaurant at this 'contemporary boutique hotel' looks the business, with its blond wood, interesting artefacts, dark sea-grass chairs and picture windows overlooking the estuary. The kitchen is also making its mark, and local fish gets a good airing in the shape of, say, sweet roast scallops with marinated fennel, slivers of radish and shellfish bisque, or crisp-skinned fillet of roast black bream with dried tomatoes and a fricassee of squid and chickpeas. Alternatives appear in the guise of roast fillet of lamb with persillade of spring vegetables and boulangère potatoes ('what a good dish!' enthused a reporter), or poached breast of local chicken with herb butter. Bitter chocolate tart with home-made cherry ice cream makes a pleasant finish. The modest wine list covers a lot of territory, with prices from £13.50.

Chefs: Ben Bass and Peter Bublik **Proprietors:** Jane and Roy Carson **Open:** Sat and Sun L 12.30 to 2.30, all week D 7 to 9 **Meals:** alc (main courses L £8 to £10, D £15 to £21) **Service:** not inc, card slips closed, 10% for parties of 6 or more **Cards:** Amex, Delta, Maestro, MasterCard, Visa **Details:** 38 seats. 38 seats outside. Vegetarian meals. No children under 12 at D. No smoking. Wheelchair access (not WC). Music. No mobile phones **Accommodation:** 12 rooms, all with bath/shower. TV. Phone. B&B £120 to £200. No children under 12

MAP 2 Frampton Mansell GLOUCESTERSHIRE

White Horse

Cirencester Road, Frampton Mansell GL6 8HZ
Tel: (01285) 760960
Website: www.cotswoldwhitehorse.com

Cooking 2 | Modern British | £27–£50

A shellfish tank (à la Rick Stein) has now been added to the culinary armoury of this aspiring Cotswold gastropub. It harbours clams, mussels, oysters and crabs, as well as lobsters (the last are generally served simply with garlic, lemon and herb butter). Other sea creatures get more contemporary treatment: seared marlin is accompanied by pineapple and chilli relish, salmon comes with pea purée, chorizo and chive cream sauce. On the meat front, expect all sorts from chicken breast with curried butternut squash and coriander cream sauce to pork and leek sausages with spring onion mash. Starters could include hot cheese fritters with wholegrain mustard sauce, while desserts might feature pistachio crème brûlée with chocolate sauce. The décor is an eclectic blend of 'the traditional and the trendy'; service is willing and on-the-ball. Wines are arranged by style, with prices from £11.75 (£2.95 a glass).

Chef: Howard Matthews **Proprietors:** Emma and Shaun Davis **Open:** all week L 12 to 2.30 (3 Sun), Mon to Sat D 7 to 9.45 **Closed:** 24 to 26 Dec, 1 Jan **Meals:** alc (main courses £9.50 to £15). Bar menu available **Service:** not inc **Cards:** Delta, Maestro, MasterCard, Visa **Details:** 45 seats. 50 seats outside. Private parties: 25 main room. Car park. Children's helpings. No smoking. No music

MAP 6 Fressingfield SUFFOLK

Fox and Goose

Fressingfield IP21 5PB
Tel: (01379) 586247
Website: www.foxandgoose.net

Cooking 3 | Modern British | £24–£61

Five centuries of history and a 'marvellous' rural location make this one-time guildhall beside the village church a highly attractive prospect. Paul Yaxley is making the most of its attributes, and the interior still has a sense of deep-rooted antiquity. By contrast, the cooking is up-to-the-minute, and there's plenty of painstaking work and dedication behind the scenes: red mullet is served with mussel tempura, crushed aubergine and a pistachio and mint pesto, while mains run to beef fillet with sprouting broccoli topped with Gorgonzola rarebit or a trio of pork (fillet, belly and cheek) served with apple and black pudding mash and red onion marmalade. And there's no slackening when it comes to desserts like hot chocolate pudding served with a chocolate 'cigarette' and rosemary and caramel ice cream. 'Unfailingly good' service continues to win applause, and the well-considered wine list shows an enthusiast's handprint; house selections are from £12.50.

Chef/Proprietor: Paul Yaxley **Open:** Tue to Sun 12 to 2 (1.45 Sat), 7 to 8.30 (8.45 Fri, 9 Sat; 6.30 to 8.15 Sun) **Meals:** alc (not Sun L; main courses £10.95 to £17.50). Set L £11.50 (2 courses) to £13.95, Set L Sun £12.95 (2 courses) to £15.95, Set D £35 **Service:** not inc, card slips closed **Cards:** Delta, Maestro, MasterCard, Visa **Details:** 48 seats. 12 seats outside. Private parties: 28 main room, 12 to 16 private rooms. Car park. Vegetarian meals. Children's helpings. No children under 9 at D. No smoking. Wheelchair access (also WC). Music

MAP 3 Funtington WEST SUSSEX

Hallidays

Watery Lane, Funtington PO18 9LF
Tel: (01243) 575331

Cooking 2 | Modern British | £30–£55

The address suggests picture-postcard 'Olde England' – as befits the terrace of ancient thatched cottages housing this downland village restaurant. Local and regional ingredients are at the heart of the enterprise, and the industrious kitchen's skills also run to baking and fish-curing. Soups have a seasonal ring (perhaps Jerusalem artichoke and hazelnut), otherwise you might start with twice-baked Stilton soufflé or galantine of guinea fowl and foie gras with red onion chutney. Main courses follow suit with, say, herb-crusted sea bass and saffron butter sauce or confit of Barbary duck with quince relish and port sauce, while desserts could run to mango and pineapple crème pot. The wide-ranging, international wine list opens with seven house recommendations from £11.75 to £13.50.

Chef: Andy Stephenson **Proprietors:** Andy Stephenson and Peter Creech **Open:** Wed to Fri and Sun L 12 to 1.15, Wed to Sat D 7 to 9.15 **Closed:** 2 wks Mar, 1 wk late Aug **Meals:** alc L (not Sun; main courses £16.50 to £18). Set L £15 (2 courses) to £18, Set L Sun £19, Set D £25 (2 courses) to £29 **Service:** not inc **Cards:** Delta, Maestro, MasterCard, Visa **Details:** 26 seats. Private parties: 16 main room. Car park. No smoking. Wheelchair access (also WC). No music

 This symbol means that there are some restrictions on smoking though it may be allowed in some eating areas.

MAP 10 Gateshead TYNE & WEAR

Baltic, Rooftop Restaurant

Centre for Contemporary Arts, South Shore Road, Gateshead NE8 3BA
Tel: (0191) 440 4949
Email: mccoys@balticmill.com

Cooking 2 | Modern British | £37–£67

Encased in a glass capsule, suspended between the four towers of the fabulous Baltic arts centre, the restaurant affords extravagant floor-to-ceiling window views of the Tyne and the reborn quayside. Even with its work cut out on a bustling lunchtime, service is enthusiastic and effective. The cooking scores hits and misses as it tries to cover a number of culinary bases, but pheasant and foie gras terrine with apple jam, subtly dressed smoked salmon and crab salad with chilli, lime and lemon, and main courses of lamb with horseradish mash, and salt and pepper sea bass with pak choi and shiitakes all worked well at inspection through a combination of restraint and balance. Appealing desserts might include baked egg tart with nutmeg and ginger crème fraîche, and the espresso is good and strong. The selection of wines is as shiny and modern as the architecture and arranged by style, but with plenty of substance. Ten options by the glass span the range, and bottles start at £14.95.

Chef: Simon Wood **Proprietors:** Eugine McCoy and Marcus Bennet **Open:** all week L 12 to 1.45, Mon to Sat D 7 to 9.45 **Meals:** Set L £21.95 (2 courses) to £24.95, Set D £30 (2 courses) to £35 **Service:** 10% **Cards:** Amex, Delta, Maestro, MasterCard, Visa **Details:** 90 seats. Private parties: 100 main room, 2 to 26 private rooms. Vegetarian meals. No smoking in 1 dining room. Wheelchair access (also WC). Music. Air-conditioned

Eslington Villa

8 Station Road, Low Fell, Gateshead NE9 6DR
Tel: (0191) 487 6017
Email: eslingtonvilla@freeuk.com

Cooking 3 | Modern European | £25–£58

This red-brick Edwardian mansion in an attractive garden on the east side of the Team Valley remains an oasis of calm on the edge of Gateshead, despite urban encroachment. French and Mediterranean influences are in evidence on the menu, which treads a reassuringly safe path through smoked duck and orange salad with celeriac rémoulade and truffle oil, tournedos of salmon with roast garlic, Puy lentils and red wine, and warm compote of plums with cinnamon ice cream. Occasionally the kitchen ventures into the realms of oyster, crab and tempura prawn with sweet chilli, or back home for chargrilled sirloin with hand-cut chips and béarnaise sauce followed by sticky toffee pudding. Fair prices characterise the 40-bin wine list, which has seven house recommendations from £11.90, plus a selection of halves.

Chef: Andrew Moore **Proprietors:** Nick and Melanie Tulip **Open:** Sun to Fri L 12 to 2, Mon to Sat D 7 to 9.45 **Meals:** alc (not Sun L; main courses £10 to £18). Set L £12.50 (2 courses) to £14.50, Set D Mon to Fri £18.50 **Service:** not inc, card slips closed **Cards:** Amex, Delta, Diners, Maestro, MasterCard, Visa **Details:** 85 seats. 16 seats outside. Private parties: 65 main room, 4 to 30 private rooms. Car park. Vegetarian meals. Children's helpings. No smoking. Music **Accommodation:** 18 rooms, 16 with bath/shower. TV. Phone. B&B £69.50 to £79.50

MAP 2 **Gillingham** DORSET

Stock Hill

Stock Hill, Gillingham SP8 5NR
Tel: (01747) 823626
Website: www.stockhillhouse.co.uk

Cooking 5 | Modern European | £36–£64

A life-size statue of a wild boar observes visitors as they meander up the beech-lined drive towards this personally appointed late-Victorian house. Peter and Nita Hauser celebrated two decades in residence during 2005, and visitors still marvel at their 'sheer professionalism in all departments'. Peter has stayed close to his Austrian roots, and dishes from his homeland are patriotically flagged on his daily menus. The results can be mightily impressive: leg of duckling in a goulash sauce with spätzli wowed an inspector, and the repertoire extends to poached pike 'cervolat' on sweet red pepper coulis and 'zweibel röstbraten' (sirloin steak accompanied by a Bohemian bread dumpling). However, other culinary influences are seldom far away: seared king scallops with Thai-spiced vegetables, breast of local chicken stuffed with crayfish tails, and even a version of Welsh rarebit have appeared of late. Desserts are, not surprisingly, in the true Viennese tradition: for example, Alsatian apple tart, and 'mohr im hemd' (chocolate steamed pudding). Unfussy, professional staff are guided by ever-watchful Nita Hauser. The international wine list acknowledges Austria, although France is the major player. Prices start at £15.90.

Chefs: Peter Hauser and Lorna Connor **Proprietors:** Peter and Nita Hauser **Open:** Tue to Fri and Sun L 12.15 to 1.30, all week D 7.15 to 8.30 **Meals:** Set L £25 to £28, Set D £35.50 to £38.50 **Service:** not inc, card slips closed **Cards:** Maestro, MasterCard, Visa **Details:** 36 seats. 12 seats outside. Private parties: 24 main room, 6 to 12 private rooms. Car park. Vegetarian meals. No children under 7; children's helpings. No smoking. No music. No mobile phones **Accommodation:** 8 rooms, all with bath/shower. TV. Phone. D,B&B £125 to £300. No children under 7

MAP 2 **Gittisham** DEVON

Combe House

Gittisham EX14 3AD
Tel: (01404) 540400
Website: www.thishotel.com

Cooking 4 | Modern British | £38–£79

'It's the scale of the grounds that impresses more than the building, Grade I listed and Elizabethan though it is,' declared a reporter when casting an eye over the 3,500 acres that surround this many-gabled house. Rooms are surprisingly small for such a grand setting, but they are matched by service that is refreshingly relaxed and unstuffy. The kitchen combines its own seasonal supply of vegetables, leaves and herbs with fine local ingredients – producers are listed on the menu – and treats them with confidence and understanding, the thrill coming from invigoratingly first-class raw materials like the 'copybook-fresh' fillet of red mullet with garlic gnocchi that was 'a simple but resounding success' at inspection. Other highlights have included roast duck breast with its deboned confit leg wrapped in filo teamed with Savoy cabbage stuffed with chorizo, and a dessert incorporating some 'really beautiful tasty young rhubarb' into a parfait with an accompanying rice pudding. A sharply chosen wine list of manageable length focuses on France and Australia and includes dozens of half-bottles. Reasonable prices start at £14.50.

Chef: Philip Leach **Proprietors:** Ruth and Ken Hunt **Open:** all week 12 to 2, 7 to 9.30 **Closed:** 2 weeks Jan **Meals:** Set L £19 (2 courses) to £25, Set D £38 to £49. Bar menu available **Service:** not inc **Cards:** Delta, Maestro, MasterCard, Visa **Details:** 100 seats. Private parties: 50 main room, 12 to 50 private rooms. Car park. Vegetarian meals. Children's helpings. No smoking. Wheelchair access (also WC). Occasional music. No mobile phones **Accommodation:** 15 rooms, all with bath/shower. TV. Phone. B&B £128 to £320. Baby facilities. Fishing

MAP 8 **Golcar** WEST YORKSHIRE

Weavers Shed

Knowl Road, Golcar HD7 4AN
Tel: (01484) 654284
Website: www.weaversshed.co.uk

Cooking 5 | Modern British | £27–£79

'We came away, as ever, feeling very happy that such honest, genuine restaurateurs have made their home in Yorkshire,' sums up the affection that visitors feel towards Stephen and Tracy Jackson's rustic restaurant-with-rooms in the hills above Huddersfield. Theirs is a classic partnership: she is an affable and calm hostess 'offering genuine and disarming hospitality', while he cooks with vigour, intelligence and an unerring feel for local and home-grown produce.

The dining room has been given an impressive contemporary face-lift, but Stephen Jackson's menus remain true to the spirit of the place. A floral logo on the menu highlights dishes involving pickings from the garden: a terrine of tomatoes with Bloody Mary sorbet, oregano and wild serpolet thyme could open the show, alongside 'summery' pea risotto with a sharp sorrel butter. Main courses embrace trencherman's helpings of calf's liver with root vegetables, and grilled line-caught sole with butter-poached leeks and Florence onions, juniper and rose bay willowherb. Elsewhere, there is impressive meat cookery in the shape of a tiny, shallot-crusted loin of delicately pink local spring lamb with a rosemary-tinged jus. Desserts are also skilfully handled, especially a 'tasting' of new season's Yorkshire rhubarb, and a 'masterful' cherry and frangipane tart with honey ice cream and a wild thyme and cherry jus. The 'always interesting' wine list has a soft spot for South-west France and a knack for picking good producers elsewhere, such as Dromana Estate in Australia and Clos Mimi in California. Add in enthusiastic commentaries and fair pricing (from £13.95), and you have 'a model of its kind'.

Chefs: Stephen Jackson, Ian McGunnigle and Cath Sill **Proprietors:** Stephen and Tracy Jackson **Open:** Tue to Fri L 12 to 2, Tue to Sat D 7 to 9 (10 Sat) **Closed:** Christmas to New Year **Meals:** alc (main courses £15 to £26). Set L £12.95 (2 courses) to £15.95 **Service:** not inc, 10% for parties of 10 or more **Cards:** Amex, Delta, Diners, Maestro, MasterCard, Visa **Details:** 36 seats. Private parties: 40 main room, 10 to 16 private rooms. Car park. Vegetarian meals. No smoking in 1 dining room. Music. No mobile phones **Accommodation:** 5 rooms, all with bath/shower. TV. Phone. B&B £65 to £85

MAP 8 **Goosnargh** LANCASHIRE

Solo

AR

Goosnargh PR3 2BD
Tel: (01772) 865206

Housed in an eighteenth-century cottage, this consistent neighbourhood restaurant has been doing great local service since 1986. Menus have an international flavour, opening with, say, chicken piri-piri with olives and croûtons (£5.50) before honey-glazed rack of lamb with minted rosemary gravy (£14.50) or thin slices of salmon cooked with cream, bean sprouts and black bean sauce. Round off proceedings with one of the house puddings (£4.50). Three-course Sunday lunch £16.90. Open Sun L and Tue to Sat D.

MAP 2 **Goring** OXFORDSHIRE

Leatherne Bottel

The Bridleway, Goring RG8 0HS
Tel: (01491) 872667
Website: www.leathernebottel.co.uk

Cooking 3 | Modern European | £35–£68

On a warm summer day, when this long, white house 'has its feet almost in the water', sit on the Thames-side terrace with an aperitif – although a winter open fire in the 'cosy, cumulative' bar is equally welcoming. The setting here may be timelessly tranquil, but the cooking isn't. Roast scallops with asparagus tips and a parsnip sauce epitomise the teaming of powerful flavours with emphatic spicing and dressings. Touches of Asian influence show in freshly picked crab served with sweet tomato salsa and wasabi lemon cream, or a main-course duck breast glazed with pomegranate and accompanied by roast chicory, green lentils and wilted pak choi. Or try roast guinea fowl breast wrapped in Parma ham with celeriac gratin and wild mushroom ragoût. Raspberry pannacotta is a refreshing alternative to a 'top-rate' sunken chocolate soufflé cake with gingered orange ice. Service is charming and attentive, and house French is £14.75.

Chef: Julia Storey **Proprietor:** Croftchase Ltd **Open:** all week L 12 to 2 (2.30 Sat, 3.30 Sun), Mon to Sat D 7 to 9 (9.30 Sat) **Closed:** 31 Dec **Meals:** alc (main courses £18 to £20). Set D Mon to Fri £23.50. Light L menu available Mon to Sat **Service:** 10%, card slips closed **Cards:** Amex, Delta, Maestro, MasterCard, Visa **Details:** 48 seats. 65 seats outside. Private parties: 48 main room. Car park. Vegetarian meals. No children under 10. No music

MAP 8 **Grange Moor** WEST YORKSHIRE

Kaye Arms

29 Wakefield Road, Grange Moor WF4 4BG
Tel: (01924) 848385

Cooking 3 | Modern British | £25–£54

These days, the isolated Kaye Arms is – strictly speaking – a brasserie living in the shell of a Yorkshire country pub. Over the last 30 years, the Quarmbys have tried to stay ahead of the pack by putting the emphasis on plates of food rather than pints of beer. Their menu still boasts a few old favourites, although these have been dusted off and reinvented: scampi and chips now comes with pea purée and tomato fondue. Elsewhere, the kitchen ups the tempo with roast wood pigeon on Puy lentil and Toulouse sausage ragoût, and grilled halibut with wild mushrooms, cream sauce, spinach and olive oil mash. Light meals and sandwiches are offered at lunchtime, while desserts include caramelised rice pudding with whisky-soaked prunes. A decent range of wines by the glass opens the promising list; prices start at £13.

Chef: Adrian Quarmby **Proprietors:** Adrian and Niccola Quarmby, and Sarah Allott **Open:** Tue to Sun 12 to 2, 7 to 9.30 (Sat D 6.30 to 9.45) **Closed:** 24 Dec to 3 Jan **Meals:** alc (main courses L £6 to £19, D £10 to £19). Light L menu available Tue to Sat **Service:** not inc **Cards:** MasterCard, Maestro, Visa **Details:** 90 seats. Car park. Vegetarian meals. No children under 14 at D. No smoking in 1 dining room. Music

MAP 8 **Grasmere** CUMBRIA

Jumble Room

Langdale Road, Grasmere LA22 9SU
Tel: 015394 35188
Website: www.thejumbleroom.co.uk

Cooking 2 | Global | £24–£57

Andrew and Chrissy Hill's splendid little restaurant is the kind of place you dream about having in your own home town: casual, honest, restorative and uncompromising in pursuit of quality. The mood is cheerful, the décor Bohemian and the cooking spot-on for what it offers. Organic ingredients surface all over the place, from the 'soul soup' and salad leaves to beer batter for the fish and chips. Scallops have been 'fantastic', local supplies are given global treatment (as in Moroccan tagine of Lakeland lamb on date, coriander and pine-nut couscous) and vegetarian options are enticing (Gruyère-topped rösti with fresh asparagus and organic salad, for example). To finish, try moist, spongy gingerbread liberally doused in custard. An organic house Rioja at £10.95 tops the short, wide-ranging list.

Chefs: Chrissy Hill, David and Trudy Clay **Proprietors:** Andy and Chrissy Hill **Open:** Easter to end-Nov and 27 Dec to 8 Jan: Wed to Sun 11 to 4, 6 to 10; from 9 Jan to 13 Apr, weekends only **Closed:** 12 to 27 Dec **Meals:** alc (main courses: L £6.95 to £10.50, D £11 to £18.50) **Service:** not inc, card slips closed **Cards:** Delta, Maestro, MasterCard, Visa **Details:** 45 seats. 10 seats outside. Private parties: 24 main room. Vegetarian meals. Children's helpings. No smoking. Wheelchair access (not WC). Music

White Moss House

Rydal Water, Grasmere LA22 9SE
Tel: (015394) 35295
Website: www.whitemoss.com

Cooking 5 | British | £45–£54

The house dates from 1730 and was bought by William Wordsworth for his son; it remained in the Wordsworth family until the 1930s. One still gets the impression of a small-scale, lived-in house with flowers everywhere, from 'the Wordsworthian daffodils' in the hall to the bold, flowery patterns on fabrics in the lounge, and the flower-patterned plates in the dining room. It is in this 'cottagey' dining room that Peter Dixon delivers his understated cooking that eschews fussy presentation and follows well-tried traditional lines.

The formula is simple and straightforward: dinner at 8pm, a five-course, fixed-price affair, with no choice until pudding. Soup opens proceedings – at inspection a 'subtle, understated' carrot, coriander, lentil and orange – then fish, say soufflé of smoked Fleetwood haddock and halibut with Westmoreland smoked cheese. Meat is 'first-rate' and local, perhaps rack of Herdwick lamb served with a crisp herb crust and a Burgundy sauce enriched with blueberries and blackberries, or roast fillet of Cumbrian pure-bred Galloway beef marinated in Coniston Old Man ale. Huntsman's pudding with Malmsey sauce proved a hit with one reporter – 'it's good to find traditional English puddings' – with a 'mercifully not over-sweet' sticky chocolate hazelnut cream slice as the alternative. Bread has been well reported, there's an interesting choice of British farmhouse cheeses to follow dessert, and service is unstuffy and informal.

The good-value wine list is oriented around French regions, each complemented by a global selection from similar grape varieties. At every level from £10.95 basics to grand cru Burgundy the same philosophy applies: top wines, excellent vintages and no makeweights.

Chefs: Peter Dixon and Ian Armstrong **Proprietors:** Susan and Peter Dixon **Open:** Mon to Sat D only 7.30 for 8 **Closed:** Dec and Jan **Meals:** Set D £35.50 **Service:** not inc, card slips closed **Cards:** Delta, MasterCard, Maestro, Visa **Details:** 18 seats. Private parties: 18 main room. Car park. Vegetarian meals. Children's helpings. No smoking. Wheelchair access (not WC). No music. No mobile phones **Accommodation:** 6 rooms, all with bath/shower. TV. Phone. D,B&B £94 to £198. Baby facilities. Fishing

MAP 6 **Great Gonerby** LINCOLNSHIRE

Harry's Place

17 High Street, Great Gonerby NG31 8JS
Tel: (01476) 561780

Cooking 7 | Modern French | £62–£90

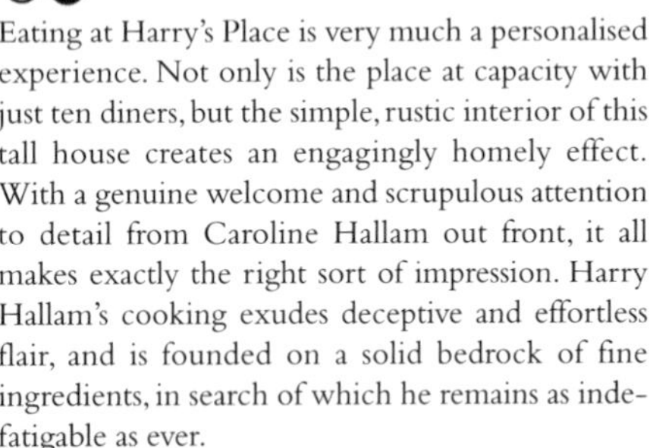

Eating at Harry's Place is very much a personalised experience. Not only is the place at capacity with just ten diners, but the simple, rustic interior of this tall house creates an engagingly homely effect. With a genuine welcome and scrupulous attention to detail from Caroline Hallam out front, it all makes exactly the right sort of impression. Harry Hallam's cooking exudes deceptive and effortless flair, and is founded on a solid bedrock of fine ingredients, in search of which he remains as indefatigable as ever.

The menu is as simple as can be, short of actually being table d'hôte. A pair of alternatives at each stage usually begins with a soup, such as mushroom with truffle oil, and another starter – perhaps a terrine of king scallops, red pepper and leeks set in Sauternes and chive jelly – before main-course options of fish or meat. The former could be lightly sautéed halibut with béarnaise, while the latter may offer Aberdeen Angus fillet with a herb and onion stuffing and a basso profundo sauce of madeira, red wine, rosemary and thyme. What impresses most is the culinary alchemist's trick of imbuing the most apparently simple of components with deep, complex flavours. That applies equally to the almost teasingly straightforward desserts of chocolate mousse garnished with red fruits, or ice cream flavoured intensely with something like apricot. Selecting from a pedigree range of British and European cheeses is the alternative. The basically Franco-Spanish wine list is perhaps a little too short for its own good, and prices are undoubtedly high. Reds start at £26 for a St-Chinian, albeit a good one, while the cheapest white is a £20 Rioja. Four comes by the glass at £4.50 and £5.

Chef: Harry Hallam **Proprietors:** Harry and Caroline Hallam **Open:** Tue to Sat 12.30 to 2, 7 to 9 **Closed:** bank hols **Meals:** alc (main courses £28.50 to £32) **Service:** not inc **Cards:** Delta, Maestro, MasterCard, Visa **Details:** 10 seats. Private parties: 10 main room. Car park. Children's helpings. No children under 5. No smoking. Wheelchair access (not WC). No music

MAP 2 **Great Milton** OXFORDSHIRE

Le Manoir aux Quat' Saisons

Church Road, Great Milton OX44 7PD
Tel: (01844) 278881
Website: www.manoir.com

Cooking 9 | Modern French | £66–£149

The Manoir has its own system of brown road signs on the A329, marking it out as the heritage site it has undoubtedly become. Now sailing confidently into its third decade, the entire enterprise is testament to the vision and creative energies of Raymond Blanc. Tarry among the cabbage patches and chervil rows before eating, the better to appreciate the industrious efforts that go into the cooking.

The principal dining room is a conservatory extension with a tent-effect ceiling and laminate floor, a joy on a summer's day when the many windows afford diverting views of others pottering in the gardens. A smaller room within the original building takes the overspill. Multinational service runs on castors throughout, managing a precise balance of correctness and unobtrusive warmth. Between them, the proprietor and Gary Jones have perfected a culinary style full of understated personal flourishes and painstaking attention to detail, which offers the seasonal best of the gardens alongside impeccably sourced meat and fish. Honed in the 1980s, the style mixes lightness and intensity, so that textures are almost apologetic in the demands they make on the palate, and yet the flavours are lingeringly powerful. Take a salad of Cornish crab. It consists of: a heap of finely shredded white meat bound in a strongly gingered yoghurt dressing topped with a small blob of oscietra, on a slice of mango; a crab claw on a slick of mango purée; a pile of brown meat in lightly Indian-spiced yoghurt with diced red pepper and onion; and some segments of blood orange and its candied zest, together with a little 'exquisitely sour' lime jelly. The time invested in the dish pays handsome dividends.

Main-course meats arrive in a number of presentations. Suckling pig appears as several slices of roast loin, a little braised cheek and some crisped, Chinese-spiced belly, the fat layer not too indecently thick but the crackling rendered to perfection. New season's Devon lamb at a May visit involved a cricket ball-sized chunk of the shank on the bone, with a pair of shimmering pink noisettes, a couple of pieces of caramelised sweetbread, and a slice of improbably tender liver. These were all supported by a 'a great exhilarating heap of green spring vegetables'.

Amid all the sighs of satisfaction, there is the odd report of less happy proceedings. Some ponder the sky-high prices when delicacy extends to small servings and simplicity, although it would be wrong to lay too much emphasis on these doubts, however. The overwhelming response is one of ringing endorsement.

Try not to miss the iced creations, whether they be taken in the form of the artist's palette of sorbets and ice creams, or the extraordinary concentration of an apple sorbet accompanying a Calvados soufflé baked inside a hollowed-out Jona Gold apple. An array of petits fours, some twinkling with gold leaf, comes with excellent arabica coffee.

The wine list documents French classics in loving detail, with many in a range of vintages. Bottles from outside the mainstream appear too: tooth-staining Alicante (£31) from Ollieux-Romanis in the Languedoc and half a dozen offerings from the Jura, for example. Listings from elsewhere are never less than serious, and California is something special. The Guide has always struggled to come to terms with the prices here, ever mindful of diners who are pushing the boat out to experience the food, but a handful of respectable options under £25, the chance to sample over a dozen finer things by the glass and a lavish spread of halves have won the day.

Chefs: Raymond Blanc and Gary Jones **Proprietor:** Raymond Blanc **Open:** all week 12.15 to 2.45, 7.15 to 9.45 **Meals:** alc (main courses £37 to £40). Set L £45 to £95, Set D £95 **Service:** not inc **Cards:** Amex, Delta, Diners, Maestro, MasterCard, Visa **Details:** 100 seats. Private parties: 8 main room, 10 to 50 private rooms. Car park. Vegetarian meals. Children's helpings. No smoking. Wheelchair access (not WC). No music. No mobile phones. Air-conditioned **Accommodation:** 32 rooms, all with bath/shower. TV. Phone. B&B £275 to £1,250. Rooms for disabled. Baby facilities

MAP 3 Great Missenden BUCKINGHAMSHIRE

La Petite Auberge

107 High Street, Great Missenden HP16 0BB
Tel: (01494) 865370

Cooking 3 | French | £39–£54

'Nothing has changed,' observed one visitor returning to the Martels' exceedingly welcoming, leisurely little restaurant after several years' absence. 'An extraordinary throwback to the seventies,' thought another reporter – no doubt referring to the ambience and the old-school, generously sauced French food. M. Martel treats well-chosen raw materials sympathetically, and any variations on his short menu tend to be dictated by the seasons. Velvety duck foie gras terrine is 'the real McCoy', likewise roast pigeon with 'vieux vinaigre' – although accompaniments have let the side down. Simple classics such as a starter of crevettes with lemon butter sauce work well, while desserts have included lemon tart and fanned-out slices of warm apple with cinnamon ice cream. The short and exclusively French wine list is realistically priced from £13.50.

Chef: Hubert Martel **Proprietors:** Mr and Mrs H. Martel **Open:** Mon to Sat D 7.30 to 10 **Closed:** 2 weeks Christmas, 2 weeks Easter **Meals:** alc D (main courses £16 to £17) **Service:** not inc **Cards:** Delta, Diners, Maestro, MasterCard, Visa **Details:** 30 seats. Private parties: 30 main room. No smoking. Wheelchair access also WC). No music. No mobile phones

MAP 6 Great Yarmouth NORFOLK

Seafood Restaurant AR

85 North Quay, Great Yarmouth NR30 1JF
Tel: (01493) 856009

Seafood cookery of days gone by in a converted pub by the quay. The menu roams around the world for gravlax (£8.50), monkfish in curry sauce (£8), and halibut with banana and grapes in white wine sauce (£17). Lobsters are from the tank, meat eaters could plump for 'surf & turf', while desserts (£5.50) are old-school favourites like crème caramel and summer pudding. Fish-friendly wines from £11.95. Closed Sat L and all Sun.

MAP 9 **Grimsby** N.E. LINCOLNSHIRE

Granary

Haven Mill, Garth Lane, Grimsby DN31 1RP
Tel: (01472) 346338
Website: www.granarygrimsby.co.uk

Cooking 1 | Seafood/Mod European | £27–£41

For almost three decades, the first floor of this converted waterside grain store has been doing sterling service as an affable, family-run seafood restaurant. The Houghtons tell us that 80 per cent of their fish comes from the Grimsby docks, and it's subjected to refreshingly unfussy treatment. Fillet of halibut arrives with black butter and capers, haddock is baked with garlicky crayfish tails and Lancashire cheese, and lemon sole is simply grilled. Meat-eaters might prefer a plate of charcuterie or beef stifado, vegetarians aren't neglected and there are cheesecakes, trifles and other 'trolley' desserts to round things off. House wine is £11.

Chef: Paul Wilson-Hundee **Proprietors:** Ron and Mary Houghton **Open:** Mon to Fri L 12 to 2, Wed to Sat D 7 to 9 **Closed:** 1 week Christmas to New Year, 1 week July, bank hols **Meals:** alc (main courses £10 to £13.50) **Service:** not inc, card slips closed **Cards:** Amex, Delta, MasterCard, Maestro, Visa **Details:** 80 seats. Private parties: 80 main room, 10 to 45 private rooms. Vegetarian meals. Children's helpings. No cigars/pipes. Occasional music

MAP 6 **Grimston** NORFOLK

Congham Hall, Orangery

Lynn Road, Grimston PE32 1AH
Tel: (01485) 600250
Website: www.conghamhallhotel.co.uk

Cooking 3 | Modern British/French | £32–£83

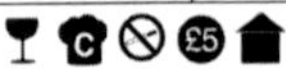

This cream-coloured Georgian manor sits in acres of park and gardens on the western edge of Grimston. A handsome dining room with peach-coloured walls and twinkling mini-chandeliers sets off Jamie Murch's classically inspired cooking. At inspection a Paris mushroom soup appetiser was earthily rich, and starter scallops with cauliflower purée and spicy beignets were nicely executed. Main-course fish is sometimes cooked a heartbeat too long, although thyme-crusted potato, roast Jerusalems and vanilla velouté make canny accompaniments to sea bass. Meat might include ballotine of apricot-stuffed partridge, with braised Savoy, game chips and a cep and truffle sauce. Attractive desserts have included clementine and ginger cheesecake with white chocolate sorbet, and there is a separate list of ice creams and sorbets for lighter appetites. An innovative wine list is arranged by styles, with ten by the glass and a useful slate of halves; prices start at £17.

Chef: Jamie Murch **Proprietor:** Von Essen Hotels **Open:** all week 12 to 1.45, 7 to 9.15 **Meals:** Set L £14.50 (2 courses) to £33, Set D £33 (2 courses) to £55. Bar L menu available Mon to Sat **Service:** not inc, card slips closed **Cards:** Amex, Delta, Diners, Maestro, MasterCard, Visa **Details:** 40 seats. 20 seats outside. Private parties: 64 main room, 4 to 18 private rooms. Car park. Vegetarian meals. Children's helpings. No children under 7 at D. No smoking. Wheelchair access (not WC). No music. No mobile phones **Accommodation:** 14 rooms, all with bath/shower. TV. Phone. B&B £99 to £350

MAP 2 **Haddenham** BUCKINGHAMSHIRE

Green Dragon

NEW ENTRY

Churchway, Haddenham HP17 8AA
Tel: (01844) 291403
Website: www.eatatthedragon.co.uk

Cooking 1 | Modern British | £28–£53

Once a manorial court, this solid-looking brick-and-tile residence, dating back to 1650, is still at the heart of village life, although it now earns its keep by providing food and drink. Menus change regularly and the kitchen buys shrewdly, whether it's Buckinghamshire lamb or Devon fish. The result is a repertoire that ranges from honest renditions of pub classics (steak and kidney suet pudding laced with Wychert Ale from the village brewery) to Gressingham duck breast with summer vegetables and flavoursome natural juices. Confit of duck with pineapple chutney makes a satisfying starter, while Malibu pannacotta on a lime and coconut macaroon with blueberries impressed at inspection. Cheery staff are overseen by hands-on proprietors, and the 60-bin wine list opens with house recommendations from £11.95.

Chefs: Paul Berry and Dean Taylor **Proprietors:** Peter Moffat and Paul Berry **Open:** all week L 12 to 2, Mon to Sat D 7 to 9.30 **Closed:** 25 Dec, 1 Jan **Meals:** alc (main courses L £8 to £17.50, D £10 to £18.50). Set D Tue and Thur £11.95 (2 courses). Light L menu available **Service:** 10% (optional) **Cards:** Delta, MasterCard, Maestro, Visa **Details:** 60 seats. 40 seats outside. Private parties: 60 main room, 8 to 14 private rooms. Car park. Vegetarian meals. No children under 7. No smoking. Wheelchair access (not WC). No music. No mobile phones at D

MAP 9 **Halifax** WEST YORKSHIRE

Design House

Dean Clough, North Bridge, Halifax HX3 5AX
Tel: (01422) 383242
Website: www.designhouserestaurant.co.uk

Cooking 2 | Modern European | £26–£57

Housed in a massive restored mill complex, this ground-floor venue looks every inch the contemporary brasserie. Owner Lee Stevens Marshall is now in the kitchen and his cooking shows some flair. Mushrooms and Stilton rarebit with red-onion marmalade makes an enjoyable starter, or you might pick a mosaic of winter game with pear chutney. Main courses follow the eclectic route: sesame-crusted salmon fillet with teriyaki sauce, and loin of lamb with blue-cheese and marjoram polenta and port jus, for example. Finish with, say, chocolate mocha tart and mascarpone cream. Tapas and light dishes dominate at lunchtime. Champagnes are given star billing; otherwise the global wine list opens with house recommendations from £11.50.

Chef/Proprietor: Lee Stevens Marshall **Open:** Mon to Fri L 12 to 2.30, Mon to Sat D 6 to 9.30 **Closed:** 26 Dec **Meals:** alc (main courses £9 to £20). Set D (not after 7pm Sat) £13.95. Tapas and light L menu available **Service:** not inc, card slips closed, 10% for parties of 15 or more **Cards:** Delta, Maestro, Mastercard, Visa **Details:** 80 seats. Private parties: 100 main room, 12 private room. Vegetarian meals. Children's helpings. No smoking. Music. Air-conditioned

Holdsworth House

Holdsworth, Halifax HX2 9TG
Tel: (01422) 240024
Website: www.holdsworthhouse.co.uk

Cooking 3 | Modern British | £27–£64

A grand seventeenth-century manor house on Halifax's northernmost edge, Holdsworth is venerable enough to have counted The Beatles among its guests. Amid the oil paintings and oak panelling, Gary Saunders offers diners a good-value, fixed-price 'luncheon', in addition to his more expansive carte. Presentations favour the classical, with citrused king prawns partnering Isle of Lewis smoked salmon, and main courses ranging from cannelloni of Anglesey sea bass with provençal vegetables and balsamic syrup, to braised Lune Valley lamb with carrot and swede mash and onions cooked in port. Seductive desserts include choux puffs with ginger cake, golden syrup and praline ice cream, or an array of English and French cheeses. The wine list, which is grouped by style, offers a broad span of choice, starting from £13.25, and one page happily reflects the fact that one of the proprietors married into the wine-making Wynn family of South Australia.

Chef: Gary Saunders **Proprietors:** Kim Pearson and Gail Moss **Open:** Mon to Fri L 12 to 2, Mon to Sat D 7 to 9.30 **Meals:** alc (main courses £11 to £20). Set L £12.95 (2 courses) to £15.95 **Service:** not inc **Cards:** Amex, Delta, Diners, Maestro, MasterCard, Visa **Details:** 50 seats. 10 seats outside. Private parties: 120 main room. Car park. Vegetarian meals. No smoking. Wheelchair access (also WC). Music. No mobile phones **Accommodation:** 40 rooms, all with bath/shower. TV. Phone. B&B £97.50 to £175. Rooms for disabled. Baby facilities

Shibden Mill Inn

Shibden Mill Fold, Shibden, Halifax HX3 7UL
Tel: (01422) 365840
Website: www.shibdenmillinn.com

Cooking 3 | Modern British | £20–£49

Tucked away in the Shibden valley overlooking Red Beck, this greatly extended seventeenth-century inn is a hive of activity. Inside is a warren of different rooms, with the restaurant reached via a steep narrow staircase. The kitchen shows enterprise and ambition, offering Nidderdale ham hock with Puy lentils and white Stilton and celeriac pudding, and gilthead bream with baby spinach, rösti and laksa sauce alongside venison and Gressingham duck terrine with peach chutney and poppy seed tuiles, or pot-roast maize-fed chicken. On Sundays there's also roast beef with home-made Yorkshire pudding and a jug of onion gravy, while chocolate torte with warm pear and plum chutney is top of the desserts. The wine list is a decent, varied slate, with prices from £10.50.

Chef: Steve Evans **Proprietor:** Mr S.D. Heaton **Open:** Mon to Sat 12 to 2, 6 to 9.30, Sun 12 to 7.30 **Meals:** alc (main courses £11 to £18). Set L £8.95 (2 courses) to £11.95. Bar menu available **Service:** not inc, card slips closed **Cards:** Amex, Delta, Maestro, MasterCard, Visa **Details:** 60 seats. 40 seats outside. Private parties: 68 main room, 1 to 8 private rooms. Car park. Vegetarian meals. Children's helpings. Music **Accommodation:** 12 rooms, all with bath/shower. TV. Phone. B&B £68 to £130

MAP 6 Hambleton RUTLAND

Hambleton Hall

Hambleton LE15 8TH
Tel: (01572) 756991
Website: www.hambletonhall.com

Cooking 7 | Modern British | £40–£120

Though close to Oakham, Hambleton Hall, on top of the promontory that juts into Rutland Water, feels thoroughly rural. The gardens and the interior colour schemes are sumptuous, and everything runs with aplomb and tireless civility. The emphasis on game – expect pheasant, grouse and woodcock in summer and autumn – and vegetables, herbs and saladings from the kitchen garden give Aaron Patterson's cooking palpable seasonality. Presentations tend to the traditional, so roast scallops come with shallot purée and smoked bacon, poulet de Bresse with morels, and Pyrenean mountain lamb with rosemary-spiked jus. Terrine carefully composed of a mosaic of chicken, veal sweetbread and foie gras is appositely teamed with a sharp apple and blackberry compote to cut its richness. Roast sucking pig comes with just enough fat to deepen the flavour plus fondant potato and a prune and Armagnac sauce that avoids being overpowering, while duck is roasted pink and tender, and partnered with a little pie of the leg meat mixed with raisins and pine nuts. Technique doesn't falter at any stage, so a passion-fruit soufflé is properly risen and contains a purée of fruit at the bottom, along with a pastry case of passion-fruit and banana sorbet, or there might a pavé of chocolate, white and dark, garnished with raspberries.

The wine list encourages experimentation, first with a page of 'wines of the moment' from £15 that are more than just mainstream basics, then by embracing quality small producers at every turn: Tim Adams and Frankland Estate in Australia, Roc d'Anglade and Domaine des Schistes in Languedoc-Roussillon, for example.

Chef: Aaron Patterson **Proprietors:** Tim and Stefa Hart **Open:** all week 12 to 1.30, 7 to 9.30 **Meals:** alc (main courses £20 to £39.50). Set L £18.50 (2 courses) to £35, Set L Sun £37.50 to £50, Set D £35 to £55. Snack menu available **Service:** not inc **Cards:** Amex, Delta, Diners, Maestro, MasterCard, Visa **Details:** 64 seats. 20 seats outside. Private parties: 64 main room, 2 to 20 private rooms. Car park. Vegetarian meals. Children's helpings. No smoking. Wheelchair access (not WC). No music **Accommodation:** 17 rooms, all with bath/shower. TV. Phone. B&B £165 to £650. Rooms for disabled. Baby listening/sitting. Baby facilities. Swimming pool

MAP 5 Hanwell OXFORDSHIRE

Moon and Sixpence

NEW ENTRY

Hanwell OX17 1HW
Tel: (01295) 730544
Email: moonand.sixpence@virgin.net

Cooking 2 | Modern British | £29–£55

Toby Hill, last listed in the 2004 Guide at Lords of the Manor, Upper Slaughter (see entry), has taken over this large village pub. It probably won't win any awards for interior design, but it does take food seriously. The tendency is towards hearty fare; food is served on large white plates and comes in generous portions. A bowl of moules marinière makes a generous starter (the first-class mussels winning praise), or there could be a warm salad of grilled chicken and crispy bacon. Main courses might turn up roast rack of lamb in a herb crust with a black olive jus, or pubby favourites like beer-battered cod with chunky chips, and there is a separate menu featuring Aberdeen Angus steaks. Desserts can be as traditional as sticky toffee pudding with home-made vanilla ice cream. Service gets the job done in an unassuming, knowledgeable way. Real ales are dispensed at the bar, and the wine list is priced just right for a pub, with five house selections at £12.

Chef: Toby Hill **Proprietors:** Rupert and Toby Hill **Open:** Tue to Sun L 12 to 2 (3 Sun), Mon to Sat D 6 to 9 **Meals:** alc (main courses £10 to £19.50) **Service:** not inc, card slips closed **Cards:** Delta, Maestro, MasterCard, Visa **Details:** 70 seats. 30 seats outside. Private parties: 50 main room, 10 to 50 private rooms. Car park. Vegetarian meals. Children's helpings. No smoking. Wheelchair access (not WC). Music

MAP 9 Harome NORTH YORKSHIRE

Star Inn

High Street, Harome YO62 5JE
Tel: (01439) 770397
Website: www.thestaratharome.co.uk

Cooking 5 | Modern British | £41–£63

In its ten years under Andrew and Jacquie Pern, the Star has become an institution: an archetypal pub ('a lovely thatched building alongside a stylish Victorian original public house') that caters to all-comers. The repertoire has a regional feel, and the

cooking is founded on first-rate, well-sourced raw materials. Although supplemented by blackboard specials, the main carte is self-sufficient in terms of interest and variety, offering starters such as grilled black pudding and pan-fried foie gras with watercress salad, apple and vanilla chutney and a scrumpy reduction, or a risotto of locally grown plum tomatoes with oregano from the herb garden, wild rocket and goats' cheese salad. A similarly wide spectrum produces main courses of lasagne of local rabbit with baby spinach, black trumpet mushrooms, mozzarella salad and white truffle oil, and carefully timed seared tuna with mussels and samphire. Well-sourced materials take in Bresse chicken with Lincolnshire Poacher and streaky saddleback bacon, squab pigeon with bubble and squeak, and fallow deer – for one visitor 'exceptional in taste and texture' and served with girolles and foie gras. Desserts have included an enjoyable chocolate and lavender torte. Ten or so wines by the glass open a list that covers all bases with aplomb. Fair prices (from £11.95) and useful tasting notes sweeten the deal.

2004 saw the opening of a satellite café in a light, bright and modern building at Scampston Hall, Malton (tel: 01944 759000), which between the hours of 10am to 5pm serves everything from sandwiches (Cotherstone cheese with pickled beetroot and celery) to light lunches (coarse country terrine with cornichon salad and crusty bread), and a range of pastries and puddings. The venue can be booked for private functions, including evenings.

Chef: Andrew Pern **Proprietors:** Andrew and Jacquie Pern **Open:** Tue to Sun L 11.30 to 2 (12 to 6 Sun), Tue to Sat D 6.30 to 9.30 **Closed:** 9 to 26 Jan **Meals:** alc (main courses £14.50 to £19) **Service:** not inc, card slips closed **Cards:** MasterCard, Maestro, Visa **Details:** 50 seats. 30 seats outside. Private parties: 36 main room, 8 to 12 private rooms. Car park. Vegetarian meals. Children's helpings. No smoking. Wheelchair access (not WC). Music **Accommodation:** 11 rooms, all with bath/shower. TV. B&B £130 to £210. Rooms for disabled

MAP 8 **Harrogate** NORTH YORKSHIRE

Drum and Monkey

5 Montpellier Gardens, Harrogate HG1 2TF
Tel: (01423) 528014

Cooking 2 | Seafood | £27–£69

This pub conversion has been packing them in for nigh on 30 years, and a change of ownership two years ago does not seem to have dinted enthusiasm. Wisely, the formula remains the same: simple, classic treatments of fish. You might start with salmon and watercress mousse, crab cocktail, or moules marinière, then go on to sea trout poached and served with asparagus hollandaise, or monkfish garnished with prawns and mushrooms and accompanied by prawn and brandy sauce. Lobster comes three ways – thermidor, steamed with garlic butter, or served cold with salad – grilled Dover sole appears in three different sizes, and seafood platters form the back-up. A simpler menu operates at lunchtime. The short, affordable list of around 30 fish-friendly wines opens at £11.95.

Chefs: Selina Leamy and Keith Penny **Proprietor:** Jan Fletcher **Open:** Mon to Sat 12 to 2.30, 5.45 to 10 **Closed:** 25 and 26 Dec **Meals:** alc (main courses £8 to £25) **Service:** not inc, card slips closed **Cards:** Delta, Maestro, MasterCard, Visa **Details:** 54 seats. No smoking. Music. Air-conditioned

Hotel du Vin & Bistro

Prospect Place, Harrogate HG1 1LB
Tel: (01423) 856800
Website: www.hotelduvin.com

Cooking 3 | Modern European | £30–£59

This striking conversion of a solid Yorkshire-stone terrace overlooking the Stray – the acres of green at Harrogate's heart – pretty much follows the successful formula of town-house hotel, relaxed restaurant and first-class wine list of the group's other branches (see entries in Birmingham, Brighton, Bristol, Henley-on-Thames, Tunbridge Wells and Winchester). The name of the game is to combine good-quality ingredients with uncomplicated modern cooking to produce a menu with broad appeal. Classics come in the form of chateaubriand with béarnaise, or lamb cutlets with Reform sauce. Fish lovers can indulge in squid and tiger prawn risotto with mint or halibut with sautéed Jerusalem artichokes and beurre rouge, and vegetarians have a reasonable choice. Desserts have generally failed to impress. Service is 'attentive, swift and efficient'. The wine list scores as highly as at most other members of the group. Over 600 bins reach from the grandest terroirs into the most remote corners of the vinous world and most look well worth a go. Prices open at around £13.50.

Chef: Gareth Longhurst **Proprietor:** MWB Group plc **Open:** all week 12 to 1.45, 7 to 9.45 **Meals:** alc exc Sun L (main courses £15 to £19). Set L Mon to Sat £12.50 (2 courses inc wine), Set L Sun £23.50, Set D Mon to Thur £17.50 **Service:** not inc, card slips closed **Cards:** Amex, Delta, Maestro, MasterCard, Visa **Details:** 90 seats. 40 seats outside. Private parties: 10 to 60 private rooms. Vegetarian meals. Children's helpings. No smoking. Wheelchair access (also WC). No music **Accommodation:** 43 rooms, all with bath/shower. TV. Phone. Room only £95 to £275. Rooms for disabled. Baby facilities

Quantro

AR

3 Royal Parade, Harrogate HG1 2SZ
Tel: (01423) 503034

Glossily designed brasserie that adds some contemporary pizazz to the Harrogate restaurant scene. Up-to-the-minute menus deal in vibrant modern dishes including ham hock terrine with pea pannacotta and apple and sage chutney (£4.75), sea bass with a warm fennel and potato salad and sauce vierge (£13.50), and banana tarte Tatin with honey parfait and praline crisp (£4.50). Light lunch menus £9.95/£12.95. Closed Sun. A sibling is at 62 Street Lane, Leeds; tel: (0113) 288 8063.

MAP 3 **Harrow** GREATER LONDON

Golden Palace

146–150 Station Road, Harrow HA1 2RH
Tel: (020) 8863 2333

Cooking 4 | Chinese | £26–£87

A parade of shops on a busy thoroughfare in Harrow may not sound like the obvious setting for a top-notch Chinese restaurant, but the Golden Palace can hold its own with the best in the business. To get a flavour of the place, join the queues for a Sunday lunch of incomparable dim sum, packed with variety, invention and bold distinctive flavours. These moreish delicacies can be as good as any around: witness steamed five-spice beef tripe with Chinese turnip, a meatless version of slithery cheung fun, and other possibilities like steamed stuffed baby squid in shrimp paste. The kitchen also covers the full Chinese repertoire with a 200-dish line-up taking in soft-shell crabs with spicy salt and chilli, shredded roast duck with preserved cabbage, charcoal-roast pork with honey, and much more. Beyond the regular menu, there are all manner of esoteric and gastronomically challenging specials, which have helped to earn the place its reputation.

Chef/Proprietor: Mr G. Ho **Open:** Mon to Sat 12 (11 bank hols) to 11.30, Sun 11 to 10.30 **Closed:** 25 Dec **Meals:** alc (main courses £5.50 to £30). Set L and D £16.50 to £24 (all min 2) **Service:** 10% **Cards:** Amex, Delta, Diners, Maestro, MasterCard, Visa **Details:** 160 seats. Private parties: 110 main room. Vegetarian meals. Wheelchair access (also WC). Occasional music. Air-conditioned **Tube:** Harrow-on-the-Hill

Ram's

AR

203 Kenton Road, Harrow HA3 0HD
Tel: (020) 8907 2022

'Pure Vegetarian Surti Cuisine' at rock-bottom prices in stylish modern surroundings not far from Kenton tube station. The Gujarati city of Surat is the source of fascinating dishes ranging from pau bhaji (spicy vegetable curry with buttered bread rolls; £3.75) and kichi (steamed rice-flour dumplings spiked with chillies) to vengan na bhartu (baked aubergines with rotla bread). Also note weekend specials like kand (steamed purple potatoes with lemon and spices). Surti dhals and rice around £4.50; thalis £5/£9 ('no sharing'). House wine £9.20. Open all week.

MAP 6 **Harwich** ESSEX

Pier Hotel, Harbourside Restaurant

The Quay, Harwich CO12 3HH
Tel: (01255) 241212
Website: www.milsomhotels.com

Cooking 2 | Seafood/English | £32–£78

Major refurbishment has seen both Pier dining options take on a stylish, contemporary new face with natural tones that echo the seafaring setting. The first-floor Harbourside Restaurant (above the more informal Ha'penny Bistro) boasts a polished pewter champagne bar that makes the best of the stunning views over the Stour and Orwell estuaries. The slick nautical styling reflects its position alongside quay and harbour, enhanced by maritime paintings by Jamie Dodds, the acclaimed Brightlingsea artist. Chef Chris Oakley's lengthy menu embraces the theme and is awash with the fruits of the sea, brought in directly from the boats. Think grilled Harwich lobster, or perhaps poached fillet of turbot served on creamed leaf spinach with a hollandaise sauce, and there are a few 'from the land' options for carnivores too, all backed by smart and friendly service. Wines are a lively, modern mix from £13.25.

Chef: Chris Oakley **Proprietor:** Paul Milsom **Open:** all week 12 to 2, 6 to 9.30 **Closed:** 25 Dec eve **Meals:** alc (main courses £12.50 to £31.50). Set L £17 (2 courses) to £21 **Service:** 10%, card slips closed **Cards:** Amex, Delta, Diners, Maestro, MasterCard, Visa **Details:** 80 seats. 30 seats outside. Private parties: 80 main room, 14 to 80 private rooms. Car park. Vegetarian meals. Children's helpings. No-smoking area. Music. No mobile phones. Air-conditioned **Accommodation:** 14 rooms, all with bath/shower. TV. Phone. B&B £70 to £175. Rooms for disabled. Baby facilities

MAP 9 **Hathersage** DERBYSHIRE

George Hotel

Main Road, Hathersage S32 1BB
Tel: (01433) 650436
Website: www.george-hotel.net

Cooking 4 | Modern British-Plus | £39–£60

This is a former coaching inn built of grey stone, with a history extending back 500 years. That might be said of several places in the Guide, but what distinguishes the George in Hathersage is the singular quality of Ben Handley's cooking. A couple staying nearby who rolled up for the Early Bird evening menu found themselves lingering for most of the evening, and indeed returning two nights later. Enterprising and successful dishes, based largely on local ingredients, have included an Oriental-style 'sweet and sticky' pork salad with roast cashew nuts, well-made wild mushroom risotto with red wine and rosemary, and roast cod with pancetta, creamed potatoes and sauce vierge. The timing of fish and meat seems never less than pinpoint-accurate, and understanding of flavour is such that a lunchtime bowl of asparagus soup with a swirl of truffle oil and good bread quite satiated one reporter. This being Derbyshire, Bakewell tart is a must, and here it is both crisp-shelled and agreeably moist. Otherwise, the home-made ice creams are well-reported. The wine list is arranged by style and keeps prices on a reasonably short leash from £14.95. Eight wines come by the glass, from £3.75.

Chef: Ben Handley **Proprietor:** Eric Marsh **Open:** all week 12 to 2.30, 6.30 to 10 **Meals:** alc (main courses £13 to £19). Early Bird menu £12 (two courses) to £14.95 (3 courses). Lounge L menu available **Service:** not inc **Cards:** Amex, Delta, Diners, Maestro, MasterCard, Visa **Details:** 50 seats. Private parties: 70 main room, 10 to 70 private rooms. Car park. Vegetarian meals. Children's helpings. No smoking. Wheelchair access (not WC). Music. No mobile phones **Accommodation:** 19 rooms, all with bath/shower. TV. Phone. B&B £80 to £165

MAP 8 **Haworth** WEST YORKSHIRE

Weavers

13–17 West Lane, Haworth BD22 8DU
Tel: (01535) 643822
Website: www.weaversmallhotel.co.uk

Cooking 3 | Modern British | £28–£51

Behind the thick millstone grit walls of a trio of knocked-through cottages, lies a convivial, rambling interior with 'tatty chic' mismatched furniture, and bobbins, shuttles and other weaving memorabilia. This isn't provincial backwater cooking, though: *viz.* starters from the main evening menu like potted confit of Lune Valley duck topped with sprouting lentils and served with rhubarb relish, or a thick slice of rare-breed pork and apple brandy terrine with plum relish and 'zingy' cucumber and gherkin salsa. Dishes blend a predominantly British style with good use of local and regional produce. Among mains, for example, Pennine-reared beef and potato pie is served in a pint pudding bowl topped with a golden-brown crust with white onion relish and Daddies sauce on the side, while breast of Gressingham duck comes perfectly pink and tender with bubble and squeak made with kale and a Seville orange and dry sherry sauce. Finish with chocolate and ginger biscuit cake with 'amazing' Yorkshire tea ice cream. House wine is £11.95, with 10 by the glass from £3.

Chefs: Colin, Jane and Tim Rushworth **Proprietors:** the Rushworth family **Open:** Wed to Fri and Sun L 12 to 2, Tue to Sat D 6.30 to 8.45 (9.15 Sat) **Closed:** 26 Dec to 4 Jan **Meals:** alc (main courses L £8 to £15, D £11 to £18). Set L £10.95 (2 courses), Set L Sun £17.50, Set D Tue to Fri £12.95 (2 courses) **Service:** not inc, 10% for parties of 7 or more **Cards:** Amex, Delta, Diners, MasterCard, Maestro, Visa **Details:** 60 seats. Private parties: 45 main room, 10 to 15 private rooms. Vegetarian meals. Children's helpings; no children under 4 after 7pm. No smoking. Music. Air-conditioned **Accommodation:** 3 rooms, all with bath/shower. TV. Phone. B&B £55 to £85. Baby facilities

MAP 3 **Haywards Heath** WEST SUSSEX

Jeremy's

Borde Hill, Balcombe Road, Haywards Heath
RH16 1XP
Tel: (01444) 441102
Website: www.homeofgoodfood.co.uk

Cooking 2 | Modern European | £32–£58

The restaurant is at the end of a long driveway, which it shares with Borde Hill Gardens. It may look like a tea room from the outside, but inside is done in modern restaurant style, with sunny-yellow walls festooned with artworks, a laminate floor, and a ceiling open to the crossbeamed roof. There has been another change of chef since last year, and indications are that the place could do with a period of stability. Inaccuracies marred too many dishes at inspection, but hope was rewarded in the form of confit duck rillettes with radicchio salad dressed in aged balsamic, and the apposite accompaniments of roast beetroot, rhubarb sauce and sun-dried tomatoes that came with a main course of smoked haddock. Simple desserts such as apple and plum crumble with cinnamon cream might well be a better bet than the more outré offerings. A list of monthly recommendations heads up the short wine list, with Italian house wines at £13.

Chefs: Rupert Gleedow and Lee Cobb **Proprietors:** Jeremy and Vera Ashpool **Open:** Tue to Sun L 12 to 2.30, Tue to Sat D 7 to 9.30 **Closed:** first week Jan **Meals:** alc (main courses £13.50 to £20.50). Set L Tue to Sat £16.50 (2 courses) to £20.50, Set L Sun £22 (2 courses) to £26, Set D Tue to Thur £16.50 (2 courses) to £20.50 **Service:** not inc, 10% for parties of 8 or more **Cards:** Amex, Diners, Maestro, MasterCard, Visa **Details:** 55 seats. Private parties: 60 main room, 60 to 120 private rooms. Car park. Vegetarian meals. Children's helpings. No smoking in 1 dining room. Wheelchair access (not WC). Music

MAP 9 **Helmsley** NORTH YORKSHIRE

Feversham Arms Hotel

Helmsley YO62 5AG
Tel: (01439) 770766
Website: www.fevershamarmshotel.com

Cooking 5 | Modern British | £31–£70

Simon Rhatigan took over this prettily situated hotel in 2003 and has transformed it into a smart 'hip, chic abode', adding a fashionable conservatory restaurant. Chef Charlie Lakin brings great technical skill to fine raw materials and delivers robust dishes that do not stint on flavour. That was certainly the case with an inspector's first course of fresh black truffle risotto with a poached duck's egg, a rich combination with real depth of flavour from a marriage of good stock and the earthy, musky punch of finely chopped truffle. More mainstream ideas might include Whitby crab salad with lemon and chervil mayonnaise, or ham hock and foie gras terrine with caramelised apple dressing. Star of the show among main courses at inspection was a crisp-skinned roast poussin carved at the table and accompanied by a delicate white boudin speckled with black truffle, carrots, crisp leeks, and a madeira jus.

There is a great deal of comfort among desserts, which have delivered 'perfectly executed' egg custard tart with a winter fruit compote, and a very citric lemon soufflé 'risen like a hot-air balloon' nicely contrasted with a sweet cassis coulis and liquorice ice cream. Service is welcoming, combining 'a relaxed, friendly and professional tone', and the wine list has reliable flavours from around the world at fair prices, starting at £16.95.

Chef: Charlie Lakin **Proprietor:** Simon Rhatigan **Open:** all week 12 to 2 (1 to 3 Sun), 7 to 9.30 **Meals:** alc (main courses L £9 to £13.50, D £17 to £22). Set L £16.95, Set D £30 **Service:** not inc **Cards:** Maestro, MasterCard, Visa **Details:** 55 seats. 30 seats outside. Private parties: 60 main room, 1 to 30 private rooms. Car park. Vegetarian meals. Children's helpings. No smoking. Wheelchair access (also WC). Music **Accommodation:** 17 rooms, all with bath/shower. TV. Phone. B&B £120 to £200. Rooms for disabled. Baby facilities. Swimming pool

MAP 6 **Hemingford Grey** CAMBRIDGESHIRE

Cock

47 High Street, Hemingford Grey PE28 9BJ
Tel: (01480) 463609
Website: www.cambscuisine.com

Cooking 2 | Modern British | £21–£49

Two separate entrances emphasise the dual identity of this neatly turned-out pub/restaurant close to the Great Ouse. Chef Chris Brading has moved to the group's latest venture: the Boathouse in El (reports please). At the Cock, home-made sausage are a fixture, and there's always a board of fish spe cials (skate with pea and mint purée, roast toma toes and salsa verde, for example). The menu i based on decent ingredients – although presentation can be 'sloppy'. Start with a baked duck parcel with sweet-and-sour cucumber before tackling braised blade steak with celeriac rösti, caramelised shallots and port. Meals end on, say, rhubarb crème brûlée. Prices on the broadly based wine list start at £9.95. The Crown & Punchbowl, Horningsea (see entry), completes the group.

Chef: Ali Longfoot **Proprietors:** Oliver Thain and Richard Bradley **Open:** all week 12 to 2.30, 6.45 to 9.30 (6.30 to 8.30 Sun); no food 25 and 26 Dec **Meals:** alc D (main courses £11 to £17). Set L Mon to Sat £8.95 (2 courses) to £11.95, Set L Sun £17.95 **Service:** not inc, card slips closed **Cards:** Maestro, MasterCard, Visa **Details:** 60 seats. 35 seats outside. Private parties: 35 main room. Car park. Vegetarian meals. Children's helpings. No children under 6 at D. No smoking. Wheelchair access (not WC). No music. No mobile phones

MAP 5 **Henley-in-Arden**
WARWICKSHIRE

Edmunds

64 High Street, Henley-in-Arden
B95 5BX
Tel: (01564) 795666

WARWICKSHIRE RESTAURANT OF THE YEAR

Cooking 5 | Modern British | £27–£56

A corner property on the tree-lined main street through the village, Edmunds is a tribute to the dedication and professionalism of Andy and Beverley Waters. Decorated throughout in colours as warm as the front-of-house welcome, it makes a comfortable setting for some accomplished modern country cooking.

One of Andy's most tenacious followers records her satisfaction with many a meal here, singling out a starter of two types of prawn served in a reduced seafood sauce topped with crisp-fried prosciutto, and a top-drawer main-course serving of steamed plaice on a bed of spinach with hollandaise. A meatier route might begin with duck three ways (rillettes, smoked and a foie gras terrine), and proceed to roasted rack of local lamb with pistachio fondant, parsnip and vanilla purée and a rich Burgundy jus. This is a kitchen that takes enough trouble over vegetarian dishes to separate the menu into starters and main courses, always a good sign. A trio of fine pre-selected farmhouse cheeses – perhaps Tête de Moine, Exmoor Blue and Fougéru, a bracken-wrapped French goats' cheese – is the savoury alternative to desserts such as an assiette of no fewer than seven classic items, taking in chocolate fondant, lemon tart, crème brûlée and superb rhubarb jelly, among others.

A French-led wine list with shorter selections from elsewhere opens with seven house wines from £12.25, or £3.25 a glass, for a South African Chenin Blanc.

Chef: Andy Waters **Proprietors:** Andy and Beverley Waters **Open:** Tue to Fri L 12 to 1.45, Tue to Sat D 7 to 9.45 **Closed:** 5 weeks throughout the year; phone to check **Meals:** Set L £7.50 (1 course) to £28.50, Set D £25.50 (2 courses) to £28.50 **Service:** not inc, card slips closed, 10% (optional) for parties of 6 or more **Cards:** Delta, MasterCard, Maestro, Visa **Details:** 42 seats. Vegetarian meals. Children's helpings. No smoking. Wheelchair access (not WC). Music

MAP 2 **Henley-on-Thames**
OXFORDSHIRE

Hotel du Vin

NEW ENTRY

New Street, Henley-on-Thames RG9 2BP
Tel: (01491) 848400
Website: www.hotelduvin.com

Cooking 4 | Modern European | £31–£62

The latest addition to the Hotel du Vin chain opened in Henley in the autumn of 2004, in premises that were once occupied by Brakspear's brewery. The transition from grain to grape has been handled stylishly, the huge dining room kitted out in the group style with central banquette seating, outsized wine bottles, and a plethora of carefully copied famous paintings of naked women, interspersed with posters from the Belle Epoque.

With starters and mains on the left side, and Simple Classics and Vegetarian to the right, the menu structure will look familiar to anyone who has eaten at the other branches. An unfussy culinary approach delivers a trio of fine scallops on onion and garlic purée with a dribble of truffle oil, as well as appealingly textured, twice-baked Gruyère soufflé. A small fillet of brill sits on a bed of lightly cooked cucumber and celery, with a chive-speckled buttery sauce to accompany, while three chops of new season's lamb are cooked appetisingly pink. Sides include pak choi with sesame oil, and dandelion and rocket salad, as well as the usual spuds and spinach, and meals end with something like filling pecan cake with 'unremittingly sweet' maple syrup ice cream and butterscotch sauce. The Guide has yet to see a copy of the wine list, but our inspector admits to 'drooling, almost visibly' so expect a corker with bottles from around £13.

Chef: Eddie Gray **Proprietor:** MWB Group plc **Open:** all week; 12 to 2, 7 to 10 **Meals:** alc (main courses £12 to £14.50). Set Sun L £23.50 **Service:** not inc **Cards:** Amex, Delta, Diners, Maestro, MasterCard, Visa **Details:** 80 seats. 40 seats outside. Private parties: 50 main room. Children's helpings. Wheelchair access (also WC). No music **Accommodation:** 43 rooms, all with bath/shower. TV. Phone. Room only £115 to £395. Rooms for disabled. Baby facilities

Three Tuns Foodhouse

5 Market Place, Henley-on-Thames RG9 2AA
Tel: (01491) 573260
Email: thefoodhouse@btconnect.com

Cooking 3 | Modern British | £32–£60

In a former life this centuries-old building was a mortuary, but nowadays it fulfils its function as a contemporary eating house with a quirky, eclectic feel. After a bright start, the set-up seems to have lost some of its edge: offhand service and a lack of care have been cited, although the kitchen still puts its faith in local ingredients and supplies from the London markets. The daily-changing menus advertise roast Irish cod with crab broth and aïoli or Cornish mackerel with Goan seasoning and roast red peppers alongside calf's liver with mash, broad beans and shallot gravy. Start with a plate of tapas and finish with lemon tart. The wine list (from £14) packs a lot of drinking into a small space. The owner recently acquired the Fox and Hounds, Christmas Common.

Chefs: Kieron Daniels and Michael Jones **Proprietor:** Kieron Daniels **Open:** all week 12 to 2.30, 7 to 10 **Meals:** alc (main courses £10 to £17). Set L £5 (1 course) **Service:** not inc, card slips closed **Cards:** Delta, Maestro, MasterCard, Visa **Details:** 27 seats. 20 seats outside. Private parties: 30 main room, 10 to 40 private rooms. No smoking. Wheelchair access (not WC). Music

To submit a report on any restaurant, please visit *www.which.co.uk/gfgfeedback*.

MAP 5 **Hereford** HEREFORDSHIRE

Castle House, La Rive

Castle Street, Hereford HR1 2NW
Tel: (01432) 356321
Website: www.castlehse.co.uk

Cooking 6 | Anglo-French | £36–£80

The handsome Georgian house, with its classic pillared entrance porch, is down a quiet back street a stone's throw from the cathedral. Interiors are not forbiddingly grand but rather homely and welcoming, with family photographs dotted about and an appealing view of a leafy stream from the dining room windows. Executive chef Stuart McLeod oversees a menu that tries out some novel combinations but doesn't overreach itself in ambition. An uneven lunch produced, for one couple, the satisfactions of a main course of confit duck on sauerkraut with red onion sauce and a show-stopping dessert of marmalade and whisky parfait with caramelised bitter oranges and a rolled-oat tuile.

At dinner, a grander touch brings on casserole of native oysters and spring onions with smoked salmon feuilleté, and main courses such as local beef fillet with sweet potato dauphinois and wild mushroom compote, or loin of lamb forestière with a faggot of the knuckle, celeriac fondant and a rhubarb infusion. Vegetarians might have fun working out what exactly a carrot and Gruyère 'compression' will consist of. An exotically spicy dessert might be mango and basil pannacotta with passion-fruit ice cream, ginger crisps and lemongrass crème fraîche. France is the main focus of the wine list, with strong global support. There are star bottles aplenty for big spenders, but the interest and value in the lower reaches impress more. Six house options from £16.95 kick things off.

Chef: Stuart McLeod **Proprietors:** Dr and Mrs A. Heijn **Open:** all week 12.30 to 2, 7 to 10 (9 Sun) **Meals:** alc L exc Sun (main courses £14 to £16). Set L Sun £21.95. alc D (main courses £18.45 to £22.95), Set D £49.95 **Service:** not inc **Cards:** Amex, Delta, Maestro, MasterCard, Visa **Details:** 32 seats. 20 seats outside. Private parties: 36 main room. Car park. Vegetarian meals. Children's helpings. No smoking. Wheelchair access (also WC). Occasional music. No mobile phones. Air-conditioned **Accommodation:** 15 rooms, all with bath/shower. TV. Phone. B&B £113.50 to £245. Rooms for disabled. Baby facilities

MAP 8 **Hetton** NORTH YORKSHIRE

Angel Inn

Hetton BD23 6LT
Tel: (01756) 730263
Website: www.angelhetton.co.uk

Cooking 4 | Modern British | £24–£55

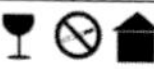

The ever-popular Angel is a Dales dining pub phenomenon, combining the informality of a bar/brasserie with a separate, more upmarket restaurant. Stone floors, oak beams, polished wooden tables and log fires are *de rigueur* in the bar, while the comfortable, elegant restaurant's two interconnecting rooms are hung with paintings and heavy drapes. Though the cooking maintains a no-nonsense, generous approach in both areas – with some crossover of dishes – there's more elaboration and refinement on the restaurant menu. The sourcing of local ingredients remains a kitchen priority, with lamb from Bolton Abbey and Newby Hall beef making an appearance, while the modern-focused dinner menu could strike out with home-made black pudding topped with foie gras on caramelised apple and a red wine sauce ('among the very best black pudding we have tasted,' enthused one couple). A moist and tasty fillet of pan-fried wild sea bass with seared scallops, rocket, asparagus and a caviar beurre blanc could follow, while desserts keep to a more homely, familiar line with mandatory sticky toffee pudding with toffee sauce and Chantilly cream. France and Italy are the prime passions of the highly individual wine list, including numerous bottles imported direct from small estates. Prices are commendably fair, with house bottles from around £13, and mature vintages are offered where appropriate.

Chef: Bruce Elsworth **Proprietor:** Juliet Watkins **Open:** Sun L 12 to 2.15, Mon to Sat D 6 to 9.30 **Closed:** 25 Dec, 1 Jan, 1 week Jan **Meals:** alc exc Sat D and Sun L (main courses £11 to £17). Set L Sun £20.90, Set D Mon to Fri 6 to 6.45 £13.20 (2 courses) to £19.25 (inc wine), Set D Sat £32.45. Bar menu available **Service:** not inc, card slips closed **Cards:** Amex, Maestro, MasterCard, Visa **Details:** 60 seats. 40 seats outside. Private parties: 40 main room. Car park. Vegetarian meals. Children's helpings. No smoking. Wheelchair access (also women's WC). No music. Air-conditioned **Accommodation:** 5 rooms, all with bath/shower. TV. Phone. B&B £120 to £170. Rooms for disabled

MAP 2 **Heytesbury** WILTSHIRE

Angel Coaching Inn

AR

High Street, Heytesbury BA12 0ED
Tel: (01985) 840330

Seventeenth-century coaching inn given a stylish 'rustic chic' makeover, driven in part by Antony Worrall Thompson. Well-hung chargrilled steaks (from £15) with various butters and sauces are the main contenders, but the carte also promises a mix of earthy and luxurious ideas: tempura scallops with Cornish crab coleslaw (£9), steamed mutton and foie gras suet pudding with red onion marmalade (£15), and iced mango parfait with hot mango rice pudding (£5), for example. Shortish, affordable wine list from £10.50; accommodation available. Open all week.

MAP 2 **Highclere** HAMPSHIRE

Marco Pierre White's Yew Tree

NEW ENTRY

Hollington Cross, Andover Road, Highclere
RG20 9SE
Tel: (01635) 253360
Website: www.theyewtree.net

Cooking 5 | Modern British/French | £32–£78

The sturdy character of this rambling old pub by the junction of a narrow lane with the busy A343 has been retained by new owners, although the emphasis on Marco Pierre White's name gives notice that food is in the ascendancy. The day-to-day running of the kitchen is in the hands of Neil Thornley, who interprets the MPW blend of traditional and modern admirably: classic *Larousse Gastronomique* (bisque of crab ... l'américaine, confit of lamb ... la dijonnaise with flageolets ... la crème) mixed with some updated pub stalwarts (kipper pâté, fishcake with hollandaise, shepherd's pie). Visitors are struck by the intensity of flavours from the word go: a risotto of first-rate, fresh crayfish, contrasting magnificently with Parmesan, pleased at every level with fine timing, a slick of bright green chive oil adding another dimension. Simplicity laced with innovation and the use of excellent ingredients also distinguishes main courses, with an 'admirably restrained' dish of venison revealing 'good meat' and spot-on mash. A raspberry soufflé has been found 'perfect'; it comes with frozen sweet yoghurt, and contrasting flavours from orange tuiles and a scattering of shortbread crumbs ('more than a garnish; they had a point'). Service has not impressed, but the nicely judged wine list (not too long, not too short) holds plenty of interest, with a good selection under £20.

Chef: Neil Thornley **Proprietors:** Marco Pierre White and Gareth Lloyd-Jones **Open:** all week L 12 to 3, Mon to Sat D 6 to 9.30 **Meals:** alc exc Sun L (main courses £10 to £27.50). Set L Sun £19.95 **Service:** not inc, card slips closed **Cards:** Amex, Delta, Diners, Maestro, MasterCard, Visa **Details:** 92 seats. 20 seats outside. Private parties: 80 main room. Car park. Vegetarian meals. Children's helpings. No smoking. Music **Accommodation:** 6 rooms, all with bath/shower. TV. B&B £60 to £120

MAP 2 **Hindon** WILTSHIRE

Angel Inn

AR

Angel Lane, Hindon SP3 6DJ
Tel: (01747) 820696

'A fabulous oasis off the A303' is one verdict on this revitalised eighteenth-century coaching inn. A roaring fire and real ales remain, but the place now has restaurant aspirations. Starters like baked blue Brie on bacon in filo (£6) might precede a rolled trio of roast duck breast, venison and pigeon with claret and vanilla-poached pear (£14), while desserts could include Cointreau and white chocolate mousse with kumquat confit (£5). Short wine list from £11.95. Accommodation. Closed Sun D.

MAP 6 **Holkham** NORFOLK

Victoria

Park Road, Holkham NR23 1RG
Tel: (01328) 711008
Website: www.victoriaatholkham.co.uk

Cooking 3 | Modern British | £35–£62

Descendants of the agriculturally renowned 'Coke of Norfolk' still own the Holkham Estate and, with it, this flint-walled, forceful-looking hotel named in honour of Queen Victoria. The décor's faded colonial charm evokes both Days of the Raj and *Out of Africa*, although most of the culinary inspiration comes from much closer to home. Game from the Estate is a feature: venison Wellington, cooked beautifully rare and served on a bed of Savoy cabbage chiffonade with bitter chocolate sauce, for example. To start, there might be 'memorable' salmon cured with vodka and beetroot, or terrine of guinea fowl with Agen prunes and pistachio vinaigrette, 'Vic's favourites' include chicken Caesar salad, while desserts could feature caramelised lemon custard with gingerbread ice cream. The eclectic wine list, arranged by style, starts at £12.50.

Chef: Neil Dawson **Proprietors:** Tom and Polly Coke **Open:** all week 12 to 2.30, 7 to 9.30 **Meals:** alc (main courses £10 to £18). BBQ menu available in summer **Service:** not inc, card slips closed **Cards:** Delta, Diners, Maestro, MasterCard, Visa **Details:** 90 seats. 150 seats outside. Private parties: 40 main room, 10 to 20 private rooms. Car park. Vegetarian meals. Children's helpings. No smoking. Wheelchair access (also women's WC). Music. Air-conditioned **Accommodation:** 16 rooms, all with bath/shower. TV. Phone. B&B £90 to £170. Rooms for disabled. Baby facilities

MAP 6 **Holt** NORFOLK

Yetman's

37 Norwich Road, Holt NR25 6SA
Tel: (01263) 713320
Website: www.yetmans.net

Cooking 4 | Modern British | £50–£67

Yetman's thrives on its own brand of very personal domesticity, which the owners have nurtured since they opened this pretty little yellow restaurant in 1988. Peter Yetman is his own man out front (he has been known to close the place if the weather is too hot), and Alison is very much her own woman in the kitchen. Don't expect refined cuisine here: direct, earthy, heart-on-sleeve dishes are the order of the day, and it's all fuelled by a dedication to well-sourced seasonal produce. Cockles in white wine and garlic sauce won over one reporter, Cornish squid is chargrilled and served with a sweet chilli jam, while roast local new season's lamb comes with a walnut stuffing and a mint and citrus sauce. Vegetables seem to have that 'just gathered' freshness, cheeses come from Neal's Yard, and desserts are uncomplicated offerings like treacle tart, vanilla pannacotta with spiced plums, or a version of the River Café's chocolate nemesis with Seville orange curd. Wines are a brief list of personal favourites chosen to match the cooking, with prices from £17.25. For an even more personal touch try a pint of Yetman's own beer.

Chef: Alison Yetman **Proprietors:** Alison and Peter Yetman **Open:** Sun L 12.30 to 2, Wed to Sat and bank hol Sun D 7 to 9.30 **Meals:** Set L and D £28.50 (2 courses) to £39 **Service:** not inc, card slips closed **Cards:** Amex, Delta, Maestro, MasterCard, Visa **Details:** 32 seats. Private parties: 20 main room. Vegetarian meals. Children's helpings. No smoking. Wheelchair access (not WC). No music

MAP 5 Holy Cross WORCESTERSHIRE

Bell and Cross AR

Holy Cross DY9 9QL
Tel: (01562) 730319

Bustling and regularly packed pub/restaurant in a lofty listed building at the foot of the Clent Hills but within reach of the M5. Daily specials beef up the regular menu, which works its way from confit of ham hock and vegetable terrine with Pommery mustard dressing (£5.50) through grilled sea bream fillet with prawn, basil and tomato linguine (£11.75) to white chocolate and rhubarb crème brûlée (£5). Around 40 wines with prices from £11.75. Open all week.

MAP 10 Holy Island NORTHUMBERLAND

Crown and Anchor Inn

Market Square, Holy Island TD15 2RX
Tel: (01289) 389215

Handily situated Northumbrian inn and an agreeable stopover for visitors to tidal Holy Island. Regularly changing menus and blackboards are dictated by ever-increasing supplies of local produce: a terrine of veal sweetbreads and black pudding (£6.50) might precede smoked salmon fishcakes with 'sunshine mayonnaise' (£14), or slow-braised lamb with bean stew. Finish with desserts like crunchy lemon sponge with mixed berries and vanilla ice cream (£4.50). Seasonal wine list with prices from £12.40. Accommodation. Closed Sun D; open weekends only Nov to Mar.

AR	Not a full entry but provisionally recommended (known as 'round-ups' in previous editions, these 'also recommended' establishments are now integrated throughout the book).

MAP 8 Honley WEST YORKSHIRE

Mustard and Punch

6 Westgate, Honley HD9 6AA
Tel: (01484) 662066
Website: www.mustardandpunch.co.uk

Cooking 3 | Modern European | £20–£56

Richard Dunn runs an industrious kitchen at his unassuming, welcoming restaurant in *Last of the Summer Wine* country, with much made on the premises, including bread, preserves, and ice cream. There is the option of set-price eating as well as a carte, and a pleasing sense of creativity runs through both. Chicken liver parfait with caramelised onion chutney is familiar enough, but more novel is pan-fried duck liver with pain d'épice, fig caramel and veal jus. Main courses might include braised ham hock with mustard seed mash, toffee apple and sage jus, and a Thai-style monkfish noodle bowl, or go for veal liver and bacon. Desserts might be chocolate molten cake, or steamed figgy pudding with star anise ice cream. An enterprising and fairly priced wine list from around the world opens at £11.95.

Chefs: Richard Dunn and Wayne Roddis **Proprietor:** Richard Dunn **Open:** Tue to Fri L 12 to 2, Mon to Sat D 6 to 9.30 **Closed:** 26 Dec to 5 Jan, 2 weeks Aug **Meals:** alc (main courses £9.50 to £18). Set L £10.50 (2 courses), Set D Mon to Fri and 6 to 7 Sat £16.95 (inc wine). **Service:** not inc **Cards:** Amex, Delta, Maestro, MasterCard, Visa **Details:** 55 seats. Private parties: 30 main room. Vegetarian meals. No smoking. Music. Air-conditioned

MAP 9 Horncastle LINCOLNSHIRE

Magpies

71–75 East Street, Horncastle LN9 6AA
Tel: (01507) 527004
Website: www.eatatthemagpies.co.uk

Cooking 5 | Modern British | £46–£55

This delightful row of low terraced cottages on the town's East Street has custard-coloured stucco walls with navy-blue shutters on its upper floor (not the traditional black-and-white façade one might expect from the name), and inside is uncluttered, decked out in shades of honey and rusty reds with well-spaced tables and white linen. There's a stylish little courtyard terrace out back for those fair-weather aperitifs.

Andrew Gilbert's pedigree shows in the enticing, fixed-price menu and the kitchen's classy output (Andrew was previously at the Old Vicarage, Ridgeway, see entry). While he mans the stoves, partner Caroline Ingall's domain is at front-of-house, heading up the black-clad team who help offer an intimate, relaxed experience. Andrew's great-value modern British repertoire uses top-quality produce (from local suppliers where possible) and delivers oodles of interest and imaginative flavour combinations. Take baked sea bass on a pineapple and chilli salad with sautéed potatoes and mango dressing, or perhaps roasted duck breast on carrot and swede mash, rösti potatoes with seared foie gras and Madeira sauce, then agonise over the choice between a classic hot chocolate fondant with chocolate mousse and bitter chocolate sorbet, or glazed lemon tart with a gin and tonic sorbet and lemon and sesame tuile.

Italy, with wines from Alfieri, Santini and Moris Farms, scores highly on a wine list scattered with good names. Bordeaux and Burgundy sensibly focus on bottles under £30, while house selections start at just £11.85.

Chef: Andrew Gilbert **Proprietors:** Caroline Ingall and Andrew Gilbert **Open:** Sun L 12 to 2.30, Wed to Sun D 7 to 9.30 **Closed:** 26 Dec to 3 Jan **Meals:** Set L and D £32 **Service:** not inc, card slips closed **Cards:** MasterCard, Maestro, Visa **Details:** 34 seats. 10 seats outside. Private parties: 36 main room. Vegetarian meals. No smoking. Wheelchair access (also WC). Music. No mobile phones. Air-conditioned

MAP 3 **Horndon on the Hill**
ESSEX

Bell Inn

High Road, Horndon on the Hill SS17 8LD
Tel: (01375) 642463
Website: www.bell-inn.co.uk

Cooking 2 | Modern European | £31–£48

In the Middle Ages, this venerable hostelry was frequented by pilgrims waiting to cross the Thames at Higham's Causeway; five centuries on it looks the part and is still in the business of providing sustenance. The kitchen tackles some ambitious-sounding ideas: ravioli of leek and parsley with truffle hollandaise and puff pastry could open proceedings, before pan-fried dorade with clam chowder and Parmesan, or bacon knuckle with celeriac purée and marrowfat pea jus. Desserts cover everything from banana crumble to rhubarb crème brûlée with star anise jelly and rhubarb sorbet. The same menu is also available in the bar (no bookings), alongside a few more robust pub-style dishes. A considerate choice of half-bottles fleshes out the reasonably priced wine list; house recommendations start at £10.25.

Chef: Finlay Logan **Proprietors:** John and Christine Vereker **Open:** all week 12 to 1.45 (2.15 Sun), 6.45 to 9.45 **Closed:** 25 and 26 Dec, bank hols **Meals:** alc (main courses £12 to £14.50). Sandwich L and bar menus available. **Service:** not inc, card slips closed **Cards:** Amex, Delta, Maestro, MasterCard, Visa **Details:** 80 seats. 36 seats outside. Private parties: 12 main room, 14 to 36 private rooms. Car park. Vegetarian meals. Children's helpings. No smoking in dining area. Wheelchair access (also WC). No music **Accommodation:** 15 rooms, all with bath/shower. TV. Phone. Room only £50 to £100. Rooms for disabled. Baby facilities

MAP 6 **Horningsea**
CAMBRIDGESHIRE

Crown & Punchbowl

High Street, Horningsea CB5 9JG
Tel: 01223 860643
Website: www.cambscuisine.com

Cooking 2 | Modern British | £25–£47

Like its stablemate The Cock in Hemingford Grey (see entry), this village pub has made the transition from local watering hole to casual country restaurant. The décor is unostentatious and so is the food, with regularly changing menus focusing on sound ingredients (including meat from rare breeds). From the printed menu Stilton pannacotta with walnuts and honey might lead you on to beef fillet with braised oxtail, shallots and Hemingford mash, or something from the blackboard listing fresh fish dishes (monkfish with Puy lentils, seafood sauce and vegetable dressing, for example). The selection of 'mix-and-match' sausages sounds intriguing, while desserts strike a rich note – chocolate tart with marmalade and crème fraîche ice cream, for instance. Thirty wines from £9.95 include ten by the glass. The Boathouse in Ely is the latest addition to the group.

Chefs: Ben Renshaw and Peter Friskey **Proprietors:** Richard Bradley, Richard Day and Oliver Thain **Open:** all week L 12 to 2.30, Mon to Sat D 6.30 to 9 (9.30 Fri and Sat) **Meals:** alc (main courses £11 to £18). Set L £9.95 (1 course) to £15.95 **Service:** not inc **Cards:** Amex, Delta, Maestro, MasterCard, Visa **Details:** 70 seats. 20 seats outside. Private parties: 30 main room, 10 private room. Car park. Vegetarian meals. Children's helpings. No smoking. Wheelchair access (also WC). No music **Accommodation:** 5 rooms, all with bath/shower. TV. B&B £59.95 to £79.95. No children

MAP 6 **Houghton Conquest**
BEDFORDSHIRE

Knife & Cleaver

AR

The Grove, Houghton Conquest MK45 3LA
Tel: (01234) 740387

Jacobean panelling graces the bar in this affluent, seventeenth-century country inn/restaurant close to John Bunyan's stamping ground. Meals in the conservatory-style restaurant make a feature of fish (chargrilled marlin with minted pea purée and a tomato and chervil dressing); otherwise expect potted duck rillettes with sweet pimento jam (£6), beef fillet with tarragon and sweet potato mash, then desserts like mango crème brûlée (£4.50). Well-spread wine list, with prices from £11.50. Accommodation. Closed Sat L and Sun D.

MAP 9 **Huddersfield**
WEST YORKSHIRE

Bradley's

84 Fitzwilliam Street, Huddersfield HD1 5BB
Tel: (01484) 516773

Cooking 2 | Medit/Mod British | £17–£52

A Huddersfield fixture for a dozen years or more, Andrew Bradley's bistro-style restaurant 'remains as popular as ever' and 'always buzzes' with diners and music. Pale wood and bold colours characterise the split-level dining room, decked out with upholstered cane chairs and polished-wood tables. The lengthy, crowd-pleasing repertoire suits both venue and ambience and is delivered via blackboard specials, fixed-price Prime Time menu, and carte. Take your pick from a fashionable modern medley, perhaps a retro-themed roast breast of corn-fed chicken stuffed with asparagus and wrapped in Parma ham, grilled sea bass fillets served with braised fennel and sauce vierge, or the more esoteric chilled Japanese-style roast beef with peanut and soya and Chinese greens to start. Though results can occasionally prove inconsistent, service is suitably enthusiastic and youthful, and the no-nonsense wine list is reasonably priced with French house opening the account at £11.50.

Chef: Stuart Nunn **Proprietor:** Andrew Bradley **Open:** Mon to Fri L 12 to 2, Mon to Sat D 6 (5.30 Fri and Sat) to 10 **Meals:** alc (main courses £9.50 to £17). Set L £6.95 (2 courses) to £7.95, Set D £14.95 to £16.95 (inc wine) **Service:** not inc **Cards:** MasterCard, Maestro, Visa **Details:** 120 seats. Private parties: 120 main room, 2 to 60 private rooms. Car park (D only). Vegetarian meals. Children's helpings. No smoking in 1 dining room. Wheelchair access (also WC). Music. Air-conditioned

Dining Rooms @ Strawberry Fair

14–18 Westgate, Huddersfield HD1 1NN
Tel: (01484) 513103

Cooking 2 | Modern European | £21–£42

The Dining Rooms are an understandably popular lunchtime (plus breakfast and afternoon tea) venue that pull in the crowds with high-quality food. The restaurant shares its town-centre real estate with a shop selling home accessories and kitchenware – and makes good use of the attractive tableware in stock. The kitchen delivers fresh, innovative dishes without a long wait, and an inspector's only lament is that the whole shebang shuts up shop in the evening. Start with 'properly smoked and perfectly cooked' haddock on a salad of plum tomatoes and watercress, or a dozen tender spears of new season's asparagus with a soft-poached egg, shaved Parmesan and parsley oil. Main-course tagliatelle with pumpkin, rocket and dolcelatte impressed an inspector, as did a rum and caramel crème brûlée. Wines on the modest, good-value list start with a brace of Chileans at £10.55.

Chefs: Glenn Varley and Rachel Miller **Proprietor:** Phillip Harrison **Open:** Mon to Sat L only 11.30 to 3 **Closed:** bank hols **Meals:** alc (main courses £6.50 to £12.50) **Service:** not inc, card slips closed **Cards:** Amex, Delta, Maestro, MasterCard, Visa **Details:** 48 seats. Private parties: 48 main room. Vegetarian meals. Children's helpings. No smoking. Wheelchair access (also WC). Music. No mobile phones. Air-conditioned

Vanilla

NEW ENTRY

73–75 Lidget Street, Lindley, Huddersfield
HD3 3JP
Tel: (01484) 646474

Cooking 2 | Modern European | £28–£43

Chris Dunn sold his interest in the Mustard and Punch, Honley (see entry), to set up his own modern bistro a few miles away. His menu has a varied, modern style, with plenty of quirky touches; presentation is good, and flavours are distinct. An eye for native produce is evident in the shape of Lishman's prizewinning sausages, Whitby crab, Yorkshire game (in a caramelised suet pudding), and lamb (served, perhaps, as a trio of shepherd's pie, kidney and best end, with swede fondant, spinach and red cabbage, and roasting juices). Among starters there might be crispy-fried scallops with black pudding, buttered spinach and a poached egg with ginger and lemongrass butter sauce, and to finish chocolate brûlée with eggnog ice cream and a sablé biscuit. Service is polite and friendly, while the wine list – a globetrotting, reasonably priced affair – starts at £10.50.

Chefs: Chris Dunn, Andrew Sharp and Alex Knott **Proprietor:** Chris Dunn **Open:** Tue to Fri L 12 to 2, Tue to Sat D 5.30 to 9.30 (10 Sat) **Meals:** alc (main courses £10.50 to £16). Set L £6.95 (2 courses) **Service:** not inc **Cards:** Delta, Maestro, MasterCard, Visa **Details:** 55 seats. Private parties: 55 main room. Vegetarian meals. Children's helpings. No smoking. Music

MAP 9 **Hull** KINGSTON UPON HULL

Boars Nest

NEW ENTRY

22 Princes Avenue, Hull HU5 3QA
Tel: (01482) 445577
Website: www.theboarsnest.co.uk

Cooking 2 | British | £25–£49

The porcine name is apt, given that these premises started life as a butcher's shop. Original tiled floors, tiled walls and meat rails high on the ceiling are true to the local vernacular, and the kitchen's view of things is very English. Beef hash with a deep-fried egg and meat juices is a typically gutsy starter; likewise smoked haddock and minted mushy pea fishcake. Pan-fried scallops with home-made piccalilli and potato salad sounds odd (but it works), while Gressingham duck breast is rolled in bubble and squeak and cooked Wellington-style. Elsewhere, you might find poached eel with mash and parsley sauce, and wild boar sausages. Vegetables are 'more than perfect', and for pudding you might consider doughnuts with chocolate sauce. Service is smiley, and the modest wine list does its job, with workaday drinking from £11.95.

Chef: Simon Rogers **Proprietors:** Simon Rogers and David Stead **Open:** Sun L 11.30 to 3, Wed to Mon D 6.30 to 10.45 **Meals:** alc exc Sun L (main courses £8.50 to £15). Set L Sun £15 **Service:** not inc, card slips closed **Cards:** Amex, Delta, Diners, Maestro, MasterCard, Visa **Details:** 32 seats. Private parties: 22 main room, 2 to 14 private rooms. Children's helpings. No smoking. Wheelchair access (also WC). Music

MAP 3 **Hunsdon** HERTFORDSHIRE

Fox & Hounds

NEW ENTRY

2 High Street, Hunsdon SG12 8NH
Tel: (01279) 843999
Website: www.foxandhounds-hunsdon.co.uk

Cooking 2 | British | £24–£49

Readers may recall James Rix from his time as head chef at the Cow Dining Room (see entry London). Since then he has upped sticks and is now to be found running the show at this family-friendly village pub close to the Hertfordshire/Essex border. The place has been given a revamp and it now combines the virtues of thriving boozer with congenial rustic restaurant. Plates and bowls are piled high, menus change daily and the kitchen delivers grilled squid with soy dressing, pigeon breast with pancetta, lightly roasted potatoes and French beans, and veal escalope atop a bed of spinach. Cheeses come with home-baked walnut and prune bread; otherwise there are traditional desserts like cherry and almond tart. House wine is £11.

Chef: James Rix **Proprietors:** James and Bianca Rix and Gemma Marsh **Open:** Tue to Sun L 12 to 3 (12 to 4 Sun), Tue to Sat D 6 to 10.30 **Closed:** 1 week Feb **Meals:** alc (main courses L £7.50 to £12, D £7.50 to £16.50). Set L Tue to Fri £10 (2 courses), Set L Sun £17.50 (2 courses) to £19.50, Set D Tue to Fri £12.50 (2 courses; 6 to 8pm only). Bar menu available **Service:** 10% (optional), card slips closed **Cards:** Delta, MasterCard, Maestro, Visa **Details:** 80 seats. 40 seats outside. Private parties: 40 main room. Car park. Vegetarian meals. Children's helpings. No smoking in 1 dining room. Wheelchair access (not WC). Occasional music

MAP 6 **Huntingdon** CAMBRIDGESHIRE

Old Bridge Hotel

1 High Street, Huntingdon PE29 3TQ
Tel: (01480) 458410
Website: www.huntsbridge.com

Cooking 4 | Modern British | £28–£64

The independent Huntsbridge Group has its base at this ivy-clothed eighteenth-century building near a bridge over the Ouse – although the set-up's tentacles also extend to the Falcon, Fotheringhay; the Pheasant, Keyston and the Three Horseshoes, Madingley (see entries). Martin Lee's cooking takes its cue from Britain's regional larder, but ingredients are subjected to forthright global treatment: baked fillet of hake comes with sprouting broccoli, marinated potatoes and tapenade, braised shoulder of Cornish lamb might be accompanied by cumin potatoes, red cabbage and parsnip crisps, while a warm salad of confit pheasant, pomegranate and walnuts suggests the Middle East. Like all Huntsbridge outlets, this is a flexible enterprise, which means you are also welcome to call in for sausage and mash, Caesar salad and BLTs. Puddings are simpler in style (Seville orange jelly with fresh egg custard), and one reporter felt the chocolate nemesis 'should not really be allowed out' (which we interpret as a compliment). For busy Sunday lunches roast beef is added to the menu.

The Huntsbridge wine lists keep pace with changing times and remains good value. As the daddy of the group, this one adds a convincing 'exceptional and rare' tier to the 'under £20'/'top-class' formula. Bottles start at £12.50, and 16 come by the glass.

Chef: Martin Lee **Proprietors:** Huntsbridge Ltd **Open:** all week 12 to 2.30, 7 (6.30 Fri/Sat) to 10 **Meals:** alc (main courses £9.75 to £22). Set L £13.50 (2 courses) to £16.75 **Service:** not inc **Cards:** Amex, Delta, Diners, Maestro, MasterCard, Visa **Details:** 100 seats. 25 seats outside. Private parties: 60 main room, 15 to 25 private rooms. Car park. Vegetarian meals. Children's helpings. No smoking. Wheelchair access (not WC). No music. No mobile phones. Air-conditioned **Accommodation:** 24 rooms, all with bath/shower. TV. Phone. B&B £95 to £190. Baby facilities

 This symbol means that the restaurant has elected to participate in *The Good Food Guide's* £5 voucher scheme (see 'How to Use the Guide' for details).

MAP 10 **Hutton Magna** CO DURHAM

Oak Tree Inn

Hutton Magna DH11 7HH
Tel: (01833) 627371

Cooking 2 | Modern European | £31–£45

Part of a row of terraced cottages by the church, this village pub/restaurant is run as a double act, with Alastair Ross in the kitchen and Claire out front. Menus are chalked above the bar and a specials board is brought round to each table. Ideas can sometimes seem over-complicated (roast fillet of turbot with provençale vegetables, salmon and basil ravioli, and champagne and chive sauce, for example), but there are plenty of good things to be had. Roast scallops wrapped with black pudding and Parma ham accompanied by parsley mash is a decent starter, ribeye steaks are served with big chips and béarnaise sauce, while vanilla pannacotta with pineapple and lemongrass compote and delicate fromage frais sorbet makes a pleasing finale. The modest wine list opens with house selections from £9.90.

Chef: Alastair Ross **Proprietors:** Alastair and Claire Ross **Open:** Tue to Sun D only 6.30 to 8.30. L bookings only **Closed:** 26 Dec, 1 Jan, 1 week Feb **Meals:** alc (main courses £12.50 to £16.50) **Service:** not inc, card slips closed **Cards:** Delta, Maestro, MasterCard, Visa **Details:** 24 seats. Private parties: 24 main room. Car park. No smoking. Music. No mobile phones

MAP 1 **Ilfracombe** DEVON

The Quay Restaurant

NEW ENTRY

11 The Quay, Ilfracombe EX34 9EQ
Tel: (01271) 868090
Website: www.11thequay.com

Cooking 2 | Modern European | £27–£115

The redeveloped harbour area of Ilfracombe offers plenty of eating options, prime among which is this stone- and brick-fronted building co-owned by Damien Hirst. Inside is a ground-floor tapas bar, with two dining rooms upstairs, one overlooking the harbour, the other (the Atlantic Room) surveying the bay. Floor-to-ceiling windows open on to a balcony, there is an aquarium set into the wall, and in the open kitchen chefs work calmly to produce some successful modern cooking. Jerusalem artichoke soup with a trio of truffled potato ravioli is smooth and pleasantly rich, or there might be rillettes of organic salmon with oscietra caviar and marinated cucumber. Hearty main courses have included pot-roast pheasant with braised chicory and pancetta, and the 'utterly fresh, lightly oily' grilled grey mullet, its skin fiercely seared to crispness, served with crushed potatoes and spinach, that so impressed an inspector. Gratin of winter fruits under a light, fluffy sabayon makes a good seasonal dessert, and chocolate marquise is made with Valrhona. Single-handed service keeps up the cheer. A short wine list is led off by an international choice of ten house wines from £12.

Chef: James O'Connor **Proprietors:** Damien Hirst and Simon Bronne **Open:** all week 12 to 3, 6 to 10 **Closed:** 25 and 26 Dec **Meals:** alc (main courses £16 to £25). Set L Mon to Sat £17.50, Set L Sun £17.50 (2 courses) to £20, Set D £45 to £85 (inc wine). Tapas menu available **Service:** 10% (optional) **Cards:** Amex, Diners, Maestro, MasterCard, Visa **Details:** 100 seats. 15 seats outside. Private parties: 25 main room, 10 to 25 private rooms. Children's helpings. No smoking. Wheelchair access (not WC). Music. Air-conditioned

MAP 8 **Ilkley** WEST YORKSHIRE

Box Tree

NEW ENTRY

35–37 Church Street, Ilkley LS29 9DR
Tel: (01943) 608484
Website: www.theboxtree.co.uk

Cooking 6 | Anglo-French | £41–£81

A long-standing stalwart of earlier editions of the Guide, the Box Tree makes a welcome return, now under the experienced auspices of Simon and Rena Gueller, veterans of great acclaim at former ventures in Harrogate and Leeds. The decorative tone has subtly but distinctly changed, from the antique-shop clutter of yesteryear to a fresher and sharper feel, and the staff's approach introduces a note of unstuffy efficiency, for which many will be thankful.

Quality home-made bread with Echiré butter, properly appetising canapés and the *de rigueur* creamy velouté amuse-bouche in a coffee cup all post notice of the culinary intent. This is serious cuisine, committed to technical excellence without reaching for outré combinations to sustain interest. A starter of white asparagus might be simply finished with sauce maltaise, or there is the option of a trio of marine hors d'oeuvres comprising dressed crab with cucumber jelly, truffled Dover sole sushi wrapped in nori, and chopped gravad lax on a gingery aspic base. Main courses gain lustre through the pedigree of their components, as is the case with gamey squab pigeon, served bright pink, with fondant potato and shredded cabbage in a powerful yet light red wine reduction. Monkfish arrives with a version of cassoulet for company, with morteau sausage and a foaming parsley sauce. Desserts make an impact too, as when a moist cake of pear and apricot, garnished with fig sorbet, has a rich caramel espuma poured over it, or when passion-fruit soufflé with hazelnut ice cream is further accompanied by a little glass of chocolate milkshake.

Interesting bottled beers and good sherries by the glass add spice to a stately wine list strong in French classics and fine bottles from Australia and California. Prices (from £15.95) are on the high side, but plentiful half-bottles increase scope.

Chef: Simon Gueller **Proprietor:** Rena Gueller **Open:** Fri to Sun L 12 to 1.30 (2 Sun), Tue to Sat D 7 to 9.30 **Meals:** alc D (main courses £19.50 to £26). Set L £18 (2 courses) to £25, Set D Tue to Thur £28 **Service:** not inc **Cards:** Delta, Maestro, MasterCard, Visa **Details:** 50 seats. Private parties: 36 main room, 14 private room. Vegetarian meals. No children under 10 at D; children's helpings. No smoking. Wheelchair access (not WC). Music. No mobile phones. Air-conditioned

Farsyde

1–3 New Brook Street, Ilkley LS29 8DQ
Tel: (01943) 602030
Website: www.thefarsyde.co.uk

Cooking 4 | Modern British-Plus | £21–£42

Having moved across town in 2003, Gavin Beedham and his team are ticking over confidently in their adopted premises opposite the parish church. The kitchen has stuck to its trusted formula of modern-brasserie-style cooking with lots of influences and a dedication to value for money across the board. Open your account with a warm salad of wood pigeon, new potatoes, pancetta, capers and roast artichokes, or kebab of Thai chicken, mango and lychee, before fillet of cod with a prawn and sesame crust on a crab, pea and pesto risotto cake with chilli jam, or fillet of beef with an oxtail casserole and horseradish mash. More fish dishes appear on the specials board, and ice creams find their way into several of the desserts: chocolate and mint with chocolate sponge and chocolate zabaglione, and coconut with banoffi cheesecake and caramelised bananas.

for example. House wines are £8.95, and the 50-bin list is a keenly priced, worldwide selection.

Chef/Proprietor: Gavin Beedham **Open:** Tue to Sat 11.30 to 1.30, 6 to 9.30 **Closed:** 25 and 26 Dec, 1 and 2 Jan **Meals:** alc (main courses £12 to £15.50). Set L 12 to 1.30 £12.95 (3 courses), Set D 6 to 7.15 £12.95 (2 courses) **Service:** not inc **Cards:** Delta, Maestro, MasterCard, Visa **Details:** 82 seats. Vegetarian meals. No smoking in restaurant, permitted in bar. Wheelchair access (also WC). Music

MAP 5 Ilmington WARWICKSHIRE

Howard Arms AR

Lower Green, Ilmington CV36 4LT
Tel: (01608) 682226

'Prosperous and stylish' sums up this sprucely remodelled 400-year-old Cotswold inn by the village green. Daily-changing blackboard menus follow the seasons and the markets for, say, twice-baked goats' cheese and thyme soufflé (£5.50), pancetta-wrapped Berkshire pork fillet with parsnip purée and Madeira sauce (£11.50), and homely desserts such as Mrs G's toffee meringue (£6). Fine choice of real ales and a short, catholic wine list with prices from £11.15. Three letting rooms. Open all week.

MAP 1 Instow DEVON

Decks

Hatton Croft House, Marine Parade, Instow
EX39 4JJ
Tel: (01271) 860671
Website: www.decksrestaurant.co.uk

Cooking 2 | Modern European | £34–£41

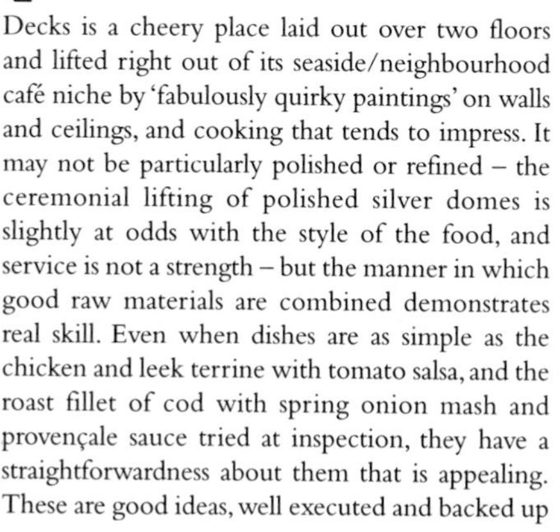

Decks is a cheery place laid out over two floors and lifted right out of its seaside/neighbourhood café niche by 'fabulously quirky paintings' on walls and ceilings, and cooking that tends to impress. It may not be particularly polished or refined – the ceremonial lifting of polished silver domes is slightly at odds with the style of the food, and service is not a strength – but the manner in which good raw materials are combined demonstrates real skill. Even when dishes are as simple as the chicken and leek terrine with tomato salsa, and the roast fillet of cod with spring onion mash and provençale sauce tried at inspection, they have a straightforwardness about them that is appealing. These are good ideas, well executed and backed up by honest-tasting desserts such as a brandy-snap of apple, raspberry and passion-fruit sorbets. House South African is £9.95.

Chef/Proprietor: Lee Timmins **Open:** Tue to Sat 12 to 2.30, 7 to 9.30 **Closed:** first 2 weeks Nov, 25 and 26 Dec, 1 Jan **Meals:** alc L (main courses £6 to £13). Set D £24.50 **Service:** not inc, card slips closed **Cards:** Delta, MasterCard, Maestro, Visa **Details:** 42 seats. 32 seats outside. Private parties: 60 main room. Vegetarian meals. Children's helpings. No smoking in 1 dining room. Wheelchair access (also WC). Music. Air-conditioned

MAP 6 Ipswich SUFFOLK

Galley AR

25 St Nicholas Street, Ipswich IP1 1TW
Tel: (01473) 281131

Busy bistro-style restaurant with a global outlook. Savoury baklava, and grilled halloumi on Moorish couscous reflect the owner's native roots; otherwise, the kitchen goes walkabout for crispy braised belly pork with coconut hot-and-sour sauce (£8), grilled Loch Duart salmon marinated with borscht and creamy dill sauce (£16), and sticky toffee pudding with marmalade ice cream (£6). House wine £12.95. Open Tue to Sat. There's a branch at 21 Market Hill, Woodbridge; tel: (01394) 380055.

MAP 5 Ironbridge SHROPSHIRE

Malthouse AR

The Wharfage, Ironbridge TF8 7NH
Tel: (01952) 433712

All-purpose inn built around a cobbled courtyard alongside the Severn, comprising a Jazz Bar (with live music) and a dimly lit, traditional restaurant dealing in straightforward modern dishes. Seared scallops with grilled Spanish black pudding (£7) and venison fillet with apple mash, green beans and red wine jus (£15.50) have been recommended from the regularly changing menus; desserts (£4) might include mixed berry crème brûlée. Thursday night is fish night. House wines from £10. Accommodation. Open all week.

MAP 3 **Jevington** EAST SUSSEX

Hungry Monk

Jevington BN26 5QF
Tel: (01323) 482178
Website: www.hungrymonk.co.uk

Cooking 2 | Anglo-French | £44–£58

The birthplace of the banoffi pie, this long-established, cottagey restaurant is a place of pilgrimage for pudding aficionados. Low doorways, snug sitting rooms and comfy sofas ooze cosy, olde English atmosphere. The menu evolves gently, yet remains comfortingly familiar; take smoked haddock and salmon kedgeree to start, then perhaps poached halibut with a lemon and saffron sauce, or marinated loin of lamb with aubergine couscous and plum sauce. Calorific desserts are predominantly homely, old-school offerings – headed by banoffi pie, of course, but bolstered by, say, melting chocolate pudding, or jam roly-poly and custard. Service is helpful and relaxed, while the French-inspired wine list has some mature clarets at its heart, but kicks off with house bottles at £14–£15.

Chefs: Gary Fisher and Matt Comber **Proprietors:** Nigel and Sue Mackenzie **Open:** Sun L 12 to 2.30, all week D 6.45 to 10 **Closed:** Dec 24 to 26, bank hol Mon **Meals:** Set L Sun £28.95, Set D £29.95 **Service:** not inc, 12.5% for parties of 7 or more **Cards:** Amex, Maestro, MasterCard, Visa **Details:** 34 seats. 12 seats outside. Private parties: 34 main room, 4 to 16 private rooms. Car park. Vegetarian meals. Children's helpings. No children under 3. No smoking. Occasional music. Air-conditioned

MAP 8 **Kendal** CUMBRIA

Bridge House

1 Bridge Street, Kendal LA9 7DD
Tel: (01539) 738855
Website: www.bridgehousekendal.co.uk

Cooking 4 | Modern British | £29–£59

A quietly elegant stone house close to one of the bridges over the river is the setting for Roger and Alena Pergl-Wilson's restaurant, and there are views of the water from one of the upstairs dining rooms. Little else distracts from the food on the plate. Roger's cooking is broadly Anglo-French, although he is not averse to slipping in ideas from elsewhere: fillet of sea bass is served with a 'piccata' of aubergine and a red pepper sauce, while grilled fell-bred lamb cutlets might appear with orange, cumin and mint butter and spiced couscous. The loyalty to Cumbrian produce also extends to smoked lake pike, Lunesdale duck (with apricot and chestnut stuffing and Madeira sauce) and Lyth Valley damsons – which might find their way into a crumble. Other desserts are more exotic: poached pear with liquorice ice cream, chocolate sauce and a sesame poppy-seed wafer, for example. The worldwide wine list is fairly priced, with house selections from £11.95.

Chef: Roger Pergl-Wilson **Proprietors:** Roger and Alena Pergl-Wilson **Open:** Tue to Sat 12.30 to 1.30, 6.30 to 9.30 **Closed:** 25 and 26 Dec **Meals:** alc D (main courses £11 to £20). Set L £13.50 (2 courses) to £17.50, Set D Tue to Fri £19.50 **Service:** not inc, card slips closed **Cards:** Delta, Maestro, MasterCard, Visa **Details:** 36 seats. Private parties: 25 main room, 10 to 25 private rooms. Vegetarian meals. Children's helpings. No smoking. Occasional music

Déjà-vu

124 Stricklandgate, Kendal LA9 4QG
Tel: (01539) 724843
Website: www.dejavukendal.co.uk

Cooking 2 | French Bistro | £25–£52

Fran and Ian Wood have exchanged bright colours and assorted furniture for a more sedate mixture of deep burgundy walls, matching upholstered chairs and pale wooden tables but have kept the unpretentious informality popular with locals. An appealing range of well-spiced and properly herbed tapas, ranging from patatas bravas with chorizo to meatballs, has been added to hearty main courses such as slow-roast pork shoulder with sage sauce, or a simple pan-fried quarter of chicken with sun-blush tomato and saffron sauce. Crunchy asparagus accompanying black truffle risotto with the right mix of bite and softness characterises the carefully attentive cooking. Puddings like profiteroles or crème brûlée are supplemented by well-sourced local ice creams and sorbets. The list of around 25 wines starts at £12 and maintains the no-fuss approach.

Chef: Fabien Bellouère **Proprietors:** Fran and Ian Wood **Open:** all week D only 5.30 to 9 (9.30 Fri and Sat) **Closed:** 25 and 26 Dec, 1 Jan, bank hol Mon **Meals:** alc (main courses £9 to £17). Tapas menu available Mon to Sat L and D 5.30 to 6.30 **Service:** not inc, card slips closed, 10% for parties of 6 or more **Cards:** Amex, Delta, Maestro, MasterCard, Visa **Details:** 36 seats. Private parties: 20 main room. Vegetarian meals. No smoking. Wheelchair access (not WC). Music. No mobile phones

MAP 5 **Kenilworth** WARWICKSHIRE

Restaurant Bosquet

97A Warwick Road, Kenilworth CV8 1HP
Tel: (01926) 852463
Website: www.restaurantbosquet.co.uk

Cooking 4 | French | £44–£60

After a quarter-century, the Ligniers certainly seem at home in Kenilworth, and their endearing double act continues to draw an appreciative audience, with Bernard at the stove while Jane is very bright and chatty at front-of-house. And, though it's easy for first-timers to miss their small, unobtrusive and narrow terraced restaurant on the main road through town, it's well worth tracking down. Inside, dark wooden floors, black leather chairs, mirrors, silk curtains and a distinctive colour scheme strike a modern edge, providing the backdrop for Bernard's quality approach to the traditional cooking of his Gallic homeland. Expect classic ingredients sprinkled with luxury items on fixed-price or carte options right from the start; take an escalope of duck foie gras served with a sweet and sour sauce, or perhaps lobster and prawn with a crumble of carrots and apricots in a ginger sauce. A fillet of Scottish beef with classic peppercorn sauce, its chips cooked in goose fat, might head the mains, alongside girolles-stuffed boned squab; in-house breads, excellent olives and 'fish of the day' mains bolster proceedings. The wine list, not unexpectedly, is patriotically French, opening with house bottles at £14.50.

Chef: Bernard Lignier **Proprietors:** Bernard and Jane Lignier **Open:** Tue to Fri L (bookings only) 12 to 1.15, Tue to Sat D 7 to 9 **Meals:** alc (main courses £19). Set L and D Mon to Fri £29.50 **Service:** not inc **Cards:** Amex, Maestro, MasterCard, Visa **Details:** 26 seats. Private parties: 30 main room. Children's helpings. No smoking. No music. No mobile phones

Simply Simpson's

101–103 Warwick Road, Kenilworth CV8 1HL
Tel: (01926) 864567

Simpson's has moved to Edgbaston, Birmingham (see entry), and the original premises have been renamed and turned into a simpler brasserie/bistro with former sous-chef Iain Miller at the helm. The output ranges from confit of duck leg salad (£5.25) to cod, chips and mushy peas (£12.50), taking in smoked haddock and spinach risotto (£5) and braised shank of lamb kleftico (£14.25) along the way. Chocolate fondant is an alternative to praline crème brûlée (£5.50). An equally wide-ranging wine list climbs steeply from £16. Closed Sun and Mon.

MAP 10 **Keswick** CUMBRIA

Swinside Lodge

AR

Grange Road, Newlands, Keswick CA12 5UE
Tel: (017687) 72948

Georgian country residence in fabulous Lakeland surroundings close to Derwent Water. Dinners are fixed price for four courses (£35) with cheese as an extra. Start with seared scallops, black pudding, hawthorn shoots and herb and apple salad before cream of celeriac and Stilton soup; main courses could be rosemary-roast fillet of Cumbrian lamb with sun-dried tomato risotto rösti and kumquat relish, while desserts might include rum pannacotta with pineapple and passion-fruit compote. House wine is £12.50. Open all week D only.

MAP 3 **Kew** GREATER LONDON

Glasshouse

14 Station Parade, Kew TW9 3PZ
Tel: (020) 8940 6777
Website: www.glasshouserestaurant.co.uk

Cooking 5 | Modern British | £32–£74

This much-favoured neighbourhood restaurant within sight of Kew Gardens tube station goes from strength to strength. Its long, glazed frontage makes it hard to miss. Also distinctive are Anthony Boyd's fixed-price menus, offering a wealth of creative choice. A coq au vin raviolo was large, near-spherical, crammed with its filling and sitting on a field mushroom that in turn rested on unctuous onion confit, and crisp Cornish mackerel arrives in a mille-feuille, under a strip of puff pastry and resting on aubergine caviar, courgettes, tomato and pesto. And considered juxtapositions produce satisfying main courses like a 'swine tasting' comprising roast Middle White pork belly with a crisped slice of Parma ham on top and morteau sausage, garnished triumphantly with choucroute, prunes and an apple tarte fine. The shorter lunch menu offers two choices per course, perhaps proceeding from pickled herrings with crème fraîche, capers and shallots, to confit rabbit leg and chorizo with creamed polenta and buttered curly kale; finish with ginger pannacotta with poached rhubarb and frosted pistachios, or raspberry baked Alaska. Helpful, chatty service makes everyone feel welcome.

Wine service, 'as helpful as ever', provides expert guidance to a long list of contemporary stars structured to appeal to all pockets. France and Italy are the focus in Europe, Australia and California in the New World, but quality isn't stinted in the shorter selections elsewhere. Prices start at £15, with over a dozen by the glass.

Chef: Anthony Boyd **Proprietors:** Bruce Poole and Nigel Platts-Mills **Open:** all week 12 to 2.30 (3 Sun), 7 to 10.30 **Closed:** 24 to 26 Dec **Meals:** Set L £2.50 (2 courses) to £25, Set L Sun £27.50, Set D £32.50 to £45 (whole table only) **Service:** 12.5% (optional), card slips closed **Cards:** Amex, Delta, Maestro, MasterCard, Visa **Details:** 65 seats. Private parties: 70 main room. Vegetarian meals. Children's helpings. No smoking. No music. Air-conditioned **Tube** Kew gardens

MAP 6 **Keyston** CAMBRIDGESHIRE

Pheasant

Loop Road, Keyston PE28 0RE
Tel: (01832) 710241
Website: www.huntsbridge.com

Cooking 2 | Modern European | £32–£63

In a peaceful little farming village on the Cambridgeshire/Leicestershire border, this member of the Huntsbridge group is a delightful old thatched inn, its white walls adorned with hanging flower baskets. At the front is a small grassed area with picnic benches in the shade of mature trees. If that's not archetypal English country pub enough, inside are low, beamed ceilings, flagstone floors, a log fire, and pink-painted walls hung with farming implements. There are two informal bar eating areas, while the main dining room is only slightly more refined. Eclectic modern menus might offer among starters an earthy, well-flavoured mushroom and thyme soup finished with a dash of truffle oil, or a large slice of guinea fowl and asparagus terrine accompanied by a first-rate fruit chutney. To follow, carefully cooked monkfish with saffron and red pepper risotto has been a highlight, selected from the blackboard of fresh fish delivered daily from Cornwall. Desserts take in mocha and cappuccino mousse with orange and polenta biscuits. The wine list follows the familiar Huntsbridge group format, with 16 engaging options by the glass followed by separate selections under and over the £20 mark. The emphasis is on elegant styles, and, while this is not the longest list in the group, it still encompasses a world of temptations.

Chef: James Claydon **Proprietor:** Huntsbridge Ltd **Open:** all week 12 to 2, 6.30 to 9.30 **Meals:** alc (main courses £10 to £22). Bar menu available **Service:** not inc **Cards:** Amex, Delta, Diners, Maestro, MasterCard, Visa **Details:** 70 seats. 20 seats outside. Private parties: 34 main room, 30 private room. Car park. Vegetarian meals. Children's helpings. No smoking. No music. No mobile phones

MAP 5 **Kibworth Beauchamp** LEICESTERSHIRE

Firenze

9 Station Street, Kibworth Beauchamp LE8 0LN
Tel: (0116) 279 6260
Website: www.firenze.co.uk

Cooking 3 | Modern Italian | £29–£60

A crash course in the Italian fine arts may be had from the interior at Firenze, crammed as it is with prints and reproductions, the impression of a litre of riches being poured into a half-litre carafe enhanced by the low, beamed ceiling. Lino Poli's bilingual menus offer a similar guide to new-wave Italian culinary arts, dealing in starters such as smoked pigeon breast with an orange and fennel salad. A page of pasta dishes precedes the fish options – including sole fillets rolled with spinach and served with saffron sauce – and then meats: rabbit might be stuffed with apple and sauced with grain mustard. Desserts bring on pannacotta with limoncello, or chocolate polenta cake. Sarah Poli is eminently capable front-of-house. The 100-strong wine list sticks with Italy from fizz through to sweeties and packs in excellent lesser-known names (Drius, Malvira, Rocca di Montegrossi) alongside the more famous Jermann and Planeta. Good-value bottles start at £12.60, and 14 come by the glass.

Chefs: Lino Poli and Stuart Batey **Proprietors:** Lino and Sarah Poli **Open:** Tue to Fri L 12 to 2, Tue to Sat D 7 to 10 **Closed:** 2 weeks Christmas to New Year, 2 weeks in summer **Meals:** alc (main courses £8.50 to £19.50). Set L £12 (1 course), Set D Tue to Thur £15 (2 courses) to £25 **Service:** not inc, card slips closed **Cards:** Delta, Maestro, MasterCard, Visa **Details:** 70 seats. Private parties: 70 main room, 16 to 20 private rooms. Vegetarian meals. Children's helpings. No-smoking area. Wheelchair access (not WC). Music. No mobile phones

MAP 5 **Kingham** OXFORDSHIRE

Mill House

Kingham OX7 6UH
Tel: (01608) 658188
Website: www.millhousehotel.co.uk

Cooking 5 | Modern British-Plus | £42–£62

The creeper-clad hotel stands in ten acres of trimly manicured lawns, with a trout stream running through, in Cotswold country between Chipping Norton and Stow. Its interiors are done in gentle shades of rust red and soft green, with botanical prints on the dining room walls. A distinct sense of vaulting ambition emanates from Paul Haywood's efforts nowadays, with a new multi-course menu dégustation now joining the other fixed-price option. Presentations aim for maximum impact: a flat cake of haggis accompanies thinly sliced rabbit ballottine with strips of trompette mushrooms and a meaty garlic cream sauce. The occasional nod to domestic cookery brings on a main course of roast cod partnered with bubble and squeak containing bits of braised beef, although its sauce is based on foie gras and there is red onion confit to boot. Gressingham duck breast comes with confit leg, parsnip purée and braised red cabbage, as well as a small 'risotto' of wheat grains, chestnuts and pancetta. Highly polished desserts take in acclaimed soufflés – perhaps of prune and Armagnac, served with crème brûlée and ice cream, both flavoured with orange blossom – as well as the signature thin apple tart made with Braeburns, while cheeses are an embarrassment of riches. The wine list essays a comprehensive tour of the great and the good at mostly fair prices. House wines, from Chile, are £14.50.

Chef: Paul Haywood **Proprietor:** John Parslow **Open:** all week 12 to 2, 6 to 9.30 **Meals:** Set L and D £28 to £40; Set L Mon to Sun £12.50 (2 courses) to £16.50 (3 courses). **Service:** not inc, card slips closed **Cards:** Amex, Delta, Diners, Maestro, MasterCard, Visa **Details:** 80 seats. 24 seats outside. Private parties: 80 main room. Car park. Vegetarian meals. Children's helpings. No smoking. Wheelchair access (also WC). Occasional music. No mobile phones **Accommodation:** 23 rooms, all with bath/shower. TV. Phone. B&B £85 to £140. Rooms for disabled. Baby facilities

This symbol means that accommodation is available at this establishment.

MAP 6 **King's Lynn** NORFOLK

Riverside

AR

27 King Street, King's Lynn PE30 1ET
Tel: (01553) 773134

Five-hundred-year-old timbered building with some of the best river views you could wish for, plus tables on the terrace in fine weather. Lunch brings on a good-value carte, taking in penne with mussels (£6.50), cottage pie (£8.75), and roast rack of lamb (£17). The dinner menu (£23.75/£29.75) offers plenty of options too: maybe duck and orange terrine, then venison medallions with redcurrant and red wine sauce, followed by lemon cheesecake. Saturday brunch from 10.30am. House wines £12. Closed Sun.

Rococo

11 Saturday Market Place,
King's Lynn PE30 5DQ
Tel: (01553) 771483

Cooking 3 | Modern British | £25–£62

This bright and contemporarily decorated restaurant is situated in an ancient building on the main market square. The menus make a virtue of simplicity, and Nick Anderson is proud of his top-quality materials provided by a well-established network of suppliers, which might show up at dinner – lunch is a simpler affair – as a straightforward dish of sautéed wild mushrooms on toasted brioche with a poached duck's egg, or a mille-feuille of smoked haddock with a cappuccino of roast garlic and chervil. The choice at main course might be between wild sea bass with roast fennel, garlic mash and a tomato and basil beurre blanc, and red snapper with spiced bulgur wheat and an orange, basil and caper sauce. Finish perhaps with caramelised rice pudding with two fruit sauces, or pear tarte Tatin flavoured with cinnamon. Reports have highlighted the kitchen's 'perfect timing' and the unhurried service. Wines are varied and sensibly priced for the most part, starting with French house white at £11.95 and red at £13.95.

Chefs: Nick Anderson and Tim Sandford **Proprietors:** Nick and Susannah Anderson **Open:** Tue to Sat 12 to 2, 7 to 10 **Closed:** 24 to 30 Dec, bank hol Mon **Meals:** alc (main courses L £8 to £11, D £12.50 to £20). Set L £10.95 (2 courses) to £14.95 (inc wine) **Service:** not inc, card slips closed **Cards:** Delta, Maestro, MasterCard, Visa **Details:** 40 seats. Private parties: 40 main room. Vegetarian meals. Children's helpings. No-smoking area. Wheelchair access (also WC). Occasional music. No mobile phones

MAP 5 **Kington** HEREFORDSHIRE

Penrhos Court

Kington HR5 3LH
Tel: (01544) 230720
Website: www.penrhos.co.uk

Cooking 3 | Mediterranean | £47–£56

Occupying a complex of farm buildings grouped around a big pond, Penrhos Court is a thoroughly distinctive enterprise, which has been in the same ownership since the 1970s. Some of the buildings are of medieval lineage, and the rough-stone floors and gnarled wood of the interiors reflect that. Four courses plus coffee is the inclusive format, with no choice for the opening soup (perhaps sweet potato and nettle) or the second course, which could be a brilliantly fresh salad of arame seaweed, carrot and cabbage in an orange vinaigrette. Main courses present a choice of four, the palm at inspection going to superb pot-roast Welsh organic chicken with chickpea mash and chillied tomato dressing, but there might also be marinated roast gilthead bream, or fillet of sea bass with creamed fennel, all served with side dishes of well-chosen vegetables. Lemon balm ice cream is just that – two scoops in a cocktail glass, as rich as clotted cream – or there might be a large helping of dark chocolate and coffee mousse. Martin Griffiths oversees front-of-house with relaxed enthusiasm. A short, serviceable wine list starts at £15.20 for Italian Nero d'Avola.

Chef: Daphne Lambert **Proprietors:** Daphne Lambert and Martin Griffiths **Open:** all week D only 7.30 to 9.30 **Closed:** Jan **Meals:** Set D £32.50 **Service:** not inc, card slips closed **Cards:** Amex, Maestro, MasterCard, Visa **Details:** 70 seats. 200 seats outside. Private parties: 75 main room, 20 private room. Car park. Vegetarian meals. Children's helpings. No smoking. Wheelchair access (also WC). No music. No mobile phones **Accommodation:** 17 rooms, all with bath/shower. TV. Phone. B&B £100 to £140. Rooms for disabled. Baby facilities

MAP 2 **Kintbury** BERKSHIRE

Dundas Arms

AR

53 Station Road, Kintbury RG17 9UT
Tel: (01488) 658263

Small inn on an island between the Kennet and Avon Canal and the River Kennet, with a dozen or so tables outside for al fresco dining. The menu might start with warm smoked duck breast salad (£5) or grilled scallops with black pasta and saffron sauce (£9.50) and move on to roast rack of English lamb or pan-fried pigeon breasts with wild mushroom risotto (£13). Commanding wine list has 100-plus top-quality bins (with prices from £14 to £200). Closed all Sun and Mon D.

MAP 9 **Kirk Deighton** NORTH YORKSHIRE

Bay Horse

Main Street, Kirk Deighton LS22 4DZ
Tel: (01937) 580058

Cooking 3 | Modern European | £24–£45

Flagstone floors and a fruit machine mark the border between bar and dining room in this revitalised village pub a few minutes' drive from the A1. Food is the main business, and wordy handwritten menus are supplemented by blackboard specials. Seafood is a strong suit, from fishcakes ('born in Australia, developed in Wiltshire, cooked by a Lancastrian, eaten in Yorkshire', says the menu) to seared king scallops with a 'little pot' of devilled whitebait, mushy peas, rocket and pancetta crisps, and salmon fillet stuffed with king prawn mousse. Alternatives might include slow-cooked confit of Yorkshire lamb stuffed with oranges and fresh rosemary, while desserts are old-stagers like sticky toffee pudding with home-made vanilla ice cream. Most wines on the short, affordable list are offered by the glass; bottle prices start at £10.95. Karl Mainey also owns the Fox and Hounds in Walton, near Wetherby; tel:(01937) 842192.

Chef: Stephen Ardern **Proprietor:** Karl Mainey **Open:** Tue to Sun L 12 to 2.15, Mon to Sat D 6 to 9.30 **Meals:** alc (main courses £7 to £15). Set L £13.50 (2 courses) to £15.50, Set D 6 to 7 £13.95 (2 courses) **Service:** not inc, 10% (optional) for parties of 7 or more **Cards:** Delta, Maestro, MasterCard, Visa **Details:** 50 seats. 16 seats outside. Private parties: 50 main room. Car park. Vegetarian meals. Children's helpings. No smoking. Wheelchair access (also WC). Music

MAP 8 **Kirkham** LANCASHIRE

Cromwellian

16 Poulton Street, Kirkham PR4 2AB
Tel: (01772) 685680

Cooking 2 | Modern British | £34–£47

The Cromwellian arouses a happy sense of nostalgia, with its reassuring domestic intimacy, charm and dependable food. Seekers after pyrotechnics may find the cooking 'safe', but there's no denying the amiable good humour of Peter and Josie Fawcett. After honing their skills here since 1986, they know by now that their customers' tastes are traditional; grilled tuna on warm niçoise salad with herb vinaigrette is about as modern as it gets. Aberdeen Angus fillet steak with port and Stilton sauce is a fixture, and the kitchen is famed for its dauphinoise-style potatoes. Bury black pudding with mushy pea 'mash' and rich brown gravy is presented without airs and graces as a starter, while desserts lean towards crumbles, tarts and sponges. The wine list has been pepped up with bottles from small French growers; house selections start at £12.

Chef: Josie Fawcett **Proprietors:** Peter and Josie Fawcett **Open:** Tue to Sat D 7 to 9 **Meals:** Set D £18 (2 courses) to £24.50 **Service:** not inc, card slips closed **Cards:** Delta, Maestro, MasterCard, Visa **Details:** 28 seats. Private parties: 12 main room, 10 to 12 private rooms. Vegetarian meals. No music. No mobile phones

MAP 5 **Knightwick** WORCESTERSHIRE

The Talbot

NEW ENTRY

Knightwick WR6 5PH
Tel: (01886) 821235
Website: www.the-talbot.co.uk

Cooking 1 | British | £31–£43

For more than two decades, Annie Clift has been the driving force behind this inn overlooking the River Teme. It's part pub, part restaurant-with-rooms, and even sports its own microbrewery; it's also the focal point for a thriving local food economy. The arrival of Jonathan Lloyd has injected some fresh young blood into this industrious, almost self-sufficient set-up, although 'good old-fashioned Aga cooking' is still its trademark. Roast breast of lamb with creamy mash and cep butter sauce, baked coley with crab sauce and nettle cakes, and sherry trifle represent the old world; grilled scallop on a pressed terrine of monkfish liver ('foie gras of the sea') is one of the new contenders. Home-brewed beers are supplemented by a respectable 50-bin wine list with prices from £11.25.

Chefs: Annie Clift and Jonathan Lloyd **Proprietors:** the Clift family **Open:** all week 12 to 2, 6.30 to 9.30 (7 to 9 Sun) **Closed:** 25 Dec eve **Meals:** alc L (main courses £11 to £14). Set L Sun £17 (2 courses) to £20, Set D £20.75 (2 courses) to £24.95. Bar menu available **Service:** not inc, card slips closed **Cards:** Amex, Delta, Maestro, MasterCard, Visa **Details:** 50 seats. 40 seats outside. Private parties: 36 main room, 25 to 35 private rooms. Car park. Vegetarian meals. Children's helpings. No smoking. Wheelchair access (not WC). No music **Accommodation:** 11 rooms, all with bath/shower. TV. Phone. B&B £48 to £80. Fishing

MAP 7 **Knossington** LEICESTERSHIRE

Fox & Hounds

6 Somerby Road, Knossington LE15 8LY
Tel: (01664) 454676
Website: www.foxandhounds.biz

Cooking 2 | Modern European | £28–£50

This village pub is covered in creepers, has a large, sloping garden to the rear, and walls that are about two feet thick. It provides a congenial backdrop for Brian Baker's modern European cooking, which makes conscientious use of local materials. Slow-roasted shoulder of lamb with roasted red pepper and pesto, or grilled halibut with roasted aubergine and herb risotto, are the kinds of Mediterranean-inspired main courses to expect, and meals are bookended with the likes of king prawns with chilli and garlic oil, and baked white chocolate and praline cheesecake. Bargain two-course deals might consist of smoked salmon with poached egg and rocket, followed by black pudding with mash and onion gravy. Wines by the glass start at £2.95 for house French, while bottles rise to the heights of Zind-Humbrecht Pinot Gris from Alsace and pedigree red Burgundy.

Chef/Proprietor: Brian Baker **Open:** Wed to Sun L 12 to 2.30, Tue to Sun D 7 to 9.30 **Meals:** alc (main courses £9.50 to £14). Set L £9.95 (2 courses) to £16.95, Set L Sun £14.95 (2 courses) to £16.95. Bar L menu available **Service:** not inc **Cards:** Delta, MasterCard, Maestro, Visa **Details:** 35 seats. 20 seats outside. Private parties: 30 main room, 14 to 18 private rooms. Car park. Vegetarian meals. Children's helpings. No smoking in 1 dining room. No music

MAP 7 **Lancaster** LANCASHIRE

Simply French

AR

27A St Georges Quay, Lancaster LA1 1RD
Tel: (01524) 843199

Converted quayside warehouse close to the Maritime Museum, now a cavernous Gallic eating place. Fruits de mer platters are one of the star turns, but the menu also takes in grilled green-lipped mussels with garlic and Pernod butter (£4.75) and confit of duck leg with port and mushroom jus (£12.50), plus specials like braised beef with green peppercorn and whisky sauce. 'Early-bird offers' are good value. Closed Mon to Fri L.

MAP 5 **Langar** NOTTINGHAMSHIRE

Langar Hall

Langar NG13 9HG
Tel: (01949) 860559
Website: www.langarhall.com

Cooking 4 | English | £28–£71

After 25 years, Imogen Skirving has her customers pretty well sussed. Many are regulars, drawn back by the generosity and hospitality that pervades her tranquil country house and a style of cooking that avoids ostentation but not imagination. A clear sense of purpose is evident from the sourcing of materials – Langar lamb, Belvoir partridge, local cheeses (there are three Stilton producers within five miles) – to a balanced menu with well-defined ideas. Seasonality is all. Output subsumes seared red mullet with broccoli and saffron sauce, along with saddle of venison with Jerusalem artichoke tarte Tatin, braised red cabbage and juniper jus, and a degree of comfort is targeted by some dishes: seared foie gras with duck egg and brioche soldiers, or fried calf's liver and bacon with creamed potatoes and caramelised onions. Desserts, too, aim for the comfort zone, and have included glazed custard tart with apple compote and whisky ice cream, alongside 'a celebration of rhubarb'. The wine list suits the mood, with the main focus on affordable Bordeaux and Burgundy.

Chef: Toby Garratt **Proprietor:** Imogen Skirving **Open:** all week 12 to 1.30, 7 to 9.30 **Meals:** alc D (main courses £13.50 to £20). Set L Mon to Thur £13.50 (2 courses) to £16.50, Set L Fri/Sat £17.50 (2 courses) to £20, Set L Sun £24.50 **Service:** 10% (optional) **Cards:** Maestro, MasterCard, Visa **Details:** 50 seats. 25 seats outside. Private parties: 50 main room, 10 to 20 private rooms. Car park. Vegetarian meals. Children's helpings. No smoking. Wheelchair access (also WC). Music **Accommodation:** 12 rooms, all with bath/shower. TV. Phone. B&B £65 to £185. Rooms for disabled. Baby facilities. Fishing

MAP 8 **Langho** LANCASHIRE

Northcote Manor

Northcote Road, Langho BB6 8BE
Tel: (01254) 240555
Website: www.northcotemanor.com

Cooking 5 | Modern British | £31–£103

At this Victorian red-brick manor house turned popular country-house hotel the large dining room offers views over the Ribble Valley. Into it, from Matthew Harris's industrious kitchen, pour Bowland Forest beef and lamb, Herdwick mutton, fruit and vegetables from local growers (including Northcote's own kitchen garden) and seasonal game. The food straddles both traditional and contemporary, and skill levels are high, notably in signature dishes of black pudding and buttered pink trout with mustard and watercress sauce ('one of those unexpectedly successful marriages'), and deconstructed Lancashire hot pot – separate lamb and potatoes – with pickled red cabbage and oyster fritter. Lightly seared scallops come with cracked wheat, a grating of black truffle and white chocolate sauce in one happy partnership, while traditional cuisine has been represented by a sparkling fresh (if pricey) Dover sole simply served with perfectly cooked vegetables. Plus there is good, well-hung prime fillet of beef with 'deep flavour' and great chips, or robust venison and mushroom pie in a dark stock. Among desserts, ginger parkin with crème caramel custard appealed to one diner, or try apple crumble soufflé with Lancashire cheese ice cream. Most reporters are happy, but some mention poor timing, small portions at steep prices, and service errors. The wine list kicks off at £16.75, includes plenty of half-bottles, and covers the globe without missing a beat. A second venture – the Three Fishes in Mitton (see entry) – is another runaway success by Craig Bancroft and Nigel Haworth.

Chefs: Nigel Haworth and Matthew Harris **Proprietors:** Craig Bancroft and Nigel Haworth **Open:** all week 12 to 1.30 (2 Sun), 7 to 9.30 (10 Sat) **Closed:** Dec 25, Jan 1 **Meals:** alc (main courses £21 to £27). Set L £20, Set D £50 to £70 **Service:** not inc **Cards:** Amex, Delta, Maestro, MasterCard, Visa **Details:** 70 seats. Private parties: 85 main room, 2 to 40 private rooms. Car park. Vegetarian meals. Children's helpings. Jacket and tie. No smoking. Wheelchair access (not WC). Music. No mobile phones **Accommodation:** 14 rooms, all with bath/shower. TV. Phone. B&B £110 to £175. Rooms for disabled. Baby facilities

MAP 9 **Langthwaite** NORTH YORKSHIRE

Charles Bathurst Inn

AR

Langthwaite DL11 6EN
Tel: (01748) 884567

The Pennine Way attracts walkers and breathtaking Arkengarthdale brings a substantial car trade to this eighteenth-century village inn. All are welcome, with sustenance in the form of daily dishes scrawled on a mirror at the end of the bar. The scope of the cooking is wide, taking in Thai-style spare ribs (£5.25) or duck terrine (£4.25), then fishcakes with hollandaise (£8.45), shank of lamb on a lentil cake with juniper jus (£11.50), or baked cod and gazpacho coulis (£9.95), before desserts such as Eton Mess or spiced plum and apple crumble (£3.75). Accommodation. Open all week.

MAP 6 **Lavenham** SUFFOLK

Great House

Market Place, Lavenham CO10 9QZ
Tel: (01787) 247431
Website: www.greathouse.co.uk

Cooking 2 | French | £27–£59

This thoroughly French and resolutely traditional restaurant may not aspire to the cutting edge of gastronomy but it remains none the less a popular venue of some long standing in the Guide, and deservedly so. The setting on Lavenham's ancient marketplace is pretty as a picture, mostly half-timbered houses with brightly painted plasterwork, though the Great House presents a Regency façade by way of a contrast. Menus change weekly and always feature a selection of 'old favourites', such as calf's liver with fresh raspberries, or poached turbot fillet with watercress sauce, alongside more unusual options such as a sausage of smoked and fresh tuna with green olives on a basil coulis. Desserts likewise range from crêpes suzette and pain perdu to Earl Grey crème brûlée. A sizeable, mostly French wine list opens with a page of house selections by the glass, half-litre or bottle, prices starting at £11.50 a bottle.

Chef: Regis Crépy **Proprietors:** Regis and Martine Crépy **Open:** Tue to Sun L 12 to 2.30, Tue to Sat D 7 to 9.30 (10 Sat) **Closed:** all Jan **Meals:** alc (main courses L Tue to Sat £9 to £13, D £14 to £19). Set L Tue to Sat £14.95 (2 courses) to £16.95, Set L Sun £23.95, Set D Tue to Fri £21.95. Snack L menu available **Service:** not inc, card slips closed **Cards:** Delta, Maestro, MasterCard, Visa **Details:** 45 seats. 30 seats outside. Private parties: 60 main room, 8 to 14 private rooms. Vegetarian meals. Children's helpings. No smoking in 1 dining room. Music **Accommodation:** 5 rooms, all with bath/shower. TV. Phone. Room only £65 to £150. Baby facilities

MAP 5 **Ledbury** HEREFORDSHIRE

Malthouse

NEW ENTRY

Church Lane, Ledbury HR8 1DW
Tel: (01531) 634443

Cooking 3 | Modern British | £34–£57

Head up a cobbled lane by Ledbury's historic Market Building to find this pleasantly out-of-the-way restaurant on two floors, with a courtyard outside for fine-weather dining. Chef/proprietor Ken Wilson aims high, with ambitious, intricate modern dishes involving all manner of components: starters such as spot-on sauté wild sea bass fillet on courgette noodles with a crisp potato 'ravioli' encasing a blob of tapenade show what he can do. Boned saddle of milk-fed lamb wrapped around a nugget of sweetbread, with a rack chop, glistening spinach and a blob of puréed squash has also passed muster, and there's no better finale than the 'tripartite' assiette of banana ice parfait, spiced banana bread and a light crunchy galette with maple and pecan ice cream. The reasonably priced wine list offers respectable drinking without greedy mark-ups; house Chilean is £12.50.

Chef: Ken Wilson **Proprietors:** Ken Wilson and Jamila Belkoniene **Open:** Sat L 12 to 1.30, Tue to Sat D 7 to 9.30 **Meals:** alc (main courses £10.50 to £18.50). Set D Tue to Fri £17.25 (2 courses) to £23 **Service:** not inc **Cards:** Maestro, MasterCard, Visa **Details:** 30 seats. 16 seats outside. Private parties: 30 main room, 14 private room. No smoking. Music. No mobile phones

MAP 8 **Leeds** WEST YORKSHIRE

Anthony's Restaurant

19 Boar Lane, Leeds LS1 6EA
Tel: (0113) 245 5922
Website: www.anthonysrestaurant.co.uk

Cooking 6 | Modern European | £39–£79

Boar Lane is a characterless city-centre thoroughfare close to the station, and passers-by not in the know would be surprised to find a restaurant of such gastronomic ambition among the everyday shops and bars. Large windows at ground level look into the bar and reception area, where customers sit on chesterfields and armchairs to study the menu. The main event takes place in the basement dining room. A curved ceiling studded with ambient lights, big semi-abstract floral paintings on the walls, plus loads of space between smartly set tables – all create a comfortingly contemporary interior.

Anthony Flinn's menu consists of a concise à la carte of four choices at each course but bolstered by a steady supply of inter-course teasers and tasters. There is also a shorter, good-value, set-price lunch menu. First comes a shot glass of foaming carrot, coconut, mint and rum, a start that failed to inspire confidence in a number of reporters and inspectors. A pre-starter of sautéed whelk with a quenelle of potted duck was much more like it, as was another with shrimps given the potted treatment and topped with ground pistachios.

Anthony's is a world where round plates are the exception, not the rule. A risotto of white onion, espresso and Parmesan air 'just gets better', according to one reporter, and seems a fixture among starters. Complex constructions and compelling flavour juxtapositions are what to expect: duck neck, for instance, soft and yielding, is filled with foie gras, accompanied by a deep-fried duck egg, its yolk oozing over the plate, some potato, a sharp dressing, and a scattering of peppery purple cress. Another starter of crab with coconut and 'ice salad' turns out to be a race against time as the frosted leaves thaw and become watery, while the fresh-tasting white crabmeat has been somewhat overpowered by the coconut. Dazzlingly fresh skate wing is expertly taken off the bone for a main course accompanied by a smoked eel and foie gras terrine, roast cod served with a crab risotto has impressed, while black pudding was the undoubted star of a dish of roast salmon cheeks and chopped mango ('eat your heart out, Bury; this was remarkable'). Thickly sliced roast ribeye comes with 'sticky cubes of brisket confit', some salsify, a skewer of 'tender, almost melting' baby squid, and pickled garlic 'ravioli'.

After the pre-dessert – perhaps apple parfait with cinnamon ice cream – lemon chiboust with barley ice cream and sumac caramel shows that the pursuit of challenging combinations carries on into the home straight. Pineapple and black olive Tatin impressed an inspector, with the chopped pineapple combining well with the earthy olives and the aroma of the accompanying cardamom ice cream. Good coffee comes with carefully crafted petits fours. Service is efficient and exudes a warmth the denizens of Leeds surely appreciate, although not all the staff are able to explain the finer points of all the dishes. The wine list is intriguingly fronted by around a dozen bottled beers, before moving on to the grape, listed by drinking style; prices start at £14.50.

Chef: Anthony James Flinn **Proprietors:** Anthony Flinn and Anthony James Flinn **Open:** Tue to Sat 12 to 2.30, 7 to 9.30 (10 Fri and Sat) **Closed:** 24 to 30 Dec, Jan, 3 to 4 May, 31 May, 5 to 10 Sept **Meals:** alc (main courses £20 to £25). Set L £20 (2 courses) to £25 **Service:** not inc **Cards:** Maestro, MasterCard, Visa **Details:** 36 seats. Private parties: 36 main room. Children's helpings. No smoking. Wheelchair access (also WC). Music. Air-conditioned

Bibis Criterion

Criterion Place, Swinegate, Leeds LS1 4AG
Tel: (0113) 243 0905
Website: www.bibisrestaurant.com

Cooking 3 | Italian | £29–£78

Big and bustling, this dependable Italian feels like the pulse of the city, particularly on a Saturday night when long queues form outside and 300 seats are brimful inside its cavernous dining room. The Art Deco styling, with tiled floors, marble-effect pillars, mirrors and candelabra, vies for attention with closely packed tables, a stainless-steel open-to-view kitchen and the Café Society cocktail bar. The menu is as expansive as the venue, a crowd-pleasing colossus to promote an agony of choice: antipasti, such as hot asparagus glazed with a citrus hollandaise, then perhaps saltimbocca alla romana, a range of pizzas and pastas, plus daily specials (possibly seared swordfish steak with chilli jam), all find their place. Sound ingredients, unpretentious cooking and attentive, friendly service hit the mark, while the compact wine list comes with a fair percentage from Italy, with house Duboeuf £14.75 and a dozen by glass from £3.50.

Chef: Piero Vinci **Proprietor:** Oliver Teodorani **Open:** all week 12 to 2.15 (3.30 Sun), 6 (5.30 Sat and Sun) to 11.30 (11 Mon and Tue, 10.30 Sun) **Closed:** 25 Dec, L 1 Jan **Meals:** alc (main courses £8.50 to £25.50). Bar menu available **Service:** 10% (optional) **Cards:** Amex, Delta, Maestro, MasterCard, Visa **Details:** 300 seats. Vegetarian meals. Children's helpings. No cigars/pipes in dining room. Wheelchair access (also WC). Music. Air-conditioned

Brasserie Forty Four

44 The Calls, Leeds LS2 7EW
Tel: (0113) 234 3232
Website: www.brasserie44.com

Cooking 4 | Modern European | £31–£66

One of the pioneers of the Leeds gastro-renaissance, this consistently reliable, bright and spacious brasserie overlooking the River Aire continues to stay in touch with the times without going over the top. The menu sets off round the world, picking up a Chinese influence here (salt-and-pepper squid with young cabbage and candied lemon) and a Middle Eastern idea there (tagine of local mutton with roasted almonds and 'plumped' fruits). 'B44's' hand-made pizzas are a staple, and the kitchen likes jokey titles: 'sausage and beans' is actually a ragoût of Morteau sausages with haricots blancs and roasted peppers, while African 'bric-à-bracs' are crisp pastries with chopped pine nuts, dried fruit, feta and spinach. For dessert, consider peanut-butter cheesecake or venture into the indulgent world of 'Chocolate Corner'. The wine list is an eclectic assortment, with good value across the range; Chilean house selections (not the cheapest on the list) are £14.95.

Chef: Jeff Baker **Proprietor:** Michael Gill **Open:** Mon to Fri L 12 to 2, Mon to Sat D 6 to 10.30 (11 Fri and Sat) **Closed:** bank hols **Meals:** alc (main courses £10.50 to £16). Set L and D (not after 7pm) £12.50 (2 courses) to £16. Light L menu available **Service:** 10% (optional), card slips closed **Cards:** Delta, MasterCard, Maestro, Visa **Details:** 110 seats. Private parties: 110 main room, 12 to 50 private rooms. Vegetarian meals. Children's helpings by prior arrangement. No pipes/cigars in dining room. Music. Air-conditioned

Dough Bistro

AR

293 Spen Lane, West Park, Leeds LS16 5QN
Tel: (0113) 278 7255

Wayne Newsome operates a bakery during the day and in the evening offers some vibrant bistro cooking. The surroundings are basic and the atmosphere lively. Start with sardine fillets with confit tomatoes and grilled polenta, followed by roast duck breast with slow-roast shallots and tamarind jus. Readers have enjoyed roast chicken stuffed with caramelised onions and sun-blushed tomatoes and served with green peppercorn sauce, and lemon tart has wowed among puddings. £23.95 for four courses. BYO drink (there's an off-licence opposite), and note credit cards are not accepted. Open Tue to Sat 7 to 9.30.

Fourth Floor Café and Bar

Harvey Nichols, 107–111 Briggate,
Leeds LS1 6AZ
Tel: (0113) 204 8000
Website: www.harveynichols.com

Cooking 4 | Modern British | £26–£54

As at other branches (see Fifth Floor, London, and Forth Floor, Edinburgh), Fourth Floor is a cool, spacious, informal room, the open-plan kitchen and hard edges here bouncing the sound back and forth. The view over rooftops may not be the most sumptuous, but the glassed-in terrace seating is a boon on fine days. Young and enthusiastic staff serve accurately rendered modern food with the emphasis on freshness. Start perhaps with a well-composed salad of smoked chicken, avocado, and grapefruit, or grilled queen scallops done under Gruyère and herbs with a reduction of Noilly Prat. Precisely timed fish is impressive (maybe grilled fillet of turbot partnered with salsify, a rich and waxy shrimp and caper butter, and a perfectly judged red wine and fish stock sauce), while a meat dish might feature fine lamb noisette with black olive potatoes and roast garlic in a balsamic reduction. Side orders of fat fries are excellent, and Yorkshire rhubarb in season should not be missed: rhubarb tarte Tatin with gingered semifreddo, for example. The short menu of bar drinks offers an attractive modern range of wines amid cocktails and some first-class beers, while the wine list proper is as fine a monument to good taste as at other branches. Prices, from £13.50, are fair for the territory.

Chef: Richard Allen **Proprietor:** Harvey Nichols **Open:** all week L 12 to 3 (4 Sat and Sun), Thur to Sat D 5.30 (7 Sat) to 10 **Closed:** 25 and 26 Dec, 1 Jan, Easter Sun **Meals:** alc (main courses £10.50 to £16). Set L £15 (2 courses) to £18, Set D £10.95 (2 courses) to £14.95. Bar menu available **Service:** 10% (optional) **Cards:** Amex, Delta, Diners, Maestro, MasterCard, Visa **Details:** 85 seats. 15 seats outside. Private parties: 200 main room. Vegetarian meals. Children's helpings. No-smoking area. Wheelchair access (also WC). Occasional music. Air-conditioned

Leodis

Victoria Mill, Sovereign Street, Leeds LS1 4BA
Tel: (0113) 242 1010
Website: www.leodis.co.uk

Cooking 3 | Brasserie/Mod British | £28–£63

Another key player in the revitalisation of the Leeds' restaurant scene, Leodis is a bullish canal-side warehouse conversion that manages to preserve the historic heritage and yet buzz like a full-on city brasserie. It's noisy and it's fun. Contemporary lighting and gleaming glass partitions blend with brick walls and old iron beams, and the place oozes polish and professionalism. The kitchen's daily-changing menu jets its way from beer-battered king prawns with sweet chilli dip to steak and kidney pudding, via Thai chicken soup, rare tuna salad niçoise, Tuscan-style braised ham hock and grilled French duck breast with mushroom and asparagus tart, garlic and thyme. Extra vegetables range from chips or mash to rocket and Parmesan. Likewise, desserts encompass the likes of hot roast peaches and plums with orange mascarpone, or treacle sponge with crème anglaise.

A well-constructed wine list runs all the way from £13.95 house to the most serious of Bordeaux, via some good fruity brasserie fare and interesting producers like Trinity Hill in New Zealand or Duclaux in Côte Rôtie. France and Italy are the strongest suits.

Chefs: Steven Kendell and John Wilks **Proprietors:** Martin Spalding, Steven Kendell and Philip Richardson **Open:** Mon to Fri L 12 to 2, Mon to Sat D 6 to 10 **Closed:** 24 and 26 Dec, 1 Jan, bank hol Mons L **Meals:** alc (main courses £8.50 to £17.50). Set L £16.95, Set D Mon to Fri 6 to 7.15 £16.95. Light L menu available Mon to Fri **Service:** 10% (optional), card slips closed **Cards:** Amex, Delta, Diners, Maestro, MasterCard, Visa **Details:** 180 seats. 60 seats outside. Private parties: 180 main room. Car park (evenings only). Vegetarian meals. Children's helpings. Wheelchair access (also WC). Music

Little Tokyo

24 Central Road, Leeds LS1 6DE
Tel: (0113) 243 9090

'The root and spice of healthy living' is the motto of this enterprising little Japanese café complete with handmade wooden tables and a Japanese garden. Bento boxes (from £11) are the mainstays, backed up by ramen, udon, and soba noodles in various guises (from £6). Also note soft-shell crab tempura, spare ribs in OK sauce, and ebi fry curry with king prawns (£7). Sushi, sashimi, and salads complete the picture. Special weekday lunches are £5.50. Alcoholic cocktails and wines from £10.50. Closed Sun.

No. 3 York Place

3 York Place, Leeds LS1 2DR
Tel: (0113) 245 9922
Website: www.no3yorkplace.co.uk

Cooking 6 | Modern European | £32–£83

A short stroll from the railway station, this smart city-centre restaurant shares a street with a diversity of entertainments, including lap-dancing. Inside is cool and chic, with a roof of glass and chairs upholstered in cream leather. Urbane, knowledgeable service and a personable, enthusiastic sommelier, are definite plus points.

The cooking idiom is unmistakably contemporary, with a striving for complexity evident in most dishes. A monster raviolo of duck confit bulges with its filling, and is finely complemented by its sweet-and-sour sauce. Equally well considered have been fish main courses like generously proportioned breaded halibut on a bed of Eastern-spiced vegetable ragoût, or sea bass on braised fennel with a mini-lasagne of crab. Meats might include impressive roast pork belly spiked with five-spice, copiously accompanied by seared foie gras, buttered spinach, Jerusalem artichoke purée, baby onions and a truffle jus. A cheese menu (choose up to five) offers outstanding quality, or there are desserts like iced lemon chiboust with lemon curd, an orange tuile, citrus marmalade and sauce Suzette, and even a rendition of Black Forest gâteau, with cherry sorbet and matching syrup. The varietally sorted wine list makes a comprehensive stab at covering most bases, not forgetting an Italian Verdicchio and an English Rondo red; prices open at £14.50 and there's choice under £25 as well as above.

Chef: Martel Smith **Proprietors:** Martel Smith and Denis Lefrancq **Open:** Mon to Fri L 12 to 2, Mon to Sat D 6.30 to 10 **Closed:** 25 to 30 Dec, bank hols (exc Good Friday) **Meals:** alc (main courses £13.95 to £20.95). Set L £14.50 (2 courses) to £18.50, Set D 6.30 to 7.30 £14.50 (2 courses) to £18.50 **Service:** 10% (optional), card slips closed **Cards:** Amex, Delta, Maestro, MasterCard, Visa **Details:** 48 seats. Private parties: 55 main room. Vegetarian meals. Children's helpings. No smoking in dining room. Wheelchair access (also WC). Music. Air-conditioned

Olive Tree

AR

Oaklands, 55 Rodley Lane, Leeds LS13 1NG
Tel: (0113) 256 9283

Renowned Greek Cypriot taverna in a converted Victorian house on the outer ring road. Plates of meze (£16.50 per head) are popular, and the kitchen's repertoire spans everything from beef stifado and lamb souvlaki (£11) to regional specialities like fried salt-cod with skordalia. To finish, try rizogalo (rice pudding with cinnamon and pistachios). Fixed-price menus £6.95 to £12.95; house wine £11.95. Open all week. High-profile owner George Psarias is hoping to hit the jackpot with his new outlet at 188–190 Harrogate Road, Chapel Allerton; tel: (0113) 269 8488.

Pool Court at 42

44 The Calls, Leeds LS2 7EW
Tel: (0113) 244 4242
Website: www.poolcourt.com

Cooking 7 | French/Mod Brit | £42–£88

Right on the river Aire, Pool Court exudes an air of relaxed gentility, with dramatic lighting at night emphasising its architectural splendour. The restaurant is on an intimate scale, its dark blue tones pointing up the waterside theme of the décor, with service fully in keeping, quietly professional and not given to rush. The cooking plies a contemporary French line, with plenty of unexpected touches. Appetisers extend not just to the now-familiar cup of soup but perhaps also to a little fondue burner filled with bubbling white wine and Gruyère. Serving scallops with a vegetable purée has become quite the norm, and here they arrive with one of carrot spiked with ginger together with a butter sauce combining citrus and Sauternes, while duck foie gras has been partnered with peanut brittle and sweetcorn sorbet. The speciality fish of the day is worth a punt: at inspection, it delivered properly timed roast turbot on a soft polenta cake in a sauce of grape must and truffle oil. Orkney beef fillet has been impressive too, served au poivre and accompanied by a fried duck egg and a neatly arranged stack of good chips. To finish, the 'Study in Chocolate' will seduce the true aficionado, consisting of a brûlée with boozy raspberries at the bottom, a chewy walnut brownie, a soufflé flavoured with coffee beans, and a chocolate cup containing honey and almond fondue. If all that sounds too much, consider the home-made ice creams and sorbets.

A thoroughly convincing wine list from £15.65 spans the world and offers much to entice in the £20 to £30 bracket, New Zealand's Palliser Estate Sauvignon Blanc (£23.65) and Finca El Retiro Malbec (£23.40) typifying the modern outlook. But there are classics aplenty too, and a range of old CVNE Riojas to top things off.

Chef: Jeff Baker **Proprietor:** Michael Gill **Open:** Mon to Fri L 12 to 2, Mon to Sat D 7 to 10 (8.30 Sat) **Closed:** bank hols **Meals:** Set L and D £25 (2 courses) to £59 **Service:** 10%, card slips closed **Cards:** Delta, Maestro, MasterCard, Visa **Details:** 38 seats. 18 seats outside. Private parties: 38 main room. Vegetarian meals. No children under 3. No smoking. Wheelchair access (also WC). Music. No mobile phones. Air-conditioned

Raja's

AR

186 Roundhay Road, Leeds LS8 5PL
Tel: (0113) 248 0411

Bastion of the Leeds Indian scene for two decades, in an Asian neighbourhood a short ride from the city centre. Lobsters and seafood are delivered fresh each day (the fish curry is haddock), and the menu is a long haul through north Indian and Punjabi dishes, taking in aloo tikka (£1), assorted tandooris, curry-house stalwarts, and specials such as handi gosht (pot-roast lamb; £6), plus a variety of vegetables (around £3.50). House wine £10.25; otherwise drink beer or lassi. Closed Sun L.

Room

AR

Bond House, The Bourse Courtyard, Boar Lane, Leeds LS1 5DE
Tel: (0113) 242 6161

Large, noisy and strikingly fashionable venue done out in shades of purple just off a thoroughfare close to Leeds station. The full menu deals out classic retro dishes with a twist: all-day breakfast terrine (£5), 'cuppa soup', chicken tikka masala with curried potato salad (£15), and even beans on toast for vegetarians. Around 40 worldwide wines from £13, with plenty by the glass. Closed Sun D. There's a branch at 1 Devonshire Gardens, Glasgow; tel: (0141) 341 0000.

Simply Heathcotes

Canal Wharf, Water Lane, Leeds LS11 5PS
Tel: (0113) 244 6611
Website: www.heathcotes.co.uk

Cooking 3 | Modern British | £27–£58

This 'no-frills modern brasserie' has wooden floors, exposed stone walls and a curved staircase up to a mezzanine bar. Besides Paul Heathcote's trademark Lancashire-influenced dishes the wide choice on the seasonal menu includes French and Italian options. Reporters have praised confit Goosnargh duck leg with braised lentils and rocket, and 'accurately timed' king prawns on a puddle of creamy cauliflower purée surrounded by sherry vinegar sauce. Main courses might include 'thick and juicy' pot roast cod fillet with 'sweet and tender' braised baby onions and broth pot flecked with saffron, or maybe roast rack of Pendle lamb with crushed carrots and peas. Finish with an 'impressive' vanilla bean ice cream with caramelised Pedro Ximenez sherry and a shot of hot espresso coffee to pour over. The global wine list is reasonably priced; house Italians start at £13.95.

Chef: Simon Peacock **Proprietor:** Paul Heathcote **Open:** Mon to Sat 12 to 2.30, 6 to 10 (11 Sat), Sun 12 to 9 **Closed:** 25 and 26 Dec, 1 and 2 Jan, bank hol Mons **Meals:** alc (main courses £10 to £19.50). Set L £10.50 (1 course) to £16, Set D 6 to 7 £10.50 (1 course) to £16. Sun all-day menu available **Service:** not inc, card slips closed **Cards:** Amex, Delta, Maestro, MasterCard, Visa **Details:** 110 seats. Private parties: 160 main room. Car park. Vegetarian meals. Children's helpings. No-smoking area. Wheelchair access (also WC). Music. Air-conditioned

Sous le Nez en Ville

The Basement, Quebec House, Quebec Street, Leeds LS1 2HA
Tel: (0113) 244 0108

Cooking 3 | Modern European | £30–£58

This informal bistro-style restaurant remains relatively unchanged over fifteen years. Choice is generous, even for lunchtime bar food, which extends from sandwiches to tapas to confit duck leg with kumquat chutney and alfalfa sprouts. Andrew Carter's restaurant menu ranges across Europe, starting with three cheese and potato dumplings with spinach and almond sauce, and pigeon breast with toasted fruit bread. Fish is a feature, whether as moules marinière, whole grilled sea bass with sea salt, herbs and lime, or roast monkfish on the bone with garlic, tomatoes and wild mushrooms. There is meat too, though – perhaps venison with black pudding, apple Tatin and caramel jus - and the vegetable sides include good old cauliflower cheese. Desserts tend towards straightforward crème brûlée, or bread-and-butter pudding with Chantilly cream and honey sauce.

A masterful collection of French wines has sound global backing. With good-value options like François d'Allaines' Saint-Aubin Premier Cru En Remilly for £26.50, the Burgundy section is no mere recitation of unattainable star names; other regions follow suit. Over a dozen house wines from under £12 also come by the glass.

Chefs: Andrew Carter and Andrew Lavender **Proprietors:** Andrew Carter and Robert Chamberlain **Open:** Mon to Sat 12 to 2.30, 6 to 10 (11 Sat) **Closed:** 24 Dec to 2 Jan **Meals:** alc (main courses £10 to £18.50). Set D 6 to 7.30 £19.95. Bar menu available **Service:** not inc **Cards:** Delta, Diners, Maestro, MasterCard, Visa **Details:** 90 seats. Private parties: 50 main room, 4 to 20 private rooms. Vegetarian meals. Music. Air-conditioned

MAP 7 **Leek** STAFFORDSHIRE

Number 64

64 St Edward Street, Leek ST13 5DL
Tel: (01538) 381900
Website: www.number64.com

Cooking 2 | Modern British | £28–£61

Dating from 1747, this red-brick building is now part of a complex owned by provisions manufacturers, Cottage Delight. It comprises a deli, patisserie, an impressive-looking cellar wine bar (with its own menu) and a quietly elegant first-floor restaurant decorated in pastel shades. Café-style snacks and light meals are served at lunchtime, but for dinner the kitchen changes up to more ambitious modern food using judiciously sourced raw materials. Goats' cheese pannacotta is a typical opener, before fillet of local beef with seared foie gras, buttered spinach, rösti and port jus, or seared halibut with truffled pommes purée, crushed mint peas, girolles and fish velouté. Finish with a 'Chocolart Trio' or something wacky like Horlicks and Malteser parfait. House wines start at £11.45.

Chef: Paul Owens **Proprietor:** Nigel Cope **Open:** all week L 12 to 2 (3 Sun), Mon to Sat D 7 to 9 (10 Sat) **Meals:** alc (main courses L £10 to £12.50, D £13 to £26). Set L £15 (2 courses) to £18. Bar and snack menus available **Service:** not inc, card slips closed **Cards:** Amex, Maestro, MasterCard, Visa **Details:** 55 seats. 28 seats outside. Private parties: 40 main room, 8 to 14 private rooms. Vegetarian meals. No smoking. Music. Air-conditioned **Accommodation:** 3 rooms, all with bath/shower. TV. Phone. B&B £65 to £95. Rooms for disabled. Baby facilities

MAP 5 **Leicester** LEICESTERSHIRE

Entropy

NEW ENTRY

3 Dover Street, Leicester
LE1 6PW
Tel: (0116) 254 8530
Website: www.entropylife.com

Cooking 6 | Modern European | £26–£71

A sharp intake of breath was heard around Leicester in 2004 with the opening of this exciting new venture in a concrete ex-warehouse not far from the station. Tom and Cassandra Cockerill's bravely named restaurant bears the same name as their first venture (a bar at 42 Hinckley Road in the city). Both have degrees in physics, and Tom has worked at the Fat Duck (see entry, Bray), which virtually amounts to the same thing.

On the ground floor are a bar and lounge area, as well as an internal window looking into the kitchen, while the restaurant space is up a flight of stairs. Here, floor-to-ceiling windows let the daylight in, and the colour scheme is two-tone monochrome. The food is anything but. A single fat scallop is sliced through, interleaved with ribbons of black truffle, set on shredded leek and sauced with a perfectly seasoned foam of cauliflower. Langoustines are whooshed up into a bavarois scented with vanilla and presented in a chilled langoustine consommé flavoured with lemongrass and ginger. Not only is there an amuse-bouche and a pre-dessert in the expected contemporary fashion, but there is also an in-betweenie before the main course, and it isn't a sorbet but rather something like a Thai salmon fishcake in mango chilli salsa.

Main courses display consummate craftsmanship, with equal pains taken for a vegetarian dish of globe artichoke tart topped with Wigmore cheese and pine nuts, with asparagus in hollandaise, sun-dried tomatoes, pea shoots and garlic flowers as for a serving of duck two ways, the leg meat in a pastilla, the breast roasted, each preparation with its own sauce.

The planning and execution of these dishes impress mightily, and the effort is maintained all the way to desserts, which might include a Tatin of peach with a tuile containing a scoop of saffron ice cream alongside a shot glass of raspberry coulis topped up with champagne. Lightness and precision have distinguished a soufflé of orange and passion fruit served with white chocolate ice cream. The wine list, almost as minimal as the décor, is surprisingly Francocentric. Prices are fair, with only a few breaking the £20 barrier. House vins de pays are £12.50.

Chefs: Tom Cockerill and Elliot Moss **Proprietors:** Tom and Cassandra Cockerill **Open:** Mon to Sat 12 to 2.30, 6 to 10 **Closed:** Christmas, bank hols **Meals:** alc (main courses £17 to £24). Set L £11.95 (2 courses) to £15.95. Bar menu available **Service:** not inc **Cards:** Amex, Delta, Maestro, MasterCard, Visa **Details:** 60 seats. Private parties: 95 main room, 1 to 20 private rooms. Vegetarian meals. Children's helpings. No smoking. Music. Air-conditioned

Opera House

10 Guildhall Lane, Leicester LE1 5FQ
Tel: (0116) 223 6666
Website: www.theoperahouserestaurant.co.uk

Cooking 2 | Modern European | £26–£70

At one time this was the Opera House Hotel, although the building itself (a conversion of two cottages dating from 1685) has also seen service as an inn, jail and antique shop. In its current incarnation it's a contemporary restaurant with discreet, brick-floored nooks and a labyrinth of vaulted cellars below. Signature dishes such as slow-roast belly pork with seared diver-caught scallops, black pudding and a honey and ginger reduction set the tone on the regularly changing fixed-price menus, which span everything from foie gras parfait with pear and cinnamon chutney to a tranche of wild sea bass with white polenta, ratatouille and pepper coulis. Desserts could range from tarte Tatin to chilled watermelon soup with honeydew and cantaloupe jelly. No-nonsense annotations are a reliable guide through an attractive international selection of wines capped by a 'private cellar' of top-class bottles. Fruity, modern house white from South Africa's Kanu is £15.

Chef: Alex Howard **Proprietors:** Noel and Val Weafer **Open:** Mon to Sat 12 to 2, 7 to 10 **Closed:** 25 Dec to 3 Jan, bank hols **Meals:** Set L £9.95 (2 courses) to £13.50 (inc wine), Set D £29.50 (2 courses) to £39.50 **Service:** 10% (optional), card slips closed **Cards:** Amex, Delta, Diners, Maestro, MasterCard, Visa **Details:** 70 seats. Private parties: 22 main room, 8 to 16 private rooms. Vegetarian meals. Children's helpings. No smoking. Music. No mobile phones. Air-conditioned

MAP 3 **Leigh-on-Sea** ESSEX

The Boatyard

8/13 High Street, Leigh-on-Sea SS9 2EN
Tel: (01702) 475588
Website: www.theboatyardrestaurant.co.uk

Cooking 1 | Modern European | £31–£69

'Somebody had good vision and a clever architect,' commented a reporter on this impressive conversion of an old boatyard by the Thames estuary. The predominance of steel, wood and glass may look a bit incongruous in a street of weatherboarded cottages, ancient pubs, chandlers and the odd still-working boatyard, but the nautical-themed décor, wide views and outside decking bring it all into focus. Modern brasserie dishes take in deep-fried squid with yellow curry salsa, meaty home-made burgers, confit duck leg with Puy lentils, and Dover sole with lemon and lime butter. Desserts, such as vanilla and star-anise pannacotta, and blackberry and apple crumble are generally well received. House Chilean is £12.95.

Chef: Jonathan Luck **Proprietor:** John Cross **Open:** Wed to Sun L 12 to 3, Tue to Sat D 6.30 to 10.30 (11 Sat) **Meals:** alc D (main courses £15 to £20). Set L £11.95 (2 courses) to £15.95. Cover £1.50 **Service:** not inc, card slips closed **Cards:** Delta, MasterCard, Maestro, Visa **Details:** 189 seats. Private parties: 180 main room, 15 to 30 private rooms. Car park. Vegetarian meals. Children's helpings. Wheelchair access (also WC). Music. Air-conditioned

AR	Not a full entry but provisionally recommended (known as 'round-ups' in previous editions, these 'also recommended' establishments are now integrated throughout the book).

MAP 5 **Leominster** HEREFORDSHIRE

Royal Oak Hotel, Déjà Vu

AR

South Street, Leominster HR6 8JA
Tel: (01568) 612610

Traditional town-centre hotel making the most of its recently launched Déjà Vu restaurant. Promising evening menus advertise dishes like potted duck with red onion relish (£4.75) before sustaining main courses such as pot-roast belly pork with creamed spinach, onion purée, and fondant potato (£13.50) or steamed haddock with gravlax sauce and braised cabbage. Finish with 'comforting' sticky toffee pudding (£4.50) or tarte Tatin (£5). Decent, 50-strong wine list with affordable drinking from £11. Open all week.

MAP 1 **Lewdown** DEVON

Lewtrenchard Manor

Lewdown EX20 4PN
Tel: (01566) 783222
Website: www.lewtrenchard.co.uk

Cooking 6 | Modern British | £29–£94

This many-gabled, mullioned Jacobean manor, its grey stone façade softened by wisteria, clematis and roses, sits idyllic and stately in its garden and park. A top-flight country-house hotel, it attracts an international clientele but still has a 'very relaxed' and endearingly timeless quality. Ornate ceilings, carved dark oak panelling, massive fireplaces and old oil paintings grace the interior. Complementing and contrasting with the traditional surroundings, Jason Hornbuckle's light, lively contemporary cooking shows flair, imagination and accomplishment. He loves themes and variations, and it's all 'tiny and gone in a few mouthfuls', but, though dishes are complex, the concept is spot on and all the many parts coalesce into a convincing whole. First-class materials, including produce from Lewtrenchard's walled kitchen garden are key, with dishes 'positively fragrant with fresh herbs'. Take a main-course roast loin of local new-season spring lamb, served with petit moussaka, baked fig and sautéed feta cheese to illustrate the style, or perhaps a fillet of John Dory, partnered by a lightly curried apple, butternut squash, peas, coriander and baby leeks. A tropical-inspired lemongrass pannacotta with coconut parfait and lychee sorbet could vie for attention with a 'huge choice' of West Country cheeses. The appealing repertoire (including a tasting option) is delivered at fixed prices, service is expectedly professional, but 'everyone's smiling and genuine', and do save space for 'irresistible bread rolls' and the 'plateful' of nibbles and appetizers.

A well-rounded global collection of wines is strongest in French classics but includes interesting, mature New World bottles too: there's a strong South African range, and 1993 Tyrell's Vat 1 Semillon from Australia looks a bargain at £33. Six house wines are priced from £13.

Chef: Jason Hornbuckle **Proprietor:** Von Essen Hotels **Open:** Tue to Sun L 12 to 1.30, all week D 7 to 9 **Meals:** Set L £12 (2 courses) to £20, Set D £35 to £37.50. Bar menu available **Service:** not inc **Cards:** Amex, Delta, Maestro, MasterCard, Visa **Details:** 35 seats. 16 seats outside. Private parties: 16 main room, 12 to 60 private rooms. Car park. Vegetarian meals. No children under 8. No smoking. Wheelchair access (not WC). Music. No mobile phones **Accommodation:** 14 rooms, all with bath/shower. TV. Phone. B&B £95 to £250. Rooms for disabled. No children under 8. Fishing

MAP 3 **Lewes** EAST SUSSEX

Circa

AR

145 High Street, Lewes BN7 1XT
Tel: (01273) 471777

A shot of fusion in glass-fronted designer premises at the heart of Lewes. The kitchen aims high, invention abounds, but results have been noticeably uneven of late. On the plus side, successes have included pressed tandoori chicken terrine and roast rhubarb and fig crumble with rhubarb ice. In between, expect things like bang-bang sea bass with a wind-dried sausage dumpling, sautéed greens and young coconut laksa. Eclectic wines from £13.50. Closed Sun. The same team also runs the Circa Brasserie (see entry below).

Circa Brasserie

AR

Pelham House Hotel, St Andrews Lane, Lewes BN7 1UX
Tel: (01273) 471333

The Brasserie, managed by the owners of Circa (see above), is part of the major conversion completed in 2004 of Pelham House into a hotel and conference centre. Enter via the large hallway into a lofty space, where muted colours and stone floors are echoed in the two adjoining dining rooms. As with the sister restaurant, complexity creeps into menus which run to pressed duck terrine, confit shallot, sour crisps and maple glaze (£8.45) as a starter. Fish seemed a strong point at inspection: grilled sea bass with garden pea risotto and beet pesto, or there might be confit duck leg, steamed potato, bok choy and Asian jus (£12.95). Bread has disappointed; finish with sticky tamarind pudding with sesame seed ice cream and palm butter sauce (£6). Open all week.

MAP 8 **Leyburn** NORTH YORKSHIRE

Sandpiper Inn

Market Place, Leyburn DL8 5AT
Tel: (01969) 622206

Cooking 3 | Modern European | £29–£47

A roadside country pub flanked by a brace of churches, the Sandpiper is an ancient, small building of rough brown stone, with plenty of dark wooden furniture and, just inside the entrance, a display of wittily captioned photographs of the kitchen team at work. Despite that, food is clearly taken seriously, with fine local materials featuring prominently. Start with a fresh salad of smoked salmon and crayfish sharply dressed with citrus, before continuing with something like expressively flavoured, gutsy beef fillet with wild mushrooms, leeks and local molasses-cured black bacon, or Whitby cod served with prawns and fennel. Desserts aim to indulge with coffee-sauced chocolate marquise, or no-frills vacherin, the bottom half a meringue disc, the top layer half mango sorbet and half vanilla ice cream. Staff are fully on the ball, and wines are a well-annotated list of 32 bins, with house Duboeuf at £11.50.

Chef: Jonathan Harrison **Proprietors:** the Harrison family **Open:** Tue to Sun 12 to 2.30 (2 Sun), 6.30 (7 Sun) to 9 (9.30 Fri and Sat) **Meals:** alc (main courses £9.50 to £16). Light L menu available **Service:** not inc, card slips closed **Cards:** Delta, Maestro, MasterCard, Visa **Details:** 40 seats. 20 seats outside. Private parties: 40 main room. Vegetarian meals. Children's helpings. No children after 8pm. No smoking. Music. No mobile phones **Accommodation:** 3 rooms, all with bath/shower. TV. B&B £55 to £90. No children

MAP 5 **Lichfield** STAFFORDSHIRE

Chandlers

AR

Corn Exchange, Conduit Street, Lichfield
WS13 6JU
Tel: (01543) 416 688

Located in the heart of Lichfield, Chandlers occupies the first floor of the former Corn Exchange. This large, buzzy place looks every inch the lively city brasserie, and delivers veal Milanese (£10.95) and chargrilled Scotch ribeye with peppercorn sauce (£12.75), and fish features strongly: grilled red snapper with Moroccan couscous and mint yoghurt (£12). Finish with lemon tart with raspberry coulis (£4.25). 'Service is effective and polite'. Changes are planned to the menu after we go to press. Open all week.

MAP 6 **Lidgate** SUFFOLK

Star Inn

AR

The Street, Lidgate CB8 9PP
Tel: (01638) 500275

This is a traditional English country pub where log fires are a draw, as well as heavy beams, oak tables, and a great atmosphere. The food attracts customers too: garlicky Mediterranean aromas waft around, hinting of fish soup (£6), paella (£14.50), scampi provençale, and Spanish-style roast lamb (£15.50). The lady behind these surprises is from Catalonia, so you can expect a wine list that is predominantly Spanish too, kicking off with house wine at £12.50. Open all week (no food Sun D).

MAP 1 **Lifton** DEVON

Arundell Arms

Lifton PL16 0AA
Tel: (01566) 784666
Website: www.arundellarms.com

Cooking 5 | Modern British | £34–£61

A rambling, ivy-clad, old coaching inn on a site dating back to Saxon times, the Arundell owns 20 miles of the river Tamar, and is a haven for fishermen and others in whom the sporting instinct runs strong. Characterful period interiors are appreciated for eschewing the tendency to chintziness, and the place has the feel of a lived-in country house, due testament to Anne Voss-Bark's long experience in the business.

With Philip Burgess moving to more of an advisory role, his long-time colleague Nick Shopland has taken up the reins in the kitchen, and capably maintains the standards set here over a number of years. The fixed-price menus showcase fine West Country produce, perhaps in the form of shellfish soup with a hot terrine of scallops and crab, or a first-course serving of sea bass with saffron, ginger and spring onions. Enterprising game cookery furnishes main courses such as a classic brace of woodcock, teamed with braised Savoy cabbage and bacon and sauced with sweet wine, while a mignon of local beef might appear with a parsley tartlet and sauce of red wine and butter. Dessert might be variations on rhubarb, gently anointed with vanilla cream, or classic sticky toffee with toffee sauce and, naturally, some clotted cream.

The wine list assumes familiarity with France but gives some helpful guidance throughout the rest of the high-calibre global selection. Good prices, an interesting line-up of halves and six house wines (from £13) also by the glass should guarantee satisfaction all round.

Chef: Nick Shopland **Proprietor:** Anne Voss-Bark **Open:** all week 12.30 to 2, 7.30 to 9.30 **Closed:** 24 to 26 Dec D **Meals:** Set L £20 (2 courses) to £24.50, Set D £34 to £40. Bar menu available **Service:** not inc **Cards:** Amex, Delta, Diners, MasterCard, Maestro, Visa **Details:** 70 seats. 25 seats outside. Private parties: 70 main room, 10 to 25 private rooms. Car park. Vegetarian meals. Children's helpings. No smoking. Wheelchair access (also WC). Music **Accommodation:** 21 rooms, all with bath/shower. TV. Phone. B&B £95 to £180. Baby facilities. Fishing

MAP 9 **Lincoln** LINCOLNSHIRE

Wig & Mitre

AR

30–32 Steep Hill, Lincoln LN2 1TL
Tel: (01522) 535190

A prime historical location and renowned flexibility (food and drink served all day, every day) are scoring points in the Hope family's enterprise. Theirs is a tried and tested formula. Cheese and mushroom soufflé (£7), crusted rack of lamb with tarragon mustard (£16.50), and vanilla cheesecake with red fruit compote (£5) are typical of the main menu. Breakfast, sandwiches and specials fill in the remaining gaps. Decent wines from £12.45. Open all week.

MAP 6 Littleport CAMBRIDGESHIRE

Fen House

AR

2 Lynn Road, Littleport CB6 1QG
Tel: (01353) 860645

Dinner at David Warne's smart Georgian house on the northern edge of Littleport begins on sofas in the lounge sipping pre-dinner drinks while studying the fixed-price four-course dinner menu (£33.25), then continues in the formal dining room. Five choices for starters and main courses might include cauliflower soup topped with poached smoked haddock, then breast of guinea fowl poached in red wine and green olives. Cheese follows, and then perhaps hot chocolate pudding with coffee cream. House wine is £14. Open Fri and Sat D only (booking essential); other times by arrangement.

MAP 6 Little Shelford CAMBRIDGESHIRE

Sycamore House

1 Church Street, Little Shelford CB2 5HG
Tel: (01223) 843396

Cooking 3 | Modern British | £35–£43

Michael Sharpe cooks while his wife Susan serves in their neat, understated country restaurant. Don't expect culinary pyrotechnics in this Cambridgeshire backwater: instead, you can look forward to confident, unshowy cooking that is perfectly tailored to a modest – almost domestic – regime that opens its doors only four evenings a week. Within these constraints, the fixed-priced menus ring the changes to reflect seasonal supplies, bringing on board starters like seared scallops with pea guacamole, chicken liver parfait, or beetroot risotto. A mid-course salad precedes main courses such as roast guinea fowl with apples and organic cider, or grilled sea trout with a citrus dressing, and to finish there are traditional recipes like steamed Cambridge pudding with clotted cream as well as brandy-snap baskets filled with interesting ice creams (Toblerone or marmalade, for example). A short, individual wine list offers good value throughout and the chance to drink some great wines with low mark-ups – Ridge Geyserville at £29.50, for example.

Chef: Michael Sharpe **Proprietors:** Michael and Susan Sharpe **Open:** Wed to Sat D only 7.30 to 9 **Closed:** Christmas to New Year **Meals:** Set D £25 **Service:** not inc, card slips closed **Cards:** Delta, Maestro, MasterCard, Visa **Details:** 24 seats. Private parties: 24 main room. Car park. Vegetarian meals. No children under 12. No smoking. No music. No mobile phones

MAP 8 Liverpool MERSEYSIDE

Chung Ku

Riverside Drive, Columbus Quay,
Liverpool L3 4DB
Tel: (0151) 726 8191
Website: www.chung-ku.com

Cooking 1 | Chinese | £18–£60

Views across the river provide an attractive backdrop to this designer Chinese restaurant. The chef has been in post since 2004, but a new owner has taken over since our last edition, and those in the know feel that the range of the menu and the level of cooking could be improved. That said, the kitchen delivers a well-tried assortment of recognisable dishes, notably a decent selection of roast meats (duck, char sui and crispy belly pork), along with crunchy soft-shell crabs and deep-fried shredded beef with spicy sauce. Set banquets are a feature. On the plus side, staff make a genuine effort to be helpful and communicative, and the well-chosen wine list promises decent drinking from £10.90.

Chef: Mr Lu **Proprietor:** Esther Ng **Open:** all week noon to 11 (10 Sun, midnight Fri/Sat) **Meals:** alc (main courses £8.70 to £14.50). Set L (2 courses) £6.50 to £9.50, Set D £19.50 (min 2) to £35 (min 4) **Service:** 10% (optional) **Cards:** Amex, Delta, Maestro, MasterCard, Visa **Details:** 300 seats. Private parties: 200 main room. Car park. Vegetarian meals. Wheelchair access (also WC). Music. Air-conditioned

Hope Street Hotel, London Carriage Works

40 Hope Street, Liverpool L1 9DA
Tel: (0151) 705 2222
Website: www.tlcw.co.uk

Cooking 5 | Modern British | £37–£58

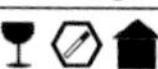

Hope Street connects the cathedrals of both denominations, each of which is worth a gander, and it is also a good place to eat. This renovated Victorian Merseyside palazzo houses impeccably modern restaurant and brasserie operations, and has caused ripples in the city since it opened in late 2003. While the brasserie menu deals in the appetising likes of flash-fried chilli squid, or pork rillettes, with deli sandwiches and 'hearty salads' too, the daily-changing restaurant menus aim for complexity and impact. These might be achieved by way of fish specials such as monkfish bundled up in Cheshire ham and tapenade, with sautéed baby turnip, Swiss chard and ratatouille in a red-wine beurre blanc, or Szechuan-peppered Lancashire duckling with its roasted liver and a tian of squash and spinach. One reader thoroughly approved a meal that began with oysters served in the shells in an aspic of their own juices, bedded on mashed potato, followed by roast saddle of venison with quince marmalade, and finishing with fig Tatin with fromage blanc sorbet. For the truly sweet of tooth, peppermint pannacotta comes with chocolate and hazelnut fudge.

The wine list packs a lot of options into seven pages. Good everyday bottles start at £12.50, but look out for smart choices all over, like Australia's Starvedog Lane Cabernet Sauvignon (£26) or Hugel's classic Jubilee Alsace Pinot Gris (£35).

Chefs: Paul Askew and Matt Locke **Proprietor:** David Brewitt **Open:** all week L 12 to 3.30, Mon to Sat D 5.30 to 9.30 **Closed:** 25 Dec D **Meals:** Set L £19 (2 courses) to £25, Set D £28 (2 courses) to £36. Brasserie menu available **Service:** not inc, card slips closed, 10% (optional) for parties of 8 or more **Cards:** Amex, Delta, MasterCard, Maestro, Visa **Details:** 70 seats. Private parties: 40 main room. Vegetarian meals. Children's helpings. No smoking in 1 dining room. Wheelchair access (also WC). Music. No mobile phones. Air-conditioned **Accommodation:** 48 rooms, all with bath/shower. TV. Phone. Room only £125 to £315. Rooms for disabled. Baby facilities

Jumbo City AR

36 Nelson Street, Liverpool L1 5DN
Tel: (0151) 708 6808

Exceedingly friendly restaurant in the heart of the city's Chinese quarter. The kitchen delivers consistently good dishes from a wide-ranging 150-dish menu: salt and pepper spare ribs and crispy-fried squid are successful appetisers, roast meats are authentically satisfying, and other recommended dishes include Szechuan seafood casserole, 'Three Treasures' (bean curd, aubergine and green pepper) with prawn stuffing, and Singapore noodles. Dim sum confined to the main menu only. Generous portions, good value.

Mei Mei AR

9 Berry Street, Liverpool L1
Tel: (0151) 707 2888

'Dim sum to die for' are arguably the star attractions in this 'unobtrusively smart' new address in the city's Chinatown. A lengthy list of intriguing items – complete with photographs – promises top-drawer steamed char sui bau (with a light, fluffy bun), scallop cheung fun, and 'increasingly moreish' turnip cake. Other choices such as spare ribs, and prawn and vegetable 'crystal' dumplings are also very acceptable. The full menu focuses on the familiar Chinese repertoire. House wine is £10. Open all week.

Other Place Bistro

29A Hope Street, Liverpool L1 9BQ
Tel: (0151) 707 7888

Cooking 2 | Modern European | £22–£47

Deep in Liverpool's cultural heartland round the corner from the Philharmonic Hall, this unpretentious modern bistro makes the most of its location, offering pre-theatre deals and light lunches to an appreciative crowd. Co-owner David Thorneycroft has now shifted most of his attention to the Other Place outlets on Allerton Road, and a new chef is at the helm in Hope Street. Some reporters think that standards have fallen off slightly in recent months, but the kitchen continues to deliver straightforward dishes like devilled lambs' kidneys before, say, monkfish with chive and fish cream risotto or roast Goosnargh duck breast with spinach and thyme jus. Close the show with Seville orange tart with mascarpone cream or whisky crème brûlée. The short, modern wine list promises plenty of zesty drinking from £11.25.

Chefs: Rhian Cradock and James Morgan **Proprietors:** David Thorneycroft, Sean Millar, Sheila Benson, Mark Benson, Chris Feeny and Philippa Feeny **Open:** Tue to Fri L 11.30 to 2.30, Tue to Sat D 6 to 10 **Closed:** 25 and 26 Dec, 1 Jan, bank hols **Meals:** alc (main courses L £4.50 to £9, D £11 to £14). Set D £21.95 (2 courses) to £24.95. Pre-theatre Set D Tue to Fri 6 to 7 £11.95 (2 courses) to £14.95 **Service:** not inc, card slips closed **Cards:** MasterCard, Maestro, Visa **Details:** 54 seats. Private parties: 30 main room, 12 to 20 private rooms. Vegetarian meals. Children's helpings. No cigars/pipes. Music

Simply Heathcotes

Beetham Plaza, 25 The Strand, Liverpool L2 0XL
Tel: (0151) 236 3536
Website: www.heathcotes.co.uk

Cooking 2 | Modern British | £27–£51

An office plaza by the Liver Building is the setting for this outpost of Paul Heathcote's gastro-empire. It is certainly chic, although the plate glass, polished granite walls and 'hard' floors can create a soulless mood, which is not helped by 'impersonal' staff. Like the décor, the food follows the 'badged' Heathcote formula. Regional produce figures large, menus are tweaked as the seasons change and the results can be impressive. Reporters have enjoyed mussels with cider and cream, smoked bacon and Savoy cabbage, and braised beef with horseradish mash, roasted root vegetables and red-wine sauce. Knickerbocker Glories are 'different every time, but uniformly excellent'; alternatively, finish with rhubarb, vanilla and elderflower summer pudding. The wine list is a lively slate with prices from £13.95.

Chef: Philip Sinclair **Proprietor:** Paul Heathcote **Open:** all week 12 to 2.30, 6 to 10 (11 Sat, 9 Sun) **Closed:** bank hols **Meals:** alc (not Sun L; main courses £8 to £16). Set L Sun £14.50 (2 courses) to £17 **Service:** not inc **Cards:** Amex, Delta, MasterCard, Maestro, Visa **Details:** 100 seats. 30 seats outside. Private parties: 40 main room. Vegetarian meals. Children's helpings. No smoking. Wheelchair access (also WC). Music. Air-conditioned

60 Hope Street

60 Hope Street, Liverpool L1 9BZ
Tel: (0151) 707 6060
Website: www.60hopestreet.com

Cooking 4 | Modern European | £27–£77

Number 60 is a dignified Georgian terrace that manages to be tranquil, even leafy, while enjoying such a central location. The Manning brothers' operation divides in two. At ground-floor level is a trim white restaurant; below is a café-bar, its walls painted raspberry red. The cooking is infectiously ambitious, with some speciality ingredients – Périgord chicken, saltmarsh lamb, Welsh black beef – supporting more local modes. Impeccably Scouse 'pea whack' fritters accompany scallops with deep-fried capers and pancetta as a starter, while main courses take in potato-coated roast halibut with smoked salmon and cabbage, or roast chicken breast with gratin potatoes, root vegetable hash and a rosemary cream sauce. Desserts such as warm date tart with spiced pecans and a chocolate and port syrup come with wine suggestions, no matter how stiff the challenge. Anyone for a deep-fried jam sandwich with Carnation milk ice cream? Service is friendly, and as on the ball as the city's European-champions football team.

Chablis from Billaud-Simon, Muscadet from Ragotière and Crozes-Hermitage from Colombier show that there's some serious Scouse nous behind the French-biased wine list, a slim volume that nevertheless manages to hit the spot for all palates and pockets.

Chef: Paul McEvoy **Proprietors:** Colin and Gary Manning **Open:** Mon to Fri L 12 to 2.30, Mon to Sat D 6 to 10.30 **Closed:** bank hols **Meals:** alc (main courses £15 to £26). Set L £12.95 (2 courses) to £15.95. Set D Mon to Sat 5 to 7 £11.95 (2 courses) to £14.95 **Service:** not inc, 10% for parties of 8 or more **Cards:** Delta, MasterCard, Maestro, Visa **Details:** 90 seats. Private parties: 90 main room, 10 to 30 private rooms. Vegetarian meals. Children's helpings. No-smoking area. Music. Air-conditioned

Ziba at the Racquet Club

5 Chapel Street, Liverpool L3 9AG
Tel: (0151) 236 6676
Website: www.racquetclub.org.uk

Cooking 3 | Modern British | £29–£72

Pale wood floors, tall windows and undressed tables convey the feel of a businesslike brasserie. The food – contemporary, if not cutting-edge – runs to some enterprising ideas – like an inspector's smoked duck breast accompanied by carrot and ginger salad with a pomegranate dressing. 'Tasty and tender' slow-roast cannon of lamb with swede and orange purée and redcurrant jus, and a 'chunky piece of fine tasting' monkfish with a good crab-herb crust served with a creamy smoked haddock and pea risotto, also featured, but the inspection highlight was a rich coffee tiramisù with walnut and raisin fudge. While there is no doubting the kitchen's skills, reports suggest under-par dishes can slip through the net. Service is friendly and helpful. An imaginative and good-value wine list is arranged by style and packed with mouth-watering prospects from £13.50.

Chef: Neil Dempsey **Proprietors:** Martin and Helen Ainscough **Open:** Mon to Fri L 12 to 2.30, Mon to Thur and Sat D 6 to 10.30 (11 Sat) **Meals:** alc (main courses £10 to £25). Set L £15 (2 courses) to £18. Snack L menu available Mon to Sat **Service:** not inc **Cards:** Amex, Delta, Maestro, MasterCard, Visa **Details:** 100 seats. Private parties: 120 main room, 12 to 22 private rooms. Vegetarian meals. Children's helpings. No smoking. No music. Air-conditioned **Accommodation:** 8 rooms, all with bath/shower. TV. Phone. Room only £105 to £150. Baby facilities. Swimming pool

 This symbol means that the wine list is well above the average.

MAP 5 **Llanfair Waterdine** SHROPSHIRE

Waterdine

Llanfair Waterdine LD7 1TU
Tel: (01547) 528214
Website: www.waterdine.com

Cooking 4 | Modern British | £30–£55

On the English side of the border between Shropshire and Powys, towards the head of the Teme Valley, this sixteenth-century inn-with-rooms puts on a homely face with its spruce décor, posies and domestic curios. Ken Adams buys locally and sets great store by the provenance of his raw materials, and the results on the plate have pleased most reporters. Typically you might find cured loin of Gloucester Old Spot pork with sarladaise potatoes and butter-bean ragoût alongside local duck breast on a confit of leeks with kumquat sauce and dauphinois potatoes, although other ingredients come from further afield: Cornish crab appears with vegetables in a terrine with mango, lime and chilli salsa, for example. Desserts encompass lemon tart with cassis sorbet and rice pudding with prune crème brûlée. An international line-up of wines at fair prices (starting at £16) hits just the right note. The Waterdine still functions as a pub, but it's 'bookings only' in the restaurant.

Chefs: Ken Adams and James Kinghorn **Proprietor:** Ken Adams **Open:** Tue to Sun L 12.15 to 1.45, Tue to Sat D 7.15 to 9, bookings only **Closed:** D 24 to 26 Dec **Meals:** alc (not Sun L, Sat D; main courses £13 to £16.50). Set L Sun £17.50, Set D Sat £28. Bar L menu available Tue to Sat **Service:** not inc, card slips closed **Cards:** Maestro, MasterCard, Visa **Details:** 24 seats. Private parties: 16 main room, 10 to 14 private rooms. Car park. No children under 8. No smoking. No music **Accommodation:** 3 rooms, all with bath/shower. TV. B&B £40 to £95. No children under 12

MAP 2 **Long Crendon** BUCKINGHAMSHIRE

Angel Restaurant

47 Bicester Road, Long Crendon HP18 9EE
Tel: (01844) 208268
Website: www.angelrestaurant.co.uk

Cooking 1 | Modern British | £34–£65

The appellation 'inn' was dropped a few years ago, although this sixteenth-century listed building is still a provider of hospitality, with bedrooms, several dining areas and a cheerfully decorated conservatory. Fish deliveries arrive daily, and specials are inscribed above the bar: 'outstanding' Scottish rope-grown mussels are steamed with smoked garlic and garden herbs, while seared fillet of sea bass comes with chargrilled vegetables, sweet chilli and basil dressing. Carnivorous appetites are not neglected, so you might see black pudding and sautéed chicken livers with sherry vinaigrette. As a finale, consider caramelised banana bavarois or panettone bread-and-butter pudding. Service is 'pleasant and prompt'.

The substantial wine list is packed with good names like Grosset in Australia and Vacheron in the Loire, and all the trendy grapes – Viognier, Roussanne, Pinot Noir – are on parade in both original French and New World incarnations. House bottles are £14.50.

Chefs: Trevor Bosch and Donald Joyce **Proprietors:** Trevor and Annie Bosch **Open:** all week L 12 to 2.30, Mon to Sat D 7 to 9.30 **Meals:** alc (not Sun; main courses £16 to £23.50). Set L £14.95 (2 courses) to £17.95 **Service:** not inc, card slips closed **Cards:** Amex, MasterCard, Maestro, Visa **Details:** 75 seats. 30 seats outside. Private parties: 25 main room, 8 to 15 private rooms. Car park. Vegetarian meals. Children's helpings. No smoking in 1 dining room. Music. Air-conditioned **Accommodation:** 3 rooms, all with bath/shower. TV. Phone. B&B £65 to £85. Baby facilities

MAP 6 **Long Melford** SUFFOLK

Scutchers

Westgate Street, Long Melford CO10 9DP
Tel: (01787) 310200
Website: www.scutchers.com

Cooking 2 | Modern British | £33–£56

Substantial bistro cooking is the hallmark of this attractively decorated restaurant, set in a converted village house. Old-fashioned richness meets a few modern 'exotics' and the chef-proprietor's focus is on good raw materials. Dishes are generously sauced and even the most ample mains come with extra vegetables and choice of spuds. The atmosphere is casual; quick meals can be had if time's too tight for a languid feast, and there's even a takeaway menu. Start with sautéed foie gras on rösti with haggis and port jus, or local asparagus in puff pastry with lemon butter and roast red pepper. Follow with crisp, pink duck breast, Cox's apples and gravy or simple Dover sole. Puddings could include iced berries with warm white chocolate sauce and spotted dick with custard. The wine list opens with single glasses from £2.50 and house bottles at £12.50. Thereafter, equal prominence is given to selections from the New and Old Worlds.

Chefs: Nick Barrett and Guy Alabaster **Proprietors:** Nick and Diane Barrett **Open:** Tue to Sat 12 to 2, 7 to 9.30 **Closed:** Christmas, 2 weeks Aug **Meals:** alc (main courses £12 to £19). Set L Tue to Fri £15 (2 courses), Set D Tue to Thur £15 (2 courses) **Service:** not inc **Cards:** Amex, Delta, Maestro, MasterCard, Visa **Details:** 70 seats. 40 seats outside. Private parties: 50 main room. Car park. Vegetarian meals. No smoking. Wheelchair access (also WC). No music. Air-conditioned

MAP 8 **Longridge** LANCASHIRE

Longridge Restaurant

104–106 Higher Road, Longridge PR3 3SY
Tel: (01772) 784969
Website: www.heathcotes.co.uk

Cooking 6 | Modern British | £28–£68

If Paul Heathcote has removed his name from what is still the flagship of his restaurant group, he's still a commanding presence in the kitchen, flanked by adjutant Leigh Myers. From outside this may look like a simple Lancashire cottage, but it's kitted out in best modern style, with a light, bright ambience alongside the original wooden panelling.

The commitment to local produce and regional methods of preparation, permeates the menus, and for one group of regulars things just get better and better: a September dinner being 'the most exquisite meal we have ever had here'. Black pudding is a constant, enjoyed on this occasion in a sizeable raviolo with a sauce featuring caramelised apple – and the herb-crusted brill with asparagus that followed was pretty neat too. It's to the credit of the cooking style that old-fangled dishes never come across as Heritage Fayre, not even when mead is used to sauce Goosnargh duck breast with buttered cabbage and turnips. Similarly, roast sucking pig from a local supplier is served with cider potatoes and baked apple, its juices spiked with sage. Side-dishes such as fat chips or cauliflower cheese may prove hard to resist, as will the crowd-pleasing desserts, which could take in a cinnamon doughnut with vanilla ice cream, or, classically, might pair black cherry ice cream with dark chocolate gâteau. Service is a treat. The wine list presents a considered line-up without fuss. It's arranged by grape variety with a dozen by the glass and bottles from £13.95.

Chefs: Paul Heathcote and Leigh Myers **Proprietor:** Paul Heathcote **Open:** Tue to Fri L 12 to 2.30, Tue to Sat D 6 (5 Sat) to 10, Sun 12 to 9 **Closed:** 1 and 2 Jan **Meals:** alc (main courses £12.50 to £24.50). Set L £14 (2 courses) to £17, Set D (not Sat 6.30 to 10) £25 **Service:** not inc, 10% for parties of 8 or more **Cards:** Amex, Delta, Diners, Maestro, MasterCard, Visa **Details:** 70 seats. Private parties: 70 main room, 8 to 18 private rooms. Car park. Vegetarian meals. Children's helpings. No smoking in 1 dining room. Wheelchair access (not WC). Music

Thyme

1–3 Inglewhite Road, Longridge PR3 3JR
Tel: (01772) 786888
Website: www.thyme-restaurant.co.uk

Cooking 3 | Modern European | £19–£61

Two terraced cottages were knocked through to create this thoroughly modern brasserie on two levels. Regulars reckon that Alex Coward has 'cranked up the cooking' here of late: dishes have been fine-tuned, tastes are clearer and presentation looks fashionable. Recent successes have included 'today's interesting and often unusual soup' (well-balanced chestnut, red onion and courgette), scallop and tiger-prawn risotto and 'the best porchetta-style suckling pig I have had'. Weekly specials like rack of Bowland lamb with fondant potato, plum and redcurrant chutney and a jus scented with lavender and honey offer even more choice, and desserts range from chocolate and orange pudding to mango and passion-fruit brûlée with sesame nougat. The modest wine list is an affordable assortment, with house 'favourites' from £11.25. There's a second branch of Thyme at the Sirloin Inn, Station Road, Hoghton, Preston; tel: (01254) 852293.

Chefs: Alex Coward and Mike Law **Proprietors:** Alex Coward and Wayne Keough **Open:** Tue to Sun 12 to 2.30, 6 to 9.30 (Sunday 1 to 8pm) **Meals:** alc (main courses £13 to £19). Set L (Tue to Sat) £7.95 (2 courses) to £9.95, Set Sun L £10.95 (2 courses) to £12.95, Set D (Tue to Fri and Sun 6 to 7.30) £8.95 (2 courses) to £10.95. Light L menu available **Service:** not inc, card slips closed **Cards:** Amex, Delta, Diners, MasterCard, Maestro, Visa **Details:** 45 seats. Private parties: 45 main room. Vegetarian meals. No smoking. Wheelchair access (also WC). Music. No mobile phones

MAP 2 Longstock HAMPSHIRE

Peat Spade

AR

Longstock SO20 6DR
Tel: (01264) 810612

'Lovely village pub' where all vegetables and meat are impeccably sourced from sustainable sources. The cooking is an eclectic mix of a modern European style with a few Asian flourishes, featuring potted salmon and Dorset crab (£5.75), organic mutton rogan josh (£9), and free-range pork faggots with mash (£8.50), with the likes of good old sticky toffee pudding (£4.50) among desserts. Sunday lunch has been well reported, and there are good vegetarian choices. Organic and biodynamic wines from £12.80 appear on the short wine list. No credit cards. Closed Sun D and all Mon.

MAP 1 Looe CORNWALL

Trawlers on the Quay

The Quay, East Looe PL13 1AH
Tel: (01503) 263593
Website: www.trawlersrestaurant.co.uk

Cooking 3 | Seafood | £39–£47

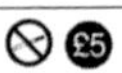

With a bang-on-the-quay setting and an atmosphere that generates a 'cheerful and holiday feeling', this popular bistro attracts locals and visitors with the quality and worth of the fresh seafood on offer. Classic preparations are the order of the day, with dishes mobilising plenty of flavours, as in a starter of crevettes stir-fried with lime, chilli, garlic and herbs, or a main course such as local cod sautéed with roast peppers, sun-blush tomatoes, parsley, olives and capers, or sautéed fillets of John Dory with crab, prawns, mussels and cream. There's choice for meat eaters too, with breast of chicken stuffed with Cornish blue cheese and walnuts in a chive cream sauce. For a resonant finale, try the dark chocolate and orange terrine. Little home-made chocolates accompany cafetière coffee, breads are all home made ('getting us off to a fine start'), and the wine list shows the same commitment to value and quality. House wine is £13.50.

Chefs: Mark Napper and Todd Varnadoe **Proprietors:** Nick Love and Mark Napper **Open:** Tue to Sat D only 6.15 to 9.15 **Closed:** 25 and 26 Dec **Meals:** Set D £23 (2 courses) to £26 **Service:** not inc **Cards:** Maestro, MasterCard, Visa **Details:** 40 seats. 12 seats outside. Private parties: 50 main room. Vegetarian meals. No smoking. Wheelchair access (not WC). Music

MAP 3 Lower Hardres KENT

Granville

Street End, Lower Hardres CT4 7AL
Tel: (01227) 700402

Cooking 4 | Modern European | £31–£51

Head south from Canterbury for a few miles and you will happen upon this substantial old roadside inn owned by the same proprietors as the Sportsman in Whitstable (see entry). It is just as good as its parent, offering a similar blend of informal pub atmosphere and classy home cooking. Top-quality local produce is the kitchen's starting point. Tender roast partridge, in season, is served with dabs of Valrhona chocolate sauce that add a hint of sweetness to the gamey meat, while super fresh gilt-head bream is cooked simply with rosemary and garlic and served with roast potatoes and greens – 'just perfect' felt an inspector. To start, the blackboard menu might offer smoked mackerel with potato salad and horseradish, or potato and wild garlic soup, and to finish, lemon tart with raspberry sauce, or rhubarb sorbet with burnt cream are typical. If there is a weak link, it is in the 'cheerfully inept' service: 'restaurant food at restaurant prices but untrained pub staff,' as one visitor put it. Prices on the short wine list start at £11, with seven selections by the large or small glass.

Chefs: Jim Shave, Ezra Gaynor, David Hart and Oliver Rose **Proprietors:** Gabrielle, Stephen, Philip and Damian Harris **Open:** Tue to Sun L 12 to 2, Tue to Sat D 7 to 9 **Closed:** 25 Dec, 1 Jan, Easter Mon **Meals:** alc L and D (main courses £11 to £18). Bar menu available Mon to Sat L **Service:** not inc, 10% for parties of 6 or more **Cards:** Delta, Maestro, MasterCard, Visa **Details:** 65 seats. 20 seats outside. Private parties: 30 main room. Car park. No-smoking area. Wheelchair access (also WC). Music. Air-conditioned

MAP 7 Lower Oddington GLOUCESTERSHIRE

Fox Inn

NEW ENTRY

Lower Oddington GL56 0UR
Tel: (01451) 870555
Website: www.foxinn.net

Cooking 1 | Modern British | £27–£48

'The Fox is always packed,' noted a reporter who has made frequent visits to this gentrified, highly attractive Cotswolds pub. It's a place that emanates upper-class, '*Country Life* magazine' rusticity, although cheerful, chatty staff banish any whiffs of pretension or snootiness. One menu (plus a specials board) applies throughout, and the kitchen delivers consistently good upbeat dishes without airs or graces. Chilled sugar-cured tuna comes with endive and shallot dressing, while seared scallops are paired with rocket and ginger. On the meat front, expect anything from Barbary duck breast with port and morello cherries to medallions of pork dijonnaise, while desserts are straightforward ideas like orange parfait with citrus sauce. Nine house wines (from £11.75) head the well-chosen wine list.

Chef: Raymond Pearce **Proprietor:** Ian Mackenzie **Open:** all week 12 to 2, 6.30 to 10 (9.30 Sun) **Closed:** 25 Dec **Meals:** alc (main courses £8.50 to £14) **Service:** not inc, card slips closed, 10% for parties of 7 or more **Cards:** Delta, Maestro, MasterCard, Visa **Details:** 80 seats. 80 seats outside. Private parties: 20 to 24 private rooms. Car park. Vegetarian meals. Children's helpings. No music **Accommodation:** 3 rooms, 2 with bath/shower. TV. B&B £45 to £95

MAP 6 **Lowick** NORTHAMPTONSHIRE

Snooty Fox

16 Main Street, Lowick NN14 3BH
Tel: (01832) 733434

Cooking 3 | Modern British | £27–£55

More of an inn than a village local, this rough-stone, many-gabled, sixteenth-century hostelry is tucked away in a surprisingly lovely part of Northamptonshire. The focus of the food here is a chill counter arrayed with steaks from well-hung Orkney Island beef: choose your preferred cut, have it cooked to your liking and enjoy it with a pile of fat chips, garlic butter or peppercorn sauce. Mersea Island rock oysters are also mainstays, and the grill/rôtisserie is deployed for other options like seared tuna with new potatoes, rocket and fennel salad. You might begin with gravlax and horseradish crème fraîche or coarse pâté with fruit chutney and finish with a plate of 'artisan-made' cheeses, warm Bakewell tart or simply strawberries and cream. The wine list is a well-spread assortment arranged by style; prices start at £12.50.

Chef: Clive Dixon **Proprietors:** Clive Dixon and David Hennigan **Open:** all week 12 to 2, 6.30 to 9.30 **Meals:** alc (main courses £10.50 to £16). Set L Mon to Sat £9.95 (2 courses) to £13.95. Bar menu available **Service:** not inc, 10% (optional) for parties of 10 or more **Cards:** Delta, Diners, MasterCard, Maestro, Visa **Details:** 120 seats. 60 seats outside. Private parties: 50 main room, 12 to 26 private rooms. Car park. Vegetarian meals. Children's helpings. No smoking in 1 dining room. Music

MAP 9 **Low Laithe** NORTH YORKSHIRE

Dusty Miller

Low Laithe, Summerbridge HG3 4BU
Tel: (01423) 780837

Cooking 4 | Anglo-French | £34–£64

Once a pub, then an antique shop, for the last twenty years this has been the Dennisons' hospitable restaurant in a quiet hamlet between Pateley Bridge and Harrogate. Brian Dennison turns out good-quality, well-cooked food, which is served in a 'sparkly-clean ... pretty and stylish' dining room fringed with antique furniture. The service, by Elizabeth Dennison, and the rural Nidderdale setting are strong points. Push the boat out with admirably fresh oysters on ice, a chicken-liver parfait, or perhaps watercress and apple soup. Follow with classically inspired roast duckling and apple sauce, supreme of partridge with bread sauce and game chips, or 'a good traditional tournedos Rossini'. End on a sweet note with the domestic delights of plum crumble and custard, or a skilfully executed lemon tart with a slightly sweet raspberry coulis perfectly counterpointing its citric sharpness. A 'small but perfectly formed' wine list has been put together 'with care and lots of personal knowledge'. Bottles are fairly priced, from £13 upwards, with plenty of scope between £20 and £30, while prices by the glass start at £3.50.

Chef: Brian Dennison **Proprietors:** Brian and Elizabeth Dennison **Open:** Tue to Sat D only 7 to 11 **Closed:** 25 and 26 Dec, 1 Jan **Meals:** alc (main courses £22). Set D £24.90 **Service:** not inc, card slips closed **Cards:** Amex, Delta, Maestro, MasterCard, Visa **Details:** 46 seats. Private parties: 32 main room, 8 to 14 private rooms. Car park. Children's helpings. No children under 9. No smoking. Occasional music

MAP 7 **Ludlow** SHROPSHIRE

Dinham Hall

Dinham, Ludlow SY8 1EJ
Tel: (01584) 876464
Website: www.dinhamhall.co.uk

Cooking 5 | Modern European | £60–£72

A hundred yards downhill from the castle, three-storey Dinham Hall turns its back on the ramparts and battlements to look out over its own lawns. The small-scale interior (the wood-floored dining

room seats only two dozen) is plainly decorated, although don't miss the enormous old fireplace. There is a real sense of things forging ahead in the kitchen here nowadays. Peter James McGregor is young, ambitious and willing to try out new ideas – in a town that scarcely lacks high-flyers.

Superbly fresh raw materials inform the cooking, which is served at a sedate pace by courteous and friendly staff. The three- or four-course dinner menu might start with something as simple as caviar-topped scallops, accompanied by warm cucumber and sauced with vermouth, or a grilled John Dory fillet on niçoise salad. Main courses ascend to appreciably greater complexity, so that roast loin of spring lamb arrives with crisp sweetbreads and roast garlic, with boulangère potatoes wrapped in locally cured bacon. An inspector's main dish of supple, thick-sliced duck breast came with fondant potato, a baked fig and a lightly spiced jus of red wine and thyme, as well as a small bed of intensely flavoured parsnip purée. Desserts, too, might seem to be piling up the ingredients, although the individual elements are straightforward enough: thus, a crème brûlée flavoured with rhubarb and tonka beans appears in the company of mandarin sorbet, chilled rhubarb and vodka soup, and almond tuiles. The wine list is a fairly basic document and is lacking one or two producers' names, but prices are eminently reasonable throughout. Eight house recommendations are around £17.

Chef: Peter James McGregor **Proprietors:** J.P. and J.E. Mifsud **Open:** all week D only 7 to 8.45 **Meals:** Set D £35 to £42.50. Light L menu available **Service:** not inc, card slips closed **Cards:** Amex, Delta, Diners, Maestro, MasterCard, Visa **Details:** 24 seats. 40 seats outside. Private parties: 44 main room, 2 to 100 private rooms. Car park. Children's helpings. No children under 8. No smoking. Wheelchair access (not WC). No music. No mobile phones **Accommodation:** 13 rooms, all with bath/shower. TV. Phone. B&B £95 to £240. Baby facilities

Hibiscus

17 Corve Street, Ludlow SY8 1DA
Tel: (01584) 872325
Website: www.hibiscusrestaurant.co.uk

Cooking 8 | French | £39–£93

Claude and Claire Bosi's stylish but unassuming restaurant is on the main street running north to south through the town. Inside are three small, interlinked rooms, with a bar area at the front, with much oak panelling and an uncluttered look. A couple of abstract paintings lighten the place, and smart glassware and floor-length table linen give an impression of serious intent.

Virtually from the moment this venture began in 2000, it was clear that Bosi's culinary intentions were equally serious. His cooking doesn't stand still but is committed to a tireless quest for new challenges, pushing back the boundaries of experimental French cuisine but with the panache to take his customers with him each step of the way. Ingredients are given their proper due, not least in that they are served generously rather than in precious micro-portions, and even when you may be thinking that the level of complexity in a dish looks set to topple the balance, the trick is nonetheless somehow brought off.

A spring lunch that began with duck confit ravioli with puréed broad beans and followed on with roast Cornish cod with a fricassee of peas and root vegetables in wild garlic froth confirmed the outstanding quality for a pair who had scarcely been able to believe it the first time. Combinations are nothing if not bold: witness a first course that brings together roast lambs' sweetbreads with calamari cooked in maple syrup, the flavours complicated by sweet red onion chutney, a scattering of lemon zest and the intriguing dryness of a foamy sauce of Assam tea. So many items may crowd on to the plate in main courses that you may be left wondering whether the dish would have been altogether bereft if one or two had been left out, but the overall excellence of an inspector's main course wasn't in question. It consisted of a large grilled breast of Challans duck of extraordinary richness, accompanied by roast shallots, their flavour rounded out with a bit of banana, wedges of melon seasoned with lemon verbena, a thin pastry tart of tiny mushrooms, and more besides. When the desire to do a lot with a dish is at its most exuberant, it might result in a main course arriving as two separate servings, as is the case with suckling pig, first roasted, served with sea urchin cream and dried apricot and cumin purée, then the slow-cooked belly with a sausage, truffle shavings and a mash of potato, turnip and vanilla.

If there are sweet fruits in the preceding courses, there are quite as likely to be vegetables, herbs and savoury ingredients in the desserts. Herb-flecked, iced olive oil parfait with cherries is one way of concluding, or there might be meadowsweet pannacotta with apple compote and a cinnamon biscuit, or the fixture tarte au chocolat served with an ice cream of Indonesian basil. Excellent Crozes-Hermitage from Domaine du Colombier (£28.50) typifies an impressive range of French wines that nonetheless keeps its feet on the ground (there's a decent Lubéron red in the house line-up for £14.75 too). Other countries have shorter selections, but half-bottles are a strength.

Chef: Claude Bosi **Proprietors:** Claire and Claude Bosi **Open:** Wed to Sat L 12.15 to 1.45, Tue to Sat D 7.15 to 9.30 **Closed:** 23 Dec to 18 Jan, 1 week Aug **Meals:** Set L £19.50 (2 courses) to £25, Set D £42.50 to £60 **Service:** not inc, card slips closed **Cards:** Delta, Maestro, Visa **Details:** 36 seats. Private parties: 36 main room. Car park. Children's helpings. No smoking. Wheelchair access (not WC). No music. No mobile phones

Mr Underhill's

Dinham Weir, Ludlow SY8 1EH
Tel: (01584) 874431
Website: www.mr-underhills.co.uk

Cooking 7 | Modern European | £51–£67

As the Teme flows under Ludlow castle walls it also passes the Bradleys' prettily sited restaurant-with-rooms. Amble through the garden (a delight in spring and summer) to the dining room: long and thin with, at one end, a cracking view over the terrace to the river. As dusk falls, lights in the foliage outside come on, the glassware gleams, and all is relaxed informality. This is one of those places that runs very much to its own rules, with a daily-changing set menu of six courses, the only choice coming at dessert stage. The system for establishing likes and dislikes beforehand doesn't always work for non-residents, so it pays to be open-minded, although there will never be anything too controversial on offer.

This is cooking that makes a virtue of simplicity and economy, and seems to please the great majority on both fronts. One fine, home-made bread opens the proceedings, a first-rate sourdough on our inspection visit, the accompanying butter sprinkled with a few flakes of salt. The first course is little more than an amuse, a May dinner beginning with a single spear of soft, chopped asparagus in a medium of chopped soft-boiled egg. This was followed by a tiny dish of delicately flavoured foie gras custard, sandwiched between sweetcorn cream and a salty, dark meat glaze top. A fish dish follows, perhaps moist, crumb-topped halibut sitting alongside a swirl of carrot velouté and a pile of spring greens, and then meat. Thin-sliced Périgord duck breast of impressive flavour, its skin smeared in wildflower honey, was arranged around a Savoy cabbage parcel of shredded vegetables. After a small pre-dessert, the majesty of the dessert menu opens up. A filo pastry tart of warm, molten dark chocolate might be offset by white chocolate ice cream, or there could be rhubarb crumble with ginger ice cream in the season.

From a range of Alsace by the estimable Ernest Burn to Kumeu River's New Zealand wines, the individual wine list makes enticing reading and has been praised for fair pricing. Six house wines come by the glass or bottle (from £13), and there's an impressive slate of halves.

Chef: Chris Bradley **Proprietors:** Chris and Judy Bradley **Open:** Wed to Sun D only 7.15 to 8.15 **Closed:** 1 week Jan, 1 week Jul **Meals:** Set D £40 to £44 **Service:** not inc, card slips closed **Cards:** Delta, Maestro, MasterCard, Visa **Details:** 30 seats. 30 seats outside. Car park. Vegetarian meals. No children under 8. No smoking. No music. No mobile phones **Accommodation:** 9 rooms, all with bath/shower. TV. Phone. B&B £95 to £210. No children under 8. Fishing

Overton Grange

NEW ENTRY

Old Hereford Road, Ludlow SY8 4AD
Tel: (01584) 873500
Website: www.overtongrangehotel.com

Cooking 3 | Anglo-French | £47–£90

A narrow, curving drive leads up to this large, Edwardian manor house on a small promontory on the outskirts of Ludlow. Inside will look familiar to frequenters of country-house restaurants, with plenty of oak panelling, swagged drapes and open fires, although a more contemporary touch has been brought to bear on the dining room. Olivier Bossut is a chef with an eye for detail, as is handsomely evidenced by excellent, labour-intensive appetisers and a pre-dessert of lavender crème brûlée that constituted 'a fine piece of workmanship' at inspection. Impressive main-course meats turn up in the shapes of a steamed squab pigeon with creamed Savoy cabbage and Périgord truffle sauce, and an impeccably timed noisette of local lamb with a parcel of wild mushrooms and an oily but flavourful liquorice sauce. These might be book-ended by well-wrought langoustine feuilleté with spinach, and desserts that favour chocolate creations, such as white chocolate croquant with a matching ice cream in a brandy-snap basket. An extensive selection of quality wines, with much to celebrate for Francophiles, looks tempting until one ponders the prices. There is precious little below £20, although proceedings open with half a dozen house selections at £19.

Chef: Olivier Bossut **Proprietor:** Franck J.S. Choblet-Metzo **Open:** Wed to Sat L 12 to 2.30, all week D 7 to 9.45 (10 Sat) **Meals:** Set L £29.50 to £39.50, Set D £39.50 to £55 **Service:** 10% (optional), card slips closed **Cards:** Delta, Maestro, MasterCard, Visa **Details:** 70 seats. Private parties: 100 main room, 12 to 100 private rooms. Car park. No children under 8. No smoking. Wheelchair access (not WC). No music. No mobile phones **Accommodation:** 14 rooms, all with bath/shower. TV. Phone. B&B £85 to £190

MAP 9 **Lund** EAST RIDING OF YORKSHIRE

Wellington Inn

19 The Green, Lund YO25 9TE
Tel: (01377) 217294

Cooking 3 | Modern British | £36–£58

At the heart of an out-of-the-way Wolds village, this pub-cum-restaurant is an all-round 'polished' affair, and, as one reporter remarked with enthusiasm, 'if it was in my village I wouldn't move house'. Traditional touches prevail, like flagstones and real beams, while the restaurant comes decked out on several levels, with white walls, more beams, lush carpeting and polished, candlelit tables; it's a modern 'posh pub' and not at all 'dusty olde worlde', successfully combining enterprising food alongside its role as the village local. The evenings-only restaurant menu trades in the kind of upmarket dishes you might be surprised to find in a country pub; take roast North Sea cod on a chilli and chorizo risotto, or perhaps pot-roast Gloucester Old Spot belly pork teamed with roasted root vegetables and a sweet cider reduction. Bar food is delivered in a tastefully converted back room, with lunch chalked on the blackboard. The contemporary list of well-reviewed wines is good value (from £11.95); seven options by the glass and a good collection of halves add to the appeal.

Chef: Sarah Jeffery **Proprietors:** Russell and Sarah Jeffery **Open:** Tue to Sat D only 6.45 to 9.15. Bar food Tue to Sun **Meals:** alc (main courses £15 to £19). Bar menu available **Service:** not inc, card slips closed **Cards:** Delta, MasterCard, Maestro, Visa **Details:** 42 seats. Private parties: 30 main room, 8 to 12 private rooms. Car park. Vegetarian meals. No children under 16. No smoking. Music. No mobile phones

MAP 1 **Luton** DEVON

Elizabethan Inn

AR

Fore Street, Luton TQ13 0BL
Tel: (01626) 775425

Nick Powell and Anne Gibbs are keeping things on track at this classic English village pub in a farming hamlet. The kitchen conjures up robust, full-flavoured dishes like mushrooms in garlic butter (£5.25) or chicken liver parfait with home-made chutney complemented by substantial main courses of fillet of salmon with crab bisque and asparagus (£13) or ribeye steak with pepper sauce (£14) and no-nonsense desserts like chocolat fudge tart (£4.50). A list of 20-plus wines starts a £10.95. Open all week.

MAP 1 **Lydford** DEVON

Dartmoor Inn

Lydford EX20 4AY
Tel: (01822) 820221
Email: info@dartmoorinn.co.uk

Cooking 3 | Modern British-Plus | £33–£55

Karen and Philip Burgess have been busy of late smartening up and refurbishing much of thei popular Dartmoor hostelry. Their intention ha always been to promote the region through festivals and other junketings and to put local producers top of their shopping list. There's little doubt that the kitchen can deliver unfussy dishes wit skill and dexterity: to start, you might choos brown shrimp risotto with crayfish and saffron, c pork terrine with spiced pears. Free-range duck served with celeriac purée and wild garlic leave and fillet of Cornish sea bass with ratatouille an roast crab oil. Vegetarians have a full menu, an desserts could vary from homespun rhubarb an treacle steamed pudding to honey parfait wit toasted pine nuts. A page of house recommendations (from £12.75) opens the enticing glob wine list.

Chefs: Andrew Honey and Philip Burgess **Proprietors:** Karen and Philip Burgess **Open:** Tue to Sun L 12 to 2, Tue to Sat D 6.30 to 9.30 **Closed:** Christmas, bank hols **Meals:** alc (main courses £12 to £19.50). Set L £14.95 (2 courses) to £17.50, Set D Tue to Thur £14.95 (2 courses) to £17.50. Bar menu available **Service:** not inc, card slips closed, 10% for parties of 10 or more **Cards:** Delta, Maestro, MasterCard, Visa **Details:** 70 seats. Private parties: 20 main room. Car park. Vegetarian meals. Children's helpings. No children under 5 Fri and Sat D. No smoking. Occasional music. No mobile phones **Accommodation:** 3 rooms, all with bath/shower. Phone. B&B £95 to £125. No children

⊘	This symbol means that smoking is not permitted.
	This symbol means that there are some restrictions on smoking though it may be allowed in some eating areas.

MAP 8 **Lydgate** GREATER MANCHESTER

White Hart Inn

51 Stockport Road, Lydgate OL4 4JJ
Tel: (01457) 872566
Website: www.thewhitehart.co.uk

Cooking 4 | Modern British | £31–£66

In an expansive Pennine setting and with its own lawns and big oak framed extension, the White Hart achieves a generous blend of ancient and modern in which the minimal co-exists with the traditional. The kitchen buys carefully and indeed produces its own Saddleworth sausages; these set the tone for the lengthy menu that draws inspiration from English tradition, with Italian twists. Mains of beef fillet, Berkshire pork loin or grilled fillet of halibut are accompanied respectively by wild mushroom ravioli, onion and sage risotto and salmon cannelloni. Starters can range from Bayonne ham, feta and olive omelette to honey-smoked duck breast with tempura ginger sushi roll and crispy noodle salad, via cod brandade with tiger prawns. Puddings, though, are more British, and might include Scotch pancakes or apple and blackberry crumble, while native cheeses are a feature. Lunches and the early evening weekday menu are worth exploring. Wines are a contemporary international mix, smartened up by some serious Bordeaux and Burgundy. Bottles start at £14.50, and a dozen come by the glass.

Chef: John Rudden **Proprietors:** Charles Brierley and John Rudden **Open:** all week 12 to 2.30, 6 to 9.30 (Sun and bank hols 1 to 7.30) **Meals:** alc (main courses £12 to £19). Set L £12.50 (2 courses) to £14.50 (3 courses), Set D Mon to Thur £34.50 to £42.50 **Service:** not inc, card slips closed **Cards:** Amex, Delta, Maestro, MasterCard, Visa **Details:** 125 seats. Private parties: 90 main room, 38 to 220 private rooms. Car park. Vegetarian meals. Children's helpings. No smoking. Wheelchair access (also WC). Music. Occasional music. No mobile phones. Air-conditioned **Accommodation:** 12 rooms, all with bath/shower. TV. Phone. B&B £80 to £130. Baby facilities

	This symbol means that the wine list is well above the average.
	This symbol means that the restaurant has a truly outstanding wine cellar.

MAP 2 **Lymington** HAMPSHIRE

Egan's

24 Gosport Street, Lymington SO41 9BE
Tel: (01590) 676165

Cooking 2 | Modern British | £23–£52

John and Deborah Egan's modest bistro-style restaurant scores with a pleasingly simple décor and capable service, and it's also prepared to invest in decent local ingredients, particularly fish. Scallops with lobster sauce and leek risotto made a good start to one meal, and the kitchen is obviously keen on involved, multi-component aggregations (boned skate wing and vegetable 'spaghetti' share the plate with a brochette of tiger prawns, prawn spring roll, and spiced lemongrass and ginger sauce). Meat receives similar treatment: marinated medallions of venison with griottine cherry sauce sit alongside a crépinette of guinea fowl breast and morel sauce, for example. Portions are ample – particularly as main courses come with side dishes of vegetables ('totally unnecessary' according to one recipient). Finish with sticky toffee pudding with toffee pear, or a salad of tropical fruits.

Chef: John Egan **Proprietors:** John and Deborah Egan **Open:** Tue to Sat 12 to 2, 6.30 to 10 **Meals:** alc D (main courses £12 to £17). Set L £9.95 (2 courses) to £12.95 **Service:** not inc **Cards:** Maestro, MasterCard, Visa **Details:** 50 seats. Private parties: 30 main room. Vegetarian meals. Children's helpings. No smoking in 1 dining room. Music

MAP 8 **Lytham St Anne's** LANCASHIRE

Chicory

5–7 Henry Street, Lytham St Anne's FY8 5LE
Tel: (01253) 737111
Email: chicory@tiscali.co.uk

Cooking 4 | Global | £26–£60

Smartly kitted out with a huge double-sided banquette neatly dividing the restaurant in two and an open-to-view kitchen giving a 'sense of theatre', this cheerful, modern restaurant serves the 'well-heeled clientele of Lytham well'. The evening menu has much of interest – lunch is a lighter affair – and its broadly European style with pan-Asian touches turns up anything from tea-smoked salmon with quail's egg won tons and a cream cheese samosa to boned and rolled suckling pig with crushed chorizo potatoes. Fish dishes have included fish and chips of 'excellent quality' and an unusual partnership of gigot of monkfish with rolled shin of beef confit, while red-blooded grills and roasts – of fillet of beef or rack of lamb – share the billing with the likes of chicken breast flavoured with lime, sun-dried tomatoes and Parmesan. Desserts range from glazed lemon tart to a trio of chocolate. Long waits have been a problem, but around two dozen wines by the glass help smooth things along. House wines are £11.95.

Chefs: Gary Cartwright, Felix Santoni and Richard Martin **Proprietors:** Gary Cartwright, Bevan Middleton, Felix Santoni and Richard Martin **Open:** all week 12 to 2 (2.30 Sun), 6 to 9.30 (10 Fri and Sat, 9 Sun) **Meals:** alc exc Sun L (main courses L £7.50 to £10, D £15 to £23). Set L Sun £17.95, Set D Sun to Thur £17.95 **Service:** not inc, card slips closed **Cards:** Amex, Delta, Maestro, MasterCard, Visa **Details:** 75 seats. Private parties: 75 main room. Vegetarian meals. Children's helpings. No-smoking area. Wheelchair access (also WC). Music. Air-conditioned

Dalmeny Hotel, Atrium

19–33 South Promenade, St Anne's on Sea FY8 1LX
Tel: (01253) 712236
Website: www.dalmenyhotel.co.uk

Cooking 2 | Modern European | £21–£59

Part of the hotel, but with its own entrance, the smart, tiered-glass Atrium has light wood floors and bistro-style furniture. 'The place to be in Lytham St Anne's on a Friday night', its sociable, noisy atmosphere is fuelled by live music, or sometimes Muzak, and the kitchen trips merrily through French-focused modern European crowd-pleasers. Standards did not always hold up at inspection, but highlights were ham hock and black pudding with home-made brown sauce, and a duo of lamb (roast fillet and confit leg) with buttered olive mash, roast seasonal vegetables and red wine jus. White chocolate and berry pannacotta with plum compote makes a good finish. Service is cheerful but can falter when things get busy. Wines start at £10.95, with most under £25.

Chef: Darren Pilling **Proprietor:** Sandra Webb **Open:** all week D only 6 to 9.30 **Closed:** 24 to 26 Dec **Meals:** alc Mon to Thur and Sat (main courses £15 to £25). Set D 6 to 7 £9.95 (2 courses) to £12.50, after 7 £15.50. Bar menu available Sun to Thur D **Service:** not inc, card slips closed **Cards:** Amex, Delta, Maestro, MasterCard, Visa **Details:** 80 seats. Private parties: 100 main room. Car park. Vegetarian meals. Children's helpings. No smoking. Wheelchair access (also WC). Music. Air-conditioned **Accommodation:** 128 rooms, all with bath/shower. TV. Phone. B&B £61.60 to £148. Rooms for disabled. Baby facilities. Swimming pool

MAP 6 Madingley CAMBRIDGESHIRE

Three Horseshoes

High Street, Madingley CB3 8AB
Tel: (01954) 210221
Website: www.huntsbridge.com

Cooking 3 | Mediterranean | £42–£65

This senior member of the Huntsbridge Group's gang of four East Anglian pub/restaurants (see entries in Fotheringhay, Huntingdon and Keyston) is a cosmopolitan-feeling thatched inn a couple of miles from Cambridge and close to the American Military Cemetery. Here Richard Stokes continues with his busy modern take on Italian cuisine, fusing British ingredients with a plethora of Mediterranean components: Portland crab is garnished with shaved fennel, celery, citron, dill, dried chilli, dandelion, bottarga (dried mullet roe) and olive oil, while roast saddle of red deer is partnered by celeriac, Fontina gratin, wild mushrooms and Tuscan black cabbage; vegetables are extra. Some less elaborate ideas, such as coda alla romana (braised oxtail in white wine) with wet polenta and Parmesan, appear on the list of 'bar grill' specials. Reports suggest occasional lapses and inconsistencies, but ample desserts like blackberry crumble with home-made blackberry ice cream have been greatly appreciated. Wine continues to hit the spot, with the well-established 'under £20' and 'top-class' categories both punching their weight. Sixteen house wines by the glass offer stimulating flavours from £3.25 to £6.50.

Chef: Richard Stokes **Proprietor:** Huntsbridge Ltd **Open:** all week L 12 to 2, Mon to Sat D 6.30 to 9.30 **Closed:** 31 Dec and 1 Jan **Meals:** alc (main courses £15 to £22). Bar/grill menu available **Service:** not inc, 10% for parties of 10 or more **Cards:** Amex, Maestro, MasterCard, Visa **Details:** 110 seats. 40 seats outside. Private parties: 60 main room. Car park. Children's helpings. No smoking. Wheelchair access (not WC). No music

MAP 1 Maidencombe DEVON

Orestone Manor

Rockhouse Lane, Maidencombe TQ1 4SX
Tel: (01803) 328098
Website: www.orestone.co.uk

Cooking 3 | Modern English | £30–£71

Down a steep, narrow lane where the land drops sharply to the sea, the hotel has fabulous views over Babbacombe Bay from its verandah, terrace and dark green dining room. The kitchen makes use of good West Country materials such as rump of lamb, roasted and served with a rosemary-scented sausage, carrot purée and pommes Anna, or crab from Start Bay, fashioned into gnocchi as an accompaniment to black bream. Grilled scallops as an inspection starter were rather outdone by their chorizo sparring partner, but a main course of roast guinea fowl was well-timed and served with Agen prunes and a well-judged marsala sauce. At dessert stage, fair pannacotta was let down by inapposite rhubarb and bland champagne jelly. A better bet might be the regional cheese selection. Wines are a fresh-faced global mix arranged by style and priced from £14.95, with a few special old bottles gathered together at the end.

Chef: Chris May **Proprietors:** Rose and Mark Ashton, Peter Morgan and Friederike Etessami **Open:** all week 12 to 2.30, 7 to 9 **Meals:** alc (main courses £12 to £24). Set L £14.75 (2 courses) to £17.95. Terrace menu available Mon to Sat **Service:** not inc, card slips closed **Cards:** Amex, Delta, Maestro, MasterCard, Visa **Details:** 50 seats. 40 seats outside. Private parties: 72 main room, 6 to 19 private rooms. Car park. Vegetarian meals. Children's helpings. No smoking. Wheelchair access (also WC). Music. No mobile phones **Accommodation:** 12 rooms, all with bath/shower. TV. Phone. B&B £69 to £225. Rooms for disabled. Swimming pool

MAP 2 Maiden Newton DORSET

Le Petit Canard

AR

Dorchester Road, Maiden Newton DT2 0BE
Tel: (01300) 320536

Attractive cottage that earns its living as a consistently reliable country restaurant. The platter of local fish has been described as 'absolutely delicious', while the menu looks further afield for ideas like seared scallops with saffron risotto and lemon butter sauce, roast Gressingham duck breast with chilli and five-spice sauce, and escalope of organic veal with wild mushrooms. Intriguing desserts such as avocado cheesecake. Dinner £24.50/£28. Around two dozen affordable wines from £14.95. Open Tue to Sat D; also L first and third Sun in month.

MAP 3 Maidstone KENT

Souffle

31 The Green, Bearsted, Maidstone ME14 4DN
Tel: (01622) 737065
Website: www.soufflerestaurant.co.uk

Cooking 3 | Modern British | £28–£60

Bearsted green and the Souffle provide stylish relief to a nondescript area, with the restaurant – tile-hung with exposed timbers inside – generating a comfortable feeling. Karen Evenden runs an efficient front-of-house, while Nick delivers an ambitious and interesting menu. Breast of Barbary duck with honey and rosemary, and roast loin of venison with a redcurrant and black pepper sauce show that the cooking has a firm English accent, although alongside these are mix-and-match dishes like osso buco of monkfish with Thai spices, coriander and coconut milk, and roast rump of lamb with Moroccan spices. Puddings along the lines of pear tarte Tatin with vanilla ice cream, a trio of crème brûlées, and prune and Armagnac soufflé have a classic ring. Wines start at £12.50 on a predominantly French list.

Chef: Nick Evenden **Proprietors:** Nick and Karen Evenden **Open:** Tue to Fri and Sun L 12 to 2, Tue to Sat D 7 to 9.30 **Meals:** alc exc Sun L (main courses £16.50 to £18). Set L £13.50 (2 courses) to £16.50, Set D Tue to Fri £22.50 **Service:** 10% (optional), card slips closed **Cards:** Amex, Delta, Maestro, MasterCard, Visa **Details:** 60 seats. 20 seats outside. Private parties: 50 main room, 10 to 25 private rooms. Car park. Vegetarian meals. Children's helpings. No smoking. Wheelchair access (also men's WC). Music. No mobile phones

MAP 8 Manchester GREATER MANCHESTER

Bridge

AR

58 Bridge Street, Deansgate,
Manchester M3 3BW
Tel: (0161) 832 0242

Re-energised Victorian city pub, proud of its roots as a watering hole but now primarily noted for its food. Local and regional ingredients define the menus, which span everything from Bury black pudding to Eccles cakes. Typical dishes might include venison carpaccio with wild watercress and horseradish cream (£6), Port of Lancaster smoked haddock chowder with baby spinach, a poached egg and Morecambe Bay shrimp dumplings (£9.50), and sherry trifle (£4). Short international wine list from £10.50. Closed Sun D.

Bridgewater Hall, Charles Hallé Room

Lower Mosley Street, Manchester M2 3WS
Tel: (0161) 950 0000

The Charles Hallé Room serves pre- and post-performance meals on concert evenings only (as well as lunch Mon to Fri). The set-price menus (£17.50/£22.50) offer the likes of mosaic of saffron and herb-scented rockfish with lobster, roast loin of venison with caramelised red cabbage and creamy game sauce, and cherry crème brûlée. Executive chef Robert Kisby zips back and forth from his main base at Le Mont (see entry), while the day-to-day running is down to Marco Tedde.

Cedar Tree

69 Thomas Street, Manchester M4 1LQ
Tel: (0161) 834 5016

More like a café than a restaurant, the Cedar Tree may not win awards for its décor, but the food is worthy of attention. Highlights of the Lebanese menu include faroug meshwi (tender chicken with garlic sauce; £8.50) and hearty kebabs (kafta halabiyeh is minced lamb with onion and parsley; £8.50). Start with hot or cold maizza, including sawda dajaj (fried chicken livers in lemon sauce; £3.50). Vegetables are well reported, and desserts run to mamoul with dates ('a sort of superior fig roll'). Open all week.

AR	Not a full entry but provisionally recommended (known as 'round-ups' in previous editions, these 'also recommended' establishments are now integrated throughout the book).

Establishment

43–45 Spring Gardens,
Manchester M2 2BG
Tel: (0161) 839 6300
Website: www.establishmentrestaurant.com

Cooking 5 | Modern British | £35–£71

Many city restaurants these days are in converted banks, but this must be one of the more eye-catching, with twin glass domes, marble pillars and even some of the old wooden counters recalling the building's days as a temple to Mammon. But food is the currency here now, and Ian Morgan's style is highly crafted modern British with gentle French inflections. Thus braised guinea fowl, 'full of gamey flavour', is sauced with red wine and attended by shallots and mushrooms, while sea trout comes with pickled cabbage, smoked bacon, broad beans and a sauce of chicken juices. Choice is wide and combinations highly intricate, although you might start out straightforwardly enough with a slice of game terrine with pear chutney, or smoked salmon hand-carved at the table. Generous portions of cheeses in fine fettle are the alternative to revamped versions of favourites such as rhubarb crumble or crème brûlée, the latter perhaps incorporating caramelised pineapple. 'Exceptional attention to detail' distinguishes the old-school service. A list beginning with a selection of 'Wines below £20' is a model of user-friendliness, but there are plenty of French classics for the unconstrained. Some 20 wines by the glass range from £3.75 to £16.

Chef: Ian Morgan **Proprietors:** Carl Lewis, Tim Molloy and Ian Morgan **Open:** Tue to Fri L 12 to 2.30, Tue to Sat D 6.30 to 10 **Closed:** bank hols **Meals:** alc (main courses £19 to £25). Set L £17.50 (2 courses) to £19.95 **Service:** not inc **Cards:** Amex, Delta, Diners, Maestro, MasterCard, Visa **Details:** 80 seats. Private parties: 12 main room, 12 to 25 private rooms. Vegetarian meals. Children's helpings. No smoking. Wheelchair access (also WC). Music

Glamorous Chinese

Wing Yip Business Centre, Oldham Road, Ancoats, Manchester M4 5HU
Tel: (0161) 839 3312

Cooking 2 | Chinese | £17–£54

£

'Sunday lunch dim sum are a serious business here, with doors opening at 11,' observed one correspondent about this restaurant attached to the Wing Yip Business Centre. Families pack the place and heated trolleys are wheeled round with all kinds of savoury and sweet morsels: steamed items including ginger-spiked beef dumplings are the pick of the bunch, although the choice extends to deep-fried minced prawns in rice paper, and turnip croquettes. Overall, some reckon that this is currently the 'most authentic' experience of its kind in Manchester. The full menu cuts a swathe through the broad Chinese repertoire, from salt-and-pepper soft-shell crab and crispy smoked chicken 'sticks' to stir-fried shredded pork with preserved mustard leaves and sliced beef (cooked just pink) with fine noodles. House wine is £9.90.

Chef: Piu Hung **Proprietor:** Tommy Hung **Open:** all week 11.30 (11 Sun) to 11.15 (11.45 Fri and Sat, 10.45 Sun) **Meals:** alc (main courses £7.50 to £18). Set L £5.95 (2 courses) to £9.95, Set D £15.50 (min 2) to £22 (min 2) **Service:** not inc, 10% for parties of 8 or more **Cards:** Delta, MasterCard, Maestro, Visa **Details:** 650 seats. Private parties: 400 main room, 1 to 100 private rooms. Car park. Vegetarian meals. Wheelchair access (also WC). Music. Air-conditioned

Greens

43 Lapwing Lane, West Didsbury, Manchester M20 2NT
Tel: (0161) 434 4259

Cooking 2 | Vegetarian | £21–£43

Since 1990 this well-organised out-of-town restaurant has been serving exciting vegetarian food to an ever-appreciative audience of Didsbury locals and visitors from further afield. Menus change every three months, and ideas are garnered from across the globe. North Country cheeses turn up frequently: for example, smoked Lancashire is fashioned into a rissole and served with mushy pea purée, while Blackstick's Blue appears in a roulade with sun-blush tomato and basil with sticky onion jam. The kitchen also gets to grips with deep-fried oyster mushrooms with Chinese pancakes and plum sauce, and Mussaman curry with potatoes, griddled baby aubergines and sticky rice, as well as 'afters' like double chocolate cheesecake and Key lime pie. The restaurant has recently been refurbished and extended, and is now licensed (house wine is £11), but you are still welcome to BYO (corkage £1.50).

Chefs/Proprietors: Simon Connolly and Simon Rimmer **Open:** Tue to Fri and Sun L 12 to 2 (Sun 12.30 to 3.30), all week D 5.30 to 10.30; booking essential **Closed:** 25 and 26 Dec, bank hols **Meals:** alc L Tue to Fri and D (main courses £7.50 to £10.50). Set L Sun £10.50 to £12.50, Set D Tue to Fri 5.30 to 7 £12.50, Set D Sun and Mon £12.50 **Service:** not inc, 10% for parties of 6 or more, card slips closed **Cards:** Delta, Maestro, MasterCard, Visa **Details:** 48 seats. 6 seats outside. Private parties: 48 main room. Vegetarian meals. Children's helpings. No smoking. Music

Koh Samui

AR

16 Princess Street, Manchester M1 4NB
Tel: (0161) 237 9511

Destination Thailand on the fringes of Chinatown. The basement dining room is sparsely decorated, service is generally pleasant, and the menu covers most staples of the cuisine, from satays to curries. Coconut cream soup with mixed seafood has impressed, and baked seafood in an unglazed clay pot, roast duck stir-fried with star anise, honey and soy sauce, and rice-stick noodles with bean sprouts have also passed muster. Separate menu of Thai desserts and ice creams. Around two dozen wines from £12. Open Mon to Fri L, Mon to Sun D.

Kosmos Taverna

AR

248 Wilmslow Road, Manchester M14 6LD
Tel: (0161) 225 9106

Long-running, hospitable taverna driven along by indefatigable Loulla Astin. Three-stage 'mezethes' banquets from £14 per person are a popular draw; otherwise, the menu plunders the traditional Greek-Cypriot repertoire for kleftiko (£10.50), pork afelia, and kodopoulo riganato (chicken breast cooked over charcoal with oregano). Desserts are mostly Greek delights like charlotta (trifle laced with rose water and orange liqueur; £3.50), halva, and yoghurt with honey. Greek house wine by the litre carafe £13. Open all week D only.

Lime Tree

8 Lapwing Lane, West Didsbury, Manchester
M20 2WS
Tel: (0161) 445 1217

Cooking 3 | Global | £24–£49

Over the last two decades Patrick Hannity's animated neighbourhood restaurant has matured and grown in confidence, thanks in part to reliable local supply lines and high-quality seasonal raw materials. Lunch and early-evening set menus offer good value, but the kitchen reveals its full mettle with a carte that could open with, say, deep-fried squid and prawn tempura with sweet chilli and ginger dressing or seared fillet of beef carpaccio with Parmesan and rocket salad. To follow, there might be pan-fried duck breast and confit of leg with bubble and squeak, lentils and jus, or grilled fillet of sea bass with a fishcake, spinach and herb butter sauce, while desserts (each listed with a recommended tipple) are mostly well-tried classics like Baileys cheesecake with chocolate ice cream, and crème brûlée with Grand Marnier. Some astute choices in France – Henry Pellé's Sancerre, Meursault from J.-P. Fichet – set the tone for a contemporary global wine list that confidently balances ambition and value. House bottles at £12.95 are boosted by ten or so wines of the month, all also by the glass.

Chefs: Jason Parker and Jason Dickenson **Proprietor:** Patrick Hannity **Open:** Tue to Fri and Sun L 12 to 2.30, all week D 5.45 to 10.30 **Closed:** 24 to 26 Dec, 1 Jan **Meals:** alc exc Sun L (main courses L £7 to £14, D £13 to £14.50). Set L Tue to Fri £14.95, Set L Sun £16.95 (inc coffee), Set D 5.45 to 6.30 £14.95 **Service:** not inc, 10% for parties of 6 or more **Cards:** Amex, Delta, Maestro, MasterCard, Visa **Details:** 90 seats. 24 seats outside. Private parties: 8 to 10 private rooms. Vegetarian meals. Children's helpings. No smoking. Wheelchair access (not WC). Music

Little Yang Sing

17 George Street, Manchester M1 4HE
Tel: (0161) 228 7722
Website: www.littleyangsing.co.uk

Cooking 1 | Cantonese | £23–£51

Over the years this popular Chinatown address has earned a reputation for its accessible and non-controversial approach to Chinese cuisine. The Cantonese thrust of the cooking is unchanged, but the owners tell us that they are now promoting healthy eating and providing nutritional information about specific dishes. 'Prawn bauble with almond flakes' and coconut chicken samosas find their way on to the dim sum list, while the full menu focuses on perennials like aromatic crispy duck and baked lobster with ginger and spring onion. Added to this are a few esoteric items such as sizzling oysters in black-pepper sauce, plus a sizeable vegetarian selection (including countless variations on 'soya-bean protein'). Chilean and Australian house wines start at £10.95.

Chef: Warren Yeung **Proprietor:** LYS Restaurants Ltd **Open:** all week 12 to 11.30 (12 Fri, 12.30 Sat, 10.45 Sun) **Closed:** 25 Dec **Meals:** alc (main courses £8 to £13). Set L £9 (2 courses) to £11, Set D £17.50 to £23 (min 2) **Service:** 10% **Cards:** Amex, Delta, MasterCard, Maestro, Visa **Details:** 220 seats. Private parties: 80 main room, 60 private room. Vegetarian meals. Children's helpings. No-smoking area. Wheelchair access (not WC). Music. Air-conditioned

Livebait AR

22 Lloyd Street, Manchester M2 5WH
Tel: (0161) 817 4110

This lively bistro in a vaulted building just off Albert Square sports lots of green and white and has an elegant, airy feel. Apart from steak and chicken, the menu is wholeheartedly dedicated to fish. Traditions are upheld with a 'splendid' Dover sole on the bone, but the repertoire takes off rapidly into the realms of clam chowder with smoked haddock and sweetcorn, and sea bass with ginger and chilli crab, stir-fried noodles and hoisin soy sauce. Starters are from £4, main courses from £10. Open all week.

Le Mont

Urbis Centre, Cathedral Gardens,
Manchester M4 3BG
Tel: (0161) 605 8282
Website: www.urbis.org.uk

Cooking 5 | Modern French | £37–£84

'For a modern urban setting Le Mont is hard to beat. The interior is spacious, comfortable and contemporary without being excessive. Add the views of the (Manchester) skyline and the architecture of the Urbis Centre and you have a cracking formula.' So wrote an impressed visitor of this restaurant on the fifth (non-smoking) and sixth (smoking) floors. Robert Kisby's bilingual menu may deliver dishes that are a lot more conservative than the bold and striking surrounds, but the style is ambitious and the technique sound. For example, 'considerable effort' went into producing miniature versions of all the starters for the assiette of hors d'oeuvres tried at inspection, ballottine of salmon, a 'retro' prawn and avocado cocktail with a lobster and mango salad, and a 'beautifully rich' terrine of confit duck among them. Pure-bred Galloway beef is used for a main-course entrecôte dijonnaise, or a classic peppered rump steak. That care over sourcing of ingredients shows again in pan-roasted venison from the Lune Valley, served with bitter chocolate sauce and caramelised winter vegetables, while the timing of fish, such as halibut on pasta with wild mushrooms and tarragon-infused white-wine sauce, is spot on. Variations on a raspberry theme worked well, delivering a sorbet, pannacotta, soufflé and crème brûlée 'each one superbly crafted', while British and French cheeses make a fine alternative. The wine list is built around some decent producers, with France topping the bill, but few are priced under £20.

Chef: Robert Kisby **Proprietor:** Northern Quarter Trust **Open:** Mon to Fri L 12 to 2.30, Mon to Sat D 7 to 10.30 **Closed:** 23 Dec to 5 Jan **Meals:** alc (main courses £19 to £30). Set L £17.95 (2 courses), Set D Mon to Thur £26.95 **Service:** 10% (optional), card slips closed **Cards:** Amex, Delta, MasterCard, Maestro, Visa **Details:** 74 seats. Private parties: 34 to 40 main rooms. Vegetarian meals. Children's helpings. No smoking in 1 dining room. Wheelchair access (also WC). No music. Air-conditioned

Market Restaurant AR

104 High Street, Manchester M4 1HQ
Tel: (0161) 834 3743

Manchester restaurants come and go, but the Market just rolls on 'day in, day out'. Like the décor, the cooking goes its own way, disregarding fads and providing a healthy mix of British classics and idiosyncratic global ideas. Expect the likes of black pudding with a potato and apple pancake (£6), Parmesan-crusted turkey breast with red pepper relish (£15), and lemon sole with smoked salmon and avocado before saffron pavlova with lemon-curd cream (£5.25). Affordable wines from £8.95. Open Wed to Fri L and Wed to Sat D.

🍷 This symbol means that the wine list is well above the average.

Moss Nook

Ringway Road, Manchester M22 5WD
Tel: (0161) 437 4778

Cooking 4 | Modern British | £29–£93

Brandishing silver domes may seem dated, but a first-time visitor rather enjoyed 'stepping back in time' here 'at the end of Manchester Airport's flight path'. Kevin Lofthouse, who has cooked here for twenty-three years, offers set-price four- and six-course tasting menus and a carte that is strong on tradition but executed with panache. His dishes are nothing if not complex; even sautéed foie gras is set on a cake of rösti, moistened with rich truffle jus and topped with a pastry crust. Successes have included classics like Swiss cheese soufflé, an inter-course minestrone soup, and loin of lamb teamed with a celeriac and parsnip purée and timbale of wild mushrooms. Meals end with the likes of coffee and Tia Maria tiramisù, glazed lemon and lime tart or well-kept British and French cheeses. Service from 'no-nonsense local Manchester staff' is low-key and polite, and the wine list, not as Francophile as it first seems, succinctly covers the world at fairly reasonable mark-ups. House wines from France and Australia start at £14.

Chef: Kevin Lofthouse **Proprietors:** Pauline and Derek Harrison **Open:** Tue to Fri L 12 to 1.30, Tue to Sat D 7 to 9.30 **Closed:** 2 weeks Christmas **Meals:** alc (main courses £19.50 to £23). Set L £19.50 (whole table only), Set D £36.50 (whole table only) **Service:** not inc, card slips closed **Cards:** Amex, Delta, Maestro, MasterCard, Visa **Details:** 65 seats. 20 seats outside. Private parties: 50 main room. Car park. Vegetarian meals. No pipes. Wheelchair access (not WC). No music. Occasional music. No mobile phones. Air-conditioned

New Emperor AR

52–56 George Street, Manchester M1 4HF
Tel: (0161) 228 2883

Worth knowing about as a respectable address deep in the heart of Chinatown. The menu covers most bases, from a regular assortment of dim sum, through roast meats, hotpots, one-plate rice and noodle dishes and so on. Set banquets (from £21.50 per person) offer familiarity in the shape of aromatic crispy duck, king prawns with ginger and spring onion, and chicken with lemon and honey sauce. House wine around £10. Open all week.

Ocean Treasure

Greenside Way, Middleton,
Manchester M24 1SW
Tel: (0161) 653 6688
Website: www.chiyip.co.uk

Cooking 2 | Chinese | £24–£58

'It is quite remarkable how a place which depends so much on English customers maintains the standard of its authentic dishes,' noted one aficionado after sampling jellyfish with pork shank in this brightly coloured, pagoda-like restaurant on the outskirts of Oldham. 'Three roasties and rice' (duck, char siu and crisp belly pork) has been exceptional, and the regular 200-dish menu embarks on a tour of the provinces with seafood as its standard-bearer: sweet-and-sour yellow croaker and 'stone-fried' Szechuan-style sea bass share the bill with kung-po king prawns, chicken in oyster sauce, and crispy shredded beef with Beijing sauce; sizzlers, noodles and dim sum complete the picture. Friday night is cabaret and disco night. The wine list has a decent range of bottles from around the world: house Duboeuf is £10.90.

Chef: Chi Keung Wong **Proprietors:** Stewart Yip and Jack Lui **Open:** all week 12 to 10.30 (11.30 Fri and Sat) **Meals:** alc (main courses £7.50 to £12). Set L £11.90, Set D £18 to £38 **Service:** not inc **Cards:** Amex, Delta, Diners, MasterCard, Maestro, Visa **Details:** 270 seats. Private parties: 270 main room, 6 to 60 private rooms. Car park. Vegetarian meals. Wheelchair access (also WC). Music. Air-conditioned

Pacific

58–60 George Street, Manchester M1 4HF
Tel: (0161) 228 6668
Website: www.pacific-restaurant-manchester.co.uk

Cooking 2 | Chinese | £31–£58

'A slightly different experience from the normal Manchester Chinatown one' was one visitor's verdict on this bright, contemporary restaurant. The upstairs dining room has been done out with vivid colours, wooden floors and modern paintings, and the menu aims to promote Chinese cuisine to a sympathetic Western clientele: customers are invited to mix and match from a choice of cooking methods and different accompaniments (Dover sole could be steamed and served with black-bean sauce, for example). Vegetarians have a full menu, and chef's specials such as 'golden' braised duck with scallops, fish lips and Chinese mushrooms are highlighted with rosettes for 'delicacy'. Appetisers include a wide assortment of dim sum, including minced beef balls with coriander and water chestnuts, or you might fancy monster deep-fried stuffed crab claws. House wine is £10.90. A related Thai restaurant operates on the ground floor.

Chef: Tim Wong **Open:** all week 12 to 3, 6 to 11 **Meals:** alc (main courses £6 to £15.50). Set L and D £20.50 to £38.50 (some min 2) **Service:** 10% **Cards:** Amex, Delta, Maestro, MasterCard, Visa **Details:** 200 seats. Private parties: 100 main room. Vegetarian meals. No-smoking area. Wheelchair access (also WC). Music. Air-conditioned

Palmiro AR

197 Upper Chorlton Road, Manchester M16 0BH
Tel: (0161) 860 7330

Upper Chorlton Road may not be the most glamorous of locations, but both the short, regularly changing menu and the cooking sing of Italy – it is no surprise that Stefano Bagnoli has built up a loyal and enthusiastic following over the past six years. Cod cheeks with anchovies and peppers (£5.75) may precede whole grilled sea bass with salmoriglio courgettes and mint (£15.50), or pistachio-crusted lamb cutlets stuffed with Parma ham (£15.75). To finish, consider pear and almond tart (£4.25). An in-depth list of Italian wines opens at around £10.50. Open Sun L and all week D.

Le Petit Blanc AR

55 King Street, Manchester M2 4LQ
Tel: (0161) 832 1000

Northern branch of the Blanc chain in the vibrant heart of the city. Like its relations, it thrives on flexibility and a positive attitude towards children. The kitchen delivers brasserie dishes including hot-smoked salmon with soused beetroot and crème fraîche (£6.50), grilled Scottish ribeye steak with home-made chips (£18) and iced chestnut and meringue vacherin with crème Chantilly (£5.50). Fixed-price menus £12 to £14.50. Forward-looking, Francophile's wine list from £12.95. Open all week. Other outlets in Birmingham, Cheltenham, Oxford and Tunbridge Wells (see entries).

Restaurant Bar & Grill

14 John Dalton Street, Manchester M2 6JR
Tel: (0161) 839 1999
Email: manchester@rbgltd.co.uk

Cooking 2 | Global | £27–£61

An agreeably informal, two-storeyed venue just off Albert Square, this specialises in eclectic brasserie cooking of a generally reliable standard. Start with duck spring rolls with plum and pineapple dipping sauce, or spicy shrimp risotto, as the mood takes you, before branching out further into tandoori-baked sea bass with mint yoghurt, or well-reported Thai green chicken curry with coconut rice. Fish is seemingly well handled, as when halibut is roasted in a crabmeat and herb crumb, and there are classic steak dishes too. Side orders of vegetables, charged extra, include pak choi with chilli and garlic or seasonal greens with chervil butter. Finish with something like chocolate brownie. Wines are a single-page international jumble rising to just under £40, with South African house wines first out of the traps at £13.

Chefs: Alan Earle and Dave Bright **Proprietor:** Individual Restaurant Company **Open:** Mon to Fri 12 to 3, 6 to 10.30, Sat and Sun 12 to 10.30 **Meals:** alc (main courses £7.50 to £17). Bar menu available **Service:** not inc, 10% for parties of 6 or more **Cards:** Amex, Delta, Diners, Maestro, MasterCard, Visa **Details:** 170 seats. Vegetarian meals. No smoking. Wheelchair access (also WC). Music. Air-conditioned

Second Floor

Harvey Nichols, 21 New Cathedral Street, Manchester M1 1AD
Tel: (0161) 828 8898
Website: www.harveynichols.com

Cooking 4 | Modern European | £26–£66

Floor-to-ceiling windows looking across Victorian rooftops to the cathedral add to the appeal of the restaurant in Harvey Nichols' Manchester branch, as does the lighting 'programmed to circulate through a range of colours'. Tables are laid with crisp, starched napery and 'classy place settings', and the menu is an appealing modern British repertoire of light, well-executed dishes. The European approach is exemplified by carpaccio of beef, foie gras fondant and roast parsnip, or a saffron risotto with mussels and baby squid, with more distant influence showing in, say, crab and sweetcorn fritters with tomato salsa and guacamole. Interesting fishy ideas might surface in the form of fillet of red snapper with carrot and Sauternes sauce, or crisp-cooked monkfish with polenta chips and tomato fondue, but the repertoire also encompasses straightforward meat dishes like Italian-style pork chop with gremolata. Breads and petits fours are well reported.

The wine list is modern and international enough for any fashionista, but opens classically with an impressive flourish of champagnes and assured ranges from the main French regions. House wines are £13.50 but the focus is on quality bottles from £20 up – except on Tuesday nights, when wines from a 'Wineshop' list are sold at retail, rather than restaurant, prices.

Chef: Robert Craggs **Proprietor:** Harvey Nichols **Open:** all week L 12 to 3 (5 Sun), Tue to Sat D 6 to 10.30 **Closed:** 25 and 26 Dec, Easter Sun **Meals:** alc (main courses £11 to £20). Set D in brasserie £11 (2 courses) to £15 **Service:** 10% (optional) **Cards:** Amex, Delta, Diners, Maestro, MasterCard, Visa **Details:** 180 seats. Private parties: 300 main room, 50 to 150 private rooms. Vegetarian meals. No-smoking area. Wheelchair access (also WC). Music. Air-conditioned

Simply Heathcotes

Jacksons Row, Deansgate, Manchester M2 5WD
Tel: (0161) 835 3536
Website: www.heathcotes.co.uk

Cooking 2 | Modern British | £27–£64

The kitchen of this northern mini-chain member (see also Leeds, Liverpool, Preston, Wrightington) deals in modern brasserie staples – risotto of broccoli and English parmesan with walnut pesto, or mussels with white wine, cream and garlic. Black pudding with a soft-boiled egg, celery salt, gems and salad cream reflects local roots, and gutsy main courses have included, in winter, slow-roast belly of Middle White pork with sea salt crackling and honey gravy, and, in summer, roast Goosnargh duck breast and golden beetroot with deep-fried sage macaroni. Service is mostly 'friendly and with an eye for detail', but ten years on the décor is 'faded'. House wines are £13.95.

Chef: Olivia Casson **Proprietor:** Paul Heathcote **Open:** Mon to Sat 12 to 2.30, 5.30 to 10 (11 Sat), Sun 12 to 9 **Closed:** bank hols **Meals:** alc (main courses £10 to £18.50). Set L £14 (2 courses) to £16, Set L Sun £14.50 (2 courses) to £17, Set D 5.30 to 7 £14 (2 courses) to £16 **Service:** 10% (optional) **Cards:** Amex, Delta, Diners, Maestro, MasterCard, Visa **Details:** 150 seats. Private parties: 200 main room, 50 private room. Vegetarian meals. Children's helpings. No smoking in dining room. Wheelchair access (also WC). Music. Air-conditioned

Stock

AR

4 Norfolk Street, Manchester M2 1DW
Tel: (0161) 839 6644

Marble pillars and an original domed ceiling set the tone in Manchester's impressively revitalised Stock Exchange Hall. Modern Italian food is the new asset, and the menu takes a regional view of things: peppered pigeon breast with watercress and citrus salad (£8), home-made gnocchi with pork sausages, fennel and chilli, and devilled calf's liver with speck and asparagus (£17.50) are bolstered by fish specials and desserts like cappuccino tiramisù. High-class, all-Italian wine list with prices from £15.95. Closed Sun.

Tai Pan

AR

Brunswick House, 81–97 Upper Brook Street, Manchester M13 6TW
Tel: (0161) 273 2798

Warehouse-like Chinese eating house above an oriental supermarket a little way from the hubbub of the city centre and Chinatown. Dim sum (from £3) range from sui mai to steamed whelks in satay sauce. The full menu covers everything from Cantonese roast meats and one-plate noodle dishes (from £6.50) to baked lobster with black-bean sauce, Szechuan lamb (£8.25) and a whole section devoted to ostrich. Westernised banquets from £15 a head. Open all week.

That Café

AR

1031 Stockport Road, Levenshulme, Manchester M19 2TB
Tel: (0161) 432 4672

Alison Eason and co. soldier on in their idiosyncratic conversion of two terraced houses. Weekly menus plunder the globe for roast pigeon, beetroot and blood orange tartlet (£7.25), Moroccan stuffed peppers, and grilled tuna on glass noodles with sweet-and-sour plums and a chilli and wasabi dressing (£14.50) before desserts like passion-fruit, mango and papaya parfait (£4.50). Early-evening menus Tue to Fri (two courses £12.95); live jazz first Wed of each month. House wine £10.25. Open Sun L and Tue to Sat D.

Yang Sing

34 Princess Street, Manchester M1 4JY
Tel: (0161) 236 2200
Website: www.yang-sing.com

Cooking 4 | Cantonese | £29–£60

A stone's throw from Manchester's Chinese arch, Yang Sing is an unmissable stone-fronted edifice with huge red banners fluttering in the wind; décor includes a classic mix of high-backed red chairs, red-clothed tables, pillars and 'mock green pagoda roofs'. Dim sum are many and varied, and the choice extends well beyond sui mai and char sui buns into the realms of shredded mooli in feather-light pastry ('layered over and over like an armadillo shell') and the textural challenges of steamed sliced pork tongues with red dates and ginger. Some recent samplings have lacked that expected touch of class – although spot-on egg custard tarts make a welcome finale. But Harry Yeung's famed repertoire has received fulsome endorsements too: 'part of the fun was just asking for "food" and being brought a marvellous array of well-selected dishes', noted one reveller. Familiar items like whole steamed sea bass and crispy beef with chilli have been mentioned, but it pays to explore the ever-changing list of specials. A serious wine list favours Burgundy but encompasses a good mix of affordable and iconic bottles from across the world at fair prices. House wines and special selections look well matched to the food and start at £12.95.

Chef: Harry Yeung **Proprietors:** Harry and Gerry Yeung **Open:** all week 12 to 10.45 (11.15 Fri/Sat, 9.45 Sun) **Closed:** 25 Dec **Meals:** alc (main courses £8 to £15.50). Set L and D from £35 (min 2) **Service:** net prices **Cards:** Amex, Delta, Maestro, MasterCard, Visa **Details:** 230 seats. Private parties: 220 main room, 20 to 140 private rooms. Vegetarian meals. Wheelchair access (also WC). Occasional music

MAP 3 **Marlow** BUCKINGHAMSHIRE

Danesfield House, Oak Room

Henley Road, Marlow SL7 2EY
Tel: (01628) 891010
Website: www.danesfieldhouse.co.uk

Cooking 3 | Anglo-French | £46–£100

A mock-Elizabethan fantasy of white stone beside the Thames, Danesfield seeks to impress. So does

the Oak Room's understated opulence (designed by Anouska Hempel), where Steven Morris creates a creditable culinary equivalent. His approach is part French, part Old English, so you might proceed from soufflé suissesse to a traditional pheasant pie with red cabbage at the same meal. Other dishes build in complexity, with scallops accompanied by artichoke fondue, asparagus spears and a lemongrass beurre blanc, while a main-course caramelised Barbary duck breast is served on pak choi, with vanilla-scented mash and a brandy and blackcurrant jus. Cheeses are Anglo-Continental, or there may be white chocolate parfait with poached strawberries. Wines are luxurious in both variety and cost (including a six-year-old Swiss white for £63). House vins de pays, Chardonnay and Grenache, are £21. The less formal, all-day Orangery brasserie has dishes like gravad lax, venison sausages and mash, and apple crumble.

Chef: Steve Morris **Open:** all week 12 to 1.45, 7 to 10 **Meals:** alc (main courses £15 to £24.50). Set L £18.50 (2 courses) to £24.50, Set D £43. Brasserie menu available **Service:** 12.5% (optional), card slips closed **Cards:** Amex, Delta, Diners, Maestro, MasterCard, Visa **Details:** 39 seats. 20 seats outside. Private parties: 8 main room, 4 to 110 private rooms. Car park. Vegetarian meals. Children's helpings. No smoking. Wheelchair access (also WC). No music. No mobile phones **Accommodation:** 87 rooms, all with bath/shower. TV. Phone. B&B £190 to £315. Rooms for disabled. Baby facilities. Swimming pool

Hand & Flowers

NEW ENTRY

West Street,
Marlow SL7 2BP
Tel: (01628) 482277

Cooking 6 | Modern British | £36–£61

Tom and Beth Kerridge moved to this white-washed pub on the outskirts of Marlow at the beginning of March 2005. He was previously head chef at the much-acclaimed Adlard's in Norwich (see entry), and so expectations were high from the outset. Low beams festooned with 'Mind Your Head' notices, plain furniture and undressed tables combine to retain the atmosphere of a country pub, as do the hanging baskets outside, but there the resemblances just about come to an end. An early inspection showed Kerridge already well into his stride. The menus are informed by a nicely judged mixture of unpretentious modern British and rustic French dishes. Superbly fresh crab fondant, a pâté with whole pieces in it, comes in a glass pot and is accompanied by brown bread and cucumber and dill chutney, while a small piece of confit bacon dressed in cider and mustard makes another hugely impressive opener, made the more satisfying with a little raviolo of minced pork and a scoop of apple purée. Purées abound, here as elsewhere, so a celeriac version turns up with a main course of sea bass, and a beetroot one with roast breast of Suffolk duck. These have been majestic dishes, however, the former encasing its fish in a meaty-looking puff pastry parcel stained with port jus, while the latter added braised Puy lentils to an otherwise predominantly red colour scheme that involved a separate copper dish of spiced red cabbage. The intricacy of the constructions works, with each dish accumulating layers of complementary flavour.

By contrast, desserts look a touch simpler. A dark chocolate cheesecake on a wafer-thin biscuit base, topped with white chocolate mousse, is sensationally rich. Otherwise, try an apple crumble tartlet with blackberry sorbet and custard. A menu of lunch specials gives the nod to the pub ethos by offering a hot salt-beef sandwich, Welsh rarebit and plum tomato omelette, and an all-day breakfast. Seven house wines by the glass, from £4 to £4.75, head up a list that moves briskly through the major countries, with a page of specials bringing up the rear.

Chef: Tom Kerridge **Proprietors:** Tom and Beth Kerridge **Open:** Tue to Sun L 12 to 2.30, Tue to Sat D 7 to 9.30 (10 Fri and Sat) **Meals:** alc (main courses £12 to £19.50) **Service:** not inc **Cards:** Amex, Delta, Maestro, MasterCard, Visa **Details:** 45 seats. 20 seats outside. No smoking in 1 dining room. Music

Vanilla Pod

31 West Street, Marlow SL7 2LS
Tel: (01628) 898101
Website: www.thevanillapod.co.uk

Cooking 5 | Modern British | £34–£74

A bright, contemporary dining room painted in caramel and brick red with cheerful modern prints on the walls and closely packed tables, the Vanilla Pod is an ambitious, fairly formal restaurant with French front-of-house staff. Start perhaps with asparagus risotto – 'a very unusual presentation topped with light greenish foam that tasted the essence of fresh asparagus' – or seared scallops on vanilla-scented pear compote. For main course, expect fashionable dishes like poached sea bass with 'delicious' braised fennel and a whoosh of fennel pollen cream, or perhaps a glossy pithiviers of chicken, foie gras and morels accompanied by a few carrots and a dark, sticky jus. Cheeses have been impressive, and among puddings might be chocolate fondant, or a classic French apricot tart, with 'lovely' light puff pastry, slightly marred by a bright blue drizzle of Curaçao syrup. A short but serious wine list from £16.50 centres on France.

Chef: Michael Macdonald **Proprietors:** Michael and Stephanie Macdonald **Open:** Tue to Sat 12 to 2, 7 to 10 **Closed:** Christmas, 2 weeks Easter, bank hols **Meals:** Set L £17.50 (2 courses) to £19.50, Set D £40 to £45 **Service:** not inc **Cards:** Amex, Delta, Maestro, MasterCard, Visa **Details:** 34 seats. 10 seats outside. Private parties: 40 main room, 8 private room. Vegetarian meals. No smoking. Wheelchair access (not WC). No music. No mobile phones

MAP 8 **Marsden** WEST YORKSHIRE

Olive Branch

Manchester Road, Marsden HD7 6LU
Tel: (01484) 844487
Website: www.olivebranch.uk.com

Cooking 4 | Modern English | £29–£58

While the food at this pub-like Pennines restaurant improves steadily, the place retains its comfortable down-to-earth informality. The menu is a mixture of stolid English fare with smatterings of Italian or Far Eastern influences. Accurate timing prevails, as in perfectly baked queen scallops served with a finely balanced lime and garlic butter and Gruyère, and slowly braised lamb shank, falling off the bone, on a bed of creamy mash surrounded by a well-made tomato sauce. Vegetables, including carrots in orange juice and broccoli bursting with freshness, are clearly well sourced and cooked respectfully. A crispy base for a 'superb' orange tart with well-flavoured vanilla ice cream shows that enthusiasm and skill go beyond the savoury department. Wines, starting at £12.95, are treated seriously, with decent classics at fair prices.

Chef: Paul Kewley **Proprietors:** Paul Kewley and John Lister **Open:** Wed to Fri L 12 to 2, Mon to Sat D 6.30 to 9.30, Sun L and D 1 to 8.30 **Closed:** first 2 weeks Jan **Meals:** alc (main courses £11 to £19). Set L £10.95 (2 courses), Set D Sun to Thur £15.50 (2 courses) to £18.50 **Service:** not inc, card slips closed **Cards:** Delta, Maestro, MasterCard, Visa **Details:** 65 seats. 15 seats outside. Private parties: 40 main room, 10 to 40 private rooms. Car park. Vegetarian meals. Children's helpings. No smoking. Wheelchair access (not WC). Music **Accommodation:** 3 rooms, all with bath/shower. TV. Phone. Room only £50 to £70. Baby facilities

MAP 2 **Marsh Benham** BERKSHIRE

Red House AR

Marsh Benham RG20 8LY
Tel: (01635) 582017

Handsomely restored red-brick and thatched pub/restaurant in a pretty hamlet close to the M4. An upbeat, affluent setting for French-inspired cooking that brings on board the likes of terrine of foie gras with a salad of fine beans and spicy apple compote (£9) and roast monkfish with potato mousseline and sauce vierge (£17). Conclude with desserts such as warm chocolate and red berry fondant (£5.50) or cheeses with home-made quince jelly. Also fixed-price bistro menus (£13.95/£16.95). House wines £13.50. Closed Sun D.

MAP 9 **Marton** NORTH YORKSHIRE

Appletree

Marton, nr Pickering YO62 6RD
Tel: (01751) 431457
Website: www.appletreeinn.co.uk

Cooking 3 | Modern British | £26–£48

In an old-stone building in a tiny village, TJ and Melanie Drew have created a civilised and friendly pub-restaurant run with a degree of individuality and flair. During their five-year tenure, they have built up an enviable network of first-rate suppliers to support home-grown and home-made produce – some of which is on sale at a shop counter within the pub. Impressive home-made grissini and bread make a fine start. There is a comforting familiarity about a twice-baked Brie and goats' cheese soufflé, or calf's liver and smoked bacon (teamed with roast red pepper, crushed potatoes and a red wine jus. An inspection meal turned up a lobster risotto that incorporated 'fantastic' home-grown coriander and went on to superb venison on a bed of wild mushroom duxelles accompanied by a chocolate sauce. 'Unbelievable generosity' is a characteristic of the kitchen too; one reporter, undecided at pudding stage, was presented with an assiette of desserts: a 'superb' pineapple tarte Tatin, poached pear with Valrhona chocolate sauce, and scoops of 'very rich' lemon curd ice cream and champagne sorbet. The balanced and wide-ranging list of wines opens at £11.

Chef: T.J. Drew Proprietors: Melanie and T.J. Drew Open: Wed to Sat 12 to 2, 6.30 to 9.30, Sun 12 to 2.30, 7 to 9 Closed: 25 Dec, first 2 weeks Jan Meals: alc (main courses £9 to £15) Service: not inc, card slips closed Cards: Delta, Maestro, MasterCard, Visa Details: 36 seats. 16 seats outside. Private parties: 26 main room, 8 to 10 private rooms. Car park. Vegetarian meals. Children's helpings. No smoking. Music

MAP 5 **Marton** SHROPSHIRE

MacCallums Restaurant, Lowfield Inn

NEW ENTRY

Marton SY21 8JX
Tel: (01743) 891783

Cooking 4 | British | £26–£46

Steve MacCallum has resurfaced a few hundred yards from his previous domain (the Sun Inn) and is now to be found in this self-named restaurant attached to the Lowfield Inn. His new dining room has its own entrance and is totally separate from the pub itself: it feels stylish and minimalist, with neutral colours and natural materials much in evidence.

Menus are dictated by supplies, and MacCallum is capable of delivering some 'stupendously impressive' dishes, notably in the fish department: 'spankingly fresh' spaghetti of crab with garlic, chilli and parsley is simplicity itself, while fillet of turbot with pea mash is finished with an exemplary chive and mustard sauce. By contrast, meat is often treated robustly: rump of lamb with a chunk of baked aubergine, new season's garlic and rosemary gravy, for example. Wild garlic also inspired the best soup one reporter had eaten 'for about 20 years', while iced toffee with bananas in rum is a trademark dessert. 'Immensely individual, enthusiastic service' is a bonus, and the affordable wine list starts at £11.50.

Chef/Proprietor: Steve MacCallum Open: Wed to Sat L 12 to 2, Tue to Sat D 6.30 to 9 Closed: 25 Dec, 1 week Apr, 1 week Aug Meals: alc (main courses £9.50 to £15.50). Set L £14 (2 courses) to £17 Service: not inc, card slips closed Cards: Delta, Diners, MasterCard, Maestro, Visa Details: 20 seats. Private parties: 24 main room, 24 to 40 private rooms. Car park. Vegetarian meals. Children's helpings. Wheelchair access (not WC). Music

This symbol means that smoking is not permitted.

Sun Inn

NEW ENTRY

Marton SY21 8JP
Tel: (01938) 561211
Website: www.suninn.biz

Cooking 2 | Modern British | £25–£47

New owners have given the Sun a major face-lift, and the dining room now has a contemporary décor and a 'positively serene atmosphere'. The kitchen dishes out large portions of home-style cooking, true to the format that chef Helen Short established at her previous venture, the Cider Press at Drybrook in the Forest of Dean. The menu offers some blasts from the past – pork and leek roulade, for instance – and items such as Cape brandy pudding point to a South African influence. Cod fillet on pea purée with asparagus and chive velouté has impressed with its good raw materials and accurate timing, and home-made breads and ice creams have garnered praise. Service can be casual, and the wine list is an international collection of 20-plus bottles from £10.95.

Chef: Helen Short Proprietors: J.A. Whateley and Helen Short Open: Wed to Sun L 12 to 2 (2.30 Sun), Tue to Sat D 7 to 9.30 Meals: alc (main courses £9 to £15). Bar L menu available Wed to Sat Service: not inc, card slips closed Cards: Maestro, MasterCard, Visa Details: 28 seats. Private parties: 28 main room. Car park. Vegetarian meals. Children's helpings. No smoking. No music

MAP 9 **Masham** NORTH YORKSHIRE

Swinton Park, Samuel's

Masham HG4 4JH
Tel: (01765) 680900
Website: www.swintonpark.com

Cooking 4 | Modern British | £28–£78

Swinton is the Victorian idea of a medieval castle, with battlements, towers and turrets, although the original house dates from the seventeenth century. It has been in the Cunliffe-Lister family since the 1880s, and Susan of that present-day ilk is responsible for the restoration of the walled garden that supplies the kitchen. With plenty of outdoor activity, together with plenty of indoor opulence, you won't be bored, and Andrew Burton, who was appointed head chef in 2004, makes his own contribution to the excitement.

The food lightly mixes country-house and modern urban modes, adding a Bloody Mary dressing to tian of Whitby crab with sautéed scallops, or serving duck as both breast and liver, with belly pork confit to boot, alongside pommes Anna, puréed shallots and a jus spiked with star anise. The celebrated venison from the estate was 'stupendously impressive' at inspection, well hung and supple, cooked pink yet properly seared, with a braised faggot including the liver, some Savoy cabbage, a purée of celeriac and deeply flavoured bay leaf jus. Desserts may be hefty, as was a large wedge of hard-glazed lemon balm tart with clear-tasting pear sorbet. Staff are all knowledge, proficiency and charm. The first-rate wine list is arranged by style – spicy fruity reds and so on – and starts with a house selection at £14.50.

Chef: Andrew Burton **Proprietors:** Mark and Felicity Cunliffe-Lister **Open:** all week 12.30 to 2, 7 to 9.30 **Meals:** Set L £14 (2 courses) to £18, Set D £40 to £49. Bar menu available **Service:** not inc, card slips closed **Cards:** Amex, Delta, Diners, Maestro, MasterCard, Visa **Details:** 60 seats. 20 seats outside. Private parties: 90 main room, 8 to 24 private rooms. Car park. Vegetarian meals. Children's helpings. No children under 8 at D. No smoking. Wheelchair access (also WC). Music. No mobile phones **Accommodation:** 30 rooms, all with bath/shower. TV. Phone. B&B £120 to £350. Rooms for disabled. Baby facilities. Fishing

MAP 1 **Mawgan** CORNWALL

New Yard

NEW ENTRY

Trelowarren, Mawgan TR12 6AF
Tel: (01326) 221595
Website: www.trelowarren.com

Cooking 2 | Modern British | £23–£58

Look for the signposts off the B3293 to the 'historic country estate' of Trelowarren: this glass-fronted former coach house is found along a one-way track punctuated by cattle-grids and 'brutal humps'. Inside is plain and pale, enlivened by vivid artwork (there is an on-site arts and crafts gallery), with a real fire to warm you on chilly evenings.

Greg Laskey is a regionalist *par excellence*, sourcing no less than 90 per cent of his raw materials from within a 20-mile radius of Mawgan. Culinary influences look to Europe, though, with asparagus going into open ravioli served with tomato confit and Parmesan, and local lamb appearing with sweet shallots in red wine accompanied by buffalo cheese and impressive fondant potato. A starter pairing of sautéed foie gras and seared scallops works well, although the dish has been overloaded with one too many subsidiary ingredients. Main courses are served with copious vegetables, all well prepared, and desserts might bring on coffee soufflé with praline ice cream, or lemon tart with rhubarb compote. The wine list, varietally arranged, darts hither and yon in search of quality, with prices opening at £12.50 for southern French selections.

Chef: Greg Laskey **Proprietor:** Ferrers Vyvyan **Open:** all week L 12 to 2.15, Mon to Sat D 7 to 9 **Closed:** Mon Sept to June, Jan **Meals:** alc (main courses L £6 to £12.50, D £12 to £17.50) **Service:** not inc **Cards:** Maestro, MasterCard, Visa **Details:** 44 seats. 20 seats outside. Private parties: 50 main room. Car park. Vegetarian meals. Children's helpings. No smoking. Wheelchair access (also WC). Music. No mobile phones

MAP 5 **Medbourne** LEICESTERSHIRE

Horse & Trumpet

Medbourne LE16 8DX
Tel: (01858) 565000
Website: www.horseandtrumpet.com

Cooking 6 | Modern British | £37–£72

'We cannot remember a better meal' is a reaction typical of those who encounter David Lennox's cooking. The setting is a sensitively converted yellow sandstone pub, and a rather grand pub it must have been, with copious original features alongside all the contemporary accoutrements you would expect of a top-flight restaurant-with-rooms.

On the dinner carte of around five choices per course the concise dish descriptions hide a great deal of skill. While this is cutting-edge cooking, it is the way flavours and textures are intelligently considered and juxtaposed that proves ultimately satisfying. Foie gras parfait brings together banana bread, smoked duck, port, celeriac and prunes, while Isle of Skye scallops arrive with beetroot risotto, orange jelly and spring onion. Main courses are painstakingly composed: roast Anjou pigeon is accompanied by lentils, spiced pastilla, pistachio, cocoa and gingerbread, and roast sea trout teamed with scallop, pimento, parsley, black olive emulsion and keta caviar. Vegetables are extra. Correspondents enthusiastically endorse the dessert combinations too: chocolate fondant with iced double cream, pistachio and toffee, for example, 'was everything I could have wished for'. And there is praise too for the value on a short-choice set-price lunch menu that offers celeriac velouté, and roast cod with cardamom gnocchi. Service is warm and friendly, and the wine list combines interest and variety, though it doesn't get into second gear under £20. House French is £18.95.

Chef: David Lennox **Proprietors:** David Lennox and Gary Magnani **Open:** Tue to Sun L 12 to 1.45 (2.30 Sun), Tue to Sat D 7 to 9.30 **Closed:** First week Jan **Meals:** alc D (main courses £16.50 to £22). Set L £16 (2 courses) to £28 **Service:** not inc, 10% for parties of 8 or more **Cards:** Delta, Diners, Maestro, MasterCard, Visa **Details:** 48 seats. 16 seats outside. Private parties: 32 main room, 8 to 16 private rooms. Vegetarian meals. No children under 12. No smoking in dining room. Wheelchair access (also WC). Music. No mobile phones **Accommodation:** 4 rooms, all with bath/shower. TV. Phone. B&B £75. Rooms for disabled

MAP 7 Melbourn CAMBRIDGESHIRE

Pink Geranium

25 Station Road, Melbourn SG8 6DX
Tel: (01763) 260215
Website: www.pinkgeranium.co.uk

NEW CHEF | Modern British | £35–£74

The Pink Geranium is pink through and through, with a thatched roof, cottage garden and yards of floral fabrics adding to the gentility of it all. A new chef arrived too late for an inspection; Kevin Barron has previously featured in the Guide at the Painswick Hotel, Painswick (see entry). His à la carte menu might kick off with pan-roasted Arisaig scallops, Cantonese pork and green tomato chutney, followed by rump of new season lamb with creamed celeriac, lamb samosa, caper jus and girolles. Finish with something like honey cheesecake with tonka bean ice cream and butterscotch sauce. The wine list has plenty of worthy names throughout France, Italy and the wider world, plus a healthy number of half-bottles. Prices start at £14.50.

Chef: Kevin Barron **Proprietor:** Lawrence Champion **Open:** Tue to Sun L 12 to 2, Tue to Sat D 7 to 9.30 **Closed:** 25 and 26 Dec, 1 Jan **Meals:** alc exc Sun L (main courses £17.50 to £26.50). Set L Tue to Sat £16.50 (2 courses) to £21.50, Set L Sun £24.50, Set D Tue to Fri £21.50 (2 courses) to £27.50 **Service:** 10% (optional), card slips closed **Cards:** Amex, Delta, Maestro, MasterCard, Visa **Details:** 60 seats. Private parties: 50 main room, 4 to 14 private rooms. Car park. Vegetarian meals. Children's helpings. No smoking. No music

Sheene Mill

Station Road, Melbourn SG8 6DX
Tel: (01763) 261393
Website: www.sheenemill.co.uk

Cooking 3 | Global | £35–£70

The setting is as attractive as ever: an instantly recognisable converted mill with its own stream and millpond where the banks are thick with trees, shrubs and wild flowers. Sheene Mill is now 'almost 100% organic', according to proprietor Steven Saunders, with supplies coming from farmers' markets and the nursery next door. Ingredients are top-notch, and there are signs that Steven is steering away from the brasserie format towards a more sophisticated restaurant setup. The kitchen embarks on a world tour for dramatic black risotto with crispy fried squid, toasted almonds and lemon oil, crispy roast belly of pork with stir-fried vegetable noodles, tamarind juice and pak choi or colourful roasted red snapper with Mediterranean vegetables, garlic froth and truffle oil. To finish, iced pineapple and aniseed mousse with black-pepper strawberries proved to be a 'beautifully constructed' and 'truly gorgeous' dessert. The wine list offers a good range, divided up by style ('aromatic, vibrant and zesty', for example); prices start at £14.50.

Chef: Steven Saunders **Proprietors:** Steven and Sally Saunders **Open:** all week L 12 to 2.30, Mon to Sat D 7 to 9.30 **Closed:** 26 Dec, 1 Jan **Meals:** Set L £18 (2 courses) to £23, Set L Sun £25, Set D £29 (2 courses) to £37.50 **Service:** 10% (optional) **Cards:** Amex, Delta, Maestro, MasterCard, Visa **Details:** 130 seats. 24 seats outside. Private parties: 100 main room. Car park. Vegetarian meals. Children's helpings. No smoking. Music. No mobile phones. Air-conditioned **Accommodation:** 9 rooms, all with bath/shower. TV. Phone. B&B £85 to £120. Baby facilities

MAP 10 Melmerby CUMBRIA

Village Bakery AR

Melmerby CA10 1HE
Tel: (01768) 881811

A 1970s blueprint for the ecologically minded enterprise of the future, still sticking to its organic guns after three decades. The hub of the place is the wood-fired oven, used for everything from organic breads and pizzas to cakes and biscuits (from £1.25). Breakfast brings raspberry porridge, Inverawe kippers and fry-ups (£8.50); lunch provides everything from open sandwiches and bruschettas to boiled ham with parsley sauce (£7.25), pasta and salads. Organic juices, beers and ciders, plus wines from £9.75. Open all week to 4.30pm.

MAP 9 **Mill Bank** WEST YORKSHIRE

Millbank

Mill Bank Road, Mill Bank, Nr Sowerby Bridge HX6 3DY
Tel: (01422) 825588
Website: www.themillbank.com

Cooking 5 | Modern European | £27–£57

Topiary in metal tubs, like sentries guarding the front steps, is the only clue that this isn't the traditional country pub you might expect to find tucked away off the A58 between Sowerby Bridge and Ripponden. The low-ceilinged dining room has wooden floors married with plain walls, contemporary artwork and modern lighting, interspersed with the occasional splash of coloured wall and carefully placed modern sculpture; there's a noticeable cosmopolitan edge, though the bar retains its flagstones and fireplace.

Modern-focused menus have a brasserie slant, listing crowd-pleasing deep-fried haddock in beer batter with chips, pea purée and tartare sauce alongside trendier poached halibut with lobster tagliatelle, slow-roast tomato and asparagus, or sucking pig with roast vegetables and black pudding hash browns. Among starters are carrot and ginger soup, or pheasant shepherd's pie and grape chutney; to finish, pistachio ice cream accompanies chocolate fondant cake, while lemon curd sponge comes with orange crème anglaise. The globetrotting wine list, arranged by style and crisply annotated, offers bags of drinking under £20, French house from £10.95 and a dozen by glass from £2.20.

Chef: Glen Futter **Proprietor:** The Millbank (Halifax) Ltd **Open:** Tue to Sun L 12 to 2.30 (4.30 Sun), all week D 6 to 9.30 (10 Fri/Sat, 8 Sun) **Closed:** 2 weeks Oct, 2 weeks Jan **Meals:** alc Mon to Sat (main courses £9 to £19). Set L £11.95 (2 courses), Set L Sun £13.25 (2 courses) to £16.95, Set D Mon to Thur £11.95 (2 courses), Set D Fri 6 to 7 £11.95 (2 courses), Set D Sun £13.25 (2 courses) to £16.95 **Service:** not inc **Cards:** Delta, Maestro, MasterCard, Visa **Details:** 60 seats. 20 seats outside. Private parties: 34 main room, 22 private room. Vegetarian meals. Children's helpings. No smoking. Music

MAP 6 **Milton Ernest** BEDFORDSHIRE

Strawberry Tree

3 Radwell Road, Milton Ernest MK44 1RY
Tel: (01234) 823633

Cooking 6 | Modern European | £41–£71

This seventeenth-century thatched cottage, with gravelled drive and shrubs, has had a sympathetic makeover inside, leaving inglenooks, stone flags and oak beams untampered with. The sparsely decorated, brightly lit dining room has comfortable chairs and is overseen with quiet efficiency by the chefs' parents, while brothers Jason and Andrew run the kitchen with flair.

An inspection confirmed that their feel for ingredients and timing and their skill in presentation do not falter. Dishes are refreshingly straightforward, with clean, clear flavours that speak of themselves. A twice-baked Stilton soufflé uses Colston Bassett, and is crisp on the outside, pungently melting within. Crab pâté comes with avocado and an impressive cucumber and tomato jelly on a plate strewn with garden herbs. Timing of meat could scarcely be more accurate, as witness properly crackled pedigree pork, served on shredded leek with a tian of potato and carrot and rich wine gravy; a fish alternative might be fried hake with king prawns, herb noodles and a bouillabaisse sauce. Desserts eschew soothing familiarity for a final fanfare. Poached pear with hazelnut ice cream, sandwiched between brandy-snap biscuits, with salted butterscotch and apple purée made a mesmerising essay in contrasts, from 'tart to mellow to salt to crisp to soft' in one heady dish. The short wine list has good notes, and enough choice under £20 for those on a budget. Prices start at £15 a bottle (£4.40 a glass) for a white French blend and a California Cabernet.

Chefs: Jason and Andrew Bona **Proprietors:** the Bona family **Open:** Wed to Fri L 12 to 1.30, Wed to Sat D 7 to 9 **Closed:** 2 weeks Jan, 2 weeks summer **Meals:** alc L (main courses £12 to £20). Set D Wed to Fri £25 (2 courses), Set D Sat £41.50 **Service:** not inc, 12.5 % for parties of 6 or more, card slips closed **Cards:** Delta, Maestro, MasterCard, Visa **Details:** 22 seats. Private parties: 22 main room, 8 private room. Car park. Children's helpings. No smoking in 1 dining room. Occasional music

MAP 2 **Minchinhampton** GLOUCESTERSHIRE

Sophie's Restaurant

AR

20 High Street, Minchinhampton GL6 9BN
Tel: (01453) 885188

French country cooking transported to a thoroughly English, Grade II listed Georgian building. Lunchtime menus are topped up with consignments of walnuts and quinces from the owners' garden in France: expect authentic dishes like mushroom and Gruyère tart (£6), then baby hake with roast fennel and tomatoes (£14), followed by crêpes with chestnut purée (£4.50). Book for Saturday evening extravaganzas where centrepieces might include gigot of salt-marsh lamb. Personally imported wines (from £9.95) are stars of the Gallic list. Open Tue to Fri L and Sat D.

MAP 3 **Mistley** ESSEX

Mistley Thorn

NEW ENTRY

High Street, Mistley CO11 1HE
Tel: (01206) 392821
Website: www.mistleythorn.co.uk

Cooking 2 | Modern European | £24–£49

Built in 1723, this relaxed and friendly inn overlooking the Stour Estuary is now enjoying the benefits of a stylish, twenty-first-century revamp. Chef/proprietor Sherri Singleton finds time to run a cookery school and has a keen eye for good local ingredients including fish from an Essex day boat, Maldon beef and organic vegetables. Menus change daily, ideas are unfussy and dishes are given some neat tweaks – rosemary skewers adding flavour to chargrilled chicken livers, for example. Seafood is well handled, witness whole brill 'a la plancha' with olive oil, smoked paprika, chilli and garlic, or seared wild halibut with cider mustard sauce. Chargrilled lamb chops come with salsa verde and 'lush, sunshiney' peperonata, while Jack Daniels pecan tart with Chantilly cream has been the pick of the desserts. House wines start at £11.70.

Chef/Proprietor: Sherri Singleton **Open:** all week 12 to 2.30, 6.30 to 9 (9.30 Sat) **Closed:** 25 Dec **Meals:** alc (main courses £8.50 to £14). Set L £10.95 (2 courses) to £13.95 **Service:** not inc, 10% (optional) for parties of 8 or more, card slips closed **Cards:** Maestro, MasterCard, Visa **Details:** 75 seats. 12 seats outside. Private parties: 50 main room, 10 to 30 private rooms. Car park. Vegetarian meals. Children's helpings. No smoking. Wheelchair access (not WC). Occasional music. Air-conditioned **Accommodation:** 5 rooms, all with bath/shower. TV. Room only £60 to £80. Baby facilities

MAP 8 **Mitton** LANCASHIRE

Three Fishes

NEW ENTRY

LANCASHIRE OF THE YEAR RESTAURANT

Mitton Road, Mitton,
Whalley BB7 9PQ
Tel: (01254) 826888
Website: www.thethreefishes.com

Cooking 5 | Modern British | £26–£50

This new venture by the Northcote Manor team (see entry, Langho), is a long, low, rambling, stone inn, clean and spare inside, and happily short of knick-knacks and horse brasses. Staff are well-informed, personable and not at all given to napkin-flourishing. Inspection showed David Edward setting a formidable early pace in the kitchen. A starter of boiled onions topped with a poached egg and a scattering of crumbled, acidulous Lancashire cheese was 'achingly simple comfort food at its best'. Free-range spare ribs, tender and 'stickily piggy', were spiced up with firm, devilled black peas. Mains brought Bowland lamb's liver with confit kidneys, spring cabbage, mash and roast garlic, 'an offal-lover's dream', and Goosnargh chicken breast with Delamere goats' cheese, cracked wheat, broad beans and celeriac – 'a goaty take on chicken Kiev', the cheese leaking out into the creamy, soupy sauce to make a dish that lingered in memory. Fish-eaters might go for Three Fishes pie: Fleetwood fish under a mash top sprinkled with Kirkham's Lancashire. With this substantial northern cooking, one can be outfaced by dessert stage. If not, try Manchester custard with raspberry jelly and banana, or chocolate and orange pudding with clotted cream. Wines are a good spread of contemporary styles from £12.50, though there's not much aimed at enthusiasts.

Chef: David Edward **Proprietors:** Craig Bancroft and Nigel Howarth **Open:** Mon to Sat 12 to 2, 6 to 9 (9.30 Fri/Sat), Sun 12 to 8.30 **Closed:** 25 Dec **Meals:** alc (main courses £7.50 to £16) **Service:** not inc **Cards:** Amex, Delta, Diners, Maestro, MasterCard, Visa **Details:** 120 seats. 60 seats outside. Private parties: 18 main room. Car park. Vegetarian meals. Children's helpings. No smoking. Wheelchair access (also WC). No music

This symbol means that the restaurant has elected to participate in *The Good Food Guide's* £5 voucher scheme (see 'How to Use the Guide' for details).

MAP 6 **Monks Eleigh** SUFFOLK

Swan Inn

The Street, Monks Eleigh IP7 7AU
Tel: (01449) 741391

Cooking 3 | Modern European | £26–£49

The interior of this thatched and timbered village pub reminded one visitor of a wine bar with its pale wood floor and cane chairs. But the Swan 'remains very much a local' with people popping in just for a drink, although blackboard menus give notice that the food here is a cut above the norm for a pub. Nigel Ramsbottom delivers seasonal menus sourced from a network of well-chosen local suppliers. You may find grilled pigeon breast coupled with a crispy smoked bacon and walnut salad, or pancakes stuffed with spinach and ricotta in a rich cheese sauce. Or there may be spicy Moroccan chicken breast, or braised lamb knuckle with Puy lentil sauce: the cooking pays allegiance to no obvious style. Simpler things are not overlooked, though; try pan-fried king prawns in garlic and parsley butter, sirloin steak with aubergine, basil, cherry compote and 'very moreish' chips, and orange and brazil nut cake coated in chocolate ganache to finish. There's a range of regional ales, eight wines by the glass, and house wine at £11.50.

Chef: Nigel Ramsbottom **Proprietors:** Carol and Nigel Ramsbottom **Open:** Wed to Sun 12 to 2, 7 to 9.30 **Closed:** 25 and 26 Dec, 1 Jan, last 2 weeks Sept **Meals:** alc (main courses L £7.50 to £16, D £9 to £16) **Service:** not inc, card slips closed **Cards:** Delta, MasterCard, Maestro, Visa **Details:** 40 seats. Private parties: 40 main room, 12 to 40 private rooms. Car park. Vegetarian meals. Children's helpings. No smoking. No music

MAP 6 **Morston** NORFOLK

Morston Hall

Morston NR25 7AA
Tel: (01263) 741041
Website: www.morstonhall.com

Cooking 6 | Modern British | £39–£65

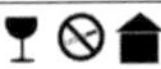

This could be a model of its kind, hidden away in north Norfolk, a couple of miles west of Blakeney. Alongside the restaurant the Blackistons run a small hotel, and the well-managed operation offers just the sort of hospitality that both travellers and locals appreciate. Nothing is posh or grand, indeed the scale is personable, almost homely, and because ambition is just right, results are invariably successful.

Galton Blackiston's daily four-course, no-choice menus are built on sound classical techniques and an abundance of regional materials – his own produce adding to that from local farmers and suppliers. Much effort goes into dishes, but they are not overworked and are characterised by clarity and accurate timing. Inspection found the kitchen very much on song, delivering a first-class pithiviers of duck with bigarade jus, then fresh, moist fillet of turbot with Puy lentils, pommes Anna and herb oil, and roast cannon of lamb with fondant potato, young fennel, aubergine caviar and a rich jus. A neat and colourful passion-fruit tart with orange sorbet rounded off the meal with 'real zing', although those after something savoury could go for well-kept British and French cheeses instead. The home-made bread, amuse-bouche and petits fours all show that the eye is not taken off the ball at any stage. Service is 'pleasant, helpful and attentive without being over-fussy'. The well-rounded wine list – long on quality, short on pretension – starts at £15; it's arranged by grape varieties and features informative background notes.

Chefs: Galton Blackiston and Samantha Wegg **Proprietors:** Tracy and Galton Blackiston **Open:** Sun L 12.30 for 1 (1 sitting), all week D 7.30 for 8 (1 sitting) **Closed:** 25 and 26 Dec, 1 Jan to 1st week Feb **Meals:** Set L £28, Set D £42 **Service:** not inc, card slips closed **Cards:** Amex, Delta, Diners, Maestro, MasterCard, Visa **Details:** 50 seats. 20 seats outside. Private parties: 20 main room. Car park. Vegetarian meals. Children's helpings. No smoking. Wheelchair access (also WC). No music. No mobile phones **Accommodation:** 7 rooms, all with bath/shower. TV. Phone. D,B&B £135 to £260. Rooms for disabled. Baby facilities

MAP 2 **Moulsford** OXFORDSHIRE

Beetle & Wedge

Ferry Lane, Moulsford OX10 9JF
Tel: (01491) 651381
Website: www.beetleandwedge.co.uk

Cooking 4 | Anglo-French | £38–£75

Set bucolically on the bank of the Thames, the Beetle & Wedge offers modern brasserie dishes with the focus on chargrilling in the Boathouse Restaurant, while the formal conservatory Dining Room is now used for private parties. Part of the

charm of this husband-and-wife operation is that there is no attempt to dissemble. Reporters feel they get fair value for money on a wide-ranging menu that runs from fish soup via seared scallops with creamed leeks and shellfish sauce to tempura chicken and tiger prawns with a soy and coriander sauce. The kitchen focuses on careful sourcing of materials – 'we still (21 years on) seek to have the highest quality of ingredients' – and cooks them accurately and in sensible combinations. Crown of local pheasant appears with baby onions and a creamy cognac sauce, and kidneys and black pudding with a grainy mustard sauce. Traditional puddings of blackcurrant and apple crumble or warm treacle sponge with home-made custard round things off. Very occasional notes – 'delicious', 'exceptional winemaker' – hint at the enthusiasm that has gone into selecting the wines, from classic Chablis by Billaud-Simon to cutting-edge Australian producer Heartland. The house selection opens at £17.50.

Chef: Richard Smith **Proprietors:** Kate and Richard Smith **Open:** all week 12 to 1.45, 7 to 9.45 **Meals:** alc (main courses £11.50 to £21.50). Cover £1 **Service:** not inc **Cards:** Amex, Delta, Diners, Maestro, MasterCard, Visa **Details:** 70 seats. 40 seats outside. Private parties: 45 main room. Car park. Vegetarian meals. Wheelchair access (also WC). Occasional music. No mobile phones **Accommodation:** 10 rooms, all with bath/shower. TV. Phone. B&B £110 to £185. Rooms for disabled. Baby facilities. Fishing

MAP 9 **Moulton** NORTH YORKSHIRE

Black Bull

Moulton DL10 6QJ
Tel: (01325) 377289
Email: sarah@blackbullmoulton.co.uk

Cooking 4 | Seafood/Mod British | £29–£69

Every inch the old-fashioned village inn although only a mile from Scotch Corner, the Black Bull has bags of character and atmosphere and draws a lively crowd. The extensive bar menu is a big draw at lunchtime, but installed to the rear of the building, forming the centrepiece of the restaurant, is a carefully maintained 1932 Pullman carriage – from the Brighton Belle – where seafood has long dominated proceedings. An extensive list of starters ranges from a simple plate of Craster smoked salmon, via a cold salad of duck, avocado, pine nuts and cherries with a citrus dressing, to hot mussels in garlic with a herb-crumb topping. Main courses might take in poached sole fillets glazed with a cheese sauce and accompanied by prawns and creamed leeks. Some presentations can seem old-fashioned, but, on the other hand, diners on the Brighton Belle probably weren't offered monkfish wrapped in smoked bacon and served with curried prawn risotto and herb oil dressing. Non-fish dishes might include herb-roast rack of lamb with leek and potato crumble, while dessert options could run to raspberry and white chocolate shortcake. Wines from the dynamic Vincent Girardin feature heavily on the strong Burgundy list, and there are canny choices from all French regions, plus short round-ups from elsewhere. Prices (from £13) are very fair.

Chef: Paul Grundy **Proprietors:** A.M.C. Pagendam and S.C. Pagendam **Open:** Mon to Sat 12 to 2, 6.45 to 10.15 **Closed:** 24 to 26 Dec **Meals:** alc (not Sat L; main courses £16 to £24.50). Set L £17.50. Bar L menu available **Service:** not inc **Cards:** Amex, Delta, Diners, Maestro, MasterCard, Visa **Details:** 100 seats. 20 seats outside. Private parties: 30 main room, 10 to 30 private rooms. Car park. Vegetarian meals. No children under 7. No smoking. No music. No mobile phones

MAP 5 **Munslow** SHROPSHIRE

Crown

NEW ENTRY

Munslow SY7 9ET
Tel: (01584) 841205
Website: www.crowncountryinn.co.uk

Cooking 3 | Modern British | £22–£51

A Grade II listed Tudor inn with a handful of guest rooms, the Crown looks every inch the part of an English country pub. Every last corner of it exudes cosy hospitality, from the flagstoned and carpeted ground floor, all dried hops and row upon row of jugs, mugs and tankards, to the dining room above, where fairy lights are twined around the ancient ceiling beams and spindle-backed chairs are all of a piece with the lacy cloths on the tables. Richard Arnold offers a menu that is several cuts above the pub norm. Start with griddled king scallops on broccoli purée with sun-dried tomato pesto, the shellfish 'crustily seared', the broccoli earthy, and go on perhaps to 'nicely pink, well-crisped' Aylesbury duck breast with raspberry vinegar jus. More vegetables than you can possibly eat arrive on side plates, but are mostly top-notch, and meals are rounded off with the likes of layered chocolate mousse and wild cherry ice cream with a brandy-snap. Service, free of pretence or affectation, is perfectly judged. A commendable short wine list looks around the world for inspiration. House wines at £11.95 are from Chile.

Chef: Richard Arnold **Proprietors:** Richard and Jane Arnold **Open:** Tue to Sun 12 to 2, 6.45 to 9 (8 Sun) **Closed:** 25 Dec **Meals:** alc exc Sun D (main courses £10 to £17). Set D Sun £13.50 to £16.50. Light L menu available **Service:** not inc **Cards:** Amex, Delta, Maestro, MasterCard, Visa **Details:** 70 seats. 20 seats outside. Private parties: 40 main room, 10 to 18 private rooms. Car park. Vegetarian meals. Children's helpings. No smoking in 1 dining room. Wheelchair access (not WC). Music **Accommodation:** 3 rooms, all with bath/shower. TV. B&B £40 to £65. Rooms for disabled. Baby facilities

MAP 2 **Nailsworth** GLOUCESTERSHIRE

Mad Hatters

AR

3 Cossack Square, Nailsworth GL6 0DB
Tel: (01453) 832615

Ingredients are mostly organic and locally sourced at this neighbourhood restaurant-with-rooms, with even pasta and ice cream prepared from scratch. Daily handwritten menus make international forays from a French base, offering pan-seared salmon with pak choi and teriyaki sauce as an alternative to halibut escalope grenobloise (£17.50). Lunch brings on more modest main courses such as cashew nut and parsnip layer (£9). Start with fish soup (£5) and round off a meal with dark chocolate tart and vanilla ice cream (£5.50). Organic wines from £11. Open Wed to Sun L and Wed to Sat D.

MAP 6 **Nayland** SUFFOLK

White Hart

11 High Street, Nayland CO6 4JF
Tel: (01206) 263382
Website: www.whitehart-nayland.co.uk

Cooking 3 | Modern European | £24–£55

For ten years, this outpost of the Roux empire has been dispensing modern European food in the context of a smartly dressed-up Suffolk village pub. A few luxurious indulgences creep on to the menu in the shape of duck salad 'gourmande' (with smoked breast, ballottine of foie gras and confit shredded leg) and sea bass fillet with cavalo nero cabbage and caviar champagne sauce, but there are less fanciful ideas as well – including mutton and oyster stew with minted dumplings and a sauce spiked with sloe gin, and game pie with potato purée (from the excellent-value lunchtime 'menu rapide'). Desserts are skilfully wrought ideas including vanilla and lychee crème brûlée and home-made ice creams and sorbets in a tuile basket. Reporters have approved of the very welcoming feel of the place and its 'faultless' service. Wines are conveniently split into price bands, starting at £11, and are a solid international mix homing in on France at the top of the range.

Chef: Carl Shillingford **Proprietor:** Michel Roux **Open:** all week 12 to 2.30, 6.30 to 9.30 **Closed:** 26 Dec to 9 Jan **Meals:** alc (main courses £10 to £17.50). Set L Mon to Sat £15.90 (2 courses) to £20.90. Bar L menu available **Service:** not inc **Cards:** Amex, Delta, Diners, MasterCard, Maestro, Visa **Details:** 50 seats. 30 seats outside. Private parties: 80 main room, 10 to 33 private rooms. Car park. Vegetarian meals. Children's helpings. Music **Accommodation:** 6 rooms, all with bath/shower. TV. Phone. B&B £74 to £105. Baby facilities

MAP 8 **Near Sawrey** CUMBRIA

Ees Wyke

Near Sawrey LA22 0JZ
Tel: (015394) 36393
Website: www.eeswyke.co.uk

Cooking 2 | British | £40–£48

Follow the winding country lanes up from Newby Bridge or cross the ferry from Bowness to find Richard and Margaret Lee's classically styled country house. In true Lakeland style, dinner revolves around a daily-changing fixed-price menu that runs to four courses (plus decent British cheeses to round things off). Local ingredients fare well, and the kitchen balances traditional ideas with some more modern gestures. Begin with Cartmel smoked salmon or figs, pancetta, goats' cheese and honey baked in puff pastry before, say, courgette and Parmesan soufflé. Main courses could range from slow-roast shoulder of Herdwick lamb to roast monkfish provençale, while comforting desserts extend to bread-and-butter pudding and a chocolate truffle 'tear' with raspberry coulis. Half a dozen house wines from £13 open the affordable list.

Chef: Richard Lee **Proprietors:** Richard and Margaret Lee **Open:** all week D only 7.30 (1 sitting) **Meals:** Set D £30 **Service:** not inc, card slips closed **Cards:** Delta, Maestro, MasterCard, Visa **Details:** 16 seats. Private parties: 20 main room. Car park. No children under 12. No smoking. No music **Accommodation:** 8 rooms, 6 with bath/shower. TV. D,B&B £72 to £170. No children under 12

MAP 8 **Nether Alderley** CHESHIRE

Wizard

Macclesfield Road, Nether Alderley SK10 4UB
Tel: (01625) 584000

Cooking 2 | Modern British | £31–£67

Once a pub, this white-painted building stands close to National Trust parkland not far from Alderley Edge. These days, it plies its trade as a country restaurant with flagstone floors, beamed ceilings and bare wooden tables laid out in three open-plan dining areas. The 'Wizard of Edge' is Paul Beattie, who heads a kitchen that deals in eclectic dishes with some voguish flourishes and occasional nods to modern pub grub (smoked haddock rösti, for example). Open, perhaps, with mouclade of mussels in a lightly curried cream sauce, move on to grilled halibut with honey, soy and sesame dressing or roast cannon of lamb, bubble and squeak and braised red cabbage, and finish off with blackberry and apple crumble with home-made custard. House wines start at £14.50.

Chef: Paul Beattie **Proprietor:** Bispham Green Brewery **Open:** Tue to Sun L 12 to 2, Tue to Sat D 7 to 9.30 **Closed:** Christmas to New Year, bank hols **Meals:** alc (not Sun L; main courses L £7.50 to £17, D £7.50 to £19). Set L Sun £18.95 (2 courses) to £22.95 **Service:** 10% (optional), card slips closed **Cards:** Amex, Delta, MasterCard, Maestro, Visa **Details:** 90 seats. 20 seats outside. Private parties: 40 main room, 10 to 40 private rooms. Car park. Vegetarian meals. Children's helpings. No smoking in 1 dining room. Wheelchair access (also men's WC). Music

MAP 2 **Nettlebed** OXFORDSHIRE

White Hart, Nettlebed Restaurant

28–30 High Street, Nettlebed RG9 5DD
Tel: (01491) 641245
Website: www.whitehartnettlebed.com

Cooking 3 | Modern British | £47–£57

The White Hart's ancient, many-gabled, red-brick-and-flint exterior conceals a stylish, minimalist interior in the Nettlebed Restaurant. A ballottine of trout with white bean salad and beetroot reduction exemplifies the kitchen's approach: precise cooking, good raw materials, and consideration of texture. Main course could include wild sea bass fillet with mussels, braised fennel and bouillabaisse sauce, or roast rump of Welsh lamb with pearl barley, sweetbread, and basil jus. Expect desserts like rhubarb tarte fine with ginger terrine and basil sorbet, or blackberry soufflé with apple sorbet. The restaurant opens just a couple of evenings a week, but the bistro – cauliflower soup, fillet of beef with cabbage, fondant potato and truffle jus, bread and butter pudding – serves lunch and dinner daily. Seventy-odd wines make a knowledgeably assembled list; house is £11.95, and eleven come by the glass.

Chef: Nick Seckington **Proprietor:** Carlton House Contract Catering **Open:** Restaurant Fri and Sat D only 6.30 to 10; bistro all week L and D **Meals:** Set D £35. Bistro and bar menus available. **Service:** not inc **Cards:** Amex, Maestro, MasterCard, Visa **Details:** 60 seats. 30 seats outside. Private parties: 100 main room, 2 to 60 private rooms. Car park. Vegetarian meals. Children's helpings. No smoking. Wheelchair access (also WC). Music **Accommodation:** 12 rooms, all with bath/shower. TV. Phone. Room only £55 to £145. Rooms for disabled. Baby facilities

MAP 5 **Newark** NOTTINGHAMSHIRE

Café Bleu AR

14 Castle Gate, Newark NG24 1BG
Tel: (01636) 610141

This stunningly designed French-style café has been plying its trade for more than ten years, its mix of regularly changing local art and live music attracting a loyal following. On the food front, the cooking might be described as Mediterranean with additions, offering roast red mullet with gnocchi and steamed mussels (£6), sea bass with tomato and garlic risotto (£14.50), and confit belly pork with buttered spring greens, roast scallop, rösti and horseradish foam. A well-chosen slate of 30-plus global wines (from £9.95) includes a handful by the glass. Closed Sun D.

MAP 7 **Newbury Park** ESSEX

Curry Special AR

2 Greengate Parade, Horns Road, Newbury Park IG2 6BE
Tel: (020) 8518 3005

Vibrant Indian restaurant, on two floors, popular with a predominantly Asian crowd, with Bollywood hits shown on a screen downstairs. A pan-Indian menu sticks to familiar dishes such as lamb tikka (£7.25), methi chicken (£7.50) or whole buttered chicken (£15), with a wide selection of breads. Vegetarians are well catered for: maybe choose tandoori paneer tikka (£7) and kofta in lababdar sauce (£5.25). House wines £10.95. Open Tue to Fri L and Tue to Sun D.

MAP 7 **Newcastle upon Tyne**
TYNE & WEAR

Barn @ the Biscuit Factory

AR

Stoddart Street, Shieldfield, Newcastle upon Tyne NE2 1AN
Tel: (0191) 230 3338

Rawhide rides into Newcastle in the shape of this funky joint housed in a defunct food factory–turned–art gallery. Wooden furniture and etchings of cowboys and American Indians set the tone, although the food is from a different world. Simple dishes work best, as in tempura cod with fries, but the kitchen also tackles South American chicken and avocado salad (£4), Greek-style lamb patties (£8), and desserts like warm rice pudding with new season's rhubarb (£4). House wine is £13. Open Mon to Sat.

Blackfriars Café Bar

Friars Street, Newcastle upon Tyne NE1 4XN
Tel: (0191) 261 5945
Website: www.blackfriarscafebar.co.uk

Cooking 3 | Global | £22–£53

A twelfth-century Dominican monastery (complete with a secluded courtyard) provides the unlikely setting for this jolly and 'very Bohemian' café/bar. Inside, the eclectic décor makes for a 'slightly irreverent', rustic environment in which to enjoy experimental bistro food. Influences are pulled in from far and wide: pork belly hotpot with chilli, beetroot, oyster mushrooms and miso has a Pan-Asian flavour, while the Med contributes risottos (a wacky combination of salmon with earthy haggis hit the spot for one reporter). Elsewhere, the Middle East is represented by baby aubergine and broad bean tagine, then it's back home for beef fillet with chips and brown ale jus. To finish, there might be a clever take on crème brûlée with mascarpone and strawberries. The 'small but perfectly formed' global wine list begins with house Duboeuf at £11. Sidney's in Tynemouth (see entry) is under the same ownership.

Chef: Andy Drape **Proprietors:** Andy and Sam Hook **Open:** Tue to Sun L 12 to 2.30, Tue to Sat D 6 to 9.30 **Closed:** D 24 to 26 Dec **Meals:** alc (main courses L £7 to £8, D £11.50 to £21.50). Set L and D Tue to Fri 6 to 7 £9.90 (2 courses) to £12.90 **Service:** not inc, 10% for parties of 6 or more **Cards:** Delta, Maestro, MasterCard, Visa **Details:** 60 seats. 30 seats outside. Private parties: 100 main room, 20 to 50 private rooms. Vegetarian meals. Children's helpings. No smoking. Wheelchair access (not WC). Music. Air-conditioned

Café 21

19–21 Queen Street, Princes Wharf, Quayside, Newcastle upon Tyne NE1 3UG
Tel: (0191) 222 0755

Cooking 5 | Bistro | £28–£74

Set amid imposing nineteenth-century banking buildings, this flagship of Terence Laybourne's mini empire (see Bistro 21, Durham) certainly stands out with its double-fronted glass façade. Wooden floors, white-clothed tables and a cool, green interior translate into an attractive, stylish modern restaurant with an informal feel. The classy food remains in upmarket brasserie mould, but the kitchen is certainly not short of ideas. The menu is varied enough to take in duck pastilla with seared foie gras and cinnamon sauce, and spring rolls of rare salmon with a ginger dipping sauce, although the broadly European strand is perhaps most representative: roast beetroot salad with goats' cheese, walnuts and lamb's lettuce, or a main course of braised beef shoulder in red wine. Timing is spot-on, flavours delight (in a well-reported roast pheasant breast with winter greens and a rich red wine jus, for example), while slow-cooked shoulder of pork with black pudding mash, braised cabbage and crisp crackling is the kind of gutsy dish at which the kitchen excels. British cheeses provide an alternative to desserts, which may include lemon posset with raspberries and shortbread. A succinct wine list offers a good range of low- to mid-priced bins, striking a balance between countries and styles, starting with house Duboeuf at £13.

Chef: Chris Dobson **Proprietors:** Terence and Susan Laybourne **Open:** Mon to Sat 12 to 2.30, 6 to 10.30 **Closed:** bank hols **Meals:** alc (main courses £13 to £21.50). Set L £14 (2 courses) to £16.50 **Service:** not inc **Cards:** Amex, Delta, Diners, Maestro, MasterCard, Visa **Details:** 60 seats. Vegetarian meals. No smoking in 1 dining room. Wheelchair access (not WC). Music. Air-conditioned

Fisherman's Lodge

Jesmond Dene, Jesmond, Newcastle upon Tyne
NE7 7BQ
Tel: (0191) 281 3281
Website: www.tomscompanies.com

Cooking 6 | Seafood/Mod British | £38–£113

The nineteenth-century lodge, reached by a long drive that runs beside a gently flowing stream, feels about as rural as it is possible to feel in a city, but the interior is smart and contemporary, with a high comfort count. The food is imaginative and well executed. Simple but beguiling combinations include 'plump and juicy' scallops served with a single roast langoustine and 'quite superbly made' truffle risotto, a trio of crab – in a samosa with ginger, as a 'ravishing' tian, and Thai-style in filo – and stuffed pig's trotter with veal sweetbreads, artichoke purée, and truffle coulis.

Main courses have a similarly sharp focus. The restaurant is known for its fish 'and you can see why', ventured an inspector, who was impressed with braised fillet of turbot and braised oxtail (with potato purée, caramelised shallots, and baby leeks). At that same meal, a sparklingly fresh piece of sea bass was served with a Noilly Prat cream sauce that 'helped to elevate the dish to dizzy heights', and a 'rich and robust' fillet of beef (with seared foie gras, wild mushrooms, caramelised onions, and a madeira jus) proved to be a 'classy delivery' of an updated version of tournedos Rossini.

Desserts, too, garner high praise: vanilla and toffee parfait with caramel milkshake and white chocolate truffles, say, or chilled passion-fruit mousse with mango froth and passion-fruit doughnuts. Service could be tightened up to match the kitchen's output, and it is a shame the wine list offers so little below £20, for it is an interesting and wide-ranging selection. House Vins de Pays d'Oc are £17.95.

Chef: Paul Amer **Proprietors:** Tom and Jocelyn Maxfield **Open:** Mon to Sat 12 to 2, 7 to 10.30 **Closed:** bank hols **Meals:** Set L £22 to £50, Set D £40 (2 courses) to £50 **Service:** not inc **Cards:** Amex, Delta, Maestro, MasterCard, Visa **Details:** 100 seats. Private parties: 60 main room, 6 to 40 private rooms. Car park. Vegetarian meals. Children's helpings. No smoking. Wheelchair access (also WC). Music. No mobile phones

Treacle Moon

5–7 The Side, Quayside, Newcastle upon Tyne
NE1 3JE
Tel: (0191) 232 5537
Website: www.treaclemoonrestaurant.com

Cooking 4 | Modern British | £53–£63

Treacle Moon is a small restaurant with a low-key ambience, its reputation being founded on high-quality cooking and a resolute focus on value on the plate. Evening starters might range from warm goats' cheese, watercress and pear salad with red onion marmalade and walnut pesto, to shredded confit duck on crispy leeks with a quenelle of black pudding and potato, scantily dressed with hazelnut vinaigrette. Move on to 'a truly delicious and savoury combination' of top-notch Angus rib-eye steak, Puy lentils, beetroot and wild mushroom duxelles, surrounded by a dark, glossy reduction of meaty jus – 'earthy, salty and sweet at the same time'. Among lighter options might be poached whiting with crab and chive crust, tomato and shallot butter and thyme jus, or maybe a gratin of truffled macaroni and Parmesan with roast asparagus and a mushroom vinaigrette. Finish off with vanilla- and rum-scented roast stone fruits, or a simple but perfect rice pudding infused with tonka beans for flavour and topped with crunchy toasted almonds. House wine starts at £3.50 a glass, and a nicely chosen selection of bottles offers plenty of choice around or under £20.

Chef: Paul Martin **Proprietors:** Tom and Jocelyn Maxfield **Open:** all week D only 7 to 10.30 **Closed:** bank hol Mons **Meals:** Set D £30 (2 courses) to £36 **Service:** not inc **Cards:** Amex, Delta, Diners, Maestro, MasterCard, Visa **Details:** 26 seats. Private parties: 26 main room. Vegetarian meals. No smoking. Music. No mobile phones. Air-conditioned

MAP 2 New Milton HAMPSHIRE

Chewton Glen

Christchurch Road, New Milton BH25 6QS
Tel: (01425) 275341
Website: www.chewtonglen.com

Cooking 5 | Modern European | £40–£145

The eighteenth-century Palladian red-brick mansion exudes a classiness that stops just short of haughty grandeur. There may be a pillared portico

entrance attended by a neo-classical statue, but the tone is more elegant country living than landed gentry. That said, the vast and splendid dining room seems designed to take the breath away, with immaculate table settings and generally polished service (though there are reports of lapses this year) fitting the bill.

Fixed-price menus dotted with supplements offer a wealth of choice, with many dishes given the obvious sheen that expensive ingredients bestow. Dressed Cornish crab is garnished with caviar, croûtons and cos, the terrine of foie gras is marinated in walnut wine, and somebody has carefully grated some hard-boiled egg to go with the oscietra and blinis. Prime cuts and fillets inform the main-course repertoire, the presentations generally with inspired ingredient listings. Venison might come with celeriac purée, roast carrots, butternut squash, parsnips and a blueberry sauce, or there could be sea bass teamed with artichokes, wild mushrooms, pak choi, bacon and mash, all discreetly sauced with white wine. A sense of bringing the palate down gently is evident in desserts such as warm ginger gâteau with poached pear, vanilla ice cream and toffee sauce, while options for a sorbet selection run to coconut, mango, lemon, pear, raspberry or passion fruit.

The weighty list of big-name wines caters to diners with well-padded wallets, although an imaginative line-up of a dozen or more by the glass from £6 offers a bolt-hole.

Chef: Luke Matthews **Proprietors:** Martin and Brigitte Skan **Open:** all week 12.30 to 1.45, 7.30 (7 Sat) to 9.30 **Meals:** alc L (main courses £20 to £35). Set L Mon to Sat £22.50, Set L Sun £37.50, Set D £59.50 to £110 (inc wine, whole table only) **Service:** 10%, card slips closed **Cards:** Amex, Delta, Diners, MasterCard, Maestro, Visa **Details:** 160 seats. 40 seats outside. Private parties: 80 main room, up to 120 private rooms. Car park. Vegetarian meals. Children's helpings; no children under 5. No smoking. Wheelchair access (also WC). Occasional music. No mobile phones. Air-conditioned **Accommodation:** 58 rooms, all with bath/shower. TV. Phone. Room only £280 to £805. Rooms for disabled. No children under 5. Swimming pool

MAP 3 Newton Longville
BUCKINGHAMSHIRE

Crooked Billet

2 Westbrook End, Newton Longville MK17 0DF
Tel: (01908) 373936
Website: www.thebillet.co.uk

Cooking 3 | Modern British | £35–£86

'The people of Newton Longville' grow vegetables and herbs for the kitchen of this immaculately thatched village pub within easy reach of Milton Keynes, although Emma Gilchrist also casts her net further afield for supplies. The restaurant is open only for dinner, when the repertoire shows plenty of ambition inspired by a catholic view of the culinary globe. Corned beef hash with Choron sauce, duck cassoulet, and pork loin with crispy Parma ham and grain mustard and apple mash represent the occidental side of things, while yellowfin tuna carpaccio with pickled ginger and a vegetable spring roll or salt and pepper skate wing with sticky rice and pak choi add an oriental note. Desserts might range from a fruity 'study on blackcurrant' to chocolate and raspberry terrine with pistachio ice cream. Similar dishes – plus upmarket sandwiches – are served at lunchtime in the traditional bar. And then there is the wine list. The fact that everything is available by the glass opens up a world of possibilities. Red wines are put into broad categories with descriptions, and the page of 'The Most Popular Wines' has plenty around the £20 mark.

Chef: Emma Gilchrist **Proprietors:** John and Emma Gilchrist **Open:** Sun L 12.30 to 2.30, Mon to Sat D 7 to 10 **Closed:** 25 and 26 Dec **Meals:** alc (main courses £11.50 to £21). Set D £45 to £65 (inc wine). Bar L menu available Tue to Sat **Service:** not inc, card slips closed **Cards:** Amex, Delta, Maestro, MasterCard, Visa **Details:** 50 seats. 50 seats outside. Private parties: 12 main room. Car park. Vegetarian meals. Children's helpings. No smoking. No music. No mobile phones

To submit a report on any restaurant, please visit *www.which.co.uk/gfgfeedback*.

NEW ENTRY	This appears after the restaurant's name if the establishment was not a main entry in last year's Guide, although it may have been a 'round-up/also recommended' in previous editions.

MAP 1 **Newton Poppleford** DEVON

Moores'

NEW ENTRY

6 Greenbank, High Street, Newton Poppleford EX10 0EB
Tel: (01395) 568100
Website: www.mooresrestaurant.co.uk

Cooking 1 | Modern British | £25–£50

New owners are making a good go of their first solo venture, and guests are made extremely welcome by Kate Moore, who runs front-of-house virtually single-handed. Recent highlights have included a well-flavoured vegetable terrine with home-made piccalilli, and a simple but excellent rhubarb and yoghurt dessert. Main courses might include generously proportioned beef Wellington, its pastry 'excellent, light and crisp', accompanied by wild mushrooms and bubble and squeak, while fish options could run to fillet of sea bream with ratatouille salsa and saffron rice. An international wine list offers bottles from around £15 and a handful by the glass from £3.50.

Chef: Jonathan Moore **Proprietors:** Jonathan and Kate Moore **Open:** Tue to Sun L 12 to 2, Tue to Sat D 7 to 9.30 **Closed:** 25 Dec, first two weeks Jan **Meals:** Set L Tue to Sat £12.50 (2 courses) to £17, Set L Sun £8.50 (2 courses) to £13, Set D £24.50 **Service:** not inc **Cards:** Delta, Diners, Maestro, MasterCard, Visa **Details:** 32 seats. Private parties: 20 main room, 12 private room. Vegetarian meals. Children's helpings. No smoking. Wheelchair access (also WC). Music. No mobile phones **Accommodation:** 3 rooms, 1 with bath/shower. B&B £30 to £50. Baby facilities

MAP 8 **Norden** GREATER MANCHESTER

Nutters

Edenfield Road, Norden OL12 7TW
Tel: (01706) 650167

Cooking 3 | Modern British | £26–£62

A mile or so down the road from their original pub, the Nutters have installed themselves in a huge manor house in over six acres of parkland. The busy décor in the interconnecting dining rooms does not please everyone. The menu promises much, from a fritter of chicken and Sandhams creamy Lancashire cheese with mizuna and tapenade dressing to a main course of pork medallions with ginger and soy dumplings and tempura spring onions. An inspection meal started somewhat inauspiciously with flash-fried haddock with Welsh rarebit and went on to a 'fine-quality' melody of Goosnargh duck – succulent, rare slices of breast, confit leg 'just the right side of salty', and a pithiviers of shredded leg meat in 'first-class' glazed pastry – accompanied by a jus of green peppercorns and chives, and concluded with coffee pannacotta with a chocolate-latticed tartlet of smooth vanilla ice cream. While sourcing is impeccable, and bread, canapés and petits fours can hardly be bettered, there are occasional notes to the effect that flavours are not as upstanding as they should be. Service can be uncommunicative. The wine list concentrates most attention on the New World, with house Australian opening proceedings at £12.95.

Chef: Andrew Nutter **Proprietors:** Andrew, Rodney and Jean Nutter **Open:** Tue to Sun 12 to 2, 6.45 to 10 **Meals:** alc exc Sun L (main courses £13.50 to £19). Set L Tue to Sat £12.95 (2 courses) to £34, Set L Sun £22 to £34, Set D £34 **Service:** not inc, 10% for parties of 10 or more **Cards:** Amex, Delta, Maestro, MasterCard, Visa **Details:** 154 seats. Private parties: 48 main room, 120 private room. Car park. Vegetarian meals. Children's helpings. No smoking. Wheelchair access (also WC). Music

MAP 5 **Norton** SHROPSHIRE

Hundred House Hotel

AR

Bridgnorth Road, Norton TF11 9EE
Tel: (01952) 730353

The Phillips family have been running the show – bar, brasserie, restaurant and hotel – for some 20 years. The kitchen is committed to serving 'interesting, quality food', and the repertoire takes in seared scallops on pea purée (£8), roast rack of lamb with savoury lentils, roast peppers and rosemary jus (£18), and tiramisù (£5). Lighter meals in the brasserie run to chicken liver pâté, and beef and venison pie (£10). A dozen global wines by the glass; house wine £14. Open all week.

AR Not a full entry but provisionally recommended (known as 'round-ups' in previous editions, these 'also recommended' establishments are now integrated throughout the book).

MAP 2 **Norton** WILTSHIRE

Vine Tree

Foxley Road, Norton SN16 0JP
Tel: (01666) 837654
Website: www.thevinetree.co.uk

NEW CHEF | Modern British | £28–£54

The minuscule hamlet of Norton comprises 15 dwellings and this unpretentious roadside pub decked out with 'tea room' furniture, busy floral-patterned curtains and old flagstone and oak floors. It provides a congenial rustic backdrop for food with a contemporary attitude. Ingredients (including fish from West Country ports) are well chosen, menus change every couple of weeks and dishes are gleaned from far and wide: hot-and-sour prawn soup sits alongside chargrilled Evesham asparagus with lemon-scented crab, while braised shoulder of Welsh salt-marsh lamb is turned into a Celtic combo with 'Irish stew' and herb dumplings. The assiette of desserts for two is a best seller, or you might single out pink champagne and wild strawberry jelly with white peach sabayon. The well-spread wine list has a big assortment by the glass. Bottle prices start at £10.95.

Chefs: Robert Strong, Tom Hooper and Ben Hallam **Proprietors:** Tiggi Wood and Charles Walker **Open:** Mon to Fri 12 to 2, 7 to 9.30 (10 Fri), Sat 12 to 2.30, 7 to 10, Sun 12 to 3, 7 to 9.30; open all day Sat and Sun in summer **Closed:** 25 Dec **Meals:** alc (main courses £9.50 to £18.50) **Service:** not inc **Cards:** Amex, Delta, Diners, Maestro, MasterCard, Visa **Details:** 80 seats. 200 seats outside. Private parties: 80 main room, 18 private room. Car park. Vegetarian meals. Children's helpings. No smoking in 1 dining room. Occasional music. No mobile phones

MAP 6 **Norwich** NORFOLK

Adlard's

79 Upper St Giles, Norwich NR2 1AB
Tel: (01603) 633522
Website: www.adlards.co.uk

Cooking 5 | Modern British | £35–£75

This old stager on the Norwich scene is in a pretty street near the Roman Catholic cathedral. Its split-level dining room is an elegant, contemporary space with wooden floors and new grey cane chairs, smartly set tables and modern artworks on display. Culinary orientation here has always kept abreast of the times; Roger Hickman has returned after a one-year stage at Tom Aikens (see entry, London), bringing some fresh, metropolitan ideas.

Presentation follows Aikens's ornately florid style, so a starter of lobster and potato salad with truffle vinaigrette and chervil mousse looked to one reporter 'like something out of the Chelsea Flower Show' – nonetheless, its flavours and freshness were utterly convincing. More in the modern mainstream was a starter of accurately roast scallops with pea purée and crisp pork belly, the purée creamy and subtle, and the meaty pork combining well with the scallops. Meat/fish juxtaposition surfaced again in a main course that used chicken jus to sauce a fried sole with fondant potato, roast baby artichoke and prawn beignet, while loin of Norfolk spring lamb might be partnered with white beans and roast fennel, the juices spiked with traditional rosemary. A pre-dessert in a shot glass heralds creations such as a buttery fig tart with burnt honey ice cream and red wine sauce. Coffee comes with various biscuits and chocolates. The wine list, with pages of good options (and plenty of halves), rightly trumpets a collection of French country wines that juxtaposes famous Daumas Gassac and Trévallon with upcomers Mas de Gourgonnier (£20) and Clot de l'Oum (£24) – both excellent value. Worthwhile house wines are £15.50.

Chef: Roger Hickman **Proprietor:** David Adlard **Open:** Tue to Sat 12.30 to 1.45, 7.30 (7 Sat) to 10.30 **Closed:** 1 week from Christmas **Meals:** alc (main courses £17 to £24). Set L £17 (2 courses) to £21 **Service:** not inc **Cards:** Amex, Delta, Diners, Maestro, MasterCard, Visa **Details:** 45 seats. Private parties: 45 main room. Vegetarian meals. No cigars/pipes. Wheelchair access (not WC). No music. Air-conditioned

Delia's Restaurant and Bar

AR

Norwich City Football Club, Carrow Road, Norwich NR1 1JE
Tel: (01603) 218705

Delia Smith, football supremo, is the driving force behind this modern restaurant attached to her beloved Norwich City Football Club. Short-choice menus are fixed price (£29.50), and the well-reported repertoire covers everything from potted Morecambe Bay shrimps or coarse country pâté to lamb's liver with Wiltshire sweet-cure bacon and crisp-fried onions, and chunky marmalade bread-and-butter pudding. Around 18 global wines from £12.50. Open Fri and Sat D only.

Mad Moose Arms, One Up Restaurant NEW ENTRY

2 Warwick Street, Norwich NR2 3LD
Tel: (01603) 627687

Cooking 2 | Modern British | £31–£59

A large cream-coloured building close to the University of East Anglia is the setting for this unpretentious, deservedly popular pub/restaurant. Wriggle through the crush in the bar/poolroom and head up the stairs to the double dining room, where the simple, minimalist bistro look of bare tables and wooden floor is softened by purple velvet curtains and low lighting. Seared scallops with lamb's lettuce, coriander, fennel and orange ceviche may feature as a starter, or pan-fried mackerel fillet teamed with chorizo sausage, curly kale and apple crisps. Meat main courses are well reported, with Gressingham duck breast served with sweet, crunchy red cabbage, creamy celeriac and a gamey cinnamon sauce, while a salad of carrots, chilli, peppers and star anise, along with buttered pak choi and coriander chickpeas make indelibly Asian partners for slow-cooked belly pork. For dessert, try peanut butter parfait with glazed bananas. Service is friendly and efficient, and the wine list comprises around 40 bins organised by style, with house selections from £11.95.

Chef: Eden Derrek **Proprietor:** H.D. Watt **Open:** Sun L 12 to 3, Mon to Sat D 7 to 9.45 **Meals:** alc (main courses £10 to £17). Bar menu available **Service:** not inc **Cards:** Amex, Diners, Maestro, MasterCard, Visa **Details:** 110 seats. 60 seats outside. Private parties: 50 main room. Vegetarian meals. Children's helpings. No smoking. Music

Tatlers

21 Tombland, Norwich NR3 1RF
Tel: (01603) 766670
Website: www.tatlers.com

Cooking 2 | Modern British | £30–£58

A solid Georgian townhouse right by the cathedral entrance, this venue has long been noted for good eating. Each of the three dining rooms is painted a different colour, but all have unclothed tables, old wooden floors and vases of lilies in common. The star dish at inspection was a vivid orange pumpkin tart, subtly sweet and delicately textured, served with chive crème fraîche. Another first course of game sausages came with buttery onions and a sustaining sauce enriched with duck liver. Mains offer a homely take on modern restaurant cooking, with sea bass appearing alongside parsnip purée, baby shallots and crispy cabbage, while French country cooking provides the inspiration for corn-fed chicken in champagne sauce with Alsace bacon and pasta. The golden treacle tart with smooth, creamy vanilla ice looks a sure-fire bet for pudding. Ten house wines start at £12.80 a bottle, or £3 a standard glass.

Chef: Chris Johnson **Proprietor:** Annelli Clarke **Open:** Mon to Sat 12 to 2, 6.30 to 10 **Closed:** bank hols **Meals:** alc (main courses £12 to £16). Set L £10 (1 course) to £18 **Service:** not inc, card slips closed **Cards:** Amex, Delta, Maestro, MasterCard, Visa **Details:** 70 seats. Private parties: 32 main room, 6 to 32 private rooms. Vegetarian meals. No smoking. Music

MAP 5 Nottingham
NOTTINGHAMSHIRE

Bees Make Honey AR

12 Alfreton Road, Nottingham NG7 3NG
Tel: (0115) 978 0109

The BYO policy is one of many appealing elements to this homespun café a few minutes' walk from the Playhouse and Theatre Royal. The blackboard menu lists a broadly Mediterranean range of dishes, from zarzuela to kleftico, via asparagus risotto. Vegetarians are well catered (spinach and feta pie, for example). Unlicensed, but BYO. Open Tue to Sat D only.

Geisha NEW ENTRY

3 The Broadway, Lace Market,
Nottingham NG1 1PR
Tel: (0115) 959 8344

Cooking 4 | Pan-Asian | £31–£144

This pan-Asian restaurant, centring on the best of Japanese technique, opened in the Lace Market district near St Mary's Church in summer 2004. The interior is predominantly black, the walls done in mosaic on themes of fish, and the lighting is fashionably low. Tables are low too, set on plinths, with seating on banquettes with bolsters, meaning the short of leg and concave of back will feel most comfortable.

Food service is in the pan-Asian style, with dishes coming to the table sequentially as soon as they are ready, and everything is meant for sharing. The full range of options, including omokase (the chef's selection of between five and ten courses) is available, and the Japanese items particularly are well rendered. Assorted vegetable tempura are properly light and crisp, garnished with soba noodles that are also fried. Slices of lobster are wrapped in basil before being fried, and are accompanied by a velvet-smooth curry sauce, and there is wagyu beef with oyster mushrooms as well as organic braised belly pork with five-spice for the discerning. More speculative dishes might include duck and foie gras gyoza dumplings with cherry jelly, or crispy harumaki chocolate roll with blueberry compote. Wines are stylistically grouped, and, while not cheap, are nothing like as steeply marked up as those at equivalent metropolitan venues. Prices start at around £13.

Chef: Anthony Sousa Tam **Proprietors:** Philip Duke, Ashley Walter and Anthony Sousa Tam **Open:** Tue to Thur D only 7 to 10, Fri and Sat D only 6 to 10.30 **Closed:** 25 and 26 Dec, 1 Jan **Meals:** alc (main courses £15 to £29.50). Set D Tue to Thur £20 to £100, Set D Fri and Sat £47 to £100. Bar menu available **Service:** 10% (optional), card slips closed **Cards:** Amex, Delta, Maestro, MasterCard, Visa **Details:** 60 seats. Private parties: 60 main room. Vegetarian meals. No children under 16. No smoking. Music. No mobile phones. Air-conditioned

Hart's

1 Standard Court, Park Row,
Nottingham NG1 6GN
Tel: (0115) 911 0666
Website: www.hartsnottingham.co.uk

Cooking 5 | Modern British | £25–£66

The décor at this city-centre address is simple enough, with wooden floors and minimalist modern art on plain walls, a central serving area the main focus. Nor does the culinary approach aim for over-embellishment, so don't expect appetisers or pre-desserts. What Alan Gleeson is good at is familiar combinations of quality ingredients cooked with skill and care. A salad of tender wood pigeon breast with seared foie gras, green beans and powerful truffle purée made a strong opener at inspection, and there is no bashfulness about serving straightforward dishes such as creamy moules marinière, or smoked salmon with avocado, crème fraîche and Avruga caviar.

Main courses show great assurance, whether for fish cookery such as crisp-skinned sea bass on baked saffron mash with a confit of peppers, or for satisfying meat dishes like loin of fallow venison with celeriac purée and a sauce teeming with juniper berries. Accomplished desserts include perfectly textured tarte Tatin with caramel ice cream, 'sublime, intense' raspberry and white chocolate cheesecake, and a salad of multifarious fruits teamed with rhubarb ice cream. Vegetarians have their own menu, and service is attentive and well drilled. A brasserie-style listing of wines, grouped by style, reveals a commendable effort to source classy, interesting bottles at ungrasping mark-ups. The base price is £12.50.

Chef: Alan Gleeson **Proprietor:** Tim Hart **Open:** all week 12 to 2, 7 to 10.30 (9 Sun) **Closed:** 26 Dec, 1 Jan **Meals:** alc (main courses £11.50 to £22.50). Set L Mon to Sat £11.95 (2 courses) to £14.95, Set L Sun £18, Set D Sun £11.95 (2 courses) to £14.95 **Service:** 12% (optional), card slips closed **Cards:** Amex, Delta, Maestro, MasterCard, Visa **Details:** 80 seats. 20 seats outside. Private parties: 80 main room, 6 to 110 private rooms. Car park (D only). Vegetarian meals. Children's helpings. No smoking. Wheelchair access (also WC). No music **Accommodation:** 32 rooms, all with bath/shower. TV. Phone. Room only £115 to £140. Rooms for disabled. Baby facilities

Restaurant Sat Bains

Old Lenton Lane, Nottingham NG7 2SA
Tel: (0115) 986 6566
Website: www.restaurantsatbains.net

Cooking 7 | Modern European | £75–£190

Chef Sat Bains is now master of all he surveys at this idiosyncratic establishment. Where once he headed the kitchen, he is now (as of May 2005) proprietor of the whole hotel – or restaurant-with-rooms, as we should perhaps more accurately style it. It's a former farm property next to the river Trent, comprising a number of red-brick buildings clustered around a gravelled courtyard. The original stone-floored dining room is now supplemented by a conservatory extension, again floored in York stone, the well-spaced tables set with ecru napery.

Bains's culinary style is breathlessly modern, with experimental combinations in the French idiom abounding. Three dinner menus are available – the basic carte, a menu dégustation and a menu surprise. The seven courses of the menu dégustation (plus various intermediate amuse-gueules) present a series of gustatory challenges. A single scallop is set on coriander-flecked kohlrabi, with a peanut brittle crisp and blobs of Granny Smith apple sauce. At the other end of the meal comes a glass made up of sundae-like layers of passion fruit, yoghurt, toffee and liquorice, the ingredients all harmonising well with each other.

The less speculative assemblages work equally well, as when sliced lobster is finished with tomato, rocket, caviar and olive oil, or when a main course of tender, well-timed quail is served with a shiitake mushroom and lightly caramelised shallots and dressed with soy sauce. The incidentals at inspection included a spoon of foie gras decorated with Earl Grey aspic, a vivid and refreshing beetroot sorbet, and a pre-dessert course of cheese on toast, which was literally that – sliced goats' cheese on thin toast, dribbled with truffle oil and presented on its baking sheet rather than on a plate. This is eye-catching food that achieves a solid strike rate, delivered by smartly attired staff who are unfailingly helpful. The brand-new and very polished wine list is arranged by styles, with gentle coaching on how each will partner food. Alternatively, simply ask for a 'tasting wine' to appear with each course on the two most expensive menus. Bottles start at £19.

Chefs: Sat Bains and John Freeman **Proprietor:** Sat Bains **Open:** Tue to Sat D only 7 to 9.30 **Closed:** first two weeks Jan, 2 weeks Aug **Meals:** Set D £55 to £140 (inc wine) **Service:** 10% (optional), card slips closed **Cards:** Amex, Delta, Maestro, MasterCard, Visa **Details:** 40 seats. Private parties: 40 main room, 10 to 28 private rooms. Car park. No children under 8. No smoking. Wheelchair access (also men's WC). Occasional music. No mobile phones. Air-conditioned **Accommodation:** 8 rooms, all with bath/shower. TV. Phone. B&B £114 to £265. Rooms for disabled

Sonny's

3 Carlton Street, Hockley, Nottingham NG1 1NL
Tel: (0115) 947 3041
Website: www.sonnys.co.uk

Cooking 3 | Global | £24–£65

This popular venue is a useful spot with an informal style and a repertoire of dishes that have evolved over the years. The short carte and even shorter set menus are peppered with ideas that attempt to please all palates – a policy that seems to work well. Among the more traditional items on the lunchtime café menu might be venison sausage with rosemary mash, and salmon fishcake, but in the restaurant be prepared for glazed artichoke, Swiss cheese, and bacon terrine to start, and roast cod with chorizo, sauerkraut, and red wine sauce among main courses. Inventive vegetarian dishes are always offered: say, a samosa of oriental stir-fried vegetables with wilted pak choi and peanut dressing. Rich desserts – perhaps bitter chocolate fondant with dark chocolate sorbet and crème anglaise – are the alternative to a selection of English and French cheeses served with quince jelly. Wines are a succinct international line-up of eminently drinkable bottles, with prices starting at £11.95.

Chef: Matt Vincent **Proprietor:** Rebecca Mascarenhas **Open:** all week 12 to 3, 7 to 10.30 **Closed:** bank hols **Meals:** alc (main courses £12.50 to £20.50). Set L £11.50 (2 courses) to £13.50, Set D Sun to Wed £13.50 (2 courses) to £16.50. Café menu available **Service:** 10% (optional), card slips closed **Cards:** Amex, Delta, Maestro, MasterCard, Visa **Details:** 86 seats. 16 seats outside. Private parties: 86 main room. Vegetarian meals. Children's helpings. No-smoking area. Wheelchair access (not WC). Music. No mobile phones. Air-conditioned

La Toque

61 Wollaton Road, Beeston,
Nottingham NG9 2NG
Tel: (0115) 922 2268
Website: www.latoqueonline.co.uk

Cooking 3 | French | £28–£63

The interior here is 'brown, brown and brown' (Venetian blinds, leather seating, tablecloths, walls, even light brown lighting), yet the effect is 'quite warm and welcoming'. Mattias Karlsson's determinedly French menus feature truffles, foie gras, and a few seasonal materials, and he does not favour simplicity: scallops, for example, being wrapped in prosciutto and served with parsnip roulade, a confit of peppers and plum tomatoes, lobster and an aged balsamic reduction. Main courses are equally ambitious. Parsnip gratin, rosemary jus, caramelized onion and 'lovely wild mushrooms' contrasted nicely with the sweetness of tarragon-crusted loin of lamb, though not all dishes balance their multiple flavours with such assurance. Complexity continues in desserts like Armagnac and roast pineapple cream soufflé with chocolate- and orange-filled brioche and pistachio nougatine parfait. The international wine list tilts to France, with fine Bordeaux and Burgundies, but there's good choice under £20 too; house French is £13.95.

Chef: Mattias Karlsson **Proprietor:** Norman Oley **Open:** Tue to Fri L 12 to 2.30, Mon to Sat D 7 to 10 **Closed:** 26 Dec to 5 Jan, first 2 weeks Aug **Meals:** alc D (main courses £18 to £20). Set L £10.95 (2 courses) to £14.95 **Service:** 10% (optional), card slips closed **Cards:** Amex, Delta, Diners, Maestro, MasterCard, Visa **Details:** 38 seats. Private parties: 28 main room. Vegetarian meals. No children under 8. No smoking in 1 dining room. Wheelchair access (also WC). Music. No mobile phones. Air-conditioned

World Service

Newdigate House, Castle Gate,
Nottingham NG1 6AF
Tel: (0115) 847 5587
Website: www.worldservicerestaurant.com

Cooking 4 | Modern British | £26–£69

The name says it all in this cool, globally inclined city-centre venue concealed behind a high brick wall in Newdigate House. A Japanese-style pebbled garden leads into the lounge bar, and the main dining area is filled with oriental statuary, a wooden prancing horse, mirrors, and window ledges set with Indonesian vases. The menu follows suit, although it happily embraces West and East: from the former you might encounter ham hock and chicken liver terrine with green beans and a quail's egg, or 'consummately simple' hickory-smoked salmon fillet with asparagus spears and hollandaise, while the latter contributes crab samosas with lime and ginger sauce, and Thai-style steamed chicken breast with jasmine rice and roast sharon fruit. To finish, soufflés are 'alert, upright and like a feather'. Alternatively, try yoghurt pannacotta with poached rhubarb and a garnish of slivers of dried rhubarb. Service is professional and courteous to a fault, while the wine list is comprehensive, eclectic and reasonably priced, with house recommendations from £13.50.

Chef: Preston Walker **Proprietors:** Dan Lindsay, Phil Morgan, Chris Elson and Ashley Walter **Open:** all week 12 to 2 (2.30 Sun), 7 to 10 (9 Sun) **Closed:** 1 to 7 Jan **Meals:** alc (main courses £12.50 to £19). Set L £11.50 (2 courses) to £15.50 **Service:** 10% (optional), card slips closed **Cards:** Amex, Delta, Maestro, MasterCard, Visa **Details:** 75 seats. 30 seats outside. Private parties: 34 main room, 8 to 26 private rooms. Vegetarian meals. Children's helpings. No smoking. Music

MAP 5 **Oakham** RUTLAND

Lord Nelson's House Hotel, Nick's Restaurant

11 Market Place, Oakham LE15 6DT
Tel: (01572) 723199
Website: www.nelsons-house.com

Cooking 4 | Anglo-French | £28–£58

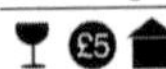

It's a warren of narrow passages inside this timber-framed building tucked away in Oakham's Market Place. Start in the lounge, nibbling olives and canapés while studying the menu, then continue in one of the two interlinked dining rooms furnished with an eye for tradition and comfort. Nick Healey's food may not aim for state-of-the-art trendiness, but he is not averse to incorporating the odd contemporary flourish. There could be a Thai fish casserole combining scallops, crevettes, mussels, and monkfish, or chicken breast with thyme-roasted sweet potatoes and grain mustard and sherry sauce, but the centre of gravity remains traditional, with chicken liver parfait and home-made green tomato chutney, or steak au poivre. Fine raw materials are evident: witness the well-timed garlicky prawns that came with shallots, peppers and white wine, or the halibut bolstered with spinach and lemon butter sauce. Puddings, too, follow tradition, among them a well-reported sticky toffee, and a bread-and-butter pudding. 'Excellent, attentive' service is relaxed but professional. A good-value international wine list (from £11.50) with loads of options by the glass is crowned by an inspiring collection of fine wines.

Chef: Nick Healey **Proprietors:** Nick and Amanda Healey **Open:** Tue to Sat 12 to 2.30 (2 Sat), 7 to 9.30 **Meals:** alc (main courses £8 to £21) **Service:** not inc, card slips closed **Cards:** Delta, Maestro, MasterCard, Visa **Details:** 46 seats. Private parties: 50 main room. Vegetarian meals. Children's helpings. No-smoking area. Music. No mobile phones **Accommodation:** 4 rooms, all with bath/shower. TV. Phone. B&B £65 to £90

 This symbol means that the wine list is well above the average.

MAP 2 **Oaksey** WILTSHIRE

Wheatsheaf

NEW ENTRY

Wheatsheaf Lane, Oaksey SN16 9TB
Tel: (01666) 577348

Cooking 2 | Modern British | £30–£52

Hidden away in a cul-de-sac opposite the village church, this seventeenth-century stone inn is basking in a new lease of life under owners Tony and Holly Robson-Burrell. Chef Darren Le Feuvre moved here from the Royalist Hotel, Stow-on-the-Wold along with knowledgeable restaurant manager Walter Jansen, and together they are transforming the pub into a serious food contender. Their sensibly planned menus comprise a short, sharp assortment of modern dishes supported by plenty of in-house endeavour (petits fours have been pronounced 'brilliant'). A salad of smoked Coln trout with pecorino and lime typifies the starters, while main courses could run from roast salmon with chorizo mash, spinach and leeks to confit of duck leg with choucroute, Parmesan mash and marjoram sauce. Desserts are trendily presented offerings like home-made bourbon and vanilla ice cream with summer fruits. House wines start at around £12.

Chef: Darren Le Feuvre **Proprietors:** Tony and Holly Robson-Burrell **Open:** Tue to Sun L 12 to 2 (3 Sun), Tue to Sat D 6.30 to 9.30 **Meals:** alc (main courses £10 to £16.50). Bar snack menu available **Service:** not inc, card slips closed **Cards:** Delta, Maestro, MasterCard, Visa **Details:** 46 seats. 12 seats outside. Private parties: 26 main room. Car park. Vegetarian meals. Children's helpings. No smoking. Wheelchair access (not WC). Music

MAP 2 **Odiham** HAMPSHIRE

Grapevine

AR

121 High Street, Odiham RG29 1LA
Tel: (01256) 701122

Crowds of regulars and families keep the mood buoyant in this cheerily decorated neighbourhood bistro. The kitchen's style is honest, no-frills home cooking. Chateaubriand is a signature dish, and the monthly menus feature items like poached skate, caper and mustard salad (£5), and sautéed calf's liver with crushed truffle potatoes, parsnips and balsamic shallots (£15); desserts (£5) range from limoncello pannacotta to caramelised lemon tart with blood orange sorbet. House wines from £11.95. Closed Sat L and Sun.

MAP 2 **Old Burghclere** HAMPSHIRE

Dew Pond

Old Burghclere RG20 9LH
Tel: (01635) 278408
Website: www.dewpond.co.uk

Cooking 4 | Anglo-French | £41–£59

Fashioned from a pair of sixteenth-century drovers' cottages, this country restaurant – set on a narrow lane close to the A34 – offers superb views over flat, open green fields (full of lambs in the spring) to the Hampshire Downs. On fair days, a split-level decked terrace at the rear provides an ideal vantage point over aperitifs. The two interconnecting dining rooms have been redecorated and deliver a Mediterranean slant with their colours of vanilla and terracotta, while walls, windowsills and display tables come crammed full of art and sculpture, acting as a changing gallery for local artists. But not much changes on Keith Marshall's well-balanced dinner-only repertoire of accomplished, non-frill-seeking dishes, and that includes the reasonable fixed price (save for a couple of supplements). Start with a salad of seared scallops with pan-fried black pudding, potato and pancetta and a chive dressing, followed by, perhaps, best end of lamb accompanied by ratatouille-filled courgettes, sun-blushed tomato, a stock reduction and gratin dauphinois. Service, headed up by a new manager, hits just the right note and is well informed.

An unfussy slate of wines mostly under £25 is forthrightly set out by styles, with a few special bottles added for treats. House wines are £13.50 and a dozen come by the glass.

Chef: Keith Marshall **Proprietors:** Keith and Julie Marshall **Open:** Tue to Sat D only 7 to 10 **Meals:** Set D £28 **Service:** not inc **Cards:** Delta, MasterCard, Maestro, Visa **Details:** 45 seats. Private parties: 45 main room, 20 to 30 private rooms. Car park. No smoking. Wheelchair access (not WC). No music

MAP 5 **Ombersley** WORCESTERSHIRE

Venture In

Ombersley WR9 0EW
Tel: (01905) 620552

Cooking 3 | Modern British/French | £29–£55

Striped window awnings and a mellow-yellow interior distinguish the Venture In from its historic half-timbered neighbours in this ancient village

bypassed by the A449. The kitchen puts its faith in a trusted network of suppliers for imaginative fixed-price menus that could feature locally sourced meat in the guise of, say, pot-roast lamb with sweet-pickled red cabbage, or beef fillet with creamed polenta, sautéed mushrooms and red-wine sauce. Toby Fletcher also pays due attention to the harvest of the sea (West Coast scallops might be served with cucumber and crème fraîche salad and beetroot dressing) and there are fortnightly fish extravaganzas on alternate Wednesday evenings. Desserts are mostly classic ideas like iced praline parfait with warm blackberry and cassis compote. The 70-bin wine list casts its net wide for interesting tipples; house selections are £13.

Chef/Proprietor: Toby Fletcher **Open:** Tue to Sun L 12 to 2, Tue to Sat D 7 to 9.30 **Meals:** Set L £16.95 (2 courses) to £19.95, Set D £31.50 **Service:** not inc, card slips closed **Cards:** Delta, MasterCard, Maestro, Visa **Details:** 34 seats. Private parties: 34 main room. Car park. Vegetarian meals. No children under 10. No smoking in 1 dining room. No music. Air-conditioned

MAP 3 **Ongar** ESSEX

Smith's

AR

Fyfield Road, Ongar CM5 0AL
Tel: (01277) 365578

'Famous for fish' boasts the menu in this long-running seafood venue (opened in 1958 but with a swish up-to-the-minute look). Haddock, plaice, skate and salmon are cooked every which way (from £11.50), lobster and bouillabaisse put in an appearance, and you might also find grilled mussels with garlic butter (£6.50), pot-roast lamb with red wine and rosemary sauce, and desserts such as lemon tart with vanilla bean sauce (£5.75). Fixed-price lunches from £9.50. Thirty-plus wines from £12. Closed Mon.

MAP 6 **Orford** SUFFOLK

Butley-Orford Oysterage

AR

Market Hill, Orford IP12 2LH
Tel: (01394) 450277

'You don't go here for plush luxury; you go for wonderful fish,' summarised a reporter, well contented with his sole in a prawn and vermouth sauce (£13). The restaurant's own oyster beds and smokehouse (try a selection from both for £9.50) complement the steady supply of fresh fish specials. Finish with lemon syllabub (£4) and wash it all down with a bottle from a good selection of white wines from £11.50. Open all week exc Sun to Thur D Oct to Apr.

Crown and Castle, Trinity

Orford IP12 2LJ
Tel: (01394) 450205
Website: www.crownandcastle.co.uk

Cooking 4 | Modern British-Plus | £32–£58

Cheerful, idiosyncratic décor creates 'a contemporary feel' in this handsome old Victorian hotel opposite Orford Castle's impressive Norman keep. Meals are unhurried, and the food (especially at lunchtime) is good value; simple table settings indicate that the focus is on the quality of what you eat rather than any unnecessary frippery. As befits a place close to the source, seafood is a strong suit: at inspection, in the form of potted brown shrimps and sea bass with shellfish stock and rouille, both of which impressed. There are good meat options too, reflecting local and seasonal choice, say pan-fried lambs' kidneys and chicken livers en croûte with sprouting broccoli and gravy, or rack of Suffolk lamb with spicy aubergine, tomato and onion ragoût and yoghurt, and pudding might turn up bitter chocolate soufflé cake or rhubarb meringue pie. Service is well drilled, and the interesting wine list is fairly priced; house wines from South Africa and Australia are £12.50.

Chefs: Ruth Watson and Max Dougal **Proprietors:** David and Ruth Watson **Open:** all week 12 to 2, 7 to 9.15 (Sat D 9.30) **Closed:** Jan 4 to 6 **Meals:** alc D (main courses £11.50 to £16.50). Set L £16.50 (2 courses) to £25, Set D Sat £32.50 to £35 **Service:** not inc **Cards:** Delta, Maestro, MasterCard, Visa **Details:** 56 seats. 60 seats outside. Private parties: 46 main room, 10 private rooms. Car park. Vegetarian meals. Children's helpings. No children under 9 at D. Wheelchair access (also WC). No music. No mobile phones **Accommodation:** 18 rooms, all with bath/shower. TV. Phone. B&B £70 to £130. Baby facilities

This symbol means that accommodation is available at this establishment.

MAP 7 **Oswestry** SHROPSHIRE

Sebastians

45 Willow Street, Oswestry SY11 1AQ
Tel: (01691) 655444
Website: www.sebastians-hotel.co.uk

At first glance you might be forgiven for thinking this was a classy English provincial tea shop, with its blue-and-white façade and chintzy interior of beams, panelling and oak floorboards. In reality, the Fishers run this sixteenth-century building as a self-styled 'hotel and restaurant', offering bistro-style food with a French provincial accent. Dishes are written *en français* with English translations and there's little here to challenge the gastronomic status quo: monthly menus open with a classic soup (potage Crécy, for example), a sorbet interrupts proceedings and there are Gallic cheeses to finish. Along the way, expect dishes like Narbonne-style poached eggs, lamb fillet with crushed potatoes and sage jus, and John Dory with braised chicory and orange sauce, as well as desserts like lemon tart with raspberry coulis. Europe and the New World share the billing on the realistically priced wine list; house recommendations start at £12.95.

Chef: Mark Sebastian Fisher **Proprietors:** Mark Sebastian and Michelle Fisher **Open:** Tue to Sat D only 6.30 to 9 **Closed:** 25 and 26 Dec, 1 Jan **Meals:** Set D £29.95 **Service:** not inc, card slips closed **Cards:** Amex, Delta, MasterCard, Maestro, Visa **Details:** 32 seats. 20 seats outside. Private parties: 50 main room. Car park. Vegetarian meals. Children's helpings. No smoking. Wheelchair access (not WC). Music. No mobile phones **Accommodation:** 8 rooms, all with bath/shower. TV. Phone. Room only £60 to £70. Rooms for disabled. Baby facilities

MAP 6 **Ovington** NORFOLK

Brovey Lair

Carbrooke Road, Ovington IP25 6SD
Tel: (01953) 882706
Website: www.broveylair.com

Cooking 5 | Fusion | £52–£66

In some ways eating at the Pembertons' café-with-rooms is like attending an extremely civilised dinner party: there's just one sitting at 7.45pm (which must be booked in advance), the kitchen is open-plan, and the set menu has no choice until dessert. The cool, contemporary décor wows and the accomplished combination of influences from the Mediterranean and Asia means that this is where the much-maligned fusion style can be seen at its best. Tina Pemberton's ideas are not revolutionary, but her dishes display passion and a genuine feel for flavour.

There is an air of excitement about a menu that opens with tiger prawns stir-fried with chilli, mint and coriander and served on a green papaya salad, then goes on to leek and celeriac soup with Bramley apple, cardamom, saffron and toasted almonds, and, as a main course, has fillet of Dover sole baked in a spicy kaffir lime and coconut marinade and accompanied by black rice, pak choi, oyster mushrooms and asparagus stir-fried in tamarind and saké, and finishes with exotic bitter chocolate mocha truffle torte. Overly attentive, chatty service adds to the dinner party ambience; go with a sense of adventure. Lunch is by three days' prior arrangement. The compact wine list is heavily, although not exclusively, skewed towards France and opens with house French and Chilean at £14.95.

Chef: Tina Pemberton **Proprietors:** Mike and Tina Pemberton **Open:** all week D only 7.45 (1 sitting). Bookings only; L by arrangement **Closed:** 25 Dec **Meals:** Set D £42.50 **Service:** 10%, card slips closed **Cards:** Amex, Maestro, MasterCard, Visa **Details:** 20 seats. 10 seats outside. Private parties: 24 main room. Car park. Vegetarian meals. No children under 16. No smoking. Wheelchair access (not WC). Music. Air-conditioned **Accommodation:** 2 rooms, both with bath/shower. TV. B&B £115 to £125. No children under 16. Swimming pool

MAP 2 **Oxford** OXFORDSHIRE

Al-Shami

AR

25 Walton Crescent, Oxford OX1 2JG
Tel: (01865) 310066

Ever-popular, colourfully decorated Lebanese haunt in a quiet Victorian terrace. Hot and cold meze are the main attraction (£2 to £4 per item), and the range spans everything from familiar hummus and tabbouleh to rarely seen nkha'at pane (fried lambs' brains). High-protein grills, kebabs and vegetarian options like mujadara (rice and lentils with fried onions; £6.50); sticky desserts (£2) and Arabic ice creams to finish. House Lebanese is £11.99; otherwise check the selection of Ch. Musar. Open all week.

Branca

111 Walton Street, Oxford OX2 6AJ
Tel: (01865) 556111
Website: www.branca-restaurants.com

Cooking 1 | Modern Italian | £24–£55

A boisterous, studenty atmosphere, all-day opening and early supper deals contribute to the appeal of this animated modern Italian brasserie. The menu covers a lot of ground, from seared smoked salmon fillet with roast garlic and leek risotto, or crab cakes with sweet pepper and chilli salsa, to roast duck breast with braised lentils and balsamic sauce. Stone-baked pizzas and pasta are mainstays, while desserts are familiar favourites like rich chocolate torta, pannacotta, and panettone bread-and-butter pudding. All thirteen regional Italian wines come by the glass, bottle (from £11.75) or 500ml 'pot', and the one- or two-course set meals include a glass of house or a Nastro Azurro.

Chef: Michael MacQuire **Proprietor:** Paul Petrillo **Open:** all week; 12 to 11.30 **Closed:** 25 and 26 Dec **Meals:** alc (main courses £9 to £17). Set L Mon to Fri 12 to 5 £5.95 (1 course), Set D Mon to Fri 5 to 7 £10 (2 courses) **Service:** not inc, card slips closed **Cards:** Amex, Delta, Diners, Maestro, MasterCard, Visa **Details:** 110 seats. Private parties: 50 main room. Vegetarian meals. Children's helpings. No-smoking area. Wheelchair access (also WC). Music. No mobile phones. Air-conditioned

Cherwell Boathouse

50 Bardwell Road, Oxford OX2 6ST
Tel: (01865) 552746
Website: www.cherwellboathouse.co.uk

Cooking 1 | Modern English/French | £23–£39

Punts can be hired at the Boathouse, but this 37-year-old Oxford institution is better known for its seductive location, overlooking a verdant stretch of the Cherwell, and its gold-standard cellar. The kitchen steers a familiar Anglo-French course (rather unevenly sometimes), and the short menu might offer fried wood pigeon breast with warm potato salad and cep cream sauce, and grilled fillet of salmon with mixed herb risotto and celeriac rémoulade, before simple desserts like rhubarb and orange crumble with bourbon cream.

Service can be slow, but the fine selection of wines at wonderfully fair prices should smooth any ruffled feathers. Bordeaux and Burgundy, properly cellared, are the heart of the list, with international contributions dotted about. House is £11.50, and around ten engaging options come by the glass.

Chef: Mark Horton **Proprietors:** The Verdin family **Open:** all week 12 to 2 (2.30 Sat/Sun), 6.30 to 10 **Closed:** 25 to 30 Dec **Meals:** Set L £12.50 (2 courses) to £21.50, Set D £23.50 **Service:** not inc, 10% for parties of 6 or more **Cards:** Amex, Delta, Maestro, MasterCard, Visa **Details:** 70 seats. 45 seats outside. Private parties: 120 main room, 10 to 50 private rooms. Car park. Vegetarian meals. Children's helpings. No smoking. Wheelchair access (also WC). No music

Chiang Mai

130A High Street, Oxford OX1 4DH
Tel: (01865) 202233
Website: www.chiangmaikitchen.co.uk

Cooking 1 | Thai | £32–£46

Hidden away down a tiny alley off the High Street, this rickety seventeenth-century timber-framed building doesn't look much from the outside, although Thai wood carvings and other artefacts in the dining room give a clue to its current identity. Most of the staples – from satays and soups to salads and stir-fries – are represented on the menu, and the kitchen also tackles more unusual specialities such as venison with Thai aubergines and red curry paste. Vegetarians might be tempted by, say, tofu tord (crisp-fried bean curd with peanut sauce), and a couple of authentic desserts include steamed sticky rice with cashews and banana. One-plate rice and noodle dishes are an affordable bet at lunchtime. House wine is £12.50; otherwise drink Singha beer.

Chef: Pun Bua-In **Proprietor:** Helen O'Malley **Open:** all week; 12 to 2.30, 6 to 10.30 **Closed:** Dec 25, bank hols **Meals:** alc (main courses £7 to £10.50) **Service:** 10% (optional), not inc **Cards:** Amex, Diners, Maestro, MasterCard, Visa **Details:** 80 seats. Private parties: 33 main room. Vegetarian meals. No smoking in 1 dining room. Wheelchair access (1 step; not WC). No music

Edamame

AR

15 Holywell Street, Oxford OX1 3SA
Tel: (01865) 246916

An ultra-cheap Japanese canteen opposite New College, serving non-formulaic food to an enthusiastic crowd. At lunchtime, the kitchen delivers a healthy selection from eponymous edamame pods (£1.50) to bowls of udon noodles (from £5) and shake furai teishoku (breaded salmon fillet with rice and miso soup, £7). Sushi Thur evening; full menu Fri and Sat. To drink, try cold oolong tea or calpis (Japanese yoghurt drink); house wine £2 a glass. No cards at lunchtime; no bookings. Open Tue to Sun L, Thur to Sat D (unusual hours).

Fishers

AR

36–37 St Clements Street, Oxford OX4 1AB
Tel: (01865) 243003

The no-nonsense Fishers formula has been going strong for 10 years, with something for every fish fan from a £5 lunch and early-evening menu (exc Sat D and Sun L) to whole New England lobster (£35.50) via various platters, oysters, and haddock and chips. Fish and seafood arrive daily to provide a carte where grilled Cornish sardines with lemon and parsley (£5) could be followed by baked Welsh sea bass with garlic and herb oil (£15). Finish with 'vaspretto' – Amaretto and espresso over vanilla ice cream. White-biased wine list from £10.95. Closed Mon L.

Gee's

61 Banbury Road, Oxford OX2 6PE
Tel: (01865) 553540
Website: www.gees-restaurant.co.uk

Cooking 2 | Modern British | £30–£74

The Gee family, who built the large Victorian conservatory for its floristry business, aptly lend their name to this lively restaurant about ten minutes from the city centre. The small bar displays vivid modern art, while the dining room comes decked out with a tiled floor, clever spotlighting, impeccably laid tables and squidgy banquettes, and young staff serve with panache and contribute to the friendly atmosphere. The kitchen's focus is modern, the emphasis on quality seasonal produce and the approach straightforward. A weekly-changing 'star dish' delivers a distinctly British experience with all the traditional trimmings (perhaps roast Gloucestershire pork belly with black pudding and apple purée), while monthly-changing lunch and dinner cartes, fixed-price options and a mid-week seafood tasting menu vie for attention. From these you might choose a creamy and moist risotto of crab, shrimps and saffron, followed by tender and richly flavoured pot-roast shank of venison with Savoy cabbage, then lemon posset. A short, fashionable wine list strikes out with house South African at £12.95.

Chef: Michael Wright **Proprietor:** Jeremy Mogford **Open:** all week 12 to 2.30 (3.30 Sun), 6 to 10.30 (11 Fri and Sat) **Closed:** 25 and 26 Dec **Meals:** alc (main courses £11 to £22). Set L £13.95 (2 courses), Set D £20.95 (2 courses) to £24.95 **Service:** not inc, 10% for parties of 5 or more **Cards:** Amex, Delta, Maestro, MasterCard, Visa **Details:** 85 seats. 60 seats outside. Private parties: 85 main room. Vegetarian meals. Children's helpings. No smoking. Wheelchair access (also WC). Music. Air-conditioned

Lemon Tree

268 Woodstock Road, Oxford OX2 7NW
Tel: (01865) 311936
Website: www.thelemontreeoxford.co.uk

Cooking 3 | Mediterranean | £27–£67

There's a touch of Mediterranean warmth about Clinton Pugh's lively brasserie, with its yellow ochre split-level dining room and doors opening on to the gravelled garden. The kitchen sources a fine range of raw materials from locally bred Charolais beef to Clonakilty black pudding (served with spring-onion mash and mustard dressing), although fish is the top attraction judging by reports: specials such as flavoursome fish soup with Parmesan and croûtons and pan-roasted flounder with caper sauce have both been endorsed. Other high points have included braised lamb shank with butternut squash and sage risotto, and rump steak with béarnaise sauce, followed closely by fig tarte Tatin with vanilla mascarpone and caramel sauce. Service is 'excellent' and the wine list is a decent slate with plenty offered by the glass; bottle prices start at £12.95.

Chef: John Pugsley **Proprietor:** Clinton Pugh **Open:** Thur to Sun noon to 11, Mon to Wed 6 to 11 **Closed:** 24 Dec to 3 Jan **Meals:** alc (main courses £9.50 to £19.50). Set L Thur to Sat £10.95 (2 courses) to £12.95. Tapas available in bar **Service:** not inc (though may change to optional charge) **Cards:** Amex, Maestro, MasterCard, Visa **Details:** 90 seats. 40 seats outside. Private parties: 90 main room. Car park. Vegetarian meals. Children's helpings. No smoking in 1 dining room. Wheelchair access (also WC). Music. No mobile phones

Liaison

NEW ENTRY

29 Castle Street, Oxford OX1 1LJ
Tel: (01865) 242944

Cooking 1 | Chinese | £30–£50

A seasoned reporter applauded the fact that this unostentatious Chinese restaurant in a 'rickety Tudor house' had the 'audacity' to serve genuinely authentic dishes in Oxford. A sizeable list of dim sum throws down the gauntlet with the likes of sautéed sea snail with curried sauce, chicken's feet in Chinese wine, and crispy custard buns alongside the more usual dumplings. The full menu navigates its way through the Chinese provinces and also embarks on a whistle-stop tour of Thailand and other parts of South-east Asia: check out the special 'home-made' dishes and peasant-style 'clay pots' like five-spice braised beef, or duck's web with fish lips. Service is considerate. House wine is £9.50.

Chef: Charles Tsang **Proprietor:** Y.K. Tsang **Open:** all week 12 to 3, 6.30 to 11.30 **Meals:** alc (main courses £7 to £10). Set D £15.95 to £19.60 **Service:** 10% (optional), card slips closed **Cards:** Delta, Maestro, MasterCard, Visa **Details:** 70 seats. Private parties: 60 main room, 15 private room. No smoking in 1 dining room. Wheelchair access (not WC). Music. Air-conditioned

Le Petit Blanc

AR

71–72 Walton Street, Oxford OX2 6AG
Tel: (01865) 510999

The original of Raymond Blanc's group of family-friendly provincial brasseries. The lively, relaxed atmosphere and flexible attitude is a winning format, especially for families. There's a prix fixe menu at £12 for two courses, a children's menu (£5.95 for 2 courses), and a carte which runs from Thai coconut and lime soup (£4.50) to pappardelle with prawns and chilli (£6.50/£12.50). Finish with pavlova of summer berries and vanilla ice cream (£5.50). Open all week. There are branches in Birmingham, Cheltenham, Manchester and Tunbridge Wells (see entries).

Sojo Restaurant

AR

6–9 Hythe Bridge Street, Oxford OX1 2EW
Tel: (01865) 202888

Affordable neighbourhood restaurant occupying a shop conversion in one of the city's Chinese enclaves. Dim sum are a good lunchtime bet, and the full menu focuses on regional specialities from Shanghai and Szechuan. The former contributes, say, sweet soy duck (£7.50) and garlic oil squid, while red peppercorn chicken and dan dan mein (minced chicken, noodles and peanut sauce; £3.50) represent the latter. Thai and Japanese dishes such as satay and salmon teriyaki also feature. Open all week.

MAP 8 **Oxton** MERSEYSIDE

Fraiche

11 Rose Mount, Oxton CH43 5SG
Tel: (0151) 652 2914
Email: fraicherestaurant@yahoo.com

Cooking 6 | Modern French | £45–£74

Tucked away in an unassuming terrace in the middle of the conservation village of Oxton near Birkenhead, this restaurant brought a breath of Fraiche air to the local dining scene when it opened a couple of years ago. Chef-patron Marc Wilkinson gained experience in France and cooking at some prestigious British addresses, before returning in triumph to his roots.

It's been quite a homecoming, as is attested by the swelling volume of local support he has garnered for supremely crafted, highly assured cooking of considerable glamour. With a subtly understated seaside theme in the décor, and well-briefed, attentive service, the stage is set for culinary fireworks. These arrive in the form of a fixed-price menu of four choices at each stage. Muscovado-glazed chicory is the cleverly sweet-bitter accompaniment to seared scallops, the combination supported by a frothy mushroom sauce. Another way of starting might be with carpaccio of mouli, earthily served with pickled girolles and a truffled poached egg, while main courses go for out-of-the-ordinary ingredients such as pink-cooked Black Face Suffolk lamb, with crisp-battered sweetbread, a baby leek, and white bean and apricot purée, or slow-cooked Loire quail with pomelo compote and boudin noir. Artistic presentations enhance ingenious desserts such as chilled chocolate coulant with passion-fruit sorbet and a cocoa and walnut crisp, or try a sweet-savoury alternative such as Mrs Bourne's Cheshire cheese served with fruitcake.

A mouthwatering selection of fine wines matured to perfection opens the imaginative wine list, which overall offers excellent value (from £15.50) and a confident mix of modern and classical styles: compare Jackson Estate New Zealand Sauvignon Blanc and Sancerre by Hubert Brochard, both at around £24.

Chefs: Marc Wilkinson and Nelson Sa **Proprietor:** Marc Wilkinson **Open:** Tue to Sat D 7 to 9 (9.30 Fri and Sat) **Closed:** first week Jan **Meals:** Set D £25 (2 courses) to £45 (whole table only) **Service:** not inc, card slips closed **Cards:** Delta, MasterCard, Maestro, Visa **Details:** 20 seats. 10 seats outside. Private parties: 20 main room. Vegetarian meals. No smoking. Wheelchair access (not WC). No music. No mobile phones

MAP 1 **Padstow** CORNWALL

The Ebb

1A The Strand, Padstow PL28 8B5
Tel: (01841) 532565

Cooking 4 | Seafood-Plus | £40–£59

Seafood is top of the agenda at this bright and airy restaurant right by Padstow harbour: supplies come from the Cornish day boats and – like the décor – the food is modern, refreshingly light and effective. Karen Scott's menus are in tune with the seasons and ideas are emphatically eclectic – so expect to find starters of seared scallops with curried banana broth and coriander, or goats' cheese bruschetta with fig jam. Main courses pick up the theme, perhaps whole baked sea bass with spicy Thai salad and toasted sesame seeds, roast cod with bacon, tomato, Savoy cabbage and cannellini bean cassoulet, or (if meat is your thing) half a poussin roasted with fennel. Place your order 24 hours in advance and you can have a Cornish blue lobster with your name on it. Finish with something filling (plum crumble with vanilla ice cream) or whimsical (cold fruit soup with elderflower sorbet). West Country merchants supply wines for the equally varied list; house selections start at £16.

Chefs: Karen Scott and Tom Rhodes **Proprietors:** Peter and Karen Scott **Open:** Wed to Mon D only 7 to 9.30 (6 to 10 in summer) **Closed:** Nov to 1 week before Easter **Meals:** alc (main courses £13.50 to £18.50) **Service:** not inc, card slips closed **Cards:** Delta, MasterCard, Maestro, Visa **Details:** 60 seats. Private parties: 36 main room, 12 to 18 private rooms. Vegetarian meals. No children under 14. No smoking. Music. No mobile phones

 This symbol means that smoking is not permitted.

Margot's

11 Duke Street, Padstow PL28 8AB
Tel: (01841) 533441
Website: www.margots.co.uk

Cooking 3 | Modern British | £31–£47

As it's only just up the street from the harbour, it's hardly surprising that seafood is a big player on the menu of this small but ever-popular, friendly bistro. The pretty blue-and-white interior echoes the location, while service is genuinely cheerful and knowledgeable, and you can linger long over your meal knowing there's only one sitting. The good-value, sensibly compact and modern-focused menus come awash with squeaky-fresh fish, perhaps grilled fillet of brill served with spinach, new potatoes and a chive butter sauce, or roast cod fillet with garlic, parsley, capers and a herb mash. Local Cornish lamb might vie for attention too, simply served with roast new potatoes and a rosemary jus, while a signature sticky toffee pudding, perhaps partnered by butterscotch sauce, could head up desserts. The short, affordable wine list stays largely under £20, opening with a five-strong house selection from £10.50 that's also available by the glass (£3.50) and carafe (£8.25).

Chefs: Adrian Oliver and Philip Cortis **Proprietors:** Adrian and Julie Oliver **Open:** Wed to Sat L 12.30 to 2, Tue to Sat D 7 to 9 **Closed:** 25 to 26 Dec, all Jan **Meals:** alc L (main courses £11.50 to £16.50). Set D £22.50 (2 courses) to £26.50 **Service:** not inc **Cards:** Amex, Delta, MasterCard, Maestro, Visa **Details:** 22 seats. Private parties: 22 main room. Vegetarian meals. Children's helpings. No smoking. Wheelchair access (not WC). Music

Rick Stein's Café

10 Middle Street, Padstow PL28 8BQ
Tel: (01841) 532700
Website: www.rickstein.com

Cooking 2 | Seafood | £31–£51

Whatever the time or weather, expect crowds in this cheap and cheerful outpost of Rick Stein's Padstow dominion. Tables fill up quickly inside the pleasantly functional dining room, there's always plenty of animated chatter and the action often spills over on to the covered courtyard. The kitchen delivers straightforward bistro food with a flexible attitude and – not surprisingly – a leaning towards fish. Salt and pepper prawns or panzanella might open the show, while main courses could include devilled gurnard, or pan-fried haddock with cannellini beans, capers and tarragon, as well as chargrilled Scottish ribeye steak with tomato and red onion salad. Puddings such as Bakewell tart with clotted cream are not a strong point. The concise wine list is peppered with a few of Rick Stein's personal favourites. Prices start at £13.50.

Chefs: Roy Brett and Paul Harwood **Proprietors:** Rick and Jill Stein **Open:** all week 12 to 3, 7 to 9.30 **Closed:** 24 to 26 Dec, 1 May **Meals:** alc (main courses £8.50 to £16). Set L and D £19.50 to £22.50 **Service:** not inc **Cards:** Delta, Maestro, MasterCard, Visa **Details:** 40 seats. 10 seats outside. Vegetarian meals. Children's helpings. No smoking. Wheelchair access (not WC). Music **Accommodation:** 3 rooms, all with bath/shower. TV. Phone. B&B £85 to £105. Baby facilities

St Petroc's Bistro

4 New Street, Padstow PL28 8EA
Tel: (01841) 532700
Website: www.rickstein.com

Cooking 2 | Bistro | £41–£55

One of Rick Stein's many enterprises in the town, St Petroc's is the budget alternative to the Seafood Restaurant (see entry right) and as such seems to have an endless flow of eager clientele. The brief menu offers six choices at each course, among which might be yellow split pea and ham soup, followed by half a roasted chicken with mash and gravy, then crème brûlée. Generally the kitchen succeeds in its efforts and the cooking is reputed for good materials, especially fish – pan-fried gurnard with sage and garlic butter gets the thumbs up – and a fairly straightforward approach. An inspection meal endorsed these two virtues but reflected on the unevenness of execution of some dishes. Wine prices start at £13.25.

Chefs: Alistair Clive and Roy Brett **Proprietors:** Rick and Jill Stein **Open:** all week 12 to 2, 7 to 10 **Closed:** 1 week at Christmas, May Day **Meals:** alc (main courses £12.50 to £16) **Service:** not inc **Cards:** Delta, MasterCard, Maestro, Visa **Details:** 55 seats. 20 seats outside. Private parties: 55 main room. Vegetarian meals. Children's helpings. No smoking. Wheelchair access (also WC). Music. Air-conditioned **Accommodation:** 10 rooms, all with bath/shower. TV. Phone. B&B £115 to £185. Baby facilities

Seafood Restaurant

Riverside, Padstow PL28 8BY
Tel: (01841) 532700
Website: www.rickstein.com

Cooking 6 | Seafood | £53–£109

This is still the flagship craft in Rick Stein's expanding flotilla of commercial ventures. Lately seen grousing for England on the BBC's *Grumpy Old Men*, the proprietor nonetheless ensures that all within this expansive, white-walled, comfortable harbourside venue remains sweetness and light. Staff are mustard-keen, their knowledge of piscatorial matters appropriately up to snuff, and there is enough elbow room between tables to set about a seafood platter without annoying the neighbours.

Much of the produce does indeed come straight off the boats and in through the kitchen door, as is evidenced by that extra dimension of marine freshness that even the best inland restaurants don't quite capture. Other items, such as oysters from Galway or Colchester, or langoustines from western Scotland, may have made a longer journey. Starter preparations are mostly hearteningly simple: crab comes just with rocket, basil and lemon-scented olive oil; scallops are served with Puy lentils and sauced with Australian Chardonnay; oysters are served in the Charentais fashion with spicy sausages. For the main business, things get a little more involved. Hake fillet turns out in Spanish livery with butter beans, tomato, chilli, and a green sauce, while the monkfish might well appear in a vindaloo. The tasting menu offers a guided tour through the repertoire, and it's all rounded off with the likes of hot chocolate fondant with praline ice cream, pannacotta with baked plums, or vanilla ice cream with old, treacly Pedro Ximenez sherry poured over it.

White wines, well matched to the menu, are the priority on the extensive wine list. The good-value house dozen from £18 to £30 will satisfy most palates, but the full list makes a rewarding read, with treats like Rudera Chenin Blanc (£24) from South Africa.

Chefs: Stéphane Delourme and Roy Brett **Proprietors:** Rick and Jill Stein **Open:** all week 12 to 2 (2.30 July and Aug), 7 to 10 **Closed:** 1 week at Christmas, 1 May **Meals:** alc (main courses £16 to £44). Set L and D £65 **Service:** not inc **Cards:** Delta, MasterCard, Maestro, Visa **Details:** 110 seats. Private parties: 40 main room. Vegetarian meals. Children's helpings; no children under 3. Wheelchair access (not WC). No music. Air-conditioned **Accommodation:** 14 rooms, all with bath/shower. TV. Phone. B&B £115 to £245. Baby facilities

MAP 2 **Painswick** GLOUCESTERSHIRE

Painswick Hotel

Kemps Lane, Painswick GL6 6YB
Tel: (01452) 812160
Website: www.painswickhotel.com

NEW CHEF | British | £32–£75

A grey-stone village on a steep hillside is the ravishing setting for this solid Palladian mansion. The grounds are relatively pocket-sized for the house, with a steep drop down from the croquet lawn to the narrow lane on which the house is situated. The interiors are done in loosely defined period style, with the extended long dining room all panels and busily patterned fabrics.

Prime meats from pedigree herds, seasonal game from local estates and fish and shellfish from the Cornish ports are the mainstays of the à la carte menus. Former sous-chef Mark Redwood is now heading the kitchen. Start with seared scallops with horseradish noodles and baby beetroot, follow it up with breast of Goosnargh duck with poached kumquat, herb couscous and braised chicory. Finish with something like dark chocolate tart with lavender ice cream. One or two reports suggest that service might be a little more cooperative.

Well-sourced Bordeaux and Burgundy precede a good-value global round-up on the unpretentious wine list, with the likes of Wither Hills Pinot Noir from New Zealand at £25. Six house options from £15 also come by the glass.

Chef: Mark Redwood **Proprietors:** Max and Jane Sabotini and Robert and Pauline Young **Open:** all week 12 to 2, 7 to 9 **Meals:** alc D (main courses £22 to £25). Set L £14 (2 courses) to £17. Light L menu available **Service:** not inc, card slips closed **Cards:** Amex, Delta, MasterCard, Maestro, Visa **Details:** 43 seats. Private parties: 60 main room, 6 to 16 private rooms. Car park. Vegetarian meals. Children's helpings. No smoking. Music. No mobile phones **Accommodation:** 19 rooms, all with bath/shower. TV. Phone. D,B&B £95 to £275

This symbol means that the chef has changed since last year's entry, and the Editor has judged that the change is of sufficient interest to merit the reader's attention.

MAP 5 **Paulerspury** NORTHAMPTONSHIRE

Vine House

100 High Street, Paulerspury NN12 7NA
Tel: (01327) 811267
Website: www.vinehousehotel.com

Cooking 3 | Modern British | £44–£53

This 300-year-old stone cottage and its delightful garden are just half a mile off the A5 south-east of Towcester. The Springetts' restaurant-with-rooms is a very personal set up, with Julie ever present out front and Marcus in the kitchen. Menus are kept short (just three choices per course), and dishes like duck liver pâté with Guinness and shallot jelly and toasted muesli bread, or saddle of venison with parsnip cream and a vanilla and ginger stock sauce, typify their style. Successes have included fillet of Gloucester Old Spot pork with truffle sauce and 'juicy' Goosnargh duck breast with red wine and treacle sauce. Desserts tend to be homely, although goats' cheese sorbet with pine nut and rosemary biscuits and local honey sounds intriguingly different. Old-school French bottles form the backbone the 70-strong wine list; house recommendations are £12.95.

Chef: Marcus Springett **Proprietors:** Marcus and Julie Springett **Open:** Tue to Fri L 12 to 2, Mon to Sat D 7 to 9.30 **Closed:** 1 week at Christmas **Meals:** Set L and D £26.95 (2 courses) to £29.95 **Service:** 12.5% (optional), card slips closed **Cards:** Delta, Maestro, MasterCard, Visa **Details:** 33 seats. Private parties: 33 main room. Car park. No smoking. Wheelchair access (not WC). No music **Accommodation:** 6 rooms, all with bath/shower. TV. Phone. B&B £59 to £85

MAP 5 **Paxford** GLOUCESTERSHIRE

Churchill Arms

Paxford GL55 6XH
Tel: (01386) 594000
Website: www.thechurchillarms.com

Cooking 4 | Modern European | £29–£50

This is a honey-coloured stone inn with a bare-bones interior (rustic floorboards, tables, junk-shop prints and nicotine-stained ceilings) in a Cotswold hamlet. But, thanks to Sonia and Leo Brooke-Little, this is no backwoods watering hole but a strongly rooted enterprise – a combination of pub and serious restaurant. Dishes are detailed on blackboards and orders taken at the bar, meals served on 'posh modern square plates', and the kitchen on the whole follows the path of judicious simplicity and allows ingredients to speak for themselves. One visitor was impressed by 'very tasty, soft-textured' breast of pigeon served with mixed herb salad and aubergine pickle; while chicken breast came with a correctly made butternut risotto, crisp bacon and red pepper sauce. Puddings – such as raspberry and white chocolate iced terrine and pineapple – have met with approval, and service has been a bit more forthcoming and helpful than we reported last year. Wines are listed on a board, too: a short, good-value, global slate opening at £10.50, with quite a few available by the glass and carafe.

Chefs: Sonya Brooke-Little and David Toon **Proprietors:** Sonya and Leo Brooke-Little **Open:** all week 12 to 2, 7 to 9 **Closed:** 25 Dec **Meals:** alc (main courses £8 to £16) **Service:** not inc **Cards:** Delta, Maestro, MasterCard, Visa **Details:** 60 seats. 60 seats outside. Private parties: 30 main room. Vegetarian meals. Children's helpings. No-smoking area. Wheelchair access (not WC). No music **Accommodation:** 4 rooms, all with bath/shower. TV. Phone. B&B £40 to £70

MAP 1 **Penzance** CORNWALL

Abbey Restaurant

Abbey Street, Penzance TR18 4AR
Tel: (01736) 330680
Website: www.theabbeyonline.com

Cooking 4 | Modern European | £35–£63

Abbey Street, steep and cobbled, leads down to the harbour, and the striking modern restaurant and next door blue-painted Abbey Hotel (also run by the Tunnicliffes) certainly stand out once you've found your bearings. Strikingly bold colours are used to good affect in the ground-floor bar, while the first-floor dining room takes from the mellow, natural end of the spectrum.

Ben Tunnicliffe cooks a good-value, set-price two- or three-course lunch and a pricier evening à la carte. His is a modern outlook with local and seasonal materials (Cornish fish is a strong point) helping to give the food its particular identity: pan-fried red mullet with black pudding, butter beans and thyme, or a fillet of turbot for main course, served with new potato, lobster and asparagus salad and roast pepper dressing. Some poor timing and heavy-handed seasoning affected an inspection meal, although the better dishes included a best end of organic lamb with blanquette of sweetbreads, and hot marmalade soufflé with malted chocolate ice cream. Service is 'impressively impeccable', and an enthusiastically annotated wine list affords reasonable choice under £20. House wine is £12.50.

Chef: Ben Tunnicliffe **Proprietors:** Ben and Kinga Tunnicliffe **Open:** Fri and Sat L 12 to 2, Tue to Sat D 7 to 10 **Closed:** Christmas **Meals:** alc D (main courses £12.50 to £21.50). Set L £18 (2 courses) to £23 **Service:** not inc **Cards:** Maestro, MasterCard, Visa **Details:** 30 seats. Private parties: 21 main room. Children 7pm dinner only. No children under 5. No smoking. No music. No mobile phones. Air-conditioned **Accommodation:** 7 rooms, 6 with bath/shower. TV. B&B £60 to £190

Bay Restaurant

NEW ENTRY

Mount Prospect Hotel, Britons Hill, Penzance TR18 3AE
Tel: (01736) 363117
Website: www.bay-penzance.co.uk

Cooking 3 | Modern British | £27–£58

Glorious views over the rooftops to the harbour and Mount's Bay are a feature of this contemporary restaurant-cum-art gallery in a likeable family-run hotel. The food is also worth more than a passing glance, thanks to the arrival of a new kitchen team headed by Ben Reeve (ex-Pickled Fish, St Ives). The menus follow the seasons, and you might open with a carefully judged contemporary combo of lightly pickled sea bass with herby couscous and marinated wild mushrooms. Main courses focus on 'the sea' (local line-caught mackerel with beetroot compote), 'the garden' (sesame-roast tofu with tempura vegetables) and 'the land' (mightily good roast chump of West Country lamb with Cornish Yarg gnocchi, and mint and honey pesto). Desserts maintain the tempo in the shape of warm chocolate truffle pudding with chocolate sauce and clotted cream. The manageable wine list is a decent global selection with house wines from around £12.

Chefs: Ben Reeve, Katie Semmens, Stuart Ball and Virkko Vendla **Proprietors:** Yvonne and Stephen Hill **Open:** all week 11.30 to 2, 6 to 9.30 **Closed:** L Oct to Apr **Meals:** alc (main courses L £7.50 to £9.50, D £13 to £18) **Service:** not inc, card slips closed **Cards:** Amex, Maestro, MasterCard, Visa **Details:** 60 seats. 16 seats outside. Private parties: 100 main room. Car park. Vegetarian meals. Children's helpings. No smoking. Music. No mobile phones. Air-conditioned **Accommodation:** 24 rooms, all with bath/shower. TV. Phone. B&B £65 to £135. Baby facilities. Swimming pool

Harris's

46 New Street, Penzance TR18 2LZ
Tel: (01736) 364408
Website: www.harrissrestaurant.co.uk

Look opposite the Sir Humphry Davy statue if you are heading down the main street towards this long-running Penzance favourite. The Harris family has been in residence here for more than three decades and they continue to serve uncomplicated food based largely on Cornish produce. Fish plays a leading role, with supplies coming from local merchants and beyond: expect anything from Falmouth mussels 'marinière' to line-caught sea bass on crispy leeks with basil pesto. The kitchen also aims for unadorned simplicity on the meat front – as in grilled smoked duck breast on rocket and endive salad, or fillet steak béarnaise. A couple of West Country cheeses are alternatives to desserts like treacle tart. Light lunches are available from Tuesday to Saturday, and eight house wines (from £12.95) open the affordable, well-spread list.

Chef: Roger Harris **Proprietors:** Roger and Anne Harris **Open:** Tue to Sat 12 to 1.45, 7 to 9.30; also Mon D in summer **Closed:** 25 and 26 Dec, 1 Jan, 3 weeks winter **Meals:** alc (main courses £16 to £29.50; L by prior arrangement). Light L menu available **Service:** 10%, card slips closed **Cards:** Amex, Maestro, MasterCard, Visa **Details:** 40 seats. Private parties: 24 main room, 20 to 24 private rooms. No children under 6. No smoking in 1 dining room. Music. No mobile phones

Summer House

Cornwall Terrace, Penzance TR18 4HL
Tel: (01736) 363744
Website: www.summerhouse-cornwall.com

The Zaino family's jolly guesthouse is 'quite insanely Med', from its riotously colourful décor and *trompe l'oeil* antique pediments to the taped Italian opera highlights. Service is infectious and the food draws inspiration from the unadorned dishes Italians cook for themselves, even though menus are written in French with English translations. They 'dare to be spare' in the kitchen, eschewing garnishes and keeping sauces to a minimum. A mound of sliced shiitake mushrooms, garlic and parsley accompanies seared scallops, beef fillet (cooked correctly blue as requested) is pepped up with a little stock-free, red-wine reduction, and brill is flavoured with Mediterranean basil. Simplicity also wins the day with desserts like roasted peppered pineapple and Bacardi sorbet. The all-Italian wine list opens at £14.

Chef: Ciro Zaino **Proprietors:** Ciro and Linda Zaino **Open:** Wed to Sun D only 7.30 to 9 **Closed:** Nov to Feb **Meals:** Set D £26 **Service:** 10%, card slips closed **Cards:** Delta, MasterCard, Maestro, Visa **Details:** 22 seats. 18 seats outside. Private parties: 26 main room. No children under 5. No smoking. Music **Accommodation:** 5 rooms, all with bath/shower. TV. B&B £70 to £95. No children under 13

MAP 5 **Pershore** WORCESTERSHIRE

Belle House

NEW ENTRY

5 Bridge Street, Pershore WR10 1AJ
Tel: (01386) 555055
Website: www.belle-house.co.uk

Cooking 3 | Modern European | £28–£43

Belle House, in a terrace of large old buildings on the main road through town, is 'quite breathtakingly beautiful' inside. Natural colours unite worm-eaten timbers and exuberant plaster mouldings, pale wood floors, square slab tables and wicker chairs with brown leather cushions. The kitchen handles good raw materials with accurate timing and consistency – for example, sparklingly fresh, crisp-skinned black bream with coleslaw, enlivened by a blob of 'intense' potato mayonnaise. The quality and presentation of a rack of lamb 'only just verging on the pink' also impressed; it came with spinach 'outstandingly full of flavour', boulangère potatoes, and 'very sweet and surprisingly strongly flavoured' tomato and basil confit. Similar precision juxtaposed an intense mango sorbet with a 'mild and subtle' tasting lime and coconut parfait. Service is well-informed, friendly and unpretentious, and house wine Pinot Grigio is £11.95 (£2.95 a glass).

Chef/Proprietor: Stephen Waites **Open:** Tue to Sat 12 to 2, 7 to 9.30 **Closed:** 25 and 26 Dec, 1st 2 weeks January **Meals:** Set L £8.50 (1 course) to £18, Set D £19 to £24. Pre-theatre menu available **Service:** not inc, card slips closed **Cards:** Amex, Delta, Diners, Maestro, MasterCard, Visa **Details:** 80 seats. Private parties: 50 main room, 36 private room. Vegetarian meals. Children's helpings. No smoking. Wheelchair access (also WC). Music. Air-conditioned

MAP 2 **Petersfield** HAMPSHIRE

JSW

1 Heath Road, Petersfield GU31 4JE
Tel: (01730) 262030

Cooking 6 | Modern British | £40–£66

Tucked away down a street leading off Petersfield's main square, JSW is a modestly proportioned restaurant filled with light from large windows, with a restrained and stylish design scheme. In the few years since it opened, Jake Watkins has taken it from strength to strength, tellingly enjoying a healthy level of out-of-town custom. As so often, local supplies have proved the making of the kitchen. All the fish is line-caught from boats on the Solent, while most of the meat is either wild or organic and supplied by a butcher in the vicinity. A couple who worked their way through the six-course tasting menu found much to commend, from an exemplary risotto of turbot and girolles to a precision-textured feuillantine of creamy rhubarb. Dishes may appear quite simple in conception, but the level of classical technique brought to bear on them is what dazzles, so that the summary offered by another reporter – 'perfection without fuss' – says it all. Combinations are soundly judged, pairing red mullet with a galette of courgettes, and pork with black pudding and Calvados sauce, and quantities don't overwhelm. The salted caramel mousse with hazelnut praline has become something of a signature dessert.

A separate vegetarian menu is offered, and deft, smiling service adds to the allure. The restaurant has built a remarkable wine cellar with a mix of recent and mature vintages, and sets Alsace and Germany in their rightful place among the classic regions. Italy, Australia and the USA pull out the stops too. Fruity house Australian is £16.50.

Chef/Proprietor: Jake Watkins **Open:** Tue to Sat 12 to 1.30, 7 to 9.30 **Closed:** 2 weeks June, last week Dec, first week Jan **Meals:** Set L £19.50 (2 courses) to £29.50, Set D £29.50 (2 courses) to £39.50 **Service:** not inc **Cards:** Delta, Maestro, MasterCard, Visa **Details:** 22 seats. Private parties: 22 main room. Vegetarian meals. No children under 8. No smoking. No music. No mobile phones

 This symbol means that the restaurant has a truly outstanding wine cellar.

MAP 1 **Peter Tavy** DEVON

Peter Tavy Inn

Peter Tavy PL19 9NN
Tel: (01822) 810348

Cooking 2 | Modern European | £23–£44

Reached down a lane past 'sundry agricultural hazards', this pretty village on the western fringes of Dartmoor feels remote, and its much-extended but down-to-earth fifteenth-century pub really looks the part. Flagged floors and tables of dark-varnished wood are backed up by archetypal beams, winter fires and local ales. Honest pub cooking at reasonable prices is the forte, with menus written on blackboards and food ordered at the bar. Lunch delivers straightforward, classic pub food (from baguettes and ploughman's to steak and Stilton pie), while the kitchen cranks up a gear at dinner: perhaps a robust version of duck liver pâté with apricot brandy, followed by monkfish with smoked garlic, or whole black bream stuffed with prawns, then coconut and lime tart. The short, equally affordable wine list kicks off with eight house selections from £9.25.

Chef: Chrissy Kilfedder **Proprietors:** Graeme and Karen Sim **Open:** all week 12 to 2, 6.30 to 9 **Closed:** D 24 Dec, 25 Dec, D 26 and 31 Dec **Meals:** alc (main courses £7 to £16) **Service:** not inc, card slips closed **Cards:** Delta, Maestro, MasterCard, Visa **Details:** 70 seats. 100 seats outside. Private parties: 45 main room. Car park. Vegetarian meals. Children's helpings. No smoking in 1 dining room. Music

MAP 7 **Pinchinthorpe** REDCAR & CLEVELAND

Brewhouse Bistro

AR

Pinchinthorpe Hall, Pinchinthorpe, nr Guisborough TS14 8HG
Tel: (01287) 630200

Part of a forward-looking venture that includes a microbrewery, restaurant, and organic kitchen garden built around a seventeenth-century manor (with accommodation). Home-reared Dexter beef has its own mini-menu (fillet steak with oxtail stockpot, for instance; £18), but the repertoire extends to breast of wood pigeon with roast garlic, beetroot and red onion salad (£6.50), and North Sea halibut with mustard lentils, capers and beurre rouge (£15) before desserts like warm pecan toffee pie with honeycomb ice cream (£4.50). Well-chosen wines from £12.50. Open all week.

MAP 5 **Plumtree** NOTTINGHAMSHIRE

Perkins

Station House, Station Road, Plumtree
NG12 5NA
Tel: (0115) 937 3695
Website: www.perkinsrestaurant.co.uk

Cooking 2 | Modern British/French | £24–£49

Off the A606 just south of Nottingham the Perkins's friendly restaurant, once a railway station, has been commended for its 'lovely ambience' and 'exceptionally considerate and helpful' staff. As well as its own herb garden, it now also boasts a smokehouse for cold-smoking meat and fish. The monthly-changing carte might offer seared tuna on ratatouille, followed by local beef sirloin with red chilli pesto, or breaded lamb noisettes in a sauce of tomatoes, bacon and rosemary; end maybe with black cherry crème brûlée with almond biscuits. The set menus change weekly, and fine-value weekday lunches (perm two courses from the three on the menu) deal in homely simplicities such as rosemary and onion cream soup and pastry-lidded fish ragout, finishing with the likes of strawberry and raspberry pavlova; the three-course Sunday lunch always includes roast beef. Wines from a short list start at £11.75, and there's plenty of choice under £20.

Chef: Marco Smeeth **Proprietors:** Tony, Wendy, Jonathan and David Perkins **Open:** Tue to Sun L 12 to 2 (2.30 Sun), Tue to Sat D 6.45 to 9.45 **Meals:** alc (not Sun L; main courses £9.50 to £14.50). Set L Tue to Sat £9.75 (2 courses), set L Sun £13.50 (2 courses) to £16.95, Set D Tue to Thur £19.50 **Service:** not inc **Cards:** Amex, Delta, Maestro, MasterCard, Visa **Details:** 73 seats. 24 seats outside. Private parties: 12 main room, 32 private room. Car park. Vegetarian meals. No smoking in 1 dining room. Wheelchair access (not WC). Occasional music. Air-conditioned

To submit a report on any restaurant, please visit *www.which.co.uk/gfgfeedback*.

MAP 1 **Plymouth** DEVON

Tanners

Prysten House, Finewell Street,
Plymouth PL1 2AE
Tel: (01752) 252001
Website: www.tannersrestaurant.co.uk

Cooking 4 | Modern British | £26–£58

Inside this fifteenth-century grey-stone pile, Plymouth's oldest domestic building, ceilings as beamed as you would expect set off slate floors and bare stone walls, and there's even a well in one of the two dining rooms.

Sourcing as much as they can locally, the Tanner brothers cook in a relatively straightforward style, with no needless gilding of lilies. Red mullet terrine comes with a salad of chargrilled romaine leaves, or you might start a little more substantially with a quail, stuffed with apricots and thyme, further texture being provided by crisp-cooked pancetta. But simplicity does not preclude culinary exertion, so a mini shepherd's pie and gratin of kohlrabi night be the partners for roast loin of lamb, while monkfish might be parcelled in ham and served with ink risotto and a sauce of red-wine-boosted pan juices. Cheeses from the West Country share a plate with French examples, or you might pick pear mousse with caramel sauce and a tuile. House wines from France, Chile and Australia, all £12.95 (£3.50 for a glass), head a list that is arranged stylistically and priced fairly.

Chef/Proprietors: Christopher and James Tanner **Open:** Mon to Sat 12 to 2.30, 7 to 9.30 **Closed:** 25 and 26 Dec, 1 Jan **Meals:** Set L £12.50 (2 courses) to £15, Set D £24 (2 courses) to £35 **Service:** not inc **Cards:** Amex, Delta, Maestro, MasterCard, Visa **Details:** 45 seats. 50 seats outside. Private parties: 30 main room, 24 private room. Vegetarian meals. Children's helpings. No smoking. Wheelchair access (also WC). Music

MAP 10 **Ponteland** NORTHUMBERLAND

Café 21

33–35 The Broadway, Darras Hall, Ponteland
NE20 9PW
Tel: (01661) 820357

Cooking 4 | Modern British | £24–£58

This popular bistro has settled into its own particular niche – when a place works this well, that's no

bad thing. And yet (although you wouldn't really notice it) Terry Laybourne sold Café 21 to his head chef of five years, Ian Lowrey, in March 2005. Reassuringly, inspection demonstrates that little has actually changed. The 'very bistro-like' interior captures the French spirit, with white paper protecting white tablecloths, simple dark wood chairs, and red quarry-tiled floors, and daily changing menus chalked on a board show the cooking aims for a broad appeal. Start with 'wonderful' crab and mango spring rolls with well-balanced sweet chilli mayonnaise, and follow with fresh halibut, simply grilled and served with a well-made tartare sauce, a bowl of 'delicious, thin' French fries and a quenelle of mushy peas, or maybe crisp, confit duck with mustard mash, fine beans, thyme and rosemary. Desserts include caramelized pineapple with coconut sorbet and chilli syrup – a hit at inspection – alongside such classics as treacle tart. Service is described as 'fabulous', and the global wine list is modest in both length and price; house wine is £12.

Chef: Ian Lowrey **Proprietors:** Ian and Susan Lowrey **Open:** Sat L 12 to 2, Mon to Sat D 5.30 (6 Sat) to 10 **Closed:** bank hols **Meals:** alc (main courses £9.50 to £19.50). Set L £12 (2 courses) to £14, Set D Mon to Fri 5.30 to 7 £12 to £14 **Service:** not inc **Cards:** Amex, Delta, Diners, Maestro, MasterCard, Visa **Details:** 68 seats. Private parties: 50 main room. Car park. Vegetarian meals. Children's helpings. No-smoking area. Wheelchair access (also WC). Music

MAP 2 **Poole** DORSET

Mansion House

Thames Street, Poole BH15 1JN
Tel: (01202) 685666
Website: www.themansionhouse.co.uk

Cooking 3 | Modern British-Plus | £28–£48

In contrast to the populist bustle of nearby Poole Quay, this Georgian townhouse exudes a graciously traditional elegance with its pillared porch, creeper-clothed exterior and civilised trappings; the mood in the cherrywood-panelled dining room can often seem as cosy as a gentlemen's club. The kitchen makes good use of carefully sourced ingredients including local meat, game and seafood garnered from Dorset, Cornwall and beyond. Reporters have been pleased with the results: one enjoyable dinner began with pan-fried scallops, mustard mash and parsley velouté before fillet of halibut with cockles and leeks. Other options might be sesame-grilled rabbit tart with mushrooms, and roast rack of Dorset lamb with a braised lamb shank shepherd's pie, followed by tropical nougat glace with pineapple sorbet and passion fruit. Lighter meals are served in the bistro. A well-conceived wine list pours plenty of good-value options into loose style categories, topped and tailed by an engaging house selection from £12.95 and a sane collection of fine wines.

Chef: Gerry Godden **Proprietors:** Jackie and Gerry Godden **Open:** Sun to Fri L 12 to 2, Mon to Sat D 7 to 9.30 (open bank hols for Sun D) **Meals:** Set L £17.50 (2 courses) to £19.25, Set D £21.95 (2 courses) to £27.45. Bistro menu available **Service:** not inc **Cards:** Amex, Delta, Diners, Maestro, MasterCard, Visa **Details:** 85 seats. Private parties: 100 main room, 14 to 36 private rooms. Car park. Vegetarian meals. Children's helpings. Under-5s must eat at 7pm at D. No smoking. Occasional music. Air-conditioned **Accommodation:** 32 rooms, all with bath/shower. TV. Phone. B&B £75 to £145. Baby facilities

MAP 1 **Porlock Weir** SOMERSET

Andrews on the Weir

Porlock Weir TA24 8PB
Tel: (01643) 863300
Website: www.andrewsontheweir.co.uk

Cooking 4 | Modern European | £29–£63

Andrew Dixon's restaurant-with-rooms is to be found where the B-road peters out by Porlock Bay. It's a sprawling Victorian villa with a pair of dining rooms done in gold and terracotta, with some diverting, specially commissioned photographs worth a gander. The kitchen is justly proud of the provenance of its materials, as is evident from the menu descriptions: braised Devon Ruby oxtail with creamed parsnips and roast squash; Minehead cod on Jerusalem artichoke risotto; slow-roast Somerset pork on sage and onion potatoes with black pudding ravioli, seared foie gras, caramelized apple and madeira jus. In the same spirit, an inspection opened with Withycombe asparagus, served with Lynmouth Bay lobster and avocado and potato salad. Uneven seasoning has been reported, including in a serving of Exmoor lamb noisette and black olive couscous (with fine aubergine purée and roast garlic), but things ended on an unambiguous high note with roast pineapple complemented by a forthright rum and vanilla caramel plus coconut ice cream. Service is by a large, well-informed team. House wines from Chile and Spain start at £14, and there's good Sancerre by Serge Laporte at £26.25.

Chef: Andrew Dixon **Proprietors:** Andrew Dixon and Rodney Sens **Open:** Wed to Sun 12 to 2.30, 6.30 to 9.30 **Meals:** Set L £12.50 (2 courses) to £15.50, Set D £28 (2 courses) to £35 **Service:** not inc, 10% for parties of 7 or more **Cards:** Delta, Maestro, MasterCard, Visa **Details:** 40 seats. Private parties: 40 main room, 20 to 25 private rooms. Car park. Vegetarian meals. Children's helpings. No children under 12. No smoking. Wheelchair access (not WC). Music **Accommodation:** 5 rooms, all with bath/shower. TV. B&B £70 to £160.

MAP 1 Porthleven CORNWALL

Critchards AR

Harbour Head, Porthleven TR13 9JA
Tel: (01326) 562407

Harbour-side seafood restaurant in a former mill, almost spoiled for choice by supplies fresh from St Ives, Newlyn and Porthleven itself. The Critchards take a global perspective, producing perhaps monkfish and prawn curry (£17), Thai-style pan-fried fillets of red gurnard, and crab, rocket and mango tempura (£15), as well as grilled lobster. There's always a meat dish too. Start with salmon ceviche (£7) and save space for desserts like lime and mascarpone cheesecake (£5). Mostly white wines from £13.95. Accommodation. Open Mon to Sat and occasional Sun D only.

MAP 1 Portscatho CORNWALL

Driftwood

Rosevine, nr Portscatho TR2 5EW
Tel: (01872) 580644
Website: www.driftwoodhotel.co.uk

Cooking 5 | Modern European | £49–£59

The Robinsons' elegantly appointed hotel sits high up in a Cornish village overlooking the sea, the expansive windows in the dining room emphasising the serenity of the view. Crisp white cloths and white-jacketed staff establish a light and airy ambience, and the modern pan-European cooking makes the most of local produce, with fish and seafood naturally showing up strongly. Lobster and fruits de mer platters can be ordered at a supplement a day in advance. A first-course tian composed of skate, shredded crab, tomato and avocado offers plenty of food for thought in itself, and might be succeeded – if you're ploughing the marine furrow – by sea bass, served with dill purée and a vinaigrette containing both smoked eel and lobster. Otherwise, consider roast foie gras, fashionably set about with beetroot, walnuts and a ginger and port jus, followed up by a main-course fricassee of pig's trotter with butter beans and morels.

Piquant flavour combinations are also at work in desserts such as rhubarb mousse with ginger savarin and orange sauce, or lime pannacotta with roasted mango and mango purée. The imaginative short wine list gives a fair shake of the stick to the southern-hemisphere countries as well as France, with prices starting at £13.

Chef: Rory Duncan **Proprietors:** Paul and Fiona Robinson **Open:** all week D only 7 to 9.30 **Closed:** mid-Dec to early Feb, except New Year **Meals:** Set D £36 **Service:** not inc, card slips closed **Cards:** Amex, Maestro, MasterCard, Visa **Details:** 40 seats. Car park. No babies in restaurant. No smoking. Music. No mobile phones **Accommodation:** 15 rooms, all with bath/shower. TV. Phone. B&B £112.50 to £200. Baby facilities. Swimming pool. Fishing

MAP 7 Poulton GLOUCESTERSHIRE

Falcon Inn

London Road, Poulton GL7 5HN
Tel: (01285) 850844
Website: www.thefalconpoulton.co.uk

Cooking 5 | European | £30–£56

The Falcon is in tiptop condition at the moment. It still lives up to its title as a freehouse, dispensing real ales and pub hospitality, but elsewhere it puts on a visibly stylish show for customers in search of food. Clever lighting, classy posies and artistic greenery create an upmarket impression, and the menus change every few weeks for maximum appeal. Raw materials are consistently good, and the kitchen shows off its prowess with confidence: scallops are perfectly timed and served with pea purée, crispy prosciutto and mint vinaigrette; soft, supple Gressingham duck breast comes with an unusual celeriac and plum tart and a highly sophisticated thyme-scented jus, and someone clearly has a real talent for making bread and pastry. Meals finish strongly with the 'wobbliest ever' vanilla pannacotta (accompanied by spiced oranges and home-made shortbread biscuits), or white chocolate parfait with honey-baked figs. Around 50 well-spread wines offer the prospect of interesting drinking at very bearable prices, house selections starting at £11.95.

Chefs: Jeremy Lockley, Will Abraham and Oliver Bellamy **Proprietor:** Jeremy Lockley **Open:** all week 12 to 2.30, 7 to 9 **Meals:** alc (main courses £10 to £16.50). Set L Sun £15 (2 courses) to £20 **Service:** not inc **Cards:** Delta, Maestro, MasterCard, Visa **Details:** 60 seats. Private parties: 30 main room, 8 to 15 private rooms. Car park. Vegetarian meals. Children's helpings. No smoking. Wheelchair access (also WC). Music

MAP 7 **Prestbury** CHESHIRE

White House

The Village, Prestbury SK10 4DG
Tel: (01625) 829376
Website: www.thewhitehouse.uk.com

Cooking 4 | Modern British | £30–£67

The original incumbents of this eighteenth-century farmhouse would hardly recognise the place these days: classy décor and a refined, luxurious atmosphere typify the intimate dining room and adjoining conservatory, and the food suits its slightly posh surroundings. The kitchen subjects sound British ingredients to modern European treatments, as in dishes like Cumbrian fell-bred beef fillet with frites, roast tomatoes, asparagus and balsamic glaze, or saddle of roe deer with venison sausage, coriander and apple. Fish is also well represented by, say, seared scallops with oriental tomato fondue and courgette fritters, or grilled Dover sole with dill and pink peppercorn butter. A tasting of miniature 'British' desserts is one option for afters; otherwise expect anything from caramel peach mascarpone torte with orange tuile to warm soft-centre chocolate fondant with cherry ice cream. 'Simply Rylands' fixed-price menus are fine value for two or three courses. The wine list is accessible and varied, with house wines from £14.25.

Chefs: Ryland Wakeham and Richard Clark **Proprietors:** Ryland and Judith Wakeham **Open:** Tue to Sun L 12 to 2, Mon to Sat D 7 to 10 **Closed:** 25 Dec **Meals:** alc (not Sun L; main courses £12 to £19.50). Set L £16.95 to £18.70, Set D Mon to Fri £15.95 (2 courses) to £21.45 **Service:** not inc **Cards:** Amex, MasterCard, Maestro, Visa **Details:** 75 seats. 12 seats outside. Private parties: 15 main room, 15 to 42 private rooms. Car park. Vegetarian meals. Children's helpings. No smoking before 2pm L and 10pm D. Wheelchair access (not WC). Music. No mobile phones **Accommodation:** 11 rooms, all with bath/shower. TV. Phone. Room only £40 to £130. No children under 10

MAP8 **Preston** LANCASHIRE

Winckley Square Chop House

23 Winckley Square, Preston PR1 3JJ
Tel: (01772) 252732
Website: www.heathcotes.co.uk

Cooking 3 | Modern British | £27–£66

The premises formerly known as Simply Heathcotes have been reborn as a two-pronged set-up, with the Olive Press in the basement and the Chop House on the ground floor. It looks set to become an asset to Preston's business district, with its contemporary décor (including an open kitchen at one end) and bullish Brit-inspired food. Paul Heathcote's much-lauded support of regional produce still defines the menu in the shape of his renowned black pudding, savoury pies and boiled Bowland ham (with farmhouse Lancashire cheese and piccalilli), augmented by Southport shrimps, Goosnargh duck, and dishes like chargrilled lamb fillets in a goats' cheese crust with balsamic onions. To finish, chocolate pot comes with one of the 'crispiest' rings of shortbread ever, or try Heathcote's signature bread-and-butter pudding with clotted cream and apricots. A jazzy modern wine list opens with house recommendations at £13.95.

Chef: Tom Lowe **Proprietor:** Paul Heathcote **Open:** all week 12 to 2.30, 6 to 10 (11 Sat) **Closed:** 25 Dec, bank hol Mon **Meals:** alc (main courses £7 to £22). Bar menu available 2.30 to 6 **Service:** not inc, 10% for parties of 8 or more **Cards:** Amex, Delta, Diners, Maestro, MasterCard, Visa **Details:** 95 seats. Private parties: 95 main room. Vegetarian meals. Children's helpings. No smoking. Wheelchair access (also WC). Occasional music. Air-conditioned

MAP 8 **Ramsbottom** GREATER MANCHESTER

Ramsons

18 Market Place, Ramsbottom BL0 9HT
Tel: (01706) 825070
Website: www.ramsons.org.uk

Cooking 4 | Italian | £29–£73

This year's entry reflects a time of change in the affairs of Chris Johnson as he adjusts his business to different times and local tastes – by the autumn of 2005 he will effectively be operating two restaurants. The old cellar café The Hideaway has been refurbished with restaurant tables and place settings from Ramsons, and will offer Tamaron Byrne's Tasting Menu at £20, while Ramsons itself will deal solely in fine dining, and to that end has been upgraded with four bespoke dining tables hand-carved from reclaimed pitch pine beams, new crockery, silverware, placemats and napkins. In Ransoms, Abdulla Naseem and Amy Bicknell continue to interpret Chris's passion for Italian cooking and prime raw materials – vegetables and dairy products are organic, meat bought from trusted local farms – alongside other, more broadly European influences. Besides appreciating the thoughtful, attentive and carefully paced service, highlights of an inspection meal were a delicate lobster bisque with lobster ravioli and saffron infusion, poached Sicilian artichoke with Amalfi lemon butter, and mains of grilled turbot with poached langoustine and roast red pepper fondant, and flashed fillet of beef with roast Jerusalem artichoke and champagne sauce. Among desserts, warm pecan pie with cardamom and ginger ice cream stood out.

Wines are all Italian, starting from £14.50 (with cheaper options in the Hideaway), and are pithily summarised in note form on the opening pages of the list before it launches into detailed descriptions. Chris Johnson himself is the best source of guidance as he hand-picks every bin and 'would fall on his sword before serving anything that did not come up to scratch'.

Chefs: Abdulla Naseem and Amy Bicknell **Proprietors:** Ros Hunter and Chris Johnson **Open:** Wed to Sun L 12 to 2.30 (1 to 3.30 Sun), Wed to Sat D 7 to 9.30 wed to sat. Hideaway Wed to Sat D only. **Meals:** alc (main courses £9.50 to £27.50). Set L £18 to £39.50. Set L Sun £20 to £25. Set D £39.50. Snack L menu available weekdays **Service:** not inc, card slips closed **Cards:** Delta, MasterCard, Maestro, Visa **Details:** 32 seats. Vegetarian meals. No smoking. Occasional music. No mobile phones

MAP 3 Ramsgate KENT

Surin AR

30 Harbour Street, Ramsgate CT11 8HA
Tel: (01843) 592001

Mrs Damrong is the life and soul of this modest Thai restaurant a stone's throw from the harbour. Her extensive menu covers all the staples, from fishcakes (£4.50) and Mussamun beef tamarind curry (£7) to stir-fries and noodles. Seafood specials such as Dover sole with asparagus or steamed sea bass with lime and chillies (£13) are worth noting. Don't miss the locally brewed 'Surin' Thai-style beer; house wines from £10.95. Open Tue to Sat L, Mon to Sat D.

MAP 8 Ramsgill NORTH YORKSHIRE

Yorke Arms

Ramsgill HG3 5RL
Tel: (01423) 755243
Website: www.yorke-arms.co.uk

Cooking 6 | Modern European | £35–£132

Nidderdale is a designated Area of Outstanding Natural Beauty, much beloved of television programme-makers. At the centre of this tiny village, all built of rough grey stone, is the creeper-clad Yorke Arms. An agreeable feeling of pastoral prosperity characterises the traditional English interiors, and the dining room is dominated by a majestically proportioned mirror. Daily specials and a tasting menu supplement the seasonally changing carte, with much in the way of local produce in evidence. Frances Atkins's style is a mixture of the homely and the highfalutin, striving to marry simplicity and originality within the modern European framework. An inspector's main-course fillet of wild Lune salmon came with a bouquet of wild mushrooms, samphire, herbed rösti, and rather full-on lemon relish as well as two separate sauces, leaving the simplicity principle some way behind, but the materials were good. Local mutton should be worth a look, when available, perhaps cooked en blanquette with cider, black pudding, roast roots and fondant potato.

British cheeses with home-made biscuits are one way to finish, if the sweeter likes of plum clafoutis with marzipan ice cream don't tempt. Service is adept at disguising its essential formality with a relaxed attitude. France is the focus of the well-chosen wine list, with the New World also given due consideration. Prices start at £15.

Chef: Frances Atkins **Proprietors:** Bill and Frances Atkins **Open:** all week L 12 to 2, Mon to Sat D 7 to 9 (residents only Sun D) **Meals:** alc (main courses £17.50 to £24). Set L Mon to Sat £17.50 (2 courses) to £21, Set L Sun £29, Set D £70 to £100 (inc wine). Bar menu available Mon to Sat L, Mon to Thur D **Service:** not inc **Cards:** Amex, Delta, Diners, Maestro, MasterCard, Visa **Details:** 60 seats. 20 seats outside. Private parties: 20 main room, 2 to 20 private rooms. Car park. Vegetarian meals. No children under 12. No smoking. Wheelchair access (not WC). Music. No mobile phones **Accommodation:** 14 rooms, all with bath/shower. TV. Phone. D,B&B £120 to £380. No children under 12

MAP 7 **Reading** BERKSHIRE

London Street Brasserie

2–4 London Street, Reading RG1 4SE
Tel: (01189) 505036
Website: www.londonstbrasserie.co.uk

Cooking 2 | Modern European | £30–£63

'A bit of a find in Reading', enthused one Berkshire reporter after visiting this personable town-centre brasserie overlooking the River Kennet. The original eighteenth-century tollhouse has been given a fresh, contemporary look, with an eclectic modern menu to match. Meat and poultry from the owner's farm show up in, say, grilled Gloucester Old Spot pork cutlet with creamed leeks and roast apple chutney, or roast rump of lamb with a basil and red-wine jus. Fish also gets a fair outing: fillets of red mullet, John Dory and red snapper with steamed vegetable ribbons, sautéed cockles, broad beans and peas, for example. Oysters and caviar have their say, and British cheeses rub shoulders with desserts like hot caramel soufflé. 'Brilliant, attentive' service is a bonus, and the good-value wine list offers interesting drinking from £13.50.

Chef: Paul Brotherton **Proprietor:** Paul Clerehugh **Open:** all week 12 to 11 **Meals:** alc L 12 to 3 and D 6.30 to 11 (main courses £12 to £20). Set L and D 12 to 7 £13.50 (2 courses) **Service:** not inc, 10% for parties of 6 or more **Cards:** Amex, Delta, Diners, MasterCard, Maestro, Visa **Details:** 70 seats. 20 seats outside. Private parties: 70 main room, 20 to 40 private rooms. Vegetarian meals. No cigars/pipes in dining room. Wheelchair access (also WC). Music. No mobile phones

MAP 3 **Reigate** SURREY

Dining Room

59A High Street, Reigate RH2 9AE
Tel: (01737) 226650
Website: www.tonytobinrestaurants.co.uk

Cooking 3 | Modern British | £35–£77

Tony Tobin's smart, cosmopolitan restaurant is in the thick of the action on Reigate's High Street, the interior done in calming hues with modern paintings on the walls. The fixed-price menu deals in contemporary brasserie-style cooking, offering main courses such as roast duck breast with chorizo risotto, or seared red bream with pak choi, vegetables stir-fried in sesame oil and sweet chilli syrup, indicating the twin Mediterranean and pan-Asian focal points. These might be flanked by a comforting opener like smoked haddock vichyssoise with a soft-poached egg, and a crowd-pulling dessert such as apple frangipane tart with Calvados cream. Extra vegetables are charged separately, and if only the regular service failings could be ironed out dining here would add up to a thoroughly happy experience. An up-to-date wine list is arranged by style, with a 'library' listing of older bottles for the high rollers. Chilean house wines in four varieties are £16.95 (£4.50 a glass).

Chef/Proprietor: Tony Tobin **Open:** Sun to Fri L 12 to 2, Mon to Sat D 7 to 10 **Closed:** Christmas, Easter Sun, bank hols **Meals:** Set L Mon to Fri £19.50, Set L Sun £28.50 (3 courses), Set D Mon to Fri £28.50 (2 courses) to £36.45, Set D Sat £34 (2 courses) to £41.95. Bar menu available **Service:** 12.5% (optional), card slips closed **Cards:** Amex, Delta, Maestro, MasterCard, Visa **Details:** 78 seats. Private parties: 50 main room, 28 private room. Vegetarian meals. Children's helpings. No smoking. Music. Air-conditioned

MAP 3 **Richmond** SURREY

Burnt Chair

5 Duke Street, Richmond TW9 1HP
Tel: (020) 8940 9488
Website: www.burntchair.com

Cooking 3 | Global | £38–£65

Weenson Oo continues to tread the same global fusion path he set out on in 1991 and the kitchen pitches its efforts appropriately, rounding up Eastern and Western flavours and influences. Multiple flavours are generally handled with assurance, turning out baked, spiced coconut butterfish with crisp-fried shallots and wilted greens, and a dish of glazed loin of pork teamed with risotto cake, papaya and sweet pepper salsa. Trenette with broad beans, rocket and pesto is a good start, black pepper and garlic prawns with seared chicken livers and balsamic is a slightly more unexpected first-course proposition. For dessert try coconut bavarois with pineapple chutney or roast apricots and lemon mascarpone. Being handy for Richmond Theatre, pre-performance two-course set dinners are speedily delivered. The wine selection espouses California with a passion from the £14.75 house wine upwards. Ace producers like Ramey, Cline and Ridge abound and ten come by the glass.

Chef: John Barry **Proprietor:** Weenson Andrew Oo **Open:** Tue to Sat D only 6 to 11 **Closed:** 2 weeks at Christmas **Meals:** alc (main courses £12.50 to £19.50). Set D £15 to £20. Cover £1 **Service:** not inc **Cards:** Delta, Maestro, MasterCard, Visa **Details:** 31 seats. Private parties: 36 main room. Vegetarian meals. Children's helpings. No smoking. Music **Tube:** Richmond

Chez Lindsay

AR

11 Hill Rise, Richmond TW10 6UQ
Tel: (020) 8948 7473

Lindsay Wotton's passion for all things Breton shows no sign of waning in her well-established Richmond rendezvous. Top billing goes to organic galettes (£3 to £9) with fillings from cheese and onions to smoked salmon with lemon and chive cream. Also expect plenty of seafood (for example, feuilleté of scallops, leeks and cider butter sauce; £14.75), meat options like steak, plus sweet crêpes (from £3). Fixed-price lunches (£14.50/£17.50) and a cut-price 'petit menu du midi' (£6.50). Gallic wines (from £12), beers and ciders. Open all week.

Restaurant at the Petersham

NEW ENTRY

Petersham Hotel, Nightingale Lane, Richmond TW10 6UZ
Tel: (020) 8939 1084
Website: www.petershamhotel.co.uk

Cooking 4 | Anglo-French | £37–£76

With bucolic views of fields, trees and the river Thames, this is about as tranquil a setting as one could wish for so close to London: enjoy it with a drink on the terrace in fine weather. The hotel restaurant is a welcoming place with comfortable furnishings and courteous, efficient staff. All this inspires confidence, bolstered by a well-structured menu, and confirmed by the first arrivals: seared scallops and boudin noir with cauliflower and celeriac, and grilled red mullet with sardine ravioli and garden-pea risotto.

For one inspector, this was ample proof that the arrival of Alex Bentley from the now defunct Monsieur Max in Hampton Hill has raised the standard of the cooking greatly. Mr Bentley has ensured a line of continuity with the trademark country-house cooking, applying quietly confident techniques to sophisticated but unshowy dishes. Main dishes are in the same vein, notably pot-roasted saddle of venison set on top of a pile of red cabbage, accompanied by a parcel of spicy stuffed cabbage and surrounded by red-wine sauce. Recommended puddings have included a rich chocolate moelleux with caramelised bananas, served with vanilla ice cream. France dominates the wine list, which runs from £18.50 for house basics to world-famous bottles, with about eight by the glass.

Chef: Alex Bentley **Proprietor:** Colin Dare **Open:** all week 12.15 to 2.15, 7 to 9.45 **Closed:** 25 and 26 Dec, 1 Jan **Meals:** alc (main courses £12 to £24). Set L Mon to Sat £16.50 (2 courses) to £22 **Service:** 10% (optional), card slips closed **Cards:** Amex, Delta, Diners, MasterCard, Maestro, Visa **Details:** 70 seats. Private parties: 70 main room, 16 to 26 private rooms. Car park. Vegetarian meals. Children's helpings. Wheelchair access (also WC). Music. No mobile phones. Air-conditioned **Accommodation:** 61 rooms, all with bath/shower. TV. Phone. B&B £135 to £235. Rooms for disabled. Baby facilities

MAP 9 **Ridgeway** DERBYSHIRE

Old Vicarage

Ridgeway Moor, Ridgeway S12 3XW
Tel: (0114) 247 5814
Website: www.theoldvicarage.co.uk

Cooking 7 | Modern British-Plus | £39–£81

It may be only just outside Sheffield, but the rustic setting includes a wild flower meadow and a wooded walk in the grounds of the rather grand old vicarage, which is 'impressive as ever' without being intimidating. Service from impeccably well-trained staff is knowledgeable and pleasant, and in the kitchen Tessa Bramley with stately authority continues to cook creatively and confidently, with a strong sense of direction and purpose. Sourcing and timing are both admirable, and combinations well considered, whether a casserole of crayfish and scallops infused with cardamom, cumin and lemon grass, or a main-course lime and ginger roasted guinea fowl with pommes Anna and saffron-braised fennel.

Dishes make a strong visual impact – baked brill fillet served with roast butternut squash, Chinese greens, candied pecans with rhubarb and star anise sauce, for instance – and classic flavour combinations are implemented with assurance. Calf's liver, partnered with foie gras, onion marmalade, bitter Seville oranges and bacon piroshki, has impressed with its interplay of sweet, livery richness and the fruit's tart acidity. A light touch and pinpoint timing have made the most of sea bass set on a galette of Jersey Royals and allied with a salad of dressed Whitby crab, mango, peas and asparagus, plus a minted pea and Muscat sauce of 'utter brilliance'. If the approach seems elaborate at times, it is not bravura for its own sake. Vicarage garden sweet woodruff ice cream (with crispy hazelnut wafer and old English raspberry sherry trifle) blends flavours of the countryside, and one reporter's tasting plate on the theme of chocolate/mocha/coffee was 'as brilliant as ever'. Meals are supported by good breads, carefully sourced and well-kept British cheeses and exemplary petits fours.

The wine list now has real stature: strong all the way from basic gluggers to a large collection of mature European classics. New is a line up of 24 wines under £20, all available by the glass. The main list is arranged by style and leans towards France, but has many international stars, particularly in Syrah and other powerful reds. Praise has been showered on a sommelier with 'real passion for the subject'.

Chefs: Tessa Bramley and Nathan Smith **Proprietor:** Tessa Bramley **Open:** Tue to Fri L 12.30 to 2.30, Tue to Sat D 6.45 (6.30 Sat) to 9.45 **Closed:** 26 Dec, 31 Dec to 7 Jan, bank hols **Meals:** Set L £25 to £49, Set D £49 **Service:** not inc, card slips closed **Cards:** Delta, Maestro, MasterCard, Visa **Details:** 46 seats. 16 seats outside. Private parties: 50 main room, 10 to 20 private rooms. Car park. Vegetarian meals. Children's helpings. No smoking. Wheelchair access (also WC). Occasional music. No mobile phones

MAP 9 **Ripley** NORTH YORKSHIRE

Boar's Head

Ripley HG3 3AY
Tel: (01423) 771888
Website: www.boarsheadripley.co.uk

Cooking 3 | Modern British | £29–£57

Pretty stone villages may be two a penny in this neck of the woods but Ripley stands out as a 'model estate village', rebuilt from scratch in the 1830s by the hereditary landlords – the Ingilby family, whose duties today include overseeing the menus and wine list at the Boar's Head. Cooking is essentially modern British – think grilled John Dory with braised endives and red-wine emulsion – but peripherals, such as the Balmoral sauce accompanying beef fillet and oxtail mash, not to mention the décor, remind the casual diner of the owners' blue-blooded credentials. Lamb shank and spring-onion tartlet with rarebit crust was the best starter at inspection. Elaborate presentations have included carved spuds shaped like mushrooms, and desserts are such as chocolate-dipped cherries on rum-and-raisin sabayon. Lord Ingilby has spent his time well, accumulating a decent, eclectic range of bottles for the wine list. Prices are fair, starting at £3 for a glass of Chilean Sauvignon.

Chef: Marc Guibert **Proprietors:** Sir Thomas and Lady Emma Ingilby **Open:** all week 12 to 2, 7 to 9.30 **Meals:** alc bistro (main courses L £12 to £15, D £12 to £20). Restaurant: Set L £15 (2 courses) to £19, Set D £32 to £36 **Service:** not inc **Cards:** Amex, Delta, Diners, MasterCard, Maestro, Visa **Details:** 46 seats. Private parties: 46 main room. Car park. Vegetarian meals. Children's helpings. No smoking. Wheelchair access (also WC). Music **Accommodation:** 25 rooms, all with bath/shower. TV. Phone. B&B £105 to £150. Rooms for disabled. Baby facilities. Fishing

MAP 3 **Ripley** SURREY

Drake's Restaurant

The Clock House, High Street, Ripley GU23 6AQ
Tel: (01483) 224777
Website: www.drakesrestaurant.co.uk

Cooking 6 | Modern French | £36–£74

An expansive common is the centrepiece of this attractive Surrey village. It isn't easy to miss the solid Georgian edifice that houses Drake's, with its pillared entrance flanked by stone urns, and the majestic clock. An aperitif on the terrace on a balmy evening is a good way to start; the garden stretches away before you, and the seats are mighty comfortable.

Steve Drake favours a modern French emphasis, although the materials are among the best our own islands can offer, with lamb and beef sourced locally, fish from Brixham, and venison from the Scottish Highlands. Finely judged lightness makes for good lunches, as was attested by the reporter who got through 'very flavoursome' salmon terrine interleaved with herbs, baked turbot on a bed of chicory and pea purée in a rich, fruity red wine sauce, and a dessert of coffee bavarois with apricot sorbet and marinated figs, all good, strong, well-balanced flavours. Others have found the balance lacking on occasion. Lamb cooked two ways – roast saddle and slow-braised fillet – presented fine meat, which was rather put in the shade by an overly assertive sauce containing chopped olives. Well-reported desserts have included banana parfait rolled in praline served with pineapple sorbet, and raspberry custard tart with raspberry sorbet. Eight wines by the glass, from £4, introduce a list that does France in thorough detail before heading off elsewhere. Prices are mostly fair.

Chef: Steve Drake **Proprietors:** Steve and Serina Drake **Open:** Tue to Fri L 12 to 1.30, Tue to Sat D 7 to 9.30 **Closed:** Christmas, 2 weeks Aug **Meals:** Set L £18 (2 courses) to £22, Set D £33.50 (2 courses) to £39.50 **Service:** not inc **Cards:** Delta, Maestro, MasterCard, Visa **Details:** 34 seats. Private parties: 34 main room, 6 to 10 private rooms. Vegetarian meals. No children under 12. No smoking. No music. No mobile phones

MAP 9 **Ripon** NORTH YORKSHIRE

Old Deanery

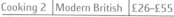

Minster Road, Ripon HG4 1QS
Tel: (01765) 600003
Website: www.theolddeanery.co.uk

Cooking 2 | Modern British | £26–£55

Known to locals and tourists alike, this seventeenth-century manor house across the road from the cathedral is now reaping the benefits of a thorough but sympathetically contemporary refurbishment. Menus reflect the up-to-the-minute outlook of the place: in the evenings the line-up of dishes runs from carpaccio of salmon with Avruga caviar, lime and coriander dressing, via duck breast with warm foie gras mousse and leek vinaigrette, or halibut fillet with mushroom purée and crab raviolo, to jasmine brûlée with lime parfait and lemongrass sorbet. Lunches are more traditional and the separate 'menu' of British and Irish cheeses is well worth investigating. The wine list, printed in striking black and white, is arranged by style ('fruit-driven unoaked' for example) and prices are realistic; eight house wines (from £14.50) start the ball rolling.

Chef: Barrie Higginbotham **Proprietor:** Express Terminals Ltd **Open:** all week L 12 to 2, Mon to Sat D 7 to 9.30 **Closed:** 25 Dec **Meals:** alc (main courses L £7.50 to £14, D £11.50 to £17.50). Set L £9.50 (2 courses) to £11.75 **Service:** not inc, card slips closed **Cards:** Delta, Maestro, MasterCard, Visa **Details:** 50 seats. 28 seats outside. Private parties: 50 main room, 12 to 20 private rooms. Car park. Vegetarian meals. No smoking. Wheelchair access (also WC). Music **Accommodation:** 11 rooms, all with bath/shower. TV. Phone. B&B £85 to £125

MAP 5 **Roade** NORTHAMPTONSHIRE

Roade House

16 High Street, Roade NN7 2NW
Tel: (01604) 863372
Website: www.roadehousehotel.co.uk

Cooking 4 | Modern British | £35–£51

'The Roade House's strong suit is its location,' writes a reporter, noting that it is 'just five minutes from Junction 15 of the M1' and 'an easy detour to avoid the horrors of motorway food'. The emphasis is placed on a contemporary menu with plenty of touchstone ideas and good ingredients – along the lines of gratin of cod, salmon, scallops and prawns, followed by braised spiced blade of beef steak. The high point at inspection was a puff-pastry case filled with baked fillet of plaice and leeks, with a light butter and chive sauce, and a particularly tasty slow-roast belly of pork with crisp crackling and a slice of crumbly, well-seasoned black pudding. Some desserts can also be first-rate, judging by prunes in cognac with cognac ice cream. Service is willing and friendly, and wines embrace a broad spectrum of modest and reasonably priced bottles and half-bottles. House wine is £12.50.

Chefs: Chris Kewley and Debbie Richardson **Proprietors:** Chris and Sue Kewley **Open:** Mon to Fri L 12 to 1.45, Mon to Sat D 7 to 9.45 **Closed:** 26 Dec to New Year **Meals:** Set L £20 (2 courses) to £23, Set D £25 (2 courses) to £30 **Service:** not inc **Cards:** Amex, Delta, Maestro, MasterCard, Visa **Details:** 45 seats. Private parties: 56 main room. Car park. Vegetarian meals. Children's helpings. No smoking. Wheelchair access (also WC). Occasional music. Air-conditioned **Accommodation:** 10 rooms, all with bath/shower. TV. Phone. B&B £60 to £83. Rooms for disabled. Baby facilities

MAP 8 **Rochdale** GREATER MANCHESTER

After Eight

2 Edenfield Road, Rochdale OL11 5AA
Tel: (01706) 646432
Website: www.aftereight.uk.com

Cooking 3 | Modern British | £29–£48

Geoff and Anne Taylor's genial Lancashire restaurant in a quiet and leafy corner of Rochdale eschews voguish minimalism and favours the enduring virtues of personable hospitality and good food. Monthly menus display a fondness for North-Country ingredients, whether corn-fed Goosnargh duck breast, Wensleydale wild boar with a Garstang Blue cheese and white port sauce, or medallions of Holme Farm venison from North Yorkshire, served in November with an elderberry sauce. Fish dishes could be smoked salmon risotto to start, then roast turbot and salad niçoise with Chardonnay sauce, and vegetarians are treated to a full menu. Local cheeses are worth investigating, and desserts might include hardy perennials like ginger pudding with crème anglaise or strawberry meringue. A quartet of house wines at £12.90 opens an extensive, well-chosen wine list.

Chef: Geoff Taylor **Proprietors:** Geoff and Anne Taylor **Open:** Sun L 12.30 to 5, Tue to Sat D 7.30 to 9.30 **Closed:** 25 and 26 Dec, 1 Jan **Meals:** alc D (main courses £14 to £17). Set L Sun £14.95 (2 courses) to £17.95 **Service:** not inc **Cards:** Amex, Delta, Diners, Maestro, MasterCard, Visa **Details:** 47 seats. Private parties: 30 main room, 15 to 20 private rooms. Vegetarian meals. Children's helpings. No smoking. Wheelchair access (not WC). Music

MAP 1 Rock CORNWALL

Black Pig

Rock Road, Rock PL27 6JS
Tel: (01208) 862622
Website: www.blackpigrestaurant.co.uk

Cooking 7 | Modern British | £57–£93

The premises are still no great shakes. A former florist's shop to which very little has seemingly been done, the Black Pig is plainly decorated inside, with a few local artworks on the walls. If the place has nothing much to look at, that at least means that there remains only the cooking to focus on. And what cooking. Nathan Outlaw has moved on to St Ervan Manor (see entry, St Ervan), but his presence is still felt, and he retains a consultative role here. Indications following a reinspection in 2005 are that under new chef, Chris Vincent, the level of achievement is not diminished. The menu is still as terse as can be, especially as regards which bit of meat you might get and how cooked, which somehow also reflects the surroundings, but the results are first-rate. Black bream as a starter comes with blackened skin – seared but subsequently poached in a colourful spring vegetable nage with lemon and rosemary. Even the most apparently humdrum of ingredients sings with astonishing freshness and quality, as is the case with tiny, bright green split peas sprinkled over a first-course serving of crisp belly pork partnered by scampi tails, the plate further garnished with light apple purée and sage.

Main courses might offer a brilliantly rendered pairing of duck breast and foie gras, alongside micro-diced beetroot, a tartlet of caramelised chicory and thyme, or a fine piece of grilled turbot with green beans, given punch by means of semolina gnocchi with shaved Parmesan and a sauce founded on potted brown shrimps. These are thoughtful dishes, constructed with a view to what will please rather than startle the palate. A dessert glass of elderflower cream tasted properly like the essence of an English summer, with good strawberries, a vanilla shortbread biscuit and the appealing lightness of a yoghurt sorbet in attendance. Or go the whole hog with bitter chocolate fondant served with pistachio ice cream and swirls of pungent coffee syrup. Colin Morris is a proficient sommelier, and the short wine list mixes and matches bottles from Western Europe and the southern hemisphere, opening with Languedoc blends at £14 a bottle, £3.75 a glass.

Chef: Chris Vincent **Proprietors:** Nicki Tigwell, Colin Morris and Nathan Outlaw **Open:** Tue to Sat D only 7 to 9.30 **Meals:** alc (main courses £22.50 to £24.50). Set D £60 **Service:** not inc **Cards:** Amex, Maestro, MasterCard, Visa **Details:** 36 seats. 16 seats outside. Private parties: 32 main room. Car park. Vegetarian meals. No children under 12. No smoking. Music. No mobile phones

St Enodoc Hotel

Rock PL27 6LA
Tel: (01208) 863394

The views across the Camel estuary are reason enough for visiting this corner of North Cornwall, and the St Enodoc Hotel is built to enjoy the very best of them. The 'smart and comfortable' interior is bolstered by the Mediterranean look of the dining room, with tiled floor and floor-to-ceiling windows. Start with roast pigeon breast with red onion tarte Tatin and raspberry vinaigrette, then move on to roast halibut with fennel cream sauce and sautéed potatoes with pancetta, lemon and sage. Desserts include chocolate and star anise terrine with spiced plums. Set L £10 to £18, D £18 to £20. Open all week.

MAP 1 Rockbeare DEVON

Jack in the Green

Rockbeare EX5 2EE
Tel: (01404) 822240
Website: www.jackinthegreen.uk.com

Cooking 3 | Global | £30–£54

This basic white-painted roadside pub contains its surprises: the bar, serving decent beer, retains a pubby feel, but walk through to the restaurant and you find warm sophistication matched by serious cooking. Blackboard specials majoring on fish supplement the succinct menu while immaculate service sets this apart from most pubs with restaurants. Unflashy elements, such as crab and avocado set in a ramekin, or rabbit with a moist, herby and carefully seasoned stuffing, are allowed to shine. Straightforward main courses also bring simple pleasures: glorious plain-cooked lemon sole served with asparagus, succulent pork loin, and superb Exmoor venison have each demonstrated immaculate timing of fine ingredients. Puddings impress less. Wines range widely in price and provenance and are supported by enthusiastic, knowledgeable staff; a helpful 'house selection' of eight, all available by the glass, introduces the list with a starting price of £10.75.

Chefs: Matthew Mason and Craig Sampson **Proprietor:** Paul Parnell **Open:** Mon to Sat 12 to 2, 6 to 9.30 (10 Fri and Sat), Sun 12 to 9.30 **Closed:** 25 Dec to 5 Jan **Meals:** alc (main courses £11.50 to £18.50). Set L and D Sun £19.75 (2 courses) to £23.95. Bar menu available **Service:** not inc **Cards:** Amex, Delta, MasterCard, Maestro, Visa **Details:** 140 seats. 20 seats outside. Private parties: 60 main room, 18 to 60 private rooms. Car park. Children's helpings. No smoking. Wheelchair access (also WC). Music. Air-conditioned

MAP 10 **Romaldkirk** CO DURHAM

Rose and Crown

Romaldkirk DL12 9EB
Tel: (01833) 650213
Website: www.rose-and-crown.co.uk

Cooking 3 | Traditional English | £25–£49

Plum in the heart of a picturesque Teesdale village, Christopher and Alison Davy's civilised inn cleverly balances the virtues of well-heeled pub and country hotel, thanks to genuine hospitality and decent food. Dinner in the oak-panelled restaurant adheres to a well-tried formula: the daily fixed-price menu might begin with deep-fried Cotherstone cheese fritters before a bowl of soup (perhaps tomato, pepper and apple); main courses range from roast fillet of local lamb with kidney and woodland mushroom casserole, madeira jus and béarnaise sauce to monkfish with braised 'tagliatelle' of vegetables, red wine and balsamic jus. As a finale, choose between desserts like dark-chocolate torte and North Country cheeses. Brasserie-style lunches and suppers are also served at the traditional bar. The extensive, well-annotated wine list includes a good showing of half-bottles and plenty by the glass; house Chilean is £12.95.

Chefs: Christopher Davy and Andrew Lee **Proprietors:** Christopher and Alison Davy **Open:** Sun L 12 to 1.30, all week D 7.30 to 9 **Closed:** 24 to 26 Dec **Meals:** Set L £16.50, Set D £26. Bar menu available **Service:** not inc, card slips closed **Cards:** Maestro, MasterCard, Visa **Details:** 24 seats. 24 seats outside. Private parties: 20 main room. Car park. Vegetarian meals. Children's helpings. No children under 6. No smoking. Wheelchair access (also WC). No music. No mobile phones **Accommodation:** 12 rooms, all with bath/shower. TV. Phone. B&B £75 to £140. Rooms for disabled. Baby facilities

MAP 2 **Romsey** HAMPSHIRE

Bertie's

AR

80 The Hundred, Romsey SO51 8BX
Tel: (01794) 830708

An airy conservatory is a new feature of this converted coaching inn bedecked with vibrant paintings. There's also been a change of chef, although current menus were not available before the Guide's deadline. The cooking seems likely to continue on similar lines, with modern bistro dishes such as tempura scallops with sauce gribiche, followed by wild sea bass with crab bisque, then desserts like iced strawberry parfait. Fixed-price menus Mon to Fri (£12.95/£15.95). Around 60 wines from £11.95. Accommodation. Closed Sun. Reports, please.

Three Tuns

58 Middlebridge Street, Romsey SO51 8HL
Tel: (01794) 512639
Email: threetunsromsey@aol.com

Cooking 3 | Modern British | £34–£61

Since taking over this 300-year-old hostelry, Belinda Baker and Ian Younger have given the Three Tuns a sophisticated, contemporary feel, with dim lighting, a slate floor and dramatic monochrome photographs on the walls. The place is now 'food focused', although it has stayed in touch with its roots and retains a clutch of local drinkers. Game from nearby Broadlands Estate and meat from a Stockbridge butcher are part of chef Matt Appleton's culinary armoury, and he serves up miniature modern dishes on trendy plates. A stack of seared scallops with sweetcorn fritters comes surrounded by a pool of intense basil foam, while basil might appear again with roast cannon of Hampshire Down lamb and red pepper and tomato jus. Truffles are also a favourite ingredient (perhaps in ravioli with guinea fowl), and Burgundy-poached pear with pear parfait makes a convincing, clear-flavoured finale. House wine is £11.75.

Chef: Matt Appleton **Proprietors:** Belinda Baker and Ian Younger **Open:** all week L 12 to 2, Mon to Sat D 7 to 9.30 **Meals:** alc (main courses £13 to £22). Bar L menu available Mon to Sat **Service:** not inc, card slips closed **Cards:** Delta, Maestro, MasterCard, Visa **Details:** 60 seats. 40 seats outside. Private parties: 40 main room. Car park. Vegetarian meals. No children under 14. No smoking. Music

MAP 2 **Rowde** WILTSHIRE

George & Dragon

AR

High Street, Rowde SN10 2PU
Tel: (01380) 723053

New owners are continuing to make food the main business at this rustic village pub. Seafood delivered daily from Cornwall is the focus of the menu: say, simply grilled sardines (£6.50) or 'exquisitely tender' salt and pepper chilli squid, followed by roast monkfish with parsnip mash and red wine jus (£16.50). Fillet steak with green peppercorn sauce (£17.50) is well reported too, and rack of lamb or a cassoulet of Wiltshire sausages (£9) are other meaty options. Apple and blueberry crumble (£5) makes a good finish. Eight wines are available by the glass from £2.75. Closed Sun D and all Mon.

MAP 7 **Roydhouse** WEST YORKSHIRE

Three Acres Inn

AR

Roydhouse HD8 8LR
Tel: (01484) 602606

Country restaurant, seafood bar, deli and hotel built around a sprawling one-time drovers' inn five miles from Huddersfield. The king-size menus take a world tour, from home-made black pudding on chorizo, butter-bean and tomato stew (£7) to a gratin of Goan lobster (£18) or pot-roast guinea fowl with cider and Calvados (£15) – not forgetting desserts such as hot banana fritters in coconut batter with rum and raisin ice cream. Fairly priced wines from £12.95. Open all week.

MAP 3 **Rye** EAST SUSSEX

Fish Café

NEW ENTRY

17 Tower Street, Rye TN31 7AT
Tel: (01797) 222226
Website: www.thefishcafe.com

Cooking 4 | Seafood/Mod European | £25–£62

This 'extremely well run' red-brick converted warehouse harbours a kitchen with attitude that serves a ground-floor café (lunch) and an upstairs restaurant with spare, modern, seafood-themed décor (dinner only). The cooking mingles modern European with Asian influences and strongly favours seafood, but what really brings the dishes to life is the combination of first-rate raw materials and perfect timing. Risotto was spot-on at inspection: 'generous, tasty, meaty chunks' of lobster with wild rocket, globe artichoke and Parmesan. Monkfish wrapped in prosciutto and stuffed with salmon mousse was equally successful. Even if 'fantastic seafood' is the main focus of the menu, there are some meat dishes – say, soy, chilli and ginger marinated beef served with noodle, vegetable and herb salad to start, followed by rump of South Downs lamb with niçoise vegetables. A dessert of cardamom pannacotta with strawberry and mint compote gained one reporter's approval, or there might be glazed passion-fruit mousse with grenadine sorbet. Breads and ices are all made in-house, service is thoroughly professional, yet relaxed and friendly, and the wine list is a good, reasonably priced selection, starting at £11.50.

Chef: Paul Webbe **Proprietors:** Paul and Rebecca Webbe **Open:** all week 12 to 2.30, 6 to 9 **Meals:** alc (main courses L £7.50 to £13, D £11.50 to £23) **Service:** not inc **Cards:** Amex, Delta, Maestro, MasterCard, Visa **Details:** 52 seats. Private parties: 68 main room, 68 private room. Vegetarian meals. No children at D. No smoking. Music. Air-conditioned

Landgate Bistro

5–6 Landgate, Rye TN31 7LH
Tel: (01797) 222829
Website: www.landgatebistro.co.uk

Cooking 4 | Modern British | £25–£40

After 25 years at their bistro just outside Rye's medieval walls, Nick Parkin and Toni Ferguson-Lees can consider themselves old hands at the restaurant game. But despite their longevity they remain as enthusiastic as ever, thanks to a loyal following and a well-established network of local suppliers. On the food front, the kitchen maintains a balance between keeping customers happy with old favourites and evolving the style to avoid stagnation. The cooking is not complicated, but honest and unfussy – salad of confit duck with Puy lentils, for example, and slow-roast belly of pork with black pudding and apple sauce. Fish and seafood have been impressive: at inspection, starters of salmon and salt-cod fishcakes with parsley sauce, and squid braised in white wine, tomatoes and garlic, then mains of poached fillet of turbot with chive hollandaise, and scallops with brill and an orange and vermouth sauce were heartily endorsed. Typical among desserts might be blood-orange sorbet or walnut and treacle tart. On the wine front prices start at £10.50 and you can drink very well for under £20.

Chef: Toni Ferguson-Lees **Proprietors:** Nick Parkin and Toni Ferguson-Lees **Open:** Tue to Sat D only 7 to 9.30 (10 Sat) **Closed:** 2 weeks Christmas, 1 week summer **Meals:** alc (main courses £10 to £14). Set D Tue to Thur £18.90 **Service:** net prices, card slips closed **Cards:** Delta, MasterCard, Maestro, Visa **Details:** 30 seats. Vegetarian meals. Children's helpings. No smoking. Music

MAP 3 St Albans HERTFORDSHIRE

Darcys

AR

2 Hatfield Road, St Albans AL1 3RP
Tel: (01727) 730777

Stylishly designed restaurant, just off the main drag, which 'aims to bring a smart cosmopolitan edge to the St Albans scene' and is a gift for the ladies who lunch (two courses £11.50). Expect elaborately dressed, round-the-world dishes along the lines of Thai-style lamb and noodle salad (£7), tuna with guacamole, pineapple, pomegranate and red pepper salsa (£15), followed by chocolate, peanut and caramel spring roll with chocolate sauce. Thirty-plus modern wines with prices from £13. Open all week.

MAP 1 St Ervan CORNWALL

St Ervan Manor

NEW ENTRY

St Ervan PL27 7TA
Tel: (01841) 540255
Website: www.stervanmanor.co.uk

Cooking 7 | Modern British | £62–£112

Not far from Padstow and a little inland, St Ervan is mentioned in the late Sir John Betjeman's autobiographical volume, *Summoned by Bells*. It is a classic Cornish village with a fine church and this elegant, grey-stone building with its double high-pitched roofs and five acres of gardens. The dining room in this former rectory is of Lilliputian proportions done in cool blue and brilliant white, with an eye-catching view over the lawns.

Nathan Outlaw, of Black Pig fame (see entry, Rock), arrived to head up the kitchen here in March 2005. Having already set a formidable pace at his previous venue, he seems scarcely to have missed a beat on the short journey to St Ervan. The drill is dinner on five nights each week, and there is a straight choice of two seasonal tasting menus of six courses each, the £20 difference between them accounted for by the value of the raw materials involved. At a spring inspection, the lower-priced option began in subtle but fine style with a bowl of creamy cauliflower soup dappled with curry oil and containing diced apple. An irreproachable saffron risotto topped with crisp-skinned sea bass followed, and was in turn succeeded by a serving of cubes of belly pork with sweet soused plums and forceful onion purée, a dish marked by astonishing clarity of flavours. Monkfish and oxtail were paired in the main course, the latter appearing as a round cake of shredded meat, together with exemplary mashed potato and mushrooms cooked in sherry vinegar with pumpkin seeds. Two well-judged desserts followed: an orange brûlée with orange and star anise sorbet, and then a baked rhubarb sponge with lavender ice cream and creamed almonds, a highly satisfying study in textural contrasts.

Eating from the grander menu might take you from lobster risotto in its own bisque, through pigeon and foie gras with fig chutney, all the way to chocolate fondant with pistachio ice cream and espresso sauce. Either way, the new chef has ensured that this is a major new arrival on the already lustrous Cornish scene. Solid collections from all French regions are complemented by a smattering of wines from elsewhere. The 'Sommelier's Selection', from £15 to £31, is a good short-cut to quality bottles.

Chef: Nathan Outlaw **Proprietors:** Allan and Lorraine Clarke **Open:** Wed to Sun D only 7 to 9 **Closed:** 20 to 27 Dec, 8 to 31 Jan **Meals:** Set D £45 to £65 **Service:** not inc, card slips closed **Cards:** Delta, Maestro, MasterCard, Visa **Details:** 20 seats. Private parties: 12 main room, 6 to 10 private rooms. Car park. No children under 14. No smoking. Wheelchair access (also WC). Music. No mobile phones **Accommodation:** 6 rooms, 5 with bath/shower. TV. B&B £90 to £225. No children under 14

MAP 1 St Ives CORNWALL

Alba

Old Lifeboat House, Wharf Road,
St Ives TR26 1LF
Tel: (01736) 797222
Website: www.alba-restaurant.co.uk

Cooking 3 | Modern European | £26–£61

A terrific view over the harbour from huge windows accompanies modern, ambitious food with bold flavours. Fish is foremost, but there's a

vegetarian menu too, and among the token meat dishes fillet of venison with a miniature game pudding, winter vegetables and port sauce has been praised. Start perhaps with wild rabbit tortellini, or skate tempura with pickled cucumber and miso, before moving on to fried fillet of John Dory with roast polenta, chargrilled leeks, black olives and romanesco sauce, or maybe roast brill with cockles in a chardonnay broth. Desserts may bring themes and variations (three flavours of crème brûlée, say) or caramelised buttermilk custard with prune and Armagnac ice cream. House wines start at £11.95, and service is discreet and helpful.

Chef: Grant Nethercott **Proprietor:** The Harbour Kitchen Co. Ltd **Open:** all week 12 to 2, 6 to 9.45 **Closed:** 25 and 26 Dec **Meals:** alc (main courses £13 to £18). Set L £18.50 (2 courses) to £22.50, set D £40, set D 6 to 7.30 (not high season) £12 (2 courses) to £15. Light L menu available **Service:** not inc, 10% for parties of 6 or more **Cards:** Amex, Delta, Maestro, MasterCard, Visa **Details:** 60 seats. Private parties: 40 main room, 20 to 40 private rooms. Vegetarian meals. Children's helpings. No smoking. Wheelchair access (also WC). Music. Air-conditioned

Porthgwidden Beach Café

AR

Porthgwidden Beach, St Ives TR26 1NT
Tel: (01736) 796791

Small seaside café related to Porthminster Beach Café (see entry below) boasting a glorious location overlooking the beach and St Ives Bay. There's been a change of chef, but the lively global approach remains: dinner might bring crispy pancetta and roast beetroot salad (£7.50) before crisp-skinned salmon with Asian greens, sticky rice and sesame dressing (£10), and desserts such as roast peach and almond tart (£5). Breakfast and light lunches too. House wine £11.50. Open all week, Apr to Sept only.

Porthminster Beach Café

Porthminster Beach, St Ives TR26 2EB
Tel: (01736) 795352
Website: www.porthminstercafe.co.uk

Cooking 4 | Global/Seafood | £25–£61

An Art Deco building looking over the beach and St Ives Bay is the setting for a winning combination: 'good food in a great location'. The atmosphere is suitably relaxed, and daily deliveries of fish form the bedrock of menus. At dinner, a Thai-style salad accompanies crispy fried squid with black spice and citrus miso, and three 'very fresh' scallops are surrounded by sweet pepper salsa. Baked cod on black olive crushed potatoes with peppered spinach and salsa verde is a typical main course, but there are meat dishes too, along the lines of fillet steak with truffle mash, baby peas and caramelised shallots. Lunch brings a smoked haddock fish soup, or salt cod and white bean pâté, followed by cheaper main dishes like chargrilled steak sandwich, or Parmesan-crumbed sardines stuffed with pine nuts and spinach and fried. Both double chocolate tart and saffron bread-and-butter pudding with honey and clotted cream have received compliments this year, but there's cheese too – resolutely Cornish and served with a pear and fig chutney. The globe-trotting wine list opens with house Italian at £11.95.

Chef: Michael Smith **Proprietors:** David Fox, Jim Woolcock, Roger and Tim Symons **Open:** all week 12 to 3.45, 6 to 10 **Closed:** Nov to mid-Mar **Meals:** alc (main courses L £6.50 to £13, D £13.50 to £24) **Service:** not inc, card slips closed **Cards:** Maestro, MasterCard, Visa **Details:** 50 seats. 70 seats outside. Vegetarian meals. Children's helpings. No smoking. Music

MAP 1 St Keyne CORNWALL

Well House

St Keyne PL14 4RN
Tel: (01579) 342001
Website: www.wellhouse.co.uk

Cooking 3 | Modern British | £36–£55

Large French and bay windows in the dining room of this secluded stone-built Victorian mansion make the most of fine views over the Looe Valley. It is all impeccably maintained with an urban sophistication to the décor that belies the rural setting. On offer is a blend of modern and traditional ideas, which engage attention with their lively approach. At inspection, a terrine of duck and foie gras with red onion marmalade, served with an assortment of wild mushrooms, whole pistachios and truffle oil, showed a balanced combination of tastes and textures, while breast of guinea fowl with buttered Savoy cabbage and crisp prosciutto was accurately cooked. Materials are top class and presentation impressive, while a light touch with desserts has brought commendation for panna-cotta with mango coulis and vanilla beignets.

Smart service is at a pace that's 'suited to such a relaxed setting'. Appreciable thought has clearly gone into sourcing good-value wines. House bottles are £12.50.

Chef: Glenn Gatland **Proprietors:** Nick Wainford and Ione Nurdin **Open:** all week 12.30 to 1.30, 7 to 8.30 **Closed:** 1 week Jan **Meals:** Set L £18.50 to £23.50, Set D £32.50 **Service:** not inc, card slips closed **Cards:** Delta, Maestro, MasterCard, Visa **Details:** 36 seats. 18 seats outside. Private parties: 36 main room. Car park. Vegetarian meals. Children's helpings; no children under 8 at D. No smoking. Wheelchair access (also WC). No music. No mobile phones **Accommodation:** 9 rooms, all with bath/shower. TV. Phone. B&B £75 to £180. Baby facilities. Swimming pool

MAP 3 **St Margaret's at Cliffe** KENT

Wallett's Court

Westcliffe, St Margaret's at Cliffe CT15 6EW
Tel: (01304) 852424
Website: www.wallettscourt.com

Cooking 3 | Modern European | £32–£68

The Oakleys are long-time custodians of this beguilingly old-fashioned hotel just north-east of Dover, a special venue for dressed-up dinners, impress-the-client lunches and stopovers en route to the ferries. It's also a place with a unique, lived-in feel. Chef Stephen Harvey takes full account of Kentish produce and supplies from further afield for dishes with modern overtones. Wood pigeon Tatin with red onion, thyme, and port reduction might open proceedings alongside seared yellowfin tuna carpaccio with red chard, mango, lime and bird's-eye chilli, while roast cod appears with tempura vegetables, Japanese soy dipping sauce, chilli and ginger jam. Local pheasant is given the full traditional treatment, and desserts are elaborate creations like iced cinnamon parfait with hot pears, figs and tawny port syrup. The extensive wine list evokes a respectable cellar with 20 by the glass and house recommendations at £14.95.

Chef: Steven Harvey **Proprietor:** Oakley Family **Open:** Tue to Fri and Sun L 12 to 2, all week D 7 to 9 **Meals:** Set L £17 (2 courses) to £19.50, Set D £35 **Service:** not inc **Cards:** Amex, Delta, Diners, Maestro, MasterCard, Visa **Details:** 70 seats. Private parties: 40 main room, 6 to 40 private rooms. Car park. Vegetarian meals. Children's helpings. No children under 8 after 8. No smoking. Occasional music. No mobile phones **Accommodation:** 17 rooms, all with bath/shower. TV. Phone. B&B £99 to £159. Baby facilities. Swimming pool

MAP 1 **St Martin's** ISLES OF SCILLY

St Martin's on the Isle

Lower Town, St Martin's TR25 0QW
Tel: (01720) 422092
Website: www.stmartinshotel.co.uk

NEW CHEF | Modern European | £58–£70

The low-slung, rustic granite building might resemble a row of cottages, but it is actually a smart hotel. On the first floor is the Tean restaurant, which overlooks the uninhabited island of the same name. In this elegantly furnished room, the accent is on modern European food with a strong inventive thrust. We were not in time to visit this year following the appointment of new head chef John Mijatovic, but the ebullient style of cooking for which the restaurant has been noted looks set to continue. Expect fillet of sea bass on a salad of exotic fruits and rocket to start, or scallop and crab ravioli in shellfish froth, followed by roast monkfish with braised fennel and garlic butter sauce, or pork loin with broad beans and button onions in a sauce of ceps. There are separate vegetarian and cheese menus, and enticements such as lime and chocolate tart with Baileys-scented cream and a bitter chocolate sorbet for the sweet of tooth. Old and New Worlds get equal shouts on the wine list, with prices from about £17.

Chef: John Mijatovic **Proprietors:** Peter and Penny Sykes **Open:** all week D only 7 to 9 **Closed:** Nov to Feb **Meals:** Set D £44.50. Bar L menu available **Service:** not inc, card slips closed **Cards:** Amex, Delta, Diners, Maestro, MasterCard, Visa **Details:** 80 seats. Private parties: 2 to 25 private rooms. Vegetarian meals. Children's helpings. No children under 9. No smoking. No music. No mobile phones **Accommodation:** 30 rooms, all with bath/shower. TV. Phone. D,B&B £120 to £340. Rooms for disabled. Baby facilities. Swimming pool. Fishing

MAP 1 **St Mawes** CORNWALL

Hotel Tresanton

27 Lower Castle Road, St Mawes TR2 5DR
Tel: (01326) 270055
Website: www.tresanton.com

Cooking 4 | Modern European | £39–£60

One reporter considers a meal at this trendy, yet understatedly elegant, waterside hotel reason enough for living in 'tourist-full' Cornwall. Service has 'loads of confidence but no fuss', and

lunch and dinner set menus offer three choices per course. The Mediterranean is at the heart of a style that puts strong emphasis on native ingredients, many from the sea: seared black bream with baby leeks and aubergine purée, or calamari with basil mayonnaise, lemon and rocket. Red meat is another strong suit – judging by chargrilled fillet of beef served with dauphinoise potatoes, and grilled rump of lamb with roast new potatoes – and vegetarians can expect the likes of gnocchi with butternut squash and wild mushrooms. Desserts include chocolate pudding with white chocolate ice cream, or try West Country farmhouse cheeses. France and Italy provide most of the wine list's hundred bottles, but those from elsewhere are interesting too; prices start at £14, but choice begins above £20.

Chef: Paul Wadham **Proprietor:** Olga Polizzi **Open:** all week 12.30 to 2.30, 7 to 9.30 **Meals:** Set L £20 (2 courses) to £26, Set D £35, snack L menu available **Service:** not inc, card slips closed **Cards:** Amex, Delta, Maestro, MasterCard, Visa **Details:** 50 seats. 60 seats outside. Private parties: 40 main room. Car park. Vegetarian meals. No children under 6 in restaurant (children's tea 5.30–6.30). Wheelchair access (not WC). No music **Accommodation:** 29 rooms, all with bath/shower. TV. Phone. B&B £212.50 to £280. Baby facilities

Rising Sun

The Square, St Mawes TR2 5DJ
Tel: (01326) 270233
Website: www.risingsunstmawes.com

Cooking 4 | Modern European | £26–£47

The idyllic village of St Mawes is tucked away in one of the many sheltered inlets of the Fal estuary, and standing at its centre, by the harbour, is this traditional whitewashed pub. The bar has a bare wooden floor, a roaring fire in winter, a welcoming atmosphere and a straightforward bar menu. To the rear is a modern conservatory extension that houses the restaurant, decorated in soft pastel shades, tables laid with crisp white linen. Set menus offer a small but balanced choice of three or four dishes per course, starting perhaps with a trio of mousses – brown crab, smoked salmon and cucumber, in neat layers reminiscent of Neapolitan ice cream, the richness of the crab balanced by the subtle salmon and refreshing cucumber. Among main courses, roast lamb has impressed, perfectly pink, tender and juicy, served with a well-flavoured gravy and a swirl of mustard sauce; while fish choices might include grilled sea bass with sesame seed dressing, with wobbly vanilla pannacotta with vanilla ice cream to finish. Wines are grouped by style, the list well annotated, with prices starting at a very fair £11 and plenty of choice by the glass.

Chefs: Ann Long and Tim Zawada **Proprietor:** John Milan **Open:** Sun L 12 to 2, all week D 7 to 9 **Meals:** Set L Sun £18, Set D £27 (2 courses) to £30. Bar menu available **Service:** not inc, card slips closed **Cards:** Delta, Maestro, MasterCard, Visa **Details:** 40 seats. Private parties: 70 main room. Car park. Vegetarian meals. No children under 12. No smoking. Wheelchair access (also WC). No music. No mobile phones **Accommodation:** 8 rooms, all with bath/shower. TV. Phone. B&B £50 to £140

MAP 1 **St Merryn** CORNWALL

Ripley's

St Merryn PL28 8NQ
Tel: (01841) 520179
Email: chefripley@aol.com

Cooking 3 | Modern British | £40–£65

Paul Ripley's bright yellow cottage restaurant stands out in its terrace in this traditional Cornish hamlet. Use of space within is maximised, with tables crammed in, and the aim is to open for lunches too in due course. Our reports this year suggest that Ripley may perhaps be stretching himself too thinly as it is. Poor judgement upset a serving of hake at inspection, which was out-shouted by its pungently garlicky, salty, saffron sauce. Over-salting, indeed, has been a recurrent theme. On the credit side, there have been reports of a technically flawless risotto of creamy squash with crispest pancetta and shavings of mature Parmesan; the rump steak is from meat that has been hung for 35 days to develop positive flavour, before being served bordelaise-style with bone-marrow butter; and breads, such as sun-dried tomato and walnut and raisin, are great. A well-chosen, concise wine selection starts at £11.95 for La Serre Merlot.

Chef/Proprietor: Paul Ripley **Open:** Tue to Sat D only 7 to 9.30; phone to check winter opening times **Closed:** 1 week at Christmas **Meals:** alc (main courses £13.50 to £17.50) **Service:** not inc, card slips closed **Cards:** Delta, Maestro, MasterCard, Visa **Details:** 32 seats. Private parties: 32 main room. No young children. No smoking. Wheelchair access (also WC). Music. No mobile phones

MAP 8 **Sale** GREATER MANCHESTER

Hanni's

4 Brooklands Road, Sale M33 3SQ
Tel: (0161) 973 6606

Cooking 2 | Eastern Mediterranean | £25–£51

£

A local culinary landmark in a converted shop by Brooklands Metrolink Station, Mohammed Hanni Al-Taraboulsy's self-named restaurant continues to serve up a colourful mix of Eastern Mediterranean and Middle Eastern dishes. In the mezze department are all kinds of palate-sharpening morsels, from falafel and borek pastries to arayes (toasted pitta bread filled with fried minced lamb) and yershig (chunks of merguez sausage). 'Specialities' include hearty stalwarts like kleftiko, stifado and a take on osso bucco using lamb; couscous comes in half-a-dozen permutations, and there's a heavy-weight battalion of kebabs and chargrills from marinated poussin to halibut and king prawns. Finish with Turkish delight, green figs with yoghurt or even halloumi cheese in filo pastry. The wine list, including a decent showing of geographically apposite bottles, starts with French and Spanish house wines at £11.95.

Chef: Mr Hoonanian **Proprietors:** Mohammed Hanni and Jennifer Al-Taraboulsy **Open:** Mon to Sat D only 6 to 10.30 (11 Fri/Sat) **Closed:** 25 and 26 Dec, 1 Jan, Good Fri, Easter Mon **Meals:** alc (main courses £11.50 to £15.50). Set D 6 to 7 £11.95 (2 courses) to £30 (min 4) **Service:** not inc, card slips closed **Cards:** Amex, Delta, Maestro, MasterCard, Visa **Details:** 50 seats. Private parties: 50 main room. Vegetarian meals. Children's helpings. Wheelchair access (not WC). Music. Air-conditioned

MAP 8 **Salford** GREATER MANCHESTER

Lowry Hotel, River Restaurant

50 Dearmans Place, Chapel Wharf, Salford M3 5LH
Tel: (0161) 827 4041
Website: www.thelowryhotel.com

Cooking 4 | Modern European | £35–£86

The former link with Marco Pierre White ended, the River Room now sails under its own colours. Picture windows overlook the Irwell and offer commanding views of the bridge that links Salford to the centre of Manchester. Smartly set tables with quality glassware set a tone of agreeable refinement, and Paul Jobling's cooking is in keeping with its surroundings. Lambs' sweetbreads with langoustines and sauce gribiche made an enterprising starter at inspection, the dressing avoiding oil and egg overload yet retaining vinegary freshness, while a main course of deboned oxtail on potato purée offered a world of earthy satisfaction. Sauces with meat are impressively deep stock reductions, rather than modish squiggles, but fish is robustly handled too, with celeriac purée and artichoke hearts the chosen partners for seared sea bass. Desserts may sound a touch seaside, but they can deliver majestic flavours, as did a banana and chocolate chip cake that came with crème anglaise and piña colada ice cream. 'Slickly professional' service ensures relaxation. The wine list is not overlong but is astutely chosen, with good names like Rijckaert in Burgundy and Craggy Range in New Zealand. House wines are £17, and plenty come by the glass.

Chef: Paul Jobling **Proprietor:** Rocco Forte **Open:** all week 12 (12.30 Sat/Sun) to 2.30 (3.30 Sun), 6 to 10.30 **Meals:** alc (main courses £18.50 to £35). Set L £18.50 (2 courses) to £20.50, Set D 6 to 7 £18.50 (2 courses) to £20.50 **Service:** 10% (optional) **Cards:** Amex, Delta, Diners, Maestro, MasterCard, Visa **Details:** 100 seats. 50 seats outside. Private parties: 12 main room, 8 to 22 private rooms. Vegetarian meals. Children's helpings. No smoking in 1 dining room. Wheelchair access (also WC). Music. No mobile phones. Air-conditioned **Accommodation:** 165 rooms, all with bath/shower. TV. Phone. B&B £205 to £1,350. Rooms for disabled. Baby facilities

MAP 2 **Sapperton** GLOUCESTERSHIRE

Bell at Sapperton

Sapperton GL7 6LE
Tel: (01285) 760298
Website: www.foodatthebell.co.uk

Cooking 4 | Modern European | £36–£54

The revitalised Bell at Sapperton, just west of Cirencester, belongs to the new breed of well-to-do Cotswold inns combining gentrified *Country Living* décor with ambitious food based around judicious sourcing of local ingredients, and it now bakes its own bread. Chef Ivan Reid changes his menus each month to make the best of fresh supplies; February's might offer home-smoked pigeon breast with rémoulade and aubergine chutney, or cutlets of Longhorn lamb with devilled kidneys and shepherd's pie, while August's could bring summer truffle risotto or warm free-range chicken salad with avocado, cucumber and Parmesan wafer. There are also regularly changing fish specials, well-chosen cheeses and desserts like passion-fruit brûlée with rosemary cake and poached mango, or Hattie Wilson's home-made ice creams. Ploughman's and other pub dishes are added to the menu at lunchtime. The serious, knowledgeably assembled wine list, arranged by style and helpfully annotated, offers plenty of quality drinking at realistic prices; house wines begin at £12.50. There are pricey French classics too, and a choice of stickies.

Chef: Ivan Reid **Proprietors:** Paul Davidson and Pat Le Jeune **Open:** all week 12 to 2, 7 to 9.30 (9 Sun) **Closed:** 25 and 26 Dec, 31 Dec **Meals:** alc (main courses £12 to £17) **Service:** not inc **Cards:** Maestro, MasterCard, Visa **Details:** 80 seats. 40 seats outside. Private parties: 12 main room. Car park. Vegetarian meals. No children under 10 in evening; children's helpings. No-smoking area. No cigars. Wheelchair access (also WC). No music. No mobile phones

MAP 8 **Sawley** LANCASHIRE

Spread Eagle

Sawley BB7 4NH
Tel: (01200) 441202
Website: www.the-spreadeagle.co.uk

Cooking 3 | Modern British | £21–£46

'An absolute gem in the lovely Ribble Valley,' says one Lancastrian of this consistently reliable seventeenth-century inn by a bend in the river above Clitheroe. Along with wonderful views from the stylish restaurant, diners can expect an assortment of globally inspired dishes like a large, 'delightfully light' tortellino of scallops and bacon with warm vichyssoise sauce, or grilled duck breast with poached pineapple, spring onions and aniseedy sauce, or that North Country classic, braised neck of lamb with black pudding and pickled red cabbage. Helpings are generous and vegetables arrive 'bursting with flavour', although one diner noted an 'over-indulgence of crushed potatoes everywhere'. Finish with local cheeses or desserts such as iced blackcurrant meringue parfait. Well-trained staff are 'a credit to the owners', and the varied international wine list opens with 11 house recommendations from £10.

Chef: Greig Barnes **Proprietors:** Nigel and Ysanne Williams **Open:** Tue to Sun L 12 to 2, Tue to Sat D 6 to 9 **Meals:** alc (not Sun L; main courses £9.50 to £16.50). Set L Tue to Fri £9.50 (2 courses) to £12.45, Set L Sun £13 (2 courses), Set D Tue to Fri 6 to 7 £10.50 (2 courses) to £13.75, set D Tue to Fri 7 to 9 £12.50 (2 courses) to £15.75. Bar L menu available Tue to Sat **Service:** not inc, card slips closed **Cards:** Maestro, MasterCard, Visa **Details:** 180 seats. Private parties: 100 main room, 10 to 50 private rooms. Car park. Vegetarian meals. Children's helpings. No smoking. Wheelchair access (also WC). Music

MAP 6 **Saxmundham** SUFFOLK

Bell Hotel

31 High Street, Saxmundham IP17 1AF
Tel: (01728) 602331
Email: thebell@saxhighstreet.fsnet.co.uk

Cooking 4 | Anglo-French | £22–£44

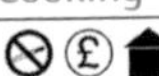

Andrew and Catherine Blackburn have been hard at work in their likeable Georgian coaching inn, upgrading bedrooms and refurbishing other parts of the hotel. Judging by feedback, this has not detracted from the quality of the food served in their uncluttered green and white dining room. Fish has been singled out, but the concise set menus and carte, cooked by Andrew (English) and served by Catherine (French), offer plenty of variety – from mille-feuille of smoked eel and potato pancakes with horseradish cream, to red snapper with pasta galette, fennel and scallops, or from terrine of foie gras with cider jelly and toasted brioche, to wild duck with braised chicory and pearl barley. As a finale, there are desserts such as chocolate tart with rosemary ice cream. 'The value for money, for Londoners spending a weekend in Suffolk, was terrific,' noted one traveller from the capital. The same could also be said of the competitively priced and beefed-up wine list; house recommendations start at £9.95

Chef/Proprietor: Andrew Blackburn **Open:** Tue to Sat 12 to 2, 6.30 to 9 **Closed:** 26 Dec, 1 Jan, spring half-term, October half-term **Meals:** alc (main courses £12.50 to £15). Set L £11.50 (2 courses) to £14, Set D £17.50. Bar, light L menus available **Service:** not inc, card slips closed **Cards:** Delta, Maestro, MasterCard, Visa **Details:** 26 seats. 15 seats outside. Private parties: 30 main room, 8 to 40 private rooms. Vegetarian meals. No smoking. No music **Accommodation:** 10 rooms, all with bath/shower. TV. B&B £40 to £80. Baby facilities

MAP 9 **Scarborough** NORTH YORKSHIRE

Lanterna

33 Queen Street, Scarborough YO11 1HQ
Tel: (01723) 363616
Website: www.lanterna-ristorante.co.uk

Cooking 3 | Italian | £34–£105

Giorgio and Rachel Alessio run the Lanterna as a full-on restaurant, a far cry from a pizzeria or pasta joint. They follow the seasons, import direct from their native land and set out their menus in traditional Italian style. Although their gastronomic roots are in Piedmont (the indigenous white truffle is given its rightful place of honour), they also take full advantage of Yorkshire's larder. Hence a long carte and a list of specialities including perhaps sanguinaccio (black pudding with polenta and caramelised onions) and fagiano (breast of local pheasant with Barbera and wild mushroom sauce), as well as daily fish specials from Scarborough market, regional staples like pollo Piemonte (chicken with rosemary and garlic sauce) and classic desserts like pears in marsala with sweet ricotta. The all-Italian wine list features big names alongside humbler offerings; house selections are £12.50.

Chef: Giorgio Alessio **Proprietors:** Giorgio and Rachel Alessio **Open:** Mon to Sat D only 7 to 10 **Closed:** 2 weeks Oct, 25–26 Dec, 1 Jan **Meals:** alc (main courses £12 to £37) **Service:** not inc, card slips closed **Cards:** Delta, Maestro, MasterCard, Visa **Details:** 30 seats. Private parties: 30 to 35 private rooms. Vegetarian meals. No smoking. Wheelchair access (not WC). Music. Air-conditioned

MAP 10 **Seaham** CO DURHAM

Seaham Hall, White Room

Lord Byron's Walk, Seaham SR7 7AG
Tel: (0191) 516 1400
Website: www.seaham-hall.com

Cooking 5 | Modern European | £36–£123

The windswept coastal location may not be to everyone's taste, but this spa hotel certainly makes its own impression. From the ever-spiralling whirlpool water feature out front to the crisp, white-walled dining room with its balustraded terrace, everything has a distinctly metropolitan air, which is enhanced by the Modern European slant of Stephen Smith's cooking. Signature dishes take in stuffed trotter with morels, onions and sage, as well as venison saddle with pumpkin purée and a seared scallop in a sauce enriched with chocolate. An inspection dinner got off to a fine start with a well-timed piece of sautéed foie gras in a spiced jus, alongside accompaniments of fig purée and half a pickled fig. Fish cooking shows up well too, exemplified by a main course of roast cod, copiously adorned with mussels and squid, the whole thing casually dressed with a splash of bouillabaisse sauce from a jug which is left on the table. A vein of nostalgia runs through desserts such as prune and Armagnac soufflé with matching ice cream, or the deconstructed version of Black Forest gâteau that comes with a shot glass of cherry granita. Good Illy coffee and simple but satisfying breads round it all out, while the service is a model of discreet efficiency.

The wine list offers a thorough world survey, but value is uneven: plenty of good bottles in the £20s – the revitalized Villa Antinori Chianti classico at £26, for example – but Sauvignon blancs look dear, especially 2002 Cloudy Bay at a whopping £70.

Chef: Stephen Smith **Proprietors:** Tom and Jocelyn Maxfield **Open:** all week 12 to 2.30, 7 to 10 **Meals:** alc (main courses £18 to £34). Set L £19.50 to £65, Set L Sun £27.50, Set D £65. Bar L menu available **Service:** not inc **Cards:** Amex, Delta, Diners, Maestro, MasterCard, Visa **Details:** 55 seats. Private parties: 55 main room, 10 to 120 private rooms. Car park. Vegetarian meals. No smoking. Wheelchair access (also WC). Music. No mobile phones. Air-conditioned **Accommodation:** 19 rooms, all with bath/shower. TV. Phone. B&B £195 to £565. Rooms for disabled. Baby facilities. Swimming pool

MAP 2 **Seaview** ISLE OF WIGHT

Seaview Hotel

High Street, Seaview PO34 5EX
Tel: (01983) 612711
Website: www.seaviewhotel.co.uk

Cooking 3 | Anglo-French | £27–£53

If you're arriving by yacht, the Seaview Hotel is a short plash from Cowes on the eastern side of Wight. Landlubbers should head for the village of the same name, and park wherever they can in the narrow streets. A major refurbishment in the spring of 2005 has rung some changes, with the addition of a new brasserie (reports, please). There's a brand new kitchen, too, from which Michael Green cooks in a straightforward style. Mussels and razor clams marinière, perhaps, or hot, cheesy crab ramekins to start, and the likes of poached haddock with Mornay sauce and spinach, or herb-crusted rack of lamb with rosemary rösti and redcurrant jus, to follow. Meals end sympathetically with maybe stem ginger pudding, served with the local brand of vanilla ice cream and butterscotch sauce. A French-centred wine list is interspersed with some classy bottles. House French is £11.95, or £4 for a large glass.

Chef: Michael Green **Proprietor:** Techaid Facilities Ltd **Open:** all week 12 to 2, 7 to 9.30 **Closed:** 24 to 26 Dec **Meals:** alc (main courses £12 to £20). Set L Sun £16.95. Bar menu available **Service:** not inc, card slips closed **Cards:** Amex, Delta, Diners, Maestro, MasterCard, Visa **Details:** 100 seats. 50 seats outside. Private parties: 50 main room, 10 to 40 private rooms. Car park. Vegetarian meals. Children's helpings. No children under 5 after 7.30pm. No smoking in 1 restaurant and 1 bar. Wheelchair access (also WC). No music. No mobile phones. Air-conditioned **Accommodation:** 17 rooms, all with bath/shower. TV. Phone. B&B £72 to £182. Baby facilities

MAP 2 **Shaftsbury** DORSET

La Fleur de Lys

AR

Bleke Street, Shaftesbury SP7 8AW
Tel: (01747) 853717

A secluded courtyard is one feature of this well-established family set-up in a converted girls' boarding house. Anglo-French cooking is the kitchen's business, with menus promising quail breasts on red lentil purée with baked garlic and smoked bacon sauce before grilled fillets of Dover sole with lemon and butter sauce, then desserts such as lemon parfait with exotic fruits in kumquat sauce. Fixed-price dinners £22.50 to £27.50; extensive wine list from £14. Accommodation. Open Wed to Sun L and Mon to Sat D.

Wayfarers

Sherborne Causeway, Shaftesbury SP7 9PX
Tel: (01747) 852821

Cooking 4 | Modern British | £30–£56

For twelve years the Newtons have provided modern, artistically presented food in comfortable, relaxed surroundings at this eighteenth-century former coaching inn just west of Shaftesbury. The elaborately worded menu reflects intricate cooking that aims to make dishes impress the eye as well as the palate. 'Sautéed tournedos of pork confit filled with duck foie gras, served with red onion jam, poached quince and caperberries' is a typical starter; so is 'warm scallop mousseline with seared scallops and dried ham "craquant" on a pea and bacon purée with rouille'. Self-taught chef Mark by and large pulls off these tricky balancing acts through a combination of first-class produce and finely honed technique, sometimes to brilliant effect. The same goes for main courses such as quail medallions filled with thyme, wild mushroom and apricot mousse, served with morels and polenta crostini; or saffron-roast red mullet on globe artichoke 'barigoule' with salt cod and langoustine boudin and saffron velouté. And if that's not too much of a mouthful, there might be iced passion-fruit and lemon-curd parfait with sesame and poppy seed wafers, basil syrup and crème fraîche sorbet to finish. Six house selections from around £13 open a predominantly French wine list.

Chef: Mark Newton **Proprietors:** Clare and Mark Newton **Open:** Wed to Fri and Sun L 12 to 1.15, Tue to Sat D 7 to 9 **Closed:** 3 weeks from 26 Dec, 2 weeks June/July **Meals:** alc (not Sun L; main courses £17.50 to £18). Set L £18.50 to £21, Set D Tue to Fri £18.50 to £21 **Service:** not inc, card slips closed **Cards:** Amex, Delta, Maestro, MasterCard, Visa **Details:** 34 seats. 6 seats outside. Private parties: 34 main room. Car park. Vegetarian meals. No children under 8 at D. Wheelchair access (also women's WC). No music **Accommodation:** 1 room with bath/shower. B&B £55 to £70. No children under 12

MAP 9 **Sheffield** SOUTH YORKSHIRE

Blue Room Brasserie

798 Chesterfield Road, Woodseats,
Sheffield S8 0SF
Tel: (0114) 255 2004

Cooking 2 | Modern European-Plus | £29–£63

Blue glass tumblers and dark blue-and-cream upholstery complement the title of this modern brasserie on Sheffield's southern outskirts. The kitchen is at home with all sorts of fresh, attractively presented dishes, whether Thai fishcakes with pickled vegetables and chilli dip, or classic grilled plaice fillets with garlic butter and square-cut home-made chips. The global treatment may also be applied to crispy pork salad with crushed peanuts and lemongrass, roast rump of lamb with ratatouille, or seared fillet of sea bass with pesto mash and sauce vierge. There's also a full menu for vegetarians (red wine risotto with porcini and Parmesan, for example), and desserts have included a splendidly fruity raspberry crème brûlée. Staff are charming and families are happily accommodated. House wine is £11.95.

Chef/Proprietor: Christian Kent **Open:** Tue to Sat D only 6 to 10 **Closed:** bank hols **Meals:** alc (main courses £9 to £22). Set D £20 to £25 **Service:** not inc **Cards:** Delta, Maestro, MasterCard, Visa **Details:** 130 seats. Private parties: 100 main room, 10 to 40 private rooms. Car park. Vegetarian meals. Children's helpings. No smoking in 1 dining room. Wheelchair access (also WC). Music. Air-conditioned

Curator's House

Botanical Gardens, Clarkehouse Road, Sheffield S10 2LN
Tel: (0114) 268 7788
Email: curatorshouse@fsmail.net

NEW CHEF | Modern British | £39–£58

Cheek-by-jowl with Sheffield Botanical Gardens, this converted early-nineteenth-century house with a conservatory offers inventive café food by day and a full-blown modern restaurant menu at night. Daytime offerings range from sandwiches and wraps with fillings like Chinese-style shredded duck to, say, home-smoked chicken salad with chilli jam and crème fraîche. Evening menus change every few months, but expect the likes of asparagus, pea and lemon thyme risotto, or roast duck with spiced pear mash and red cabbage, before desserts such as chocolate and orange mousse with white chocolate ice cream. A few 'special' bottles bump up the excellent-value wine list, which opens at £3.25 a glass, £12.50 a bottle.

Chef: Lee Mangles **Proprietors:** Malcolm and Lesley Donaldson **Open:** all week L 11.30 to 2.30, Tue to Sat D 7 to 10 **Closed:** 25 Dec **Meals:** alc (main courses: L £4.50 to £9.50, D £15 to £18) **Service:** not inc, card slips closed **Cards:** Delta, Diners, Maestro MasterCard, Visa **Details:** 56 seats. 24 seats outside. Private parties: 56 main room. Vegetarian meals. Children's helpings. No smoking. Wheelchair access (also WC). Occasional music. Air-conditioned

To submit a report on any restaurant, please visit *www.which.co.uk/gfgfeedback*.

Greenhead House

84 Burncross Road, Chapeltown, Sheffield S35 1SF
Tel: (0114) 246 9004

Cooking 2 | Modern European | £30–£61

On the northern edge of Sheffield, this cottagey-looking stone house is the place to go for the country house experience. After an aperitif in the 'front-room-style' lounge, move into an intimate gold and red dining room with well-spaced, white-clad tables, candles, and flowers. Neil Allen cooks a light Friday lunch carte and four-course dinners priced according to the main course choice, keeping pace with current trends without gimmickry. Potted brown shrimps coupled with a small asparagus salad with lemon and tarragon dressing launched an inspection meal that included an intermediary gin-and-tonic granita, tender lobster blanquette, and a crème brûlée of well-balanced espresso flavour. Well-made sauces and 'delicious' bread drew praise, as did 'delightfully charming' service. The well-spread global wine list includes house Italian at £14.50.

Chef: Neil Allen **Proprietors:** Neil and Anne Allen **Open:** Fri L 12 to 1, Wed to Sat D 7 to 9 **Closed:** Dec 25 to Jan 1, 2 weeks Easter, 2 weeks Aug **Meals:** alc L (main courses £9.50 to £10.50). Set D £36 to £40 **Service:** not inc, card slips closed **Cards:** Amex, Delta, Maestro, MasterCard, Visa **Details:** 32 seats. Private parties: 32 main room. Car park. Vegetarian meals. Children's helpings. No children under 7. No smoking. Wheelchair access (not WC). No music. No mobile phones

Rafters

220 Oakbrook Road, Nether Green, Sheffield S11 7ED
Tel: (0114) 230 4819
Website: www.raftersrestaurant.co.uk

Cooking 3 | Modern European | £40–£51

'A decent neighbourhood restaurant' thought one visitor to this first-floor restaurant (up a steep, narrow staircase) above an estate agent west of the city centre. It's a small, almost semicircular venue and, besides the spoke-like eponymous ceiling beams, has brick-red walls with matching curtains, carpets, upholstery and napery. The kitchen's short modern repertoire includes standards like chicken and duck liver parfait with Victorian chutney, or bread-and-butter pudding layered with dried winter fruits and served with a butterscotch sauce. Prime raw materials are handled with respect

(Gressingham duck on artichoke, pea and sage risotto; chargrilled Aberdeen Angus fillet with field mushrooms and creamed spinach), and the highlight of an inspection meal was halibut served with a classic sauce Dugléré, chickpea gâteau and buttered asparagus. Five house bottles at £11.95 open a well spread list.

Chefs/Proprietors: Marcus Lane and Michael Sabin **Open:** Thur to Sat and Mon D only 7 to 9.30 **Closed:** 25 and 26 Dec, bank holidays **Meals:** Set D £27.50 **Service:** not inc, 10% for parties of 8 or more, card slips closed **Cards:** Amex, Delta, Diners, Maestro, MasterCard, Visa **Details:** 38 seats. Private parties: 40 main room. Vegetarian meals. No children under 5. No smoking. Music. No mobile phones. Air-conditioned

Richard Smith at Thyme

32-34 Sandygate Road, Crosspool,
Sheffield S10 5RY
Tel: (01142) 666096
Website: www.thymeforfood.co.uk

Cooking 5 | Mod British/Medit | £27–£79

It may be well west of the city centre, just off the A57, but Richard Smith's cool, contemporary eatery is very much a modern British urban restaurant. The long, spacious, off-white dining room with glass screens at one end, blue water-glasses and big foodie pictures on the walls combines smartness and informality. The unpretentiously written menu, which deals in the best brasserie tradition, sounds plain, even brusque ('Yorkshire fish and chips, tartare sauce, scraps, mushy peas'), but this only heightens the gosh factor when the plate arrives. East Coast crab spring roll sounds (and looks) like a Stateside dish, the crisp roll cut on the oblique and the halves upended to flank sliced avocado, pink grapefruit segments and toasted almonds, with a small salad of crabmeat and frisée dressed in lobster oil adding further incident. French-style foie gras terrine comes with compotted Yorkshire rhubarb to prevent it getting uppity; other bits of abroad get a look-in, too – there's Irish stew, and even a version of chicken Kiev. Long, slow cooking is often the sign a kitchen means business, and lamb shoulder emerges from seven hours' controlled braising as faultless, thickly rolled, melting meat with peas, button onions, superb dauphinoise and, naturally, the braising juices. But desserts are where the presentational stops are really pulled out, witness a 'mushroom' of caramel parfait on a crisp meringue stalk (not so much a deconstructed as an exploded pavlova) with passion-fruit cream and passion-fruit sorbet. To cap it all, staff appear 'fantastically well trained'.

For all this ambition it is heartening to see that the wine list has not taken on airs and continues to provide a large slate of good-value basics from £13 before cracking into some canny international choices, such as Diamond Valley in Australia and E. Burn in Alsace. Smart French options top things off. There's a café in Glossop Road, Broomhill, and the Druid Inn, Birchover (see entry) is also in the fold.

Chef: Simon Wild **Proprietors:** Richard and Victoria Smith **Open:** all week 12 to 1.45 (2.45 Sun), 6 to 9.30 (10 Fri/Sat) **Meals:** alc (not Sun L; main courses £14 to £28). Set L Mon to Sat £12 (2 courses) to £16, Set D (Mon to Fri 6 to 7) £16 to £24. Snack L menu available **Service:** not inc, 10% for parties of 12 or more **Cards:** Amex, Maestro, MasterCard, Visa **Details:** 80 seats. Private parties: 60 main room, 15 to 30 private rooms. Vegetarian meals. Children's helpings. No smoking in 1 dining room. Wheelchair access (also WC). Music

Supper Club

AR

289 Abbeydale Road South, Sheffield S17 3LB
Tel: (0114) 235 0101

Originally Carriages, more recently Browns, this is the latest reincarnation of this modern venue on the edge of the city. Seared scallops with chorizo and olive oil mash (£7) make a creditable starter, and the menu follows with, say, saddle of lamb with a mini shepherd's pie (£13), beef Wellington, or wild mushroom and Emmental ravioli. Bringing up the rear are in-vogue ideas like strawberry shots with chocolate fondue (£5.50). Wines from £9.95. Open Tue to Sat D only.

MAP 8 **Shelf** WEST YORKSHIRE

Bentley's

12 Wade House Road, Shelf HX3 7PB
Tel: (01274) 690992
Website: www.bentleys-foodandwine.co.uk

Cooking 3 | Modern British | £19–£49

A simple terraced building on a busy roadside, Bentley's is traditional Yorkshire through and through, from the cosy fireplace and stone stairs to the plain, stone-flagged dining rooms downstairs. Chintzy it ain't. Cooking of a homely style scores some palpable hits. Crab cakes served on salad leaves have good, fresh flavour, and the hearty main courses, such as crisp-skinned sea bass on roast Mediterranean vegetables with a couple of plump scallops, or beef fillet with deeply rich bourguignon sauce and seductive creamy mash, manage to satisfy. High-intensity lemon tart comes with lemon-curd sauce and matching sorbet. Wines are arranged by style and take in plenty of dependable names, with house selections from France (£10.50) and Australia (£13.25).

Chefs: Paul Bentley and Anthony Bickers **Proprietors:** Paul and Pamela Bentley **Open:** Tue to Fri L 12 to 2, Tue to Sat D 6.30 to 9.30 **Closed:** 25 and 26 Dec, first week Jan **Meals:** alc (main courses £11 to £18). Set L £9.50 (2 courses) to £10.95 **Service:** not inc, card slips closed **Cards:** Delta, Maestro, MasterCard, Visa **Details:** 68 seats. Private parties: 24 main room, 10 to 24 private rooms. Vegetarian meals. Children's helpings. No smoking. Music. No mobile phones. Air-conditioned

MAP 2 Shepton Mallet SOMERSET

Blostin's

AR

29–33 Waterloo Road, Shepton Mallet BA4 5HH
Tel: (01749) 343648

The restaurant is small – not a dozen tables – but the cooking is practised, for the Reeds have been here for 21 years. 'He well knows what he can do,' observed a reporter of Nick Reed's cooking, which spans everything from asparagus with Parma ham and hollandaise to crab and prawn tartlets with cucumber salad and sauce grelette (£6.50), from herb-crusted rack of lamb with rosemary jus to fillet of brill with crayfish tails, caperberries and herb butter (£16). Desserts are a high point: warm chocolate tart (£4), and Somerset apple cake ('the best of its kind I have had'). House wine £11.95. Open Tue to Sat D only.

Charlton House Hotel, Mulberry Restaurant

Shepton Mallet BA4 4PR
Tel: (01749) 342008
Website: www.charltonhouse.com

Cooking 5 | Modern British | £37–£84

Charlton House may operate as an elaborate shop window for the Mulberry brand but Roger and Monty Saul have eschewed the fussiness often found in country-house hotels, revelling instead in 'a rather bohemian look and feel'. The dining room occupies a large conservatory, and, although more formal than the rest of the public rooms, creates a striking look with lots of fabrics in varying colours and patterns draped over windows, chairs and tables.

Simon Crannage took over the kitchen early in 2005 and inspection revealed plenty of conscientious effort evident in both the sourcing of materials and the flair with which they are cooked. The repertoire includes some unusual but accomplished combinations. Roasted quail served with pancetta coleslaw, a sausage made of the leg, fried quail's egg, crisp bacon and a Granny Smith reduction, as a first course, manages to combine richness and simplicity in the one dish. Presentation ensures that the dishes look the part, whether roast halibut with artichoke purée, warm salad of young vegetables and carrot vinaigrette, or a pairing of slow-roast sirloin and braised blade with horseradish and a cep purée. Desserts have let the side down a little: white and dark chocolate terrine with cherry sorbet and praline was 'overwrought and unsatisfying'. Service is 'very correct'. Roger Saul's enthusiasm for wine rubs off on a sparky list that sets a host of bright, modern flavours against classical styles from around the world. Bottles start at £18 and there are numerous choices by the glass and in half-bottles.

Chef: Simon Crannage **Proprietors:** Roger and Monty Saul **Open:** Fri to Sun L 12.30 to 2.30, all week D 7.30 to 9.45 **Meals:** Set L £16 (2 courses) to £20, Set D £49.50 **Service:** not inc, 10% for parties of 8 or more **Cards:** Amex, Delta, Diners, Maestro, MasterCard, Visa **Details:** 60 seats. 20 seats outside. Private parties: 90 main room, 10 to 70 private rooms. Car park. Vegetarian meals. Children's helpings. No smoking. Wheelchair access (also WC). Occasional music. No mobile phones. Air-conditioned **Accommodation:** 25 rooms, all with bath/shower. TV. Phone. B&B £130 to £425. Rooms for disabled. Baby facilities

MAP 2 Sherborne DORSET

The Green

The Green, Sherborne DT9 3HY
Tel: (01935) 813821
Website: www.thegreensherborne.co.uk

Cooking 2 | Modern European | £31–£50

Michael and Judith Rust have found their niche in this old ochre-stone building, which now ticks over as a relaxed, well-supported neighbourhood restaurant. The freshness of their ingredients has impressed, and intense flavours come through in

dishes such as grilled fillets of Cornish red mullet with herb couscous, tomato and olive dressing. Overall, the food treads a Modern-European path, taking in anything from honey-glazed confit of duck with Savoy cabbage, smoked bacon, almondine potatoes, baked quince and redcurrants to unadorned grilled lemon sole with lemon and lime butter. To finish, expect desserts like vanilla and banana crème brûlée or lemon meringue roulade with raspberry coulis. A cluster of Languedoc wines heads the affordable, well-spread list; prices begin at £14.95.

Chef: Michael Rust **Proprietors:** Michael and Judith Rust **Open:** Tue to Sat 12 to 2, 7 to 9 **Closed:** 1 week Sept, Christmas, 2 weeks Feb, 1 week May, bank hols **Meals:** alc L (main courses £9 to £15). Set D £16.95 (1 course) to £28.50 **Service:** not inc, card slips closed **Cards:** Delta, Maestro, MasterCard, Visa **Details:** 45 seats. 10 seats outside. Private parties: 45 main room, 10 to 22 private rooms. Vegetarian meals. Wheelchair access (not WC). No music. Air-conditioned

MAP 3 Shere SURREY

Kinghams

Gomshall Lane, Shere GU5 9HE
Tel: (01483) 202168
Website: www.kinghams-restaurant.co.uk

Cooking 3 | Modern English | £33–£65

An ancient, half-timbered, red-tiled building with brickwork set at crazy angles is home to Paul Baker's solo enterprise. Within the low-beamed twin dining rooms, a carte of ambitious modern dishes deals in the likes of venison marinated in juniper and bay garnished with poached pear in ginger, while a separate listing of daily fish specials might take in monkfish medallions on spiced shallot purée, or darne of brill on orange and mustard sauce. An awareness of big-city fashion brings in touches such as a first course of five fish preparations (smoked trout, gravad lax, marinated herrings, smoked haddock brandade and spiced prawns), while populist desserts include 'gooey chocolate pudding' on white and dark chocolate sauces. The wine list covers a lot of ground within a limited compass, opening with a group of house selections from £11.95.

Chef/Proprietor: Paul Baker **Open:** Tue to Sun L 12 to 2, Tue to Sat D 7 to 9.30 **Closed:** 25 Dec to 6 Jan **Meals:** alc exc Sun L (main courses £11 to £23). Set L Tue to Sat £14.95 (2 courses), Set L Sun £15.95 (2 courses) to £19.95, Set D Tue to Thur £15.95 (2 courses) **Service:** not inc **Cards:** Amex, Delta, Diners, Maestro, MasterCard, Visa **Details:** 47 seats. 20 seats outside. Private parties: 48 main room, 20 to 28 private rooms. Car park. Vegetarian meals. No smoking. Wheelchair access (not WC). Occasional music. No mobile phones

MAP 2 Shinfield BERKSHIRE

L'Ortolan

NEW ENTRY

Church Lane, Shinfield RG2 9BY
Tel: (0118) 988 8500
Website: www.lortolan.com

Cooking 6 | Modern French | £42–£139

The red-brick former vicarage will be well known to many Guide users from previous incarnations. Along with the village church, church hall and manor, it forms one side of a stretch of road passing through Shinfield, and has a new conservatory extension alongside neatly tended flowerbeds and a fountain. The interior is done out in soft, natural shades, with a huge mirror in the dining room. After a brief interregnum, Alan Murchison has returned to the stoves here. The focus, as it always has been, is on excellent raw materials delivered to you via the medium of formidable technical skill, with complex constructions and polished presentation abounding. Three superb, meaty scallops, which have made the trip from Skye, sit on little discs of Jerusalem artichoke, accompanied by a purée of the vegetable garnished with hazelnuts and a salad containing Serrano ham. The classic pairing of chicken liver and foie gras is celebrated in a parfait that comes with a slice of peppercorned foie gras terrine, the fruity garnish taking the form of spiced fig.

Fish comes in for meaty treatments in the modern style, so that John Dory may be paired with smoked ham and white beans, as well as a velouté of peas and white truffle, but meats themselves are more mainstream. Rabbit comes with mustard sauce, and roast leg of milk-fed Pyrenean lamb with niçoise vegetables in various guises. Artistry is really let rip at dessert stage, when soft meringue, strawberry sorbet and vanilla parfait are fashioned into something that looks like a giant mushroom. With all the little extras expected from dining at this level, it adds up to a convincing performance, although one that might be better enjoyed if the overall pace of service could be made more consistent.

A fanfare of delicious wines by the glass opens a list strong in French classics and well chosen in the regions. The rest of the world maintains high standards, and Germany has a louder shout than in most establishments. Prices open at £20 for a decent Rioja Crianza. A resourceful sommelier has been applauded.

Chef: Alan Murchison **Proprietor:** Newfee Ltd **Open:** Tue to Sat 12 to 2.30, 7 to 10 **Meals:** alc (main courses £25 to £34). Set L £18 (2 courses) to £23, Set D £55 to £99 (inc wine) **Service:** 12.5% (optional), card slips closed **Cards:** Amex, Delta, Diners, Maestro, MasterCard, Visa **Details:** 84 seats. Private parties: 60 main room, 8 to 18 private rooms. Car park. Vegetarian meals. Children's helpings. No smoking. Wheelchair access (also WC). No music

MAP 2 **Shipham** SOMERSET

Daneswood House

Cuck Hill, Shipham BS25 1RD
Tel: (01934) 843145
Website: www.daneswoodhotel.co.uk

Cooking 2 | Modern British | £39–£68

The three-storey Victorian building sits on a spur of the Mendips called Cuck Hill, with a ravishing view down the steep drop from its perch. Take aperitifs on the cane furniture in the conservatory, before going into one of the two linked dining rooms, where handsome green and gold wallpaper and novelty *objets* catch the eye. The menus aim for distinctiveness, teaming seared scallops with belly pork and Jerusalem artichoke purée, or serving sea bass with ratatouille and a red pepper reduction. A slice of terrine at a spring dinner was chunkily comprised of lambs' sweetbreads, oyster mushrooms and tarragon, and garnished with sun-dried tomatoes and reduced balsamic. Local beef fillet comes bedded on sweet potato mash with braised red cabbage and sauced with whisky and grain mustard. Chilled rice pudding at inspection was lifted by seasoning with lemon and came with stewed gingered rhubarb. The wine list, strong in Bordeaux and Burgundy, has plenty of half-bottles and a generous page of house wines from £10.95.

Chef: Ross Duncan **Proprietors:** David and Elise Hodges **Open:** Sun to Fri L 12 to 2, all week D 7 to 9.30 **Closed:** 24 Dec to 5 Jan **Meals:** alc (main courses £15 to £22). Set L Mon to Fri £15.95 (2 courses), Sun £19.95 (3 courses), Set D Fri £29.95 **Service:** not inc, card slips closed **Cards:** Amex, Delta, Diners, Maestro, MasterCard, Visa **Details:** 50 seats. Private parties: 35 main room, 10 to 14 private rooms. Car park. Vegetarian meals. Children's helpings. No smoking. Wheelchair access (also WC). Occasional music. No mobile phones **Accommodation:** 17 rooms, all with bath/shower. TV. Phone. B&B £89.50 to £150. Baby facilities

MAP 2 **Shurdington** GLOUCESTERSHIRE

The Greenway

Shurdington GL51 4UG
Tel: (01242) 862352
Website: www.thegreenway.co.uk

Cooking 5 | Modern French | £41–£81

This Elizabethan Cotswold manor house built with Lancashire wool money gone posh is now a high-rolling country hotel. There may well be croquet on the lawn, and the dining room affords a verdant view through swagged muslins. Kenny Atkinson's cooking aims for the kind of ornate refinement often expected in such surroundings, and many dishes demonstrate speculative combinations. Main courses might be typified by honey-glazed pork belly presented with creamed cauliflower, black pudding, roast pineapple, baby onions and – just for good measure – seared scallops. Much of it works well, as was attested by the reporter who ate ravioli of pig's cheek with morels and scallops, and finished with a pineapple version of tarte Tatin. A vegetarian menu deals in the likes of pea, parsley and Parmesan risotto with cress salad and lemon oil. The often hesitant continental service has needled a few reporters, but clearly not the one whose car had scarcely drawn up before a morning-coated young man rushed to open the door. House bottles are £25.50 on a wine list with less substance than its weight suggests.

Chef: Kenny Atkinson **Proprietor:** Von Essen Hotels **Open:** all week 12 to 2.30, 7 to 9.30 **Meals:** Set L Mon to Sat £21, Set L Sun £25, Set D £45 to £55 **Service:** not inc **Cards:** Amex, Delta, Maestro, MasterCard, Visa **Details:** 56 seats. 24 seats outside. Private parties: 56 main room, 10 to 20 private rooms. Car park. Vegetarian meals. Children's helpings. No smoking. Music. No mobile phones **Accommodation:** 21 rooms, all with bath/shower. TV. Phone. B&B £99 to £280. Rooms for disabled

MAP 9 Sinnington NORTH YORKSHIRE

Fox and Hounds

AR

Sinnington YO62 6SQ
Tel: (01751) 431577

Genteel eighteenth-century coaching inn tucked away in a quiet village at the start of the renowned Riverside and Woodland Walks. Tradition rules at lunchtime, but the dinner menu aims higher with the likes of twice-baked Stilton soufflé with caramelised pear (£5.50), veal escalope filled with Parma ham, dolcelatte and sage (£13.50), and fish specials such as roast monkfish with pea and apple mint risotto. Finish with, say, lemongrass crème brûlée with coconut sorbet (£4.75). Accommodation. Open all week.

MAP 8 Skipton NORTH YORKSHIRE

Le Caveau

86 High Street, Skipton BD23 1JJ
Tel: (01756) 794274

Cooking 2 | Anglo-French | £24–£49

A cosy place with pleasant service, Le Caveau is a good facility for locals, set among the shops on Skipton's picturesque High Street. Quaint stone walls and a barrel-vaulted ceiling strung with a myriad fairy lights lie beneath street level in two small dining rooms. The menu offers plenty of sound staples and the cooking style is possibly a little 'retro' – witness garlic mushrooms, goats' cheese salad, fruity black pudding with port wine sauce. An inspector found some ingredients lacking in verve, but a timbale of Mediterranean vegetables and feta cheese set in pesto jelly passed muster, while apple and blackberry crumble with well-made crème anglais was 'a perfect nursery-food pud'. In between, one might find halibut perched on aromatic couscous with lemon sauce, or roast duck with prune and Armagnac gravy. A nice, reasonably priced wine list gathers about 70 bottles from around the world, starting with Georges Duboeuf house wines at £11.95.

Chef: Richard Barker **Proprietor:** Brian Womersley **Open:** Tue to Fri L 12 to 2, Tue to Sat D 7 to 9.30 (5.30 to 9.45 Sat) **Meals:** alc (main courses L £7 to £11, D £12 to £17). Set L £15.95, Set D £22.50 **Service:** not inc **Cards:** Amex, Delta, Maestro, MasterCard, Visa **Details:** 30 seats. Private parties: 30 main room, 8 to 16 private rooms. Vegetarian meals. Children's helpings. No smoking. Music

MAP 7 Smart's Hill KENT

Spotted Dog

AR

Smart's Hill TN11 8EE
Tel: (01892) 870253

Food is high on the agenda at this fifteenth-century rural hostelry. Beer-battered cod and chips (£10) and ribeye steak will please the die-hards, while more adventurous palates might be stimulated by modern cooking that puts the emphasis firmly on local produce: Chiddingstone oak-smoked salmon with Bloody Mary dressing (£7) and boned and rolled leg of Penshurst lamb with confit tomato (£10.50). In addition, there are imaginative lunchtime sandwiches and desserts like glazed lemon tart (£5). House wine £11.50. Open all week.

MAP 9 Snainton NORTH YORKSHIRE

Coachman Inn

NEW ENTRY

NORTH YORKSHIRE NEWCOMER OF THE YEAR

Pickering Road West,
Snainton YO13 9PL
Tel: (01723) 859231
Website: www.coachmaninn.co.uk

Cooking 4 | Modern British | £28–£47

'It's a very good set-up' is how one visitor summed up this village inn just west of Scarborough. Roger Gorman previously worked as Stephen Bull's head chef in London and Herefordshire, and his cooking is highly polished and unpretentious, based on good local supplies. Everything is made on the premises, from the 'fantastic' bread, via 'divine' sauces to ice creams, and sensible-length menus keep things uncluttered and centred on the main ingredients, perhaps in the form of duck confit with piccalilli and apple and celery salad. Main courses might include wild salmon with a casserole of summer vegetables – offset by 'a really beautiful mayonnaise' and an intense, fresh tomato sauce – or slow-roast belly of pork coupled with black pudding and served with caramelised apple and prune and Calvados sauce. Side vegetables are teamed with good hollandaise, and to finish there's homely sticky toffee pudding with rum and butterscotch sauce or chocolate and pistachio brownie with chocolate sauce and vanilla ice cream. Service from a friendly young team is led by Mrs Gorman. A well-chosen and unpretentious global wine list is arranged by style, with a few special bottles to spice things up. House wines are £11.50, and nine or more come by the glass.

Chef: Roger Gorman **Proprietors:** Helen Patrick and Patricia Clairmont **Open:** Thur to Tue 12 to 2 (2.30 Sat and Sun), 7 to 9 (9.30 Fri and Sat) **Meals:** alc (main courses £9 to £14) **Service:** not inc, 10% for parties of 7 or more **Cards:** Delta, Maestro, MasterCard, Visa **Details:** 40 seats. 24 seats outside. Private parties: 8 to 10 private rooms. Car park. Vegetarian meals. Children's helpings. No smoking. Wheelchair access (not WC). Music. No mobile phones **Accommodation:** 5 rooms, all with bath/shower. TV. B&B £52 to £85

MAP 6 Snettisham NORFOLK

Rose and Crown AR

Old Church Road, Snettisham PE31 7LX
Tel: (01485) 541382

Seriously extended fourteenth-century inn with a child-friendly attitude and easy access to the delights of the Norfolk coast. The kitchen mixes modern ideas with pub favourites, putting terrine of Asian duck with chilli and peanut dressing (£5.75) and crispy-fried cod with guacamole and roast sweet potatoes (£13) alongside fish and chips and chargrilled burgers. Specials like scorched tuna with pak choi and yam sag aloo add variety, while desserts include rice pudding with rhubarb compote (£5). Around 40 wines from £11.50. Accommodation. Open all week.

MAP 3 Southall GREATER LONDON

Brilliant

72–76 Western Road, Southall UB2 5DZ
Tel: (020) 8574 1928
Website: www.brilliantrestaurant.com

Cooking 3 | North Indian | £24–£61

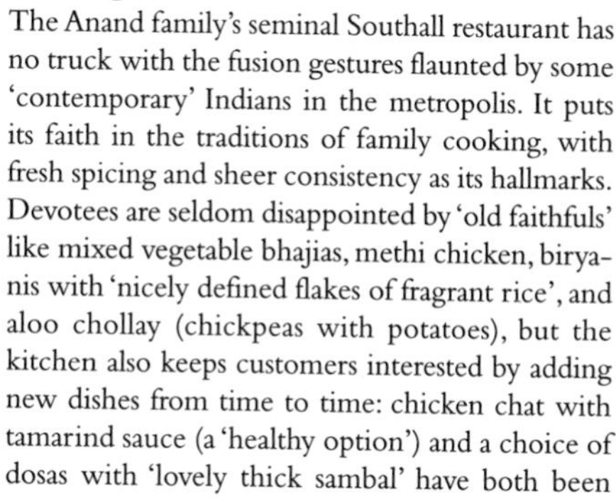

The Anand family's seminal Southall restaurant has no truck with the fusion gestures flaunted by some 'contemporary' Indians in the metropolis. It puts its faith in the traditions of family cooking, with fresh spicing and sheer consistency as its hallmarks. Devotees are seldom disappointed by 'old faithfuls' like mixed vegetable bhajias, methi chicken, biryanis with 'nicely defined flakes of fragrant rice', and aloo chollay (chickpeas with potatoes), but the kitchen also keeps customers interested by adding new dishes from time to time: chicken chat with tamarind sauce (a 'healthy option') and a choice of dosas with 'lovely thick sambal' have both been given the thumbs-up. Rice is spot on, chapatis are properly light, and the selection of breads now includes cleverly folded romali roti. House wine is £9, although lassi and Indian beer are probably more appropriate.

Chef: Davinder Anand **Proprietors:** Kewal and Davinder Anand **Open:** Tue to Fri L 12 to 2.30, Tue to Sun D 6 to 11.30 **Meals:** alc (main courses £4.50 to £15). Set L and D £17.50 **Service:** not inc, card slips closed **Cards:** Amex, Delta, Diners, Maestro, MasterCard, Visa **Details:** 250 seats. Private parties: 120 main room, 120 to 130 private rooms. Car park. Vegetarian meals. Children's helpings. No smoking in 1 dining room. Wheelchair access (also WC). Music. Air-conditioned

Gifto's Lahore Karahi 

162–164 The Broadway, Southall UB1 1NN
Tel: (020) 8813 8669

Noise, crowds and action on Broadway – Southall's, that is! This vast eating arena specialises in Pakistani cooking with an authentic punch: in the snack department (from £1.25 to £2.50) expect samosas, aloo tikka, puris, et al., although most of the action centres on the tandoor, which delivers everything from jumbo prawns to quail (£4.50). 'Tawa' hotplate specials include lamb and kidney, while curries (around £7) go native with kingfish, brains, and haleem (crushed lentils with lamb). Unlicensed, but BYO (no corkage). Open all week.

Madhu's

39 South Road, Southall UB1 1SW
Tel: (020) 8574 1897
Website: www.madhusonline.com

Cooking 3 | North Indian | £24–£50

The recent, contemporary makeover may well have brought this branch of the Anand Brothers' empire to the attention of people who would not normally venture out to Southall, and the kitchen responds by delivering consistent food to all-comers. Aloo tikki with its rich tamarind sauce is a reliable staple, although marinated prawns achar cooked delicately in the tandoor is now reckoned to be the pick of the starters. Jeera chicken is served on the bone in a sauce spiked with cumin, while fish masala has plenty of 'bite'. Rice is dependably good and breads are 'much improved'. Well-drilled staff reflect Southall's truly multicultural face. The well-considered wine list opens with house Bordeaux at £9.

Chefs: Harsandeep Bhanot and J.P. Singh **Proprietors:** Sanjay and Sanjeev Anand **Open:** Mon and Wed to Fri L 12 to 3, Wed to Mon D 6 to 11.30 **Closed:** Dec 25, L bank hols **Meals:** alc (main courses £6 to £12). Set L and D £17.50 to £20 **Service:** not inc, card slips closed **Cards:** Amex, Delta, Maestro, MasterCard, Visa **Details:** 102 seats. Private parties: 45 main room, 25 to 35 private rooms. Vegetarian meals. Wheelchair access (also WC). Music. Air-conditioned

Three Tuns Hotel, Mehfil

NEW ENTRY

45 The Green, Southall UB2 4AR
Tel: (020) 8606 8811
Website: www.mehfil.co.uk

Cooking 2 | Indian | £27–£46

'A classy addition to the vibrant Southall dining scene,' concluded an aficionado after visiting this 'serious' newcomer with an ace up its sleeve. The setting may be unpromising (a modest hotel with a pleasant, airy restaurant complete with a dance floor), but the owners have secured the services of a chef who learned his craft at the prestigious Oberoi Hotel in Mumbai. The kitchen prides itself on good ingredients and authentic spicing, and the expertise shows in, say, dry-cooked bhindi and 'top-class' gulab jamun. Tandooris – especially chicken tikka and king prawns – are of a high standard, other dishes such as chicken methi hit the button, and the supporting cast of vegetables, breads and rice also deserves applause. The brief wine list is a promising slate, with decent drinking from £10.95.

Chefs: Bhim Singh Nagee and Ameer Kahn **Proprietor:** Arun Handa **Open:** all week 12 to 3, 6 to 11 (11.45 Fri and Sat) **Meals:** alc (main courses £4 to £9). Set L £5.95 (1 course) to £6.95 (2 courses) **Service:** not inc, card slips closed **Cards:** Amex, Delta, Maestro, MasterCard, Visa **Details:** 90 seats. Private parties: 164 main room. Car park. Vegetarian meals. Children's helpings. No smoking. Wheelchair access (also WC). Music. Air-conditioned **Accommodation:** 31 rooms, all with bath/shower. TV. Phone. B&B £40 to £69. Rooms for disabled

 This symbol means that smoking is not permitted.

MAP 2 **Southampton** HAMPSHIRE

White Star Tavern

NEW ENTRY

28 Oxford Street, Southampton SO14 3DJ
Tel: (023) 8082 1990
Website: www.whitestartavern.co.uk

Cooking 3 | Modern British | £25–£64

At first glance this former hotel for ocean-going passengers looks like a contemporary watering hole. Push through the crush, however, and at the back is a panelled, banquette-lined, open-plan dining room catering for gastro-pub appetites, its cosmopolitan style reflected in Damian Brown's confident food. It is not difficult to appreciate the menu's wide appeal as it hops from brightly flavoured dishes like tempura Dublin Bay prawns with oriental salad and soy and lime dressing, and parfait of foie gras and chicken livers with pear chutney and a toasted brioche – both hits at inspection – to well-timed roast skate wing with fondant potato, wilted spinach, deep-fried capers and a red wine butter, and ballottine of corn-fed chicken and Agen prunes served with celeriac purée, asparagus and morels. While a few luxury materials add to the sense of extravagance, the kitchen never forgets it is there to please, turning out beer-battered fish and chips with pea purée. The simplicity of desserts is another plus, judging by a first-class selection of sorbets and a lemon tart with white chocolate ice cream and candied orange zest. The wine list is a short, globetrotting slate with plenty under £20. House wine is £12.95.

Chef: Damian Brown **Proprietors:** Matthew Boyle and Mark Dodd **Open:** Mon to Sat 12 to 2.30 (3 Fri and Sat), 6.30 to 9.30 (10 Fri and Sat), Sun 12 to 9 **Closed:** 25 and 26 Dec, 1 Jan **Meals:** alc (main courses £8.50 to £18.50). Set L £12.95 (2 courses) to £14.95, Set D £24.95. Bar menu available **Service:** not inc, 10% for parties of 6 or more **Cards:** Amex, Delta, Maestro, MasterCard, Visa **Details:** 70 seats. 40 seats outside. Private parties: 80 main room, 4 to 6 private rooms. Vegetarian meals. Children's helpings. No smoking. Wheelchair access (also WC). Music. Air-conditioned

MAP 7 **South Cadbury** SOMERSET

Camelot

AR

Chapel Road, South Cadbury BA22 7EX
Tel: (01963) 440448

Arthurian associations explain the name of this solid-looking stone hostelry at the foot of the prehistoric hill fort called Cadbury Castle. By contrast, the kitchen lives in the present, delivering modern ideas like duck and foie gras ballottine with roast beetroot and buckwheat salad (£7), followed by fillet of brill with pak choi, tomato and black-bean sauce (£14.25). There are also lighter dishes such as tagliatelle with rabbit and artichokes, plus desserts such as mulberry and ricotta cheesecake (£4.25). Fairly priced wines from £9.75. Open all week.

MAP 8 **South Crosland** WEST YORKSHIRE

King's Arms

23/25 Midway, South Crosland HD4 7DA
Tel: (01484) 661669

Cooking 4 | Modern European | £23–£52

Dating from the 1930s, this country pub looks across to Almondbury and the tower and hill fort on Castle Hill. It has really come to life since Tracy Lightowlers moved in and revitalised the place in 2003; drinkers gather in the bar, others opt for the sofas and wood-burning stove in the lounge, but most attention centres on the open-plan restaurant. The kitchen delivers an eclectic choice of modern dishes beginning with potato soup with leeks and Stilton fritters, or confit of belly pork with scrumpy apple and five spices, then braised shoulder of lamb with Savoy cabbage and rosemary, or roast cod with curry-flavoured mussel and potato broth. Desserts like dark chocolate fondant with rum parfait and pistachio anglaise complete the picture. 'Lite bite' set-price menu choices could include ham hock and parsley risotto to start and poached smoked haddock with champ and a poached egg to follow; smart sandwiches involve crumpets, blinis and focaccia, as well as good old bread. A handful of award-winning 'wines of distinction' heads the thoughtfully assembled list; house wines start at £11.50.

Chefs: Edd Bowen and Richard Greenway **Proprietor:** Tracy Lightowlers **Open:** Tue to Fri and Sun L 12 to 2 (4 Sun), Tue to Sat D 6 to 9 (9.30 Fri/Sat) **Meals:** alc (main courses £11 to £15). Set L £12 (2 courses) to £15, Set D Tue to Fri £12 (2 courses) to £15 **Service:** not inc **Cards:** Maestro, MasterCard, Visa **Details:** 42 seats. Private parties: 42 main room. Car park. Vegetarian meals. Children's helpings. No smoking. Wheelchair access (also men's WC). Music

MAP 8 **Southport** MERSEYSIDE

Tyndall's

AR

23 Hoghton Street, Southport PR9 0NS
Tel: (01704) 500002

Creditable French-style and Continental cooking in a converted brick and bay-windowed town house opposite the Little Theatre. Two-course midweek deals are good value from £12.95. 'Gourmet' menus run along the lines of sautéed king prawns with garlic mayonnaise (£8) and roast rack of lamb with mint and redcurrant gravy (£14.50) – or you can splash out with a celebratory Mediterranean seafood platter (£47.50 per couple). Two dozen drinkable wines from £12.95. Open Tue to Sat D.

Warehouse Brasserie

30 West Street, Southport PR8 1QN
Tel: (01704) 544662
Website: www.warehousebrasserie.co.uk

Cooking 3 | Global | £22–£54

'It was hard to believe we were in Southport and not on the Med,' commented one reporter, opening a meal here with excellent tapas, although this genteel Victorian resort turns out to be as packed with trendsetting luminaries as Cannes in the season. As the Warehouse goes gently upmarket (its owner is now at work on a new luxury hotel), the plaudits continue to flow. A soup of the famed Formby asparagus impressed one reader mightily, as did the main course of 'pink, moist, succulent' Bowland Fell lamb on Mediterranean vegetables with minted pesto. Fish options might cover chargrilled monkfish, Thai-spiced with chilli, ginger, lime and coriander, and there are more homely Lancashire dishes such as bangers and mash, or fisherman's pie. Indulge yourself at the end with roasted peanut and caramel chocolate torte. Service is commended as 'efficient and effective', and the wine list aims to cover a fair bit of ground in a few short leaps. Prices open at £9.95.

Chefs: Marc Vérité and Darren Smith **Proprietor:** Paul Adams **Open:** Mon to Sat 12 to 2, 5.30 to 10.15 **Closed:** 25 and 26 Dec, 1 Jan **Meals:** alc (main courses £8 to £15.50). Set L £10.95 (2 courses) to £12.95, Set D Mon to Thur £12.95 (2 courses) to £14.95 **Service:** not inc, 10% for parties of 8 or more **Cards:** Delta, Maestro, MasterCard, Visa **Details:** 100 seats. Private parties: 100 main room, 12 to 18 private rooms. Children's helpings. Wheelchair access (also WC). Music. Air-conditioned

MAP 2 Southrop GLOUCESTERSHIRE

Swan at Southrop NEW ENTRY

Southrop GL7 3NU
Tel: (01367) 850205

Cooking 2 | Modern British | £28–£55

Graham Williams, a co-owner of Bibendum (see entry, London), can now be found overseeing proceedings at this creeper-clad pub in a sleepy south Cotswolds village. The Swan still has its public bar and skittle alley, although the focus is now on the food served in the revamped dining area. Chef James Parkinson is also ex-Bibendum, and his cooking has a cosmopolitan edge. Dishes such as steak tartare and escargots Bourgogne can be ordered as starters or main courses, and fish is well sourced: crab vinaigrette keeps things simple, and you can also expect more involved ideas like poached wild halibut with planchada beans, chorizo, squid, olives and oregano. Meat options might include roast loin of Middle White pork with fondant potato and petits pois, while sticky toffee pudding is a decent dessert. House wine is £12.50, and the list is a well-chosen slate favouring the Old World.

Chef: James Parkinson **Proprietors:** Ian Mackenzie, Graham Williams and James Parkinson **Open:** all week L 12 to 2.30 (3 Sat and Sun), Mon to Sat D 7 to 10 **Closed:** 25 Dec **Meals:** alc (main courses £8.50 to £18) **Service:** not inc, card slips closed **Cards:** Maestro, MasterCard, Visa **Details:** 60 seats. 15 seats outside. Private parties: 60 main room, 15 to 50 private rooms. Vegetarian meals. Children's helpings. No music. No mobile phones

MAP 2 Southsea HAMPSHIRE

Bistro Montparnasse

103 Palmerston Road, Southsea PO5 3PS
Tel: (023) 9281 6754
Website: www.bistromontparnasse.co.uk

Cooking 3 | Modern European | £28–£49

From the blue-painted shopfront with its chunky gold lettering to the bright orange walls and bare wooden floors, the bistro presents an honest openness. A lively interest in the cooking and sourcing of materials has been maintained over seven years, while menu descriptions have resisted complexity for its own sake. At lunchtime, roast tomato soup, or smoked haddock and pea velouté bake may precede pan-fried ribeye steak with a red wine reduction, and a vegetarian option: perhaps herb risotto with Parmesan. The dinner menu is no less straightforward, with perhaps griddled king prawns with garlic butter, pan-fried Gressingham duck breast with sweet wine, baby onions and grapes or rabbit, mushroom and mustard casserole. Finish with crème brûlée or lemon and cherry sponge. Wines start at £12 a bottle, and about ten come by the glass.

Chef: Kevin Bingham **Proprietors:** John Saunders and Kevin Bingham **Open:** Tue to Sat 12 to 1.45, 7 to 9.30 **Closed:** 2 weeks Mar, 2 weeks late Sept to early Oct **Meals:** Set L £14.50 (2 courses) to £17.50, Set D £22.50 (2 courses) to £27.50. Light L menu available **Service:** not inc **Cards:** Amex, Delta, Maestro, MasterCard, Visa **Details:** 30 seats. Private parties: 30 main room, 12 to 30 private rooms. Vegetarian meals. No smoking Wheelchair access (not WC). Music

MAP 6 Southwold SUFFOLK

Crown Hotel

90 High Street, Southwold IP18 6DP
Tel: (01502) 722275
Email: crownreception@adnams.co.uk

Cooking 4 | Modern British-Plus | £30–£46

Southwold is the nerve centre of Adnams the brewers, the Crown its flagship. The company not only brews beer but is also a wine merchant of some repute, so the chances are that if you slake your thirst one way or the other in this unspoilt seaside town, you will have bought into the Adnams experience. The Crown makes the most of its image as a traditional eighteenth-century coaching inn, although it has been dolled up in recent times, and it operates as a pub, wine bar, restaurant and small hotel. Whether you eat in the spacious and comfortable bar or in the plusher more formal restaurant, the food is familiar Modern European, as demonstrated by a spring meal in the restaurant that opened with gravad lax with lemon and dill dressing and red mullet with saffron, fennel and orange salad. This was followed by whole grilled lemon sole with brown shrimp and parsley butter and a 'lovely, rich, tasty' navarin of lamb. Desserts might take in glazed lemon tart with crème fraîche, and service is assured even when under pressure.

The full wine list runs to over 250 bins but the short slate of 20 good-value options by the bottle (from £11.25) or glass may be all most diners need. Both reflect the expertise of the Adnams team.

Chef: Sue Miles **Proprietor:** Adnams Brewery Plc **Open:** all week 12.30 to 1.30, 7.30 to 8.45 **Meals:** Set L £18.50 (2 courses) to £21.50, Set D £24 (2 courses) to £29. Bar menu available **Service:** not inc **Cards:** Delta, Maestro, MasterCard, Visa **Details:** 24 seats. Private parties: 24 main room. Car park. Vegetarian meals. Children's helpings; no children under 8 at D. No smoking. Wheelchair access (also WC). No music. No mobile phones **Accommodation:** 14 rooms, 13 with bath/shower. TV. Phone. B&B £80 to £168. Baby facilities

MAP 9 **Sowerby** WEST YORKSHIRE

Travellers Rest

Steep Lane, Sowerby HX6 1PE
Tel: (01422) 832124

Cooking 3 | Modern British-Plus | £26–£48

'Fly in by helicopter,' suggests the owner of this remote, stone-walled pub/restaurant perched high on the moors between Sowerby Bridge and Cragg Vale; alternatively, take a route map and follow the Yorkshire byways. Inside, a stone chimney breast with a wood-burning stove separates the bar from the immaculately laid dining area. Bar meals and blackboard specials can be as pubby as home-made steakburger on focaccia, but the full evening menu ventures into the world of seared scallops on pea purée with crispy pancetta and mint oil, roast rump of lamb with crushed baked potato, pak choi and mint pesto, and savoury polenta cake with goats' cheese and slow-roast tomato 'stack'. To finish, there are desserts like ginger parkin with rhubarb ripple ice cream and hot spiced syrup. House wine is £9.50

Chef: Darren Collinson **Proprietor:** Caroline Lumley **Open:** Sat and Sun L 12.30 to 3, Wed to Sun D 6 to 9.30 (10 Sat, 8.30 Sun) **Meals:** alc (main courses £8.50 to £18). Set L Sun £16.95, Set D Wed £20 **Service:** not inc **Cards:** Delta, Maestro, MasterCard, Visa **Details:** 80 seats. 40 seats outside. Private parties: 100 main room. Car park. Vegetarian meals. No children under 9. No smoking in restaurant, permitted in bar. Wheelchair access (not WC).Music

NEW ENTRY	This appears after the restaurant's name if the establishment was not a main entry in last year's Guide, although it may have been a 'round-up/also recommended' in previous editions.

MAP 9 **Staithes** NORTH YORKSHIRE

Endeavour

1 High Street, Staithes TS13 5BH
Tel: (01947) 840825
Website: www.endeavour-restaurant.co.uk

Cooking 4 | Modern British/Seafood | £33–£50

This little fishing village north of Whitby was the birthplace of Captain James Cook, whose ship provides the name for Brian Kay and Charlotte Willoughby's enterprising, seafood-orientated restaurant. The kitchen is newly refurbished and the lower dining room redecorated, but the place is run with an appealing absence of flourish, the formidable quality of the ingredients and cooking allowed to speak for themselves. Why bother with farmed Greek red mullet, when incomparable specimens come from the Whitby boats? These may well end up perched with king prawns for company atop a tower of tomato, pear and rocket. Another commended starter is crab cakes with a chilli tomato dip and green salad, while meatier tastes might be served by chunky pork and venison terrine. 'Deliciously fresh and cooked à point,' wrote one reporter of a main course of halibut on celeriac mash topped with crisp Parma ham in a red wine jus, and a mature-tasting fillet steak with chickpea mayonnaise went down well too. Generous vegetable servings accompany main dishes, and meals end with suitably zingy rhubarb compote with ginger parfait, or a dessert assiette, perhaps encompassing lemon posset, crème brûlée, chocolate tart with marinated kumquats, and prune and Armagnac ice cream. The short, serviceable wine list opens with five French and Chilean house selections at £11.50.

Chefs/Proprietors: Brian Kay and Charlotte Willoughby **Open:** Tue to Sat D 7 to 9 **Closed:** 25 and 26 Dec, 1 Jan **Meals:** alc D (main courses £13 to £17) **Service:** not inc **Cards:** Amex, Delta, Diners, Maestro, MasterCard, Visa **Details:** 36 seats. Private parties: 16 main room, 16 private room. Car park. Vegetarian meals. No smoking. Music. No mobile phones **Accommodation:** 3 rooms, all with bath/shower. TV. B&B £70 to £80. Baby facilities

	This symbol means that accommodation is available at this establishment.

MAP 6 **Stamford** LINCOLNSHIRE

Oakhouse Restaurant

11 All Saints Place, Stamford PE9 2AR
Tel: (01780) 756565
Website: www.oakhouserestaurant.com

Cooking 2 | Modern British | £24–£58

'Without exception the food, wine and service has been excellent,' rang one endorsement of this younger sibling of the World Service (see entry, Nottingham). It appeals partly because of the flexibility it offers: a proper à la carte lunch as well as dinner, but also a set-price option at each (except dinner on Friday and Saturday). A three-course lunch for £16.75 is good going, given that it might include home-cured gravad lax, fried fillet of bream, and fig and almond tart. Despite an occasionally bold dish such as confit duck leg with pak choi, cashews, bean sprouts and hoisin dressing, flavours tend not to be exotic, relying rather on pesto to infuse roasted wild sea bass, or caramelised apples to set off a slow-roasted pork belly. Crème brûlée is a familiar way to finish, or try steamed syrup pudding with crème anglaise. House wine is from £12.25.

Chefs: Chris Elson, Chris Archer **Proprietors:** André Vazquez, Chris Elson and Ashley Walter **Open:** all week L 12 to 2.30 (3 Sun), Mon to Sat D 6.30 to 10 **Meals:** alc (main courses £10.50 to £18.50). Set L Mon to Fri £9.95 (2 courses) to £13.50, Set L Sat and Sun £14 (2 courses) to £16.75, Set D Mon to Thur £17.50 **Service:** not inc, 10% for parties of 8 or more **Cards:** Amex, Delta, Maestro, MasterCard, Visa **Details:** 80 seats. 40 seats outside. Private parties: 80 main room, 10 to 20 private rooms. Vegetarian meals. Children's helpings. Wheelchair access (also WC). Music

MAP 6 **Stanton** SUFFOLK

Leaping Hare

Wyken Vineyards, Stanton IP31 2DW
Tel: (01359) 250287
Website: www.wykenvineyards.co.uk

Cooking 2 | Modern European | £34–£51

A medieval barn makes a 'lovely, high, airy space with light-coloured timber' for the restaurant and informal café at Wyken Vineyard. Simplicity characterises the cooking; 'fresh tasting' slices of focaccia with a bottle of olive oil for drizzling prepare the way for starters like seared scallops with citrus oil and watercress salad, or pressed Wyken pheasant and rabbit terrine served with fig chutney. Uncomplicated treatment of good-quality ingredients shows in a main-course cannon of Suffolk lamb with roast fondant potatoes, aubergine and celeriac and 'a little pool of tasty, meaty gravy', while orange-scented pannacotta with raspberry sorbet makes an upbeat finale. The compact wine list includes Wyken Vineyards bottles from £14.50 (£3.50 a glass).

Chef: Nick Claxton Webb **Proprietors:** Kenneth And Carla Carlisle **Open:** all week L 12 to 2, Fri to Sat D 7 to 9 **Closed:** 24 Dec to 5 Jan **Meals:** alc (main courses £12 to £17), Set L Mon to Fri £15.95 (2 courses) to £18.95. Light L menu available **Service:** not inc, 10% for parties of 6 or more **Cards:** Maestro, MasterCard, Visa **Details:** 70 seats. 30 seats outside. Private parties: 65 main room. Car park. Vegetarian meals. Children's helpings. No smoking. Wheelchair access (also WC). No music

MAP 2 **Stanton Fitzwarren** WILTSHIRE

Stanton House Hotel, Rosemary

NEW ENTRY

The Avenue, Stanton Fitzwarren SN6 7SD
Tel: (01793) 861777
Website: www.stantonhouse.co.uk

Cooking 3 | Japanese | £22–£65

A fabulous Elizabethan-style mansion is the setting for this conference hotel now owned by Honda – whose huge complex is nearby. The place is geared up for the company's high-flyers, with state-of-the-art facilities including two restaurants: Mount Fuji is for 'no-shoes' dining, while Rosemary is a more westernised room with clean lines and tranquil views. It may not present itself as an option for the general public, but anyone who is interested in Japanese cuisine ought to give it a try. Ingredients are out of the top drawer – witness the dazzling selection of palate-cleansing sashimi arranged on a glass plate – and the kitchen shows off its skills with a flamboyant assortment of ultra-crisp fish tempura (including 'unbelievably tender' octopus). Braised ox tongue is served with miso sauce, teriyaki chicken comes with egg-fried sushi rice, and it's worth finishing with the bizarre combination of silky green tea ice cream, aduki beans and fruit gelatine. Malt whiskies outnumber sakés; alternatively, there are 20 wines from £11.50.

Chef: Tsutomotu Igarashi **Proprietor:** Hkc (UK) **Open:** all week 12 to 2, 6 to 10 **Meals:** alc (main courses £5 to £24) **Service:** not inc **Cards:** Delta, Maestro, MasterCard, Visa **Details:** 80 seats. Private parties: 100 main room, 8 to 100 private rooms. Car park. Vegetarian meals. Children's helpings. No smoking. Wheelchair access (also WC). Music. Air-conditioned **Accommodation:** 82 rooms, all with bath/shower. TV. Phone. B&B £65 to £150. Rooms for disabled. Baby facilities

MAP 5 **Stathern** LEICESTERSHIRE

Red Lion Inn

2 Red Lion Street, Stathern LE14 4HS
Tel: (01949) 860868
Website: www.theredlioninn.co.uk

Cooking 2 | Modern British-Plus | £23–£49

Like its elder brother, the Olive Branch in Clipsham (see entry), this congenial country inn deep in the hunting shires has put its home village squarely on the gastronomic map. Local produce is taken seriously here (check out the map of suppliers on the back of the menus); that said, the kitchen casts its net wide, offering steamed mussels with Thai spices and serving roast chicken breast with pearl barley risotto and garlic sausage. Potted prawns, sausages and mash, and fish and chips please the diehards, and Sunday lunch includes decent roasts. Soups – perhaps watercress, or Jerusalem artichoke – are full-flavoured, but desserts such as bread-and-butter pudding can play second fiddle to the rest of the repertoire. The wine list is an enthusiast's slate liberally peppered with bin-ends, curios and 'fine and rare' vintages. Prices start at £10.95.

Chef: Phil Lowe **Proprietors:** Ben Jones, Sean Hope and Marcus Welford **Open:** all week L 12 to 2 (3 Sun), Mon to Sat D 7 to 9.30 **Closed:** 1 Jan **Meals:** alc (main courses £9.50 to £16.50). Set L Mon to Sat £11.50 (2 courses) to £13.50, Set L Sun £15.50 **Service:** not inc, card slips closed **Cards:** Delta, Maestro, MasterCard, Visa **Details:** 60 seats. 30 seats outside. Private parties: 20 main room. Car park. Vegetarian meals. Children's helpings. No smoking in 1 dining room. Wheelchair access (not WC). Occasional music

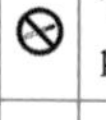	This symbol means that smoking is not permitted.
	This symbol means that there are some restrictions on smoking though it may be allowed in some eating areas.

MAP 3 **Stedham** WEST SUSSEX

Hamilton Arms

AR

School Lane, Stedham GU29 0NZ
Tel: (01730) 812555

The Hamilton Arms was one of the first pubs to introduce authentic Thai food, yet it doesn't deter locals and visitors from enjoying the pubby atmosphere, real ales and traditional bar food like cottage pie and lasagne. The Thai menu (also available to take away) delivers a long list of popular items such as satays, stir-fries, tom yum soups, and curries, with typical offerings including pla muek (battered squid with sweet-and-sour sauce; £4.25), and pud Thai (fried rice noodles with shrimps, crab and ground peanuts; £6). House wine £9.50. Closed Mon.

MAP 2 **Stockbridge** HAMPSHIRE

Greyhound

31 High Street, Stockbridge SO20 6EY
Tel: (01264) 810833

Cooking 4 | Modern British | £44–£78

Gentrified chic sums up the remodelled Greyhound, which makes the most of its setting by the River Test. Inside, there's room for a few drinkers at the bar, but the place is driven from its kitchen. Former chef Darren Bunn has upped sticks for Dublin, but Helene Schoeman makes a very worthy successor, judging by early feedback. Dishes can seem deceptively simple, but they are shot through with big flavours, contrasts, colour and touches of finesse. A 'cultured' risotto of avocado and chorizo made a great start to one meal before perfectly timed Gressingham duck breast with pea purée, a 'croquette' packed with duck rillettes and some vibrant adornments; seafood also grabs attention, whether a classic fishcake with poached egg and chive beurre blanc, or black bream fillet on well-timed saffron and broad bean couscous. Desserts are top-drawer offerings such as 'oozing' chocolate fondant with fresh mint and chocolate chip ice cream. The wine list focuses on France, plus Italy and Australia, and juggles stars and affordable bottles with élan. Madiran and

Savoie at £15 are intriguing choices amid an international range of house wines.

Chef: Helene Schoeman **Proprietor:** T.C. Fiducia **Open:** all week L 12 to 2.30, Mon to Sat D 7 to 9.30 **Closed:** 25 and 26 Dec, 1 Jan, bank hols D **Meals:** alc (main courses £12 to £23). Bar menu available **Service:** 10% (optional), card slips closed **Cards:** Delta, Maestro, MasterCard, Visa **Details:** 46 seats. 70 seats outside. Private parties: 40 main room. Car park. Vegetarian meals. Children's helpings. No smoking in 1 dining room. Wheelchair access (not WC). Occasional music

MAP 2 **Stockcross** BERKSHIRE

Vineyard at Stockcross

Stockcross RG20 8JU
Tel: (01635) 528770
Website: www.the-vineyard.co.uk

Cooking 7 | Anglo-French | £42–£113

Flames lap over the surface of the water feature that greets the arriving eye, and the surrounding villa is so Napa Valley that you could be forgiven for thinking you aren't in Berkshire any more. Once inside, there are more obvious English country-house design references, but set against a backdrop of more of that American West Coast airy spaciousness, the lushness and plushness of it all accentuated by quality furnishings and expensive artworks. John Campbell is at the forefront of the modern gastronomic movement in the UK, with combinations intended to challenge as well as titillate. To seasoned diners, some of his cooking will seem quite familiar by now. Newcomers might need a while to get their bearings. A risotto of peas, lambs' sweetbreads and Assam foam might set the ball rolling, and the momentum might carry you through to a pairing of braised oxtail with turbot, or roast John Dory with confit of belly pork, garlic soubise and a sauce of sherry. A roast Anjou squab was a fine, precisely timed inspection starter, partnered with celeriac and red chard. Unexpected sweetness is often a component of the new British cooking, so this dish also contained black treacle, which just managed to unbalance it.

Portions are modest, the better perhaps to emphasise their unconventionality. Roast saddle of lamb, impressively tender, has been accompanied by pea and mint risotto and a delicate chocolate jelly. Sheer technical panache is much in evidence, as when that combination of oxtail and vanilla-topped turbot, with accompanying mash, is brought off with great aplomb, and when an airy brûlée for dessert is matched with strawberries and a concentrated jelly of black olives and Pedro Ximénez, the last lending the whole dish a 'seductive kick'. Cheeses were not all in prime condition at inspection, but imaginative, expertly made petits fours ended things on a high. Service can be a trifle disjointed but is friendly enough.

California dreaming is the order of the day on the impressive wine list. Sir Peter Michael's unimpeachable credentials as a wine producer in the USA have resulted in a section dedicated to the great western state. The separate 'International List' is also a tour-de-force, with particular strength in Bordeaux and Italy, and plenty of options around the £20 mark.

Chef: John Campbell **Proprietor:** Sir Peter Michael **Open:** all week 12 to 1.45, 7 to 9.45 **Meals:** Set L £22 (2 courses) to £75, Set D £29 (2 courses) to £75 **Service:** not inc, card slips closed **Cards:** Amex, Delta, Diners, Maestro, MasterCard, Visa **Details:** 70 seats. Private parties: 120 main room. Car park. Vegetarian meals. Children's helpings. No smoking. Wheelchair access (also WC). Music. No mobile phones. Air-conditioned **Accommodation:** 49 rooms, all with bath/shower. TV. Phone. B&B £180 to £670. Rooms for disabled. Baby facilities. Swimming pool

MAP 6 **Stoke Holy Cross** NORFOLK

Wildebeest Arms

82–86 Norwich Road, Stoke Holy Cross
NR14 8QJ
Tel: (01508) 492497
Email: mail@animalinns.co.uk

Cooking 2 | Modern European | £25–£54

'There is some serious cooking here,' affirmed one correspondent after a visit to this neat-and-tidy roadside pub/restaurant some four miles south of Norwich. African artefacts, masks and musical instruments add a touch of exoticism to the interior, although the kitchen takes most of its inspiration from Europe. Smoked salmon and saffron risotto and seared beef fillet with shaved pecorino, wild rocket and herb leaf salad are typical starters, before basil-roast chicken breast with cocotte potatoes, roast celeriac, leeks, sautéed chanterelles and truffle jus or Gressingham duck breast with sauté Alsace lardon cabbage and redcurrant jus. Following on, expect the likes of vanilla pannacotta with mango salad and rhubarb sorbet or raspberry Bakewell tart with white chocolate ice cream. The seriousness extends to the wine list, a winner for its inspired selection (particularly in France and Australia), accurate notes and generally very fair prices. House bottles are £11.95.

Chef: Daniel Smith **Proprietor:** Henry Watt **Open:** all week 12 to 2, 7 to 9.30 **Closed:** 25 and 26 Dec **Meals:** alc (not Sun L; main courses £9.95 to £18.50). Set L £11.95 (2 courses) to £14.95, Set D (not Sat) £15 to £18.50 **Service:** not inc, card slips closed **Cards:** Amex, Delta, Diners, Maestro, MasterCard, Visa **Details:** 60 seats. Private parties: 60 main room. Car park. Vegetarian meals. Children's helpings. No-smoking area. Music

MAP 2 Stoke Row OXFORDSHIRE

Crooked Billet

AR

Newlands Lane, Stoke Row RG9 5PU
Tel: (01491) 681048

High-profile country pub, famed for its countless TV appearances, in an extremely remote setting – although everyone seems to find it. Ambitious cooking and global flavours are typified by warm truffled wild mushroom tartlet with tomato and broad bean salad, seared tuna niçoise with sautéed baby squid, roast Mediterranean vegetables and salsa verde, and passion-fruit mousse charlotte with vanilla ice cream, strawberries and raspberry coulis. Open all week.

MAP 2 Stoke-sub-Hamdon SOMERSET

Priory House Restaurant

NEW ENTRY

1 High Street, Stoke-sub-Hamdon TA14 6PP
Tel: (01935) 822826
Website: www.theprioryhouserestaurant.co.uk

Cooking 5 | Modern British | £32–£61

Built of warm, ochre-coloured Ham stone, this Somerset village is in the enviable position of being very near no fewer than three National Trust properties with noteworthy gardens, and the village's priory, dating from the fourteenth century, is owned by the NT too. It also boasts Peter and Sonia Brooks's small restaurant on a corner of the main road. To one side is a tiny terrace with outdoor tables for drinks, while the interior is done out in beige and navy, with fruit and flower prints on the walls, as well as some framed French menus.

This is the first restaurant venture for the owners, and indications are that they pretty much hit the ground running. While Sonia Brooks capably runs front-of-house, Peter is a hard-working chef, producing as much as he possibly can himself from irreproachable materials and achieving impressive results without feeling the need to strive after breathless novelty. A hefty serving of calves' sweetbreads with Puy lentils and sauce gribiche made a robust start to an inspection visit, the offal coated in peppery breadcrumbs, the lentils both buttery and acid-sharp, the sauce properly made. This was followed by loin of local wild venison, of 'immaculate timing', sliced around a cluster of blueberries, served with a rösti of celeriac that just lacked a little crunch. An alternative starter choice might be a tripartite terrine of smoked fish (salmon, mackerel and trout) with green peppercorn cream, with main courses such as beef fillet with seared foie gras. Fine pastry work distinguishes desserts such as apricot and almond tart with 'gorgeous' Amaretto ice cream. A compact, mostly well-chosen wine list jumbles Old and New Worlds together, with house wines from £14 and wines by the glass from £4.50.

Chef: Peter Brooks **Proprietors:** Peter and Sonia Brooks **Open:** Sat L 12 to 2, Tue to Sat D 7 to 9.30 **Closed:** first 2 weeks Nov, last week May, first week June, bank hols **Meals:** alc (main courses £16.50 to £19.50). Set L £14.50 (2 courses) to £19.50 **Service:** not inc, card slips closed **Cards:** Maestro, MasterCard, Visa **Details:** 25 seats. Private parties: 30 main room. No children under 7. No smoking. Wheelchair access (not WC). Music

MAP 5 Stow-on-the-Wold GLOUCESTERSHIRE

Old Butchers

AR

7 Park Street, Stow-on-the-Wold GL54 1AQ
Tel: (01451) 831700

As the Guide went to press, Peter and Louise Robinson moved across town from their former premises, the Kings Arms, to the Old Butchers, on the site of what was Hamiltons. The menu shows Mediterranean leanings in dishes such as mackerel with green olives, garlic and oregano (£5), or prosciuto crudo with cantaloupe melon (£6) among starters. Move on to roast Looe lemon sole with brown shrimps and capers (£15), or calf's liver with slow-cooked onions and Italian bacon. Finish with brown bread ice cream, or a plate of British cheeses. House wine is £12. Reports please. Open all week.

Unicorn Hotel

NEW ENTRY

Sheep Street, Stow-on-the-Wold GL54 1HQ
Tel: (01451) 830257
Website: www.birchhotels.co.uk

Cooking 2 | Modern European | £31–£52

This stone-built inn stands beside the Fosse Way, with the parish church behind. A very English interior includes patterned carpets and curtains, fruit and veg prints on walls, and a Welsh dresser loaded with plates. Michael Carr cooks good rustic food, enhancing well-sourced British ingredients with a little Mediterranean technique. Start with two chargrilled sardines with chopped garlic and a pile of wild rocket and lemony green olives, then roast duck breast, its fat well-rendered, with a potato, celeriac and Jerusalem artichoke mash, spring greens and a forthright port sauce. Fish-eaters might pick grilled halibut with broad beans and new potato salad. In February, our inspector enjoyed a scoop of Christmas pudding ice cream along with banana and blackcurrant versions, or try pear and fig – poached and roast respectively – with honey-and-whisky ice cream. The short pub-style wine list has one or two in each colour from most countries, rising to Château Beau-Site 1995 at £39.

Chef: Michael Carr **Proprietor:** Birch Hotels and Inns **Open:** all week D only 7 to 9. Bar L and D menu available **Closed:** 1 October **Meals:** alc (main courses £10 to £15.50) **Service:** not inc **Cards:** Amex, Delta, Diners, Maestro, MasterCard, Visa **Details:** 55 seats. Private parties: 40 main room. Vegetarian meals. Children's helpings. No smoking. Music **Accommodation:** 20 rooms, all with bath/shower. TV. Phone. B&B £60 to £160. Baby facilities

NEW ENTRY	This appears after the restaurant's name if the establishment was not a main entry in last year's Guide, although it may have been a 'round-up/also recommended' in previous editions.

⊘	This symbol means that smoking is not permitted.
⊘	This symbol means that there are some restrictions on smoking though it may be allowed in some eating areas.

MAP 5 **Stratford-upon-Avon** WARWICKSHIRE

Russons

8 Church Street, Stratford-upon-Avon CV37 6HB
Tel: (01789) 268822

Well-liked bistro in a central location with a strong showing of seafood on the long menu – check the blackboard for daily specials such as monkfish, salmon and scallop brochette (£13), or grilled lemon sole with crab butter (£14). Sturdy meat dishes take in boeuf bourguignonne and braised lamb shoulder. Start with chicken satay (£5.50) or seafood-stuffed tomato and fill up on blackberry and apple crêpes (£4.75). Wines from £11.95. Closed Sun and Mon.

MAP 1 **Strete** DEVON

Kings Arms

Dartmouth Road, Strete TQ6 0RW
Tel: (01803) 770377
Website: www.kingsarmsdartmouth.co.uk

Cooking 4 | Seafood | £33–£63

The Kings Arms, a large, white-painted eighteenth-century building with an impressive cast-iron balcony, ably fills the role of traditional village pub, but also attracts outsiders for its jolly atmosphere and excellent food. The seasonally changing main menu is usually bolstered by a couple of daily specials, and there is also a light lunch menu of snack dishes and one-plate meals – both are slanted towards fish dishes. The latter might offer River Yealm oysters on ice with local Hannaford's pork chipolatas and coarse-grain mustard, a heavenly combination for one reporter, or pan-fried soft herring roes on green peppercorn toasts, featuring plump, creamy roes. The main menu lists starters of mackerel escabèche with rhubarb and ginger jelly, or tuna carpaccio with tiger prawn tempura and chilli dipping sauce, followed by rack of lamb with celeriac mash and a port and rosemary jus, or pan-fried skate wing 'au poivre' with a red wine reduction. Finish with orange and Grand Marnier crème brûlée or the excellent West Country cheeses with oatcakes. Bread is home-made and might include the splendid beer bread made with Otter Ale, while wines include ten house selections at a reasonable £12.50 a bottle (£3.35 a glass).

Chef: Rob Dawson **Proprietors:** Rob Dawson and Virginia Heath **Open:** Tue to Sun L 12 to 2 (3 Sun), Tue to Sat D 7 to 9 **Meals:** alc (main courses £12 to £16.50). Light menu available Sun D and Mon **Service:** not inc **Cards:** Amex, Delta, Maestro, MasterCard, Visa **Details:** 30 seats. 60 seats outside. Private parties: 30 main room. Car park. Vegetarian meals. Children's helpings. No smoking. Occasional music

Laughing Monk AR

Totnes Road, Strete TQ6 0RN
Tel: (01803) 770639

Unchanging, personally run restaurant in a converted Victorian schoolhouse. Menus take account of local produce for dishes with a familiar ring: starters like Fowey mussels or game terrine with pickled vegetables and red onion chutney (£5.25) could be followed by herb-crusted rack of lamb or grilled fillet of West Country beef on rösti with grain mustard and brandy sauce (£16.50). Around two dozen international wines with prices from £11.50. Open Sun L and Tue to Sat D.

MAP 2 **Stuckton** HAMPSHIRE

Three Lions

HAMPSHIRE RESTAURANT OF THE YEAR

Stuckton, Fordingbridge SP6 2HF
Tel: (01425) 652489
Website: www.thethreelionsrestaurant.co.uk

Cooking 6 | Anglo-French | £31–£61

In the sylvan setting of two acres of gardens with the New Forest beyond, this family-run restaurant-with-rooms certainly enjoys a prime site. Well-spaced, smartly dressed tables and the amenable approach of Jane Womersley out front help to create a relaxed feel, and Mike Womersley's menus will not blind you with culinary science. Salad of forest mushrooms, home-made gravad lax, whole glazed Dover sole, and Scotch fillet with roast shallots, suggest that the cooking will do exactly what it says on the tin, and so it does. These laconic descriptions belie dishes of immense concentration and flair, however, as was attested by the reader who enjoyed the starter pairing of sautéed scallops and shrimps, before following on with brilliantly timed turbot in a tarragon sauce. The lime parfait to finish was pretty nifty, too. The trick seems to be, in the opinion of another, 'the freshest ingredients cooked simply so that one can enjoy their full flavour'. Truffle-studded guinea fowl, well-chosen vegetables to match each main course, and glazed strawberries with lemon-balm ice cream were among the highlights for her. Finally, last year we suggested the coffee could do with a little improvement, a wish that seems to have been fulfilled.

The wine list is short, French-biased and chosen with precision, and a good showing of halves is a bonus. House is £12.75 but most bottles are over £20.

Chef: Mike Womersley **Proprietors:** Mike and Jayne Womersley **Open:** Tue to Sun L 12 to 2, Tue to Sat D 7 to 9 (9.30 Sat) **Meals:** alc (main courses £15 to £19). Set L £15.75 **Service:** not inc **Cards:** Delta, Maestro, MasterCard, Visa **Details:** 60 seats. 20 seats outside. Private parties: 60 main room, 10 to 30 private rooms. Car park. Vegetarian meals. Children's helpings. No smoking. Wheelchair access (not WC). No music. No mobile phones **Accommodation:** 7 rooms, all with bath/shower. TV. B&B £65 to £115. Rooms for disabled. Baby facilities

MAP 7 **Studland** DORSET

Shell Bay AR

Ferry Road, Studland BH19 3BA
Tel: (01929) 450363

'A haven of peace' for some, 'lively fun' for others – either way, this is in a glorious location by Poole harbour. Fish is one of the kitchen's strong points, with oysters, langoustines and lobsters topping the bill; also on the full evening menu might be Dorset crab, avocado and peach gâteau (£9), followed by baked halibut with samphire, roast fennel and kumquat jam (£17) and chargrilled fillet steak with wild New Forest mushrooms. Live music Sun D. Closed Mon.

MAP 2 **Sturminster Newton** DORSET

Plumber Manor

Sturminster Newton DT10 2AF
Tel: (01258) 472507
Website: www.plumbermanor.com

Cooking 2 | Anglo-French | £32–£54

Keeping a success successful requires much hard work, and the continuing popularity of the Prideaux-Brune family's seventeenth-century ancestral manor is largely down to their hands-on approach. In welcoming, homely, country-house

surroundings, Brian Prideaux-Brune's set menus (with optional 'à la carte supplements') amiably combine traditional British and French elements, taking in crab mousseline with crevettes in a light curry sauce, or wild mushroom mille-feuille with brandy, basil and cream. Good timing and balance show in main courses like tender beef fillet wrapped in Parma ham with a rich mushroom and red wine sauce, or loin of pork with 'excellent crackling', apple sauce and sage-flavoured gravy. Then the dessert trolley dispenses strawberry mille feuille, 'fresh' cheesecake and 'superb' mango mousse. Wines are mostly French, with some carefully chosen New World examples; prices from £12.50.

Chef: Brian Prideaux-Brune **Proprietor:** Richard Prideaux-Brune **Open:** Sun L 12.30 to 1.30, all week D 7.30 to 9 **Closed:** Feb **Meals:** Set L Sun £21, Set D £26 **Service:** not inc, card slips closed **Cards:** Amex, Diners, Maestro, MasterCard, Visa **Details:** 60 seats. Private parties: 44 main room, 12 to 24 private rooms. Car park. Vegetarian meals. Children's helpings. No smoking. Wheelchair access (also WC). No music **Accommodation:** 16 rooms, all with bath/shower. TV. Phone. B&B £95 to £170. Rooms for disabled. Baby facilities

MAP 1 **Summercourt** CORNWALL

Viner's Bar and Restaurant

Carvynick, Summercourt TR8 5AF
Tel: (01872) 510544

Cooking 4 | Modern European | £25–£51

Kevin and Jane Viner's farmhouse-style restaurant now extends over two floors, increasing covers and creating extra lounge space in the bar. The kitchen keeps faith with local produce where possible, and it is not difficult to appreciate the menu's wide appeal as it hops from traditional moules marinière, or chicken liver parfait with 'wonderful' pear chutney, to the indulgence of a duo of grilled duck breast and confit leg served with a cider jus, or the contrast of slowly pot-roast lamb shoulder with roast pepper, goats' cheese and chorizo. Generous portions may put a stop on pudding for some, but apple strudel with cinnamon syrup and vanilla ice cream, or poached pears with a rich chocolate sauce and espresso ice cream should not be missed. Service has been a distinct let-down. Wines, however, are a good-natured collection of bottles, mostly under £20. Half a dozen house wines are all £11.85.

Chefs: Kevin Viner and Neill Farrelly **Proprietors:** Jane and Kevin Viner **Open:** Sun L 12.30 to 3, all week D 6.30 to 9.30 **Closed:** 4 weeks winter. Possible reduced opening hours winter; phone to enquire **Meals:** alc D (main courses £13.50 to £17.50). Set L £13.60 (2 courses) to £15.70. Bar menu available **Service:** not inc **Cards:** Delta, Maestro, MasterCard, Visa **Details:** 90 seats. 40 seats outside. Private parties: 50 main room, 10 to 30 private rooms. Car park. Vegetarian meals. Children's helpings. No smoking in 1 dining room. Wheelchair access (not WC). Occasional music

MAP 3 **Surbiton** SURREY

French Table

85 Maple Road, Surbiton KT6 4AW
Tel: (020) 8399 2365
Website: www.thefrenchtable.com

Cooking 4 | French/Mediterranean | £26–£58

Eric and Sarah Guignard's popular little establishment, an older sibling of the Food Room (see entry, London) is set in a parade of shops a quarter of a mile from Surbiton station and is very much in the style of a French provincial neighbourhood restaurant. There is good value for money to be found here, particularly if you look in for a set lunch, when you could expect the likes of deep-fried skate with sauce gribiche and roast magret of duck with celeriac purée. The evening carte reveals a preference for the Mediterranean: terrine of confit duck with dried fruits, and cauliflower velouté with truffle-flavoured crème fraîche are among starters, and cod with tomato confit, squid ink pasta, deep-fried squid and pistou, or saddle of rabbit stuffed with carrot and sage with cocoa bean purée, potato fondant and grain mustard sauce follow on. Desserts range from apple tarte Tatin to ginger bread-and-butter pudding with caramelised pear and vanilla ice cream, while the wine list favours France, and particularly its regions, but allows others a look-in. House wines are £11.95.

Chef: Eric Guignard **Proprietors:** Eric and Sarah Guignard **Open:** Wed to Fri and Sun L 12 to 2.30, Tue to Sat D 7 to 10.30 **Closed:** 25 and 26 Dec, 1st week Jan, last 2 weeks Aug **Meals:** alc D (main courses £10.50 to £15.50). Set L £12.50 (2 courses) to £15.50, Set L Sun £17.50 **Service:** 12.5% (optional), card slips closed **Cards:** Delta, Maestro, MasterCard, Visa **Details:** 48 seats. Vegetarian meals. Children's helpings. No-smoking area. Wheelchair access (not WC). Music. Air-conditioned

MAP 6 **Sutton Gault**
CAMBRIDGESHIRE

Anchor Inn

Sutton Gault CB6 2BD
Tel: (01353) 778537
Website: www.anchor-inn-restaurant.co.uk

Cooking 3 | Modern British | £24–£53

Despite its remote location in the wide-open expanses of the Fens by the New Bedford River (actually a straight canal, also known as the Hundred Foot Drain), this atmospheric inn manages to pull in customers from near and far. The interior is a labyrinth of low-ceilinged, panelled rooms in true old English style, but the food strikes a more contemporary European note. Expect starters like guinea fowl, chicken and lime terrine with beetroot salad or pan-fried red mullet on fennel with vanilla and olive sauce before chargrilled haunch of Denham Estate venison with braised red cabbage, baby spinach and chocolate jus or roast red pepper risotto with tapenade and rocket salad. If crème brûlée doesn't take your fancy, finish with something offbeat like lemongrass pannacotta with chilli sauce. Around 50 well-chosen bottles make up a pleasing, individual wine list, and prices, from £10.95, are fair.

Chef: Barbara Jordan **Proprietors:** Robin and Heather Moore **Open:** all week 12 to 2, 7 to 9 (6.30 to 9.30 Sat) **Closed:** 26 Dec **Meals:** alc exc Sun L (main courses £11.50 to £17.50). Set L Mon to Fri £10 (2 courses) to £14.50, Set L Sun £17 (2 courses) to £21 **Service:** not inc **Cards:** Amex, Delta, Maestro, MasterCard, Visa **Details:** 70 seats. 40 seats outside. Private parties: 35 main room. Car park. Vegetarian meals. Children's helpings. No smoking in 1 dining room. Wheelchair access (also WC). No music. No mobile phones **Accommodation:** 2 rooms, both with bath/shower. TV. Phone. B&B £50 to £120. No children

MAP 7 **Sutton on the Forest**
NORTH YORKSHIRE

Rose & Crown

AR

Main Street, Sutton on the Forest YO61 1DP
Tel: (01347) 811333

Regenerated village pub with stripped-back modern décor suggesting a rural bistro. Expect a short menu of modern-sounding dishes like marinated tuna loin with vegetable salad and a sweet chilli and ginger dressing (£6.50), and breast of chicken with Parmesan and chive mash, wilted spinach and grain mustard velouté (£13), followed by desserts such as lemon posset with berry compote. Real ales and a decent choice of wines. Closed Sun D and Mon.

MAP 6 **Swaffham** NORFOLK

Strattons

4 Ash Close, Swaffham PE37 7NH
Tel: (01760) 723845
Website: www.strattonshotel.com

Cooking 3 | Modern European | £48–£58

With particular attention paid to recycling, regionalism, organic produce and seasonality, Les and Vanessa Scott have for years shown an environmental sensitivity. Their beautiful Breckland (an area of forests and ancient heaths covering part of Suffolk and Norfolk) house has nine stylish and individual rooms and a smart dining room decorated in natural colours punctuated with vivid pictures and sculptures. The menu is a fixed-price affair, with local producers and suppliers name-checked throughout. Start with pan-fried Castle Acre chicken livers on garlic croûtes, or Beachamwell celeriac and Parmesan soup. An inspection dinner kicked off with good home-made hummus with sesame wafers, some rather oily aubergine and a well-made roast vine tomato ice cream. Main courses might pair roast scallops with asparagus and parsnip sauce, or roast shoulder of Papworth pork with Nicola potatoes, creamed celeriac and caramelised Falstaff apples. A taster course of tiptop British cheeses is included in the set price, and to finish there might be espresso mousse pudding with chocolate and chilli sorbet. Service makes a real effort to please. The wine list, arranged by style, has intelligent and informative notations and plenty of choice under £20.

Chefs: Vanessa Scott and Maggie Cooper **Proprietors:** Les and Vanessa Scott **Open:** Mon to Sat D only 7 to 9 (residents only Sun D) **Closed:** 1 week at Christmas **Meals:** Set D £37.50 **Service:** not inc **Cards:** Amex, Delta, Maestro, MasterCard, Visa **Details:** 20 seats. Private parties: 20 main room. Car park. Vegetarian meals. Children's helpings. No smoking. Music. No mobile phones **Accommodation:** 9 rooms, all with bath/shower. TV. Phone. B&B £80 to £200. Rooms for disabled. Baby facilities

To submit a report on any restaurant, please visit *www.which.co.uk/gfgfeedback.*

MAP 2 Swanage DORSET

Cauldron Bistro

AR

5 High Street, Swanage BH19 2LN
Tel: (01929) 422671

Quality ingredients fresh from the sea have long been the secret to the success of this town-centre restaurant close to the quay, with French posters adding to the classic bistro atmosphere. 'Firm, juicy' scallops have been a recent success, whether seared with lemon, garlic and balsamic or as classic coquilles St Jacques (£7). Specials call on both sea and land for the likes of New Forest roe deer on bubble and squeak (£16.50) or 'very enjoyable' local lobster. Invigorate the palate with ginger ice cream and cranberry sauce (£4.75). Wines from £10.95. Open Thur to Sun.

MAP 9 Tadcaster NORTH YORKSHIRE

Singers

16 Westgate, Tadcaster LS24 9AB
Tel: (01937) 835121
Website: www.singersrestaurant.co.uk

Cooking 2 | Modern European | £23–£45

Singers is a long-running asset to the Tadcaster scene, and it discreetly promotes its musical theme in low-ceilinged premises that look a bit like a bow-windowed café. Early-evening deals boost the numbers midweek and there are plenty of flexible options on the full fixed-price menu. Dishes change regularly and the kitchen is generous with its cream sauces, which can overwhelm otherwise well-timed raw materials: fillet of sea bass is served with queenies, capers and tomato, ribeye steak might come on celeriac mash. Starters range from smoked chicken and leek broth to beef carpaccio and – to finish – the splendid ginger and rhubarb crumble is 'nearly as good as you can get'. 'Soprano whites' and 'tenor reds' set the tone on the fairly priced wine list; house George Duboeuf is £11.95.

Chefs: Adam Hewitt and John Appleyard **Proprietor:** Philip Taylor **Open:** Tue to Sat D only 6 to 9.30 **Closed:** 25 Dec to 1 Jan **Meals:** Set D Tue to Thur 6 to 7 £14.95, Set D Tue to Thur £13.95 (1 course) to £17.95 (2 courses), Set D Tue to Sat £21.95 **Service:** not inc, card slips closed **Cards:** Delta, Maestro, MasterCard, Visa **Details:** 38 seats. Private parties: 38 main room. Vegetarian meals. No smoking. Wheelchair access (not WC). Music. Air-conditioned

MAP 2 Tadpole Bridge OXFORDSHIRE

Trout

AR

Tadpole Bridge SN7 8RF
Tel: (01367) 870382

Pub/restaurant in a picturesque setting on the bank of the Thames. Offal and some interesting vegetables (from the owners' garden in season) breathe fresh life into standards, as in roast rump of lamb with artichoke purée and sweetbreads (£17), which could be preceded by poached ox tongue with beetroot and horseradish (£6). Look also to the blackboard for Cornish-sourced seafood specials like sautéed devilled crab, or pan-fried fillet of red mullet with mango salsa. A serious wine list opens with good-value bottles from £10.95. Closed Sun D.

MAP 3 Taplow BERKSHIRE

Cliveden, Waldo's

Taplow SL6 0JF
Tel: (01628) 668561
Website: www.clivedenhouse.co.uk

Cooking 5 | Modern European | £86–£103

The former country residence of the Astors is as grand a pile as you'll come upon. A long drive leads to the magnificent front portal, and plenty of punctilious staff usher you down to dinner. Down, because Waldo's is a basement room, albeit one stately enough to have paintings hanging in vertical stacks on the walls. Overspill bookings may be catered for in the adjacent bar area, where soft music – anything from grand opera to Tom Jones – plays. A changing of the guard in the kitchens just before Christmas 2004 brought Daniel Galmiche on to the scene as executive chef. Dinner – at a whopping £65 – might start with an excellent trio of firm, sweet Scottish scallops with well-dressed herb salad, or an impressive dish of langoustines sandwiched mille-feuille fashion with wafers of seaweed, accompanied by a purée of caramelised cauliflower. Beef fillet is full of flavour, sturdily backed up by a good jus and a salad of sautéed duck foie gras and watercress. Desserts may well be the highlights, imaginatively offering pineapple as a deep-fried beignet scented strongly with lemongrass, and partnered with light-textured coconut sorbet and mango sauce. Some unevenness at inspection included an overcooked piece of sea bass with tough pasta.

The wine list is magnificent, with Spain, Germany and Austria all making strong showings alongside the more expected gems from France and California, but prices are high. A request for house white might yield Limoux Chardonnay by Dom. Bégude at £28 a pop. Options by the glass are £5 to £44.

Chef: Daniel Galmiche **Proprietor:** Von Essen Hotels **Open:** Tue to Sat D only 7 to 9.30 **Closed:** first 2 weeks Jan, second and third weeks Aug **Meals:** Set D £65. Cover £1 **Service:** not inc **Cards:** Amex, Delta, Diners, Maestro, MasterCard, Visa **Details:** 28 seats. Private parties: 12 to 60 private rooms. Car park. No children under 12. Jacket and tie. No smoking. No music. No mobile phones. Air-conditioned **Accommodation:** 39 rooms, all with bath/shower. TV. Phone. B&B £335 to £950. Rooms for disabled. Baby facilities. Swimming pool

MAP 2 **Taunton** SOMERSET

Castle Hotel

Castle Green, Taunton TA1 1NF
Tel: (01823) 272671
Website: www.the-castle-hotel.com

Cooking 7 | Modern British | £41–£77

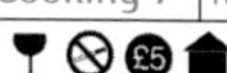

The grandeur of what began life as a Norman fortress is impossible not to love. Some say the wisteria smothering the frontage is the largest single example in the country. And the interiors are awash with heraldic features, Gothic arches, hand-coloured prints and deep, deep sofas, while the formally got-up staff sport calf-length aprons.

Many an accomplished chef has passed through here over the years, and Richard Guest is firmly in that lineage. He describes his menus as 'determinedly British and seasonal'. A salad of the month might therefore open proceedings: in May, it involved broad beans, asparagus and leaves with roundels of very tender, lightly smoked pork and a perhaps over-discreet dressing. Another starter to watch for might be scrambled duck egg with locally smoked eel dressed in lightly curry-scented oil. These days not many places dare to offer scallops as a main course. Here, they came seared, accompanied by four versions of celeriac – roast slices, marinated cubes, deep-fried thin chips and quenelles of purée. Meat is royally treated, such as the Ruby Red Devon beef that comes as roast fillet, with a braised faggot, a tiny steamed oxtail pudding and a sauce built on ox tongue. The exhibition dessert is a bitter chocolate tart made with the good stuff (73% cocoa solids), its enveloping richness contrasted with the tartness of steeped oranges.

The wine list is a roll-call of bottles from quality estates supplied by A-list merchants. Bordeaux leads, featuring a winning mix of pricey classed growths and model minor properties, like 1999 Vieux Château Gaubert at £33. Bottles start at £16.50, and there are plenty of halves and a range of fruity options by the glass. The big, bold and modern Brazz on the same site is available if you want a more informal experience.

Chef: Richard Guest **Proprietor:** the Chapman family **Open:** all week L 12.30 to 2.30, Mon to Sat D 7 to 10.30 **Meals:** Set L £13.50 (1 course) to £45, Set D Mon to Thur £13.50 (1 course) to £25, Set D Mon to Sat £38 (2 courses) to £45. Bar L menu available **Service:** 12.5% (optional), card slips closed **Cards:** Amex, Delta, Diners, Maestro, MasterCard, Visa **Details:** 70 seats. 30 seats outside. Private parties: 70 main room, 20 to 70 private rooms. Car park. Children's helpings. No smoking. Wheelchair access (also WC). No music. No mobile phones **Accommodation:** 44 rooms, all with bath/shower. TV. Phone. B&B £130 to £300. Rooms for disabled. Baby facilities

Willow Tree

3 Tower Lane, Taunton TA1 4AR
Tel: (01823) 352835

Cooking 6 | Modern British | £35–£60

This relaxed, two-floored restaurant makes pleasing first impressions, but it is Darren Sherlock's food that is the main attraction. He focuses squarely on quality ingredients and on seasonality, which he backs up with some precise cooking. Modern partnerships include a salad of roast quail with a toasted sesame-seed and chickpea purée and a honey dressing, and luxuries come in the shape of ballottine of foie gras, alongside humbler materials such as mussels cooked in cider and served in a puff-pastry pot.

Dishes retain their essential simplicity, thanks to assured handling of fine raw materials: huge, juicy and creamy scallops are teamed with slightly caramelised cubes of butternut squash, perfectly crisped pancetta and dark green pesto, and a main course of first-class pork belly ('meaty and tender' and with 'Grade A crackling') comes with braised red cabbage and boulangère potatoes. Behind the straightforwardness, though, lies a high degree of sophistication, for example in a fillet of fresh, succulent ling coupled with an exemplary clam chowder.

Direct appeal and bold simplicity characterise desserts, too: a rich coconut crème brûlée, say, or a 'we can taste it still' assiette of milk chocolate mousse, dark chocolate sorbet with slivers of stem ginger, and white chocolate 'fluff' with a raspberry coulis. Service, led by Rita Rambellas, is well up to the food, and wines, too, offer value and variety, with four good sherries served by the glass and house Chilean at £12.95, £3.75 per glass.

Chef: Darren Sherlock **Proprietors:** Darren Sherlock and Rita Rambellas **Open:** Tue to Sat D only 6.30 to 9.30 **Closed:** 4 weeks from 25 Dec, all Aug **Meals:** alc D (main courses £14 to £19) **Service:** not inc **Cards:** Delta, Maestro, MasterCard, Visa **Details:** 32 seats. 10 seats outside. Private parties: 32 main room, 10 to 20 private rooms. Vegetarian meals. No smoking. Wheelchair access (not WC). Music. No mobile phones

MAP 1 **Tavistock** DEVON

Horn of Plenty

Gulworthy, Tavistock PL19 8JD
Tel: (01822) 832528
Website: www.thehornofplenty.co.uk

Cooking 6 | Modern British | £35–£73

Set in five acres of gardens and orchards, this welcoming Devon retreat boasts a conservatory with soul-soothing views over the Tamar Valley towards Dartmoor. A fire crackles in the lounge on chilly days, and the elegant L-shaped dining room makes a suitable setting for Peter Gorton's accomplished cooking, which is expressed through fixed-price lunch and dinner menus, the former including coffee. Dinner offers a slightly wider choice with the main ingredients a little grander. A starter might comprise scallops and king prawn with pumpkin gnocchi, baby pak choi and a sauce of white wine and ginger, or grilled sea bass with marinated vegetables in a vinaigrette, while main courses bring on dishes of venison, beef, partridge, brill, or a vegetarian assiette. That brill might be tricked out with asparagus, saffron and chives, while the partridge is balanced on a potato and parsnip rösti and sauced with port. The rich and sustaining sauces are a particular strength, but dishes manage to retain balance. Among desserts might be passion-fruit bavarois with tropical fruit jelly and coconut sorbet, or a platter of West Country cheeses. The wine list is a little cornucopia of its own, with pedigree Burgundies in both colours, and one or two good Portuguese and Italian reds to go at. The house selection opens at £13.50 (£3.50 a glass).

Chef: Peter Gorton **Proprietors:** Peter Gorton and Paul Roston **Open:** Tue to Sun 12 to 2, all week D 7 to 9 **Closed:** 24 to 26 Dec **Meals:** Set L £25, Set D £42 **Service:** not inc, 10% for parties of 10 or more **Cards:** Amex, Delta, Maestro, MasterCard, Visa **Details:** 60 seats. 15 seats outside. Private parties: 70 main room, 2 to 15 private rooms. Car park. Vegetarian meals. Children's helpings. No smoking. Wheelchair access (also WC). Occasional music. No mobile phones **Accommodation:** 10 rooms, all with bath/shower. TV. Phone. B&B £110 to £230. Rooms for disabled. Baby facilities

MAP 12 **Teddington** GREATER LONDON

Wharf

AR

22 Manor Road, Teddington TW11 8BG
Tel: (020) 8977 6333

Converted boathouse overlooking Teddington Lock, with views of the Thames and a covered terrace for al fresco dining. Fish fares well on a menu that runs from moules marinière (£7.50) to roast brill with leeks, red onions and lemon thyme (£17.50) and confit of duck with Toulouse sausage and cassoulet. Finish with, say, spiced mango and mascarpone crème brûlée (£5.50). Separate bar and private dining on the 'First Floor'. House wine £12.75. Closed Sun D.

MAP 7 **Teffont Evias** WILTSHIRE

Howard's House

Teffont Evias SP3 5RJ
Tel: (01722) 716392
Website: www.howardshousehotel.co.uk

Cooking 3 | Modern British-Plus | £37–£67

In quintessential English countryside complete with a winding lane and a diminutive stream, this extended seventeenth-century dower house is a real charmer, guaranteed to elicit 'oohs' from first-timers and regulars alike. Nick Wentworth's cooking reflects the seasons and he buys carefully, although you can expect plenty of French accents along the way. A trio of local game comes with pommes Maxime and cassis jus, Wiltshire pork puts in a regular appearance, while fish is from Brixham: herb-crusted fillet of brill with chive mash, wilted leeks and ginger sauce, or confit of wild halibut with parsnip purée, caramelised chicory, saffron and vanilla dressing, for example. To finish, the kitchen may dream up hot mandarin and satsuma soufflé with cinnamon pannacotta and mulled wine syrup. The wine list plunders France before considering the rest of the world. House selections start at £13.50.

Chef: Nick Wentworth **Proprietor:** Noele Thompson **Open:** Tue to Thur and Sun L 12.30 to 1.45, all week D 7.30 to 9 **Meals:** alc D (main courses £20 to £24). Set L £19.50 (2 courses) to £23.50, Set D £25.95 **Service:** not inc **Cards:** Amex, Delta, Maestro, MasterCard, Visa **Details:** 26 seats. 12 seats outside. Private parties: 40 main room. Car park. Children's helpings. No smoking. Wheelchair access (not WC). No music **Accommodation:** 9 rooms, all with bath/shower. TV. Phone. B&B £95 to £165

MAP 2 **Tetbury** GLOUCESTERSHIRE

Calcot Manor

NEW ENTRY

Tetbury GL8 8YJ
Tel: (01666) 890391
Website: www.calcotmanor.co.uk

Cooking 3 | Modern British | £34–£77

Calcot Manor describes itself as an old English farmhouse, 'but it must have been some farm' thought one who found a large, elegant house with a flagstoned hall and big stone fireplaces. Outbuildings have been converted to provide accommodation and a health spa, while the Conservatory Restaurant is a more recent addition, its menu blending a predominantly modern British style with wider European influences. An inspector experienced mixed results but found success in a starter of seared foie gras teamed with ginger-poached rhubarb, and a main course of seared loin and braised neck of Highgrove lamb with pea and mascarpone cappelletti, braising juices and mint oil. Desserts run to vanilla crème brûlée with warm pears poached in red wine (served cold at inspection). Service is generally prompt, and there's nothing wrong with the fine, extensive wine list that lower prices wouldn't fix. Stick with the house French at £17. Also on the premises, the Gumstool Inn is a modern version of a country pub – ideal for large family groups – offering a cheerful menu of soups, casseroles, cod and chips and the like.

Chef: Michael Croft **Proprietor:** Richard Ball **Open:** all week 12 to 2, 7 to 9.30 **Meals:** alc (main courses L £7 to £14.50, D £16 to £20) **Service:** not inc **Cards:** Amex, Delta, Diners, Maestro, MasterCard, Visa **Details:** 100 seats. 50 seats outside. Private parties: 100 main room, 10 to 100 private rooms. Car park. Vegetarian meals. Children's helpings. No smoking. Wheelchair access (also WC). Music. Air-conditioned **Accommodation:** 30 rooms, all with bath/shower. TV. Phone. B&B £160 to £360. Rooms for disabled. Baby facilities. Swimming pool

Trouble House

Cirencester Road, Tetbury GL8 8SG
Tel: (01666) 502206
Website: www.troublehouse.co.uk

Cooking 5 | Modern European | £34–£57

Rural and unpretentious, the Trouble House welcomes with a series of open-plan rooms quietly decorated with traditional hop garlands and lots of food-themed pictures. The relaxed, easy-going feel is very much in keeping with Michael Bedford's classy yet unpretentious cooking. His approach is comparatively simple, but the simplicity has a great deal of skill and much culinary good sense to underpin it. Well received starters have included shellfish linguini 'of impeccable freshness', with cockles, mussels, clams and scallops, marjoram and dried tomatoes, and a foie gras terrine with Monbazillac jelly and pickled grapes. Among mains may be grilled rump of veal with café de Paris butter and snails braised in Côtes du Rhone, or braised pig's trotter stuffed with black pudding and chicken mousse and served with a 'very rich and sumptuous' mash of mixed rough root vegetables. Finish perhaps with a selection of ices served 'at exactly the right temperature', or the dessert plate for two ('an absolute bargain') also comes highly recommended. Bread is praised, the service by a young team is pleasant and attentive, and the wine list's 60 bins offer a well-chosen world tour at manageable prices.

Chef: Michael Bedford **Proprietors:** Michael and Sarah Bedford **Open:** Tue to Sun L 12 to 2.30, Tue to Sat D 7 to 9.30 **Closed:** Christmas and New Year **Meals:** alc (main courses £12 to £18) **Service:** not inc **Cards:** Amex, Delta, Maestro, MasterCard, Visa **Details:** 52 seats. 24 seats outside. Car park. Children's helpings. No children under 10 at D. No smoking in 1 dining room. Wheelchair access (also WC). Music

MAP 5 **Titley** HEREFORDSHIRE

Stagg Inn

Titley, nr Kington HR5 3RL
Tel: (01544) 230221
Website: www.thestagg.co.uk

Cooking 5 | Modern British | £25–£50

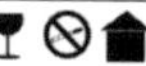

Nicola and Steve Reynolds are proud Herefordians who have turned this trimly presented roadside country pub into a shrine to the

best of local produce. The farming country round about supplies the kitchen with fine meats, organic cider and perry, and what market gardeners don't supply, the proprietors grow themselves. Deep umber hues and undressed tables lend an air of solidity to the surroundings.

First courses in particular impress. Pear and blue cheese tart is 'a lovely squishy pile of stuff all melting into itself', with short pastry underpinning it all, while four fat juicy scallops, seared outside, opalescent within, are hugely impressive. Meats are accorded regal treatment in main courses such as mustard-glazed beef fillet on potato rösti with red-wine sauce, or saddle of venison with wild mushrooms and kümmel. Zingy and fresh desserts use sharp fruit flavours to good effect, whether for 'simple and restrained' passion-fruit jelly in a moat of its own juice, or lemon tart with cassis sorbet. Service, mostly by youngsters, is 'friendly and helpful'. The compact wine list is all about good flavours at fair prices, from £12.50 fruity house basics via the rich Veritas Cabernet Sauvignon-Merlot (£19.90) to a handful of classic bottles.

Chefs: Steve Reynolds, Grant Powell, Mathew Handley **Proprietors:** Nicola and Steve Reynolds **Open:** Tue to Sun L 12 to 2, Tue to Sat D 6.45 to 9.45 **Closed:** first 2 weeks Nov, 25 and 26 Dec, May Day bank hol, 1 week spring, Tue after bank hols **Meals:** alc (not Sun L; main courses £12.50 to £16.50). Set Sun L £14.50 **Service:** not inc, card slips closed **Cards:** Delta, Maestro, MasterCard, Visa **Details:** 70 seats. 20 seats outside. Private parties: 30 main room, 18 to 30 private rooms. Car park. Children's helpings. No smoking. No music **Accommodation:** 5 rooms, all with bath/shower. TV. B&B £50 to £110

MAP 7 Todmorton WEST YORKSHIRE

Old Hall

Hall Street, Todmorden OL14 7AD
Tel: (01706) 815998

Cooking 2 | Modern British | £26–£51

This 'imposing manor house' in the centre of Todmorden is nevertheless 'very relaxed inside'. Mullioned windows, wood panelling, flagstone floors and huge fireplaces contribute to the serenely comfortable ambience, helped along by smart, friendly service. Menus incorporate plenty of appealing combinations often using local ingredients: smoked Knowl End trout fishcakes with watercress and mustard dressing, for example, or a filo parcel of R. S. Ireland's black pudding with pear, chives and pine nuts and a red-pepper coulis. Care extends to 'perfectly pink' rack of saltmarsh lamb, served with fennel, roasted carrots and a thyme and orange jus, and other main-course options might run to blackened monkfish with pickled spiced vegetables and a mint labneh. At the dessert stage raspberry and hazelnut roulade with red fruit coulis has been given the thumbs-up. Eight house wines from £11.95 head a good-value list that encompasses a wide variety of grapes and styles.

Chefs: Chris Roberts and Peter Windross **Proprietors:** Nick and Madeleine Hoyle **Open:** Thur, Fri and Sun L 12 to 2 (2.30 Sun), Tue to Sat D 7 to 9 (9.30 Sat) **Closed:** 25 Dec, first week Jan, day after bank hols **Meals:** alc (main courses £12.50 to £16). Set L £8.50 (2 courses), Set L Sun £16 **Service:** not inc, 10% for parties of 10 or more **Cards:** Delta, Diners, Maestro, MasterCard, Visa **Details:** 70 seats. 20 seats outside. Private parties: 26 main room, 10 to 50 private rooms. Vegetarian meals. Children's helpings. No smoking. Music. No mobile phones

MAP 1 Topsham DEVON

Galley

41 Fore Street, Topsham EX3 0HU
Tel: (0845) 602 6862

Idiosyncratic 'restaurant-with-cabins' in a converted 300-year-old cottage overlooking the Exe estuary. Fish is the main business, and organic produce is vigorously supported. The dinner menu (£28.50/£34.95) brings on board a duo of Caribbean-style mussels and clams, cumin-crusted fillets of brill on celeriac purée, and grilled sea bass fillets 'nestled upon pesto and lavender-crushed potatoes' wrapped in banana leaves. 'Eccentric-named desserts' like Flirtatious Sensory Therapy (chocolate fondue 'with essential oils'). Thoughtfully selected wines from £12.95. Closed Sun L and Mon L.

La Petite Maison

35 Fore Street, Topsham EX3 0HR
Tel: (01392) 873660
Website: www.lapetitemaison.co.uk

Cooking 4 | Modern British | £32–£47

Look out for the hanging blue sign and black-and-white frontage on a bend in the road, where the Pestells ply their trade. Douglas cooks an enticing, intelligible menu featuring carefully sourced West

Country produce, with most of the vegetables sent in by an organic supplier, while his wife handles the welcoming and efficient service out front. Jerusalem artichokes and watercress join forces in a soup garnished with truffle oil, while a straight-bat version of moules marinière uses Teign Valley mussels in the expected winey, creamy broth. Outdoor-reared pork from Somerset appears as herb-crusted medallions, teamed with the belly slow-roasted, supported by creamy leeks, caramelised apples, dauphinois potatoes and a cider jus, while Lyme Bay brill comes with vegetable 'spaghetti' and a chive beurre blanc. Round things off with Chocolate Collection (mousse, torte and ice-cream), or lemon tart with matching sorbet and a strawberry coulis. The wine list kicks off with three from Devon and Cornwall before setting off around the globe. Plenty of choice below £20 will cheer, and there are wines by the glass from £3.25.

Chefs: Douglas and Naomi Pestell **Proprietors:** Douglas and Elizabeth Pestell **Open:** Tue to Sat 12.30 to 2, 7 to 10 **Closed:** Closed Oct to Mar exc bookings **Meals:** Set L £17.95 (2 courses) to £20.95, Set D £23.95 (2 courses) to £28.95 **Service:** not inc, card slips closed **Cards:** Delta, Maestro, MasterCard, Visa **Details:** 30 seats. Private parties: 26 main room. Vegetarian meals. No smoking. Music

MAP 1 **Torquay** DEVON

Elephant

NEW ENTRY

DEVON NEWCOMER OF THE YEAR

3–4 Beacon Terrace,
Torquay TQ1 2BH
Tel: (01803) 200044
Website: www.elephantrestaurant.co.uk

Cooking 5 | Modern British | £28–£58

In a terrace of elegant late-Georgian houses, this newcomer – open since September 2003 – is under the same ownership as the nearby Orestone Manor hotel (see entry, Maidencombe). The elephantine theme emerges in the form of pictures of the beasts disporting themselves at fountains and in jungles.

Views of the bay enhance the mood in the first-floor bar, where simple snacks are served, as well as the ground-floor restaurant. Local meats and fish are the mainstays of Simon Hulstone's kitchen, with Brixham crab, Start Bay scallops, Teign mussels, Crediton duckling and South Devon beef all featuring proudly. Those scallops are modishly teamed with Spanish morcilla and a salt-cod croquette, as well as cauliflower and almond purée. Another good inspection dish was a cake-like wedge of foie gras terrine, layered with duck confit, under a carapace of caramelised apple. Fish cookery is as sensitive as one hopes for, with correct timing bringing out the quality of a fillet of sea bass that also gained from its pairing with truffled Savoy cabbage and herbed scampi tortellini. Side dishes of extra veg are available for the extra-hungry, although it may be worth pacing yourself so as not to miss out on the accomplished desserts, which include fine crème brûlée with wobbly apple and pear jelly and yoghurt sorbet, and an altogether challenging-sounding bitter chocolate and olive oil truffle, with raspberry and red-pepper jelly, passion-fruit coulis and hibiscus. Full-strength coffee comes with excellent petits fours. A barman who's a dab hand with the cocktail shaker, as well as a good, single-page wine list with masses of choice by the glass (from £3.50), make for enticing drinking. All in all, this is an exciting addition to the previously under-endowed Torquay scene.

Chef: Simon Hulstone **Proprietors:** Peter Morgan, Friedericke Etessami, and Rose and Mark Ashton **Open:** Mon to Sat 11.30 to 2.30, 5 to 9.30 (open all day Sun on bank hol weekends) **Closed:** Tue during winter **Meals:** alc (main courses £12.50 to £20.50). Set L £13.75 (2 courses) to £22.50, Set D (Mon to Thur 6 to 7) £13.75 to £16.75. Bar menu available **Service:** not inc, card slips closed **Cards:** Amex, Delta, Maestro, MasterCard, Visa **Details:** 65 seats. Private parties: 50 main room, 15 to 25 private rooms. Vegetarian meals. Children's helpings. No smoking in 1 dining room. Wheelchair access (also WC). Music. No mobile phones. Air-conditioned

No 7 Fish Bistro

7 Beacon Terrace, Torquay TQ1 2BH
Tel: (01803) 295055
Website: www.no7-fish.com

Cooking 1 | Seafood | £29–£50

Graham and Jill Stacey's unpretentious, popular, family-run bistro presents a welcoming face. Set just a little way up from the harbour in a terrace of elegant Regency houses, it's awash with the fruits of the sea just as the name promises. Walls are decorated with fishy *objets d'art* and prints, tables are laid with navy-blue and cream oilcloths and there's even a life-size wooden figure of a straw-boatered fishmonger. And there's no doubting the freshness of the raw materials or the simple honesty of the cooking: blackboard specials account for 70 per cent of the repertoire's haul, with the choice dependent on the daily catch, but think whole Brixham plaice or Dover sole, perhaps cod with lobster-claw thermidor sauce, or monkfish baked with black pepper and sea salt. Whites not unsurprisingly dominate the affordable wine list, with house setting sail at £11.

Chefs: Oliver and Paul Stacey **Proprietors:** Graham and Jill Stacey **Open:** Wed to Sat L 12.15 to 1.45, Tue to Sat D 7 to 9.45 (6 to 10.15 summer); also open Mon D June and Oct, Sun and Mon D July to Sept **Closed:** 1 week Nov, Christmas and New Year, 2 weeks Feb **Meals:** alc (main courses £10 to £17.50) **Service:** not inc **Cards:** Amex, Delta, Maestro, MasterCard, Visa **Details:** 38 seats. Private parties: 20 main room. Vegetarian meals. Children's helpings. Wheelchair access (not WC). Music. No mobile phones. Air-conditioned

MAP 1 **Totnes** DEVON

Effings

50 Fore Street, Totnes TQ9 5RP
Tel: (01803) 863435

Cooking 2 | Modern European | £30–£57

'Every town should have a place like this,' reckoned a reporter after visiting this unusual outfit in funky Totnes. Foodwise, it amounts to little more than five tables crammed into an upmarket deli, but its integrity is seldom in doubt. The daytime menu relies heavily on assemblages (plates of tapas, pâtés etc.), cakes and pastries, and at lunchtime a blackboard lists a few cooked dishes. The results are emphatically fresh (witness hot goats' cheese tart with peperonata), exotic salads have a starring role (local free-range duck breast with oriental dressing, orange segments and pickled ginger), and there's generally a peasant-style offering like osso bucco milanese. To finish, don't miss the 'luscious' home-made ice creams. Quibbles focus on the lack of choice and some high prices, although cheery, enthusiastic service goes some way to make amends. The wine list limits itself to around a dozen bottles from £13.75.

Chefs: Karl Rasmussen and Karen Miller **Proprietors:** Jacqueline Williams and Michael Kann **Open:** Mon to Sat L only 12 to 2.15 **Closed:** bank hols **Meals:** alc (main courses £11 to £23.50) **Service:** net prices, card slips closed **Cards:** Delta, Maestro, MasterCard, Visa **Details:** 14 seats. Private parties: 14 main room. Children's helpings. No smoking. Wheelchair access (also WC). No music. No mobile phones. Air-conditioned

Wills

2/3 The Plains, Totnes TQ9 5DR
Tel: (0800) 056 3006
Website: www.willsrestaurant.co.uk

Cooking 3 | Modern European | £29–£62

This Regency house opposite Australian explorer William Wills's statue has a bistro on the ground floor, open for lunch and dinner, and upstairs a restaurant – two elegant little rooms in pastel shades – doing dinner only. Dishes are based on decent local ingredients. Big 'bouncy' scallops with cauliflower purée and smoked venison were 'the daddy of all starters' for one diner, or try boudin of quail stuffed with wild mushrooms served with roast fig tart Tatin. Main courses favour classic European ideas like pan-fried sea bass with leek and potato cake, lobster and chive dressing, or Devon beef fillet with dauphinoise potato, madeira and foie gras jus. Finish with strawberry and cracked pepper parfait with spearmint salsa, or chocolate and banana strudel. Wines are a tempting global selection with prices from £12.50.

Chef: Craig Purkiss **Proprietors:** Philip Silverston and Jenny Priest **Open:** all week L 12 to 2.30, Tue to Sat 7 to 9.30 **Closed:** May bank hols **Meals:** alc (main courses £9 to £19) **Service:** not inc **Cards:** Amex, Delta, Maestro, MasterCard, Visa **Details:** 42 seats. 20 seats outside. Private parties: 30 main room. Vegetarian meals. Children's helpings. No smoking. Music

MAP 1 **Tresco** ISLES OF SCILLY

Island Hotel

AR

Tresco TR24 0PU
Tel: (01720) 422883

Look forward to stunning views from this sophisticated hotel on the 'island of flowers'. Fresh seafood looms large on the fixed-price dinner menus (£37.50) in the shape of, say, chargrilled monkfish with braised Puy lentils and chorizo. Away from fish, you could start with roast belly pork with Savoy cabbage and oyster sauce and close proceedings with dark chocolate and orange brûlée. Light meals on the terrace at lunchtime. The wine list is a serious tome, with prices from £16. Open all week.

MAP 10 Troutbeck CUMBRIA

Queens Head Hotel AR

Townhead, Troutbeck LA23 1PW
Tel: (015394) 32174

Pedigree seventeenth-century coaching inn with awesome views of the Troutbeck Valley and the Garburn Pass. Evening sustenance comes in the shape of crab and avocado salad with basil crostini (£6.50) and roast Cartmel venison with field mushroom confit and a redcurrant and red wine sauce (£16), followed by that Lakeland classic: 'wonderful' sticky toffee pudding with maple syrup ice cream. Baguettes and light dishes such as confit of duck on celeriac rémoulade at lunchtime. House wines £10.50. Accommodation. Open all week.

MAP 3 Tunbridge Wells KENT

Hotel du Vin & Bistro

Crescent Road, Tunbridge Wells TN1 2LY
Tel: (01892) 526455
Website: www.hotelduvin.com

Cooking 4 | Modern European | £33–£61

One of the strengths of the Hotels du Vin is that, although they form a small chain of similar venues, each feels like a one-off. In Royal Tunbridge Wells, the dining room is hung with wine pictures and dried hops, candles flicker on dark wooden tabletops, the glassware is good, and the army of staff all know what they are doing. As at other branches, Simple Classics and vegetarian dishes supplement the main menu. From the former a small portion of saffron risotto with sautéed squid was creamy and richly seafoody, while the more inventive starters have included a spring roll of cod and prawns, served with saffron mayonnaise and (somewhat overpowering) green guindilla chillies. An inspection main course offered roast duck magret of impeccable timing and seasoning, with risi e bisi and a tomato butter sauce, although a serving of roast guinea fowl with crustless quiche of spinach and chorizo was rather let down by tired-tasting fondant potato. The Valrhona chocolate tart with kumquat compote is 'simply orgasmic' to a true chocoholic, or there might be humble gooseberry crumble with custard. The wine list is another gem from the Hotel du Vin chain, with sommeliers ready and willing to talk you through the options. There's a decent number by the glass and good choice around the £20 mark.

Chef: Matt Green-Armytage **Proprietor:** MWB Group plc **Open:** all week 12 to 1.45, 7 to 9.45 **Meals:** alc (not Sun L; main courses £12 to £15.50). Set L Sun £23.50 **Service:** not inc **Cards:** Amex, Delta, Diners, Maestro, MasterCard, Visa **Details:** 80 seats. 30 seats outside. Private parties: 80 main room. Car park. Vegetarian meals. Children's helpings. No smoking. Wheelchair access (also WC). No music **Accommodation:** 35 rooms, all with bath/shower. TV. Phone. Room only £95 to £250. Rooms for disabled. Baby facilities

Le Petit Blanc AR

Five Ways, Lime Hill Road,
Tunbridge Wells TN1 1LJ
Tel: (01892) 559170

Newest link in the Blanc chain (see entries in Birmingham, Cheltenham, Manchester and Oxford), overlooking the Victoria Shopping Centre. Like its siblings, it offers flexible brasserie food, good-value set menus and a warm welcome for children. Expect modern European dishes like grilled chicken Caesar salad (£6), seared king scallops with fennel purée (£17.50) and roast Lincolnshire belly pork with apple sauce, followed by summer berry pavlova. The wine list (from £12.95) is peppered with Raymond Blanc's regional French favourites. Open all week.

Thackeray's

85 London Road, Tunbridge Wells TN1 1EA
Tel: (01892) 511921
Website: www.thackeraysrestaurant.co.uk

Cooking 6 | Anglo-French | £27–£83

'We are so lucky to have this place in Tunbridge Wells,' declares a grateful resident who finds the fixed-price lunch menus ample reason to return frequently. The restrained elegance of this Georgian house on the Common seems to put visitors at ease, as does the solicitous tone of service, which holds the line between formality and familiarity.

The cuisine is Anglo-French, with a high degree of polish, and, while dishes look impeccably modern, they nonetheless have a solid foundation of classical principles. A tian of Devon crab comes with avocado and a little roulade of smoked salmon, while scallops are teamed with black pudding and caramelised apple in a sauce of Fleurie. There is no coyness about mixing 'high' and 'low' ingredients, so a starter of sea bass from the no-choice Market Menu might come with braised lentils and a champagne beurre blanc. Cooking methods may not be the most obvious either, with salmon baked in Chinese leaf, or fillet steak roast in a wild mushroom and herb crust. The same care goes into desserts such as fig tart flavoured with vanilla and lemon thyme, served with an ice cream combining honey and green peppercorns. The wine list essays a brisk tour of western Europe and the southern hemisphere, and opens with a wide choice by the glass from £3.75; bottle prices start at £12.95.

Chef: Richard Phillips **Proprietors:** Richard Phillips and Paul Smith **Open:** Tue to Sun L 12 to 2.30, Tue to Sat D 6 to 10.30 **Meals:** alc (not Sun L; main courses £16 to £24.50). Set L Tue to Sat £12.95 (2 courses) to £13.95, Sun £26.50, Set D £18.50 to £55 **Service:** 12.5% (optional), card slips closed **Cards:** Amex, Delta, Diners, Maestro, MasterCard, Visa **Details:** 54 seats. 30 seats outside. Private parties: 35 main room, 6 to 16 private rooms. Vegetarian meals. Children's helpings. No smoking. Wheelchair access (not WC). Music. No mobile phones. Air-conditioned

MAP 3 **Twickenham**
GREATER LONDON

A Cena

418 Richmond Road, Twickenham TW1 2EB
Tel: (020) 8288 0108
Website: www.acena.co.uk

Cooking 2 | Italian | £24–£57

Just over Richmond Bridge on the Twickenham side – so really more a Richmond neighbourhood Italian – A Cena sits unobtrusively behind a glass frontage in a long parade of shops. The long, split-level room with a bar at one side is decked out with dark bare boards, paper-clothed wooden tables and a variety of wooden church- or kitchen-style chairs. Large mirrors amplify the space, and candlelight over dinner heightens the relaxed, informal mood. Genuine, imaginatively prepared Italian food is delivered via an appealing, sensible-length carte and fixed-price lunch offerings; think crab bruschetta with almond aïoli followed by veal osso bucco in bianco with risotto milanese and gremolata. Among the desserts, pannacotta with rhubarb and mint has met with praise. Good breads land on the table as you arrive, service is efficient and friendly, and the patriotic, all-Italian wine list offers house from £12.50 with eight by glass from £3.

Chef: Nicola Parsons **Proprietors:** Tim and Camilla Healy **Open:** Tue to Sun L 12 to 2.30, Tue to Sat D 7 to 10.30 **Meals:** alc D (main courses £8.50 to £21). Set L £12 (1–2 courses) to £14 **Service:** not inc **Cards:** Amex, Delta, Maestro, MasterCard, Visa **Details:** 55 seats. Vegetarian meals. Children's helpings. No pipes/cigars. Wheelchair access (not WC). Music. Air-conditioned

Brula Bistrot

43 Crown Road, St Margaret's, Twickenham TW1 3EJ
Tel: (020) 8892 0602
Website: www.info@brulabistrot.com

Cooking 2 | French | £23–£55

The name is a part-conjunction of Bruce Duckett's and Lawrence Hartley's first names (in case you were wondering), and their unassuming neighbourhood restaurant has the appendage 'bistrot' to emphasise its intentions. Robust 'cuisine grand-mère' defines the cooking, typified by dishes such as roast fillet of beef with turnip dauphinois, bone marrow and red wine sauce, or confit of Barbary duck leg with beetroot boulangère and mustard sauce. Away from meat, there might be Burgundy snails in garlic butter, and sautéed king scallops with creamed endive followed by desserts such as crème brûlée, or plum and almond tart. The wine list is a brief, well-chosen slate, opening with vins de pays at £11.50. A new branch, La Buvette, is at 6 Church Walk, Richmond; tel: (020) 8940 6264.

Chefs: Jamie Russel and Buck Carter **Proprietors:** Lawrence Hartley and Bruce Duckett **Open:** all week 12.30 to 2.30, 7 to 10.30 **Closed:** Christmas, 1 Jan **Meals:** alc (main courses £11 to £15). Set L £11 (2 courses) to £13 **Service:** not inc **Cards:** Delta, Maestro, MasterCard, Visa **Details:** 45 seats. 6 seats outside. Private parties: 50 main room, 10 to 14 private rooms. Vegetarian meals. Children's helpings. Wheelchair access (not WC). No music. No mobile phones

Ma Cuisine

6 Whitton Road, Twickenham TW1 1BJ
Tel: (020) 8607 9849

Cooking 3 | French Regional | £26–£43

Apart from the menu being in both French and English, this cheerful bistro would not seem out of place across the Channel. John McClements' cooking is an accomplished and single-minded

rendition of French country cuisine given a gloss of sophistication by tip-top raw materials and a dash of imagination. Alongside familiar grilled sardines in garlic butter, and ballottine of foie gras are oyster soup flavoured with truffles, and black pudding en croûte with Dijon mustard sauce. Main courses could range from rabbit with tarragon sauce and potato purée to entrecôte of veal with Puy lentils and cep cream, while desserts might feature anything from lemon tart to chocolate pot with coffee cream. The set-price lunch menu is particularly good value. Service is on the ball, and the mainly French wine list kicks off at £12.50. There is a second Ma Cuisine, located in a former post office, at 9 Station Approach, Kew; tel: (020) 8332 1923.

Chef: John McClements **Proprietors:** John McClements and Dominique Séjourné **Open:** all week 12 to 2.30, 6.30 to 10.30 **Meals:** alc (main courses £8 to £14). Set L £11.95 (2 courses) to £15.50 **Service:** 10% (optional), card slips closed **Cards:** Delta, Maestro, MasterCard, Visa **Details:** 70 seats. Private parties: 30 main room. Vegetarian meals. Children's helpings. No smoking. Music

McClements

2 Whitton Road, Twickenham TW1 1BJ
Tel: (020) 8744 9610
Website: www.mcclementsrestaurant.com

Cooking 6 | French | £43–£94

The jewel in John McClements's crown (see also Ma Cuisine, above) is a popular and reliable neighbourhood restaurant two minutes from the railway station, and it 'has a pleasantly relaxed feel'. Its principal focus is contemporary, cosmopolitan cooking based on a foundation of well-sourced materials, and the style is appealing without being flamboyant, with well-thought-out combinations. In the capable hands of Daniel Woodhouse, the fixed-price dinner menu runs to some six options per course: terrine and mousse of foie gras with madeira and mushroom jelly, lingot beans and leaves to start, or seared scallops with peas, confit onion, pea shoots salad and a red wine and langoustine sauce. Fish is well represented among main courses, with perhaps roast fillets of John Dory (accompanied by warm beetroot lyonnaise, creamed leek, salsify and ravigote dressing) finding a place alongside loin of pork with a potato and apple cake, truffled leek and casserole. A couple in for lunch found staffing numbers 'lavish' and the quality of service 'high', and enjoyed a 'finely sculpted' artichoke salad with pickled ceps and a mushroom vinaigrette, and a warm salad of white beans with black pudding, confit chicken wings and a bacon sauce, and puddings of roast pineapple (with rum and raisin ice cream) and hazelnut nougatine (with peach ice cream). We weren't sent a full version of the wine list, but reports suggest the choice by the glass is good, and there are plenty of options around £20.

Chef: Daniel Woodhouse **Proprietor:** John McClements **Open:** Tue to Sat 12 to 2, 7 to 10.30 **Closed:** 26 to 30 Dec **Meals:** Set L £25, Set D £34 (2 courses) to £60 **Service:** 10% (optional), card slips closed **Cards:** Amex, Delta, Diners, Maestro, MasterCard, Visa **Details:** 40 seats. Private parties: 60 main room. No children under 12. No smoking. No music. No mobile phones. Air-conditioned

MAP 10 **Tynemouth** TYNE & WEAR

Sidney's

3–5 Percy Park Road, Tynemouth NE30 4LZ
Tel: (0191) 257 8500
Website: www.sidneys.co.uk

Cooking 3 | Modern British | £21–£55

'Northumbrian black pudding with onion confit and Black Sheep beer syrup' suggests a touch of regionality in this colourful contemporary brasserie downriver from Newcastle's metropolitan bustle. The kitchen also has proud environmental allegiances, serving steaks from 'traceable British herds' and cod 'from sustainable Icelandic waters', and there's a global flavour to dishes like chermoula-marinated whole trout with chana dhal, and fillet of Caledonian Crown beef with sweet potato mash and mushroom jus. Start with tandoori king prawns, mustard and dill sauce, or teriyaki duck salad, and finish with strawberry fool, or plum and star anise jelly with white chocolate shortbread. The list of around 25 wines offers good-value drinking from £11. Andy Hook also runs the Blackfriars Café Bar in Newcastle (see entry).

Chefs: Christopher Slaughter **Proprietors:** Andy and Sam Hook **Open:** Mon to Sat 12 to 2.30, 6 to 9.30 **Closed:** bank hols exc Good Friday **Meals:** alc (main courses £10.50 to £20). Set L £9 (2 courses) to £12, Set D Mon to Fri £12 (2 courses) to £15 **Service:** not inc, 10% (optional) for parties of 6 or more **Cards:** Amex, Delta, Maestro, MasterCard, Visa **Details:** 50 seats. Private parties: 30 main room, 20 to 22 private rooms. Vegetarian meals. Children's helpings. No smoking. Music. Air-conditioned

MAP 5 Ullingswick HEREFORDSHIRE

Three Crowns

Ullingswick HR1 3JQ
Tel: (01432) 820279
Website: www.threecrownsinn.com

Cooking 4 | Modern British | £37–£47

A restaurant extension was added in 2005, but in other respects the scene at this sixteenth-century brick and timbered pub is unchanged. 'Charming bucolic décor, rustic napkins, beautiful setting,' reports one. Brent Castle cooks ultra-modern pub food, limiting choice to six items per course but scoring some palpable hits. Soufflés – perhaps Gruyère and spinach – have been described as 'historic', while mussels have been successfully paired with chorizo. Meat appears to be well timed – as in sirloin of Aberdeen Angus with tarragon sauce, fries and watercress salad – and fish is treated innovatively: osso bucco of monkfish, for example, with a red wine butter sauce, salsify and Puy lentils, or grilled skate with asparagus, nutmeg mash and a warm green salsa. Desserts include 'excellent' bread-and-butter pudding, or there could be Medjool date and pecan pudding with banana and Malibu ice cream. The bar menu offers cheaper, lighter options. The compact wine list, starting with French house at £14, has a decent cross-section of styles topped up by a blackboard list of pricier specials.

Chef/Proprietor: Brent Castle **Open:** Tue to Sun 12 to 3, 7 to 10 (9 Sun) **Closed:** 2 weeks from L 24 Dec **Meals:** alc (main courses £14.50). Bar menu available **Service:** not inc, card slips closed **Cards:** Maestro, MasterCard, Visa **Details:** 75 seats. 30 seats outside. Private parties: 45 main room, 24 to 36 private rooms. Car park. Children's helpings. No smoking. Wheelchair access (also WC). No music **Accommodation:** 1 room, with bath/shower. TV. B&B £95. Baby facilities

MAP 10 Ullswater CUMBRIA

Sharrow Bay

Ullswater CA10 2LZ
Tel: (01768) 486301
Website: www.sharrowbay.co.uk

Cooking 6 | English | £51–£75

This sympathetically extended nineteenth-century villa is Britain's original country-house hotel, famous for its unrivalled view over Ullswater. There are luxurious lounges, open fires, flower arrangements, and beautiful antiques, and the dining rooms have a formality about them which is offset by staff who are 'professional without being obsequious'. Johnnie Martin and Colin Akrigg head the kitchen, delivering five-course lunches and six-course dinners (with an intermediate sorbet), but there are a few nods towards modernity in the French-accented English dishes. Food is rich but ingredients in all departments are top drawer and treated with respect. Lobster and red mullet terrine impresses for its fresh 'unadulterated seafood' flavour as well as a spoonful of light tomato marmalade served with it. Sautéed tuna on niçoise salad has been praised, while a main-course noisette of local venison is 'top-notch meat', served pink, with braised red cabbage, celeriac purée and a brandy and port sauce, components that 'complemented each other perfectly'. The signature dessert of sticky toffee pudding is never off the menu, while a stunningly presented lemon meringue parfait with raspberry coulis is among the alternatives.

The 'helpful' Sharrow Selection offers a short-cut to some enjoyable wines from £17.50, also available by the glass. The main list musters authoritative gravitas in classic French regions and doesn't falter in the southern hemisphere, but the breadth of choice in the £20 to £30 range is perhaps its most rewarding feature. A strong hand of whites from Alsace, the Loire and Germany is a bonus.

Chefs: Johnnie Martin and Colin Akrigg **Proprietor:** Sharrow Bay Hotels Ltd **Open:** all week 1, 8 (1 sitting) **Meals:** Set L £38.75, Set D £49.75. Light L menu available **Service:** not inc **Cards:** Amex, Delta, Maestro, MasterCard, Visa **Details:** 60 seats. Private parties: 40 main room, 40 private room. Car park. Vegetarian meals. No children under 13. No smoking. Wheelchair access (also WC). No music. No mobile phones. Air-conditioned **Accommodation:** 24 rooms, 23 with bath/shower. TV. Phone. D,B&B £160 to £460. Rooms for disabled. No children under 13

MAP 8 Ulverston CUMBRIA

Bay Horse

Canal Foot, Ulverston LA12 9EL
Tel: (01229) 583972
Website: www.thebayhorsehotel.co.uk

Cooking 3 | Country-House | £34–£64

This eighteenth-century inn's simple conservatory dining room has impressive views out over Morecambe Sands. Once comfortably ensconced, consider the weekly changing carte and fixed price

menu (you can mix and match them). Arrive by 7.30pm for dinner at 8 (lunch brings the choice of a cheaper restaurant carte or popular bar lunches). Highlights have included a 'hefty plate' of smoked duck breast with mango, salad and Cumberland sauce, then roast quail stuffed with apricot, prune and ginger with a juniper and thyme jus, or rack of saltmarsh lamb in a herb and crumb crust. Fish might take in poached sea bass fillets with deep-fried king prawns served in a white wine and fresh herb cream sauce. To finish, Cape brandy pudding and Baileys chocolate mousse have both provoked enthusiastic comments. Service nicely balances efficiency and friendliness, and the New World dominates a savvy wine list that combines quality and fair prices – starting at £15.50.

Chef: Robert Lyons **Proprietors:** John Tovey and Robert Lyons **Open:** Tue to Sun L 12 to 2, all week D 7.30 for 8 (1 sitting) **Closed:** 23 to 25 Dec **Meals:** alc (main courses, L £9.50 to £16.50, D £22.50 to £24.50). Set D £28.50 **Service:** not inc, card slips closed **Cards:** Amex, Maestro, MasterCard, Visa **Details:** 50 seats. Private parties: 50 main room. Car park. Vegetarian meals. No children under 12 at D. No smoking. Wheelchair access (also WC). Music. No mobile phones **Accommodation:** 9 rooms, all with bath/shower. TV. Phone. B&B £80 to £110. No children under 12

MAP 5 **Upper Slaughter**
GLOUCESTERSHIRE

Lords of the Manor

Upper Slaughter GL54 2JD
Tel: (01451) 820243
Website: www.lordsofthemanor.com

Cooking 6 | Modern European | £37–£116

The seventeenth-century former rectory would make a good setting for a period murder mystery, and the name of the village in which it lies seems positively to invite it. With floor-to-ceiling mullioned windows looking out over parkland, and a colossal floral display in the centre of the dining room, there can be no doubting the elevated tone of the place. Les Rennie works carefully with local suppliers to ensure freshness and quality, and there is a vigorous streak of culinary daring running through his menus. Braised belly pork may well be served with a roast scallop and smoked mash and seasoned with curry oil, while red mullet is paired refreshingly with tomato sorbet. Tuna carpaccio has been well reported as a starter, while sautéed foie gras with tamarind ice cream and aged balsamic has become a popular signature dish. Desserts have included pear tarte Tatin with rosemary ice cream and blue cheese pannacotta, and exceptional basil crème brûlée, in which the savoury herb flavour imparts remarkable lightness to a normally rich concoction. Complaints about the brusqueness of service flow thick and fast in readers' reports. Wines are a so-so international selection at strong mark-ups, with Chilean Chardonnay and Merlot at the base prices of £18 and £20 respectively.

Chef: Lee Rennie **Proprietor:** Empire Ventures **Open:** all week 12.30 to 2, 7 to 9.30 (10 Fri and Sat) **Meals:** Set L £17.50 (2 courses) to £21.50, Set D £49 to £79. Bar/terrace L menu available (exc Sun) **Service:** 10%, card slips closed **Cards:** Amex, Delta, Diners, Maestro, MasterCard, Visa **Details:** 50 seats. 25 seats outside. Private parties: 50 main room, 8 to 30 private rooms. Car park. Vegetarian meals. Children's helpings. No children under 10. No smoking. No music. No mobile phones **Accommodation:** 27 rooms, all with bath/shower. TV. Phone. B&B £99 to £310. Rooms for disabled. Baby facilities

MAP 2 **Upton Scudamore**
WILTSHIRE

Angel Inn

Upton Scudamore BA12 0AG
Tel: (01985) 213225
Website: www.theangelinn-wiltshire.co.uk

Cooking 4 | Modern British | £25–£52

Walk through the walled garden and terrace to reach this restored sixteenth-century village inn on the fringes of Salisbury Plain. Inside, there's a long, high-ceilinged bar and a sizeable dining room with bare tables and golden-yellow walls hung with pictures for sale. The kitchen takes care with ingredients: witness a fine T-bone steak cooked exactly as requested and served with salted chips. Regular consignments of fish from Brixham are the starting point for dishes like Chinese-style roast monkfish with pak choi and a soy, garlic and ginger sauce, or seared fillet of brill with squid ink and crayfish tail risotto. Classic ideas are often given an unexpected twist, as in, say, courgette carpaccio ('a fine fresh green confection,' according to one recipient) with grilled artichokes and black olive and tomato salsa, while desserts feature some impressive offerings, like pecan tart with walnut ice cream. The short wine list is priced from £12.95.

Chef: Paul Suter **Proprietors:** Carol and Tony Coates **Open:** all week 12 to 2, 7 to 9.30 **Closed:** 25 and 26 Dec, 1 Jan **Meals:** alc (main courses L £8 to £12, D £12 to £20) **Service:** not inc **Cards:** Maestro, MasterCard, Visa **Details:** 60 seats. 40 seats outside. Private parties: 30 main room. Car park. Vegetarian meals. Children's helpings. No smoking in dining room. Wheelchair access (not WC). Occasional music **Accommodation:** 10 rooms, all with bath/shower. TV. Phone. B&B £70 to £80. Rooms for disabled

MAP 1 Virginstow DEVON

Percy's

Coombeshead Estate, Virginstow EX21 5EA
Tel: (01409) 211236
Website: www.percys.co.uk

Cooking 4 | Modern British | £53–£63

When the Bricknell-Webbs opened here in 1996, there was not much to the enterprise beyond the 400-year-old long house in which the restaurant is sited, and a barn with guest rooms. Now a thriving cottage industry is in full swing, with the 130-acre, organically certified estate supplying much of the kitchen's provender, and the day boats at Looe accounting for a fair proportion too. Spinach tagliatelle with wild mushrooms, assertively seasoned with thyme, made a good inspection opener, and was followed up by perfectly timed monkfish with vegetable and ginger julienne and creamy saffron sauce. Venison haunch roasted rare and served on creamed potatoes, cabbage and spinach derived plenty of powerful, gutsy flavour from its seasonings of rosemary and green peppercorns, and crisp-shelled lemon tart with strawberries and herb-scented ice cream was a successful way to finish. There are also fine English farmhouse cheeses. Wines are a carefully chosen short selection from all over the world, with house bottles at £16.

Chef: Tina Bricknell-Webb **Proprietors:** Tony and Tina Bricknell-Webb **Open:** all week 12 to 1.30, 6.30 to 9 **Meals:** Set L £20 (2 courses), Set D £40 **Service:** not inc **Cards:** Delta, Maestro, MasterCard, Visa **Details:** 36 seats. Private parties: 40 main room, 10 to 14 private rooms. Car park. Vegetarian meals. No children under 12. No smoking. Wheelchair access (also WC). No music. No mobile phones **Accommodation:** 11 rooms, all with bath/shower. TV. Phone. B&B £90 to £210. Rooms for disabled. No children under 12. Fishing

MAP 3 Wadhurst EAST SUSSEX

Best Beech Inn

AR

Mayfield Lane, Wadhurst TN5 6JH
Tel: (01892) 782045

Tile-hung pub/restaurant deep in beech woods. New chef Stephan Santin tackles modern-sounding dishes like goats' cheese and beetroot filo parcels with a beetroot reduction (£5.75) and robust slow-braised lamb shank with creamy mash, baby fennel and red wine jus (£15) before desserts such as chocolate brûlée with coffee ice cream (£6). Lighter dishes such as roast salmon Caesar salad (£8) are served in the bistro adjacent to the bar. Eclectic wine list with prices from £12.95. Accommodation. Closed Sun D.

MAP 7 Wakefield WEST YORKSHIRE

Brasserie Ninety Nine

Trinity Business Park, Wakefield WF2 8EF
Tel: (01924) 377699

Ignore the location – a business park not far from Wakefield city centre – and focus on the food in this 'boldly modern' brasserie. Breakfast from 8am burgers in the bar, and a menu of in-vogue restaurant dishes like seared scallops with apple pannacotta and sage risotto (£9) and loin of venison with spiced red cabbage and vanilla jus (£18) Desserts such as rhubarb and ginger tart (£6) disappointed at inspection. Reasonably priced wine from £11.95. Closed Sun.

Wolski's

Monarch House, George Street,
Wakefield WF1 1NE
Tel: (01924) 381252

Vast bar/restaurant occupying three floors of converted wine merchant (circa 1910). Seafood (some from Wolski's own boat) is a strong suit expect anything from salt-baked sea bass with lemon and basil oil (£15) to lobsters and specials like Dover sole with prawn and caper butter Otherwise, the menu runs from crispy duck with pancakes and hoisin sauce (£6) to a trio of chocolate desserts. Early-evening menus from £10.95 house wines from £11.95. Banqueting and conference facilities. Closed Sun.

MAP 6 **Walberswick** SUFFOLK

The Anchor AR

Walberswick IP18 6UA
Tel: (01502) 722112

The Anchor in trendy 'Hampstead-by-the-Sea' has been given a new lease of life by owners Sophie and Mark Dorber. Improvements are continuing apace, with plans for the décor and kitchen. Sophie cooks a modern menu where seared scallops come with bacon, fennel and mixed leaves (£6.75/ £10.25) and salmon fishcake with parsley sauce and hand-cut chips (£8.25). Rosemary and vanilla pannacotta with strawberry coulis (£4.25) made an impressive finish for one reporter. Mark is something of a beer guru (he runs the White Horse in Parsons Green, London), so check out the pumps and range of bottles. Open all week.

MAP 9 **Walkington** EAST RIDING OF YORKSHIRE

Manor House AR

Northlands, Walkington HU17 8RT
Tel: (01482) 881645

Long-serving timbered country-house hotel now showing 'a lot of ambition' under Annie Pickering, whose 'very pleasant, efficient young staff' are much applauded. Set dinner at £34.50 (plus supplements) runs to four courses, with main courses taking in perhaps a Yorkshire lamb assiette comprising hotpot, shepherd's pie, faggots of shank, and sautéed liver, or cod three ways: in a herby breadcrumbed crust, a fishcake, and in Masham ale batter. Start with pigeon breast with a broad bean and smoked bacon ragoût and finish with iced Baileys parfait with a blueberry and thyme jus. Wines from £12.75. Closed Sun D.

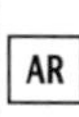

Not a full entry but provisionally recommended (known as 'round-ups' in previous editions, these 'also recommended' establishments are now integrated throughout the book).

MAP 5 **Warwick** WARWICKSHIRE

Findons

7 Old Square, Warwick CV34 4RA
Tel: (01926) 411755
Website: www.findons-restaurant.co.uk

Cooking 2 | Modern European | £33–£59

In an elegant, large-windowed Georgian building in the corner of Old Square, Findons delivers sound modern dishes amid chandeliers and gilt-framed mirrors. The accent is broadly Mediterranean, with starters including seared Brixham scallops with Sbiroli tagliatelle and sambuca and lobster broth (a bestseller, say the owners), or potato gnocchi with wild mushrooms, basil and ricotta cream. Fillet of English beef may come with polenta cake, red onion, Gorgonzola and red wine sauce, or roast chump of lamb with cannellini and borlotti bean ragoût. Some of the desserts sound a French note: brioche bread-and-butter pudding with crème Chantilly, and lemon tart with berry and cassis coulis. The list of forty-odd wines begins with house Italians at £12.95 (£3.50 a glass).

Chefs: Michael Findon and Renato Ramalho **Proprietor:** Findon & Williams Ltd **Open:** Mon to Sat D only 6.30 to 9.30 **Closed:** 26 Dec to 3 Jan **Meals:** alc D (main courses £13 to £18). Set D Mon to Fri (2 courses) £25 **Service:** not inc, 10% (optional) for parties of 6 or more **Cards:** Delta, Maestro, MasterCard, Visa **Details:** 40 seats. 25 seats outside. Private parties: 30 main room, 8 to 14 private rooms. Vegetarian meals. No children under 11. Wheelchair access (not WC). Music

Rose and Crown NEW ENTRY

30 Market Place, Warwick CV34 4SH
Tel: (01926) 411117
Website: www.peachpubs.com

Cooking 2 | Bistro | £30–£44

'Eat... Drink... Sleep' is the message behind this substantial three-storey hostelry bang in the centre of town. Inside it's a product of the contemporary school of pub design, with theatrical lighting, high-backed wicker chairs and old floorboards. Drinkers pack the bar and the music pounds. The kitchen delivers bright modern bistro food ranging from build-it-yourself deli boards to fashionable ideas like salmon niçoise and noisettes of lamb with spiced couscous and mint salsa, all based on impressively good raw materials. Weekly specials such as faggots and mash or whole roast megrim with sautéed potatoes and chorizo oil add variety, and you could finish off with a 'sophisticated' ginger pannacotta with chunky pineapple compote. Service is youthful and international but has been 'negligent' and the two-hour time limit on tables is worth noting. Thirty, fairly priced global wines start at £10.50.

Chef: Nigel Brown **Proprietor:** Lee Cash **Open:** all week 12 to 2.30 (3 Sun), 6.30 to 10 (9.30 Sun) **Closed:** 25 Dec **Meals:** alc (main courses £9.50 to £13.50) **Service:** not inc **Cards:** Amex, Delta, Diners, MasterCard, Maestro, Visa **Details:** 100 seats. 40 seats outside. Private parties: 25 main room, 20 to 25 private rooms. Vegetarian meals. No smoking in 1 dining room. Wheelchair access (also WC). Music **Accommodation:** 5 rooms, all with bath/shower. TV. Phone. B&B £65

MAP 10 **Watermillock** CUMBRIA

Rampsbeck Country House Hotel

Watermillock, Ullswater CA11 0LP
Tel: (017684) 86442
Website: www.rampsbeck.fsnet.co.uk

Cooking 3 | Anglo-French | £38–£70

The plush dining room at this 'lovely manor house' overlooks Ullswater, and welcoming, well oiled service pampers visitors. The food on the fixed-price menus is just as comforting: roast quail with wild mushrooms ragoût and fried quail's eggs to start, say, or hand-dived scallops with guacamole, pimento chutney and lime and coriander dressing. Then, this being a country-house hotel, a choice of soups with the four-course dinner, perhaps cauliflower with truffle oil, or mussel and saffron. Mains could bring fried halibut with a mushroom croustade, poached oyster and cucumber spaghetti, or, for carnivores, roast venison fillet with creamed beetroot, sauté potatoes and garlic confit. Finish with roast pineapple plus passion-fruit ice cream, or British and Irish cheeses. A good-value international wine range, divided into idiosyncratic style categories, has succinct tasting notes.

Chef: Andrew McGeorge **Proprietors:** Tom and Marion Gibb and M.J. MacDowall **Open:** all week L 12 to 1 (bookings only) and D 7 to 8.30. Bar L menu available **Meals:** Set L £28, Set D £38 to £44.50 **Service:** not inc, card slips closed **Cards:** Delta, Maestro, MasterCard, Visa **Details:** 40 seats. Private parties: 40 main room, 8 to 15 private rooms. Car park. Children's helpings. No children under 7. No smoking. No music. No mobile phones **Accommodation:** 19 rooms, all with bath/shower. TV. Phone. B&B £75 to £250

MAP 8 **Wath-in-Nidderdale** NORTH YORKSHIRE

Sportsman's Arms

Wath-in-Nidderdale, Pateley Bridge HG3 5PP
Tel: (01423) 711306

Cooking 4 | Anglo-French | £34–£57

Ray and June Carter have clocked up more than a quarter of a century at this immensely likeable seventeenth-century hostelry reached via a packhorse bridge off the road to the head of Nidderdale. Inside, the whole place is still done out in the style of a country inn, with rustic antique furniture, wall clocks and mirrors. Fish gets top billing, and a section of the menu to itself: typically the results are classic rather than fashionable – Scottish salmon is poached and served with cucumber beurre blanc, Whitby cod is roasted and set on top of bacon mash with garlic butter. Game also has its say (perhaps a pairing of pheasant and grouse breast with two different sauces) and guinea fowl finds itself in exotic company with pomegranate risotto and asparagus jus. Starters range from herring roes on toast to sauté lambs' kidneys Turbigo, while desserts have included intensely fruity summer pudding as well as apple and bilberry pie. France is the inspiration for the wine list, and prices are very fair.

Chefs: Ray Carter and Seth Marsland **Proprietors:** Jane and Ray Carter **Open:** Sun L 12 to 2.30, Mon to Sat D 7 to 9 **Closed:** 25 Dec **Meals:** alc (main courses £10.50 to £18.50). Set L Sun £28. Bar menu available **Service:** not inc, card slips closed **Cards:** Delta, Maestro, MasterCard, Visa **Details:** 50 seats. 45 seats outside. Private parties: 45 main room, 6 to 12 private rooms. Car park. Vegetarian meals. Children's helpings. No smoking. Wheelchair access (not WC). Occasional music. No mobile phones **Accommodation:** 13 rooms, all with bath/shower. TV. Phone. B&B £60 to £120. Rooms for disabled. Fishing

MAP 2 **Wells** SOMERSET

Goodfellows

NEW ENTRY

5 Sadler Street,
Wells BA5 2RR
Tel: (01749) 673866

Cooking 6 | Seafood | £23–£77

Guide readers may recall Adam Fellows from his time at Charlton House, Shepton Mallet (see entry). This, his first solo venture, has taken him to the centre of Wells and the site of the former Ritcher's restaurant, which has undergone a thoroughly modern makeover involving slate, brushed steel and pale grey-green walls. The resulting Goodfellows – a mix of fishmonger and deli, café, restaurant and state-of-the-art open kitchen – is spread over two floors linked by a spiral staircase, opening for dinner on just three nights a week; lunch caters for town-centre shoppers and businesses with light snacks and a good-value, fixed-price menu.

Bread of superlative quality is home-made, and all raw materials are first-rate (fish, the main focus, is delivered daily from Brixham). A modern vein runs through the repertoire, with flavour combinations as forthright as the décor: a starter of ballottine of organic salmon with artichoke and fennel salad and an interesting rocket and walnut pesto was an impressive start to an inspection meal that went on to 'nicely timed' fillets of sea bream with basil-crushed potato, roast Mediterranean vegetables and sauce vierge. Fillet of beef takes care of non-fish eaters. That skills extend beyond fish is apparent from a 'beautifully wobbly' pannacotta served with mixed berries and an intense grappa sorbet, or try a strawberry plate of chilled soup, fraisier cake, and strawberry and pistachio ice cream. Sad to say, service can be a little patchy under pressure. The compact, global wine list starts at £12.95.

Chef: Adam Fellows **Proprietors:** Adam and Martine Fellows **Open:** Tue to Sat L 12 to 2.30, Thur to Sat D 6.30 to 9.30 **Meals:** alc (main courses L £6.50 to £20, D £17 to £28). Set L £12.50 (2 courses) to £15, Set D £29 **Service:** not inc, card slips closed **Cards:** Amex, Maestro, MasterCard, Visa **Details:** 40 seats. 10 seats outside. Private parties: 20 main room, 8 to 12 private rooms. Vegetarian meals. Children's helpings. No smoking. Music

 This symbol means that the wine list is well above the average.

MAP 3 **Welwyn Garden City** HERTFORDSHIRE

Novelli at Auberge du Lac

Brocket Hall, Welwyn Garden City AL8 7XG
Tel: (01707) 368888
Website: www.brocket-hall.co.uk

Cooking 6 | Modern French | £45–£121

Jean-Christophe Novelli's country base is part of this swish golf/conference/hotel complex in the grounds of Brocket Hall. The Auberge overlooks an ornamental lake, a scene to inspire tranquil contentment, like the sympathetic service. Children are welcomed as warmly as their elders. Novelli has never been content simply to turn out renditions of French classics, and the menus contain much to surprise, while still firmly anchored in sound culinary logic. Caramelised veal sweetbread comes on a crisp potato galette, with prawn ravioli for company, or smoked salmon might be served warm with its own mousse, Cornish crab and a trendily frothy sauce of cucumber. Mains bring on assertive fish dishes such as turbot with sautéed girolles and roast artichokes, or richly earthy meats like Pyrenean milk-fed lamb leg with thyme tortellini, garlic-creamed French beans and lamb jus, or perhaps both together, as in the fashionable marriage of rolled pork fillet with scallops, a trotter stuffed with sage and apple, and a sauce of shellfish bisque. Frothy sauces might accompany desserts too – a Malibu version appeared with roast pineapple and pineapple sorbet on a spring menu – or there is a fine Anglo-French cheese trolley. Alongside the carte there are weekday fixed-price lunches and dinners, a Sunday lunch and a five-course tasting menu.

The wine list, overseen by a team of sommeliers on hand with ready advice, is very fine, with pages and pages of French classics, and pedigree selections from elsewhere, but prices are high. A large slate of wines by the glass opens at £5 for Chilean Sauvignon or a Negroamaro from Salento.

Chef: Jean-Christophe Novelli **Proprietor:** CCA International **Open:** Tue to Sun L 12 to 2.30, Tue to Sat D 6.30 to 10.30 **Meals:** alc (not Sun L; main courses £21 to £36). Set L Tue to Sat £28.50, Set L Sun £35, Set D £45 (Tue to Fri) to £65 **Service:** 10% (optional), card slips closed **Cards:** Amex, Delta, Diners, Maestro, MasterCard, Visa **Details:** 70 seats. 50 seats outside. Private parties: 70 main room, 4 to 18 private rooms. Car park. Vegetarian meals. Children's helpings. No smoking. Music. No mobile phones. Air-conditioned **Accommodation:** 16 rooms, all with bath/shower. TV. Phone. Room only £125 to £175. Rooms for disabled. Fishing

MAP 2 **West Bay** DORSET

Riverside Restaurant

West Bay DT6 4EZ
Tel: (01308) 422011
Website: www.thefishrestaurant-westbay.co.uk

Cooking 3 | Seafood | £27–£71

To reach this veteran among South Coast seafood restaurants you need to cross the walkway over the river: the building is surrounded by water, which adds to the charm and provides visitors eating in the bare-boarded dining room with interesting views 'enhanced by the reflection of lights from surrounding areas'. In all, it's plain, unpretentious and uncluttered. Since 1964, the Watsons have prided themselves on dispensing high-quality fish from Dorset boats and letting the ingredients do the talking. The results are straight and true, whether it's a plate of garlic prawns, a bowl of scallop and crab chowder, or something more luxurious like roast turbot with lobster sauce, or baked gilthead bream with a lemongrass, lime and coriander stuffing. Desserts have also been praised: poached damsons with lemon custard, and a 'lovely combination' of 'brûléed' figs with pistachio and marsala syrup, for example. The wine list sensibly focuses on whites that let the fish take centre stage. Prices are good, and options by the glass take in quality names like Vatan in Sancerre and New Zealand's Jackson Estate (both £4.75 for 175ml).

Chefs: Nic Larcombe and George Marsh **Proprietors:** Arthur and Janet Watson **Open:** Tue to Sun and bank hol weekends L 12 to 2.15, Tue to Sat and bank hol weekends D 6.30 to 8.30 **Closed:** 1 Dec to 12 Feb. Phone for evening opening variations Feb to Mar and Oct to Nov **Meals:** alc (main courses £10.50 to £27.50). Set L Tue to Fri exc July and Aug £13.50 (2 courses) to £16.50 **Service:** not inc, card slips closed **Cards:** Delta, Maestro, MasterCard, Visa **Details:** 75 seats. 30 seats outside. Private parties: 80 main room, 10 to 20 private rooms. Vegetarian meals. Children's helpings. No smoking. Wheelchair access (also women's WC). Occasional music

MAP 3 **Westfield** EAST SUSSEX

Wild Mushroom AR

Woodgate House, Westfield Lane, Westfield
TN35 4SB
Tel: (01424) 751137

Paul and Rebecca Webbe make a hands-on team in this converted Victorian property with a conservatory. Their international menu moves from sardine and potato terrine with capers and shallots (£4.75) through roast Gressingham duckling with caramelised pears and cassis sauce (£13.50) and Scottish beef fillet with – of course – wild mushroom sauce to glazed passion-fruit mousse with a matching syrup and grenadine sorbet (£5.25). International wines from £11.50. Closed Sat L, Sun D and all Mon.

MAP 2 **West Stoke** WEST SUSSEX

West Stoke House AR

Downs Road, West Stoke PO18 9BN
Tel: (01243) 575226

Big, rambling country house in a peaceful, civilised setting close to the Downs. The kitchen works to short fixed-price menus (three courses £35) in the modern Euro-mould of braised pork cheeks with rillettes of rabbit and purées of celeriac and apple, followed by baked cod with crushed saffron parsnips, broccoli hollandaise and bouillabaisse sauce, then strawberry soufflé with vanilla ice cream and sauce anglaise. House wines £13. Accommodation. Open Wed to Sun L and Wed to Sat D.

MAP 9 **West Tanfield** NORTH YORKSHIRE

Bruce Arms

Main Street, West Tanfield HG4 5JJ
Tel: (01677) 470325
Website: www.brucearms.com

Cooking 4 | Modern English | £33–£54

Geoff and Jan Smith's 'wonderful old pub' makes a good base for soaking up the landscape and atmosphere of an appealing corner of Yorkshire. Stone-flagged floors, a splendid fireplace and shelves of dusty books create a deliberately antiquated feel, as do 1940s copies of *The Daily Telegraph*, old Yorkshire tea tins, even a wind-up telephone. But look again, and you notice racks of wines and an 'ever-changing' blackboard menu firmly entrenched in the twenty-first century. A chowder of Cornish scallops with croûtons and crispy bacon starts things off heartily before roast Dales lamb with tarragon sauce, fillet of Masham beef, or organic salmon with asparagus and hollandaise. Desserts are an equally familiar bunch: perhaps rhubarb and apple Betty with ice cream or chocolate mousse. The creditable, all-round wine list includes house recommendations from £11.95.

Chef: Geoff Smith **Proprietors:** Geoff and Jan Smith **Open:** Sat and Sun L 12 to 2, Tue to Sat D 6.30 to 9.30 **Meals:** alc (main courses £13 to £18.50) **Service:** not inc, card slips closed **Cards:** Maestro, MasterCard, Visa **Details:** 60 seats. 20 seats outside. Private parties: 28 main room. Car park. Vegetarian meals. No smoking in 1 dining room. Music. No mobile phones **Accommodation:** 3 rooms, all with bath/shower. TV. B&B £40 to £60

MAP 2 Weymouth DORSET

Crab House Café

Fleet Oyster Farm, Ferryman's Way, Weymouth DT4 9YU
Tel: (01305) 788867

The former Abbotsbury Seafood Bar is in new hands. It always was an appealing spot overlooking Chesil Beach and the Isle of Portland (outside seating enables customers 'to watch the sunset over the lagoon'), but now there's a 'certain Spartan smartness' about it and early reports (more, please) suggest that it is much improved. Expect first-class seafood on a daily-changing menu: say, half a dozen oysters (£7) from the café's oyster farm next door, or fish chowder (£6.50), then roast red mullet (£10), or black bream baked with lemon-grass and ginger (£14). House wine £11.95. Closed Sun D, Mon D and all Tue.

Perry's

4 Trinity Road, Weymouth DT4 8TJ
Tel: (01305) 785799

Long-serving, family-run seafood restaurant by Weymouth's Old Harbour. Ultra-fresh fish is used simply for dishes like steamed mussels with garlic, white wine and cream (£7), grilled Dover sole, and roast cod with tomatoes, chorizo and butter beans (£14); otherwise, choose something meaty like fillet of pork with Calvados sauce. Mango sorbet with lime syrup, meringue and pineapple (£5) is one way to finish. Popular, chatty and unpretentious. Keenly priced wines from £10.95. Open Tue to Sun L, all week D.

MAP 9 Whitby NORTH YORKSHIRE

Greens

AR

13 Bridge Street, Whitby YO22 4BG
Tel: (01947) 600284

Rising star in the Whitby firmament, near the swing bridge on the south side of town. Locally landed fish is Rob Green's forte, and the blackboard menus reflect the day's catch. Salt and pepper squid with two sauces (£7) is a typical opener, while main courses might include line-caught halibut, sea bass, and roast fillet of turbot with a ragoût of queen scallops (£19). Yorkshire meat is a good alternative, and desserts (£5.25) might feature chocolate mousse with whisky and oranges. Vins de pays £12.50. Open Fri to Sun L and all week D.

Magpie Café

14 Pier Road, Whitby YO21 3PU
Tel: (01947) 602058
Website: www.magpiecafe.co.uk

Cooking 2 | Seafood | £21–£49

'Should be a national ambassador for Great British fish and chips,' implored a fan of this remarkable Yorkshire seaside café. Be prepared to queue – although recent extensions to the harbour-side building mean that you can now shelter inside on inclement days. Fish comes direct from the nearby market (no doubts about freshness here), and regular species like cod, haddock and skate are served with a coating of crunchy batter and crisp golden chips. The kitchen also shows off its talents with specials ranging from Whitby crab cakes with crème fraîche tartare sauce to seared tuna on spicy aubergine lasagne, and there are all manner of homely puddings to round things off, including jam roly-poly and hazelnut meringue topped with strawberries. A pot of tea often does the trick; otherwise, there are fish-friendly wines from £9.95.

Chefs: Ian Robson and Paul Gildroy **Proprietors:** Ian Robson and Alison McKenzie-Robson **Open:** all week 11.30 to 9 **Closed:** 19 to 26 Dec, 1 Jan, 8 Jan to 3 Feb **Meals:** alc (main courses £6 to £15) **Service:** not inc, card slips closed **Cards:** Delta, Maestro, MasterCard, Visa **Details:** 130 seats. Private parties: 45 main room, 20 to 36 private rooms. Vegetarian meals. Children's helpings. No smoking. Wheelchair access (also WC). Occasional music. Air-conditioned

MAP 2 Whitchurch HAMPSHIRE

Red House

21 London Street, Whitchurch RG28 7LH
Tel: (01256) 895558

Cooking 3 | Global | £29–£55

Not far from the River Test and Whitchurch's working silk mill, this restored sixteenth-century coaching inn is part pub, part casual restaurant. Any allusions to 'red' are confined to two doors – one leading to the bar, the other to the dining room. The short menu (bolstered by daily specials) promises colourful-sounding, modern dishes like duck leg ballottine with pistachio mousse, pineapple and chilli salsa, and roast rump of lamb with glazed baby carrots and couscous bouillon. Piscophiles could choose Brixham scallops with pea velouté and chorizo lardons, or lemon sole fillets poached with spinach, bacon and crème fraîche, while steak-fanciers have their own specials board. Desserts might include French lemon tart with vanilla ice cream. Service is friendly. Ten house wines (from £10.95) head the short worldwide list.

Chef: Shannon Wells **Proprietors:** Shannon and Caroline Wells **Open:** all week 12 to 2, 6.30 (7 Sun) to 9.30 **Meals:** alc (main courses £9 to £17.50). Bar menu available **Service:** not inc, 10% for parties of 8 or more, card slips closed **Cards:** Maestro, MasterCard, Visa **Details:** 38 seats. 40 seats outside. Private parties: 28 main room. Car park. Vegetarian meals. Children's helpings; no children under 8 at D. No smoking in 1 dining room. No music. No mobile phones

MAP 8 Whitewell LANCASHIRE

Inn at Whitewell AR

Whitewell BB7 3AT
Tel: (01200) 448222

Sedate, upmarket inn hidden away in the Trough of Bowland. Olde-worlde décor but modern restaurant food along the lines of seared scallops with black pudding and creamed leeks (£7.75) and poached Goosnargh chicken breast with herb dumplings and a blue cheese beignet (£14), followed by desserts like sticky toffee pudding (£4). Alternatively, eat, say, fish pie in the bar. The heavyweight wine list is worth exploring (prices from £10.90), and you can buy bottles from the Vintner's Shop. Accommodation. Open all week.

MAP 2 Whitley WILTSHIRE

Pear Tree Inn NEW ENTRY

Top Lane, Whitley, nr Melksham SN12 8QX
Tel: (01225) 709131

Cooking 4 | Modern British-Plus | £29–£53

Set in its own large garden this attractive stone-built house doubles as unpretentious local pub and restaurant. Owners Martin and Debbie Still have a chef – Stephen Terry – who has featured in the Guide over the years in some high-profile (and high scoring) places. He demonstrates his undoubted skill in finely balanced dishes such as perfectly cooked beef fillet with blue-cheese polenta and chorizo, with wilted beetroot leaves providing a contrasting earthy-tasting bed for the meat, or mint-scented pesto imparting a 'summery feel' to a dish of lamb cutlets. Start with crispy pork belly with fennel, rocket, lemon and capers, and finish with a modern take on old pub-grub friends like sticky date pudding, delivered here as a turret of tender sponge with an exceptional butterscotch sauce, or a smooth, rich but light cinnamon cheesecake served with apple compote. Service is efficient, as is the annotated wine list, which shows careful selection within a sensibly limited range; bottles start at £13.50. As the Guide hits the presses we hear Stephen Terry's departure is imminent. Reports please.

Chef: Stephen Terry **Proprietors:** Martin and Debbie Still **Open:** all week 12 to 2.30 (3 Sun), 6.30 to 9.30 (10 Fri and Sat, 9 Sun) **Closed:** 25, 26 and 31 Dec, 1 Jan **Meals:** alc (main courses £11.50 to £18). Set L £14 (2 courses) to £16 **Service:** not inc **Cards:** Delta, Maestro, MasterCard, Visa **Details:** 70 seats. 20 seats outside. Private parties: 40 main room. Car park. Vegetarian meals. Children's helpings. No-smoking area. Wheelchair access (also WC). No music **Accommodation:** 8 rooms, all with bath/shower. TV. Phone. B&B £75 to £90. Rooms for disabled

MAP 3 Whitstable KENT

JoJo's NEW ENTRY

209 Tankerton Road, Whitstable CT5 2AT
Tel: (01227) 274591

Cooking 4 | Modern European | £22–£37

'Meze, meat and fish' – JoJo's self-appointed subtitle – is a fair description of the food served in the tiny front room of this striking blue-painted Victorian terraced house. Nikki Billington uses

prime local materials as well as ideas, techniques and impeccable sourcing to produce her take on modern tapas. Cannon of lamb, seared, thinly sliced and served with tsatsiki, has met with praise, as have aubergine fritters, perfectly timed goujons of haddock with garlic mayonnaise, and battered squid 'of such delicacy that I don't think I've had anything like it'. Accompaniments are important too: candied red pepper and pear are served with Tuscan salami, and candied pear crops up again partnering kefalotiri, a nutty, hard Greek goats' cheese. Skills of a different kind bring exceptional baklava, or there could be strawberry pavlova. Paul Watson makes an amiable front-of-house host. Unlicensed.

Chefs: Nikki Billington and Sarah Hannell **Proprietors:** Nikki Billington and Paul Watson **Open:** Wed to Sun L 12.30 to 2.30, Wed to Sat D 6.30 to 10.30 **Meals:** alc (main courses £3 to £6.50). Unlicensed; BYO £1 **Service:** not inc **Cards:** none **Details:** 20 seats. 15 seats outside. Private parties: 16 main room. No smoking. Wheelchair access (not WC). Music. No mobile phones

Sportsman

Faversham Road, Seasalter, Whitstable CT5 4BP
Tel: (01227) 273370

Cooking 4 | Modern European | £30–£53

It may not be the prettiest of settings and this white-painted pub face can appear bleak and remote, but everyone is here for the food. Bare wooden floors and rustic tables provide an unfussy backdrop for Stephen Harris's commendably direct approach to cooking. Much care goes into the sourcing of ingredients – from within ten miles, where possible – with bread baked in-house and hams and bacon cured on the premises. Dishes are chalked up on a blackboard, so choosing can involve a bit of legwork, but, once decisions are made, the informal, casual service follows restaurant routines. As simplicity is one of the keynotes here, first courses make use of simple assemblies: bresaola cured in white wine and spices, Serrano ham and tomato bruschetta, or a plate of smoked eel with horseradish and soda bread. Timing of fish is accurate – witness turbot fillet braised in vin jaune with morels – while a range of more assertive but complementary flavours are brought together in crispy duck with smoked chilli salsa and sour cream. Shepherd Neame ales appear alongside a bright list of fairly priced wines, which opens at £10.95, with six available by the glass.

Chefs: Stephen Harris, Dan Flavell, Natalie Toman and Vicky Harper **Proprietors:** Stephen, Philip and Damian Harris **Open:** Tue to Sun L 12 to 2 (3 Sun), Tue to Sat D 7 to 9 **Closed:** 25 and 26 Dec **Meals:** alc (main courses £11 to £18) **Service:** not inc, card slips closed **Cards:** Delta, Maestro, MasterCard, Visa **Details:** 50 seats. Private parties: 40 main room. Car park. Children's helpings. No smoking in 1 dining room. Wheelchair access (not WC). Occasional music

Wheelers Oyster Bar

8 High Street, Whitstable CT5 1BQ
Tel: (01227) 273311

Cooking 2 | Seafood | £28–£42

Behind a cheerful pink and blue frontage, this tiny venue crams in a small bar counter where you can stand and enjoy smoked salmon sandwiches and bowls of seafood, among other snacky dishes, and to the rear a cosy parlour dining room where a full menu of imaginative modern fish dishes is served. Consistently high standards have been achieved of late, one reporter's meal opening with a crab cake 'that was all crab', served with a tart, mustardy rémoulade and dried apple crisps, followed by a well-timed sea bass fillet with a caramelised, saffron-scented risotto cake topped with a large chunk of squid in light, crisp tempura batter and a huge stuffed piquillo pepper. The dining room is unlicensed, but corkscrews are provided, and for something to use them on, the handily placed off-license across the road should suffice. Limited space means booking is essential.

Chef: Mark Stubbs **Proprietor:** Delia Fitt **Open:** Thur to Tue 1 to 7.30 (7 Sun) **Meals:** alc (main courses £14.50 to £18). Light menu available **Service:** not inc **Cards:** none **Details:** 16 seats. Vegetarian meals. Children's helpings. No smoking. Wheelchair access (not WC). No music. Air-conditioned

Whitstable Oyster Fishery Co. AR

Royal Native Oyster Stores, Horsebridge Road, Whitstable CT5 1BU
Tel: (01227) 276856

The bare-boarded Victorian oyster store, facing a shingle beach, has casually furnished dining rooms, a vague nautical theme, blackboard menus and great displays of seafood. The aim is simplicity: oysters (Whitstable native and rock), chargrilled sardines, or deep-fried squid, followed by whole sea bass roasted with garlic and rosemary, or whole lobster with potato salad, with maple syrup brûlée or chocolate and walnut brownie with white chocolate ice cream to finish. Closed Mon.

Williams & Brown Tapas

48 Harbour Street, Whitstable CT5 1AQ
Tel: (01227) 273373

Cooking 2 | Tapas | £32–£53

The eponymous pair clearly understand the merits of attention to detail – no surprise, given that they run a highly regarded delicatessen across the street from this neat, simple but cramped tapas bar. The emphasis is firmly on freshness and seasonality, and the menu ranges from Spanish regional specialities to 'modern urban tapas'. A platter of cured meats, chorizo in cider, or Manchego and membrillo are among the more familiar dishes, while chicken livers roasted with garlic, or lamb chops served with spiced lentils really catch the eye. There's a strong seafood element too: simple chargrilled sardines, or mussels with a tomato ragoût, or twice-cooked octopus (braised, then chargrilled). House wine is £12.95.

Chefs/Proprietors: Christopher Williams and David Brown **Open:** Wed to Mon L 12 to 2 (2.30 Sat, 2.45 Sun), Wed to Sat and Mon D (also Sun June-Aug) 6.30 to 9 (6 to 9.30 Sat) **Closed:** 25 and 26 Dec, 1 and 2 Jan **Meals:** alc (main courses £7 to £13) **Service:** 10% (optional) **Cards:** none **Details:** 35 seats. Private parties: 40 main room. Vegetarian meals. No smoking. Music. No mobile phones. Air-conditioned

MAP 2 **Wickham** HAMPSHIRE

Old House

NEW ENTRY

The Square, Wickham PO17 5NU
Tel: (01329) 833049
Website:
www.theoldhousehotelandrestaurant.co.uk

Cooking 1 | Modern British | £32–£60

The Old House is at one end of Wickham's large, oblong square, a creeper-covered façade and arched entrance leading in to quite an acreage of space given over to dining. James Dickson cooks a mixture of styles, with a few old favourites sitting tentatively among some more speculative modern dishes. The latter tendency might see a meal opening with duck ravioli served with pickled cucumber and hoisin dressing, while the former brings on lime-dressed crab and avocado tian, followed by marinated lamb with garlic mash. Technical ability is clearly marked in a dish of honey-glazed duck breast with morello cherries, fondant potato and spinach, the components of which were all in good order at inspection. Main courses are served with a cornucopia of not strictly necessary vegetables in the country-pub style. Hot chocolate soufflé is made with the best gear and has an admirably balanced white chocolate ice cream for company. The fairly ordinary wines are divided between the hemispheres and start at £12.95.

Chefs: James Dickson, David Cameron and Francis Devrainne **Proprietors:** Paul, Lesley and James Scott **Open:** all week L 12 to 2.30, Mon to Sat D 6.30 to 9.30 **Closed:** 26 to 30 Dec **Meals:** alc (main courses £12 to £21.50). Set L £14.95 (2 courses) to £19.95. Light L menu available Mon to Sat **Service:** not inc, card slips closed, 10% for parties of 8 or more **Cards:** Amex, Delta, Maestro, MasterCard, Visa **Details:** 80 seats. 24 seats outside. Private parties: 68 main room, 14 to 68 private rooms. Car park. Vegetarian meals. Children's helpings. No-smoking area. Wheelchair access (also WC). Music. No mobile phones **Accommodation:** 12 rooms, all with bath/shower. TV. Phone. B&B £50 to £150. Rooms for disabled. Baby facilities

MAP 8 **Wilmslow** CHESHIRE

Heddy's

AR

100–102 Water Lane, Wilmslow SK9 5BB
Tel: (01625) 526855

Pan-Middle Eastern cooking in a popular, hands-on neighbourhood restaurant close to the centre of town. Heddy Ghazizadeh's long menu covers a lot of ground, from authentic meze (from around £6 to £8) via couscous (from £10.50) to moussaka and kiniov judig (poussin in red wine with garlic and spices). Desserts embrace baklava (£3.50), rum baba, and Turkish delight. Persian specials at weekends. Wide-ranging, worldwide wine list (from £12.50) with a promising Lebanese contingent. Open Tue to Fri L and Mon to Sat D.

NEW ENTRY	This appears after the restaurant's name if the establishment was not a main entry in last year's Guide, although it may have been a 'round-up/also recommended' in previous editions.

MAP 5 **Winchcombe** GLOUCESTERSHIRE

5 North Street

Winchcombe GL54 5LH
Tel: (01242) 604566

Cooking 6 | Modern European | £34–£77

This hugely accomplished restaurant neatly proves good things come in small packages. The door opens into the larger of two tiny rooms, done in 'shoe-tan red', with beamed ceilings and bare varnished tables creating a rustic ambience. Sounds from the kitchen, such as tireless hand-whisking one February evening, speak of the pride and pains taken by Marcus Ashenford.

There is a hint of cuisine de terroir in the culinary thinking, although the construction of dishes is more complex than that. The precision of timing and seasoning is exemplary – notwithstanding an unfashionably generous hand with the salt – and dishes impress for their depth and resonance. A chunk of buttery, roasted hake sits on baby spinach amid a wreath of tiny mussels, casseroled with tomatoes and shallots, in a dark and fragrant sauce of crab bisque. After a pause for breath, a main course might be breast, leg and liver of duck, with celeriac fondant, 'mushy peas' (no purées here) and a 'strong and interesting' sauce of burnt orange. Another main might pair monkfish with sweet-and-sour chicken wings, plus baby fennel and a reduction sauce spiked with five-spice. Desserts tend to be simpler, and may feature fine, fragile pastrywork, perhaps encasing figs and orange segments, served with a scoop of intense honey ice cream. Kate Ashenford manages the front-of-house with great assurance and neither need nor space for any assistance. Choice on the shortish wine list cramped below £20, though house Sauvignon and Merlot are £13.50.

Chef: Marcus Ashenford **Proprietors:** Marcus and Kate Ashenford **Open:** Wed to Sun L 12 to 2, Tue to Sat D 7 to 9 **Closed:** 2 weeks Jan, 1 week Aug **Meals:** Set L £21.50, Set D £25 to £48.50 **Service:** not inc **Cards:** Amex, Delta, Maestro, MasterCard, Visa **Details:** 26 seats. Private parties: 26 main room. Vegetarian meals. Children's helpings. No smoking. Wheelchair access (not WC). Music. No mobile phones

 This symbol means that the restaurant has elected to participate in *The Good Food Guide's* £5 voucher scheme (see 'How to Use the Guide' for details).

Wesley House

High Street, Winchcombe GL54 5LJ
Tel: (01242) 602366
Website: www.wesleyhouse.co.uk

Cooking 3 | Modern British | £27–£60

John Wesley stayed here twice in the eighteenth century, hence the name. Inside, contemporary lighting, opulent flower arrangements and vivid abstract oils make a galvanic contrast with black beams and walls of white plaster or Cotswold stone. Nor is Martin Dunn's cooking in the least olde-worlde. A rémoulade of celeriac and pear accompanies a slice of duck confit and foie gras terrine, while Jerusalem artichokes make not a mere soup but a frothy 'cappuccino' garnished with a poached egg. Head-turning main courses have involved slow-braising lamb shank, its robust textures counterpointed with saffron mash, or pairing roast sea bass with brown shrimps on a fondue of leeks. To finish, lemon thyme crème brûlée comes with honey and ginger ice cream, while an earthy sorbet of cranberries and port might complement mandarin soufflé. France, Italy and the New World comprise most of the wine list, with house selections from £14 for Pays d'Oc Sauvignon or Merlot.

Chef: Martin Dunn **Proprietor:** Matthew Brown **Open:** all week 12 to 2, Mon to Sat D 7 to 9.30 **Closed:** 25 and 26 Dec **Meals:** alc L (main courses £17.50 to £21.50). Set L (2 courses) £12.50 to £16, Set L Sun £18.50 (2 courses) to £21.50, Set D £29.50 (2 courses, not Sat) to £35; bar L menu available **Service:** not inc **Cards:** Amex, Delta, Maestro, MasterCard, Visa **Details:** 70 seats. Private parties: 70 main room, 26 private room. Children's helpings. No smoking. Wheelchair access (not WC). Occasional music. No mobile phones. Air-conditioned **Accommodation:** 5 rooms, all with bath/shower. TV. Phone. B&B £65 to £110. Baby facilities

MAP 2 **Winchester** HAMPSHIRE

Chesil Rectory

1 Chesil Street, Winchester SO23 0HU
Tel: (01962) 851555
Website: www.chesilrectory.co.uk

Cooking 6 | Modern French | £41–£83

Built in the fifteenth century, this half-timbered building is the 'oldest house in Winchester' according to the owners. It wears its antiquity well. There are no fancy decorations, simply beams and plain

white walls, creating a fresh, uncluttered look that throws the focus onto the food and allows it to shine. Fine and luxurious ingredients underpin cooking that is marked by precise timing that makes the most of their flavours, and by imaginative combinations such as Beaufort cheese and baby spinach soufflé with parsnip and five-spice and a cep fricassee, or a rich white Alba truffle consommé with a Challans duck confit. Choice – five items per course – might include a main-course fillet of Buchan beef Rossini with confit cep and a port and truffle sauce, or fillet of John Dory with surf clams and scallops, lyonnaise potatoes and a Noilly Prat sauce. Vegetarians might revel in a porcini and white truffle risotto. Finish with an assiette of crème brûlée (coffee and Tia Maria, chocolate-orange and vanilla), or a trio of mandarin (soufflé with mandarin anglaise, sorbet and bavarois). The cellar's French backbone is fleshed out with reliable bottles from elsewhere, but its sixty, mostly youngish bins yield little under £20; house wines from £16.

Chef: Robert Quéhan **Proprietors:** Carl and Anna Reeve **Open:** Tue to Sat 12 to 1.30, 7 to 9.30 **Closed:** first 2 weeks Aug **Meals:** Set L £20 (2 courses) to £25, Set D £45 **Service:** not inc, 12.5% for parties of 7 or more, card slips closed **Cards:** Amex, Delta, Diners, Maestro, MasterCard, Visa **Details:** 45 seats. Vegetarian meals. No smoking in 1 dining room. Music. No mobile phones

Hotel du Vin & Bistro

Southgate Street, Winchester SO23 9EF
Tel: (01962) 841414
Website: www.hotelduvin.com

Cooking 4 | Modern European | £40–£56

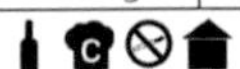

This elegant, early-Georgian town house was the original Hotel du Vin; it feels less corporate than some of its newer brethren, and the recent change of ownership has brought little change. An impeccable half-baguette presented on the wooden lid of a Chianti case with a bottle of Planeta olive oil makes a fine first impression. For starters, sample perhaps soused herrings with Russian salad, or a fresh-tasting fig and blue cheese tart with a thin drizzle of truffled honey. 'Simple Classics' have their own category among main courses – chargrilled ribeye with frites and café de Paris butter, and coq au vin, for instance – or go for a more unusual pairing of salmon, brandade and white asparagus with wilted spinach. Raspberry charlotte has been described as 'a thing of beauty'. Few other places can match the wine list for panache, or the enthusiasm and knowledge of its sommeliers. France dominates, but the Italian selection could put some specialists to shame and there is depth around the globe, including many unusual bottles. Wines start at £13 but are not listed in price order, so it's worth scouring the whole list for goodies to suit your pocket.

Chef: Andy Clark **Proprietor:** MWB Group plc **Open:** all week 12 to 1.45, 7 to 9.45 **Meals:** alc exc Sun L (main courses £14.50 to £15.50). Set L Sun £23.50 **Service:** not inc **Cards:** Amex, Delta, Diners, Maestro, MasterCard, Visa **Details:** 65 seats. 25 seats outside. Private parties: 48 main room. Car park. Vegetarian meals. Children's helpings. No smoking. Wheelchair access (also WC). No music **Accommodation:** 24 rooms, all with bath/shower. TV. Phone. Room only £115 to £185. Rooms for disabled. Baby facilities

Wykeham Arms

75 Kingsgate Street, Winchester SO23 9PE
Tel: (01962) 853834

Cooking 2 | International | £32–£54

Right next to the town's famous school, this fine old eighteenth-century inn with its cluttered interior and 'whimsical memorabilia' works well as a neighbourhood restaurant. Inspiration is gleaned from hither and yon, and although the menu manages to offer dishes such as wok-fried harissa and honey beef with sesame noodles and raita dressing, and sea bass and king scallops with cocotte potatoes and saffron cream, there is not always the capacity to live up to the promise on the menu: dishes have been on occasion 'lukewarm' and 'bland', with the balancing of sauces 'leaving a lot to be desired'. Desserts are a highlight, and warm chocolate brownie and treacle tart were praised at inspection. The hefty global wine list deals in fair mark-ups and a decent selection by the glass. House French is £11.95.

Chef: Alex Jones **Proprietors:** Peter and Kate Miller **Open:** all week L 12 to 2.30 (1.45 Sun), Mon to Sat D 6.30 to 8.45 **Closed:** 25 Dec **Meals:** alc L (main courses £5.75 to £13.75) alc D (main courses £11 to £18). Set L Sun £14.50 (2 courses) to £18.50. Light L menu available **Service:** not inc, card slips closed **Cards:** Amex, Delta, Diners, Maestro, MasterCard, Visa **Details:** 80 seats. 80 seats outside. Car park. Vegetarian meals. No children under 14. No music. No mobile phones **Accommodation:** 14 rooms, all with bath/shower. TV. B&B £57 to £135. No children under 14

This symbol means that the chef has changed since last year's entry, and the Editor has judged that the change is of sufficient interest to merit the reader's attention.

MAP 2 Winchmore Hill BUCKINGHAMSHIRE

Plough

AR

Winchmore Hill HP7 0PA
Tel: (01494) 721001

Once famed for its connections with *Carry On* queen Barbara Windsor, now a gastro-pub with aspirations. The current owners are the team behind Thackeray's in Tunbridge Wells (see entry), although the food has yet to make a real impact. The kitchen shows its worth with dishes like braised Gloucester Old Spot belly pork with chorizo, black pudding and apple purée (£12.50). Starters might include scallops with confit vegetables and saffron cream (£8.50), and you could finish with plum tart (£5.50). International wines from £12.95. Closed Sun D and all Mon.

MAP 8 Windermere CUMBRIA

Gilpin Lodge

Crook Road, Windermere LA23 3NE
Tel: (015394) 88818
Website: www.gilpinlodge.com

Cooking 6 | Modern British | £40–£72

Gilpin Lodge has an agreeably lived-in feel, thought one reporter, in that it's smart and stylish yet friendly and cheering at the same time, with blazing fires and plenty of indoor greenery as well as no fewer than four dining rooms. A former Victorian country home, it sits a couple of miles from Lake Windermere, basking in all the majestic tranquillity the Lake District has to offer.

Chris Meredith's cooking style is described by the proprietors as 'classically based modern international/British', which just about covers all bases. Fixed-price menus are the norm, with a surprisingly wide range of choice at each stage. A soup such as carrot and cumin might kick things off of an evening, to be succeeded by a dish like tortellini of haggis with winter vegetable broth, which delighted our inspector for its silky pasta and soft, herbed filling. An intermediate sorbet – perhaps cassis – precedes the main-course business. Roast cod, the flesh well timed, the skin crisp, has been robustly served with casseroled pork loin, braised vegetables and cured local ham, while breast of guinea fowl is tenderly gamey, its copious accompaniments including some wild mushrooms. There is nothing flamboyant about the preparations, only excellent raw materials treated with sensitivity: witness a professional tarte Tatin of deeply caramelised but sharp-tasting apples, served with nigh-on-flawless vanilla ice cream. With good breads and petits fours, it all adds up to the whole package. Wines are a competently chosen, if not earth-shaking, collection at mark-ups that shouldn't cause palpitations. Nine house selections may be ordered by the glass from £4.50 to £5.25.

Chef: Chris Meredith **Proprietors:** John and Christine Cunliffe **Open:** all week 12 to 2, 7 to 9 **Meals:** Set L Mon to Sat £20 (2 courses) to £25, Set L Sun £26, Set D £42.50. Light L menu available **Service:** not inc **Cards:** Amex, Delta, Diners, Maestro, MasterCard, Visa **Details:** 70 seats. 18 seats outside. Private parties: 20 main room. Car park. Vegetarian meals. No children under 7. No smoking. Wheelchair access (not WC). No music. No mobile phones **Accommodation:** 14 rooms, all with bath/shower. TV. Phone. D,B&B £160 to £290. Rooms for disabled. No children under 7

Kwela's

AR

4 High Street, Windermere LA23 1AF
Tel: (015394) 44954

'Original and excellent enterprise' bringing a taste of modern African cooking to the touristy Lake District. 'Kwela' is shanty-town jazz, and the kitchen struts its culinary stuff with braai (BBQ) pork ribs with roast mealies (corn fritters), pan-fried scallops with mango salsa (£6), two versions of traditional bobotie, and ostrich steak with figs, shallots and celeriac mash (£15.50). Cape Malay brandy pudding (£4.25) is a classic way to finish. Ecologically inclined wines from £10. Open Tue to Sun D only.

Holbeck Ghyll

Holbeck Lane, Windermere LA23 1LU
Tel: (015394) 32375
Website: www.holbeckghyll.com

Cooking 7 | Modern British/French | £40–£75

'This is a youthful but cosy establishment clearly on the rise' was one enthusiastic endorsement of the relaxed and unpretentious approach at this nineteenth-century house with views across Lake Windermere towards the Old Man of Coniston and the Langdale Pikes. The décor is restrained by Lakeland standards, which endears it to all-comers, but it's the Nicholsons' juggling with the delicate balance between value for customers and a healthy bottom line for the business that impressed one visitor, who enjoyed a good-value set lunch with 'successful extras included'.

David McLaughlin delivers the goods with assurance, and the operation appears in perfect harmony with itself and its surroundings. Perhaps the biggest attraction of the food is that it combines high quality with approachability. Nothing intimidates, yet no corners are cut. Ideas are as simple as roast loin of venison with celeriac and juniper, or roast squab pigeon with confit cabbage and madeira sauce, but fine ingredients, real flavours and proper textures lift dishes out of the ordinary. Among first courses, there could be roast scallops with celeriac and balsamic dressing, terrine of duck confit with pear and foie gras, or a luxurious salad of warm langoustines with lobster and celeriac rémoulade, preceded by an amuse-bouche of, say, truffled potato soup with confit onion and bacon. British, Irish and French cheeses are a strong point, and desserts are as good as anything else, sometimes playing on a theme such as an assiette of apple, or a chocolate plate. Quality is high on the mostly French wine list. Very little comes in under £20, but there's a good line-up of half-bottles and the six by the glass for around £5 are significantly better than basic.

Chef: David McLaughlin **Proprietors:** David and Patricia Nicholson **Open:** all week 12.30 to 2, 7 to 9.30 **Meals:** Set L £22.50 (2 courses) to £27.50, Set D £47.50. Light menu available **Service:** not inc, card slips closed **Cards:** Amex, Delta, Diners, Maestro, MasterCard, Visa **Details:** 55 seats. 25 seats outside. Private parties: 65 main room. Car park. Vegetarian meals. No children under 8. No smoking. Wheelchair access (also WC). No music. No mobile phones **Accommodation:** 21 rooms, all with bath/shower. TV. Phone. B&B £135 to £250. Rooms for disabled. Baby facilities

Jerichos

Birch Street, Windermere LA23 1EG
Tel: (015394) 42522
Website: www.jerichos.co.uk

Cooking 5 | Modern British | £36–£54

Chris and Joanne Blaydes have been settled in the centre of Windermere since 1998. Their restaurant makes a strikingly louche impression as one enters, with its plum colour scheme, subdued lighting and pictures in the Toulouse-Lautrec idiom evoking a Naughty '90s feel (1890s, that is). The kitchen is open-plan, giving some idea of the intense effort that goes into producing your dinner.

Quite a lot has already gone into writing the menu descriptions, but the food is hearteningly more straightforward than it sounds, and all the better for it. A bowl of soup combines roast plum tomatoes, red onions and thyme and is topped with a blob of Pernod-laced Greek yoghurt, while a dish of pasta noodles is tossed with local smoked sausage, peppered green beans and Parmesan. This is 'feisty, subtle and confident food', thought one who went on to enjoy a main course of pan-fried cod on sun-dried tomatoes and toasted almonds with crushed new potatoes and spinach. Premium Scottish beef is traditionally served with a reduction of red wine, mustard butter and thin, crisp chips. Finish with beautifully judged pear and ginger frangipane tart with mascarpone and crème anglaise. Wines are categorised according to the food groups they might match, the recommendations broad-minded enough to suggest that you might want to drink a Chilean Chardonnay with beef, or a Chianti Classico with fish. Seven house selections come at £13, or £3.50 a glass.

Chef: Chris Blaydes **Proprietors:** Chris and Joanne Blaydes **Open:** Tue to Sun D only 6.45 to 9.30 **Closed:** last 2 weeks Nov, first week Dec, 25 and 26 Dec, 1 Jan **Meals:** alc (main courses £14 to £17.50) **Service:** not inc **Cards:** Delta, Maestro, MasterCard, Visa **Details:** 36 seats. Private parties: 14 to 24 private rooms. Vegetarian meals. No children under 12. No smoking. Music

Miller Howe

Rayrigg Road, Windermere LA23 1EY
Tel: (015394) 42536
Website: www.millerhowe.com

Cooking 4 | English Country-House | £31–£68

A grand white house with panoramic Wordsworthian views over Lake Windermere, Miller Howe has always been about living it up. Arched windows and downlighters confer an almost absurdly romantic air on the dining room, and the cooking does its best to round off the experience of being thoroughly cosseted. The six-course Menu Gourmand is one way of enjoying the package, but there are possibly more adventurous dishes among the alternatives on the carte. Foie gras and liquorice terrine with spiced pear chutney might be one of them, to be followed by lamb in three forms – best end, confit shoulder and the tongue in ravioli – or perhaps sea bass in a risotto with baby clams and vanilla. Desserts such as rhubarb crumble with vanilla ice cream or lemon tart with lime sorbet make for an impressive finish. House wines from £17.50 bring up the rear on a deeply classical list. Halves are in plentiful supply for the price-conscious.

Chef: Paul Webster **Proprietor:** Charles Garside **Open:** all week L 12.30 to 2, Mon to Fri D 6.45 to 8.45, Sat D 8pm (1 sitting) **Meals:** alc D (main courses £18.50). Set L Mon to Sat £19.50, Set L Sun £21.50, Set D £42. Light L menu available **Service:** 10% (optional), card slips closed **Cards:** Amex, Delta, Maestro, MasterCard, Visa **Details:** 65 seats. 40 seats outside. Private parties: 40 main room, 30 private room. Car park. Vegetarian meals. Children's helpings. No smoking. Wheelchair access (also WC). Music. No mobile phones. Air-conditioned **Accommodation:** 15 rooms, all with bath/shower. TV. Phone. D,B&B £95 to £350. Rooms for disabled. No children under 8

Samling

Ambleside Road, Windermere LA23 1LR
Tel: (015394) 31922
Website: www.thesamling.com

Cooking 4 | Modern British | £59–£98

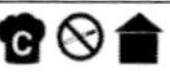

This white, pocket-sized country hotel occupies 67 acres of sweeping Lakeland countryside, with commanding views down to Windermere. The public rooms are small, with a rather lived-in feel, and the dining room is simply kitted out with bare wooden floors and tables. New chef Nigel Mendem arrived in early 2005 and shows clear potential, as was suggested by inspection dishes such as scallops with artichoke risotto and sherry vinegar caramel, or a charmingly presented main-course assiette of full-flavoured lamb encompassing slow-cooked shoulder, glazed 'chateaubriand', and a tiny tartlet of shepherd's pie, all served on a heap of lightly cooked shredded cabbage. Fish options might include turbot fillet with a gâteau of potato and salsify and a sauce of white wine cream. A complimentary item such as passion-fruit mousse in a liqueur glass heralds the arrival of impressive desserts such as caramelised pear with lemon and thyme sorbet on raisin pain perdu. Coffee comes with a fine array of petits fours. The wine list makes commendable efforts in the New World as well as in France, but mark-ups are pretty forbidding throughout. Two reds and three whites are served by the glass at £6.

Chef: Nigel Mendem **Proprietor:** Tom Maxfield **Open:** all week 12 to 2, 7 to 10 **Meals:** Set L and D £45 to £65 **Service:** not inc, card slips closed **Cards:** Amex, Delta, Maestro, MasterCard, Visa **Details:** 22 seats. 8 seats outside. Private parties: 22 main room. Car park. Children's helpings. No smoking. Music. No mobile phones **Accommodation:** 11 rooms, all with bath/shower. TV. Phone. B&B £175 to £395

MAP 1 Winkleigh DEVON

Pophams

Castle Street, Winkleigh EX19 8HQ
Tel: (01837) 83767

Cooking 5 | Modern British | £35–£48

In 2006 Melvyn Popham and Dennis Hawkes will be celebrating 20 years at the helm of this gloriously idiosyncratic, much-loved restaurant. For the uninitiated the place is open only two days a week, lunchtimes only, although there are two sittings on each day; booking is essential. The menu is chalked on a board and is cooked in the background by Melvyn, while Dennis explains and deals with wine (strictly bring your own).

If the ambience feels only one step up in scale from eating with friends at home, the cooking echoes that tone. Leek and watercress soup was a cheering starter from a January menu, or there may be a cod and salmon fishcake with creamy curry sauce, or a salad of Granny Smith and Roquefort with smoked bacon. Main courses are simple and substantial, the meats accurately timed to retain moistness and savour. Best end of local lamb is cooked in puff pastry with a spinach stuffing and sauced with madeira. Leave room for a pudding such as rhubarb shortbread tart with strawberry sauce, or the near-legendary sticky toffee pud with clotted cream. The whole experience is rounded off by good strong coffee, replenished with enthusiasm.

Chef: Melvyn Popham **Proprietors:** Dennis Hawkes and Melvyn Popham **Open:** Thur and Fri L only 11.45 to 2.30 **Closed:** Feb **Meals:** alc (main courses £17 to £19) **Service:** not inc **Cards:** none **Details:** 10 seats. No children under 16. No smoking. Occasional music. No mobile phones. Air-conditioned

MAP 1 Winsford SOMERSET

Royal Oak Inn AR

Winsford TA24 7JE
Tel: (01643) 851455

Gentrified thatched pub in Exmoor National Park with centuries of history and a good line in hospitality. Sustenance comes in the shape of bar lunches and more elaborate restaurant menus featuring a tian of salmon and crab with tomato and pesto dressing (£5), seared fillet of duck with forest berries, sweet potato crisps and veal jus (£11), and old-school desserts like bread-and-butter pudding (£4.75). France heads the wine list; prices from £12.95. Accommodation. Open all week.

MAP 9 **Winteringham** NORTH LINCOLNSHIRE

Winteringham Fields

Winteringham DN15 9PF
Tel: (01724) 733096
Website: www.winteringhamfields.com

Cooking 9 | Provincial French/Swiss | £51–£130

As the Guide is going to press we get the news we've all been dreading: Germain and Annie are selling up. New owners Colin and Rebecca McGurren, we are told, plan to run it in the same way with the same team. Which does make a lot of sense in the circumstances. Continuity is guaranteed with the presence of Robert Thompson in the kitchen, now in his second year of heading-up the team. The absence of Germain – his drive and vision – is going to leave a large hole, but the Schwabs themselves have shown great faith in Mr Thompson.

This is most people's idea of what a place in the country should be: the garden a riot of colour on a summer's day, the house an impeccably renovated, comfortable and inviting place that retains its original beams and uneven floors. Fully dressed tables and a tiled floor make for the right balance of tone. Annie Schwab MBE is, by general consent and national honour, one of the most accomplished front-of-house practitioners in the country, and she's going to be missed.

The feedback from inspectors and readers encompassed in this review are from the last six months of the Schwabs' reign, but Thompson was at the stoves. A digest of the kitchen's order book sent to us reveals the unwavering commitment to quality: game such as rabbit, hare, pheasant and woodcock come from the Roxby estate, fish from the Grimsby catch, Aberdeen Angus beef from Grantown-on-Spey, oysters from Co. Louth in Ireland, not to mention goats' milk products sourced locally.

These all find their way on to menus that combine genuine originality with sensitivity to the raw materials and extraordinary levels of technical proficiency. Appetisers alone will astonish: one dinner opened with truffle beignets accompanied by a glass of mashed Corsican ewes' cheese with a topping of sorrel sauce and then, once seated at table, a further presentation of pressed scallops and baby leeks sparsely dressed in fine olive oil. Seasonings are built up in complex layers but always support their main ingredient, so that a first course of sea bass fillet is bedded on aromatic wild rice that has been moistened with a lightly curried vinaigrette, the whole dish sauced with creamy coriander.

Choice will prove difficult. Fish dishes may be adapted for serving as starters or mains, while the meat offerings may take in two servings of lamb (roast rump and braised shoulder), duck breast and confit leg, glazed pig's trotter with duck gizzards, or veal tenderloin with the sweetbreads en ragoût. The vivid artistry continues into desserts that might encompass a liquorice soufflé rolled in orange powder, served with liquorice ice cream and grapefruit marinated in cardamom, or a creamy, gently smouldering, chilli-speckled mousse with poached rhubarb under a nougatine pyramid, surrounded by scooplets of goats' milk yoghurt sorbet. The wine list is nicely poised between Old World and New and packed with good names. Prices are on the high side, starting at £22. Some of the details listed below may well change under the new regime. It seems strange to say it, but reports, please.

Chef: Robert Thompson **Proprietors:** Colin and Rebecca McGurren **Open:** Tue to Sat 12 to 1.30, 7 to 9.30 **Closed:** 2 weeks at Christmas, last week Mar, first 10 days Aug **Meals:** alc (main courses £30 to £38). Set L £32, Set D £42 to £75 **Service:** not inc, card slips closed **Cards:** Amex, Delta, Maestro, MasterCard, Visa **Details:** 42 seats. Private parties: 8 main room, 6 to 10 private rooms. Car park. No smoking. Wheelchair access (not WC). No music. No mobile phones **Accommodation:** 10 rooms, all with bath/shower. TV. Phone. B&B £95 to £205. Rooms for disabled

MAP 6 **Witchford** CAMBRIDGESHIRE

Needhams

186 Main Street, Witchford CB6 2HT
Tel: (01353) 661405
Website: www.needhamsrestaurant.co.uk

Cooking 2 | Modern European | £25–£54

There's nothing too ostentatious or eye-catching about the décor at Luke and Verity Pearson's neatly maintained local eating place. The kitchen delivers interesting, modern dishes with confidence and professionalism. Fried goats' cheese beignets with slow-roast cherry tomatoes and sweet piquant peppers has been a successful starter, while main courses have ranged from a combo of monkfish with saffron linguine, bacon, Parmesan and grilled queen scallops to roast rack of English lamb stuffed with Parma ham and rosemary with a confit of new potatoes and garlic. To finish, pineapple and stem ginger crème brûlée is a decent version, or you might try pretty-looking mulled frozen fruit parfait with sweet red wine sauce. The reasonably priced wine list opens with house recommendations from £10.75.

Chef: Luke Pearson **Proprietors:** Luke and Verity Pearson **Open:** Tue to Sun L 12 to 1.30 (2.30 Sun), Tue to Sat D 7 to 9 (6.30 to 9.30 Fri/Sat) **Closed:** 1 to 20 Jan **Meals:** alc (not Sun L; main courses £12.50 to £20). Set L £17.25 **Service:** not inc **Cards:** Amex, Delta, Maestro, MasterCard, Visa **Details:** 64 seats. Private parties: 90 main room, 20 to 90 private rooms. Car park. Vegetarian meals. Children's helpings. No smoking. Wheelchair access (also WC). Music

MAP 3 **Woburn** BEDFORDSHIRE

Paris House

AR

Woburn, Woburn Park MK17 9QP
Tel: (01525) 290692

It's rather fitting that Peter Chandler's cooking is classical French, for his unusual restaurant was originally built for the 1878 Paris Exhibition and re-erected piece by piece on the Woburn Estate. Set meals range from £22 (lunch only) to a £60 gastronomique menu, while the pricey £55 carte features foie gras and prune terrine with caramelised apples, monkfish osso bucco, and rack of lamb with sweetbreads, with a hot raspberry soufflé to finish. An extensive, but expensive, wine list complements it all. Closed Sun D and all Mon.

MAP 5 **Wolverhampton** WEST MIDLANDS

Bilash

AR

2 Cheapside, Wolverhampton WV1 1TU
Tel: (01902) 427762

'Very on show', smart Indian that sets out its stall in the centre of town opposite the Civic Centre. Fish dishes are well reported (for example, maacher shami kebab with tamarind sauce; £6); otherwise, the regularly changing menu embraces everything from chicken tikka to lal marecher gosht (spicy hot lamb with red pepper; £14) and Bangladeshi potato curry (£10). Set lunches £11. Around three dozen wines, with six by the glass. Closed Sun.

MAP 6 **Woodbridge** SUFFOLK

Captain's Table

3 Quay Street, Woodbridge IP12 1BX
Tel: (01394) 383145
Website: www.captainstable.co.uk

Cooking 3 | Modern European | £25–£46

A family-friendly attitude and summer meals *al fresco* in the walled garden are two virtues of Jo and Pascal Pommier's unassuming local restaurant close to the theatre. And the kitchen delivers value for money and generous helpings of straightforward bistro food based on decent supplies of fresh local produce (especially seafood). Prawns Thermidor, braised lamb shank with mustard mash, and fillet of cod with tartare butter sauce and boulangère potatoes are typical, while desserts range from home-churned ice creams to chocolate and pecan nut tart. In the mornings, the place takes on the role of local café with coffee and home-made scones, while sandwiches, omelettes and simpler dishes are offered at lunchtime. The short, affordable wine list starts with vins de pays at £9.95.

Chef: Pascal Pommier **Proprietors:** Jo and Pascal Pommier **Open:** Wed to Sun L 12 to 2, Wed to Sat D 6.30 to 9.30 (Sun D, Mon L/D also at bank holiday weekends) **Closed:** 2 weeks Jan **Meals:** alc (main courses £6.50 to £15.50) **Service:** not inc, card slips closed **Cards:** Delta, Maestro, MasterCard, Visa **Details:** 50 seats. 30 seats outside. Private parties: 34 main room, 19 to 34 private rooms. Car park. Vegetarian meals. Children's helpings. No smoking. Wheelchair access (not WC). No music

Riverside

AR

Quayside, Woodbridge IP12 1BH
Tel: (01394) 382587

There's more to this updated cinema (the oldest in the country) than just seeing the latest blockbuster; there's also a restaurant offering a good-value carte or a dinner and film deal for £25. The kitchen takes a modern view of things: say, bruschetta with rare beef, tapenade and mizuna (£8), pan-fried sea bass with saffron mash and citrus dressing (£12), and triple chocolate brownie with pistachio cream (£4). Service is 'discreet and professional', and the global wine list starts the ball rolling at £12, with plenty by the glass. Closed Sun D.

MAP 5 **Worcester** WORCESTERSHIRE

Brown's

AR

24 Quay Street, South Quay, Worcester WR1 2JJ
Tel: (01905) 26263

A Worcester landmark on the bank of the Severn, this former grain mill celebrated 25 years' trading in 2005. Lunchtime visitors have endorsed the kitchen's 'light yet assured touch': spring vegetable risotto (£5.50) could precede roast Gressingham duck breast with turnip gratin and roast balsamic beets (£15), before desserts like gooseberry and elderflower fool (£5.50). Fixed-price dinner menus £27.50 to £39.50. Well-chosen global wines from £14.95. Closed Sat L, Sun D and Mon.

MAP 7 **Worleston** CHESHIRE

Rookery Hall

Worleston CW5 6DQ
Tel: (01270) 610016
Website: www.handpicked.co.uk/rookeryhall

Cooking 4 | Modern European | £35–£79

This Georgian mansion in lush Cheshire countryside now has all the trappings of the modern hotel. The dining room is large, red and elegant, with mahogany panelling and fine plaster ceiling mouldings. Lighting is low, including candles on tables, and the high-backed chairs offer solid support.

In Craig Malone's finely honed country-house repertoire ingredients like foie gras, scallops, sea bass, spring lamb and Gressingham duck take starring roles. Terrine of ham hock and roast foie gras, with apple jelly and brioche, is a well-reported starter, while mains eliciting plaudits this year have been poached chicken with mushroom and truffle risotto, and roast saddle of venison with rösti, winter vegetables and a juniper jus. Foie gras often pops up in fish dishes too, perhaps allied with monkfish, pancetta and an oyster and Muscat sauce, or accompanying roast salmon with spiced lentils and herbed crème fraîche. Desserts, encompassing a variety of techniques, range from chilled pineapple soup with pannacotta and coconut ice cream to chocolate fudge soufflé with passion-fruit sorbet. Friendly service neatly balances formality and informality, and the extensive wine list has been assembled by a real enthusiast, with explanatory notes heading each section. A good slate of wines by the glass starts at £4.50.

Chef: Craig Malone **Proprietor:** Hand Picked Hotels **Open:** Sun to Fri L 12 to 2, all week D 7 to 9 **Meals:** alc (main courses £16.50 to £25). Set L £15.50 (2 courses) to £19.50, Set D £29.50 **Service:** not inc **Cards:** Amex, Delta, Maestro, MasterCard, Visa **Details:** 50 seats. 24 seats outside. Private parties: 60 main room, 20 to 60 private rooms. Car park. Vegetarian meals. Children's helpings. No smoking. Wheelchair access (also WC). No music. No mobile phones **Accommodation:** 46 rooms, all with bath/shower. TV. Phone. Room only £145 to £280. Rooms for disabled. Baby facilities

MAP 8 **Wrightington** LANCASHIRE

Mulberry Tree

9 Wood Lane, Wrightington Bar, Wrightington WN6 9SE
Tel: (01257) 451400

Cooking 4 | Modern British | £35–£64

'The Mulberry Tree seems to be going from strength to strength,' enthused an inspector. Housed in a big, square, traditional pub-looking building, the dining areas are split between a bar and a more formal restaurant, but the standard of cooking is fairly similar in each. The kitchen makes efforts to seek out local ingredients, and they pop up on menus that might start with Szechuan salt-and-pepper king prawns with chilli and sweet-and-sour salsa, or warm Morteau sausage with a soft-poached egg, crushed new potatoes, and seasonal leaves. Move on to roast cod loin – 'a truly magnificent piece' – with wilted rocket, chorizo, and balsamic 'juice', or a whole small plaice with prawns, shrimps, and anchovy and caper butter. Portions are generous, so sweet-toothed diners be warned. There's a good distribution of world wines and prices on the 60-strong list, starting with house selections from £12.75.

Chefs: Mark Prescott and Kevin Wigglesworth **Proprietors:** James Moore and Mark Prescott **Open:** all week 12 to 2 (3 Sun), 6 to 9.30 (10 Sat, 9 Sun) **Closed:** 26 Dec, 1 Jan **Meals:** alc exc Sun L (main courses £13.50 to £20). Set L Sun £22.50. Bar menu available **Service:** 10% (optional), card slips closed **Cards:** Delta, Maestro, MasterCard, Visa **Details:** 70 seats. 20 seats outside. Private parties: 40 main room. Car park. Vegetarian meals. No children under 14 exc Sun L. No smoking. Wheelchair access (not WC). Music. No mobile phones. Air-conditioned

Simply Heathcotes NEW ENTRY

Wrightington Hotel, Moss Lane, Wrightington WN6 9PB
Tel: (01257) 478244
Website: www.heathcotes.co.uk

Cooking 2 | Modern British | £28–£57

The newest Heathcotery is on the first floor of the Wrightington Hotel, near M6 junction 27. The unmistakeable style shows strong local and regional influences in tried-and-trusted modern brasserie dishes. Black pudding partners a Lancashire cheese fritter, or accompanies roast sucking pig (with 'crisp crackling', fondant potato and baked apple). Or choose lamb chump with green olives and rustic hummus, crushed wild garlic, lemon and rosemary, and finish with bread-and-butter pudding. Light snacks or quick meals are available, there's a children's menu, and the Sunday fixed-price lunch includes brunch dishes like scrambled eggs with smoked salmon, alongside roast beef and Yorkshire pudding. Wines offer choice under £20, plus some fine bottles (at a price); house Italian is £13.95.

Chef: Gary Birkett **Proprietor:** Paul Heathcote **Open:** all week 12 to 2.30 (9 Sun), 6 to 10 (11 Sat) **Closed:** 27 December, 1 January, bank hol Mons **Meals:** alc (not Sun L; main courses £10 to £16). Set L £11.95 (1 course), Set L Sun £14.50 (2 courses) to £17 **Service:** not inc **Cards:** Amex, Delta, Maestro, MasterCard, Visa **Details:** 75 seats. Private parties: 100 main room, 10 to 20 private rooms. Car park. Vegetarian meals. Children's helpings. Wheelchair access (also WC). Music. Air-conditioned **Accommodation:** 75 rooms, all with bath/shower. TV. Phone. B&B £65 to £115. Rooms for disabled. Baby facilities

MAP 2 **Wytham** OXFORDSHIRE

White Hart AR

Wytham OX2 8QA
Tel: (01865) 244372

Oxford types already know about the 'great atmosphere...great service, great décor' at this surprisingly rural pub just off the Oxford ring road. A recent 'classy' outdoor seating area, enclosed by Cotswold walling and shrubs, is an added attraction. Steaks, sausages, lamb and mint burger (£11) and other pub staples show up on the regular menu. A smoked salmon plate (£7.50) is a decent bet, perhaps followed by whole sea bass (£17), with summer pudding (£5) to finish. Global wines from £14.95. Open all week.

MAP 10 **Yarm** STOCKTON-ON-TEES

Chadwick's

104B High Street, Yarm TS15 9AU
Tel: (01642) 788558

Cooking 3 | European-Plus | £26–£52

Chadwick's, with 'almost the only modern exterior' in this street of ancient buildings and one of the largest shop fronts, is hard to miss. The décor creates an informal atmosphere, suited to this 'continental style restaurant/café'. Simple, French- and Mediterranean-inspired menus conceal exotics like Thai beef salad, or black pudding spring rolls with pineapple dunk, amid antipasto of Italian meats or goats' cheese tarte fine. Straightforward modern main dishes might include seared salmon with buttered spinach and parsley cream, or calf's liver and bacon with black pudding mash and onion gravy, or cassoulet of duck confit with Toulouse sausage, pork rib and garlic mash. Finish with chocolate and almond brownie with pistachio ice cream. The shortish wine list covers a range of styles and countries, and represents fair value, starting at £11.95.

Chefs: David Brownless and Steven Conyard **Proprietor:** David Brownless **Open:** Mon to Sat 11.30 to 2.30, 5.30 to 9.30 **Closed:** 2nd week Oct, bank hol Mons **Meals:** alc (main courses, L £7 to £12, D £10.50 to £17). Tapas menu available Mon to Fri 5.30 to 6.30 **Service:** not inc **Cards:** Delta, Maestro, MasterCard, Visa **Details:** 70 seats. Private parties: 70 main room. Vegetarian meals. Children's helpings. No smoking. Music. Air-conditioned

MAP 2 **Yarmouth** ISLE OF WIGHT

George

Quay Street, Yarmouth PO41 0PE
Tel: (01983) 760331
Website: www.thegeorge.co.uk

Cooking 7 | Modern British | £63–£76

The George is a seventeenth-century town house that once stood in majestic near-isolation near Yarmouth quay, as may be noted from the painting of it that hangs above the fireplace in the lounge. Although the town has grown around it now, it retains a pleasing period feel, enhanced by the dark panelling and mulberry paintwork of the main restaurant. Heavy drapes at the windows conspire to give an atmosphere of being quite cut off from the outside world.

Kevin Mangeolles has been cooking here for a decade, and has quietly worked up a head of steam, so that the Restaurant (as distinct from the Brasserie, elsewhere on the ground floor) is the premier eating spot on the Isle of Wight. A three-course, fixed-price dinner menu is on offer, and, far from dealing in the faded haute cuisine of some sleepy backwater, centres on intelligent re-creations of classical ideas. Foie gras appears in the guise of a crème brûlée, a creamy mousse with white sugar top and a thin layer of brioche at the bottom, surrounded by streaks of nicely acidic cherry purée with crumbled pistachio.

Main courses up the ante still further, as was evidenced at inspection. A moist and flavourful piece of halibut was skinned and served with puntette, a 'risotto' of rice-sized pasta in an outstanding shellfish sauce, as well as several ingenious-looking constructions that turned out to be langoustine tails topped with cooked salmon mousse. There is a genuine sense that everything has been carefully considered, road-tested and honed to a high level before it finds its way on to the menu. Thus, a chunky duck breast is relieved of both fat and skin, roasted pink, rested, then carved simply into two, and scattered with fragments of nougatine, a novel take on crisp, honey-roasted skin.

New techniques being a hallmark of the menu throughout, the trio of chocolate desserts comprises white chocolate truffle and thyme ice cream, a soup of Manjari chocolate, and a deep-fried crunchy ball of chocolate that, on being broken, pours forth molten orange-scented chocolate. Non-chocoholics might gravitate towards a rhubarb and cardamom trifle, delicately spiced and full of different kinds of soft texture, served in an old-fashioned cocktail glass. With efficient, personable and helpful service to boot, this is a fine enterprise that deserves wholehearted support.

The wine list shows a French bias but puts on no airs. The main business is condensed into two pages arranged in price order from £16.75, with much at £25 or below. Some very old clarets add an unexpected twist. The brasserie, open all week for lunch and dinner, is another useful address on the Isle, and is also under the auspices of Kevin Mangeolles.

Chef: Kevin Mangeolles **Proprietors:** John Illsley and Jeremy Willcock **Open:** Tue to Sat D only 7 to 10. Brasserie open all week L and D **Meals:** Set D £46.50 **Service:** not inc, card slips closed **Cards:** Amex, Maestro, MasterCard, Visa **Details:** 30 seats. Private parties: 35 main room, 25 private rooms. Vegetarian meals. No music. Air-conditioned **Accommodation:** 17 rooms, all with bath/shower. TV. Phone. B&B £130 to £242.50

MAP 2 **Yattendon** BERKSHIRE

Royal Oak

The Square, Yattendon RG18 0UG
Tel: (01635) 201325
Website: royaloakyattendon.com

Cooking 4 | Modern British | £30–£63

At the heart of a picturesque and affluent village, this 'truly English' sixteenth-century, red-brick inn (now a restaurant-with-rooms) oozes smart country charm. Brick walls and old beams set the backdrop in the brasserie for closely packed white-clothed tables, while the more formal restaurant has pale blue walls hung with botanical prints and windows with smart drapes. The same menu serves both, while the cottage-style garden proves the perfect fair-weather setting for aperitifs; the Oak's crackling winter fire does the job in winter. Jamie Mould shows his pedigree via appealing, modern-focused menus that deliver stylish combinations without over-complication. Take mushroom risotto with ceps and truffle to open, and perhaps best end of lamb served with root vegetable dauphinois, stuffed baby artichoke, and French beans to follow. A classic dark chocolate fondant complemented by 'vibrantly flavoured' rum and raisin ice cream proves a sterling finish. Service, by mainly French staff, is professional yet informal, while the roving wine list, also Gallic-led, offers six house bottles at £15 and eight half-bottles.

Chef: Jamie Mould **Proprietor:** W.R.C. Boyle **Open:** all week 12 to 2.30, 7 to 9.30 (10 Sat, 9 Sun) **Closed:** 1 Jan **Meals:** alc (main courses £13 to £19). Set L Mon to Fri £12 (2 courses) to £15, Set L Sun £19.50 (2 courses) to £23.50 **Service:** 10% (optional) **Cards:** Amex, Delta, Maestro, MasterCard, Visa **Details:** 65 seats. 50 seats outside. Private parties: 30 main room, 12 private room. Vegetarian meals. Children's helpings. No smoking in 1 dining room. Wheelchair access (not WC). No music. No mobile phones **Accommodation:** 5 rooms, all with bath/shower. TV. Phone. B&B £75 to £130. Baby facilities

	This symbol means that smoking is not permitted.
	This symbol means that there are some restrictions on smoking though it may be allowed in some eating areas.

MAP 9 **York** NORTH YORKSHIRE

Blue Bicycle

34 Fossgate, York YO1 9TA
Tel: (01904) 673990
Website: www.thebluebicycle.com

Cooking 3 | Mod European/Seafood | £30–£60

Very central, with 'rustic' wooden furniture and simple table settings, this lively, unpretentious restaurant majors in fish. The repertoire takes in Thai-style mussels, grilled sardines with bacon, Cajun fish stew, and halibut poached in red wine. Carnivores are not excluded, though: Yorkshire beef fillet comes with champ and a carrot and caraway stir-fry, and chicken breast might be accompanied by pea risotto, black pudding spring roll and wild mushroom confit. Straightforward desserts run from sticky toffee to chocolate orange terrine. Lunches are lighter affairs, with perhaps goats' cheese and red onion tart, or lamb and rosemary bangers and mash on offer, as well as things like fishcake and chips and tuna steak. The well-chosen wine list starts at £13 and offers good choice under £20 and 18 by the glass.

Chef: Kenny Noble **Proprietor:** Anthony Stephenson **Open:** all week 12 to 2.30, 6 to 9.30 (9 Sun) **Closed:** 25 and 26 Dec, 1 and 2 Jan **Meals:** alc (main courses: L £8 to £14, D £14.50 to £19.50). **Service:** 10% (optional) **Cards:** Delta, Maestro, MasterCard, Visa **Details:** 83 seats. Private parties: 40 main room. Vegetarian meals. Children's helpings. No smoking. Wheelchair access (not WC). Music **Accommodation:** 2 rooms, all with bath/shower. TV. B&B £150. Rooms for disabled

Melton's

7 Scarcroft Road, York YO23 1ND
Tel: (01904) 634341
Website: www.meltonsrestaurant.co.uk

Cooking 5 | Modern European | £28–£59

'Why we don't go more often is a mystery,' one couple berated themselves, having clocked up a mere ten visits in three years to Michael and Lucy Hjort's modestly proportioned restaurant not far from the station. What they return for, when they do, are careful renditions of classic French-orientated cooking, with the accent on seasonal freshness. A spring menu offered starters of mussels cooked with apples, cider and Calvados, or Whitby crab risotto, before main courses that run from the tried and true (skate wing with brown butter, for instance) to the decidedly less familiar: perhaps poached ox tongue with sauce charcutière, potato fondant, parsnip purée and cabbage. Vegetarian alternatives might include aubergine, mozzarella and roast pepper charlotte with salsa verde. A dinner in May that ended with passion-fruit tart had its recipients determined to extract the recipe from the kitchen, and there has also been white chocolate parfait with rhubarb, or spiced soufflé with rum sauce. The friendly and professional approach of staff is much appreciated. A well-chosen global wine list opens with house bottles at £13.50 and many options available by the half-litre carafe. Clear tasting notes give excellent guidance throughout.

Chefs: Michael Hjort and Annie Prescott **Proprietors:** Michael and Lucy Hjort **Open:** Tue to Sat L 12 to 2, Mon to Sat D 5.30 to 10 **Closed:** 3 weeks at Christmas, 1 week Aug **Meals:** alc (main courses £13 to £19). Set L and D 5.30 to 6.15 £19 **Service:** not inc **Cards:** Delta, Maestro, MasterCard, Visa **Details:** 42 seats. Private parties: 36 main room, 14 to 18 private rooms. Vegetarian meals. Children's helpings. No smoking. Wheelchair access (not WC). Music. No mobile phones. Air-conditioned

Melton's Too

25 Walmgate, York YO1 9TX
Tel: (01904) 629222
Website: www.meltonstoo.co.uk

Cooking 2 | Modern European | £23–£41

Aka Mtoo, this bare-boarded, more informal sibling of Melton's (see above) is a café/bar/bistro serving from breakfast to dinner. In its warren of rooms on two floors, bare-brick or white-painted walls and modern unclothed tables give a relaxed, warm, friendly feel, and, what with the all-in-one menu (including sandwiches, salads and light bites too) and separate tapas and specials boards, there's plenty of choice. They aim to serve good, simple food using the best ingredients (local and regional where possible) at reasonable prices, and there's a modern Mediterranean slant in some of generously portioned dishes – cassoulet of duck and Toulouse sausage, or Moroccan lamb and apricot tagine with cinnamon and couscous – interspersed among more familiar offerings (vegetables extra).

Modest pricing extends to a short wine list starting with organic house Italians (£11.80).

Chef: Karl Smith **Proprietors:** Michael and Lucy Hjort **Open:** all week 10.30 to 10.30 (9.30 Sun) **Closed:** 25 and 26 Dec, 1 Jan **Meals:** alc (main courses £6.60 to £11.90) **Service:** not inc **Cards:** Delta, Maestro, MasterCard, Visa **Details:** 120 seats. Private parties: 40 main room, 20 to 60 private rooms. Vegetarian meals. Children's helpings. No smoking. Wheelchair access (also WC). Music. Air-conditioned

Middlethorpe Hall

Bishopthorpe Road, York YO23 2GB
Tel: (01904) 641241
Website: www.middlethorpe.com

Cooking 3 | Modern English | £35–£72

First impressions of this magnificent William and Mary mansion not far from the racecourse are bound to summon up superlatives. The stately grandeur of the interior endures unchanged, although there's a new man in the kitchen. Like his predecessor, Lee Heptinstall is in the business of creating delicate miniatures – a single seared scallop here, a 'truly magnificent' piece of turbot 'no bigger than a school rubber' there – but the results may not always live up to expectations. That said, the kitchen takes its work seriously: fillets of John Dory are served on tomato risotto, a cube of slow-cooked rare-breed belly pork comes with potato mousseline, black pudding, and baby carrots. To finish, cinnamon crème brûlée is accompanied by an excellent home-made flapjack. Prices are tailored to the tourist and Ascot market, and the 'impressive' wine list rockets into the financial stratosphere. House selections start at £16.50.

Chef: Lee Heptinstall **Proprietor:** Historic House Hotels Ltd **Open:** all week 12.30 to 1.30, 7 to 9.45 **Closed:** D 24 Dec, L 25 Dec, D 31 Dec (residents only) **Meals:** Set L £17 (2 courses) to £23, Set D £39 to £48 **Service:** net prices, card slips closed **Cards:** Amex, Delta, Maestro, MasterCard, Visa **Details:** 60 seats. Private parties: 56 main room, 12 to 56 private rooms. Car park. Vegetarian meals. No children under 8. Jacket. No smoking. Wheelchair access (not WC). Occasional music. No mobile phones **Accommodation:** 29 rooms, all with bath/shower. TV. Phone. B&B £115 to £460. Rooms for disabled. No children under 9. Swimming pool

Rish

7 Fossgate, York YO1 9TA
Tel: (01904) 622688
Website: www.rish-york.co.uk

NEW CHEF | Modern British | £30–£72

On a quiet, cobbled street some way off the York tourist trail, Rish is the very model of a modern restaurant. Split into two levels, with a bustling, deep-windowed bar for gawpers on ground-floor level, and a gentler, candlelit ambience in the restaurant upstairs. A new chef was appointed as we went to press. Good suppliers are key to the success, along with a modern and creative cooking style, for which the place has become locally renowned. Expect fried barramundi fillet with ratatouille and wilted spinach to start, followed by belly pork cannelloni with apple and vanilla, accompanied by monkfish cheeks and citrus sauce, or Stilton-glazed roast beef fillet with stewed leeks and creamed wild mushrooms. Finish with passion-fruit tart and orange-blossom honey ice cream. More reports, please. An international grab-bag of wines is fronted by 13 served by the glass from £3.95.

Chef: Matthew Weeks **Proprietors:** Sam and Maria Abu Rish **Open:** Tue to Sat 12 to 2, 6.30 to 9.30 (10 Fri and Sat) **Closed:** 25 to 27 Dec, 1 and 2 Jan **Meals:** alc (main courses £12 to £23). Set L £15 to £18.50, Set D 6.30 to 7 £15 (2 courses) to £18.50 **Service:** 10% (optional) **Cards:** Amex, Delta, Maestro, MasterCard, Visa **Details:** 62 seats. Private parties: 32 main room, 10 to 32 private rooms. Vegetarian meals. Children's helpings. No smoking in 1 dining room. Wheelchair access (also WC). Music

This symbol means that the chef has changed since last year's entry, and the Editor has judged that the change is of sufficient interest to merit the reader's attention.

Scotland

MAP 11 Aberdeen ABERDEEN

Silver Darling

Pocra Quay, North Pier, Aberdeen AB11 5DQ
Tel: (01224) 576229

Cooking 6 | Seafood | £37–£69

Perched atop a grey-granite, castellated former custom house, just behind the harbourmaster's office, with floor-to-ceiling windows giving views over the harbour and bay, Silver Darling has the feel of the deck of a ship. Running a predominantly seafood restaurant, Didier Dejean takes inspiration from his native France, and demonstrates a resolutely modern and innovative approach to cooking. Dishes sometimes involve several components but don't lose sight of the big picture, as in a skilfully prepared dish of lightly seared king scallops in a pecan crust sitting on 'subtle, soft' fennel mash set about with a frothy almond emulsion with crisp pancetta, or a main-course red snapper complemented by three towers of al dente courgettes filled with pea purée, alongside tomato and basil pasta and basil and chive dressing. Other ideas can be plainer: fillet of sea bass, 'bursting with sea flavour', with mushrooms, diced red peppers, fennel, red onions, cabbage and dill in a piquant dressing. Highly rated desserts include four flavours of parfait – apple, banana, pistachio, and caramel – served in shot glasses, and a simple white chocolate mousse with chopped poached pear. Service is generally friendly and unstuffy but was somewhat disorganised at inspection, and wines are a mainly French selection, with house Bergerac £16.50.

Chef: Didier Dejean **Proprietors:** Didier Dejean and Karen Murray **Open:** Mon to Fri L 12 to 1.45, Mon to Sat D 7 (6.30 Sat) to 9.30 **Closed:** 2 weeks from 24 Dec **Meals:** alc (main courses L £11.50 to £13.50, D £18.50 to £22.50) **Service:** not inc **Cards:** Amex, Delta, Diners, Maestro, MasterCard, Visa **Details:** 50 seats. Private parties: 55 main room, 10 private room. No smoking. Music

MAP 11 Aberfeldy PERTHSHIRE & KINROSS

Farleyer

Aberfeldy, PH15 2JE
Tel: (01887) 820332

New owners Jake and Kim Schamrel have stamped their mark on this extensively transformed, historical residence in tranquil grounds rolling down to the Tummel valley. Billed as 'restaurants & rooms', it offers modern dishes like wild duck rillettes topped with apple and sage curd (£5.75), smoked trout and wild mushroom risotto with scallops in lobster sauce (£15.50), and roast pineapple with sweetened fromage blanc (£5). Welcoming, family-friendly atmosphere. Open all week.

MAP 11 Archiestown MORAY

Archiestown Hotel

Archiestown, AB38 7QL
Tel: (01340) 810218

A new team is now installed in this eighteenth-century hotel dominating the village square. The owners have made a few cosmetic changes, and the recently appointed chef seems to be following in his predecessor's footsteps. Openers like home-smoked duck with ruby grapefruit and a berry coulis (£7) make way for pork fillet filled with haggis in whisky cream sauce (£16.50), or baked salmon and halibut in filo, while the dessert board lists things like summer pudding with clotted cream (£5). Open all week.

MAP 11 Achiltibuie HIGHLAND

Summer Isles Hotel

Achiltibuie IV26 2YG
Tel: (01854) 622282
Website: www.summerisleshotel.co.uk

Cooking 5 | Modern European | £43–£74

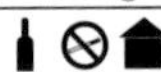

This is virtually as remote as it's possible to get on the Scottish mainland, the hotel lying in wait at the end of a 15-mile single-track road, and the experience is quite something.

Chris Firth-Bernard is justly proud of his commitment to quality Scottish produce, particularly seafood. Lunchtime provides a gentle limber-up in the lighter form of locally smoked salmon, Lochinver oysters, Summer Isles crab, or a whole seafood platter, but it is at dinner that the stops are really pulled out. A five-course set menu doesn't just stick to the starter/fish/meat formula, but may well mix it up by beginning with roast saddle of rabbit with leeks and thyme, with Stilton soufflé intervening before a main course of grilled turbot, paired with mussels steamed over white wine and saffron. Another night produced smoked haddock and potato soup to start, then Angus fillet carpaccio with a piquant relish, with seared West Coast scallops to follow, splashed in vermouth and served on a mound of buttery champ. A dessert trolley then heaves into view, bearing such temptations as dark-chocolate roulade with strawberries and banana flan, before a selection of predominantly Scottish cheeses served with dates, figs, celery and grapes.

Comprehensive coverage of the major French regions broadens into a scintillating global wine list. Talked-about bottles come from all over – there is even California's almost mythical Screaming Eagle for a four-figure sum – but the main focus is on proper grown-up wines at sensible prices, including a dozen clarets at £20 or below.

Chef: Chris Firth-Bernard **Proprietors:** Mark and Gerry Irvine **Open:** all week L 12.30 to 2, D 8 (1 sitting) **Closed:** 17 Oct to 1 Apr **Meals:** alc L (main courses £19 to £30). Set D £47. Bar menu available **Service:** net prices, card slips closed **Cards:** Maestro, MasterCard, Visa **Details:** 30 seats. Car park. Children's helpings. No children under 8. No smoking. Wheelchair access (also WC). No music. No mobile phones **Accommodation:** 13 rooms, all with bath/shower. Phone. B&B £75 to £240. Rooms for disabled. No children under 8. Fishing

MAP 11 Annbank SOUTH AYRSHIRE

Enterkine House

Annbank KA6 5AL
Tel: (01292) 520580
Website: www.enterkine.com

Cooking 4 | Modern European | £30–£61

Where other enterprises might expand and lose their charm, Enterkine House, a substantial 1930s white-painted building surrounded by 310 acres of rolling wooded countryside, has held on to its intimate country-house atmosphere by keeping a sense of scale and retaining a relaxed, informal mood. Meals in the smart dining room have a real sense of occasion about them, which the cooking more than lives up to. The set-price dinner is four courses, though all the little extras make it feel like more, and the cooking style is basically classic French but shows a variety of modern influences. Terrine of Scottish pheasant and pistachio with red onion marmalade and truffled red chard salad is a typical starter, or there might be pan-fried West Coast scallops with butternut squash and Ebly wheat risotto and shellfish sauce. Next comes saddle of Kingussie venison with braised red cabbage, fondant potato, game pithiviers and juniper red wine jus, or pan-fried sea bass with spiced couscous, Parma ham, asparagus, olive tapenade and yellow pepper sauce, and to finish, perhaps dark chocolate tulip filled with wild strawberries, mascarpone and Glayva mousse. Prices on the hefty Francocentric wine list start at £18.

Chef: Paul Moffat **Proprietor:** Oswald Browne **Open:** all week 12 to 2.30, 7 to 9 **Meals:** Set L £16.50 (2 courses) to £18.50, Set D £21.95 (2 courses) to £37.50 **Service:** not inc, 10% for parties of 6 or more, card slips closed **Cards:** Amex, Delta, Diners, Maestro, MasterCard, Visa **Details:** 40 seats. Private parties: 70 main room, 12 private room. Car park. Vegetarian meals. Children's helpings. No smoking. Wheelchair access (also WC). Music **Accommodation:** 6 rooms all with bath/shower. TV. Phone. B&B £55 to £160. Rooms for disabled. Baby facilities

To submit a report on any restaurant, please visit *www.which.co.uk/gfgfeedback*.

MAP 11 **Anstruther** FIFE

Cellar

24 East Green, Anstruther KY10 3AA
Tel: (01333) 310378

Cooking 6 | Modern Seafood | £32–£63

One street back from the harbour, the Jukes' renowned seafood restaurant is now in its twenty-fourth year. 'There's a long list of very regular visitors who already know what they want when they arrive,' says chef/proprietor Peter Jukes. A tiny lounge, with bare stone walls, flagstones and a grandfather clock, leads to the spacious dining room, which continues the exposed-stone-wall theme but adds a tiled floor, beams and candlelit tables, while an open winter fire adds cheer alongside unstuffy service led by Susan Jukes. The cooking blends accomplished sophistication with skilled simplicity, the approach treating the freshest seasonal produce with due respect; there's no over-elaboration, so flavours shine. Crayfish bisque topped with melted cheese ('reminiscent of a true French bisque') gets things off to a flying start, and spinach and nutmeg soup, or wild mushroom risotto might be among non-fish openers. 'Wonderfully fresh and tender' steamed fillet of wild sea bass impressed at inspection with its timing and with its well-matched accompaniments (spinach, leeks and a Chablis and mussel chowder), as did grilled halibut with a dollop of basil mash and a macedoine of green beans, pak choi, peas, pine nuts and smoked bacon. There's the odd concession to meat eaters – perhaps medallions of beef with wild mushrooms, sautéed onions and Dijon sauce – while desserts might run to a terrine of layered chocolate mousses. The wine list picks out excellent producers throughout France and takes similar pains on the global tour that follows. Reasonable prices start at £15, and highlights include Jubilee Pinot Gris from Hugel in Alsace at £32.50.

Chef/Proprietor: Peter Jukes **Open:** Wed to Sun L 12.30 to 1.30, Tue to Sun D 7 to 9 **Closed:** Sun winter, 24 to 26 Dec, 1 Jan **Meals:** Set L £16.50 (2 courses) to £19.50, Set D £28.50 (2 courses) to £37.50 **Service:** not inc **Cards:** Amex, Delta, Diners, Maestro, MasterCard, Visa **Details:** 40 seats. Private parties: 40 main room. Children's helpings. No children under 8. No smoking. Wheelchair access (not WC). No music

MAP 11 **Ardeonaig** STIRLING

Ardeonaig Hotel

Ardeonaig FK21 8SU
Tel: (01567) 820400
Website: www.ardeonaighotel.co.uk

Cooking 3 | South African/Scottish | £40–£58

On the south shore of Loch Tay and surrounded by ten acres of gardens, the Gottgens' hotel is more than just a centre for the fishing fraternity. They have, admittedly, much to keep them occupied (including beats on the Dochart and Tay rivers), but it is not necessary to know one end of a rod from the other to eat here. Primary ingredients are generally straightforward – venison, salmon, cod, lamb, calf's liver – but their treatments owe a lot to Peter Gottgens' native South Africa. Starters might include roast quail with wild girolle mushrooms and honey and pinotage glaze, and main courses team roast Shetland salmon with Cape Malay pickled vegetables and lime, and roast loin of lamb with a pinotage and rosemary wine sauce. Even desserts enter into the spirit of things, with chocolate mielie-meal pudding considered something of a house speciality. An all-day menu is available in the bar and has produced a 'superb' baked south-coast gilthead bream. The wine list focuses on serious bottles from South Africa, including boutique producers like Meinert and De Toren, although some important names are notably absent. House red is £13.50.

Chef: Peter Gottgens **Proprietors:** Peter and Sara Gottgens **Open:** all week 12 to 10 **Meals:** Set L £22.50 (2 courses) to £35, Set D £27.50 (2 courses) to £49.50. Bistro menu available **Service:** not inc **Cards:** Delta, Maestro, MasterCard, Visa **Details:** 50 seats. 50 seats outside. Private parties: 54 main room. Car park. Vegetarian meals. No children under 12 in dining room. No smoking. Music. No mobile phones **Accommodation:** 20 rooms, all with bath/shower. Phone. B&B £35 to £140. No children under 12. Baby facilities. Fishing

 This symbol means that accommodation is available at this establishment.

MAP 11 **Auchterarder** PERTHSHIRE & KINROSS

Andrew Fairlie at Gleneagles

Auchterarder PH3 1NF
Tel: (01764) 694267
Website: www.andrewfairlie.com

Cooking 7 | Modern French | £80–£116

The world-famous golfing resort of Gleneagles played host to the G8 summit in July 2005. Dating from the 1920s, the hotel was designed in the style of a French château, with the landscaping of the grounds inspired by Capability Brown. As well as golf, there is shooting, fishing and an equestrian centre, making it altogether a sportsperson's paradise. Andrew Fairlie's restaurant, an autonomous business, takes its place within this overall context with a due sense of occasion. Understated elegance is the decorative mood, with Ionic columns and panelled walls lightened by paintings by Archie Forrest, for whom Fairlie himself has evidently found time to sit. Staff, who are expert at putting diners at their ease, are fully conversant with what's going on in the kitchen.

Fixed-price menus, presented as a brochure, run the gamut of contemporary luxuries, with local Glenearn lamb a particular feature. It might appear as ultra-tender noisettes, bright pink inside, with Puy lentils, vegetable brunoise, upstanding aubergine caviar, and a blob of superior mayonnaise verdant with mint leaves. Fish is handled with confidence too, pairing halibut, for example, with chorizo and fennel confit, while pork arrives three ways: braised belly with apple, medallions interleaved with paper-thin bacon, and tête de porc topped with black pudding and a quail's egg. Book-ending these main dishes on the three-course menu might be remarkable home-cured lobster smoked over old whisky casks, sauced with herb and lime butter, or roast Skye scallops with parsley butter and garlic crisps, while desserts do creative things with fine chocolate, or match eloquent coconut parfait with pineapple carpaccio and a topping of mashed mango, the pineapple strewn with lime zest and pink peppercorns.

A brilliantly conceived and, surprisingly, not overlong wine list balances fine French classics with top contemporary names from around the globe. Wines by the glass, from £7.50 to £13.50, are special too. In sum, a heart-stopping list at heartbreaking prices (from £25).

Chef/Proprietor: Andrew Fairlie **Open:** Mon to Sat D only 6.30 to 10 **Closed:** 24 and 25 Dec, 3 weeks Jan **Meals:** Set D £55 to £75 **Service:** not inc **Cards:** Amex, Delta, Diners, Maestro, MasterCard, Visa **Details:** 38 seats. Car park. Vegetarian meals. No children under 12. No smoking. Wheelchair access (also WC). Music. Air-conditioned

MAP 11 **Auldearn** HIGHLAND

Boath House

Auldearn IV12 5TE
Tel: (01667) 454896
Website: www.boath-house.com

Cooking 5 | Franco-Scottish | £47–£73

Boath House is a lovely Georgian property with a porticoed entrance and 20 acres of parkland. Inside, contemporary styling may overlay classical features, but Don and Wendy Matheson offer a full-on country-house hotel package. Charles Lockley's dinners run along a clear format, starting with something to nibble over aperitifs on plush sofas in the modish lounge, followed by five courses in the intimate dining room (choice only at main course and dessert stages) from a repertoire that is familiar to regulars but does not pall with time. It manages to combine local produce, a few luxuries and some contemporary ideas, and the menu normally starts with a soup, perhaps white bean with Chinese truffle and Parmesan. First courses have turned up rich partnerships of pear Tatin, foie gras and roast wood pigeon, while main courses range from organic cod with an open raviolo of ham knuckle, scallops and yellow split peas, to saddle of red deer with celeriac purée and ceps, via cannon of Shetland lamb and pressed shoulder with dauphinois potatoes and caramelised sweetbreads. Fourth course is cheese: perhaps Dunsyre Blue with baby onion and sprouted chervil salad. To finish, chocolate and nutmeg soup with morello cherries is an interesting idea, as is roast forced rhubarb with poppy seed and ginger parfait and grenadine syrup. France dominates the wide-ranging wine list, but there is little under £20. Six house wines start at £15.50.

Chef: Charles Lockley **Proprietors:** Don and Wendy Matheson **Open:** Thur to Sun L 12.30 to 1.15, all week D 7 to 8.15 **Closed:** 1 week at Christmas **Meals:** Set L £32.50, Set D £45 **Service:** not inc **Cards:** Amex, Maestro, MasterCard, Visa **Details:** 28 seats. Private parties: 28 main room, 8 private room. Car park. Children's helpings. No smoking. Wheelchair access (also WC). Occasional music. No mobile phones **Accommodation:** 6 rooms, all with bath/shower. TV. Phone. B&B £90 to £220. Rooms for disabled. Baby facilities. Fishing

MAP 11 **Ballantrae** SOUTH AYRSHIRE

Glenapp Castle

Ballantrae KA26 0NZ
Tel: (01465) 831212
Website: www.glenappcastle.com

NEW CHEF | French | £74–£89

This rambling, impressive mansion in the Scottish baronial style, all turrets and castellated walls, was built in the 1870s for the Deputy Lord Lieutenant of Ayrshire (so whatever was the Lord Lieutenant's house like?). New chef, Matt Weedon, arrived into these opulent surroundings in June 2005. The no-choice, five-course dinner menu (plus coffee) continues, and may take you from ballottine of foie gras with smoked duck and celeriac remoulade, through Isle of Arran scallops with cauliflower purée and bacon, then Scottish beef fillet with a herb crust and red wine sauce, with a Scottish cheese (perhaps mille-feuille of Dunsyre blue with truffle honey and port) intervening before the dessert. French classics abound on the pricey list, and there is a good slate of dessert wines. Prices start at £25, and half-a-dozen excellent wines by the glass are a uniform £6.50.

Chef: Matt Weedon **Proprietors:** Graham and Fay Cowan **Open:** all week D 7 to 9 **Closed:** 1 Nov to 1 Apr **Meals:** Set D £55, light L menu available **Service:** not inc, card slips closed **Cards:** Amex, Maestro, MasterCard, Visa **Details:** 40 seats. Private parties: 34 main room, 2 to 22 private rooms. Car park. No children under 6 in dining room. Children's helpings. No smoking. Wheelchair access (also WC). No music **Accommodation:** 17 rooms, all with bath/shower. TV. Phone. D,B&B £255 to £515. Rooms for disabled. Baby facilities

MAP 11 **Ballater** ABERDEENSHIRE

Balgonie Country House

Braemar Place, Ballater AB35 5NQ
Tel: (013397) 55482
Website: www.balgonie-hotel.co.uk

Cooking 4 | Modern Scottish | £32–£62

The style of this Edwardian house is comfortable rather than luxurious, and the place has been confidently run by the Finnies for 15 years. Daily changing set lunch and dinner menus make good use of prime raw materials in a culinary style that isn't afraid of elaborate refinement, as in monkfish served with a garlic croûte and blood orange oil, and terrine of foie gras with truffle oil and griottine brioche. Flavours are carefully built up so as to maximise the impact of the dish: roast pigeon, for example, arrives with a parsnip tarte Tatin, red cabbage marmalade and a beetroot and red wine sauce, and sea bass with black olive risotto and pesto sauce. Inventiveness continues through to desserts of vanilla yogurt terrine with mulled berries, and pistachio parfait, and chocolate marquise with Advocaat and ginger ice cream. The place is run without flourish or pretence, service is attentive and efficient, and France remains the speciality on a wine list that has house Crozes Hermitage at £19.50, though most bottles are over £20.

Chef: John Finnie **Proprietors:** John and Priscilla Finnie **Open:** all week 12.30 to 2 (reservations only), 7 to 9 **Closed:** 6 Jan to 12 Feb **Meals:** Set L £19.50, Set D £37.50 **Service:** not inc, card slips closed **Cards:** Amex, Delta, Diners, Maestro, MasterCard, Visa **Details:** 30 seats. Car park. Children's helpings. No smoking. Wheelchair access (also WC). No music **Accommodation:** 9 rooms, all with bath/shower. TV. Phone. B&B £65 to £150

Darroch Learg

Braemar Road, Ballater AB35 5UX
Tel: (013397) 55443
Website: www.darrochlearg.co.uk

Cooking 6 | Modern Scottish | £47–£64

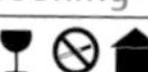

Perched on a forested rise on the western approach road to Ballater, Darroch Learg is a good-looking late Victorian mansion with steeply pitched slate roofs and dormer windows. Inside, the public rooms are spacious and welcoming, with tartan upholstery and crackling log fires, and dinner (plus Sunday lunch) served in a conservatory dining room.

The pick of local supplies makes its way to David Mutter's kitchen, including Highland beef, Deeside lamb, venison from the Glen Muick estate, wild mushrooms and soft fruits, with seafood from the western coasts. Pasta, breads and various relishes are all produced in-house. These prime ingredients are then handled with all due confidence and care, producing dishes such as beef fillet with horseradish risotto, caramelised roots and an oxtail sauce, or fillet of sole with smoked bacon, new potatoes and parsley velouté, served with a salad of tomatoes and Parmesan. Satisfied customers who opted for the Taster menu found themselves embarked on a seven-course journey from Arbroath smokie tortellini with roasted scallops, Sauternes sauce and curry oil, to warm chocolate fondant, with Scottish cheeses to finish. Just before the main course came a snail, with braised lettuce and a sauce of wild garlic. Presentations are pleasing to the eye, service is keen, and the price-quality ratio is in good balance. The wine list offers plenty of choice in the mid-20s, and demonstrates confidence, especially when selecting from Bordeaux and Burgundy. The 'brief encounters' page is well worth exploring.

Chef: David Mutter **Proprietors:** the Franks family **Open:** Sun L 12.30 to 2, all week D 7 to 9 **Closed:** Christmas, last 3 weeks Jan **Meals:** Set L £21, Set D £37.50 to £43.50 **Service:** net prices, card slips closed **Cards:** Amex, Delta, Diners, Maestro, MasterCard, Visa **Details:** 48 seats. 8 seats outside. Private parties: 62 main room. Car park. Vegetarian meals. Children's helpings. No smoking. Wheelchair access (2 steps; also men's WC). No music **Accommodation:** 17 rooms, all with bath/shower. TV. Phone. B&B £45 to £160. Rooms for disabled. Baby facilities

Green Inn

9 Victoria Road, Ballater AB35 5QQ
Tel: (013397) 55701
Website: www.green-inn.com

Cooking 4 | Modern Scottish/French | £33–£46

New owners Trevor and Evelyn O'Halloran, assisted by son Chris in the kitchen, have returned this restaurant-with-rooms to the pages of the Guide after a three-year absence. The building isn't an inn any more, although it does stand opposite the village green in a modest Victorian street. 'Smart and stylish' sums up the refurbished interior, with attention now focused on the airy, salmon-pink conservatory dining room.

Menus offer limited choice, but no shortage of invention. Saucing is a strong point – witness the wild mushroom accompaniment to roulade of Peking duck with creamed sweet white corn and pan-seared foie gras. The quality of fish and meat also points up seared red mullet with a 'palette' of sweet garlic and parsley coulis, and roast fillet of roe deer ('bursting with flavour') with wild mushroom ravioli, creamy celeriac and apple purée, and raspberry vinegar and port jus. To finish, impeccable sabayon lemon tart is served with warm cherries and honeyed mascarpone cream. France forms the backbone of the well-annotated wine list; house recommendations start at £15.95.

Chefs: Chris and Evelyn O'Halloran **Proprietors:** Trevor and Evelyn O'Halloran **Open:** Mon to Sat D only 7 to 9 **Meals:** Set D £28.50 (2 courses) to £33.50 **Service:** not inc, card slips closed **Cards:** Amex, Delta, Maestro, MasterCard, Visa **Details:** 30 seats. Private parties: 30 main room. Vegetarian meals. No smoking in 1 dining room. Wheelchair access (not WC). Music **Accommodation:** 2 rooms, both with bath/shower. TV. B&B £35 to £60. Baby facilities

MAP 11 Balquhidder STIRLING

Monachyle Mhor

Balquhidder FK19 8PQ
Tel: (01877) 384622
Website: www.monachylemhor.com

Cooking 5 | Modern Scottish | £32–£59

The pink-painted country house is reached along six miles of single-track road. Although it could not be more peaceful, gastronomically this is no sleepy backwater. Tom Lewis is scrupulous about the origins of his raw materials, sourcing many of the ingredients locally, and his cooking exhibits great clarity and sense of purpose. Drawing largely on French classical ideas, with a contemporary style, a few luxuries and a fair bit of workmanship and organisation, he turns out a very appealing menu: a bowl of pumpkin soup with roast pumpkin seed topping, pan-fried breast of quail with a fine bean salad and foie gras butter, and crab thermidor with a herb crust. Frequently, off-beat accompaniments are used in counterpoint to the central elements in dishes: fillet of sea bass for example, with roast chestnuts, ginger, Brussels sprouts and a speck and coriander jus, or slow-roast belly pork teamed with roast partridge and served with Turkish aubergine compote. Chocolate mocha tart, vanilla cheesecake with preserved cherries, or Baileys pannacotta with prunes soaked in brandy syrup are suitably indulgent desserts. A short wine list of sense and style stays mostly under £25.

Chef/Proprietor: Tom Lewis **Open:** all week 12 to 1.45, 7 to 8.45 **Meals:** alc L (main courses £14). Set L Sun £22.50, Set D £38 **Service:** not inc **Cards:** Maestro, MasterCard, Visa **Details:** 40 seats. Private parties: 24 main room, 6 to 12 private rooms. Car park. No children under 12. Children's helpings. No smoking. Wheelchair access (also WC). Occasional music **Accommodation:** 11 rooms, all with bath/shower. TV. Phone. B&B £95 to £220.

MAP 11 **Blairgowrie** PERTHSHIRE & KINROSS

Kinloch House Hotel

Blairgowrie PH10 6SG
Tel: (01250) 884237
Website: www.kinlochhouse.com

Cooking 5 | Scottish | £30–£62

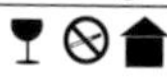

A haven for gracious living and a base for shooting, fishing, golf and visits to distilleries, castles and gardens, this grand country-house hotel boasts a classy, spacious and formal dining room with service to match. Dishes are soundly traditional and based on well-sourced local meat, seafood and game, and some vegetables and herbs are grown in a restored Victorian walled garden. Saucing is rich and well balanced, and timing is 'impeccable'. Start perhaps with breast of wood pigeon, served 'so rare that its blood oozed into the Madeira sauce', accompanied by light, smooth foie gras ravioli and a contrastingly sharp onion marmalade. An inter-course soup is then served, such as 'simple yet profoundly satisfying' wild mushroom. Move on to loin of roe deer with dauphinois potatoes, roast salsify, chestnuts, red cabbage, and a port and juniper sauce, or go for lamb with its sweetbreads, pea purée, garlic potatoes, and rosemary sauce. Baked apple with sultana and vanilla ice cream is a simple yet 'perfectly executed' dessert. Burgundy takes pride of place in a chiefly Francophile wine list that offers plenty of options by the glass (£5 to £10) and house bottles from £14.50, with ample choice at the high end. Even the cheapest bottles are decanted. Commendably, there are three pages of half-bottles.

Chefs: Bill McNicoll and Graeme Pallister **Proprietors:** the Allen family **Open:** all week 12 to 2, 7 to 9 **Closed:** 16 to 29 Dec **Meals:** alc L (main courses £8.50 to £15). Set D £39.50. Light L menu available **Service:** not inc, card slips closed **Cards:** Amex, Maestro, MasterCard, Visa **Details:** 50 seats. Private parties: 50 main room, 8 to 20 private rooms. Car park. Children's helpings. No children under 7 at D. Jacket. No smoking. Wheelchair access (also men's WC). No music. No mobile phones **Accommodation:** 18 rooms, all with bath/shower. TV. Phone. D,B&B £95 to £360. Rooms for disabled. Baby facilities. Swimming pool

 This symbol means that smoking is not permitted.

MAP 11 **Cairndow** ARGYLL & BUTE

Loch Fyne Oyster Bar

Clachan, Cairndow PA26 8BL
Tel: (01499) 600236
Website: www.loch-fyne.com

Cooking 2 | Seafood | £28–£63

A great deal has happened to the Loch Fyne brand since this ground-breaking venture opened its doors: branches now flourish throughout the country, but the original ethos of environmental care and sustainability remains. Seafood 'direct from our shores and smokehouse' is the theme, and it is the group's policy to eschew fish from endangered species. Oysters lead the pack, closely followed by smoked salmon, kippers, mussels and pickings from the local boats. A few uncomplicated cooked dishes such as queen scallops with garlic butter flesh out the repertoire, and the Glen Fyne meat range is becoming increasingly popular – hence the presence of, say, venison and sirloin steak with mustard sauce on the menu. House bottles at £10.95 head the short list of affordably priced, youthful wines.

Chef: Tracy Wyatt **Proprietor:** Loch Fyne Oysters Ltd **Open:** all week 9 to 9 (may close earlier Nov to Mar) **Closed:** 25 and 26 Dec, 1 and 2 Jan **Meals:** alc (main courses £9 to £25) **Service:** not inc **Cards:** Amex, Delta, Diners, Maestro, MasterCard, Visa **Details:** 120 seats. 20 seats outside. Private parties: 40 main room. Car park. Vegetarian meals. Children's helpings. No smoking. Wheelchair access (also WC). Occasional music. No mobile phones

MAP 11 **Clachan-Seil** ARGYLL & BUTE

Willowburn Hotel

Clachan-Seil, by Oban PA34 4TJ
Tel: (01852) 300276
Website: www.willowburn.co.uk

Cooking 3 | Modern Scottish/French | £45–£53

First-time visitors declared themselves 'absolutely delighted to enjoy such balanced, imaginative cooking in a dining room overlooking Clachan Sound and a garden full of small birds and ducks.' This long, whitewashed house idyllically set on an island accessed by a road bridge has a relaxed feel, more restaurant-with-rooms than a hotel. Daily changing four-course dinners make excellent use of first-rate produce, local lobster appearing on a dill and mascarpone cheesecake with garden salad and lemon sauce. Potato scones come with roast venison medallions, hazelnut stuffing and game chips, while roast rack of lamb has sun-dried tomato and pine nut risotto and a red wine sauce. Start with crab wrapped in marinated salmon, and try a second-course pea and pear soup, or a sorbet. Finish maybe with banana tart Tatin with vanilla ice cream and lime snaps, or Scottish cheeses with oatcakes. Wines run from £13.

Chef: Chris Wolfe **Proprietors:** Jan and Chris Wolfe **Open:** all week, D only; 7 to 7.30 **Closed:** Dec 1 to Mar 1 **Meals:** Set D £34 **Service:** not inc, card slips closed **Cards:** Delta, Maestro, MasterCard, Visa **Details:** 20 seats. Car park. Vegetarian meals. No children under 8. No smoking. Music. No mobile phones **Accommodation:** 7 rooms, all with bath/shower. TV. D,B&B £76 to £156. No children under 8

MAP 11 **Colbost** HIGHLAND

Three Chimneys

Colbost, Dunvegan IV55 8ZT
Tel: (01470) 511258
Website: www.threechimneys.co.uk

Cooking 5 | Modern Scottish | £63–£84

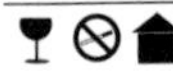

On a single-track road leading straight as a die in the direction of Skye's northwest coast, the Spears' hotel and restaurant is impeccably remote. The whole property is bounded by a white picket fence, while the view over the loch is aptly haunting. Ceilings are low, the décor faintly maritime, with a modern triptych on a wave theme and an antique anchor among the adornments. Shirley Spear is taking more of a back seat these days, having appointed a new head chef, Michael Smith, in 2004. That hasn't marked a break with the established style, and dishes such as dressed Bracadale crab with avocado salsa and lime and coriander dressing, or carpaccio of local smoked haddock with peat-smoked salmon, eggs mimosa and herb salad, look secure.

The format is for a possible four-course menu, with the intermediate second course being a soup or perhaps a serving of plain, daisy-fresh oysters. Multi-faceted main courses have taken in citrus-baked halibut with scallops, crisp potatoes, fine beans and Seville orange sauce, as well as pedigree meats such as loin and kidney of Highland lamb with pearl barley, black kale, and a sauce of mushrooms and madeira. Such a stalwart among desserts has the marmalade pudding with Drambuie custard been that it is now preceded with the accolade 'The Famous...'. Scottish cheeses with Hebridean oatcakes may well prove equally hard to resist. A fine collection of wines has pitched up at this far-flung outpost and prices (from £17.95) reflect the mileage. France is at the heart of the list, but quality remains high in the shorter listings from elsewhere. Half-bottles are a strength.

Chefs: Shirley Spear and Michael Smith **Proprietors:** Eddie and Shirley Spear **Open:** Mon to Sat L 12.30 to 2, all week D 6.30 to 9.30 **Closed:** 13 to 19 Dec, 9 to 28 Jan **Meals:** Set L £18 to £25, Set D £48 to £55 **Service:** not inc **Cards:** Amex, Delta, Maestro, MasterCard, Visa **Details:** 30 seats. 6 seats outside. Car park. Vegetarian meals. No children under 8 at D. No smoking. Wheelchair access (not WC). No music **Accommodation:** 6 rooms, all with bath/shower. TV. Phone. B&B £145 to £240. Rooms for disabled. Baby facilities

MAP 11 **Crinan** ARGYLL & BUTE

Crinan Hotel, Westward Restaurant

Crinan PA31 8SR
Tel: (01546) 830261
Website: www.crinanhotel.com

Cooking 4 | Modern European | £57–£68

The Westward Restaurant at this substantial white-painted hotel on the shore has 'soul-calming' views of the coast, and you can watch the sun setting over the Western Isles. White walls are aptly hung with striking seascapes, tables are well spaced and service is 'pleasant and helpful'. The cooking shows healthy ambition and an emphasis on fresh, quality produce from an abundant local larder of seafood and organic produce. Prawns, lobsters and clams are brought in daily by local boats to within 50 yards of the hotel, so they don't come much fresher. The kitchen is now headed by Nicola Tanguy (who worked with the outgoing chef, Ben Tish), but the approach stays the same: a set-price, four-course menu, changing daily, offering around four choices at each turn with a no-choice intermediate dish, perhaps tomato velouté. 'Perfectly cooked' pan-fried Loch Fyne scallops might come teamed with braised belly pork and cauliflower purée to start, to be followed by 'well-timed' poached West Coast wild salmon accompanied by tagliatelle, spring vegetables and 'delicately but effectively flavoured' horseradish velouté, or roast saddle of Argyll venison with Puy lentils and fondant potato. A warm chocolate soufflé or new season's cherry clafoutis might head up desserts. The wide-ranging global wine list has a six-strong house selection at £18.50 and a dozen halves.

Chef: Nicola Tanguy **Proprietors:** Nicolas and Frances Ryan **Open:** all week D only 7 to 8.30 (9 summer) **Meals:** Set D £42.50. Bar menu available **Service:** not inc, card slips closed **Cards:** Maestro, MasterCard, Visa **Details:** 40 seats. 20 seats outside. Private parties: 60 main room, 20 to 40 private rooms. Car park. Children's helpings. No smoking. Wheelchair access (also WC). No music **Accommodation:** 20 rooms, all with bath/shower. TV. Phone. D,B&B £85 to £310. Rooms for disabled. Baby facilities

MAP 11 **Crossmichael** DUMFRIES & GALLOWAY

Plumed Horse

Main Street, Crossmichael DG7 3AU
Tel: (01556) 670333
Website: www.plumedhorse.co.uk

Cooking 6 | Modern European | £34–£61

'Crossmichael,' writes a reporter, 'is a one-street linear settlement with absolutely nothing going on.' Nothing, that is, apart from Tony Borthwick's singular restaurant, at which he had just had an altogether splendid lunch. If you're heading north from Castle Douglas, you will likely miss it, as the sign is only visible southbound, but it's a small, whitewashed building next to the village pub. Scallops and white fish from Kirkcudbright, local meats and speciality products such as Loch Arthur Cheddar form the backbone of the inventive, expertly realised menus. The intensity of frothy langoustine bisque makes a powerfully persuasive opener, garnished as it is with a langoustine mousse deftly stuffed with Avruga. Elsewhere, ballottine of grouse and foie gras was an impeccable autumn starter, served with Cumberland sauce and a pastry cup of leaves dressed in truffle oil, and sea trout and scallops make a fine double act, partnered with cucumber spaghetti and a fennel velouté. Main courses are multi-layered and complex: roast halibut comes with a scallop, dauphinois potatoes with anchovy, herbed salsify, and a sauce built on smoked ham and herbs. If truffles and foie gras feature widely, they are nonetheless used with a clear understanding of what they contribute to a dish. More down-to-earth dishes, which work equally well, include roast pork loin with a roll of prune-stuffed belly, alongside beetroot and red cabbage stew and mash.

Salted chocolate caramel tart is one dessert option, or there may be passion-fruit délices with white chocolate ice cream. An individual selection of wines centres on France, with international back-up mainly from Italy and Australia. Prices start at £14.

Chefs: Tony Borthwick and Malcolm Kirkpatrick **Proprietor:** Tony Borthwick **Open:** Tue to Fri L 12.30 to 1, Tue to Sat D 7 to 8; also open one Sun L per month **Closed:** Christmas, 2 weeks Jan, 2 weeks Sept **Meals:** alc (main courses £19). Set L Mon to Sat £21, Set L Sun £24 (3 courses), Set D £42.50 **Service:** not inc, card slips closed **Cards:** Delta, Maestro, MasterCard, Visa **Details:** 28 seats. Private parties: 24 main room, 10 to 24 private rooms. No smoking. Wheelchair access (also WC). Occasional music. No mobile phones. Air-conditioned

MAP 11 **Cupar** FIFE

Ostlers Close

25 Bonnygate, Cupar KY15 4BU
Tel: (01334) 655574
Website: www.ostlersclose.co.uk

Cooking 5 | Modern Scottish | £31–£59

The vibrant Mediterranean red interior of the Grahams' small, friendly restaurant sets the tone for the high-powered, confident cooking on offer. A plethora of local produce informs dishes such as a first-course halibut fillet with stir-fried Glamis sea kale and pesto oil, seafood soup traditionally served with rouille, or the main-course medley of Pittenween market fish sauced with chervil butter. Roast fillet of Scots beef has brown lentils and oxtail to accompany it, in a sauce fired up with horseradish, while reporters once again endorse the roe venison, which comes with wild mushrooms in a textbook red-wine sauce. A plate of chocolate variations is one way to finish, but praise has also been accorded a dish of roast pineapple with mango ice cream and coconut cream. Fine presentation distinguishes dishes throughout. Service is a model of efficient informality.

Everything on the 'decent and sensibly priced' wine list looks well worth trying, whether the reliable Casillero del Diablo Chilean house red (£14.50), zesty Wither Hills Sauvignon from New

Zealand at £19.50 or second wines from Bordeaux like La Ferme d'Angludet (£25.50).

Chef: James Graham **Proprietors:** James and Amanda Graham **Open:** Sat L 12.15 to 1.30, Tue to Sat D 7 to 9.30 **Closed:** 25 and 26 Dec, 1 and 2 Jan, 2 weeks Easter, 2 weeks Oct **Meals:** alc (main courses L £10 to £14, D £16 to £19) **Service:** not inc, card slips closed **Cards:** Amex, Delta, Maestro, MasterCard, Visa **Details:** 26 seats. Private parties: 22 main room. Vegetarian meals. Children's helpings; no children under 6 at D. No smoking. Wheelchair access (also WC). No music. No mobile phones

MAP 11 **Dalry** NORTH AYRSHIRE

Braidwoods

Drumastle Mill Cottage, Dalry KA24 4LN
Tel: (01294) 833544
Website: www.braidwoods.co.uk

Cooking 6 | Modern Scottish | £32–£60

'Hard to find, but worth the search' was how one reporter wrote up his visit to Braidwoods for us. Fashioned from two rooms of an old Ayrshire cottage, the restaurant is intimate and attractive, with floral displays to delight the eye and a high gleam on the glassware. Nicola Braidwood warm-heartedly leads the front of house, ensuring everybody feels at home.

Dinner is a three- or four-course affair, with an intermediate option of soup (perhaps sweetcorn and crab) or a salad (Parma ham and avocado with Stilton and caper vinaigrette) coming before the main course. A whole roasted boneless quail is a favoured starter, stuffed with either spinach or black pudding, and served on Puy lentils or roast beetroot. Main courses bring forth such regional treasures as West Coast turbot cooked in chicken juices with a pea purée, or Highland red deer on winter roots with a sauce infused with thyme. 'Simple but elegant' lunch dishes have included curried prawn soup, grilled sea bass, and lemon tart, while one reader reckoned the 'wonderfully light' bread-and-butter pudding to be 'the best of its kind anywhere'. Coffee comes with superlative hand-made chocolates. Two stylish Beaujolais from Vissoux attest to the keen attention to detail on a manageable wine list with no makeweights. Just the four house wines (£14.95 and £16.95 per bottle) come by the glass.

Chefs/Proprietors: Keith and Nicola Braidwood **Open:** Wed to Sun L 12 to 1.30 (Sun L Sept to May only), Tue to Sat D 7 to 9 **Closed:** first 2 weeks Sept, 25 and 26 Dec, first 3 weeks Jan **Meals:** Set L Wed to Sat £17 (2 courses) to £20, Set L Sun £25, Set D £33 to £38 **Service:** not inc, card slips closed **Cards:** Amex, Delta, Diners, Maestro, MasterCard, Visa **Details:** 24 seats. Private parties: 14 main room. Car park. No children under 12 at D. No smoking. No music. No mobile phones

MAP 11 **Dornoch** HIGHLAND

Quail

Castle Street, Dornoch IV25 3SN
Tel: (01862) 811811
Website: www.2quail.com

Cooking 4 | Modern European-Plus | £50–£59

An air of carefully nurtured domesticity hangs over the Carrs' modest restaurant-with-rooms close to the centre of town, although the mood can seem too regimented for some people. 'Dinner from 7.30' means just that, and the pace can be slow throughout the evening. Michael Carr runs the kitchen and works to a short classically inclined menu, opening the show with a little appetiser soup in a cup. Reporters have enjoyed cheese soufflé and gnocchi with prawns, or you might choose something more modern like seared Skye scallops with pea purée, crispy bacon and sesame oil. Then comes tournedos Rossini, orange-crusted turbot with a fricassee of cherry tomatoes, or 'perfectly cooked' venison in port and truffle sauce. Summer pudding converted one visitor; otherwise, consider bitter chocolate tart with coconut ice cream. The wine list is a decent assortment 'full of old favourites', particularly from France. House wine is £14.

Chef: Michael Carr **Proprietors:** Michael and Kerensa Carr **Open:** Tue to Sat D only 7.30 to 9.30 **Closed:** Tue and Wed Apr to Oct, 1 week at Christmas, 2 weeks Feb/Mar, bank hols **Meals:** Set D £35.50 **Service:** not inc **Cards:** Amex, Delta, Maestro, MasterCard, Visa **Details:** 12 seats. Private parties: 10 main room. No children under 8 exc babies. No smoking. Wheelchair access (not WC). Occasional music. No mobile phones **Accommodation:** 3 rooms, all with bath/shower. TV. Phone. B&B £60 to £90. No children under 8 exc babies. Baby facilities

MAP 11 **Dufftown** MORAY

La Faisanderie

2 Balvenie Street, Dufftown AB55 4AD
Tel: (01340) 821273
Website: www.dufftown.co.uk/placestoeat

Cooking 3 | Franco-Scottish | £23–£47

There's the feeling of a relaxed French bistro about La Faisanderie, with its wooden floors, yellow walls and tablecloths, a namesake stuffed pheasant and Gallic music: quite a find in a town proudly famous for its whisky distilleries.

Eric Obry cooks a Franco-Scottish menu, where gamey flavours abound from the abundant local larder. The fish of the day – according to the menu, 'prepared how the chef's feeling' – might be crisp-skinned grilled halibut with tapenade and a herby onion compote, and medallions of local estate venison might be paired with a 'refreshingly sharp' beetroot and rowanberry jelly, black truffle and a Burgundy glaze. Turnip and saffron soup has been a well-received starter, and to finish go for perhaps a hot chocolate fondant with crème fraîche and, not surprisingly, whisky crème anglaise. Service is unobtrusive and cheerful, while the short French wine list opens at £9.90.

Chef: Eric Obry **Proprietors:** Eric Obry and Amanda Bestwick **Open:** Fri to Sun L 12 to 1.30, Wed to Mon D 6 to 8.30 (7 to 9 Fri and Sat) **Closed:** Wed D Nov to Mar, first 3 weeks Nov, 25, 26 and 31 Dec, 1 and 2 Jan **Meals:** alc (main courses £9.50 to £17). Set L £12.20 (2 courses) to £15.10, Set D £24 **Service:** not inc, card slips closed **Cards:** Delta, Maestro, MasterCard, Visa **Details:** 30 seats. Private parties: 16 main room. Children's helpings. No-smoking area. Wheelchair access (also WC). Music

MAP 11 **Dundee** DUNDEE

Dil Se AR

101 Perth Road, DD1 4JA (01382) 221501.

This Bangladeshi-run restaurant has a modern glass frontage and a menu that, whilst including most of the usual suspects (Madras, bhuna et al), has much that catches the eye. A daily special might be Mas Bangla, salmon marinated in lime, tumeric and chilli then fried in mustard oil with garlic onion, tomato and aubergine. Desserts include mangoes when in season, perhaps caramelised and served with vanilla ice cream. The dining room is smart and spacious, and the service 'professional and polite'. Open all week.

AR	Not a full entry but provisionally recommended (known as 'round-ups' in previous editions, these 'also recommended' establishments are now integrated throughout the book).

MAP 4 **Dunkeld** PERTHSHIRE & KINROSS

Kinnaird

Kinnaird Estate, by Dunkeld PH8 0LB
Tel: (01796) 482440
Website: www.kinnairdestate.com

Cooking 6 | Modern European | £47–£83

An Edwardian mansion in extensive grounds in the Tay valley, Kinnaird aims to impress but not intimidate. The experience is usually held to be a sympathetic one, the welcome full of warmth, as is the fire that crackles against the northern chill. Trevor Brooks leads a kitchen team brimming with confidence, sourcing supplies from as far afield as Rungis market in Paris and as close to home as the back garden. The style is country house for the twenty-first century, with flourishes of gently applied novelty adding interest to the foundation of prime cuts and rich sauces. Foie gras and game terrine is a banker, but you might not expect to find it garnished with pineapple and chilli chutney. Scallops are accompanied with tortellini of Arbroath smokie, the pleasing pungency of the dish enhanced by a smoky butter velouté sauce. Main courses try out some unusual seasonings: Szechuan pepper with roast squash and beetroot purée as the garnishes for corn-fed duckling, for example, while gnocchi with tea-marinated prunes might be one of the partners for roast partridge. Manjari chocolate makes an aromatic mousse, supported by passion-fruit coulis and pistachio croquant, or there might be a medley of fruit flavours, as in orange and poppy-seed cake with poached satsumas, sweet-and-sour melon salsa and lemon custard.

Clarets running back to the long-lived 1964 Ch. Latour sound the fanfare for a list that is strong on both pedigree and range. Mark-ups are merciless, although there is some relief in the southern hemisphere. A selection of six by the large glass is uniformly priced at £7.50.

Chef: Trevor Brooks **Proprietor:** Constance Ward **Open:** all week 12.30 to 1.45, 7 to 9.30 **Meals:** Set L £30, Set D £50. Light L menu available **Service:** not inc, card slips closed **Cards:** Amex, Maestro, MasterCard, Visa **Details:** 36 seats. Private parties: 36 main room, 15 to 36 private rooms. Car park. No children under 12. Jacket and tie at D. No smoking. Wheelchair access (also WC). No music. No mobile phones **Accommodation:** 9 rooms, all with bath/shower. TV. Phone. D,B&B £195 to £450. Rooms for disabled. No children under 12. Fishing

MAP 11 Edinburgh EDINBURGH

Atrium

10 Cambridge Street, Edinburgh EH1 2ED
Tel: (0131) 228 8882
Website: www.atriumrestaurant.co.uk

Cooking 1 | Modern European | £31–£68

Andrew and Lisa Radford's Atrium has become something of a stalwart on the Edinburgh eating scene, although at an inspection meal the cooking seemed to have lost some of its spark. Highlights from the lunchtime carte have included crusty home-made bread, a tender roast quail accompanied by Serrano ham salad, scallops on a bed of tomato and basil concassé, and 'well-cooked' loin of lamb with some good creamed spinach, although its accompanying jus, fondant potato and ratatouille might have benefited from a return visit to the drawing board. For dessert, chocolate pithiviers with espresso crème anglaise has been pronounced 'excellent'. There are also two- or three-course lunch and dinner deals teamed with recommended wines from an interesting wine list of some 300 bins, all of which are available by the glass – just as well, as there is little under £20. House wines open at £16.

Chefs: Neil Forbes and Andrew Jenkins **Proprietors:** Andrew and Lisa Radford **Open:** Mon to Fri L 12 to 2, Mon to Sat D 6 to 10 (all week L and D during Festival) **Closed:** 25 and 26 Dec, 1 and 2 Jan **Meals:** alc (main courses £17 to £22). Set L £13.50 (2 courses) to £17.50, Set D £25 **Service:** not inc, 10% for parties of 5 or more **Cards:** Amex, Delta, Diners, Maestro, MasterCard, Visa **Details:** 80 seats. Private parties: 180 main room. Vegetarian meals. Children's helpings. No smoking. Wheelchair access (also WC). No music. Air-conditioned

Balmoral, Number One

1 Princes Street, Edinburgh EH2 2EQ
Tel: (0131) 557 6727
Website: www.roccofortehotels.com

Cooking 6 | Modern European | £36–£125

No. 1 Princes Street is about as prestigious an address as it's possible to have in the Scottish capital, and the Balmoral makes the most of its cachet. The hotel is furnished opulently, with private banqueting suites and conference facilities aplenty. Within the main dining room, an air of light formality reigns, with smart banquette seating and subtle lighting, a plethora of watercolours on the walls, and mirrors augmenting the sense of space. Jeff Bland oversees a full-dress, à la carte menu, with canapés, a cup of truffle-oiled soup, excellent home-made breads, a pre-dessert and oodles of friandises with coffee all taking their expected places. Seared scallops with cauliflower pannacotta and a purée of raisins and capers stood out at inspection as a skilfully composed starter, with main courses of veal two ways (roast fillet and a foie gras-stuffed braised parcel), and roast loin of hare with angelotti pasta and a sumptuous beetroot reduction demonstrating the kitchen's pitch-perfect timing of meats. A fish option might be halibut with beignets of smoked brandade, in a sauce of red wine and pancetta. The textural contrasts of a dessert of orange savarin in a moat of rhubarb soup with rhubarb jelly cubes and a foaming lemon sauce impressed an inspector, or there might be flaky mango mille-feuille with coconut pannacotta and 'beguilingly subtle' rum and lime sorbet. 'Professionally attentive, yet unobtrusive' service is what it's all about.

A quality line-up by the glass opens a contemporary global wine list strong in Chile, South Africa, Australia and Italy, with prices from £19. France, however, is the main focus, including numerous distinguished bottles from Bordeaux, Burgundy and Champagne.

Chef: Jeff Bland **Proprietor:** Rocco Forte Hotels **Open:** Mon to Fri L 12 to 2, all week D 7 to 10 (10.30 Fri and Sat) **Closed:** first week Jan **Meals:** alc (main courses £22.50 to £25.50). Set L £16.95 (2 courses) to £19.95, Set D £60 to £95 (inc wine) **Service:** not inc, 12.5% for parties of 6 or more **Cards:** Amex, Delta, Diners, Maestro, MasterCard, Visa **Details:** 50 seats. Private parties: 60 main room. No children under 12. No-smoking area. Wheelchair access (also WC). Music. No mobile phones. Air-conditioned **Accommodation:** 188 rooms, all with bath/shower. TV. Phone. Room only £120 to £1,325. Rooms for disabled. Swimming pool

Blue Bar Café

10 Cambridge Street, Edinburgh EH1 2ED
Tel: (0131) 221 1222

Cool oasis for culture vultures, above the Traverse Theatre and near the Lyceum and the Usher Hall. Choose anything from a speedy 'Light Blue' dish like smoked chicken Caesar salad (£5.50) to something more 'leisurely', such as whole sea bream with spring onion and wasabi mash (£14) or lamb shank with balsamic lentils. Bring the curtain down with chocolate and pecan tart with cinnamon ice cream (£4.50). Carefully selected wines from £13.95. Closed Sun (exc during Festival).

The Bonham

35 Drumsheugh Gardens, Edinburgh EH3 7RN
Tel: (0131) 623 9319
Website: www.thebonham.com

Cooking 3 | Modern European | £27–£62

The spacious dining room of this refined modern hotel in Edinburgh's West End is modishly furnished in sage greens, with understated prints and polished wooden tables. Michel Bouyer offers a seasonally influenced menu, with palpable hits including 'succulent and firm' home-cured gravad lax, and accomplished meat cookery in the form of rabbit leg on golden polenta with julienned root vegetables, or braised Tamworth pork with thin garlic mash and green fusilli pasta. Desserts include crunchy and creamy nougat glace with honey and rosemary syrup and dried fruits, or stewed plum gratin with lemongrass sabayon. Service is 'courteous, if leisurely'. Wines evince a commendable attempt to source some interesting flavours, particularly among reds. The list opens with Australian Chardonnay and Shiraz at £14.50.

Chef: Michel Bouyer **Proprietor:** Peter Taylor **Open:** all week 12 to 2.30 (12.30 to 3 Sun), 6.30 to 10 **Meals:** alc D (main courses £11.50 to £22). Set L £13.50 (2 courses) to £16 **Service:** not inc, card slips closed, 10% for parties of 6 or more **Cards:** Amex, Delta, Diners, Maestro, MasterCard, Visa **Details:** 52 seats. Private parties: 60 main room, 1 to 70 private rooms. Car park. Vegetarian meals. Children's helpings. No smoking. Wheelchair access (also WC). Music **Accommodation:** 48 rooms, all with bath/shower. TV. Phone. B&B £108 to £195. Rooms for disabled. Baby facilities

Café St Honoré

34 NW Thistle St Lane, Edinburgh EH2 1EA
Tel: (0131) 226 2211
Website: www.cafesthonore.com

Cooking 3 | Modern Bistro | £30–£56

Café St Honoré has become an Edinburgh institution through a combination of longevity and uniqueness: inside, it looks as if it's in a back street in Montmartre, rather than 'just off Thistle Street'. Menus reflect the décor and, despite contemporary touches (like sautéed squid with mussels, chillies, ginger and spring onion), stay firmly on classic French territory, including such perennial favourites as steak au poivre, sautéed chicken livers with prunes, and lamb shank with haricot beans, garlic and rosemary. Results on the plate are mostly consistent, with occasional misses among the hits; much the same can be said of friendly but sometimes patchy service, though reporters mostly come away pleased. Ten house wines from £12.45 open the wine list.

Chefs: Chris Colverson and Hannah Barclay **Proprietors:** Chris and Gill Colverson **Open:** all week 12 to 2.15, 5.30 (6 Sat/Sun) to 10 **Closed:** 3 days Christmas, 3 days New Year **Meals:** alc (main courses L £9 to £14.50, D 7 to 10 £15 to £20). Set D Mon to Fri 5.30 to 6.45, Sun 6 to 7.15 £14.95 (2 courses) to £19.95 **Service:** not inc, 10% (optional) for parties of 8 or more **Cards:** Amex, Delta, Diners, Maestro, MasterCard, Visa **Details:** 56 seats. Private parties: 44 main room, 8 to 18 private rooms. Vegetarian meals. Children's helpings. Non-smoking area. Wheelchair access (not WC). Music

Channings

15 South Learmonth Gardens, Edinburgh EH4 1EZ
Tel: (0131) 315 2225
Website: www.channings.co.uk

Cooking 5 | Modern Scottish | £24–£57

It's a slick operation: service is beyond reproach and Hubert Lamort's cooking is on the rise, understated and delivering dishes of often astounding quality. At inspection, a tiny glass of warm oyster soup topped with a perfect wispy oyster fritter was a top-drawer opener. Crab tartare came next, served in two thimblefuls flanked by blood-red peppery flourishes of shiso cress and a slick of cream with warm Colombo spice. This appealing mix of traditional simplicity with the influence of foreign climes was carried through to impeccably timed fillets of sole finished in a simple beurre blanc and teamed with nothing more than a segment of ripe juicy grapefruit and a small rope of herby fettucine. The same care goes into desserts such as a 'perfect' soufflé with a molten centre and a glossily textured milk chocolate with nougatine in a buttery, thin pastry case that formed part of an assiette of chocolate. These were the highlights of a seven-course tasting menu, but as the Guide goes to press the restaurant was to close for refurbishment to incorporate the hotel's other restaurant, Ochre Vita (which will close), and a new à la carte menu will be introduced. Therefore, some of the details below may change; reports, please.

Chef: Hubert Lamort **Proprietor:** Peter Taylor **Open:** Tue to Sat 12 to 2, 6.30 to 10 **Meals:** alc (main courses £12.50 to £22). Set L £16 to £19 **Service:** not inc, card slips closed **Cards:** Amex, Delta, Diners, Maestro, MasterCard, Visa **Details:** 36 seats. Private parties: 36 main room, 10 to 20 private rooms. No smoking. Music. No mobile phones **Accommodation:** 46 rooms, all with bath/shower. TV. Phone. B&B £105 to £185. Baby facilities

David Bann

56–58 St Mary's Street, Edinburgh EH1 1SX
Tel: (0131) 556 5888
Website: www.davidbann.com

Cooking 2 | Vegetarian | £22–£40

This is a restaurant with a mission. The food is strictly vegetarian (with several dishes marked as vegan), and David Bann's stated aim is 'to bring vegetarian food into the mainstream by making it stylish and flavoursome'. He achieves this with an eclectic cooking style, drawing ideas from all over the Mediterranean and Asia. Among starters, crispy vegetable parcels are served with papaya and cucumber salad, chilli jelly, spiced roast garlic, tomato salsa and mango relish, and main courses range from the locally inspired walnut, hazelnut and mushroom haggis to kaffir lime paneer croquettes served with jasmine and coriander rice and spiced roti. Finish with malt whisky pannacotta, or meringue, lime and ginger parfait. The short, realistically priced wine list starts at £10.80.

Chef/Proprietor: David Bann **Open:** all week 11 to 10 (10.30 Fri and Sat) **Closed:** 25 and 26 Dec, 1 and 2 Jan **Meals:** alc (main courses £7 to £11) **Service:** not inc, 10% for parties of 8 or more **Cards:** Amex, Delta, Maestro, MasterCard, Visa **Details:** 86 seats. Private parties: 40 main room. Children's helpings. No smoking. Wheelchair access (not WC). Music. Air-conditioned

Fishers

1 Shore, Leith, Edinburgh EH6 6QW
Tel: (0131) 554 5666

Long-running bistro 'on the shore', which lives up to its name with a fondness for fish. Open your account with grilled queen scallops with orange and chilli syrup (£5.50) before baked finnan 'haddie' or grilled fillets of plaice with wilted spinach and a shrimp and mussel broth (£11.50). Lamb's liver with braised red cabbage is a meat option, and homespun desserts could include warm chocolate fudge cake with ice cream (£4.75). House wine £11.95. Open all week. Related to Fishers in the City (see entry, below).

Fishers in the City

58 Thistle Street, Edinburgh EH2 1EN
Tel: (0131) 225 5109
Website: www.fishersbistros.co.uk

Cooking 2 | Seafood | £24–£66

There are no prizes for guessing that fish is the kitchen's main concern in this relaxed metropolitan venue. Loch Fyne oysters and steamed west coast mussels share the stage with some overtly ambitious ideas: seared king scallops are served with a curried banana Tatin topped with lime, orange and turmeric cream cheese, while sea bass fillet arrives on ginger-scented steamed kale with a cashew, chilli and thyme cream sauce. Meat eaters could be offered loin of lamb on roast red pepper and pistachio mash, and vegetarians have their own menu. An array of farmhouse cheeses stands proud alongside simple desserts like sticky toffee pudding. Fifteen wines by the glass open a good-value list, with bottles from £11.95. Fishers' elder sibling is in Leith (see above).

Chef: Brendan Sugars **Proprietors:** James Millar and Graeme Lumsden **Open:** all week 12 to 10.30 **Closed:** 25 and 26 Dec, 1 Jan **Meals:** alc (main courses £8.50 to £24) **Service:** not inc, 10% for parties of 6 or more **Cards:** Amex, Delta, Maestro, MasterCard, Visa **Details:** 85 seats. Private parties: 50 main room, 30 to 50 private rooms. Vegetarian meals. No smoking in 1 dining room. Wheelchair access (also WC). Music. Air-conditioned

Forth Floor

Harvey Nichols, 30–34 St Andrews Square, Edinburgh EH2 2AD
Tel: (0131) 524 8350
Website: www.harveynichols.co.uk

Cooking 4 | Modern British | £39–£71

The restaurant forms part of Harvey Nichols' Edinburgh branch and is, as one enthusiastic visitor found, 'buzzing, very busy, bustling, modern and trendy'. There is evident enthusiasm in the kitchen too, and an eye for interesting combinations, such as pancetta-wrapped Oban scallops with smoked Brie fondue and fried cauliflower, or smoked garlic and spring onion croquettes with ratatouille and wild mushrooms. At the same time, there are much more straightforward ideas, as in slow-baked chump of lamb with roast sweet potatoes and confit shallots. Seafood has been praised this year: 'startlingly tasty' langoustine risotto and 'perfectly cooked' sea bass with pickled fennel, although there are reports of 'minuscule' starter portions. Desserts indulge with dark chocolate mousse with cherry compote and vanilla froth, or coffee and walnut bombe with white chocolate sauce. The long, global wine list is packed with producers at the top of their form – no tired old names here – with wines arranged by style in the New World and by regions throughout Europe. The cream of Bordeaux is available at stratospheric prices, but the smart money is on the healthy range of own-label bottles, from £13.50 for Sauvignon Blanc to £22.50 for Hautes-Côtes de Nuits.

Chef: Stuart Muir **Proprietor:** Harvey Nichols **Open:** all week L 12 to 3 (3.30 Sat and Sun), Tue to Sun D 6 to 10 **Meals:** alc (main courses £14.50 to £24). Set L Mon to Fri £24.50 (2 courses), Set L Sat £19.50 (2 courses). Brasserie menu available **Service:** 10%, card slips closed **Cards:** Amex, Delta, Diners, Maestro, MasterCard, Visa **Details:** 85 seats. 32 seats outside. Private parties: 160 main room. Children's helpings. No-smoking area. Wheelchair access (also WC). Music. Air-conditioned

Haldanes

39A Albany Street, Edinburgh EH1 3QY
Tel: (0131) 556 8407
Website: www.haldanesrestaurant.com

Cooking 2 | Modern Scottish | £42–£79

Set in the basement of a city-centre Georgian house, Haldanes is a comfortable, unstuffy place that strikes a balance between the relaxed and formal ends of the spectrum. A strong Scottish theme underscores the operation, yielding starters such as West Coast scallops (served with morcilla and beetroot chutney) and haggis (with mustard mash, roasted neeps and whisky sauce). The food aims to be satisfying rather than mould-breaking, offering mains of fish – perhaps sea bass with crab and ginger mousse and tiger prawn bisque – or breast of chicken with creamed greens and a tarragon and mustard butter sauce, and homely puddings of banana and toffee meringue tart with rum and raisin syrup, or a duo of chocolate bavarois.

A stimulating international collection of wines, including the excellent South African Martin Meinert, extends to a page of mature clarets and other expensive treats. House bottles start at £14 and eight worthwhile options come by the 250ml glass for £4 to £9.

Chefs: George Kelso and Steven Falconer **Proprietors:** George and Michelle Kelso **Open:** Mon to Fri L 12 to 1.45, all week D 5.45 to 9.30, pre-theatre set D Mon to Sat 5.45 to 7.30 **Closed:** 25 and 26 Dec **Meals:** alc D (main courses £16 to £26). Set L and D £18.50 (2 courses) **Service:** not inc **Cards:** Amex, Delta, Diners, Maestro, MasterCard, Visa **Details:** 60 seats. 10 seats outside. Private parties: 26 main room, 10 to 60 private rooms. Vegetarian meals. Children's helpings. No smoking. No music

Kalpna

2–3 St Patrick Square, Edinburgh EH8 9EZ
Tel: (0131) 443 4418

Cooking 3 | Indian Vegetarian | £21–£47

For more than two decades Ajay Bhartdwaj's restaurant has been a bastion of the Edinburgh scene, and it remains one of the true champions of Indian vegetarian cooking. The title 'Kalpna' suggests 'creative imagination', and the kitchen lives up to its name. A few South Indian dishes such as masala dosa make an appearance, but the main input is from Gujarat, with some nods to Rajasthan. The menu includes distinctive interpretations of classics such as bhindi masala and dhal tarka, but it pays to check out the list of specialities: khoya kaju is prepared from reduced cream, cashews, sultanas and pistachios, while dam aloo Kashmiri is baked stuffed potatoes with two contrasting sauces. Thalis are intended for one person, and there are affordable buffets at lunchtime. Indian wines from Grover Vineyards are worth investigating; otherwise the short list provides appropriate drinking from £10.50.

Chef/Proprietor: Ajay Bhartdwaj **Open:** Mon to Sat 12 to 2, 5.30 to 10.30 **Closed:** 25 Dec, 1 Jan **Meals:** alc (main courses £4.50 to £10.50). Set L £5.50, Set D £12.50 to £15 **Service:** 10%, card slips closed **Cards:** MasterCard, Visa **Details:** 65 seats. Private parties: 75 main room, 20 to 35 private rooms. Vegetarian meals. No smoking. Wheelchair access (not WC). Music

Off the Wall

105 High Street, Edinburgh EH1 1SG
Tel: (0131) 558 1497
Website: www.off-the-wall.co.uk

Cooking 2 | Modern Scottish | £32–£72

In a first-floor room, and sharing a stairway with a backpackers' hostel, Off the Wall looks out over the tourist hub of the Royal Mile. David Anderson's cooking aims for diamond-hard modernity, serving pigeon breast with creamed Jerusalem artichokes, chanterelles and port-laced juices as a satisfying winter starter, with perhaps sea bass and mussels in red wine sauce, or Barbary duck breast with salsify and red cabbage to follow. Desserts continue in the same vein, with tiramisù spiked with sambuca, and hazelnut and syrup tart partnered with apple fritter, vanilla ice cream and butterscotch sauce. The rate of service can be head-spinningly quick on a slow night. A gentler pace might allow you time to enjoy one of the many decent bottles on the wine list. Prices open with an Argentinian Sauvignon at £13.95.

Chef: David Anderson **Proprietors:** David Anderson and Aileen Wilson **Open:** Tue to Sat 12 to 2, 7 to 10 (all week 12 to 2, 6 to 10.30 during Festival) **Closed:** 25 and 26 Dec, 1 and 2 Jan **Meals:** alc D (main courses £20 to £22). Set L £16.50 (2 courses) to £19.95 **Service:** not inc **Cards:** Amex, Maestro, MasterCard, Visa **Details:** 44 seats. Private parties: 44 main room, 20 to 44 private rooms. Children's helpings. No-smoking area. No cigars/pipes in dining room. Occasional music

Restaurant Martin Wishart

54 Shore, Leith, Edinburgh
EH6 6RA
Tel: (0131) 553 3557
Website: www.martin-wishart.co.uk

Cooking 7 | Modern French | £38–£91

Occupying white end-terrace premises in the rejuvenated dockside development at Leith, Martin Wishart's restaurant is well supported and wholeheartedly admired in reports. A gentle, even slightly bland interior – all cream walls and coffee tones, with oil paintings on a country-house scale – is the backdrop for some spectacular culinary pyrotechnics. Seasonally changing menus reflect the pride of Scottish produce, with Aberdeenshire smoked haddock, organic smoked salmon, Shetland lamb and game all featuring, the last typically in a showcase main course such as woodcock cooked in Armagnac with wild mushrooms, artichokes and pomme cocotte. Combinations are daring but supremely successful, as when 'super-model-thin' ravioli packed with loads of lobster comes with big-flavoured deep-fried trotter. Certain dishes are mentioned repeatedly in dispatches. The Challans duck rubbed in spices, served with foie gras, pear chutney, and cucumber and white radish aigre-doux is never less than 'a technical *tour de force*', while shin of beef, braised to unimaginable softness and accompanied by veal sweetbreads, pomme purée and a red wine jus, is a masterpiece of intensity.

Fish is handled with equal vigour, so expect creamed Brussels sprouts, salsify, spätzli and a chicken stock jus to turn up with fillets of John Dory, or there may be a pairing of roast turbot and langoustines sauced with truffle butter supported by braised leeks. Matching soufflé and sorbet ensembles (perhaps raspberry or blackberry) score highly at dessert stage. More unusually a banana is wrapped in a chocolate crêpe and served with rum and raisin ice cream and sauce créole. Cheeses are out of the top drawer too.

Wines by the glass from a selection of over a dozen have appealed to reporters, with the charming young sommelier adding a touch of theatre to their presentation. The bottle list (from £19.50) enthusiastically explores all corners of the world and turns up rare treats, including Savennières from Domaine de la Monnaie (£40).

Chef/Proprietor: Martin Wishart **Open:** Tue to Fri L 12 to 2, Tue to Sat D 7 to 10 **Meals:** alc (main courses £22 to £26). Set L £20.50, Set D £50 to £55 **Service:** not inc **Cards:** Amex, Delta, Maestro, MasterCard, Visa **Details:** 45 seats. Private parties: 45 main room. Vegetarian meals. No smoking before 2.30pm and 10.30pm. Wheelchair access (also WC). Music. No mobile phones

Rhubarb at Prestonfield

NEW ENTRY

Priestfield Road, Edinburgh EH16 5UT
Tel: (0131) 225 1333
Website: www.rhubarb-restaurant.com

Cooking 4 | Modern European | £47–£86

Prestonfield was built in 1687 as the home of Edinburgh's Lord Provost to a design by Sir William Bruce, the architect of Holyroodhouse

Palace. It has always had a reputation for opulent entertaining, the more so since it became a hotel in the mid-twentieth century. James Thomson acquired the place in 2003 and set about giving it a £2 million refurbishment. Dusky reds, aubergine and glimmering greens combine in the lush restaurant décor, with golden-roped drapes at the windows and stargazer lilies on the tables creating a feeling of grand luxe. Kenny Coltman aims for the same kind of lustrous sheen in his cooking. Velvet-textured ravioli with roast butternut squash and pecorino Mornay sauce made a fine inspection starter, while a main-course ballottine of hare with vegetables roasted in heather honey delivered meat of good, robust flavour. Fish features strongly, as in a bold-as-brass main course of sea bass with a stew of oxtail, brown lentils and port. As one would expect from the name, an assiette of rhubarb is a signature dessert, but there might also be a rich, ripe, tart terrine of orange and pink grapefruit, appealingly complemented by a sorbet of Lady Grey tea. Repair to the lounge, with its seventeenth-century Cordoba leather walls, for excellent coffee and petits fours.

The wine list is ambitious enough to split countries, as well as France, into individual regions and leans towards prestige bottles. House wines are £16, and a dozen or so by the glass compensate for the rather thin choice below £25.

Chef: Kenny Coltman **Proprietor:** James Thomson **Open:** all week 12 to 3, 6 to 11 **Meals:** alc (main courses £18 to £30). Set L £16.95 (2 courses). Bar menu available **Service:** not inc, card slips closed **Cards:** Amex, Delta, Diners, Maestro, MasterCard, Visa **Details:** 100 seats. Private parties: 100 main room, 8 to 50 private rooms. Car park. Vegetarian meals. No children under 12. No smoking. Wheelchair access (also WC). Music **Accommodation:** 24 rooms, all with bath/shower. TV. Phone. B&B £195 to £275. Rooms for disabled

Skippers

1A Dock Place, Leith, Edinburgh EH6 6LU
Tel: (0131) 554 1018
Website: www.skippers.co.uk

Cooking 1 | Seafood | £24–£68

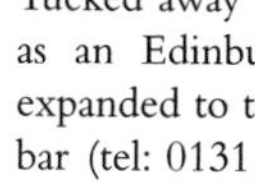

Tucked away in Dock Place and widely regarded as an Edinburgh institution, Skippers recently expanded to take in the adjacent Waterfront wine bar (tel: 0131 554 7427) and the two now offer similar food. Seafood is the name of the game, supplies coming mostly from Scottish boats, and simplicity rules at the stove (seared halibut fillet with smoked salmon and salsa verde, for example). Steamed Shetland mussels with chilli and coconut was considered the star dish at inspection. Desserts ('relatively large portions and tiny spoons') are mostly perennials like sticky toffee pudding. The short wine list favours whites, with George Duboeuf house selections at £11.50.

Chef: Mary Walker **Proprietors:** Karen and Gavin Ferguson **Open:** all week 12.30 to 2, 6 to 10 **Closed:** 25 and 26 Dec **Meals:** alc (main courses L £7 to £20, D £12 to £25). Set L £7.95 to £12.95 (2 courses), Set D Sun to Thur £19.95 **Service:** not inc, 10% for parties of 6 or more **Cards:** Amex, Delta, Maestro, MasterCard, Visa **Details:** 60 seats. 20 seats outside. Private parties: 60 main room. Vegetarian meals. Children's helpings. No smoking in 1 dining room. Wheelchair access (also WC). Music. No mobile phones

Suruchi Too

AR

121 Constitution Street, Leith, Edinburgh EH6 7AE
Tel: (0131) 554 3268

Sari meets kilt in this offbeat Indian restaurant, where the menu advertises Subcontinental dishes with a broad Edinburgh accent. Samosas ('a licht pastry stappit wi mixed vegetable servit wi a flavourfu dookin sauce'; £4) and haggis fritters feature among 'sterters'; tandooris include a cauliflower version, and main courses range from dakshni murgh masala ('a curry wi teeth'; £8.75) to lamb korma 'cookit in toothfae spices'. Decent choice of rice and 'breid'. House wine £10.95. Open all week. The original is at 14A Nicolson Street; tel: (0131) 556 6583.

Tower Restaurant

Museum of Scotland, Chambers Street, Edinburgh EH1 1JF
Tel: (0131) 225 3003
Website: www.tower-restaurant.com

Cooking 2 | Seafood/Modern British | £39–£85

'Hip place, good design and engaging service,' sums up this modern restaurant perched atop the Museum of Scotland (there is a lift) giving splendid roof-skimming views towards the castle. The sensibly compact, Mediterranean-influenced menus hit just the right note, and the cooking is typically 'of a high standard', utilising sound ingredients, appealing presentation and little pretension. The fixed-price lunch is considered good value, and the carte delivers the likes of smoked halibut with potato salad and lime and coriander dressing, then rack of black-face Borders lamb with niçoise vegetables, or calf's liver with a red onion and shallot tart Tatin and crispy bacon. Almond and Amaretto cheesecake with brandy-soaked prunes might head up the repertoire of puddings, while the wine list is a suitably modern global affair, with prices starting at £14.

Chef: Gavin Elden **Proprietor:** James Thomson **Open:** all week 12 to 5, 5 to 11 **Closed:** 25 and 26 Dec **Meals:** alc (main courses L £9.50 to £23, D £14.50 to £27). Set L £11 (2 courses), Set D 5 to 6.30 £12.50 **Service:** not inc, 10% for parties of 8 or more **Cards:** Amex, Diners, Maestro, MasterCard, Visa **Details:** 85 seats. 45 seats outside. Private parties: 85 main room. Vegetarian meals. Children's helpings. No smoking. Wheelchair access (also WC). Music. Air-conditioned

Valvona & Crolla Caffè Bar

19 Elm Row, Edinburgh EH7 4AA
Tel: (0131) 556 6066
Website: www.valvonacrolla.com

Cooking 3 | Italian | £24–£50

V&C is a gastronomic institution that has been doing Edinburgh proud for years, passing from one generation of the Contini family to the next. During the Festival it opens three evenings a week, although its stock-in-trade is all-day eating (and shopping), with lunch the main event. Ingredients from Italian artisan producers team up with the cream of Scotland's larder, and the result is a line-up of emphatically rustic, peasant-style dishes steeped in the traditions of the Mediterranean. Classic antipasti open the show before linguine with cremini mushrooms and dried porcini, calf's liver alla veneziana, or pizza topped with buffalo mozzarella, Parma ham, rocket, and pan-fried Swiss chard. There are lively salads too, and several pure-Italian torte ranging from limone to mandorle (with almonds and fresh fruit). The short wine list of around a dozen by the glass or bottle (from £9) is enough to get the mouth watering, but the full shop wine list, covering Italy in loving detail and looking far beyond its borders, is on offer too, with just £4 added to the retail price.

In October 2004, the Continis opened the Valvona & Crolla Vincaffè at 11 Multrees Walk (tel: 0131 557 0088) – Edinburgh's glitzy new shopping thoroughfare built around Harvey Nichols. It has become phenomenally successful, queues often stretch outside the glass-fronted building and it pleases the crowds with a flexible menu – although prices can seem high. The familiar V&C repertoire of crostini, antipasti, pizzas and pasta is bolstered by additional dishes like grilled steak with rocket and olive oil. Vincaffè shares the same magisterial wine list as the original.

Chef: Mary Contini **Proprietors:** Philip and Mary Contini **Open:** Mon to Sat 8 to 6.30, Sun 11 to 5 (L served 11.45 to 3.30). Also open Thur to Sat D during Festival **Closed:** 25 and 26 Dec, 1 and 2 Jan **Meals:** alc (main courses L £8 to £14, D £10 to £18) **Service:** not inc **Cards:** Amex, Maestro, MasterCard, Visa **Details:** 80 seats. Private parties: 80 main room. Vegetarian meals. Children's helpings. No smoking. Wheelchair access (also WC). Music. Air-conditioned

Vintners Rooms

The Vaults, 87 Giles Street, Leith, Edinburgh EH6 6BZ
Tel: (0131) 554 6767
Website: www.thevintnersrooms.com

Cooking 4 | French | £31–£63

The restaurant is in two sections in the basement of a historic port building. A huge stone fireplace houses a live fire on chilly days in the bar area, which is hung with oriental rugs, while the fine plasterwork in the dining room has been atmospherically smirched by a mass of flickering candles. Patrice Ginestière mixes ancient and modern modes in his accomplished French cooking, offering smoothly enjoyable pumpkin velouté, or pairing foie gras and lobster in a terrine served with mango salsa, before a main course as traditional as duck confit served on cabbage and smoked bacon. Salmon tartare may be simply dressed with crème fraîche and chives, but then halibut appears in a broth of mussels and saffron. Desserts are similarly contrasting: strawberries come with olive confit and thyme sorbet, and hot chocolate fondant with pistachio ice cream. Reporters commend the service. Upmarket French bottles dominate the wine list, but there are interesting and affordable alternatives from all over France – like Crozes-Hermitage from Remizières (£23) – and stimulating choices from further afield. House Muscadet is £16.

Chef: Patrice Ginestière **Proprietor:** The Vintners Rooms Ltd **Open:** Tue to Sat 12 to 2, 7 to 10 **Meals:** alc (main courses £16 to £22). Set L £14.50 (2 courses) to £18 **Service:** 10% (optional) **Cards:** Amex, Delta, Maestro, MasterCard, Visa **Details:** 65 seats. Private parties: 30 main room. Vegetarian meals. Children's helpings. No smoking in 1 dining room. Wheelchair access (not WC). Music

Witchery by the Castle

Castlehill, Royal Mile, Edinburgh EH1 2NF
Tel: (0131) 225 5613
Website: www.thewitchery.com

Cooking 3 | Modern Scottish | £32–£96

The name evokes the Gothic theatricality and rich setting of this restaurant (under the same ownership as the nearby Tower, see entry), housed in a sixteenth-century building by the castle gates. The dimly-lit Witchery, 'quite mysterious and atmospheric', features dark-oak panelling, tapestries, antique candlesticks, leather chairs and flagged floors, while the Secret Garden has a spectacular painted ceiling and views over a topiary- and urn-filled terrace. However, without a magic wand, it's only possible on booking to *request* a table in a specific dining room.

The menu, in contrast to the surroundings, offers a surprisingly contemporary spin on modern classics, based around prime raw ingredients and including a good array of seafood. Think classic pressed terrine of foie gras with quince jelly and toasted brioche, grilled sea bass served with roast fennel, a bouillabaisse sauce and rouille, or perhaps roast rack of black-face lamb partnered by niçoise vegetables. Finish with a blood orange crème brûlée. The wine list is quite a tome, but clear and careful annotation aids navigation. It starts from £15.95 with a basic house dozen by bottle or glass, and moves on to a very impressive global range.

Chef: Douglas Roberts **Proprietor:** James Thomson **Open:** all week 12 to 4, 5.30 to 11.30 **Meals:** alc (main courses £15 to £30). Set L £12.50 (2 courses), Set D 5.30 to 6.30 and 10.30 to 11 £12.50 (2 courses) **Service:** not inc, 10% (optional) for parties of 8 or more **Cards:** Amex, Delta, Diners, Maestro, MasterCard, Visa **Details:** 90 seats. 15 seats outside. Private parties: 40 and 50 main rooms. Vegetarian meals. Music **Accommodation:** 7 rooms, all with bath/shower. TV. Phone. B&B £275

	This symbol means that the wine list is well above the average.
	This symbol means that the restaurant has a truly outstanding wine cellar.

MAP 11 **Ednam** BORDERS

Edenwater House

Ednam TD5 7QL
Tel: (01573) 224070
Website: www.edenwaterhouse.co.uk

Cooking 4 | Modern British | £41–£50

Once the local manse, this foursquare hotel benefits from lovely views over the borderlands between the upper Tweed valley, Ettrick Forest and Yarrow Braes. Jacqui and Jeff Kelly offer a classic, country-house dinner menu of four courses with no choice: you might begin with leek and fennel soup with crème fraîche before herb-crusted John Dory with spinach, asparagus and tarragon beurre blanc. Next could come spiced fillet of Borders beef on a rösti with stuffed mushrooms, glazed chicory, courgettes and port jus, and you could round things off with pineapple and bananas poached in Malibu syrup with coconut ice cream. Occasionally the formula is tweaked: a light dish such as seared scallops on smoked salmon and asparagus risotto might open the show, and cheese-based 'savouries' like fresh pear with whipped Roquefort sometimes find their way on to the menu. The wine list has been put together with personal enthusiasm and understanding; vins de pays are £12.50.

Chef: Jacqui Kelly **Proprietors:** Jacqui and Jeff Kelly **Open:** Wed to Sat D only 8pm (1 sitting) **Closed:** first 2 weeks Jan **Meals:** Set D £35 **Service:** net prices, card slips closed **Cards:** Delta, Maestro, MasterCard, Visa **Details:** 16 seats. Private parties: 16 main room. Car park. No children under 10. No smoking. Wheelchair access (not WC). No music. No mobile phones **Accommodation:** 4 rooms, all with bath/shower. TV. B&B £50 to £95. No children under 10

MAP 11 **Elie** FIFE

Sangster's

51 High Street, Elie KY9 1BZ
Tel: (01333) 331001
Website: www.sangsters.co.uk

Cooking 4 | Modern British | £27–£55

Right on the main street of a picturesque East Neuk coastal town, Bruce Sangster's eponymous restaurant occupies a smartly painted dwelling that could be mistaken for an eating house somewhere in France. Beyond the frontage you will find a patriotically Scottish lounge and an intimate dining room with starched white cloths and generously spaced tables. Dinner can run to four courses and it's an admirably short, carefully conceived selection of modern dishes. Proper attention is paid to supplies, whether it's seared Isle of Mull dived scallops (with a chilli, ginger, galangal and coriander dressing) or slow-braised shin of beef (with dark-ale juices, 'scorched' winter root vegetables and horseradish mash). An intermediate course (twice-baked cheese soufflé or Cullen skink, for example) is listed between starters and mains, while desserts could range from iced hazelnut, honey and lime parfait with poached pear, to warm brioche whisky and sultana pudding. Wines are a sassy modern mix and every bottle pulls its weight. Prices are good, starting with £14 house.

Chef: Bruce Sangster **Proprietors:** Bruce and Jacqueline Sangster **Open:** Wed to Fri and Sun L 12.30 to 1.45, Tue to Sat D 7 to 9.30 **Closed:** 25 and 26 Dec, first 3 weeks Jan **Meals:** Set L £15.75 to £17.75, Set D £25 (2 courses) to £32.50 **Service:** not inc, card slips closed **Cards:** Delta, Diners, Maestro, MasterCard, Visa **Details:** 28 seats. Private parties: 16 main room. No children under 12. No smoking. No music. No mobile phones

MAP 11 **Eriska** ARGYLL & BUTE

Isle of Eriska

Ledaig, Eriska PA37 1SD
Tel: (01631) 720371
Website: www.eriska-hotel.co.uk

Cooking 4 | Scottish | £48–£58

Follow the brown road signs off the A828. The journey along narrow lanes may seem to take an age, but eventually you trundle across a thrillingly rickety-sounding bridge on to the island, and the house looms up. The dining room is dimly lit of an evening, with striped curtains closed against the outer world in winter. Working to a fixed-price formula with a pair of choices each for starter and main course, and a soup interposed between, Robert MacPherson scores some hits. Lightly grilled mackerel on shellfish risotto has made a generous February opener, and halibut as a main course gains from being bedded on buttery mash and accompanied by a bundle of baby leeks. At inspection, duck breast had lost a fair amount of its lustre through overcooking but was offset by its partner, a properly flavourful confit leg. Saddle of roe deer with salsify, thyme gnocchi and sauce forestière was the meat option on a spring menu. A trolley of cheeses in good condition appears after the dessert choice (perhaps pistachio pannacotta topped with passion-fruit jelly), or there might be a chunky savoury such as smoked haddock on toast. Wines are a Francocentric selection, with some competitive prices for those prepared to forage. Vins de pays are £9, and there is an abundance of halves.

Chef: Robert MacPherson **Proprietors:** the Buchanan-Smith family **Open:** all week D only 8 to 9 (L residents only) **Closed:** Jan **Meals:** Set D £38.50 **Service:** not inc, card slips closed **Cards:** Amex, Delta, Maestro, MasterCard, Visa **Details:** 44 seats. Private parties: 40 main room, 20 private room. Car park. Children's helpings. No smoking. Wheelchair access (also WC). No music. No mobile phones. Air-conditioned **Accommodation:** 22 rooms, all with bath/shower. TV. Phone. B&B £140 to £360. Rooms for disabled. Baby facilities. Swimming pool

MAP 11 **Fairlie** NORTH AYRSHIRE

Fins

Fencefoot Farm, Fairlie KA29 0EG
Tel: (01475) 568989
Website: www.fencebay.co.uk

Cooking 2 | Seafood | £28–£70

The speciality here is fish and crustacea (you can buy it at their farm shop too). The on-site smokehouse provides smoked salmon, trout and kippers, the owner's boat brings crabs, lobsters and mackerel, and oysters come from a local farm. The interiors (white-painted stone walls, bare boards, homely furniture, fishy ornaments and ship prints, or the new conservatory) are honest and uncomplicated, like the cooking. The freshest of produce is treated with sensible simplicity – be it a smoked salmon sauce partnering seared king scallops, or perhaps a halibut fillet teamed with squat lobster tails, langoustines and chardonnay sauce, or a straightforward hot seafood platter; there's steak in a pink peppercorn and whisky sauce, too. Portions are generous, the atmosphere relaxed and friendly, and an affordable wine list begins at £11.80.

Chefs: Jane Burns, Gary Brown and Paul Harvey **Proprietors:** Jill and Bernard Thain **Open:** Tue to Sun L 12 to 2.30, Tue to Sat D 7 to 9 (6.30 to 9.30 Sat) **Closed:** 25 and 26 Dec, 1 and 2 Jan **Meals:** alc (main courses £9.50 to £28). Set L Tue to Fri £12 to £14.50 **Service:** not inc, card slips closed **Cards:** Delta, Maestro, MasterCard, Visa **Details:** 50 seats. Private parties: 50 main room. Car park. No children under 7 at D. No smoking. Wheelchair access (also WC). Music. No mobile phones

MAP 11 **Fort William** HIGHLAND

Crannog

Town Pier, Fort William PH33 6PD
Tel: (01397) 705589
Website: www.crannog.net

Cooking 2 | Seafood | £26–£61

Fisherman Finlay Finlayson set up Crannog on the principle of integration – forging direct links with the local boats and establishing his own smokehouse. The results on the plate have been so impressive that many visitors hotfoot it to the smokery to buy extra supplies before leaving town. Langoustines from Loch Linnhe and Loch Eil are a star turn, but there is much more besides: Cullen skink is a robust broth, fishcakes are served on chilli cream, and roast Mallaig cod is advertised with creamy mash and parsley sauce. Finish with home-made ice creams or Scottish cheeses. House wine is £13.95. The restaurant was battered by severe weather and had to relocate to temporary premises for the 2005 season but will reopen on the pier in 2006: check for details.

Chef: Robert Ramsay **Proprietor:** Finlay Finlayson **Open:** all week 12 to 2.30, 6 to 9 (10 Apr to Oct) **Closed:** D 24 Dec, 25 and 26 Dec, D 31 Dec, 1 Jan **Meals:** alc (main courses £9 to £23) **Service:** not inc **Cards:** Delta, Maestro, MasterCard, Visa **Details:** 66 seats. Private parties: 30 main room. Vegetarian meals. Children's helpings. No smoking. Wheelchair access (also WC). Music

Inverlochy Castle

SCOTLAND GFG 2006 COMMENDED

Torlundy, Fort William PH33 6SN
Tel: (01397) 702177
Website: www.inverlochycastlehotel.com

Cooking 6 | Modern European | £48–£89

On the A82, just past the ruins of its namesake, the old thirteenth-century castle itself, Inverlochy is as grand as grand gets. The sumptuous lounge, with gallery, real fire, piano, chessboard and much reading matter invites one to unwind, while the dining rooms boast solid old oak dressers, silver figurines of game birds, and pretty appetising views over the hotel's own lake, from which you might fish a trout and have it cooked for dinner. It's jacket and tie order, please note, even if there are only two of you in the dining room, the assumption perhaps being that you wouldn't want to let yourself down.

Matthew Gray is achieving great things here, turning out dishes not only replete with fine ingredients, but demonstrating a versatile range of proficient technique too. The white meat of Isle of Barra crab is almost subliminally mayonnaised and is sandwiched between savoury-seasoned crackers, with creamy avocado purée to add lustre, while fillet of veal with truffled celeriac beignets delivers magisterial flavours, and is moist and satisfying even though the sauce is merely a fast-setting, syrupy pan reduction. Sticky toasted hazelnuts and creamed leeks round it all off. Or you might go for carpaccio of Scots beef with horseradish bavarois, followed by roast turbot with baby artichoke ragoût and ceps. Desserts look and taste dramatic, with banana and yoghurt sorbet accompanying cinnamon crème brûlée, while a winter caramel assemblage offered cardamom-scented parfait, ice cream and caramel-poached pear. Service is warm and professional.

The cover of the wine list shows bottles of Pétrus, Grange, Mouton-Rothschild et al. hob-nobbing before the fine highland view. House champagne is vintage Pommery Louise, and everything in the French-biased international collection is smart. Prices (from £30), however, will vex anyone who needs to check their bank statements.

Chef: Matthew Gray **Proprietor:** Inverlochy Castle Ltd **Open:** all week 12.30 to 1.45, 6.30 to 9 **Closed:** 8 Jan to 3 Feb **Meals:** Set L £23 (2 courses) to £28.50, Set D £52.50. Light L menu available **Service:** not inc **Cards:** Amex, Delta, Maestro, MasterCard, Visa **Details:** 50 seats. Private parties: 30 main room, 2 to 50 private rooms. Car park. Vegetarian meals. Children's helpings. Jacket and tie. No smoking. Wheelchair access (also WC). No music. No mobile phones **Accommodation:** 17 rooms, all with bath/shower. TV. Phone. B&B £220 to £580. Baby facilities. Fishing

MAP 11 **Glasgow** GLASGOW

Brian Maule at Chardon d'Or

176 West Regent Street, Glasgow G2 4RL
Tel: (0141) 248 3801
Website: www.brianmaule.com

Cooking 4 | French/Mediterranean | £30–£78

Despite aiming for a high degree of refinement, Brian Maule's restaurant manages to be relaxing and friendly as well. Laminate flooring, frosted-glass screens and white walls create an airy, modern feel, and a separate bar area is usually convivially abuzz. The cooking works to a fairly traditional European template, with no alarming combinations, but achieves some impressive results. A spring first course of asparagus in a white truffle dressing was flawlessly timed, and finished with shaved Parmesan for maximum impact, while main courses of fried tuna with mixed peppers on chilli couscous, and carefully handled pork fillet with smooth mash and al dente green beans each pleased a pair of reporters. Scottish cheeses are properly the stars of the fine selection, all of which are kept in good nick, or you might opt for a dessert such as lemon posset with a compote of red fruits and rhubarb. The six-course Celebration Menu gives a reliable cross section of the repertoire.

The wine list is bursting with good options under £25, even in Bordeaux and Burgundy, and seems canny when it comes to prestigious bottles: 1996 Ch. Gruaud-Larose (£63) should be hitting its stride now, and there's the fabulous 1983 Ch. Cos d'Estournel at £148.

Chef/Proprietor: Brian Maule **Open:** Mon to Fri L 12 to 2, Mon to Sat D 6 to 9.30 **Closed:** 2 weeks Jan, bank hols **Meals:** alc (main courses £19 to £23). Set L and D 6 to 7 £15.50 (2 courses) to £18.50, Set D £48.50 **Service:** not inc **Cards:** Amex, Delta, Maestro, MasterCard, Visa **Details:** 96 seats. Private parties: 96 main room, 6 to 96 private rooms. Vegetarian meals. No smoking. Music. No mobile phones

Buttery

652 Argyle Street, Glasgow G3 8UF
Tel: (0141) 221 8188
Email: the_buttery@hotmail.co.uk

Cooking 5 | Modern Scottish | £37–£72

'One of the city's dining gems', the Buttery, surrounded by twentieth-century flats and apartments, has an atmosphere of old-world solidity, and buzzes with a real spirit of hospitality. Willie Deans places well-sourced materials at the heart of things, and the sensibly short menus feature Scottish produce in abundance; Blairgowrie beef, perhaps, or Lochwinnoch venison, and first-class fish and shellfish. Lunch is more straightforward than dinner, although dishes are equally well executed, witness Isle of Mull mussels and finnan haddock with crispy bacon, tomatoes, shallots, white wine and parsley, and saffron- and yoghurt-infused codling with crisp leeks and a Thai salad of tiny grains, chilli oil and fried asparagus. Vegetables and accompaniments are highly worked: loin of venison, for example, has come in an apple and balsamic sauce partnered by miniature goats' cheese and tarragon spätzli, cranberry and crab apple chutney, and a gâteau of winter roots. Finish with deep-fried mango and lime rice pudding with toffee sauce and pavlova ice, or pear and orange marmalade strudel with spiced citrus confit and Amaretto ice, declared 'outstanding' by a recipient. Wine coverage is extensive, although prices are skewered towards the higher end. House red and white are £18.

Chef: Willie Deans **Proprietor:** Ian Fleming **Open:** Tue to Fri L 12 to 2, Tue to Sat D 6 to 10 **Meals:** alc L (main courses £12 to £15). Set L £16, Set D £34 (2 courses) to £38 **Service:** not inc **Cards:** Amex, Maestro, MasterCard, Visa **Details:** 60 seats. Private parties: 65 main room, 10 to 36 private rooms. Car park. Vegetarian meals. Children's helpings. No smoking. Wheelchair access (also WC). Music. Air-conditioned

Café Ostra

The Italian Centre, 15 John Street,
Glasgow G1 1HP
Tel: (0141) 552 4433
Website: www.cafeostra.com

Cooking 1 | Seafood | £22–£55

This multi-level venue in Glasgow's Italian Centre has the same owners as Gamba (see below) and also focuses primarily on seafood. Fish soup is full-blooded ('with a great gingery undertone' and basil oil drizzled on top), and the all-day menu pleases the crowds with generously filled smoked salmon omelettes, grilled sardines with salsa relish, and egg noodles with tiger prawns, roast cashews, red pepper and oyster sauce. Meat-eaters might prefer Cajun-spiced chicken with sticky rice, while desserts could include pear and raspberry cheesecake. The straightforward, fish-friendly wine list offers 11 by the glass, and bottle prices start at £11.95.

Chef: John Gillespie **Proprietors:** Alan Tomkins and Derek Marshall **Open:** all week 12 to 10 (10.30 Fri and Sat) **Closed:** 25 and 26 Dec, 1 and 2 Jan **Meals:** alc (main courses £7 to £18). Set L £5.95 (1 course) to £7.95 (2 courses) **Service:** not inc, 10% for parties of 6 or more **Cards:** Amex, Delta, Maestro, MasterCard, Visa **Details:** 90 seats. 90 seats outside. Private parties: 90 main room, 16 to 26 private rooms. Vegetarian meals. Children's helpings. No smoking in 1 dining room. Wheelchair access (not WC). Music. No mobile phones. Air-conditioned

étain

The Glass House, Springfield Court, Glasgow G1 3JX
Tel: (0141) 225 5630
Website: www.conran.com

Cooking 3 | Modern Scottish | £37–£62

The Glasgow outpost of Terence Conran's far-flung gastronomic empire is a stylish room with low lighting, where light background jazz music and amiable, well-trained staff create a relaxed atmosphere. The cooking owes more to France than anywhere else, though it is based largely on quality native produce, particularly fine Scottish seafood, as in glazed Loch Fyne oysters with champagne sabayon, or steamed scallops with braised flageolets and a bacon and ginger velouté. Typically earthy meat options include slow-roasted belly of Lancashire pork with black pudding, roast apples and celeriac rémoulade, and twice-cooked veal breast with morels, wild leeks and young turnips, and to finish, choose perhaps iced rhubarb parfait with ginger and rhubarb mousse, or hot banana soufflé with caramel sauce. The wine list is a compact edition of the usual Conran magnum opus. France is detailed and chosen with flair and other sources stand up well. Australian house red is £18 and around a dozen interesting options come by the glass from £4.

Chef: Geoffrey Smeddie **Proprietor:** Conran Restaurants Ltd **Open:** all week L 12 to 2.30 (Sun 3), Mon to Thur D 7 to 11 (Fri and Sat D 6.30 to 11) **Closed:** Dec 25, Jan 1 **Meals:** Set L £16 to £18.50, Set D £24 to £35 **Service:** 12.5% (optional), card slips closed **Cards:** Amex, Delta, Diners, Maestro, MasterCard, Visa **Details:** 59 seats. Private parties: 60 main room. Smoking in lounge only. Wheelchair access (also WC). Music. Air-conditioned

Gamba

225A West George Street, Glasgow G2 2ND
Tel: (0141) 572 0899
Website: www.gamba.co.uk

Cooking 3 | Seafood | £30–£82

'Gamba has become something of a Glasgow institution and has outlasted many of its more fashionable rivals,' noted one Scottish reporter. Its main claim to fame is fresh seafood served in uncomplicated, contemporary fashion, often with some Asian add-ons. Prices can seem high, but the kitchen generally delivers the goods: seared swordfish with chilli relish, rocket and Parmesan has plenty of bite and flavour, and grilled langoustines ('huge beasts, full of flavour') are doused with excellent herb and garlic oil. Away from the fish, there are limited alternatives like fillet of Angus beef with madeira, shiitake mushrooms and Puy lentils, or asparagus, blue cheese and apple risotto, while desserts might include rosemary and raspberry crème brûlée. The list of around 50 global wines kicks off with house selections from £14.95. Café Ostra (see entry, opposite) is under the same ownership.

Chef: Derek Marshall **Proprietors:** Derek Marshall and Alan Tompkins **Open:** Mon to Sat 12 to 2.30, 5 to 10.30 **Closed:** 25 and 26 Dec, 1 and 2 Jan **Meals:** alc (main courses £13 to £25). Set L and D 5 to 6 £15.95 (2 courses) to £17.95 **Service:** not inc, 10% for parties of 6 or more **Cards:** Amex, Delta, Maestro, MasterCard, Visa **Details:** 66 seats. Private parties: 66 main room. Vegetarian meals. No children under 14. No smoking before 2pm and 10pm. Music. No mobile phones. Air-conditioned

No. Sixteen

NEW ENTRY

16 Byres Road, Glasgow G11 5JY
Tel: (0141) 339 2544

Cooking 2 | Modern British | £25–£52

'The food, not the setting', is the point in this bijou, 'chastely furnished' venue, where elbow room is at a premium and private conversations are inadvisable. In the kitchen, Allan Heaney delivers nattily presented modern dishes perked up with modish sauces and dressings. Sweet seared scallops with smoked haddock and lemon oil are set off by a piquant, frothy chive purée, while baked halibut with toasted almond and red pepper couscous, tapenade and cumin sauce is full of contrasts. Meat alternatives might include soy-braised belly pork, or chump of lamb with balsamic-roast onions, Roquefort and pine-nut salad. Vegetables are simple but 'amazingly good', and it's worth finishing with zingy iced winter berry terrine. The well-chosen wine list has plenty of good-value drinking from £13.95.

Chef: Allan Heaney **Proprietors:** Margaret and Ronald Campbell **Open:** Mon to Sat 12 to 2.30, 5.30 to 10, Sun 12.30 to 3, 5.30 to 9 **Closed:** 2 weeks from 24 Dec **Meals:** alc (main courses £12 to £16.50). Set L and D Sun to Fri 5.30 to 6.30 £11.50 (2 courses) to £13.50 **Service:** not inc, card slips closed, 10% for parties of 8 or more **Cards:** Delta, Maestro, MasterCard, Visa **Details:** 40 seats. Private parties: 40 main room. Vegetarian meals. No smoking. No music. No mobile phones

Rococo

NEW ENTRY

202 West George Street, Glasgow G2 2NR
Tel: (0141) 221 5004
Website: www.restaurantrococo.co.uk

Cooking 3 | Modern European | £34–£71

In a semi-submerged basement a stroll from the city centre, a white-tiled floor, smart tables and dark brown leather upholstery, plus repro classical paintings, mirrors and wall-mounted abstracts in sea-blue glass, make an eye-catching setting for Mark Tamburrini's cooking. His style – fresh and light, with French and rustic Italian influences entwined – has produced a refreshing timbale of flaked salmon in lime mayonnaise, or a classic parfait of chicken liver and foie gras, with orange and raisin compote and a honey dressing. Forthright seasoning characterizes main dishes like seared monkfish with lyonnaise potatoes, spinach, and a sauce built around shallots and bacon. A supplement on the fixed-price menu buys roast fillet of Buccleuch beef with truffled green beans, cocotte potatoes and onion confit, all sauced with port. At inspection a gooey crème brûlée was appealingly spiked with lemon. Service is pin-sharp, and reliable names like Hugel, Torres and Antinori populate a stylish but pricey wine list topped by some very smart Bordeaux. House bottles from £17.95.

Chef: Mark Tamburrini **Proprietors:** Alan and Audrey Brown **Open:** all week 12 to 3, 5 to 10 (10.30 Fri/Sat) **Closed:** 1 Jan **Meals:** alc L (main courses £18.50 to £25.50). Set L £14 (2 courses) to £18, Set L Sun £20, pre-theatre D Mon to Thur 7 to 9.30, Fri to Sun 7 to 10.30 £14 (2 courses) to £18, Set D £29 (2 courses) to £36.50, Set D Sun £25 **Service:** not inc, 10% for parties of 8 or more **Cards:** Amex, Delta, Diners, Maestro, MasterCard, Visa **Details:** 70 seats. Private parties: 80 main room, 8 to 20 private rooms. Vegetarian meals. Children's helpings. No-smoking area. Music. Air-conditioned

Rogano

11 Exchange Place, Glasgow G46 6LT
Tel: (0141) 248 4055
Website: www.rogano.co.uk

Cooking 3 | Seafood | £33–£100

Fitted out at the same time and in the same Art Deco style as the *Queen Mary*, Rogano is reputedly Glasgow's oldest restaurant. It's certainly a grand dining room, with a slightly old-fashioned, formal air, and (with its attached café and oyster bar) has more than a touch of a Parisian brasserie about it. Known for its seafood, the kitchen takes few risks with the cooking of it – lemon sole is plainly grilled, halibut poached and served with Parmesan risotto – but starts with prime ingredients, mostly from the posher end of the spectrum: scallops, for instance, and lobster, either thermidor or grilled with béarnaise sauce. There's also an occasional non-fish dish, such as roast ostrich with red cabbage, or breast of guinea fowl with marmalade glaze and turnip purée. The restaurant's £16.50 set lunch looks its best value, and house wines start at £16, although they do not appear on the wine list.

Chef: Andrew Cummings **Proprietor:** Spirit Group **Open:** all week 12 to 2.30, 6.30 to 10.30 **Closed:** 25 Dec, 1 Jan **Meals:** alc (main courses £18.50 to £35). Set L £16.50. Bar and café menus available **Service:** 12.5% (optional), card slips closed **Cards:** Amex, Delta, Diners, Maestro, MasterCard, Visa **Details:** 65 seats. Private parties: 70 main room, 6 to 30 private rooms. Vegetarian meals. No smoking before 2pm L, 10pm D. Wheelchair access (not WC). No music. No mobile phones. Air-conditioned

78 St Vincent

78 St Vincent Street, Glasgow G2 5UB
Tel: (0141) 248 7878
Website: www.78stvincent.com

Cooking 1 | Modern Scottish | £27–£72

Originally the Phoenix Assurance Building, this stunning piece of Glasgow Belle Epoque makes a fine setting for a restaurant, recalling the *grand luxe* of marbled Parisian brasseries. Menu options look almost as expansive as the space itself, with breakfast served from 8.30 on weekday mornings, and plenty of up-to-the-minute global cooking on offer. Haggis, neeps and tatties with wholegrain mustard sauce makes a satisfyingly spicy starter, and prime Scottish beef fillet comes decked out with seared foie gras, truffled green beans and balsamic jus for those who really want to live it up. Finish with lemon and lime mousse, or pannacotta with intensely flavourful peppered strawberries. The carefully annotated wines are arranged alphabetically by country, with house selections at £13.95.

Chef: Ryan Napier **Proprietors:** Frederick and Julie Williams **Open:** all week 12 to 3, 5 to 10 (10.30 Fri and Sat) **Closed:** 1 Jan **Meals:** alc exc Sat D (main courses L £7.50 to £11, D £14 to £24.50). Set L and D 5 to 7 £12.50 (2 courses) to £15.50, Set D Sat £24.95 (2 courses) to £29.95 **Service:** not inc, 10% for parties of 6 or more **Cards:** Amex, Delta, Diners, Maestro, MasterCard, Visa **Details:** 100 seats. Private parties: 100 main room, 6 to 16 private rooms. Vegetarian meals. Children's helpings. No-smoking area. Wheelchair access (also WC). No music. No mobile phones

Stravaigin

28 Gibson Street, Glasgow G12 8NX
Tel: (0141) 334 2665
Website: www.stravaigin.com

Cooking 2 | Global | £24–£66

This bustling basement in studenty Hillhead now has comfortable dark leather banquettes and light wood tables. Global menus with plenty to catch the eye revolve around the tangy spicing beloved of ebullient youth. Pickled langoustines and scallop corals in noodle salad, served in a glass, make a sharply flavoured starter, while lamb chops glazed with muscovado and mustard are robustly flavoured, if outshouted by a searing chilli and mint salsa. Chargrilled Angus sirloin with roast squash and a gravy combining pesto, dried tomatoes and rosemary might be gentler. Home-made ice creams are winners, especially the fig version. A good-value wine list starts at £13.25

Chef: Daniel Blencowe **Proprietor:** Colin Clydesdale **Open:** Fri to Sun L 12 (12.30 Sun) to 2.30, Tue to Sun D 5 to 11 **Closed:** 25 Dec, 1 Jan **Meals:** alc (main courses £13.50 to £22.50). Set D 5 to 7 £11.95 (2 courses) to £14.95. Café bar menu available **Service:** not inc **Cards:** Amex, Delta, Diners, Maestro, MasterCard, Visa **Details:** 70 seats. Private parties: 70 main room. Vegetarian meals. Children's helpings. No smoking. Music. Air-conditioned

Stravaigin 2

8 Ruthven Lane, Glasgow G12 9BG
Tel: (0141) 334 7165
Website: www.stravaigin.com

Cooking 2 | Global | £24–£58

The younger sister of Colin Clydesdale's restaurants (see entry above) is a straightforward mews house conversion in the lively West End. Exposed pipes, white walls, slate tiles and pine tables are the backdrop to some ambitious modern cooking. A poor effort at a starter risotto at inspection was soon outshone by a vibrant Thai-style salad of crab, coconut and glass noodles with flavours of ginger, lime, caramel and chillied peanuts, while the true Scottish understanding of beef is evident in a huge, juicy, lustily flavoured steak of Angus sirloin served with butter-tossed mushrooms, truffle and shallot mash and a sauce of merlot. Home-made ice creams such as the pleasingly creamy, melting rum and raisin version get enthusiastic nods. A concise list of wines majors in southern Europe and the southern hemisphere, opening at £13.45.

Chef: Andrew Mitchell **Proprietor:** Colin Clydesdale **Open:** all week 12 (11 Sat and Sun) to 11 **Closed:** 25 Dec, 1 Jan **Meals:** alc (main courses £11 to £20). Set L and D 5 to 7 (6 Fri and Sat) £11.95 (2 courses) to £14.95 **Service:** not inc **Cards:** Amex, Delta, Diners, Maestro, MasterCard, Visa **Details:** 74 seats. Private parties: 30 main room. Vegetarian meals. Children's helpings. No smoking 12 to 2 and 5 to 10. Wheelchair access (also WC). Music. Air-conditioned

Ubiquitous Chip

12 Ashton Lane, Glasgow G12 8SJ
Tel: (0141) 334 5007
Website: www.ubiquitouschip.co.uk

Cooking 4 | Scottish | £40–£61

Set in a quaintly winding back lane in the West End, a short step from the Hunterian Museum, this Glasgow institution has stayed the course. Accounts agree that the place to be on a sunny day is out on the courtyard patio, with trailing greenery all around. The Chip has always ploughed a speculative culinary furrow, producing radically experimental food long before others had entered the field. Ian Brown maintains that tradition, with starters such as a sausage of Dumfries rabbit, pear and pistachio served with basil cabbage, and main courses that the uninitiated might misread as dialect poetry – viz. Scrabster-landed ling on clapshot, with chilli-roasted red pepper and crispy seaweed as accompaniments. The fine Scots produce that glistens through the menu like veins of quartz even extends to saddle of Perthshire wild boar, with crushed paprika potatoes, wilted spinach and Calvados vinaigrette. Desserts may come garnished with tuiles, such as a coconut one with blackcurrant burnt cream and liquorice ice cream. Staff are friendly and knowledgeable. There's a brasserie upstairs.

The wine list is strong on classics, and the selections from Bordeaux, Burgundy and Germany are handled with aplomb. There is a well-balanced Italian collection, and a good range of Rioja, but an imaginative line-up from Australia steals the show. House wines are £14.95.

Chef: Ian Brown **Proprietor:** Ronnie Clydesdale **Open:** all week 12 to 2.30 (12.30 to 3 Sun), 5.30 (6.30 Sun) to 11 **Meals:** Set L £22.80 (2 courses) to £28.65, Set D £33.80 (2 courses) to £38.95. Bar menu available noon to 7 **Service:** not inc **Cards:** Amex, Delta, Diners, Maestro, MasterCard, Visa **Details:** 125 seats. Private parties: 70 main room, 20 to 55 private rooms. Vegetarian meals. Children's helpings. Wheelchair access (also WC). No music. Air-conditioned

MAP 11 Glenlivet MORAY

Minmore House

AR

Glenlivet AB37 9DB
Tel: (01807) 590378

Personally run, stone-built country mansion in the heart of Glenlivet Crown Estate close to the Malt Whisky Trail. Set lunches and dinners (£25 to £35) are typified by roast red pepper and almond soup before grilled prawns glazed with a '14-herb butter sauce', then rack of Highland lamb with roast fennel, haricot beans and minted hollandaise, with a dessert like mango, passion-fruit and Grand Marnier soufflé. Open all week.

MAP 11 Gullane EAST LOTHIAN

Greywalls Hotel

Muirfield, Gullane EH31 2EF
Tel: (01620) 842144
Website: www.greywalls.co.uk

Cooking 3 | Modern British | £58–£70

Despite its name, Greywalls is a golden-stoned building of semi-circular construction, designed by Lutyens with gardens by Gertrude Jekyll, the design aristocracy of the fin-de-siècle. All is comfortable and inviting within, and it has been noted with stifled hurrahs that the dress code has been relaxed of late.

New chef David Williams has brought a gently applied touch of modernism to the fixed-price dinner menus of three courses plus coffee. Thus a single seared scallop arrives with asparagus and a curry velouté, and a seared fillet and braised brisket of Angus beef appears in the same main course in the company of grapes. Although combinations don't always seem to be the most felicitous, there is no doubting the technical skill of dishes such as a whole roast quail with cream-sauced mushrooms, or pork loin on fondant potato with over-abundant sweet apple purée. Apple strudel rolls were a good dessert at inspection, the accompanying crème brûlée even better, for all that they didn't seem to belong together. The wine list, racy limericks and all, plays to old-school strengths with oodles of well-cellared clarets and a good slate of Burgundy. But the house selection from £16.50 takes a global view and the US leads some interesting New World listings.

Chef: David Williams **Proprietor:** Giles Weaver **Open:** all week, D only 7.30 to 9 **Closed:** Nov to Mar **Meals:** Set D £45 **Service:** not inc, card slips closed **Cards:** Amex, Delta, Maestro, MasterCard, Visa **Details:** 50 seats. Private parties: 40 main room, 2 to 20 private rooms. Car park. Vegetarian meals. No smoking. Wheelchair access(also WC). No music **Accommodation:** 23 rooms, all with bath/shower. TV. Phone. B&B £135 to £270. Rooms for disabled. Baby facilities

La Potinière

34 Main Street, Gullane EH31 2AA
Tel: (01620) 843214
Website: www.la-potiniere.co.uk

Cooking 6 | Modern British | £29–£58

A large, two-tone dining-room in terracotta and white, a net-curtained former shop window at the front, one rug on a wooden floor, half a dozen tables: this is as straightforward as catering establishments get. Within these simple surroundings, Mary Runciman and Keith Marley have made a resounding success of a venue that had been a Guide stalwart under previous ownership for many years.

The four-course dinner menu offers a pair of choices for starter and main course, with a fixed second course intervening, and a choice of two desserts or cheese, as well as coffee, to finish. Memorable results are obtained from often quite modest means: one starter has been a tartlet of Isle of Mull Cheddar, its topping as loosely textured as scrambled egg, served with exemplary red onion marmalade and rocket. A tripartite terrine of duck – confit, roast and foie gras – is unexpectedly substantial and well set off by a spoonful of sweet-spiced cherry compote. The intermediate course may well be a soup, such as a wondrously concentrated essence of smoked salmon topped with chopped fennel and crème fraîche, before the main business brings on steamed halibut with a spring vegetable brunoise and Pernod-scented sauce, the fish exactly timed, and with crushed potatoes adding another texture. A meat alternative could be roast venison fillet with dauphinois potatoes and juices spiked with damson gin, before dessert presents three ways with apple, or a parfait of white chocolate, lemon and cinnamon. Fine petits fours come with coffee, breads are highly praised, and there is the full panoply of extras too, with an appetiser and pre-dessert each appearing in a shot glass. A relatively brief wine list has plenty of classical French stuff and opens with house Spanish and Argentinian at £15.50, or £3 a glass.

Chefs: Mary Runciman and Keith Marley **Proprietor:** Mary Runciman **Open:** Wed to Sun 12.30 to 2, 7 to 9 **Closed:** 2 to 3 weeks Jan, Sun D Oct to Mar, Christmas, bank hol Mon **Meals:** Set L £16.50 (2 courses) to £19, Set D £36.50 **Service:** not inc, card slips closed **Cards:** Maestro, MasterCard, Visa **Details:** 28 seats. Private parties: 28 main room. Car park. Children's helpings. No smoking. Wheelchair access (also WC). No music. No mobile phones

MAP 11 **Inverkeilor** ANGUS

Gordon's

32 Main Street, Inverkeilor DD11 5RN
Tel: (01241) 830364
Website: www.gordonsrestaurant.co.uk

Cooking 5 | Modern Scottish | £31–£58

The A92 bypasses the village of Inverkeilor, between Arbroath and Montrose, so tranquillity reigns at Gordon and Maria Watson's sympathetically run restaurant-with-rooms. The décor in sober rust-brown, cream and black makes a restrained backdrop for some fairly dazzling culinary pyrotechnics.

A home-made wholemeal baguette flavoured with walnut and rosemary kicked things off in fine style at an autumn lunch. Memorable dishes then took in fennel-scented halibut with salmon and leek risotto and chive beurre blanc, which delivered waves of gustatory satisfaction, the fish impressively timed, the texture of the rice spot-on, and an equally successful main course of tenderly seared Perthshire venison with red cabbage compote and a sprinkling of wild mushrooms. A streak of well-wrought inventiveness brings on starters such as scallops teamed with cauliflower pannacotta and white truffle dressing, while the desserts might pair best Valrhona chocolate in a meltingly-centred soufflé pudding with accompanying Horlicks ice cream. Leave a little space for the truffles and Scottish tablet that come with coffee. Breakfasts too are exquisite. The fairly priced wine list is arranged by grape variety and covers all the usual geographic bases; house wines are £11.95.

Chefs: Gordon and Garry Watson **Proprietors:** Gordon and Maria Watson **Open:** Wed to Fri and Sun L 12 to 1.45, Tue to Sat D 7 to 9 **Meals:** Set L £22, Set D £38 **Service:** not inc, card slips closed **Cards:** Delta, Maestro, MasterCard, Visa **Details:** 24 seats. Private parties: 20 main room. Car park. Vegetarian meals. No smoking. Wheelchair access (not WC). No music. No mobile phones **Accommodation:** 3 rooms, 2 with bath/shower. TV. B&B £55 to £90. No children under 6

MAP 11 **Inverness** HIGHLAND

Culloden House Hotel, Adams Dining Room

Culloden, Inverness IV2 7BZ
Tel: (01463) 790461
Website: www.cullodenhouse.co.uk

Cooking 2 | International | £37–£63

One visitor to this opulent Palladian mansion thought it was 'quite entertaining to sit in a drawing room with a 24-foot ceiling crowned with Adam plasterwork while you study the menu'. Fixed-price dinners run to four courses, perhaps opening with marinated West Coast scallops wrapped in Loch Fyne smoked salmon encased in filo pastry, before a bowl of creamy white onion soup or refreshing fennel, orange and pumpkin seed salad. Steamed fillet of halibut with smoked haddock mousse on creamed spinach has also been given a vote of confidence, or you might opt for collops of Scottish beef with horseradish rösti and foie gras mousse. Vanilla parfait with passion-fruit sorbet is 'out of this world' when it comes to desserts. The wine list is lengthy and varied, but there's precious little below £25.

Chef: Mike Simpson **Proprietor:** Edward Cunningham **Open:** all week 12.30 to 2, 7 to 9 **Closed:** Christmas **Meals:** alc L (main courses £12.50 to £17). Set D £33 to £38 **Service:** 10% (optional), card slips closed **Cards:** Amex, Delta, Diners, Maestro, MasterCard, Visa **Details:** 60 seats. Private parties: 40 main room, 2 to 24 private rooms. Car park. Vegetarian meals. Children's helpings. No children under 10. No smoking. No music. No mobile phones **Accommodation:** 28 rooms, all with bath/shower. TV. Phone. B&B £85 to £290. No children under 10. Baby facilities

Dunain Park AR

Inverness IV3 8JN
Tel: (01463) 230512

The Nicolls all pull together in this secluded grey-stone Georgian mansion, which has been in the family for some 20 years. Dinner runs to four courses, opening with a soup (curried parsnip, for example) before starters like smoked haddock rarebit (£7). Main courses (£17) range from glazed loin of spiced pork with apple and black pudding to red mullet fillet on cod mousseline with Puy lentil ratatouille. Desserts (£7) are from the buffet. Lengthy international wine list from £15.50. Open all week D only.

Chef: Loic Lefebvre **Proprietor:** Barry Larsen **Open:** Tue to Sun 12 to 2.30, 7 to 9.30 **Meals:** alc L (main courses £8 to £14). Set L £14 (2 courses), Set D £34 (2 courses) to £62 (inc wine) **Service:** not inc, card slips closed, 12.5% for parties of 6 or more **Cards:** Amex, Diners, Maestro, MasterCard, Visa **Details:** 45 seats. 16 seats outside. Private parties: 50 main room, 8 to 70 private rooms. Car park. Vegetarian meals. Children's helpings. No smoking. Wheelchair access (not WC). Music. No mobile phones **Accommodation:** 30 rooms, all with bath/shower. TV. Phone. B&B £95 to £170. Rooms for disabled. Fishing

Glenmoriston Town House

NEW ENTRY

20 Ness Bank, Inverness IV2 4SF
Tel: (01463) 223777
Website: www.glenmoristontownhouse.com

Cooking 4 | Modern French | £28–£88

As seen on TV (Gordon Ramsay's Kitchen Nightmares, second series), this three-storey, greystone hotel is on a leafy street on the east bank of the Ness. A couple of alternative lighting features and some framed ink-wash pictures (the style of which perhaps gives the restaurant its name – Abstract) draw the eye in an otherwise minimal decorative scheme.

French chef Loic Lefebvre applies modern French technique to mostly local Highland ingredients – which is one way of celebrating the Auld Alliance – and our inspection visit found a kitchen clearly growing in confidence. Foie gras raviolo is fashioned of delicate pasta and partnered by asparagus, pancetta and herbs, while smooth chickpea purée and a crustacean bouillon are the medium for sweet West Coast scallops. Meats are of impeccable provenance, with milk-fed local lamb getting the palm. It involved sections of leg, rack and shoulder, together with a mini skewer of heart, liver and kidney, well accompanied by stuffed baby artichoke and a sage and basil jus. Fish options have included bravely slow-cooked John Dory in seaweed butter with local clams and a watercress coulis. Cheeses are tiny portions of mostly French specimens in tiptop condition from a trolley, or you might opt for banana and chocolate mille-feuille with hazelnut ice cream. France is also the predominant focus of the wine list, with many highfalutin choices at stiffish prices. The baseline is £14.50 for a Languedoc Sauvignon, and there are eight reds and whites by the glass from £5.60.

Restaurant Chez Christophe

16 Ardross Street, Inverness IV3 5NS
Tel: (01463) 717126
Website: www.chezchristophe.co.uk

Cooking 4 | Modern French | £43–£65

High ambitions in the unlikely setting of an Inverness guesthouse characterise this intimate restaurant owned and run by Frenchman Christophe Magie and his Scottish wife. He mans the stoves, she is an efficient, friendly hostess. M. Magie's cooking is a sophisticated take on 'new and traditional French cuisine' built around Scottish produce, and he intersperses little extras into his fixed-price dinners, beginning with a complimentary 'assiette de bouche a oreilles'. Fish/meat combos are a favourite device, as in a terrine of roast monkfish, mango, celeriac and ham, or a main-course tarte Tatin of roast hand-dived scallops with duck confit and root vegetables, although monomaniac meat-eaters might fancy, say, cannon of lamb with a casserole of white cocoa beans and garlicky roasting jus. A fitting finale might be prune and Armagnac tart, which one correspondent rates among his 'top ten puddings'. The wine list is undiluted French, with house Côtes de Gascogne at £16.

Chef: Christophe Magie **Proprietors:** Christophe and Carol Magie **Open:** Tue to Sat D 7 to 9 **Closed:** Christmas, 1 Jan **Meals:** Set D £23.95 (2 courses) to £39.50 (5 courses, whole table only) **Service:** not inc **Cards:** Delta, Maestro, MasterCard, Visa **Details:** 16 seats. Private parties: 14 main room, 6 to 14 private rooms. No children under 12. Wheelchair access (also WC). Music. No mobile phones

Rocpool

1 Ness Walk, Inverness IV3 5NE
Tel: (01463) 717274

Cooking 3 | Modern European | £26–£56

Rocpool, named after a famed Sydney restaurant, has a riverside setting in a street of Victorian houses. It's a thoroughly contemporary affair, stylish yet relaxed, with pale wood-block flooring, dark blue banquettes and smartly dressed tables, while mirrors give the narrow room – with a tapas bar on a lower level at the far end – an illusion of space. Steven Devlin cooks a wide range of accomplished dishes with a fashionably modern-European accent that admirably suits the surroundings but shows assured restraint – 'there's no experimentation for its own sake'. Think linguine with seared king prawns, pancetta, garlic and chilli, then grilled lamb cutlets with spiced couscous and mint salsa, followed by passion-fruit pavlova with Chantilly cream. Simpler early-evening and lunch menus complement the carte. Service is friendly and efficient, while the global wine list (with a penchant for Italy) offers a dozen by the glass and house South African at £12.95.

Chef: Steven Devlin **Proprietors:** Adrian Pieraccini and Steven Devlin **Open:** Mon to Sat 12 to 2.30, 5.45 to 10 **Closed:** 25 Dec, 1 Jan **Meals:** alc (main courses L £8 to £10, D £9 to £18). Set L £7.95 (2 courses), Set D Mon to Fri 5.45 to 6.45 £9.95 (2 courses) **Service:** not inc **Cards:** Amex, Delta, Diners, Maestro, MasterCard, Visa **Details:** 55 seats. Private parties: 55 main room. Vegetarian meals. Children's helpings. No smoking while others eat. Wheelchair access (also WC). Music. Air-conditioned

MAP 11 Killiecrankie PERTHSHIRE & KINROSS

Killiecrankie House Hotel

Killiecrankie PH16 5LG
Tel: (01796) 473220
Website: www.killiecrankiehotel.co.uk

Cooking 3 | Scottish/Global | £42–£50

Designed as a private residence for a local minister in 1840, this hotel is not far from the site of the Battle of Killiecrankie (a Jacobite victory in 1689). With a rustic, wood-panelled bar, a conservatory for informal bar meals, and a more formal dining room, 'it is a country retreat of character with no illusions of grandeur'. Even better, the short, well-judged menu fulfils its promise, taking native produce as a starting point: scallops from the West Coast (in a puff-pastry case with pesto sauce), venison from the Highlands (with broccoli, cauliflower, dauphinois potatoes and a redcurrant and port jus), and local Aberdeen Angus beef, although the barramundi on a spring menu doubtless came from further afield. Dinner is a five-course affair, incorporating a cheese course and desserts such as dark-chocolate mousse flan with red syrup and strawberries. Bar food is also available for lunch and dinner.

Tim Waters' wine-trade experience translates into a substantial list that celebrates quality, affordable bottles from around the globe: witness Etienne Pochon's Crozes-Hermitage at £20.90 or Neil Ellis Groenekloof Sauvignon Blanc from South Africa at £21.90. There's top Bordeaux at fair prices too and a wealth of recommendations for matching wine and food.

Chef: Mark Easton **Proprietors:** Tim and Maillie Waters **Open:** all week D only 6 to 8.30 **Closed:** Jan to Easter **Meals:** Set D £25 (2 courses) to £37. Bar L and D menu available **Service:** not inc, card slips closed **Cards:** Delta, Maestro, MasterCard, Visa **Details:** 32 seats. Private parties: 16 main room, 6 to 12 private rooms. Car park. Vegetarian meals. Children's helpings; no children under 9. No smoking. Wheelchair access (not WC). No music. No mobile phones **Accommodation:** 10 rooms, all with bath/shower. TV. Phone. D,B&B £79 to £198. Rooms for disabled

MAP 11 Kingussie HIGHLAND

The Cross

Tweed Mill Brae, Ardbroilach Road, Kingussie PH21 1LB
Tel: (01540) 661166
Website: www.thecross.co.uk

Cooking 5 | Modern British | £29–£46

Katie and David Young took over this homely restaurant-with-rooms in 2003, and have maintained its longstanding reputation for warmth and good food. Tables are smartly togged up, with white damask, Villeroy and Boch plates and posies, and there are discreet watercolours on the walls.

The format is a fixed-price dinner menu of three courses plus coffee, with an appetiser cup of soup to start, perhaps Cullen skink with a swirl of cream if you're in luck. An inspection visit confirmed the confidence and subtle sense of adventure in the cooking, serving home-smoked Gressingham duck with spiced mango chutney and couscous as one possible starter, or setting off the molten richness of a goats' cheese soufflé with pesto for another. Main courses try out some unusual fish preparations, perhaps teaming John Dory with tomato, cardamom, braised chicory and roasted new potatoes. Meats, meanwhile, are top-notch. Salt-crusted chicken with an accomplished risotto of asparagus and Parmesan and a little wilted spinach was a hit on a May evening, while rack of Shetland salt-marsh lamb was pink, tender and altogether irreproachable, accompanied classically by ratatouille and dauphinoise. Fine judgment of sugar levels characterised a chocolate espresso cake dessert with caffè latte cream. Plenty more chocolate – as well as sweet Scots tablet – comes with the coffee.

The wine list is based on personal preferences and is full of affordable ways to enjoy fine wines. Bordeaux's best second wines lead the charge from France and New World contributions include bottles from Jackson Estate at very reasonable prices. A short list – house wines in effect – opens at £17.50.

Chefs: Becca Henderson and David Young **Proprietors:** David and Katie Young **Open:** Tue to Sat D only 7 to 8.30 **Closed:** Dec 25, Jan **Meals:** Set D £28.50 to £38.50 **Service:** net prices, card slips closed **Cards:** Amex, Delta, Maestro, MasterCard, Visa **Details:** 20 seats. Private parties: 24 main room. Car park. No smoking. Wheelchair access (also WC). No music. No mobile phones **Accommodation:** 8 rooms, all with bath/shower. TV. Phone. D,B&B £100 to £250

MAP 11 Largoward FIFE

Inn at Lathones

By Largoward, St Andrews KY9 1JE
Tel: (01334) 840494
Website: www.theinn.co.uk

Cooking 2 | Modern European | £30–£57

The Inn is a largely single-storeyed complex on the A915 not far from St Andrews. Clean white interiors with lowish ceilings and downlighters indicate that the emphasis is very much on the cooking, which might well turn up on square glass plates. Pedigree meats are treated with respect, so that a serving of 'moist and flavourful' braised belly pork with Spanish accompaniments of chorizo, morcilla, beans and cabbage is 'a success in all departments'. First courses at inspection were a little shy on the palate, although a terrine of scallop and haddock wrapped in nori with a dill dressing was well enough constructed. Three riffs on crème brûlée – lemon and raspberry, white chocolate and (best of all) liquorice and vanilla – make for an interesting comparative tasting. Staff are 'pleasant, helpful and confident'. The wine list has a lot to offer between the £12.50 baseline and £25, perhaps Life from a Stone Sauvignon from South Africa (£19) or Uruguayan Cabernet Franc (£15.50). Interesting names fill the middle ground and a spread of superstar wines at high prices tops things off.

Chef: Martin Avey **Proprietor:** Nick White **Open:** all week; 12 to 2.30, 6 to 9.30 **Closed:** Dec 25 and 26, Jan 3 to 16 **Meals:** alc (main courses £10.50 to £19). Set L £11.50 to £15.50 **Service:** not inc **Cards:** Amex, Delta, Diners, Maestro, MasterCard, Visa **Details:** 34 seats. Private parties: 50 main room, 10 to 40 private rooms. Car park. Vegetarian meals. Children's helpings. Wheelchair access (not WC). Music. No mobile phones **Accommodation:** 13 rooms, all with bath/shower. TV. Phone. B&B £100 to £200. Rooms for disabled. Baby facilities

MAP 11 Linlithgow WEST LOTHIAN

Champany Inn

Champany Corner, Linlithgow EH49 7LU
Tel: (01506) 834532
Website: www.champany.com

Cooking 4 | Scottish | £37–£95

For more than two decades this has been a shrine to Scottish beef, thanks to Clive and Anne Davidson's serious allegiance to the subject. Their cluster of old farm buildings has developed over the years and now includes a bar in the hayloft, an all-week Chop and Ale House and a grandly appointed octagonal restaurant; the Davidsons are also planning to open a shop on the site, where customers can buy their unrivalled raw materials and wines to take home.

Carcasses are treated with due respect (three weeks hanging in an ionised chill room is the norm), and the cooking is done on specially designed stoves. Choose from hunks of prime Aberdeen Angus sirloin, ribeye, porterhouse or whatever (steaks can be butchered to your requirements) and decide if you want a sauce (Stilton and port, for example). Quality is second to none, but it comes at a price. Alternatives to steak appear in the shape of double lamb chops, whole lobsters, and even deep-fried cod. Start with oysters, hot-smoked salmon (cured in the

Davidsons' own 'smokepot'), or West Coast scallops with asparagus hollandaise, and finish with, say, vanilla crème brûlée. Like the steaks, the wine list is sizeable and of the finest quality, but at a price. Classical France is given lavish attention, but of all the countries South Africa and Spain stand out in comparison with other lists of similar ambition. Own-label white is £14.50, and a dozen are proffered by the glass.

Chefs: Clive Davidson, David Gibson and Kevin Hope **Proprietors:** Clive and Anne Davidson **Open:** Mon to Fri L 12.30 to 2, Mon to Sat D 7 to 10 **Closed:** 25 and 26 Dec, 1 and 2 Jan **Meals:** alc (main courses £17.50 to £35.50). Set L £16.75 (2 courses). Bistro menu available **Service:** 10%, card slips closed **Cards:** Amex, Diners, Maestro, MasterCard, Visa **Details:** 50 seats. 20 seats outside. Private parties: 50 main room, 6 to 30 private rooms. Car park. No children under 8. Wheelchair access (also WC). No music **Accommodation:** 16 rooms, all with bath/shower. TV. Phone. B&B £95 to £125. Rooms for disabled

MAP 11 Lochinver HIGHLAND

Albannach

Baddidarach, Lochinver IV27 4LP
Tel: (01571) 844407
Website: www.thealbannach.co.uk

Cooking 6 | Modern Scottish | £57–£68

Colin Craig and Lesley Crosfield have been running this tall, nineteenth-century house for sixteen years, and their unobtrusive professionalism and hard work shows, above all, in the five-course, no-choice dinners cooked with restraint and skill. There has always been a line of invention in the menus, as well as a sense of season: warm tartlet of crab with croft leaves and vine tomato chutney, then aubergine terrine with red pepper dressing, and roast saddle of wild roe deer on crushed beetroot, with potato and thyme galette, truffled squash and game port sauce. Lesley Crosfield proudly champions local produce, whether it is seafood, meat or vegetables. Seafood might be hand-dived Lochinver scallops teamed with roast monkfish tails and served with saffron and seaweed rice, while lamb and beef come from Moray pastures, and bread and oatcakes are made on the premises. Desserts such as chocolate tartlet with orange pannacotta and peaches poached in Sauternes, or lime torte with orange and ginger sauce and berry fruit basket are preceded by Scottish and French cheeses, and followed by petits fours.

The wines, chosen with assurance, are mature bottles at fair prices. All countries have much of interest, but France is the strongest suit. Bottles start at £13, and there is also an impressive list of halves.

Chefs/Proprietors: Colin Craig and Lesley Crosfield **Open:** Tue to Sun D only 8pm (1 sitting) **Closed:** Mid Nov to Mid Mar **Meals:** Set D £45 **Service:** not inc **Cards:** Maestro, MasterCard, Visa **Details:** 16 seats. Private parties: 20 main room. Car park. No children under 12. No smoking. No music. No mobile phones **Accommodation:** 5 rooms, all with bath/shower. Phone. D,B&B £110 to £250. No children under 12

MAP 11 Melrose BORDERS

Burt's Hotel AR

Market Square, Melrose TD6 9PL
Tel: (01896) 822285

Owned and run by the Henderson family for more than three decades, this hotel is very much at the heart of town life. Fixed-price dinners in the restaurant (three courses £31.75) run along the lines of home-made duck sausage with poached apricots and orange sauce, then mixed seafood grill with saffron pasta and tiger prawn fumet, before iced coffee mousse with Balmoral shortbread. A separate bar menu is available. House wine £12.95. Open all week. New chef: reports please.

MAP 11 Moffat DUMFRIES & GALLOWAY

Limetree

High Street, Moffat DG10 9HG
Tel: (01683) 221654
Website: www.limetree-restaurant.co.uk

Cooking 2 | Modern British | £23–£38

Standing at the north end of Moffat's High Street, a bare couple of miles off the A74, the Limetree makes an ideal waypoint for motorway-floggers seeking civilised sustenance. Its simple set-price meals are along the lines of smoked haddock and bacon risotto, followed by roast rump of lamb, and then chocolate St Emilion. Prime materials have included venison and sea bass, while modern and imaginative dishes run to grilled, spiced belly pork with carrot and white radish pickle, soy and coriander, and slow-roast duck breast teamed with sage roast potatoes, chestnuts, apple and thyme. 'Gracious, unobtrusive, attentive and unhurried' service is everything most people would ask. The wine list is modest but fairly priced, starting at £11.95 and with eight by the glass from £3.25.

Chef: Matt Seddon **Proprietors:** Matt and Artemis Seddon **Open:** Sun L 12.30 to 2.30, Tue to Sat D 6.30 to 9 **Closed:** 2 weeks Oct **Meals:** Set L £13.50 (2 courses) to £16.75, Set D £17 (2 courses) to £21 **Service:** not inc, card slips closed **Cards:** Delta, Maestro, MasterCard, Visa **Details:** 25 seats. Private parties: 25 main room. Children's helpings. No smoking. Wheelchair access (not WC). Music. No mobile phones

Well View

Ballplay Road, Moffat DG10 9JU
Tel: (01683) 220184
Website: www.wellview.co.uk

Cooking 4 | Franco-Scottish | £23–£44

Well View is a peaceful Victorian villa, its name reflecting the popularity of Moffat as a spa town in the nineteenth century. The feel inside is of a superior B&B, with pretty floral curtains and striking flower arrangements setting the tone in the dining room, where guests sit together at one long, communal table. John Schuckardt oversees front-of-house operations with smooth panache and impeccably 'correct' manners, while his wife Janet and daughter Lina prepare the no-choice-until-pudding menu, their style characterised by fairly traditional dishes enhanced by imaginative modern touches and cooked with some flair. A typical dinner might commence with a smooth, well-balanced cream of tomato soup given bite with the addition of harissa, followed by Thai smoked salmon with melon and tarragon dressing, before a main course of Aberdeen Angus beef fillet on roasted root vegetables with red-wine sauce and dauphinois potatoes. A selection of fine cheeses comes next, then a choice perhaps of crème brûlée, a fruity, spicy panettone bread-and-butter pudding, or baked ginger cheesecake. The wine list has been carefully compiled, with no excessive mark-ups. Prices start at £14.

Chefs: Janet Schuckardt and Lina Schuckardt **Proprietors:** Janet and John Schuckardt **Open:** Sun L 12.30 (1 sitting), all week D 7.30 (1 sitting) **Meals:** Set L Sun £16, Set D £30 **Service:** none, card slips closed **Cards:** Amex, Delta, Maestro, MasterCard, Visa **Details:** 16 seats. Private parties: 10 main room, 6 to 10 private rooms. Car park. No children under 8 at D. No smoking. No music. No mobile phones **Accommodation:** 3 rooms, all with bath/shower. TV. B&B £70 to £110.

MAP 11 Muir of Ord HIGHLAND

Dower House

Highfield, Muir of Ord IV6 7XN
Tel: (01463) 870090
Website: www.thedowerhouse.co.uk

Cooking 2 | Modern British | £51–£61

Converted from a thatched farmhouse in the early 1800s, and later extended over the years, this low building in cottage ornée style has been Robyn and Mena Aitchison's home-from-home since 1989. After browsing the evening's menu (no choice for the first two courses) over a drink in the drawing room, you are ushered to your table for eight. Proceedings might begin with beetroot risotto, before a darne of halibut with bean broth and garlic mayonnaise, or – on another night – a salad of sautéed John Dory with orange and basil, then fillet of beef with herb relish. To finish, choose between carefully nurtured Scottish cheeses and a dessert like peaches baked in marsala. It is all very straightforward, a touch formal and exactly what you might expect. A serviceable list of sound wines kicks off with house French at £17.

Chef: Robyn Aitchison **Proprietors:** Robyn and Mena Aitchison **Open:** all week D only 8 to 9.30 (L by arrangement) **Closed:** 25 and 26 Dec **Meals:** Set D £38 **Service:** not inc, card slips closed **Cards:** Delta, Maestro, MasterCard, Visa **Details:** 26 seats. 6 seats outside. Private parties: 28 main room. Car park. Children's helpings. No children under 5. No smoking. Wheelchair access (also WC). No music. No mobile phones **Accommodation:** 5 rooms, all with bath/shower. TV. Phone. B&B £65 to £155. Rooms for disabled. Baby facilities

MAP 11 Newton Stewart DUMFRIES & GALLOWAY

Kirroughtree House AR

Newton Stewart DG8 6AN
Tel: (01671) 402141

Imposing country-house hotel with a 'modernised baronial feel' to comfortable, spacious rooms. Fixed-price four-course dinners (£32.50) take account of Scottish produce, including seafood, Kirroughtree venison, and 'well-kept' farmhouse cheeses. Expect buffalo mozzarella with tomato and basil oil, followed by cream of pumpkin soup, then corn-fed chicken breast with Arran mustard mash and Albufeira sauce, rounded off by pear sablé with Kirsch sabayon and melba sauce. Extensive wine list opens at £15.75. Open all week.

MAP 11 Oban ARGYLL & BUTE

Ee-Usk

North Pier, Oban PA34 5QD
Tel: (01631) 565666
Email: eeusk.fishcafe@virgin.net

Cooking 1 | Seafood | £27–£68

At the end of the pier, this bright, modern venue maximises the view: large plate-glass windows look across Oban harbour and the sea, and bobbing fishing boats add to the sense of atmosphere. Given the restaurant's location, it is perhaps no surprise that fish has the most important role to play on the menu. Local scallops, crab, lobster and creel-caught langoustines are likely to make their appearance, the latter perhaps as a main course with chilli and ginger or a cocktail sauce. A simple plate of locally smoked salmon has been praised, and simplicity is also a feature of a 'beautifully cooked' main-course halibut with a creamy leek sauce. Crème brûlée is a good way to finish. House wine is £13.50.

Chef: Marianne MacDonald **Proprietors:** Alan and Callum Macleod **Open:** all week 12 to 3, 6 to 10 (9 Nov to Mar) **Meals:** alc (main courses £9 to £29.50) **Service:** not inc **Cards:** Delta, Maestro, MasterCard, Visa **Details:** 108 seats. 24 seats outside. Private parties: 18 to 28 private rooms. Children's helpings. No children under 8 at D. No smoking. Wheelchair access (also WC). Music

Waterfront AR

1 The Railway Pier, Oban PA34 4LW
Tel: (01631) 563110

Fish and seafood specialist a few steps from the harbour. The boats might bring pollack, hake, skate, mackerel or wild sea trout, while regular items include Inverawe smoked salmon and langoustine tails (£8.50), followed by cod fillet in a tomato and olive crust on caper mash (£14). Fillet steak caters for carnivores, and desserts (£4.25) take in familiar sticky toffee pudding and crème brûlée. Separate lunchtime and early-evening menu. Short wine list from £12.10. Open all week.

MAP 11 Peat Inn FIFE

Peat Inn

Peat Inn KY15 5LH
Tel: (01334) 840206
Website: www.thepeatinn.co.uk

Cooking 5 | Scottish | £38–£80

A century-old photograph of this now white-washed, stone-built, former coaching inn at a crossroads in the centre of the village adorns the menu cover. It establishes the place's history, a history to which the Wilsons can justifiably feel they have contributed, having been running the place as a restaurant-with-rooms since the early 1970s.

Two fixed-price menus – one of three courses, the other of half a dozen – supplement the main carte. The cooking is perceptibly modern, while keeping its feet on the ground; outlandish combinations are eschewed in favour of the authority conferred by good materials. Venison offal (liver and kidney) are served on onion confit in a rich red-wine sauce to make a robust opener, or there are seafood options such as a salad of kiln-smoked salmon with langoustines in citrus dressing. For mains, monkfish may come in its now familiar wrapping of Parma ham, with tagliatelle and herbed velouté, while a take on cassoulet involves a convocation of lamb, pork and duck with flageolets. The dessert list may entice with the likes of nougat glace with passion-fruit sorbet, or a little pot of chocolate with rosemary shortbread. It has been noted that the youngish service could do with a little more drilling.

A profound knowledge of French wines lies behind the rather special wine list. It wears its seriousness lightly, so expect clear, unpretentious guidance where snobbery and obfuscation might be the norm. Each region is joined by top-notch global counterparts, and half-bottles abound. Prices, from £16, are very fair for the quality.

Chefs: David Wilson and Richard Turner **Proprietors:** David and Patricia Wilson **Open:** Tue to Sat 12.30 for 1, 7 to 9.30 **Closed:** 25 Dec, 1 Jan **Meals:** alc (main courses £16.50 to £24). Set L £22, Set D £32 to £48 **Service:** not inc, card slips closed **Cards:** Amex, Delta, Maestro, MasterCard, Visa **Details:** 48 seats. Private parties: 24 main room, 12 private room. Car park. Vegetarian meals. Children's helpings. No smoking. Wheelchair access (also WC). No music. No mobile phones **Accommodation:** 8 rooms, all with bath/shower. TV. Phone. B&B £95 to £175. Rooms for disabled

MAP 11 **Perth** PERTHSHIRE & KINROSS

Let's Eat

77 Kinnoull Street, Perth PH1 5EZ
Tel: (01738) 643377
Website: www.letseatperth.co.uk

Cooking 3 | Modern European | £27–£48

'Hard to believe that we are now in our tenth year,' writes Tony Heath of his popular bistro/restaurant. Endorsements this year have noticed the hospitality and the ability to make people feel relaxed quickly. Despite an occasional interloper, such as tiger prawns with a classic seafood dressing, the focus is firmly on native materials in the form of locally landed sea bass or lightly blackened fillet of Stornoway salmon served with herb-crushed tomatoes and tomato, olive oil and saffron sauce. Fish is the main preoccupation and the slate of fishy specials should not be ignored, although tenderloin of lamb with twice-cooked confit of shoulder, braised white beans, potato gratin and rosemary jus, or fillet of Scotch beef with a madeira and red wine jus show meat is given due attention. Finish perhaps with steamed ginger pudding with vanilla sauce and rhubarb ice cream, and drink from a serviceable and sensibly priced wine list that starts with Chilean red and white at £11.50.

Chefs: Tony Heath, Lewis Pringle and Steven McPhee **Proprietors:** Tony Heath and Shona Drysdale **Open:** Tue to Sat 12 to 2, 6.30 to 9.45 **Closed:** 25 and 26 Dec, 1 and 2 Jan, 2 weeks Jan, 2 weeks Jul **Meals:** alc (main courses L £9 to £12, D £10 to £18.50) **Service:** not inc, card slips closed **Cards:** Amex, Delta, Maestro, MasterCard, Visa **Details:** 65 seats. Private parties: 70 main room. Vegetarian meals. Children's helpings. No smoking. Wheelchair access (also WC). Music

63 Tay Street

63 Tay Street, Perth PH2 8NN
Tel: (01738) 441451
Website: www.63taystreet.co.uk

Cooking 4 | Modern Scottish | £30–£47

The Wares' minimally decorated, neighbourhood-style restaurant does pull in the local crowds. The bright, airy dining room on the embankment is set to a backdrop of the river Tay and slopes of the Kinnoull Hills. Cool white walls and wooden floors are offset by red-upholstered chairs and lively paintings that give the small room a modern edge. Jeremy's sensibly compact and clearly priced menus (one-priced starters, likewise mains and desserts) have a contemporary focus underpinned by classical technique and a reliance on quality produce and simplicity. The abundant Scottish larder provides plentiful local game (perhaps a haunch of venison served with braised red cabbage, a potato and olive cake, and red wine jus) or Scottish seafood (seared Skye scallops partnered by an oyster beignet, red wine risotto and herb oil). And you could start with warm duck and black pudding salad, or chicken liver and foie gras parfait, and end on triple chocolate terrine with chocolate ice cream. Good breads, friendly and efficient service with a formal edge (napkins placed on laps), and a characterful international mix of wines arranged by style, with eight house wines from £11.25 also available by the glass.

Chef: Jeremy Wares **Proprietors:** Shona and Jeremy Wares **Open:** Tue to Sat 12 to 2, 6.30 to 9 **Closed:** 2 weeks Christmas, last week Jun, first week July **Meals:** alc (main courses L £9.50, D £15.50) **Service:** not inc, card slips closed **Cards:** Amex, Delta, Maestro, MasterCard, Visa **Details:** 34 seats. Private parties: 34 main room. Vegetarian meals. No smoking. Wheelchair access (also WC). No music

MAP 11 **Plockton** HIGHLAND

Plockton Hotel

Harbour Street, Plockton IV52 8TN
Tel: (01599) 544274
Website: www.plocktonhotel.co.uk

Cooking 2 | Modern Scottish | £21–£54

There isn't much to Plockton beyond a straggle of whitewashed cottages on the edge of Loch Carron, and this waterfront hotel. The desolate tranquillity is what one comes for, of course – that and the fresh, marine-based cookery on offer here. Sweet-pickled herrings and prawns in a salad make a good starter, as do Plockton smokies, a gratinated dish of flaked smoked mackerel with crème fraîche, mozzarella and tomato. Mains embrace the legendarily generous seafood platters, as well as poached salmon with lime leaves and peppercorns, and traditional fish and chips with beer-battered haddock. End with textbook sticky toffee pudding, or an immaculate version of cranachan. A short wine list draws the line at £17.95 (apart from champagne), and there are wines by the glass from Argentina and South Africa at £2.75.

Chefs: Alan Pearson and Gordon Mair **Proprietors:** Mr and Mrs T. Pearson, and Alan Pearson **Open:** all week 12 to 2.15 (12.30 to 2.15 Sun), 6 to 9.15 **Closed:** 25 Dec, first 2 weeks Jan **Meals:** alc (main courses L £6.50 to £18.50, D £8 to £18.50) **Service:** not inc, card slips closed **Cards:** Amex, Delta, Maestro, MasterCard, Visa **Details:** 60 seats. 40 seats outside. Private parties: 55 main room. Vegetarian meals. Children's helpings. No smoking. Wheelchair access (also WC). Music. No mobile phones **Accommodation:** 11 rooms, all with bath/shower. TV. Phone. B&B £45 to £100. Rooms for disabled. Baby facilities

Plockton Inn

AR

Innes Street, Plockton IV52 8TW
Tel: (01599) 544222

Prawns with garlic butter (£6.25) and skate wing with black butter (£10) are typical of the locally landed seafood specialities on offer at this unpretentious village inn. Contributions from the inn's smokehouse come in the shape of a platter of fresh and cured seafood (£14), but while fish remains the main business there's also honey-glazed duck breast (£11.50) and haggis with clapshot. Finish with Scottish cheeses or sticky toffee pudding (£3.50). Scottish real ales and around 20 global wines from £9.50. Accommodation. Open all week.

MAP 11 **Port Appin** ARGYLL & BUTE

Airds Hotel

Port Appin PA38 4DF
Tel: (01631) 730236
Website: www.airds-hotel.com

Cooking 5 | Modern Scottish | £33–£73

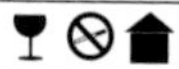

Sitting a few yards from the rusticated Appin lighthouse, the Airds is a whitewashed hotel of modest dimensions. In the low-ceilinged dining room, where a long bay window looks over Loch Linnhe, the approach is warm and unpretentious. Paul Burns favours gentle country-house cuisine, with no startling combinations but a solid backbone of fine Scots produce informing highly polished dishes. A winter lunch began with sea bass escabèche crowned with three roast langoustines, combining 'bracing freshness' with skill in seasoning and timing, followed by a main course of tender best end of Perthshire lamb with olive-oiled mash, roast vegetables, trompettes and a viscous madeira jus. A perceptible richening up occurs at dinner, when roast beef fillet might be accompanied by seared foie gras, potato rösti and red wine sauce, and wild salmon by honeyed aubergines and hollandaise. Desserts use plenty of fruit, in the likes of warm pineapple with green peppercorns and orange sauce, or Grand Marnier jelly set with citrus segments. Coffee comes with fine petits fours, perhaps including chocolate-coated lemon curd ice cream on a stick. Excellent house wines from £16 signal a serious approach, with most emphasis on a good range of Burgundy. Countries beyond France chip in a couple of well-chosen bottles apiece and half-bottles maintain the standard.

Chef: Paul Burns **Proprietors:** Shaun and Jenny McKivragan **Open:** all week 12.30 to 1.45, 7.30 to 9 **Closed:** last week Nov, 4 to 25 Jan **Meals:** Set L £17.95 (2 courses) to £21.95, Set D £47.50. Light L menu available **Service:** not inc, card slips closed **Cards:** Delta, Maestro, MasterCard, Visa **Details:** 30 seats. Private parties: 50 main room. Car park. Vegetarian meals. Children's helpings. No children under 8 at D. No smoking. No music. No mobile phones **Accommodation:** 12 rooms, all with bath/shower. TV. Phone. D,B&B £185 to £360. Baby facilities

MAP 11 **Portpatrick** DUMFRIES & GALLOWAY

Knockinaam Lodge

Portpatrick DG9 9AD
Tel: (01776) 810471
Website: www.knockinaamlodge.com

Cooking 5 | Modern European | £32–£69

'The feeling is of complete isolation,' noted one visitor to this secluded Victorian lodge set on its own inlet. But those who negotiate the long and occasionally rutted track are quickly cheered by a warm welcome, log fires, a clubby bar and comfortable lounge. Tony Pierce's classically influenced cooking suits the style of the house admirably and the formula of a set-price four-course dinner with no choice has never stifled his sense of adventure – this is cooking that shows finesse, depth of flavour and startling freshness. Typical of the format might be a 'quite beautiful, rich, deeply flavoured, just lip-smacking beef consommé with a very light boudin blanc-style mushroom sausage', then asparagus wrapped in smoked salmon with a 'light, frothy' hollandaise, and monkfish with creamy mash, green beans and baby fennel. When meat forms the centrepiece it could be roast breast of Gressingham duck with a Dubonnet and orange sauce, or roast fillet of Aberdeen Angus beef with a globe artichoke mousse and a madeira and thyme reduction. Desserts have no trouble keeping up and run the gamut from classic lemon tart to crème de menthe soufflé. Bread, canapés and petits fours are first-rate. France and Italy take pride of place on the informative wine list, with minor contributions from other countries. Affordable bottles from £14 mingle with the big names and old vintages; ten are promised by the glass.

Chef: Tony Pierce **Proprietors:** David and Sian Ibbotson **Open:** all week 12 to 2, 7 to 9 **Meals:** Set L Mon to Sat £35, Set L Sun £22.50, Set D £45 **Service:** not inc **Cards:** Amex, Maestro, MasterCard, Visa **Details:** 40 seats. 12 seats outside. Private parties: 40 main room, 12 to 18 private rooms. Car park. Vegetarian meals upon request. Children's helpings. No children under 12 after 7pm. No smoking. Wheelchair access (not WC). Music **Accommodation:** 9 rooms, all with bath/shower. TV. Phone. D,B&B £130 to £370. Baby facilities

MAP 11 **St Andrews** FIFE

Seafood Restaurant

The Scores, Bruce Embankment, St Andrews KY16 9AB
Tel: (01334) 479475
Website: www.theseafoodrestaurant.com

Cooking 4 | Seafood | £38–£67

'Almost effortless enjoyment,' concluded a reporter after visiting this dramatically situated restaurant perched like a glass box on the St Andrews foreshore. At night the building glows like an iridescent jewel, and it boasts a sleek contemporary interior with refined table settings and smart high-backed chairs. Like its elder brother in St Monans, (see entry) it offers flexible fixed-price menus dominated by fashionable fish dishes. You might begin with a salad of lobster and mango with chilli sauce and parsley pesto, or seared diver-caught scallops on citrus salad with a grape and hazelnut dressing, before a plate of Kilbrandon oysters. Main courses range from grilled fillet of cod dusted with Cajun spices served with roast fennel and garlic and herb butter, or baked fillet of halibut crusted with macadamia nuts with stir-fried vegetables and chilli and coconut sauce, to roast breast of Gressingham duck with leg confit, red onion marmalade and red wine and thyme jus. Finish with, say, Drambuie and raspberry mousse. There is plenty of choice by the glass and half-bottle on the wine list, which starts at £16 and has much of interest under £30.

Chefs: Craig Millar, Neil Clarke and Michael Speed **Proprietor:** Roybridge Ltd **Open:** all week 12 to 2.30 (12.30 to 3 Sun), 6.30 to 10 **Closed:** 25 and 26 Dec, 1 Jan **Meals:** Set L £20 (2 courses) to £24, Set D £30 (2 courses) to £40 **Service:** not inc, 12.5% for large parties **Cards:** Amex, Maestro, MasterCard, Visa **Details:** 60 seats. 30 seats outside. Private parties: 65 main room. No children under 12 at D. Wheelchair access (also WC). No music. No mobile phones. Air-conditioned

MAP 11 **St Margaret's Hope** ORKNEY

The Creel

Front Road, St Margaret's Hope KW17 2SL
Tel: (01856) 831311
Website: www.thecreel.co.uk

Cooking 7 | Seafood/Modern Scottish | £40–£51

Though the cream-painted exterior of the Craigies' restaurant-with-rooms overlooking a bay in remote Orkney may be ever so humble, it hides a fine dining experience that constitutes a must-do for those touring the Scottish islands. Inside is a tiny sitting room and a pair of dining rooms that wear the air of a modest bistro, with stone floor and bare pine tables, but where Alan Craigie offers some truly diverting fish and seafood cookery.

With so many species in danger from overfishing, the menus here make more sense than ever. There's megrim in the green crab bisque, and roasted wolf fish with aubergine casserole among the mains. The former was 'intoxicatingly strong' at inspection, its generous intensity offset by a trail of cream on the surface, and a slice of chunky ham terrine with beetroot chutney and pesto-dressed leaves was another refreshingly simple beginner. Artful textural contrasts were the result of pairing hake and scallops in a main course, which gained further from the accompaniments of braised spinach and garlicky, mustardy mash, while meat-eaters will appreciate the likes of pot-roasted shoulder of beef topped with sweetly rich red-pepper marmalade. More marmalade, this time of the conventional citrus variety, cropped up in an ice cream served with profoundly concentrated lemon tart, or there could be white chocolate pannacotta with roasted, balsamic-marinated plums. It is all convivially overseen by Joyce Craigie: 'she is a natural, with not one iota of ostentation about her'.

A compact wine list is arranged by style, with 'zesty' whites looking particularly tempting with the fish. Four house selections are £10 to £14.50.

Chef: Alan Craigie **Proprietors:** Joyce and Alan Craigie **Open:** all week D only 7 to 9 **Closed:** mid-Oct to Easter **Meals:** alc (main courses £18 to £18.50) **Service:** not inc, card slips closed **Cards:** Maestro, MasterCard, Visa **Details:** 40 seats. Private parties: 34 main room. Car park. Children's helpings. No smoking. Wheelchair access (also WC). No music **Accommodation:** 3 rooms, all with bath/shower. TV. B&B £55 to £100. Baby facilities

MAP 11 **St Monans** FIFE

Seafood Restaurant

16 West End, St Monans KY10 2BX
Tel: (01333) 730327
Website: www.theseafoodrestaurant.com

Cooking 5 | Seafood | £38–£67

Originally a fisherman's cottage, then a pub, this highly appealing restaurant is best viewed from the seashore, and it's perfectly placed to make the most of fine vistas over the rocky harbour towards the Bass Rock and Edinburgh. It's easy to imagine old sea dogs drinking at the bar, but moving through to the restaurant can seem like a culture shock: here the style is contemporary, with formal table settings, copies of Rennie Mackintosh chairs and waitresses clad in black. Diligently sourced raw materials are at the heart of the kitchen's business, and the results strike a classy, contemporary note. Ideas can be as simple as seafood chowder or as intricate as seared hand-dived scallops with goats' cheese and basil mousse, sweet-and-sour butternut squash, and pumpkin seed dressing. Main courses sustain the contrast and invention: grilled fillet of cod comes with confit potatoes, crushed peas and hollandaise, while baked fillet of halibut is given a herb crust and served with pancetta, crab and mushroom risotto, and Thai coconut sauce. There's always an alternative for meat eaters, and it's show time when it comes to desserts such as a mille-feuille of sesame brittle with poached pears and brambles with rose-water emulsion. Wines are a sassy mix of contemporary and classic bottles starting at £16 and with a host of palate-pleasers in the mid-£20s, from which most of the inspiring selection by the glass is drawn. Plenty of halves too. The Seafood Restaurant, St Andrews (see entry), is run along similar lines.

This symbol means that the wine list is well above the average.

Chefs: Craig Millar and George Scott **Proprietor:** Roybridge Ltd **Open:** Wed to Sun 12 to 2.30 (12.30 to 3 Sun), 6.30 to 9.30 **Closed:** 25 and 26 Dec, 1 Jan **Meals:** Set L £20 (2 courses) to £24, Set D £30 (2 courses) to £40 **Service:** not inc **Cards:** Amex, Delta, Maestro, MasterCard, Visa **Details:** 45 seats. 30 seats outside. Private parties: 45 main room. Children's helpings. No smoking. Wheelchair access (also WC). No music. No mobile phones

MAP 11 **Sheildaig** HIGHLAND

Tigh an Eilean Hotel

Shieldaig IV54 8XN
Tel: (01520) 755251
Email: tighaneileanhotel@shieldaig.fsnet.co.uk

Cooking 3 | Modern Scottish | £48–£63

In a bewitching, end-of-the-world hamlet with enchanting views over Loch Torridon, Tigh an Eilean (literally 'the house opposite the island') is in a delightful spot. The hotel (a converted pub) looks emphatically Scottish, but menus are emblazoned with ideas that the chef-patron has gleaned from his travels – oxtail slow-cooked with Rioja and chorizo, or chocolate macadamia nut cake with chocolate and chilli ice cream, for example. Back home, shellfish is from local boats, white fish is landed in Kinlochbervie and game comes from Scotland's moors and estates: expect anything from escalope of organic salmon and Puy lentils with hot orange vinaigrette, or venison with celeriac and apple purée, to a galette of raspberry cranachan and some fine cheeses. The wine list is a well-balanced slate with house selections from £12.70.

Chef: Christopher Field **Proprietors:** Christopher and Cathryn Field **Open:** all week D only 7 to 8.30 **Closed:** end Oct to mid-Mar **Meals:** Set D £37.50. Bar menu available **Service:** not inc **Cards:** Delta, Maestro, MasterCard, Visa **Details:** 26 seats. Vegetarian meals. Children's helpings. No smoking. Wheelchair access (also WC). No music. No mobile phones **Accommodation:** 11 rooms, all with bath/shower. B&B £62.50 to £130. Baby facilities

MAP 11 **Stein** HIGHLAND

Loch Bay AR

1–2 Macleod Terrace, Stein, Isle of Skye IV55 8GA
Tel: (01470) 592235

This shore-side cottage restaurant has much to recommend it, but the most powerful draw is the finest of fish, prepared with confident simplicity. Look to the blackboard for freshly landed specials, while among regular dishes organic salmon comes poached or grilled (£12), and there may be lobster, oysters *au naturel*, and scallops sautéed with lime and coriander. Scottish ice creams (£3.75) and cheeses (£5.50) seem the appropriate way to finish. Fish-friendly wine list from £9.95. Closed Sat L and all Sun.

MAP 11 Stonehaven ABERDEENSHIRE

Tolbooth

AR

Old Pier, Stonehaven AB39 2JU
Tel: (01569) 762287

Affable seafood restaurant housed in Stonehaven's oldest building by the pier and the harbour. Enjoy fine views and regularly changing menus along the lines of hot-smoked monkfish carpaccio with sweet-pickled cucumber salad and gazpacho sorbet (£6), and seared scallops with caramelised chicory and citrus balsamic dressing (£17). Meat alternatives could include confit of duck with stir-fried pak choi, while desserts might feature lemon-curd brûlée with lemon confit (£5.25). House wine £12.95. Closed Sun and Mon.

MAP 11 Strathyre STIRLING

Creagan House

Strathyre FK18 8ND
Tel: (01877) 384638
Website: www.creaganhouse.co.uk

Cooking 4 | French/Scottish | £34–£48

The setting for this family-run restaurant-with-rooms is an extended seventeenth century farmhouse, its stately baronial hall where stone lions guard an imposing fireplace giving dining here a grand feel. By way of contrast, the cooking takes an impeccably modern line. Meat from Perthshire farms and produce from local small holdings provide the foundations for some enterprising dishes, ranging from the noisette and cutlet of rabbit Rossini tried at inspection to a perfectly timed main course of collop of venison with an 'unctuous' Bergerac sauce that had also been used to braise the accompanying cinnamon pear. On a more classical note, the short set-price menus might also offer Scotch broth, supreme of chicken marsala (inducing a 'Proustian recall of childhood outdoor-reared fowl' in one reporter), and Aberdeen Angus fillet steak cooked 'your favourite way'. A choice of two desserts follows, perhaps a rich chocolate mousse cake combining Nutella with Green and Black's organic chocolate, or a 'suitably gooey' sticky toffee, with Scottish cheeses as an alternative. A selection of eight wines by the glass from £2.15 opens a well-annotated list that shouldn't stretch anyone's budget too far. Bottle prices start at £11.20.

Chef: Gordon Gunn **Proprietors:** Gordon and Cherry Gunn **Open:** Fri to Wed (Fri to Mon from 24 Nov to 20 Dec) D only 7.30 (1 sitting) **Closed:** 5 to 23 Nov, 22 Jan to 3 Mar **Meals:** Set D £22.50 to £29.50 **Service:** not inc, card slips closed **Cards:** Maestro, MasterCard, Visa **Details:** 14 seats. Private parties: 35 main room. Car park. Children's helpings. No children under 10 at D. No smoking. Wheelchair access (not WC). No music. No mobile phones **Accommodation:** 5 rooms, all with bath/shower. B&B £65 to £110. Rooms for disabled. Baby facilities

MAP 11 Stromness ORKNEY

Hamnavoe

AR

35 Graham Place, Stromness, KW16 3BY
Tel: (01856) 850606

Cheerful cottagey restaurant off the main street in Stromness, dedicated to feeding locals and visitors to the island. Expect substantial, 'no-frills country cooking' with plenty of local seafood: crab gratin (£5.25), peppered monkfish (£15), and baked haddock fillet {£14.50), for example. Alternatives might include pork, guinea fowl and green peppercorn terrine, and grilled sirloin steak, and desserts run to poached pears with Orkney raspberry ice cream and Cointreau sauce (£4). Rudimentary wine list from £9.80. Open from 6.30 Tues to Sun in summer, and Fri, Sat and Sun Oct to April.

MAP 11 Strontian HIGHLAND

Kilcamb Lodge

Strontian PH36 4HY
Tel: (01967) 402257
Website: www.kilcamblodge.co.uk

Cooking 4 | French/Scottish | £34–£48

Perched on the edge of a sea loch, Kilcamb is a family-sized house decorated in comfortable, homely fashion, with watercolours on the walls and the atmosphere softened with ferns and chintz. Abundant West Coast seafood features strongly on the menus, together with Stornoway black pudding, game from the nearby Mingarry estate, and hot-smoked salmon from Orkney. Choice comes in trios on the four-course menu, with the exception of a soup after the starter. A spring dinner might thus proceed from oak-smoked halibut brandade with a fluffy oatcake, sautéed leeks and herbed crème fraîche, through celeriac soup garnished with some of that Orkney salmon, to a main course of roasted loin of hare with pork belly, turnip fondant, truffled polenta, game chips and a thyme jus. At Easter weekend, there was the option of a deep-fried Easter egg with 'cream egg pastry cream', but if you fear for your arteries, go for something like rhubarb and orange compote instead. Wines are arranged by grape variety and the list focuses on affordable bottles from £15 with a few smarter options.

Chefs: Neil Mellis, William Fowler and Alistair Berry **Proprietors:** Sally and David Fox **Open:** Tue to Sun L 12 to 2, all week D 7.30 to 8.30 **Closed:** 2 Jan to 1 Feb **Meals:** alc L (main courses £7.50 to £12), Set D £38 **Service:** not inc, card slips closed **Cards:** Amex, Delta, Maestro, MasterCard, Visa **Details:** 26 seats. Private parties: 26 main room. Car park. Vegetarian meals. No children under 12. No smoking. Music. No mobile phones **Accommodation:** 12 rooms, all with bath/shower. TV. Phone. B&B £75 to £220. No children under 12. Fishing

MAP 11 **Swinton** BORDERS

Wheatsheaf

Main Street, Swinton TD11 3JJ
Tel: (01890) 860257
Website: www.wheatsheaf-swinton.co.uk

Cooking 3 | Modern Scottish | £27–£51

At this congenial cross between a restaurant-with-rooms and a classic country inn chef John Keir uses the abundant Scottish larder intelligently, his menus and blackboard specials agreeably balancing conservative and imaginative ideas. In his modern-focused dishes local seafood and game sometimes get Mediterranean or more distant touches: think grilled Eyemouth crab with pak choi, shiitake spring roll and sweet chilli sauce, then maybe peppered wild venison fillet on creamed celeriac with a juniper and redcurrant sauce. Finally vanilla-pod crème brûlée and rhubarb compote may jostle with a chocolate brownie with Malteser ice cream and chocolate sauce. The 150-strong, reasonably priced, globe-trotting wine list offers ten house by bottle and glass (from £11.95 or £2.95 respectively) backed by a decent selection of half bottles and an array of 35 malt whiskies.

Chefs: John Keir and Richard Wylie **Proprietors:** Chris and Jan Winson **Open:** all week 12 to 2, 6 to 9 (8 Sun) **Closed:** 25 to 27 Dec, 31 Dec, 1 Jan **Meals:** alc (main courses: L £7.50 to £10, D £11 to 18). Light L menu available **Service:** not inc, card slips closed **Cards:** Delta, Maestro, MasterCard, Visa **Details:** 45 seats. Private parties: 30 main room, 18 private room. Car park. Vegetarian meals. Children's helpings. No smoking. Wheelchair access (not WC). Occasional music. No mobile phones **Accommodation:** 7 rooms, all with bath/shower. TV. Phone. B&B £65 to £128. Baby facilities

MAP 11 **Troon** SOUTH AYRSHIRE

Lochgreen House

Monktonhill Road, Southwood, Troon KA10 7EN
Tel: (01292) 313343
Website: www.costley-hotels.co.uk

Cooking 5 | Franco-Scottish | £32–£61

The solid and reassuring building in the Scottish Arts and Crafts style – beautifully set in 30 manicured acres – is noted for the genteel comfort of its handsomely appointed interior. To match the rich fabrics and fine furniture in the dining room, luxury items abound on the menu in the shape of foie gras with seasonal chutney, or salmon and lobster terrine (served with baby leeks, lemon and dill crème fraîche and citrus fruit dressing), yet the food does not rely altogether on these for effect. Pride is taken in regional materials, and Andrew Costley's cooking offers some appealing ideas: poached suprême of chicken with a wild mushroom mousseline and spring vegetables, or a duo of slow-cooked and roast Ayrshire lamb teamed with crushed minted potatoes and fine beans with a smoked bacon and shallot jus. Fish is a strength too, taking in steamed Atlantic halibut with velouté potatoes and a blanquette of Shetland mussels flavoured with Pernod and chives. The general pampering tone induced by soft textures continues in desserts such as vanilla bavarois with a liquid apple centre, and an enterprising warm coconut rice pudding with grilled exotic fruits and mango sorbet. France is in the ascendancy on a wine list that has good drinking for under £25. House wines start at £16.95, and there are nine by the glass from £4.15.

Chefs: Andrew Costley, Willie Pike and Martin Hollis **Proprietors:** Costley & Costley Hoteliers Ltd **Open:** all week 12.30 to 2, 6.30 to 9 **Meals:** alc L Mon to Sat (main courses £9 to £14.50), Set L Sun £23. Set D £37.50 **Service:** not inc, card slips closed **Cards:** Amex, Delta, Diners, Maestro, MasterCard, Visa **Details:** 165 seats. 120 seats outside. Private parties: 95 main room, 30 to 120 private rooms. Car park. Children's helpings. No smoking. Wheelchair access (also WC). Music. Air-conditioned **Accommodation:** 44 rooms, all with bath/shower. TV. Phone. B&B £99 to £170. Rooms for disabled

MacCallums Oyster Bar

The Harbour, Troon KA10 6DH
Tel: (01292) 319339

Cooking 3 | Seafood | £28–£67

Head for the Seacat terminal and you'll find MacCallums overlooking the harbour where the fishing boats tie up. The owners run a wet-fish shop in Glasgow, so top-quality seafood is the starting point – not only oysters but also lobsters, mussels, langoustines, sole, squid, and hake – and the kitchen wisely takes a minimal approach to much of it. There are crab claws with saffron and basil mayonnaise to start, or scallops with spinach and herb butter, then a seafood platter, cod with braised lentil aïoli and roast fennel, or the day's whole grilled fish to follow, with token meat and vegetarian dishes thrown in. Desserts have included iced lemon parfait and sticky toffee pudding, and a short list of wines, mostly white and under £20, starts with house French at £11.60.

Chefs: Stuart Wilson and Robin Gray **Proprietors:** John and James MacCallum **Open:** Tue to Sun L 12 to 2.30 (3.30 Sun), Tue to Sat D 6.30 to 9.30 **Meals:** alc (main courses £8.50 to £25.50) **Service:** not inc **Cards:** Delta, Maestro, MasterCard, Visa **Details:** 43 seats. Private parties: 43 main room. Car park. Wheelchair access (not WC). Music

MAP 4 **Aberaeron** CEREDIGION

Harbourmaster Hotel

Pen Cei, Aberaeron SA46 0BA
Tel: (01545) 570755
Website: www.harbour-master.com

Cooking 3 | Modern Welsh | £29–£52

As its name suggests, the Heulyns' azure blue, refurbished building on the quayside was once the harbourmaster's residence. The bar dispenses local Welsh ales as well as wines (ten by the glass), with one side a locals' area and the other a modern restaurant that echoes its location, with pale blue walls, paintings of beach scenes and metal fish sculptures, while floorboards and solid wooden tables lend an appropriately informal note. Menus, like the surroundings, are suitably unpretentious, are chalked up on the board and printed daily, and come patriotically written in Welsh with English translations. Fish holds a strong hand, with fresh local produce the mainstay, competently cooked and well presented to bring the best out of main ingredients. Think fillet of poached lemon sole served with celeriac rösti and beurre rouge sauce, or chargrilled fillet of Ceredigion lamb partnered with minted risotto and a thyme jus, Celtic cheeses or pear Tatin with crème fraîche to finish, while a friendly-priced, compact wine list provides the accompaniment (from £11.50) alongside informal yet efficient service.

Chef: Sebastian Bodewes **Proprietors:** Glyn and Menna Heulyn **Open:** Tue to Sun L 12 to 2, Mon to Sat D 6.30 to 9 **Meals:** alc (not Sun L; main courses L £10.50 to £12.50, D £13.50 to £17.50). Set L Sun £16.50 **Service:** not inc, card slips closed **Cards:** Delta, Maestro, MasterCard, Visa **Details:** 40 seats. Car park. Vegetarian meals. Children's helpings. No smoking. Wheelchair access (also WC). Music **Accommodation:** 9 rooms, all with bath/shower. TV. B&B £55 to £125. No children under 5. Baby facilities

 This symbol means that accommodation is available at this establishment.

MAP 7 **Aberdaron** GWYNEDD

Ship Inn AR

Aberdaron LL53 8BE
Tel: (01758) 760204

Chef Matthew Vernau and his partner worked at Plas Bodegroes (see entry, Pwllheli) before moving to this family-run hotel in a tourist village at the tip of the Lleyn Peninsula. It is still early days, but the revamped menu promises good things in the shape of warm tomato and mozzarella tart (£4.50) and slow-cooked lamb shank with mint and rosemary (£9.75). Desserts show 'a touch of Bodegroes class': crème brûlée with poached plums (£3.50), for example. Wines from £8.95. Note: no bookings. Open all week summer; ring to confirm winter opening.

MAP 7 **Aberdovey** GWYNEDD

Penhelig Arms Hotel

Terrace Road, Aberdovey LL35 0LT
Tel: (01654) 767215
Website: www.penheligarms.com

Cooking 2 | British | £24–£53

'It's very stylish for a seaside pub,' writes a regular of this narrow building sandwiched between the road and the steep cliffs overlooking the Dovey estuary. Made up of a number of small rooms, it exudes an air of enthusiasm, thanks not least to the amiable and unpretentious Robert Hughes, who 'hovers diligently and is thoroughly charming'. Ambition on the daily-changing menu runs from avocado with Thai-spiced prawns to fresh-tasting fillets of red mullet served, at inspection, with rather muted notes of garlic and ginger. Sourcing is impeccable, and the cooking makes an honest impression: for example, in lamb shank braised in red wine with red onions, rosemary and balsamic vinegar, and vanilla cheesecake. Robert Hughes shares his passion for wine through a generously priced list that opens with 18 contemporary options by the glass. The Italian section has been bolstered over the past year, but it's the unerring eye for quality throughout that really impresses. Bottles start at £11.

Chefs: Bronwen Shaw and Jason Griffiths **Proprietors:** Robert and Sally Hughes **Open:** all week 12 to 2.30, 7 to 9.30 **Closed:** 25 and 26 Dec **Meals:** alc L (main courses £7.50 to £14.50). Set L Sun £16, Set D £27. Bar menu available **Service:** not inc, card slips closed **Cards:** Delta, Maestro, MasterCard, Visa **Details:** 36 seats. Private parties: 24 main room. Car park. Vegetarian meals. Children's helpings. No smoking. No music. No mobile phones. Air-conditioned **Accommodation:** 15 rooms, all with bath/shower. TV. Phone. D,B&B £58 to £158

MAP 7 **Abersoch** GWYNEDD

Porth Tocyn Hotel

Bwlchtocyn, Abersoch LL53 7BU
Tel: (01758) 713303
Website: www.porth-tocyn-hotel.co.uk

Cooking 4 | Modern European | £31–£58

The Fletcher-Brewer family created this hotel from a row of lead-miners' cottages on the Lleyn peninsula. Cardigan Bay recedes into the distance with Snowdonia for a backdrop, and the relaxed tranquillity of the setting is echoed within the walls of the hotel.

Buffet and light lunches demonstrate the care taken in looking after guests, but it is in the evenings that Louise Fletcher-Brewer really shines. Her cooking is a convincing marriage of traditional skills and up-to-date flavours, with Stilton dumplings going into the oxtail soup, and oysters Mornay served on grain mustard and lime couscous. For main courses, roast best end of Welsh lamb may be familiarly served with potato rösti, steamed green veg and a claret sauce, but then fish might have you all at sea, when baked cod comes with a rarebit topping, vegetable spaghetti, braised lettuce and sugar snaps, and a dressing of warm pesto. If a dessert such as coffee crunch cheesecake doesn't grab you, there is the option of a savoury like devils on horseback, or black pudding and caramelised apple with cider syrup. It is all brought forth with an endearing lack of ceremony. A well-balanced international mix of wines has something for everyone, from Chilean Chardonnay at £13.50 to a handful of clarets with a bit of age.

Chefs: Louise Fletcher-Brewer and Michael Beaty **Proprietors:** the Fletcher-Brewer family **Open:** Sun L 12.15 to 2, all week D 7.30 to 9 (7.15 to 9.30 peak season) **Closed:** mid-Nov to mid-Mar **Meals:** buffet L Sun £21.25, Set D £30.50 (2 courses) to £37. Light L menu available Mon to Sat **Service:** not inc, card slips closed **Cards:** Maestro, MasterCard, Visa **Details:** 50 seats. 30 seats outside. Car park. Vegetarian meals. Children's helpings; no very young children at D. No smoking. No music. No mobile phones **Accommodation:** 17 rooms, all with bath/shower. TV. Phone. B&B (continental breakfast) £62 to £154. Rooms for disabled. Baby facilities. Swimming pool

MAP 4 **Bassaleg** NEWPORT

Junction 28

Station Approach, Bassaleg NP10 8LD
Tel: (01633) 891891
Website: www.junction28.com

Cooking 2 | Modern European | £22–£51

Bustling, noisy and populist, this converted railway station overlooking the Usk prosaically takes its name from the nearest M4 exit: when crowds descend on the place, it packs them in with 'ruthless professionalism' (note the early-evening 'flyer' menu). The long carte covers all sorts of cuisines and styles, with straightforward, generous dishes in abundance. Fish lovers could look forward to stir-fried squid in a filo basket, or pan-fried red snapper on braised Little Gem lettuce with Burgundy and pink peppercorn cream, while meat eaters might home in on a warm salad of lambs' kidneys with mange-tout and prosciutto. Well-executed desserts include vanilla and white chocolate pannacotta with exotic fruit salsa. The worldwide wine list offers decent value from £11.50.

Chef: Jean-Jacques Payel **Proprietors:** Jon West and Richard Wallace **Open:** all week L 12 to 2 (4 Sun), Mon to Sat D 5.30 to 9.30 **Closed:** 26 Dec, 1 Jan, last week July, first week Aug **Meals:** alc exc Sun L (main courses £8 to £16). Set L Mon to Sat £10.95 (2 courses) to £12.95, Set L Sun £11.95 (2 courses) to £13.95, Set D 5.30 to 7 £13.95 **Service:** not inc, card slips closed **Cards:** Amex, Delta, Maestro, MasterCard, Visa **Details:** 160 seats. Private parties: 60 main room, 14 private room. Car park. Vegetarian meals. Jacket and tie. No smoking. Wheelchair access (also WC). Music. Air-conditioned

 This symbol means that smoking is not permitted.

MAP 7 **Beaumaris** ISLE OF ANGLESEY

Café Neptune

NEW ENTRY

First Floor, 27 Castle Street, Beaumaris LL58 8AP
Tel: (01248) 812990

Cooking 4 | Seafood | £23–£66

Looking smart and fashionable, this first-floor modern-day restaurant (above an upmarket fish-and-chip shop run by the same management) gets marks for its striking monochromatic décor, excellent service, and interesting menu. It sets its sights on an appealing mix of both established and contemporary ideas, with fish (much of it local) featuring prominently but not exclusively. A generous plate of seafood laksa bursting with scallops and tiger prawns, Arbroath smokies, or maybe steamed Anglesey mussels lead on to main courses like pan-fried red mullet topped with crayfish tails and served with shiitake mushrooms, pea purée, and a mound of couscous laced with a 'delicious semi-sweet stock', or 'utterly pink, tender and tasty' lamb rack chops with Puy lentils and red onion confit. Pineapple Tatin makes a good finish, and the short, globetrotting wine list kicks off with house selections from £12.95.

Chefs: Ernst Van Halderen and Martyn Rae **Proprietors:** Andrew and Christine Pulford **Open:** Mon to Sat 12 to 2.30, 6 to 9.30, Sun 12 to 9.30 **Meals:** alc (main courses £5 to £25) **Service:** not inc **Cards:** Amex, Delta, Maestro, MasterCard, Visa **Details:** 48 seats. Private parties: 50 main room. Children's helpings. No smoking. Music. Air-conditioned

Ye Olde Bulls Head

Castle Street, Beaumaris LL58 8AP
Tel: (01248) 810329
Website: www.bullsheadinn.co.uk

Cooking 4 | Modern European | £48–£73

'Ye Olde' isn't wrong. The former coaching inn near the famous castle can trace its lineage back to the fifteenth century, and it caters for all-comers with a snug bar, a relaxing lounge, a modern brasserie with its own chef, and a smart restaurant up in the eaves of the oldest part of the building. Refurbished in 2005, the restaurant is an elegant, comfortable room, with well-dressed candlelit tables and Wedgwood china, but with the old beams retaining a hint of venerability.

Lee Scott is the new chef, coming to Beaumaris with a bundle of experience at other smart addresses under his belt. An early indication of the potential came with an inspection starter of slow-cooked belly pork with truffled creamy mash, apple confit and mustard jus, in which all the components balanced each other to create a satisfying whole. Equally thoughtful in its construction is a main course of peppered saddle of lamb with a spectacular array of apt accompaniments, including baby turnips, caramelised onions, fondant potato, squash purée, confit garlic and wilted spinach. Finish with rhubarb and custard, in which the latter element is accounted for by a creamy pannacotta, while the rhubarb appears as a fruity jelly base, with ginger ice cream and a piece of ginger shortbread adding counterpoint. Presentations all look highly professional and eye-catching, and there is fine coffee to finish. Wines hit the spot in all French regions and imaginative shorter selections elsewhere sustain the quality focus. Bottles start at £14.50 and four good house wines come by the bottle, glass or carafe.

Chef: Lee Scott **Proprietor:** Rothwell & Robertson Ltd **Open:** Mon to Sat D only 7 to 9.30; also open Sun L bank hols **Closed:** 25 and 26 Dec, 1 Jan **Meals:** Set D £33 to £45. Brasserie menu available L and D **Service:** not inc **Cards:** Amex, Delta, Maestro, MasterCard, Visa **Details:** 45 seats. Private parties: 25 main room. Car park. Vegetarian meals. No children under 7. No smoking. No music. No mobile phones **Accommodation:** 13 rooms, all with bath/shower. TV. Phone. B&B £70 to £98.50. Baby facilities

MAP 7 **Betws-y-coed** CONWY

Ty Gwyn Hotel

AR

Betws-y-coed LL24 0SG
Tel: (01690) 710383

Centuries-old, white-painted coaching inn at the 'Gateway to Snowdonia National Park' in the wooded vale of Conwy. The kitchen works to a crowd-pleasing international menu, taking in starters like Thai-marinated julienne of fillet steak (£5.50), before seared venison fillet with red wine and wild mushrooms (£14), or fillet of sea bass with crab and Brie en croûte. Finish with, say, orange, ginger and elderflower cheesecake (£3.50). Open all week.

MAP 4 Brecon POWYS

Barn at Brynich

AR

Brynich, Brecon LD3 7SH
Tel: (01874) 623480

A converted seventeenth-century hay barn is the setting for this family-friendly enterprise in Brecon Beacons National Park. Local and organic ingredients fare well on a menu that promises a warm salad of Penclawdd cockles (£5) and daube of Welsh black beef with balsamic-roast shallots and root purée (£12) as well as 'flame grills'. Familiar desserts (£4.25) range from crème brûlée to sticky toffee pudding. House wine £8.50. Self-catering cottages and caravan park/campsite available. Open all week exc Mon Nov to May.

Tipple 'n' Tiffin

Theatr Brycheiniog, Brecon LD3 7EW
Tel: (01874) 611866

Sharing and grazing is the idea behind Richard and Louise Gudsell's laid-back café-style rendezvous in the Brecon Theatre. All plates and bowls are priced from £6 to £8, organic ingredients receive enthusiastic support, and the world is their larder: home-cured charcuterie, crispy duck legs on kumera (New Zealand sweet potato) and butternut squash rösti, and slow-roast Tamworth pork ribs in hoisin marinade with chilli noodles are typical. Finish with local ice creams or home-made desserts (£4). A fistful of wines from £10. Closed Sun.

MAP 4 Broad Haven PEMBROKESHIRE

Druidstone

Druidston Haven, Broad Haven SA62 3NE
Tel: (01437) 781221
Website: www.druidstone.co.uk

Cooking 1 | Global | £27–£55

The Bells' cliff-top hotel overlooking St Bride's Bay is full of clutter and runs on tolerance and good humour. The kitchen emphasises locally grown produce and is moving towards organic, treating mainly familiar ideas in lively style. After starters like potato and mushroom soup, or terrine de campagne with Shropshire apple chutney, there's lots of fish (say, fillet of St Bride's sea bass with tomatoes, olives and fresh herbs), and vegetarians are well catered for with the likes of wild mushroom risotto, while hearty appetites might favour ale-braised beef with herb dumplings and Marmite roast parsnips. Finish with red berry sherry trifle. House wine is £8.80.

Chefs: Angus Bell, Jon Woodhouse and Guy Morris **Proprietors:** Rod, Jane and Angus Bell **Open:** Sun L 12.30 to 2.30, Mon to Sat D 7.30 to 9.30 **Meals:** alc (main courses £11 to £21). Bar menu also available **Service:** not inc, card slips closed **Cards:** Amex, Delta, Maestro, MasterCard, Visa **Details:** 36 seats. 50 seats outside. Private parties: 36 main room, 8 to 12 private rooms. Car park. Vegetarian meals. Children's helpings. No smoking. Wheelchair access (not WC). Occasional music **Accommodation:** 11 rooms, 5 with bath/shower. B&B £39 to £130. Baby facilities

MAP 4 CAPEL DEWI CARMARTHENSHIRE

Y Polyn

NEW ENTRY

Capel Dewi SA32 7LH
Tel: (01267) 290000
Email: ypolyn@hotmail.com

Cooking 3 | Modern British | £29–£56

In a rural spot, Y Polyn is a 200-year-old pseudo-Tudor pub with a number of appealing features in its updated interior, including a wood-burning stove, white-painted stone walls hung with artwork (for sale) and bare wooden tables. The menu offers wholesome, honest dishes, which, although based on excellent native produce, including black beef and Carmarthen ham, have a distinctly Gallic accent. Robust flavours and hearty portions are a given, as in authentically thick and richly flavoured French-style fish soup with rouille, croûtons and Gruyère, which might be followed by cassoulet with lots of tender lamb, pork and chunks of Toulouse sausage in a rich stew of haricot beans, or coq au vin with a well-reduced, well-flavoured sauce. Tarte au citron or plum tarte Tatin make appropriate puddings to conclude a meal, and to wash it down there is a modest selection of wines priced from £11.50.

Chefs: Sue Manson and Maryann Wright Proprietors: Mark and Sue Manson, and Simon and Maryann Wright Open: Tue to Fri and Sun L 12 to 2.30, Tue to Sat D 7 to 9.30 Meals: alc L (main courses £8.50 to £16.50). Set D £25.50 Service: not inc, card slips closed Cards: Delta, Maestro, MasterCard, Visa Details: 40 seats. 20 seats outside. Private parties: 40 main room. Car park. Vegetarian meals. Children's helpings. No smoking in 1 dining room. Wheelchair access (also WC). Music

MAP 7 **Capel Garmon** CONWY

Tan-y-Foel

Capel Garmon, nr Betws-y-coed
LL26 0RE
Tel: (01690) 710507
Website: www.tyfhotel.co.uk

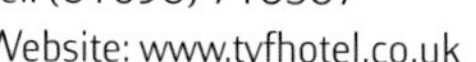

Cooking 6 | Modern British-Plus | £58–£69

High on the hills above the Conwy valley is this seventeenth-century stone farmhouse, its squat outline emerging from behind stunted trees. It has magnificent vistas over Snowdonia to the north-west but, amid all the majesty of the scenery, its own garden is a modest little patch, with mature firs and topiary to distinguish it. The Pitmans have decorated the place stylishly, with a bamboo floor and light wooden panelling in the tranquil, comfortable dining room. Janet Pitman cooks a daily-changing, fixed-price dinner menu with a pair of alternatives for each course. On a winter menu the choice might be seared gingered tuna with crisp-fried laverbread in a dressing of black treacle, chilli and sesame seeds, followed by rare-roast loin of Welsh mountain lamb with parsnip purée and winter roots, sauced with port, balsamic and mint. A spring opener that dazzled for imagination and technical proficiency involved interleaving slices of turbot and smoked salmon and grilling them – sabayon-fashion – under a golden velouté sauce. Fish as a main course might be spice-crusted monkfish, three pieces on neat mounds of buttered spinach, along with hugely moreish fried aubergine, saffron potatoes, and a tomato and lemon sauce.

The overall feeling of lightness and precision is carried through to desserts, with perhaps baked vanilla custard with a shot glass of spirit-soaked fresh apricot, or finish with Welsh and Continental cheeses. The Pitmans' daughter Kelly assists with front-of-house duties efficiently and charmingly. Wines on the global list are of a universally high standard, with meaningful tasting notes to provide guidance. Unusual choices like Seghesio Arneis (£27) from California or an excellent dry German Riesling Spätlese from Bürklin-Wolf (£39) add real character. Bottles start at £19 and plenty come in halves.

Chef: Janet Pitman Proprietors: Mr P.K. and Mrs J.C. Pitman Open: all week D only 7.30 to 8.15 Closed: mid-Dec to mid-Jan Meals: Set D £39 Service: not inc Cards: Maestro, MasterCard, Visa Details: 12 seats. Car park. No children under 7. No smoking. No music. No mobile phones Accommodation: 6 rooms, all with bath/shower. TV. Phone. B&B £99 to £160. No children under 7

MAP 4 **Cardiff** CARDIFF

Armless Dragon

97–99 Wyeverne Road, Cathays,
Cardiff CF24 4BG
Tel: (029) 2038 2357
Website: www.armlessdragon.co.uk

Cooking 2 | Modern Welsh | £19–£45

Even though this particular dragon may not be able to wave the flag, it's an apt symbol for Paul Lane's commitment to indigenous Welsh produce. He wages his campaign in an unadorned neighbourhood bistro, often looking beyond his own backyard for inspiration. Mixed platters of appetisers from 'land, sea and earth' kick off proceedings on his blackboard menus before, say, roast chicken breast (organic, of course) with purple sprouting broccoli and beetroot 'potch', or wild sea bass with mash, mussels and saffron cream. Laver balls with ginger-pickled vegetables is a signature dish, while desserts span everything from warm cinnamon bread-and-butter pudding to figs in spiced balsamic syrup with honey and ginger ice cream. The wide-ranging, international wine list promises respectable drinking from £8.90.

Chef/Proprietor: Paul Lane Open: Tue to Fri L 12 to 2, Tue to Sat D 7 to 9 (9.30 Fri and Sat) Closed: 25 Dec, bank hols Meals: alc (main courses £12 to £18). Set L £10 (2 courses) to £12 Service: not inc, card slips closed Cards: Amex, Delta, Maestro, MasterCard, Visa Details: 45 seats. Private parties: 50 main room. Vegetarian meals. Children's helpings. No smoking in 1 dining room. Wheelchair access (not WC). Music

This symbol means that there are some restrictions on smoking though it may be allowed in some eating areas.

Brazz

NEW ENTRY

Wales Millennium Centre, Bute Place, Cardiff Bay, Cardiff CF10 5AL
Tel: (029) 2045 9000
Website: www.brazz.co.uk

Cooking 1 | Modern Brasserie | £28–£59

The latest branch of the Brazz chain (see entries in Exeter and the Castle in Taunton) occupies a desirable chunk of prime real estate in the Wales Millennium Centre (aka Cardiff Opera House). Like its siblings, it thrives on flexibility, serving snacks and meals seven days a week: choose the buzz and bustle of the glass and steel brasserie or opt for the quieter surroundings of the carpeted restaurant. The menu serves its purpose with 'grazing' plates, 'super-sandwiches' and salads, bolstered by pasta, fish (hefty salmon fishcakes with creamed leeks, and mixed seafood casserole), grills and braises ('flavourful' Welsh ribeye steak). Desserts range from sheep's milk ice cream to tiramisù, and there's a handy selection of round-the-world wines from £11.95.

Chef: Simon Kealy **Proprietor:** Brazz plc **Open:** all week 12 to 3, 6 to 10.30 (11 Fri and Sat) **Meals:** alc (main courses £9 to £17.50). Bar menu available 11 to 6 **Service:** 10% (optional), card slips closed **Cards:** Amex, Delta, Maestro, MasterCard, Visa **Details:** 120 seats. 80 seats outside. Private parties: 120 main room, 20 to 80 private rooms. Vegetarian meals. Children's helpings. No smoking. Wheelchair access (also WC). Music. Air-conditioned

Da Castaldo

5 Romilly Crescent, Canton, Cardiff CF11 9NP
Tel: (029) 2022 1905
Website: www.dacastaldo.com

Cooking 2 | Modern Italian | £26–£55

Since opening, this pleasant, modern-looking Italian has developed into a well-liked, informal restaurant with a very personal stamp. Owner Antonio Castaldo recently handed over the reins in the kitchen and moved out front – although he has been known to return to the stoves when the mood takes him. The style of food is unchanged. Robust trattoria fare is bolstered by a few specials, classics are capably handled (saltimbocca alla romana and porcini mushroom risotto, for example) and there are a few contemporary flourishes such as a perfectly executed warm salad of plump scallops with marsala and parsley sauce. Desserts follow the traditional path, with tiramisù, cassata and budino di cioccolato (hot chocolate sponge). Italy overshadows the rest of the world on the decent-value wine list; prices begin at £10.95.

Chefs: Carlos Rodriguez and Rodrigo Gonzalez **Proprietors:** Antonio and Cheryl Castaldo **Open:** Tue to Sat 12 to 2, 7 to 10 (10.30 Sat) **Meals:** alc (main courses £11 to £17). Set L £8.95 (1 course) to £15.95 **Service:** not inc, card slips closed **Cards:** Delta, Maestro, MasterCard, Visa **Details:** 45 seats. Private parties: 45 main room. Vegetarian meals. Children's helpings. No smoking. Wheelchair access (not WC). Music. Air-conditioned

Le Gallois

6–10 Romilly Crescent, Canton, Cardiff CF11 9NR
Tel: (029) 2034 1264
Website: www.legallois-ycymro.com

Cooking 5 | Modern French-Plus | £30–£72

With a name like Padrig Jones there's no doubting the chef is home grown ('Gallois' translating to 'Welshman'), but his cooking is fundamentally Gallic: confident, complex and impressive, and high on ambition. The family-run Gallois has a smart, upbeat, cosmopolitan edge and a buzzy, bustling atmosphere. The cooking is based around classics with a contemporary spin, using quality fresh produce (blending ingredients sourced direct from the markets in Paris with the best local and regional produce) in innovative combinations. The sophisticated menus take a fixed-price approach, delivering main courses along the lines of pan-seared brill with herb-poached leeks, seared scallops, pomme purée and a Barolo sauce, between a starter of perhaps duck pastilla with seared foie gras and cinnamon sauce, and tarte Tatin served with Roquefort ice cream. Service, by young French staff, fits the bill, while the resolutely Francophile wine list offers house vin de pays at £13.95.

Chef: Padrig Jones **Proprietors:** the Jones and Dupuy families **Open:** Tue to Sat 12 to 2.30, 6.30 (6 Tue to Thur) to 10.30 **Meals:** Set L £14.95 (2 courses) to £17.95, Set D £30 (2 courses) to £35 **Service:** 10% (optional), card slips closed **Cards:** Amex, Delta, Maestro, MasterCard, Visa **Details:** 60 seats. Private parties: 60 main room. Car park. Vegetarian meals. Children's helpings. No-smoking area. Wheelchair access (also WC). Occasional music. Air-conditioned

Gilby's

NEW ENTRY

Old Port Road, Culverhouse Cross, Cardiff CF5 6DN
Tel: (029) 2067 0800
Website: www.gilbysrestaurant.co.uk

Cooking 2 | Modern European | £28–£65

A renovated tithe barn is the setting for Anthony Armelin's restaurant in a patch of Welsh countryside behind the television studios. The dining room occupies a vast high-raftered space broken up by screens and glass partitions, which help to create a feeling of uncluttered intimacy. Lunches and early-evening 'flyer' menus are good value, and the carte deals in modern European food. The kitchen handles simple ideas confidently: witness a 'properly made' wild mushroom risotto with sun-dried tomato tapenade and Parmesan wafers, or calf's liver with sweet-cured bacon, roast shallots, and a red wine and veal jus. Elsewhere, there's a tendency to overcomplicate, as in medallions of monkfish with crispy Serrano ham, Parmesan-tossed baby spinach, borlotti beans, gnocchi, roast red pepper coulis and basil oil. Desserts include an up-to-date version of bread-and-butter pudding. House wine is £12.95.

Chefs: Anthony Armelin and Michael Jones **Proprietor:** Anthony Armelin **Open:** Tue to Sun L 12 to 2.30 (3.30 Sun), Tue to Sat D 5.45 to 10 **Closed:** 1 week at Christmas, 1 week at Whitsun, 2 weeks Sept **Meals:** alc exc Sun L (main courses £15 to £20). Set L Tue to Sat £12.95 (2 courses), Set L Sun £17.95, Set D 5.45 to 7.30 (6.30 Sat) £16.95 **Service:** not inc **Cards:** Amex, Delta, Maestro, MasterCard, Visa **Details:** 100 seats. 28 seats outside. Private parties: 18 main room. Car park. Vegetarian meals. Children's helpings. No smoking in 1 dining room. Wheelchair access (also WC). Music

Izakaya Japanese Tavern

Mermaid Quay, Cardiff Bay, Cardiff CF10 5BW
Tel: (029) 2049 2939
Website: izakaya-japanese-tavern.com

Cooking 3 | Japanese | £23–£49

Overlooking the rejuvenated vistas of Cardiff Bay, this enterprising venture provides a taste of genuine 'everyday' Japanese food. 'Izakaya' suggests a traditional drinking house with food, and this place has all the expected trappings, from bamboo screens to paper lanterns. The menu is a full-colour affair, and the idea is to order, share and eat at your own pace. Most aspects of the cuisine are covered, and there's plenty to applaud: reporters have enjoyed ika natto (raw squid with fermented soy beans), and, from the yakimono section, splendid yaki soba noodles with vegetables and fiery kimuchi (pickled cabbage). Maguro steak (pan-fried tuna with shiitake and shimeji mushrooms) has also passed the 'super-fresh' test. A full range of hot and cold sakés is available, along with several teas (including a 'Welsh' version). House wine is £11.50.

Chefs: Yoshiko Evans and Akira Shiraishi **Proprietors:** Iestyn and Yoshiko Evans **Open:** Mon to Sat 12 to 2, 5 to 10.30, Sun 12 to 9.30 **Closed:** 25 Dec, 1 Jan **Meals:** alc (main courses £2 to £9). Set L and D £17 to £30 **Service:** not inc **Cards:** Amex, Delta, Diners, Maestro, MasterCard, Visa **Details:** 95 seats. 10 seats outside. Private parties: 80 main room, 12 to 25 private rooms. Vegetarian meals. No-smoking area. Wheelchair access (also WC). Music

Le Monde

AR

60–62 St Mary's Street, Cardiff CF10 1FE
Tel: (029) 2038 7376

Live-wire city-centre venue with a 'no bookings' policy and its own way of doing things. Join the queue, choose from the meat and fish displays, check the salad bar and find a table. Chargrilling is applied to everything from sirloin steaks (£14) to Cornish lobster; other items range from yellowtail snapper fillet with lemon butter to duck breast with hoisin sauce (£13). Start with, say, baked mussels (£4.75). House wine £10.95. Closed Sun. There's also a branch at The Pavilion, Triangle West, Clifton, Bristol; tel: (0117) 934 0999.

Woods Brasserie

The Pilotage Building, Stuart Street, Cardiff CF10 5BW
Tel: (029) 2049 2400

Cooking 2 | Modern European | £30–£60

By the water's edge in the old pilotage building overlooking Cardiff Bay, Woods is every inch the humming city brasserie, right down to its shining metal, blond woodwork and bright lights. The place has its own infectious energy – thanks partly to 'wonderful hosts' and friendly staff. The kitchen takes a contemporary view of things, embracing crispy pigs' trotters with celeriac and apple salad and baked cannon of lamb on rösti with cherry tomato and garlic dressing, as well as Caesar salad, fish and chips and Bakewell tart. The wine list contains some intriguing, little-known European names, with prices from £14.95.

Chef: Sean Murphy **Proprietor:** Choice Produce Ltd **Open:** all week L 12 to 2 (3 Sun), Mon to Sat D 7 to 10 (6.30 to 10 Sat) **Meals:** alc (main courses £10 to £18.50). Set L £12.50 (2 courses) to £15.50, Set D £29.95 (min 8) **Service:** not inc, 10% (optional) for parties of 6 or more **Cards:** Amex, Delta, Diners, Maestro, MasterCard, Visa **Details:** 80 seats. 30 seats outside. Private parties: 50 main room, 30 to 50 private rooms. Vegetarian meals. Children's helpings. No smoking. Wheelchair access (also WC). Music. Air-conditioned

MAP 4 **Castlemorris** PEMBROKESHIRE

Tides

AR

Llangloffan Farm, Castlemorris SA62 5ET
Tel: (01348) 891383

Enterprising venture linked to the Llangloffan Farm and Cheese Centre. In the evening, carefully sourced ingredients point up dishes like local goats' cheese and tomato tart (£6.25) and organic chicken breast with sweet Thai dressing (£15). Fish also fares well: Abercastle crabs or sea bass with basil-infused cream sauce. Honest desserts (£5) include white chocolate and raspberry tart. Café food at lunchtime. House wine £11. Open Apr to Oct Mon to Sat L and Wed to Sat D; Nov to Mar Fri and Sat D only.

MAP 4 **Clytha** MONMOUTHSHIRE

Clytha Arms

Clytha NP7 9BW
Tel: (01873) 840206
Website: www.clytha-arms.com

Cooking 3 | Modern Welsh | £29–£55

A welcoming hostelry not far from Abergavenny and Raglan Castle, the Clytha Arms manages to cater for locals dropping in for real ales and bar snacks, overnight guests, and seekers after good, locally based food. Longhorn beef, wild boar from Usk, organic poultry from Chepstow and fish from West Wales boats all feature on the enterprising menus. Look to the blackboard for fish and shell-fish options, or choose a plate of charcuterie with celeriac rémoulade, or leek and laverbread rissoles with beetroot chutney, with main courses running the gamut from monkfish in fino sherry with herb risotto, to roast duck with burnt orange, sauced with shiraz. A patriotic selection of Welsh cheeses is the alternative to desserts such as meringue garnished with red fruits, or chocolate pancake with rum cream.

An ambitious slate of wines features both classics and new trends likes Heartland Petit Verdot from Australia (£17.80); the result is tempting bottles at good prices in all regions. House wines are just £11.95 and there is a well-considered page of half-bottles.

Chefs: Andrew and Sarah Canning **Proprietors:** Beverley and Andrew Canning **Open:** Tue to Sun L 12.30 to 2.15 (2.30 Sun), Tue to Sat D 7 to 9.30 **Meals:** alc (main courses £12 to £20). Set L and D £18.95. Bar menu available (exc Sat eve) **Service:** not inc, card slips closed **Cards:** Amex, Delta, Diners, Maestro, MasterCard, Visa **Details:** 60 seats. 30 seats outside. Private parties: 45 main room, 10 to 20 private rooms. Car park. Vegetarian meals. Children's helpings. No smoking. No music **Accommodation:** 4 rooms, all with bath/shower. TV. Room only £50 to £90. Baby facilities

MAP 7 **Colwyn Bay** CONWY

Café Niçoise

124 Abergele Road, Colwyn Bay LL29 7PG
Tel: (01492) 531555

The kitchen at this congenial neighbourhood bistro in a row of terraced houses brings on board ingredients from local and faraway sources for simple modern dishes. Expect everything from salad of pan-fried scallops with truffle dressing (£6) and loin of Welsh lamb with celeriac purée and red wine sauce (£15) to roast barramundi with green-lipped mussels and spring vegetable pilau. The assiette of desserts (£6.75) is a well-liked – if substantial – assortment. Carefully selected wines from £12. Closed Sun, Mon and L Tue.

NEW ENTRY	This appears after the restaurant's name if the establishment was not a main entry in last year's Guide, although it may have been a 'round-up/also recommended' in previous editions.

MAP 7 **Conwy** CONWY

Castle Hotel, Shakespeare's Restaurant

NEW ENTRY

High Street, Conwy LL32 8DB
Tel: (01492) 582800
Website: www.castlewales.co.uk

Cooking 3 | Modern Welsh | £27–£55

At the heart of historic Conwy, this coaching inn has been tastefully revamped since 2000 and is making itself a reputation, thanks largely to the food served in its spacious Shakespeare's restaurant. Painted scenes from the bard's plays decorate the walls, and the menu celebrates Welsh produce in a respectful, modern way. A starter of crispy belly pork on 'our own recipe' black pudding with a white bean purée impressed an inspector, as did a duo of Welsh lamb with pease pudding and cardamom-glazed carrots. There are also more distant influences, reflected in, say, seared fillet of local sea bass with coconut and coriander risotto, ginger-scented pak choi and tomato pickle. An admirable selection of Welsh cheeses sits alongside desserts like rhubarb and walnut tart with 'pink peppercorn' poached rhubarb. The wine list provides plentiful everyday drinking (from £11.75) and some grander stuff for special occasions.

Chefs: Graham Tinsley and Gareth Dwyer **Proprietor:** Castle Hotel Conwy Ltd **Open:** Sun L 12.30 to 2.30, all week D 7 to 9.30 **Closed:** 25 and 26 Dec **Meals:** alc (main courses £16 to £20). Set L Sun £14.95 (2 courses) to £16.95. Bar menu available **Service:** 10% (optional), card slips closed **Cards:** Amex, Delta, Maestro, MasterCard, Visa **Details:** 100 seats. 12 seats outside. Private parties: 60 main room. Car park. Vegetarian meals. Children's helpings. No smoking. Wheelchair access (also WC). Music **Accommodation:** 28 rooms, all with bath/shower. TV. Phone. B&B £72 to £290. Baby facilities

MAP 4 **Crickhowell** POWYS

Bear Hotel

High Street, Crickhowell NP8 1BW
Tel: (01873) 810408
Website: www.bearhotel.co.uk

Cooking 2 | Modern Welsh | £26–£55

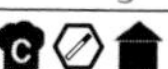

This fifteenth-century coaching inn has been run by the Hindmarshes for nigh on three decades, and it gives every impression of being the social hub of this small market town. Certainly the kitchen attempts to please all palates with grilled lamb burgers and steamed game pudding in the bar, and more ambitious cooking in the restaurant: grilled sardines with tomato tart, chorizo, aubergine caviar and tapenade dressing, for example, or slow-roast shoulder of lamb and herb-crusted loin with dauphinois potatoes, confit hotpot vegetables and parsnip purée. Treacle sponge or sticky toffee pudding may turn up at dessert stage. Service is friendly and prices kind, with house wines £10.50.

Chef: Justin Howe **Proprietors:** Stephen and Judy Hindmarsh **Open:** Sun L 12 to 2, Tue to Sat D 7 to 9.30 **Meals:** alc exc Sun L (main courses £12.50 to £21). Set L Sun £16.95. Bar menu available **Service:** not inc **Cards:** Amex, Delta, Maestro, MasterCard, Visa **Details:** 80 seats. 40 seats outside. Private parties: 60 main room. Car park. Vegetarian meals. Children's helpings. No smoking in 1 dining room. Wheelchair access (also WC). Music. Air-conditioned **Accommodation:** 34 rooms, all with bath/shower. TV. Phone. B&B £59 to £144. Rooms for disabled. Baby facilities

Beaufort

AR

Beaufort Street, Crickhowell NP8 1AD
Tel: (01873) 810402

Updated town-centre coaching inn now functioning as a stylish modern restaurant. The cooking is in the hands of a new team, who draw on Welsh meat and Cornish fish for a carte that travels from tian of crab with ratatouille and squid ink dressing (£6.50) via rump of Brecon lamb with basil mash and tagine sauce (£15.25) to lemon posset with summer fruit compote. A separate seafood menu is also on offer. Closed Mon in winter.

Nantyffin Cider Mill Inn

Brecon Road, Crickhowell NP8 1SG
Tel: (01873) 810775
Website: www.cidermill.co.uk

Cooking 2 | Modern Welsh-Plus | £26–£57

In existence since the sixteenth century, this erstwhile drovers' inn and cider mill beside the River Usk is a big and popular place. Fish and shellfish are listed on a blackboard, not the printed menu – an indication of the importance the kitchen gives to good sourcing – and could take in seared fresh scallops with wild rocket and chilli jam to start, followed by a simply grilled whole lemon sole with parsley and lemon butter. Organically reared and free-range meats and poultry from the inn's own farm in Llangynidr predominate, with the likes of confit of lamb with creamed herb mash and rosemary garlic sauce, or steamed beef and vegetable pudding with rich red-wine and onion sauce delivered in generous portions. To finish, there could be good old treacle tart, or sticky toffee pudding, alongside a selection of Welsh cheeses.

An imaginative and good-value line-up of wines is arranged by style. Bottles start at £13 and well-rated contemporary names abound, including Hureau in Saumur, Vauroux in Chablis and Shadowfax in Australia.

Chef: Sean Gerrard **Proprietors:** Sean Gerrard and Glyn and Jess Bridgeman **Open:** Tue to Sun L 12 to 2.30, Tue to Sat D 6.30 to 9.30 **Closed:** 25 and 26 Dec **Meals:** alc (main courses £8 to £17). Set L Tue to Fri £10 (2 courses) to £12.95, Set D (Tue to Thur) £10 (2 courses) to £12.95 **Service:** not inc, card slips closed **Cards:** Amex, Delta, Maestro, MasterCard, Visa **Details:** 100 seats. 45 seats outside. Private parties: 60 main room. Car park. Vegetarian meals. Children's helpings. No smoking. Wheelchair access (also WC). No music **Accommodation:** 23 rooms, all with bath/shower. TV. Phone. B&B £90 to £120. Swimming pool. Fishing

MAP 4 Cwmbach POWYS

Drawing Room AR

Cwmbach LD2 3RT
Tel: (01982) 552493

In the middle of nowhere, on the A470 'twixt Cwmbach and Newbridge-on-Wye', this Georgian country residence has been taken over by Colin and Melanie Dawson, who put the Talkhouse, Pontdolgoch, on the map a few years ago. Expect spick and span décor, piped jazz and a short menu that might include Cardigan Bay crab and avocado salad (£8), Welsh black beef fillet with a panaché of baby vegetables and chestnut and mushroom purée (£19.50) and lemon sabayon tart with honeyed mascarpone (£6.25). House wines from £12.95. Accommodation. Closed Sun and Mon.

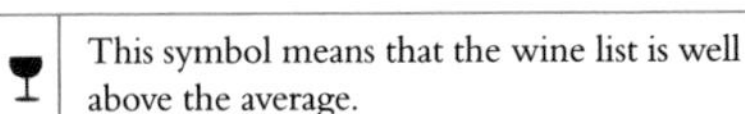

🍷	This symbol means that the wine list is well above the average.
🍾	This symbol means that the restaurant has a truly outstanding wine cellar.

MAP 7 Dolgellau GWYNEDD

Dylanwad Da

2 Ffôs-y-Felin, Dolgellau LL40 1BS
Tel: (01341) 422870
Website: www.dylanwad.co.uk

Cooking 2 | Bistro | £26–£44

The name means something like 'good influence', and is a play on chef-patron Dylan Rowlands' name. It signifies a refreshingly down-to-earth town-centre venue on a restrained scale, catering for barely more than two dozen covers when full, and mostly opening just three nights a week. Choose from a fixed-price menu or the carte for cooking that achieves great consistency. Sesame-dressed salad of Chinese-style pork might be followed by Burgundy lamb casserole, or smoked haddock and mushroom bake by Spanish chicken with tomato and chorizo sauce, as different styles are mixed and matched. Finish with apple and mincemeat pancake with vanilla ice cream, or stewed fruits with honey and cinnamon. Service wears a smile. There are no slouches on the short wine list, which benefits from Dylan Rowlands' personal enthusiasm. Most bottles are under £20 and represent exceptional value.

Chef/Proprietor: Dylan Rowlands **Open:** Thur to Sat (Tue to Sat Easter, Whit bank hol and summer) D only 7 to 9. Open for coffee and cakes 11 to 3. **Closed:** Feb **Meals:** alc (main courses £10 to £15). Set L and D £17.50 **Service:** not inc **Cards:** none **Details:** 28 seats. Private parties: 28 main room. Vegetarian meals. Children's helpings. No smoking. Wheelchair access (not WC). Music. No mobile phones

MAP 7 Eglwysfach POWYS

Ynyshir Hall

Eglwysfach SY20 8TA
Tel: (01654) 781209
Website: www.ynyshir-hall.co.uk

Cooking 8 | Modern British | £42–£108

The lane to Ynyshir Hall is a cul-de-sac, ending in an RSPB nature reserve with a hide from which you can spy on the ducks. Therapy Weekends of various kinds are a feature at the hotel, but, to some, simply being there is therapeutic enough. The expansive grounds are crammed with rhododendrons, and the hall – once a favoured retreat of

Queen Victoria – sits in a natural amphitheatre of wooded hills. Rob and Joan Reen have been working hard since 1989 to achieve and maintain the high standards with which the place is run. Rob's own bright watercolours and oils hang everywhere, and the front-of-house works in a major key, with free-flowing conversation and a distinct absence of standing on ceremony making guests feel at ease.

In Adam Simmonds, who joined the team in early 2004, they also have an outstanding chef. 'There seems to be no end to his imagination,' commented our inspector, 'which is innovative without being outlandish or unbalanced, and textural combinations are as carefully thought out as flavour combinations.' Although dishes are complex, every detail seems to belong, and the raw materials, including meats from a nearby butcher with his own abattoir, are exceptional.

A springtime feature dish was two fillets of red mullet, laid across a slice of foie gras, in turn bedded on a slew of crisp-textured Puy lentils, alongside a pool of thinly puréed melon, an astonishing exercise in original contrasts. An October dinner opened with a flawless risotto of firm langoustines, given depth by a mixture of ceps and truffles. Langoustines might also turn up in a main course with loin of rabbit, making for a subtle yet compelling juxtaposition of flavours, sauced with a complex stock reduction and adorned with spring vegetables. The traditional British fondness for fruit and game combinations might be celebrated in autumn with a serving of neatly jointed, tender roast grouse with salsify, puréed celeriac and blackberries, another consummately accomplished dish.

'Heaven in a copper pot' was one reporter's verdict on her dessert of a plum soufflé, 'risen to dizzy heights', with a scoop of cardamom ice cream dropped into the centre, and a high-octane plum sauce added. Should the cheese selection beckon, expect not merely a plate of Celtic and French samples but also a soufflé of Stinking Bishop, sorbets of apple and celery, and a glass of port to boot. It all adds up to the finest dining in Wales.

The wine list focuses on Bordeaux and Burgundy with vintages going all the way back to 1945 and picks out the key players in other regions. Solid selections elsewhere are led by Italy. A dozen desirable house recommendations from £18 to £45 also come by the glass and there's a notable collection of halves.

Chef: Adam Simmonds **Proprietors:** Rob and Joan Reen **Open:** all week 12.30 to 1.30, 7 to 8.45 **Closed:** 3 Jan to 1 Feb **Meals:** Set L £29.50 to £34.50, Set D £52 to £70. Light L menu available Mon to Sat **Service:** not inc, card slips closed **Cards:** Amex, Delta, Diners, Maestro, MasterCard, Visa **Details:** 32 seats. Private parties: 24 main room, 14 private room. Car park. Vegetarian meals. No children under 9. No smoking. Wheelchair access (not WC). Occasional music. No mobile phones **Accommodation:** 9 rooms, all with bath/shower. TV. Phone. B&B £110 to £350. No children under 9

MAP 4 **Felinfach** POWYS

Felin Fach Griffin

Felinfach LD3 0UB
Tel: (01874) 620111
Website: www.eatdrinksleep.ltd.uk

Cooking 3 | Modern British | £28–£54

Out in the wilds between the Black Mountains and the Brecon Beacons, this old stone hostelry continues to do its job as a provider of sustenance. The Inkins now grow some of their own produce and buy just about everything else locally: expect full-blooded, earthy flavours across the board. Wood pigeon on crushed new potatoes with black winter truffle, and skewered quail with braised Puy lentils and cep cappuccino set the tone, before venison with autumn fruits and dauphinois potatoes, ribeye steak with béarnaise and chips, or tuna with aubergine caviar and sauce vierge. Desserts have a boozy Continental flavour – perhaps yoghurt mousse with sangria fig compote, or vanilla crème brûlée with piña colada. Welsh cheese ploughman's and open sandwiches are tacked on at lunchtime. The well-chosen wine list kicks off with 'open wines' from £2.80 a glass, £11.95 a bottle.

Chef: Ricardo van Ede **Proprietors:** Charles and Edmund Inkin **Open:** Tue to Sun and bank hol Mon L 12.30 to 2.30 (3 Sun), all week D 7 (6.30 Apr to Aug) to 9.30 **Closed:** 24 to 26 Dec **Meals:** alc (main courses L £8 to £10, D £10.50 to £16.10) **Service:** not inc, card slips closed **Cards:** Delta, Maestro, MasterCard, Visa **Details:** 50 seats. 30 seats outside. Private parties: 60 main room, 10 to 25 private rooms. Car park. Vegetarian meals. Children's helpings. No smoking in 1 dining room. Wheelchair access (also WC). Music **Accommodation:** 7 rooms, all with bath/shower. Phone. B&B £60 to £115. Baby facilities

MAP 7 Glanwydden CONWY

Queen's Head

AR

Glanwydden LL31 9JP
Tel: (01492) 546570

For more than 20 years Robert and Sally Cureton have been welcoming and feeding all-comers to their neat and tidy village pub/restaurant. Sautéed local mussels topped with smoked Llanrwst Cheddar, dressed Conwy crab, and rack of Welsh lamb in a mustard and rosemary crust fly the flag, but the kitchen also branches out for Thai crispy duck (£12.50), and belly pork with black pudding and an apple and Calvados jus (£10.50). Accommodation in nearby Storehouse Cottage. Open all week.

MAP 7 Harlech GWYNEDD

Castle Cottage

Y Llech, Harlech LL46 2YL
Tel: (01766) 780479
Website: www.castlecottageharlech.co.uk

Cooking 2 | Modern Welsh | £40–£50

The sitting rooms and tiny bar of this simple restaurant close to Harlech Castle are a 'positive hotchpotch' taking in a collection of hats and a selection of ornaments and pictures of pigs. There's no fancy menu-speak here, and the broadly contemporary dishes offer as much local produce as the kitchen can muster, with some interesting twists and turns. Warm barbecue chicken with bacon, mango and croûtons on a mixed-leaf salad with poppy-seed dressing has been declared a 'delicious start to the meal', while cream of asparagus soup is served with separate pots of Gruyère and croûtons. Main courses maintain a modern focus, from 'tiny pink noisettes' of loin of lamb with a piquant ratatouille strudel and a port and rosemary jus, to Dover sole served with a skewer of fresh prawns and a dish of tarragon mayonnaise. Desserts, however, proved uneven at inspection, and service doesn't quite match the kitchen's output. The succinct, well-chosen wine list favours New World countries and offers good value from £13.95.

Chefs: Glyn Roberts and Ryan Britland **Proprietors:** Glyn and Jacqueline Roberts **Open:** all week D only 7 to 9 **Closed:** 3 weeks Jan **Meals:** Set D £27.50 **Service:** not inc, card slips closed **Cards:** Delta, Maestro, MasterCard, Visa **Details:** 45 seats. Private parties: 45 main room. Vegetarian meals. Children's helpings. No smoking. Wheelchair access (not WC). No music. No mobile phones **Accommodation:** 7 rooms, all with bath/shower. TV. B&B £60 to £110. Rooms for disabled. Baby facilities

Maes-y-Neuadd

Talsarnau, Harlech LL47 6YA
Tel: (01766) 780200
Website: www.neuadd.com

Cooking 4 | Modern Welsh | £26–£58

Little changes at this granite, slate-roofed manor house, where the combination of outdoor pursuits (great walking country) and indoor comfort is still a beguiling one. Views of surrounding Snowdonia are impressive, rooms are comfortable, and the whole place feels warm and inviting. Much of the success derives from Peter Jackson's admirably straightforward style, which makes good use of local raw materials, including its own garden for fruit, vegetables and herbs. At lunchtime, old favourites of rillettes of game with home-made chutney, beef and ale stew with dumplings, or grilled pork chops with apple compote are found alongside a deep-fried parcel of smoked duck and ginger, and salmon in a black olive crust. Dinner offers more complexity and less choice: expect pan-fried sea bass with spaghetti of vegetables and olive oil dressing, for example, then fillet of Welsh beef topped with oyster mushroom mousse served with garlic potatoes. To finish, interesting Welsh cheeses vie for attention with bananas and strawberries glazed with a coconut sabayon. The wine list aims to please, with a page of options under £16 and a New World-first format, but France takes the honours, with reliable names in all regions and some classics in older vintages. Nine come by the glass.

Chefs: Peter Jackson and John Jones **Proprietors:** Peter and Lynn Jackson, and Peter and Doreen Payne **Open:** all week 12 to 1.45, 7 to 8.45 **Meals:** alc L Mon to Sat (main courses £7 to £11). Set L Thur £12.95 (2 courses, inc wine), Set L Sun £15.75, Set D £33 to £37. Tapas and light menu available **Service:** not inc **Cards:** Amex, Delta, Maestro, MasterCard, Visa **Details:** 60 seats. 20 seats outside. Private parties: 50 main room, 2 to 15 private rooms. Car park. Vegetarian meals. Children's helpings. No children under 8 in restaurant after 7pm. No smoking. Wheelchair access (also WC). Occasional music. No mobile phones **Accommodation:** 16 rooms, all with bath/shower. TV. Phone. B&B £65 to £165. Rooms for disabled. Baby facilities

MAP 7 Hawarden FLINTSHIRE

Hawarden Brasserie

68 The Highway, Hawarden CH5 3DH
Tel: (01244) 536353
Website: www.thehawardenbrasserie.com

Cooking 2 | Modern European | £28–£51

Mark Jones and Neal Bates set up shop in these intimate village premises in 1998 and subsequently added the more spacious Brasserie 10/16 to their portfolio (see entry, Chester, England). The Hawarden original boasts a cool, cream interior and it takes a straightforward modern approach to things culinary, serving sea bass with wok-fried vegetables, saffron potatoes, crème fraîche and red-pepper coulis, and pan-fried duck breast with celeriac and parsnip mash, apple fritters, honey, orange and Calvados sauce. Goats' cheese, aubergine and red-pepper terrine might set the ball rolling, while desserts could include baked lemon tart with lime sorbet and raspberry coulis. 'Express' weekday lunches are a promising deal and the wine list provides keenly priced drinking from £9.95.

Chef: Mark Jones **Proprietors:** Neal Bates and Mark Jones **Open:** Mon to Fri and Sun L 12 to 2, all week D 6 to 9.15 (9.45 Fri and Sat) **Meals:** alc (main courses £10 to £17.50). Set L £9.95 (2 courses), D £11.95 (2 courses). Light L menu available **Service:** not inc **Cards:** Amex, Delta, Maestro, MasterCard, Visa **Details:** 60 seats. Private parties: 30 main room, 18 to 24 private rooms. Vegetarian meals. Children's helpings. Music

MAP 7 Hendrerwydd DENBIGHSHIRE

White Horse Inn

Hendrerwydd LL16 4LL
Tel: (01824) 790218
Website: www.white-horse-inn.co.uk

Cooking 2 | Modern European | £30–£53

Overlooking the rich acres of the Clwyd Valley north of Ruthin, this animated country pub/restaurant successfully blends traditional watering hole with understated modern dining room. 'Extra mature' Welsh steaks loom large on the menu, but you could also choose Chinese-style sea bass, or roast duck breast with spiced plum, red wine and orange sauce. Start with filo-wrapped Thai prawns with sweet chilli sauce, or smoked salmon, leek and sweet potato cakes with chive sauce, and conclude with apple and cinnamon crumble, bread-and-butter pudding, or cheeses from Wales or France. Locals and walkers in the bar can now feast on spit-roast chicken and pork (pre-ordering essential). The lively wine list (from £10.95) is peppered with attractive bottles and it's worth dipping into the special 'cellar selection'.

Chefs: Ruth Vintr, Chris Hurst and Graham Ryder **Proprietors:** Ruth and Vit Vintr **Open:** Tue to Sun 12 to 2.30, 6 to 9.15 (8.30 Sun in spring/summer, closed Sun evening in winter) **Closed:** 25 and 29 Dec, 1 Jan, bank hols **Meals:** alc (main courses £11.50 to £18). Bar menu available **Service:** not inc, card slips closed **Cards:** Delta, Maestro, MasterCard, Visa **Details:** 70 seats. 30 seats outside. Private parties: 35 main room. Car park. Vegetarian meals. No children under 12 after 9.30pm. No music

MAP 4 Laugharne CARMARTHENSHIRE

Cors

Laugharne SA33 4SH
Tel: (01994) 427219

Cooking 3 | Modern Welsh | £34–£54

'An enchanting Victorian gentleman's residence', this restaurant is set in well-tended gardens where trees and bog plants grow among sculptures, slated areas and swards of lawn. The kitchen makes full use of local produce, combining sewin, salt-marsh lamb in a rosemary and garlic crust, and Pembrokeshire black beef with ingredients from further afield. Cheese finds its way into a number of starters: figs with Gorgonzola and Parma ham, carpaccio with Parmesan shavings, pears with Roquefort, and a signature dish of smoked haddock 'crème brûlée'. Sewin with new season's asparagus, dauphinois potatoes, and lemon hollandaise was judged 'difficult to better' at a spring dinner, and desserts have included a lightly textured, rich chocolate torte, and lemon tart. The short wine list pulls together some interesting bottles, starting with house French at £11.50, £3 a glass.

Chef/Proprietor: Nick Priestland **Open:** Thur to Sat D only 7 to 9.30 **Closed:** 25 and 26 Dec, 1 Jan **Meals:** alc (main courses £15 to £20) **Service:** not inc **Cards:** none **Details:** 28 seats. 20 seats outside. Private parties: 24 main room. Car park. Vegetarian meals. No children under 8. No smoking in 1 dining room. Wheelchair access (not WC). Music **Accommodation:** 2 rooms, both with bath/shower. B&B £40 to £80. No children under 8

MAP 4 **Letterston** PEMBROKESHIRE

Something's Cooking

AR

The Square, Letterston SA62 5SB
Tel: (01348) 840621

Platefuls of golden-battered cod (£5) or haddock, mountains of chips, and Pembrokeshire crab cakes with home-made tartare sauce are the specialities of this well-regarded fish-and-chip restaurant. With its children's menu and the flexibility of eating in or taking away, it's a godsend to families on holiday. Start with potted shrimps (£3.25) or a jug of prawns (£3.50), and finish with meringue with lemon cream, or apple and apricot pie. In between there are non-fishy items like barbecued spare ribs (£6.75), and teapot refills are free. Closed Sun and Mon; open Mon July, Aug and bank hols.

MAP 7 **Llanarmon Dyffryn Ceiriog** WREXHAM

West Arms

NEW ENTRY

Llanarmon Dyffryn Ceiriog LL20 7LD
Tel: (01691) 600665
Website: www.thewestarms.co.uk

Cooking 3 | Anglo-French | £31–£57

Standing in the Ceiriog valley at the foot of the Berwyn mountains in a 'seriously remote location', this whitewashed, creeper-clad hotel has been welcoming guests since 1670. The 'gem of an olde-worlde country pub' has an interior consisting of a warren of rooms with slate floors, beams, antiques and log fires, and young, cheery staff are all part of the deal. Making the most of local ingredients, the kitchen might turn out a starter of smoked duck in a salad of watercress, roast walnuts and orange with a port and redcurrant dressing. To follow, roast fillet of organic Welsh lamb comes with a buttery shallot sauce and minted mangetout, while chargrilled smoked chicken breast on steamed leeks, bacon and avocado finished with a sweet chilli and satay sauce has been described as 'seriously delectable and unusual'. Finish with orange pannacotta with roast figs, or mango and white chocolate cheesecake. The wine list has a number of French and New World bottles under £20, with own-label Chilean red and white at £14.95.

Chef: Grant Williams **Proprietors:** Gill and Geoff Leighford **Open:** Sun L 12 to 2, all week D 7 to 9 **Meals:** alc L (main courses £8.50 to £17). Set D £27.95 (2 courses) to £32.90. Bar menu available **Service:** 10% **Cards:** Delta, Maestro, MasterCard, Visa **Details:** 80 seats. 25 seats outside. Private parties: 55 main room. Car park. Vegetarian meals. Children's helpings. No smoking. Music **Accommodation:** 15 rooms, all with bath/shower. TV. Phone. B&B £53.50 to £174. Rooms for disabled. Baby facilities. Fishing

MAP 7 **Llanberis** GWYNEDD

Y Bistro

43–45 High Street, Llanberis LL55 4EU
Tel: (01286) 871278
Website: www.ybistro.co.uk

Cooking 2 | Modern Welsh | £37–£59

Danny and Nerys Roberts opened the doors of their unassuming restaurant in 1979, and their aspirations remain the same: to serve simple, fresh food in a relaxing atmosphere. These are laudable aims, and they get them right. The kitchen makes use of local ingredients, and the repertoire shows influences from far and wide, reflected in starters such as tempura-fried king scallops with Bloody Mary jelly and avocado salsa. On the whole, the style is contemporary, which is to say that it relies on some traditional ideas but brightens them up with, say, vegetable polenta cake and watercress sauce with a grilled fillet of brill, or caramelised shallots and pomegranate sauce to accompany breast and confit leg of guinea fowl. Moules marinière and ribeye with pepper sauce have raised appreciative murmurs, as has the home-made bread, and brown sugar meringues with whipped cream and crushed hazelnuts make a fine finish. House wine is £12.

Chef: Nerys Roberts **Proprietors:** Danny and Nerys Roberts **Open:** Mon to Sat D only 7.30 to 9.45 **Closed:** first 2 weeks Jan, Mon in winter **Meals:** alc (main courses £14 to £20) **Service:** not inc, card slips closed **Cards:** Delta, Maestro, MasterCard, Visa **Details:** 40 seats. Private parties: 44 main room. Vegetarian meals. No smoking in 1 dining room. Wheelchair access (not WC). No music

MAP 4 **Llandewi Skirrid** MONMOUTHSHIRE

Walnut Tree Inn

Llandewi Skirrid NP7 8AW
Tel: (01873) 852797
Website: www.thewalnuttreeinn.com

Cooking 4 | Mediterranean/Italian | £36–£64

The unassuming whitewashed, slate-roofed inn looks much like any other pub, but it is 'now a more modern restaurant' inside. The small front bar has been turned into a lounge with a couple of deep armchairs and a sofa where you can have drinks and read the menu before going on into the restaurant – now much larger than in the old days, with lots of room between the polished wooden tables. This provides a backdrop for modern Italian cooking that takes in starters like roast pigeon with creamed leek and crispy smoked speck – the highlight at inspection – or well-reported scallops and saddle of rabbit wrapped in Parma ham. There is much that satisfies – roast cutlet of lamb and aubergine with potato and goats' cheese gratin, or a crème caramel with poached rhubarb – although reports this year have also highlighted inconsistencies. Service remains 'totally efficient and pleasant'. House wine is £13.50.

Chef: Spencer Ralph **Proprietor:** Francesco Mattioli **Open:** Tue to Sun L 12 to 2.30, Tue to Sat D 7 to 9.30 **Meals:** alc (main courses £15 to £21.50) **Service:** not inc **Cards:** Maestro, MasterCard, Visa **Details:** 65 seats. 20 seats outside. Private parties: 25 main room, 10 to 25 private rooms. Car park. Vegetarian meals. Children's helpings. No-smoking area. Wheelchair access (not WC). Music. Air-conditioned

MAP 7 **Llandrillo** DENBIGHSHIRE

Tyddyn Llan

Llandrillo LL21 0ST
Tel: (01490) 440264
Website: www.tyddynllan.co.uk

Cooking 7 | Modern British | £35–£76

The two-storey grey-stone Georgian house in the Vale of Edeyrnion has been home to Bryan and Susan Webb's hotel since 2002. In summer, meals can be taken on the verandah, with the lush lawns and ornamental fountain as a backdrop. Comfortable armchairs and glowing fires abound inside, and the candlelit dining room is done out in restful Wedgwood blue.

Returning to his native Wales from London was a smart move for Webb, whose cooking has always celebrated the twin virtues of regionality and simplicity. Appetisers alone indicate the commitment, with tiny Glamorgan sausages, salmon mousse, and delicate tartlets of leeks and laverbread on parade at inspection. Griddled scallops are a signature starter that is well worth revisiting – a ring of lightly seared shellfish around a pile of rocket with small spoonfuls of a subtle vegetable relish. Similarly, impeccably fresh langoustines are thought to need nothing more than some well-made mayonnaise and a fine leafy salad. Local lamb comes in for expected plaudits – bright pink cutlets of the loin partnered with tapenade, couscous, roast artichoke and purple-sprouting broccoli – or there might be osso buco served with saffron risotto and gremolata, or the robustness of roast monkfish with lentils and salsa verde. The linking theme is the confidence to serve first-rate ingredients with as little disguise or flummery as possible, a principle that extends to the chocolate plate that musters pastry-wrapped ganache, mousse, and ice cream, while a more experimental impulse might also bring on grilled pineapple with chilli and coconut sorbet, where the sharp, fiery and sweet flavours all pull together magnificently.

As with the food, so with the wine. The list's arrangement by detailed styles is unfussy and clear, and each section unveils a lovingly sourced selection of bottles. California is a constant theme, with stars like Kistler and Sean Thackray and several vintages of Joseph Phelps Insignia joining some fine mature clarets as a final flourish. Half-bottles all look tempting, as do the numerous options by the glass, and prices (from £13.50) are eminently fair.

Chef: Bryan Webb **Proprietors:** Bryan and Susan Webb **Open:** Fri to Sun L 12.30 to 2 (1 to 2.30 Sun), all week D 7 to 9.30 **Closed:** 2 weeks Jan **Meals:** Set L Fri and Sat £19.50 (2 courses) to £25, Set L Sun £21.50, Set D £32 (2 courses) to £42 **Service:** not inc **Cards:** Maestro, MasterCard, Visa **Details:** 36 seats. 14 seats outside. Private parties: 60 main room, 8 to 40 private rooms. Car park. Vegetarian meals. Children's helpings. No smoking. Wheelchair access (also WC). Occasional music. No mobile phones **Accommodation:** 13 rooms, all with bath/shower. TV. Phone. B&B £60 to £200. Rooms for disabled. Baby facilities

MAP 7 **Llandudno** CONWY

Bodysgallen Hall

Llandudno LL30 1RS
Tel: (01492) 584466
Website: www.bodysgallen.com

Cooking 4 | Modern British | £30–£69

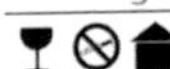

Despite being perched on a high ridge not far south of the Great Orme, Bodysgallen manages to blend in among its surroundings, with just the tips of its chimneys visible from most approaches. It is a country-house hotel in the full-dress style, with comfortable lounges furnished with log fires and the kinds of sofas that seem designed to lull you off to sleep.

It would be unwise to succumb to slumber, though, and miss John Williams's thoroughly accomplished, modern British cooking. There is a gently inventive impulse at work in the conceptions of dishes, which might involve partnering Conwy mussels and scallops with a lightly curried carrot gâteau as one starter, or saucing a warm goats' cheese mousse with cider caramel for another. There is the option of a mid-meal sorbet – too sweet for some – or dive straight into imaginative main courses such as roast medallion of veal with butternut squash, pak choi and Cassis sauce, or fillet of wild sea bass with a leek and lobster tart and lobster butter sauce. For dessert, banana, chocolate and peanut butter torte will prove popular. The wine list majors on France but makes more than a nod to other countries, and every region mixes stars and value options – even Bordeaux. House bottles start at £14.50.

Chef: John Williams **Proprietor:** Historic House Hotels Ltd **Open:** all week 12.30 to 1.45, 7 to 9.30 **Meals:** Set L £17.50 (2 courses) to £19.50, Set D £38. Light L menu available **Service:** net prices, card slips closed **Cards:** Amex, Delta, Maestro, MasterCard, Visa **Details:** 60 seats. Private parties: 55 main room, 30 to 55 private rooms. Car park. Vegetarian meals. No children under 8. Jacket. No smoking. Wheelchair access (also WC). Occasional music. No mobile phones. Air-conditioned **Accommodation:** 35 rooms, all with bath/shower. TV. Phone. B&B £125 to £300. Rooms for disabled. No children under 8. Swimming pool

Richard's

AR

7 Church Walks, Llandudno LL30 2HD
Tel: (01492) 875315

An old name, but new owners at this long-running, stone-walled bistro. Expect 'good strong flavours' and eclectic dishes along the lines of Vietnamese hot-and-sour fishcakes on pickled cucumber salad, or grilled goats' cheese salad with toasted hazelnuts, before crisp-skinned barbecued duckling with cherry and Cassis sauce, or poached halibut thermidor. Desserts include mascarpone and vanilla cheesecake with strawberry coulis. Three courses £24.95. 'Decent wine list', with prices from £12.95. Open Tue to Sat D only.

St Tudno Hotel, Terrace

Promenade, Llandudno LL30 2LP
Tel: (01492) 874411

Website: www.st-tudno.co.uk

Cooking 5 | Modern European | £31–£68

The Victorian hotel on Llandudno's sweeping seafront hardly looks any different from its neighbours; inside, though, the St Tudno is a cut above the rest. The revamped Terrace Restaurant has been well received ('all taupe and navy blue – very elegant'), service is well drilled, and reporters have been generous with their praise of Stephen Duffy's cooking. Local and seasonal produce forms a bedrock, and the kitchen constructs dishes carefully and elaborately around simple but forthright flavour combinations. How about a puff pastry tart of 'squeaky-fresh' red mullet with a tapenade crust, or a 'piquant and delicious' Thai crab cake with pickled cucumber, seared scallops, chilli and orange dressing for starters? Follow that with steamed loin of monkfish with risotto of langoustine, cauliflower purée and a crisp noodle galette, or stick to fillet of Welsh black beef with a red wine sauce, wild mushrooms, glazed shallots, hand-cut chips and béarnaise. The fine materials, craftsmanship and the unsparing attention to detail are visible in a tasting of pistachio dessert – brûlée, ice cream and soufflé – and in an intense peach tea jelly with raspberry foam, grape coulis and a vanilla biscuit.

Features on favoured wine producers including d'Arenberg in Australia and Austrian star Willi Opitz add extra meat to the sizeable global wine list. Classic French wines from excellent vintages are at the core, including plenty in half-bottles. An engaging house line-up opens at £14.50, with around ten by the glass.

Chef: Stephen Duffy **Proprietors:** Martin and Janette Bland **Open:** all week 12.30 to 1.45, 7 to 9.30 (9 Sun) **Meals:** alc D (main courses £17.50 to £22.50). Set L Mon to Sat £15 (2 courses) to £18, Set L Sun £19.50. Bar menu available **Service:** not inc, card slips closed **Cards:** Amex, Delta, Diners, Maestro, MasterCard, Visa **Details:** 60 seats. Private parties: 40 main room. Car park. Vegetarian meals. Children's helpings. No children under 5 at D. No smoking. Wheelchair access (not WC). Occasional music. No mobile phones. Air-conditioned **Accommodation:** 18 rooms, all with bath/shower. TV. Phone. B&B £75 to £230. Baby facilities. Swimming pool

MAP 7 Llanfyllin POWYS

Seeds AR

5 Penybryn Cottages, Llanfyllin SY22 5AP
Tel: (01691) 648604

Mark and Felicity Seager make a great team at this totally unpretentious cottage restaurant. Honest, uncomplicated food is their trademark, and the whole place is 'stamped with authenticity'. Evening menus are fixed price (£21-£23); Sunday lunch is a blackboard of bistro dishes like warm tomato and dolcelatte pastry (£4), fillet steak with green peppercorn sauce (£15), and old-fashioned bread-and-butter pudding (£3.75). The 150-strong wine list is a corker, and prices are 'not grabbing'. Open Thur to Sun L and Wed to Sat D.

MAP 4 Llangammarch Wells POWYS

Lake Country House

Llangammarch Wells LD4 4BS
Tel: (01591) 620202
Website: www.lakecountryhouse.co.uk

Cooking 4 | Modern British | £40–£65

This imposing Victorian house with its Tudor-style façade is in a splendid elevated setting in the Irfon valley, with the river tumbling southwards beyond the well-trimmed sweeping lawns. An enormous lounge and elegant dining room await within, and although the tone is professionally solicitous it soon relaxes as the spread of exciting canapés arrives. A no-choice soup starts things off in fine style, a silky oyster velouté with leeks and chives finding favour at an inspection visit. The remaining courses showcase Sean Cullingford's preferred idiom, which seems characterised by great intricacy, with some main dishes taking four or five lines to describe on the menus. A starter might turn up on two plates, involving poached Cornish haddock on pak choi with shallot and garlic cream, some seared scallop slices and a shot glass of mushroom consommé. So far, so modish. Twice-baked Roquefort soufflé is more traditional and is accompanied by pear (albeit poached in red wine) and rocket. The labour-intensiveness of it all pays off in main courses like meaty-textured turbot fillet served with pancetta, Savoy cabbage, roast salsify, confit garlic, Parmentier potatoes and a Sauternes sauce, which manages to retain impressive balance. The cheese trolley has a number of well-kept Welsh specimens to recommend it, while dessert options run to green apple parfait with rhubarb compote, apple sorbet and cumin nougatine. The wine list opens with an enticing round-up of affordable bottles from £17 but really hits its stride with top growers in Burgundy and mature Bordeaux. Short international selections make up the balance.

Chef: Sean Cullingford **Proprietors:** J.P. and J.E. Mifsud **Open:** all week 12.30 to 1.45, 7.15 to 9.15 **Meals:** Set L £24.50, Set D £37.50 **Service:** not inc, card slips closed **Cards:** Amex, Delta, Diners, Maestro, MasterCard, Visa **Details:** 40 seats. 12 seats outside. Private parties: 80 main room. Car park. Vegetarian meals. Children's helpings. No children under 8 at D. No smoking. Wheelchair access (also WC). No music. No mobile phones **Accommodation:** 19 rooms, all with bath/shower. TV. Phone. B&B £110 to £245. Rooms for disabled. Baby facilities. Fishing

MAP 4 Llanrhidian SWANSEA

Welcome to Town

Llanrhidian SA3 1EH
Website: www.thewelcometotown.co.uk

Cooking 3 | Classical/Modern Welsh | £27–£59

Despite its name, this self-styled bistro occupies a defunct 300-year-old pub on the north Gower coast overlooking the Loughor estuary. Inside, it is smart, comfortable and cottagey, with white walls, dark beams and a tiny bar. Welsh black beef and lamb, local seafood and other close-to-home ingredients make their presence felt on the short, modern menus: free-range chicken and wild mushroom raviolo is served on buttery braised leeks with cep sauce, seasonal asparagus appears as a mille-feuille, and steamed fillet of 'native' sea bass comes on crushed new potatoes with chive velouté. Desserts are a strong point, judging by a 'masterly' cappuccino brûlée, and an iced raspberry parfait on pistachio meringue. The short world-wide wine list opens with a clutch of bottles from the Languedoc at £12.

Chef: Ian Bennett **Proprietors:** Ian and Jay Bennett **Open:** Tue to Sun L 12 to 2, Tue to Sat D 7 to 9.30 **Closed:** 25 to 27 Dec, last two weeks Feb, 24 Oct to 2 Nov **Meals:** alc (main courses £15 to £19). Set L £12.95 (2 courses) to £15.95 **Service:** not inc, card slips closed **Cards:** Maestro, MasterCard, Visa **Details:** 40 seats. 20 seats outside. Private parties: 35 main room. Car park. Vegetarian meals. Children's helpings. No smoking. Wheelchair access (not WC). Music. No mobile phones

MAP 7 Llansanffraid Glan Conwy CONWY

Old Rectory Country House

Llanrwst Road, Llansanffraid Glan Conwy LL28 5LF
Tel: (01492) 580611
Website: www.oldrectorycountryhouse.co.uk

Cooking 5 | Modern French/British | £57–£78

Michael and Wendy Vaughan are well embarked on their third decade of operations at this country house not far from Conwy. Gutted by fire in the eighteenth century, the house was renovated in the Georgian style in 1810. It is reached by a steep drive, and is packed with fine antiques, some in glass display cases. Michael Vaughan runs the front-of-house with exceedingly personable aplomb, so that the air of a particularly jovial house party reigns most evenings.

Wendy cooks a no-choice menu for starter and main, with options for desserts or cheese to follow. The drill is generally, though by no means always, fish then meat, as was the case at a January dinner that began with translucently cooked, artichoke-scaled cod fillet with sharp celeriac rémoulade and a creamy wholegrain mustard sauce, and proceeded to loin of Welsh mountain lamb – pink, sweet and tender – crusted with anchovies and olives, and served with a tartlet of leeks, laverbread and ricotta, and boulangère potatoes. Another occasion might produce roast wood pigeon with orange and thyme, followed by pork tenderloin with a polenta cake and Calvados sauce. A long plate of three desserts is the signature way to finish, the selections perhaps taking in intense chocolate fondant, papaya-crowned vanilla pannacotta, and refreshing grapefruit sorbet. Clear tasting notes, fair prices and plenty of half-bottles result in an user-friendly and approachable wine list.

Chefs: Wendy Vaughan and Chris Jones **Proprietors:** Michael and Wendy Vaughan **Open:** Tue to Sat and bank hol Sun D only 7.30 for 8.15 (1 sitting) **Meals:** Set D £39.50 **Service:** not inc, card slips closed **Cards:** Delta, Maestro, MasterCard, Visa **Details:** 14 seats. Car park. Children's helpings. No children under 5 exc babies. No smoking. No music **Accommodation:** 6 rooms, all with bath/shower. TV. Phone. B&B £79 to £169. No children under 5 exc babies

MAP 4 Llanwrtyd Wells POWYS

Carlton House

Dol-y-coed Road, Llanwrtyd Wells LD5 4RA
Tel: (01591) 610248
Website: www.carltonrestaurant.co.uk

Cooking 6 | Modern British | £34–£63

A large, foursquare town house painted deep brick-red is home to the Gilchrists' efficiently run hotel. It exudes confidence and relaxation in the right proportions, the twin effects of Alan's capable handling of front-of-house and Mary Ann's experienced skill in the kitchen. An Easter meal delivered plenty of satisfaction in the successive forms of a reconstructed version of avocado crab, the fruit and meat mashed, shredded and layered then topped with an avocado salsa, before halibut served with braised cucumber in linguine guise, with a smoky dressing of butter, lemon and parsley. While a lot of work will have gone into many of the dishes, they somehow never seem overwrought. Scallops are briefly seared and served with Hay-on-Wye air-dried ham and salads with a walnut vinaigrette, after which fillet of local beef might appear alongside a fried polenta cake, sautéed mushrooms, buttered baby leeks and a classic madeira jus. Interesting takes on everyday desserts have included pairing dark chocolate mousse with a peach 'samosa', or poaching fresh figs in spiced Shiraz, accompanied by cinnamon ice cream. The wine list briskly tours the world, not forgetting Wales and fitting in a good range of half-bottles. Chilean and Italian house wines are £12 a bottle, £3.25 a glass.

Chef: Mary Ann Gilchrist **Proprietors:** Alan and Mary Ann Gilchrist **Open:** Mon to Sat D only 7 to 8.30 (L bookings only) **Meals:** alc (main courses £22 to £26). Set D Mon to Thur £25 **Service:** not inc, card slips closed **Cards:** Delta, Maestro, MasterCard, Visa **Details:** 14 seats. No smoking. No music. No mobile phones **Accommodation:** 6 rooms, 5 with bath/shower. TV. B&B £45 to £90

Lasswade Country House AR

Station Road, Llanwrtyd Wells LD5 4RW
Tel: (01591) 610515

A congenial family-run hotel in an Edwardian house close to Llanwrtyd Wells station. Roger Stevens is 'pro-organic', and he makes full use of locally grown produce for a daily fixed-price menu (£26.50) that might open with terrine of ham hock and purple sage with tomatoes and apple chutney, before poached wing of skate with salsa verde, or roast duck breast with beetroot and pear compote. Desserts could include gooseberry syllabub with ginger shortbread. Accommodation. Open all week D only.

MAP 7 **Machynlleth** POWYS

Wynnstay

Maengwyn Street, Machynlleth SY20 8AE
Tel: (01654) 702941
Website: www.wynnstay-hotel.com

Cooking 2 | Modern Welsh | £23–£48

The Wynnstay is an enormous, reputedly haunted, Georgian coaching inn on the main route through Machynlleth. There is a pizzeria to the rear of the premises, but we focus here on the main restaurant, which is distinguished by its orange-yellow colour scheme and a high shelf crammed with decorative china. The cooking uses good local supplies where possible, bringing in air-dried beef and garnishing it with shavings of Llanboidy cheese, and local mallard, the breast served in a main course with champ, Savoy cabbage and an orange and liquorice gravy. Seared scallops were well timed at inspection, served with a couple of creamy corals and a cake of crisp, oily ratatouille, but were let down by heavy peppering, while the rump of lamb main course, with broad beans and roughly crushed potatoes with black olives, offered irreproachable meat but was cooked well past pink. Finish with treacle and walnut tart with custard, or hot chocolate fondant with banana ice cream. The Italian-led wine list shows imagination and has been painstakingly annotated. House wines are £8.50 for a half-litre carafe, or £3 for a standard glass.

Chefs: Gareth Johns and Jim Hamilton **Proprietors:** Charles and Sheila Dark **Open:** Sun L 12 to 2, all week D 6 to 9 **Meals:** Set L £10.95 (2 courses) to £12.95, Set D £25 (2 courses) to £30. Bar menu available **Service:** not inc, card slips closed **Cards:** Amex, Delta, Diners, Maestro, MasterCard, Visa **Details:** 40 seats. Private parties: 50 main room. Car park. Vegetarian meals. Children's helpings. No smoking. Wheelchair access (not WC). Occasional music **Accommodation:** 22 rooms, all with bath/shower. TV. Phone. B&B £55 to £110. Baby facilities

MAP 2 **Nant-y-derry** MONMOUTHSHIRE

Foxhunter

Nant-y-derry NP7 9DN
Tel: (01873) 881101
Website: www.thefoxhunter.com

Cooking 4 | Modern European | £34–£69

This may once have been a typical country pub, but not much solo drinking goes on here now. The tiny bar is effectively a reception area, a place to study menus while sipping an aperitif, with the rest of the pub (warmed by wood burning stoves) given over to tables for eating; but the whole place remains pleasingly informal. Some of Matt Tebbutt's ideas are out of the familiar brasserie mould (spiced sausages with grilled peppers, for example, or hake with buttered spinach and parsley sauce), but the repertoire also encompasses starters like goujons of cod with Thai dip, and a whole baked Vacherin for two to share. Although reports this year have been mixed, good-quality ingredients are evident – in chicken and wild mushroom stew with sprout tops and mash, and in rack of local lamb with creamed Savoy cabbage and bacon – and incidentals such as bread are 'excellent'. Bread-and-butter pudding makes a good finish. A confident wine list presents a well-balanced portfolio from around the world. House wines are £13.50 (£2.50 a glass).

Chef: Matt Tebbutt **Proprietors:** Matt and Lisa Tebbutt **Open:** Tue to Sat 12 to 2.30, 7 to 9.30 **Closed:** 25 and 26 Dec, 2 weeks Feb **Meals:** alc (main courses £15 to £22). Set L £18 (2 courses) to £22 **Service:** not inc, 10% for groups of 8 or more **Cards:** Delta, Maestro, MasterCard, Visa **Details:** 60 seats. 15 seats outside. Private parties: 32 main room, 12 to 32 private rooms. Car park. Vegetarian meals. Children's helpings. No smoking. Wheelchair access (also WC). Music

MAP 2 Newport NEWPORT

Chandlery

77–78 Lower Dock Street, Newport NP20 1EH
Tel: 01633 256622
Website: www.chandleryrestaurant.co.uk

Cooking 4 | Modern European | £22–£57

Described by one visitor as 'period with twenty-first-century makeover' this two-storey restaurant has a light and airy feel. The repertoire draws mainly on European conventions and produces many classic combinations using best-quality Welsh produce; comfort, rather than innovation, is the watchword. One diner started with fresh diver scallops accompanied by rösti potato, black pudding and fresh leaves with lemon dressing, went on to tender, pink, best end of salt marsh lamb with a classic accompaniment of flageolet beans and a rustic mash of potato, swede and chives, then finished with assiette of chocolate. But there might also be crab and sweetcorn spring roll to start, and main courses of seafood bourride, or saddle of venison with braised potatoes, thyme-roast beetroot and a jus flavoured with Black Mountain liqueur. Bread has been well reported; finish maybe with passion fruit and Jersey yoghurt bavarois with pink grapefruit sorbet, or else Welsh farmhouse cheeses. A short wine list offers choice under £20 with six house wines kicking off at £12.95. 'Very helpful, friendly' service puts diners at their ease.

Chefs: Simon Newcombe and Carl Hammett **Proprietor:** Simon Newcombe **Open:** Tue to Fri L 12 to 2, Tue to Sat D 7 to 10 **Closed:** 1 week at Christmas **Meals:** alc L and D (main courses £9.50 to £17). Set L £9.95 (2 courses) to £12.95 **Service:** not inc, 10% (optional) for parties of 6 or more **Cards:** Amex, Delta, Maestro, MasterCard, Visa **Details:** 80 seats. Private parties: 40 main room, 10 to 60 private rooms. Car park. Vegetarian meals. Children's helpings. No smoking. Wheelchair access (also WC). Music. Air-conditioned

MAP 4 Newport PEMBROKESHIRE

Cnapan

East Street, Newport SA42 0SY
Tel: (01239) 820575
Website: www.cnapan.co.uk

Cooking 2 | Modern British | £23–£44

Since 1984, the Coopers and the Lloyds have been custodians of this listed town house in one of Pembrokeshire's coastal jewels (not to be confused with the Newport in South Wales, see entry above). Mother and daughter beaver away productively in the kitchen, making the most of carefully sourced ingredients (including organic vegetables and local seafood). Light lunches are a snip for dishes like smoked salmon and crab tart, while the main menu might start with Anglesey eggs, or fragrant chicken and coriander cakes, before grilled chunks of marinated Welsh lamb on a bed of spinach and apricots. To finish, expect homespun desserts like damson sorbet or ginger steamed pudding. The commendable wine list includes a couple of organics; house selections are £10.50.

Chef: Judith Cooper **Proprietors:** Eluned and John Lloyd and Michael and Judith Cooper **Open:** Wed to Sat and Mon L 12 to 2, Wed to Sun and Mon D 6.45 to 8.45 **Closed:** 25 and 26 Dec, early Jan to mid-March **Meals:** alc L (main courses £7.50 to £11). Set D £21 (2 courses) to £26.50 **Service:** not inc, card slips closed **Cards:** Delta, Maestro, MasterCard, Visa **Details:** 35 seats. 30 seats outside. Car park. Vegetarian meals. Children's helpings. No smoking. Wheelchair access (not WC). Music **Accommodation:** 5 rooms, all with bath/shower. TV. B&B £38 to £76. Baby facilities

MAP 4 Pembroke PEMBROKESHIRE

Old Kings Arms AR

13 Main Street, Pembroke SA71 4JS
Tel: (01646) 683611

This venerable hostelry, owned by the Wheeler family since 1952, remains the hub of local life. Fish from local boats figures strongly on the menu, which covers a lot of ground, from tartare of salmon with citrus topping (£4.75) and monkfish in garlic and parsley butter (£15.50) to pork fillet flamed in brandy with caramelised apples. Homespun desserts (£3.75) include lemon posset. Light meals in the bar. Forty-plus affordable wines from £8.75. Accommodation. Open all week.

MAP 7 Penmaenpool GWYNEDD

Penmaenuchaf Hall

Penmaenpool LL40 1YB
Tel: (01341) 422129
Website: www.penhall.co.uk

Cooking 2 | Modern British | £31–£68

This well-appointed Victorian retreat surveying the Mawwddach estuary from its 21 acres is relaxed and friendly, serene and dignified –

civilised, in short. The kitchen's pursuit of freshness and quality shows in home-made bread, ice cream and petits fours, and industry is apparent throughout: in the herb gnocchi and pommes mousseline with a fillet of beef, or the stuffed cabbage and madeira jus with a roast squab pigeon. Fish understandably features, with varied and appropriate treatments ranging from a Mediterranean-style starter of seared tuna with a salad of confit tomatoes, new potatoes and herb oil, to main-course roast brill with a ragoût of bacon and celery and a red wine jus. Finish with lavender crème brûlée with champagne sorbet.

The wine list, sparkling with interest, starts with three wines of the month and engaging house bottles (including d'Arenberg's Stump Jump) from £14.75. Prices are good, and succinct Bordeaux and Burgundy offerings neatly balance affordability and the desirability. Half-bottles abound.

Chefs: Justin Pilkington, Anthony and Tim Reeve **Proprietors:** Mark Watson and Lorraine Fielding **Open:** all week 12 to 2, 7 to 9.30 (9 Sun) **Meals:** alc D (main courses £20 to £24.50). Set L £15.95 (2 courses) to £17.95, Set D £32.50 **Service:** not inc, card slips closed **Cards:** Delta, Diners, Maestro, MasterCard, Visa **Details:** 34 seats. 8 seats outside. Private parties: 50 main room, 8 to 16 private rooms. Car park. Vegetarian meals. Children's helpings. No children under 6. No smoking. Wheelchair access (also WC). Music **Accommodation:** 14 rooms, all with bath/shower. TV. Phone. B&B £75 to £180. No children under 6 exc babes in arms. Baby facilities. Fishing

MAP 7 **Portmeirion** GWYNEDD

Hotel Portmeirion

Portmeirion LL48 6ET
Tel: (01766) 772440
Website: www.portmeirion-village.com

Cooking 3 | Modern Welsh-Plus | £27–£58

The Italianate village overlooking the Traeth estuary with views to the distant Cambrian Mountains is a rapturous place in which to stay (either in the hotel or in cottages in the village itself). The hotel building is at the bottom of the site by the water's edge, and the curvilinear dining room overlooking the estuary has 'a feel of dining in an ocean liner'. The kitchen seeks out Welsh produce and subjects it to European treatments, praise being registered for an amuse-bouche of a quenelle of crab and avocado with olive oil and dill, a Mediterranean-influenced starter of 'sweet, slow-cooked and jammy' tarte Tatin of plum tomatoes and basil balanced by pesto and balsamic, and a main-course fillet of beef with truffled rösti, baby onions, mushrooms and crispy pancetta with red wine jus. A tendency towards over-complication has been observed by some reporters.

The wine list combines a lively global range with a solid collection of Bordeaux that mixes classic names with newcomers like Roc de Cambes (£34), although Burgundy lovers may feel short-changed. Six house options, all £13.50, also come by the glass (£3.50).

Chefs: Billy Taylor and David Doughty **Proprietor:** Portmeirion Ltd **Open:** all week 12.30 to 2, 6.30 to 9 **Meals:** Set L £17.50 to £18.50, Set D £32.50 to £37.50 **Service:** not inc **Cards:** Amex, Delta, Diners, Maestro, MasterCard, Visa **Details:** 100 seats. Private parties: 100 main room, 10 to 30 private rooms. Car park. Vegetarian meals. Children's helpings. No smoking. Wheelchair access (also WC). No music. No mobile phones **Accommodation:** 51 rooms, all with bath/shower. TV. Phone. Room only £120 to £240. Rooms for disabled. Baby facilities. Swimming pool

MAP 7 **Pwllheli** GWYNEDD

Plas Bodegroes

Nefyn Road, Pwllheli LL53 5TH
Tel: (01758) 612363
Website: www.bodegroes.co.uk

Cooking 6 | Modern Welsh | £29–£70

The perfectly proportioned Georgian manor house is set in secluded gardens, with an avenue of 200-year-old beech trees at the back, but manages not to feel too manorial. A comforting homely feel is helped by the absence of a formal reception desk, and the L-shaped dining room, while spacious and elegant, has a wooden floor, tramline spotlights and lots of colourful modern art on the walls. Chris and Gunna Chown, who have been running the place since the mid-1980s, have set a consistently high standard. Chris's cooking is low key in presentation, based on sound Welsh ingredients (start perhaps with seared halibut in Carmarthen ham served with leeks and laverbread in dill sauce), but with some inspiration coming from further afield. Thai-style monkfish and prawn curry with coconut and coriander is more soup than curry but spicily rewarding nonetheless. Enterprising dishes at inspection included thin-sliced braised lamb's heart sparsely stuffed with sage and apricot on sweet potato purée, a bold restaurant dish if ever there was, and a main course combining tender guinea fowl breast and celeriac chips with pommes dauphinois and a well-reduced madeira sauce. Successful fish treatments have included griddled sole with scallops and salt-cod mash in lemon butter sauce, and a fine rhubarb sorbet accompanied a dessert centred on apple-studded cinnamon biscuits with elderflower custard.

The wine list offers abundance for all-comers, from £14.50 house wines and much else below £25 to a fine cellar of French classics, among which a 1983 Ch. Margaux (£345) shines brightest. Alsace is another strength, and New World countries are approached with equal verve. Dozens of half-bottles too.

Chef: Chris Chown **Proprietors:** Chris and Gunna Chown **Open:** Sun L 12.30 to 2.30, Tue to Sat D 7 to 9.30 **Closed:** Dec to Feb **Meals:** Set L £17.50, Set D £38 **Service:** not inc, card slips closed **Cards:** Delta, Maestro, MasterCard, Visa **Details:** 40 seats. Private parties: 40 main room, 12 to 16 private rooms. Car park. No smoking. Wheelchair access (also WC). Occasional music. No mobile phones **Accommodation:** 11 rooms, all with bath/shower. TV. Phone. B&B £50 to £170. Baby facilities

MAP 4 Reynoldston SWANSEA

Fairyhill

Reynoldston SA3 1BS
Tel: (01792) 390139
Website: www.fairyhill.net

Cooking 4 | Modern Welsh | £33–£64

The ivy-covered, early-Georgian house, set in the middle of the Gower peninsula, is surrounded by 24 acres of gardens and woodlands and a kitchen plot that grows produce for the table. It is an elegant, restful, friendly place offering both a carte and a good-value fixed-price deal at lunchtime and a set-price menu at dinner. Local, often organic, materials play a part in the food's success, from vegetables via shellfish to Welsh black beef, and the cooking displays a high degree of skill and judgement. While some dishes may rely on traditional combinations such as scrambled eggs and smoked salmon, or roast breast of duck with Seville orange sauce, others explore some less usual territory: griddled sausage of chicken with Llanboidy cheese and laverbread with mustard broth. Desserts extend from an unusual brochette of marinated fruits with coconut Condé and Cointreau sabayon to bread-and-butter pudding with whisky cream. Full, serious attention is given to Bordeaux and Burgundy on the lengthy wine list, with top names well represented. Pretty much every other region turns up a combination of interesting, affordable and sought-after bottles, and two pages of very drinkable wines under £20 will make all-comers feel welcome.

Chefs: Paul Davies and Bryony Jones **Proprietors:** Paul Davies and Andrew Hetherington **Open:** all week 12.30 to 2, 7.30 to 9 **Closed:** 26 Dec, first 3 weeks Jan **Meals:** alc L exc Sun (main courses £14 to £18.50). Set L Mon to Sat £14.95 (2 courses) to £18.95, Set L Sun £24.50, Set D £29.50 (2 courses) to £37.50 **Service:** not inc, card slips closed **Cards:** Delta, Maestro, MasterCard, Visa **Details:** 60 seats. 20 seats outside. Private parties: 40 main room, 4 to 40 private rooms. Car park. Vegetarian meals. Children's helpings. No children under 8 at D. No smoking. Wheelchair access (not WC). Music. No mobile phones **Accommodation:** 8 rooms, all with bath/shower. TV. Phone. B&B £130 to £250. No children under 8

MAP 5 Rockfield MONMOUTHSHIRE

Stone Mill

AR

Rockfield NP25 5SW
Tel: (01600) 716273

Expect a 'happy, smiling, courteous' welcome at this sympathetically converted sixteenth-century cider mill close to the Wye Valley. Home produce and local supplies dictate the menus, which come bang up to date with 'month-hung' bresaola, crab ravioli with salsa verde (£6.25), and loin of Monmouthshire lamb with crushed potatoes, Savoy cabbage and pancetta (£16). Ricotta soufflé with caramelised figs (£4.75), and chocolate tiramisù are part of the 'grand finale'. House wines £11.50. Accommodation in self-catering cottages. Closed Sun D and all Mon.

MAP 4 St Fagans CARDIFF

Old Post Office

Greenwood Lane, St Fagans CF5 6EL
Tel: (029) 2056 5400
Website: www.old-post-office.com

Cooking 3 | Modern European | £31–£63

Set in a small rural hamlet in a very modern extension at the back of an old post office building, this minimalist but comfortable restaurant is cast very much in the modern brasserie mould. The menu knows how to dispense comfort – in the shape of Roquefort soufflé with pears poached in mulled wine, with hazelnut dressing – and how to play to the gallery, with tian of Cornish crab, and fillet of Welsh beef with sautéed field mushrooms. Other options range from roast breast of wood pigeon with a roasted root-vegetable tartlet and red-wine and parsley jus, to sea bream with a rocket and fennel farci, rösti potato, braised cabbage and tomato and chickpea jus. Finish with butterscotch tart with chocolate parfait and vanilla ice cream, or aniseed parfait served with blackberry compote, poached rhubarb and raspberry sorbet. Around 40 varied, well-chosen wines start at £14.95.

Chef: Wesley Hammond **Proprietor:** Woods Group **Open:** Thur to Sun L 12 to 2, Wed to Sat D 7 to 9 **Meals:** Set L £13.95 (2 courses) to £15.95, Set D £28.95 (2 courses) to £35 **Service:** not inc, 10% for parties of 6 or more **Cards:** Amex, Delta, Diners, Maestro, MasterCard, Visa **Details:** 26 seats. Private parties: 26 main room. Car park. Vegetarian meals. Children's helpings. No smoking. Wheelchair access (also WC). Music. Air-conditioned **Accommodation:** 6 rooms, all with bath/shower. TV. Phone. B&B £70 to £80. Rooms for disabled

MAP 4 **Salem** CARMARTHENSHIRE

Angel

Salem, nr Llandeilo SA19 7LY
Tel: (01558) 823394

Cooking 4 | Modern British | £32–£55

Rod Peterson and Liz Smith have not only given the Angel a sumptuous face-lift but have turned it into 'the place to eat in our county', according to one local fan. Inside, it has the feel of a sophisticated country restaurant, and the food makes exemplary use of locally sourced ingredients, from Gower crab and Burry Port mussels to Usk Valley venison (served with foie gras boudin, sweet red onions and port jus). Peterson is a thoughtful, confident chef, equally adept at slow-cooking belly pork and deep-frying cod in tempura-style 'cold spring water batter'. He often 'signs' dishes with a crisp parsnip fashioned like a quill, although his real forte is pastry work and desserts: try, say, silky coffee ice cream semifreddo served in a coffee cup with sablé biscuits, or lemon tart with lime custard sauce. Breads are excellent, and Welsh cheeses are sourced from within a 30-mile radius of the restaurant. The short, affordable wine list opens with George Duboeuf house selections at £12.95.

Chef: Rod Peterson **Proprietors:** Rod Peterson and Liz Smith **Open:** Wed to Sat L 12 to 2, Tue to Sat D 7 to 9 **Meals:** alc (main courses £12 to £19) **Service:** not inc **Cards:** Delta, Maestro, MasterCard, Visa **Details:** 70 seats. Private parties: 90 main room. Car park. Vegetarian meals. Children's helpings. No smoking. Music

MAP 2 **Skenfrith** MONMOUTHSHIRE

Bell at Skenfrith

Skenfrith NP7 8UH
Tel: (01600) 750235
Website: www.skenfrith.co.uk

Cooking 2 | Modern British | £29–£57

'The Bell is a very nice and relaxed place to be,' thought one reporter, taken with the simple, spacious open-plan interior and low-beamed ceiling. Its success is down to the efforts of William and Janet Hutchings and their policy of sourcing high-quality supplies locally and seasonally (blackboards list producers). Although recent reports note some inconsistency in the cooking, the kitchen still turns out some impressive dishes, including a starter of seared scallops with purées of cauliflower and red pepper. Equally convincing has been a tender, flavourful breast of Aylesbury duckling with an intense red-wine shallot sauce, while the featured fish might be salmon served with saffron and lemon risotto. Desserts run to a tarte Tatin of pineapple infused with white rum essence and served with a pear sorbet. Snacks and simpler dishes are also available.

Twin passions for claret and fine cognac in no way blinker William Hutchings to other strata of the wine world, and his globetrotting list is a delight whatever your budget or level of interest. Half-bottles are a particular strength and there's a baker's dozen by the glass too. Prices, from £10, are commendably fair.

Chef: Kurt Fleming **Proprietors:** William and Janet Hutchings **Open:** all week 12 to 2.30, 7 to 9.30 (9 Sun) **Closed:** 2 weeks late Jan/early Feb, Mon Nov to Mar **Meals:** alc (main courses L £14.50 to £16, D £15 to £21). Set L Sun £14.50 (2 courses) to £18.50 **Service:** not inc, card slips closed **Cards:** Amex, Delta, Maestro, MasterCard, Visa **Details:** 80 seats. 36 seats outside. Private parties: 20 to 40 private rooms. Car park. Vegetarian meals. Children's helpings; no children under 8 at D. No smoking. Wheelchair access (also WC). Music **Accommodation:** 8 rooms, all with bath/shower. TV. Phone. B&B £70 to £170

AR	Not a full entry but provisionally recommended (known as 'round-ups' in previous editions, these 'also recommended' establishments are now integrated throughout the book).

MAP 4 **Solva** PEMBROKESHIRE

Old Pharmacy

NEW ENTRY

5 Main Street, Solva SA62 6UU
Tel: (01437) 720005
Website: www.theoldpharmacy.co.uk

Cooking 2 | Modern Welsh-Plus | £32–£76

Martin Lawton seeks out local ingredients for his beamed and flagged converted cottage restaurant on the main street of this harbour village, but the culinary horizons are broad, with flavours drawn from all over the world. In particular, the menu exploits locally landed seafood: perhaps crab enchiladas to start, or a main course of sea bass in a rich bisque sauce with a tartlet of king prawns and mixed seafood. Solva lobsters are a speciality, served with tiger prawns and garlic butter, or as part of a seafood extravaganza, with moules marinière and a filo basket of crab. Meat eaters can pick something like Welsh black beef fillet steak served with red pepper purée, roast shallot and garlic 'and a drizzle of black treacle', and among the puddings are pecan and treacle tart. Service is cheerfully on the ball, and a decent list of good-value wines opens at £12.90.

Chefs: Matthew Ricketts and Tom Phillips **Proprietor:** Martin Lawton **Open:** all week D only 5.30 to 9.30 **Closed:** 24 to 26 Dec **Meals:** alc (main courses £12 to £36) **Service:** not inc, card slips closed **Cards:** Delta, Maestro, MasterCard, Visa **Details:** 75 seats. 10 seats outside. Private parties: 50 main room, 16 to 24 private rooms. Vegetarian meals. Children's helpings. No smoking. Wheelchair access (also WC). Music

MAP 4 **Southerndown** VALE OF GLAMORGAN

Frolics

52 Beach Road, Southerndown CF32 0RP
Tel: (01656) 880127
Email: dougwindsor34@aol.com

Cooking 1 | Modern European | £23–£57

One of the few bright spots along this patch of coast overlooking the Bristol Channel, Frolics is a small, comfortable ground-floor shop conversion with a basement overflow. Doug Windsor obviously approaches things with an open mind, offering starters such as lobster thermidor won tons with crushed pea and Parmesan salad and cured bacon, or carpaccio of monkfish and smoked salmon with tabbouleh salsa and wild leaves. Main courses might include rump of Welsh mountain lamb with a chicken, kidney and madeira pudding, or pan-seared calf's liver with truffle mash and French onion soup. Desserts such as Welsh whisky bread-and-butter pudding do the business, while the sharp, modern wine list has helpful notes and six house bottles from £11.95.

Chef/Proprietor: Doug Windsor **Open:** Tue to Sun L 12 to 2.30, Tue to Sat D 6.30 to 10 **Closed:** 26 Dec **Meals:** alc (main courses £14 to £18.50). Set L Tue to Sat £9.95 (2 courses) to £12.95, Set L Sun £12.95 (2 courses) to £14.95 **Service:** not inc, card slips closed, 10% for parties of 8 or more **Cards:** Amex, Delta, Diners, Maestro, MasterCard, Visa **Details:** 50 seats. 6 seats outside. Private parties: 30 main room, 12 to 30 private rooms. Car park. Vegetarian meals. Children's helpings. No smoking in dining room. Music

MAP 4 **Swansea** SWANSEA

La Braseria

28 Wind Street, Swansea SA1 1DZ
Tel: (01792) 469683
Website: www.labraseria.com

Cooking 1 | Spanish | £26–£57

After two decades bringing a taste of Spain to downtown Swansea, Manuel Tercero handed over the reins to his son in 2005. Little else is likely to change in this relentlessly busy, 200-seat 'bodega'. The procedure is as follows: find a table, note its number, then order at one of the counters (downstairs is mostly meat and poultry; upstairs is seafood). Cooking techniques are ultra-simple and the chargrill is given plenty of use for everything from steaks, suckling pig, and ostrich to bass, lobster, and tiger prawns. Whet your appetite with, say, stuffed mushrooms or gravlax and finish with a pudding if you have room. Tapas are served in the Champagne Bar. Spanish and French wines (from £11.25) share the limelight on the lengthy list.

Chef: P. Vaughan **Proprietor:** D. Tercero **Open:** all week 12 to 2.30, 7 to 11.30 **Closed:** D 24 Dec, 25 and 26 Dec, 1 Jan **Meals:** alc (main courses £8 to £24). Set L £8.50 (2 courses). Tapas menu available **Service:** not inc, card slips closed **Cards:** Amex, Delta, Diners, Maestro, MasterCard, Visa **Details:** 205 seats. Private parties: 120 main room. Vegetarian meals. Wheelchair access (also WC). Music. Air-conditioned

Didier & Stephanie

56 St Helens Road, Swansea SA1 4BE
Tel: (01792) 655603

Cooking 4 | French | £24–£45

Since opening in 2000 Didier Suve and Stephanie Danvel have made this large terrace house ten minutes from the centre the best Gallic venue in town. Simple pine décor predominates in an otherwise cream-walled room, with wooden floors, panelling and furniture. Tables are topped with dark green cloths, chairs have hymn-book holders on the back, and the feel is informal, slightly dated, but relaxed, warm and welcoming. Though menus are bilingual, there's no doubting the nationality of the unashamedly native French cooking. Croustillant of black pudding with mustard dressing, or salmon rillette with dill lead on to pan-fried beef fillet served with a black pepper sauce, or rabbit casserole with a Dijon mustard sauce. Apple tarte Tatin and crème fraîche is just one pleasant way to finish. Excellent-quality ingredients, beautifully warm and crunchy French bread (which arrives as soon as you're seated), a decent selection of French farm cheeses and a reasonably priced, patriotic wine list (starting with house at £10.90 a bottle, £2.10 by glass) are further attractions.

Chefs/Proprietors: Didier Suve and Stephanie Danvel **Open:** Tue to Sat 12 to 2, 7 to 9 **Meals:** alc D (main courses £13 to £16). Set L £8.90 (1 course) to £16 **Service:** not inc, card slips closed **Cards:** Delta, Maestro, MasterCard, Visa **Details:** 28 seats. Private parties: 26 main room. Music. Air-conditioned

Hanson's

Pilot House Wharf, Trawler Road,
Swansea SA1 1UN
Tel: (01792) 466200

Cooking 3 | Modern British/Seafood | £24–£54

At the far end of Swansea Marina, Hanson's is above a fishing tackle centre – reached via a spiral staircase – and is a light, bright, and uncluttered room, with most of the 12 tables having a good view of the port. Seafood is the focus of the daily-changing blackboard menu. Winter visitors were impressed by the precision and freshness of it all, enjoying a starter of scallops and smoked bacon with swede and potato mash, balsamic sauce and tomato coulis, and main courses of chargrilled sea bass with dill butter and rich, creamy seafood spaghetti, and baked cod in a sun-dried tomato and mozzarella glaze with Mediterranean vegetables. If you've set your heart on fillet steak or venison loin look no further than the printed menu, where vegetarians will find the likes of baked sweet pepper with roast vegetables and Mediterranean crumble. Finish with a satisfyingly rich dark chocolate and raspberry torte. With representatives from Old and New Worlds, the list of 30-plus wines starts at £10.95 for vins de pays and stays mostly under £20.

Chef: Andrew Hanson **Proprietors:** Helen Tennant and Andrew Hanson **Open:** Tue to Sat L 12 to 2, Mon to Sat D 6.30 to 9.30 **Closed:** D 24 Dec, 25 and 26 Dec, most bank hols **Meals:** alc (main courses £10 to £20). Set L £10.95 (2 courses) to £13.95 **Service:** not inc, card slips closed **Cards:** Delta, Maestro, MasterCard, Visa **Details:** 50 seats. Private parties: 50 main room. Vegetarian meals. Children's helpings. Music

Knights

614–616 Mumbles Road, Swansea SA3 4EA
Tel: (01792) 363184

Fish gets top billing in this friendly restaurant on Mumbles seafront overlooking Swansea Bay. Check the daily specials for piscine offerings like dressed local crab salad, or baked fillet of hake puttanesca; otherwise, the menu deals in global, bistro-style favourites like goats' cheese and red onion tartlet with hummus (£4.50), Welsh lamb shank with roast Mediterranean vegetables and Moroccan sauce (£13.50), and fillet steak with celery, Roquefort and port sauce. Closed Sun D and Mon (also Tue in winter).

The Mermaid

AR

686 Mumbles Road Swansea SA3 4EE
Tel: (01792) 367744

Bustling coffee lounge and restaurant on Mumbles seafront. Great views of Swansea Bay can also be enjoyed from outside tables in summer. Seafood features strongly and dishes are ambitiously conceived, as in red mullet with a Welsh rarebit, crayfish and leek crust, served with a saffron and crab cream and poached grapes (£13). Start with game terrine and pear chutney (£5) and wind things up with glazed gooseberry tart (£4.50) or Welsh cheeses. Two-course L £9.95. Wines from £10.95. Open all week L and Tue to Sat D.

P.A.'s

AR

95 Newton Road, Mumbles, Swansea SA3 4BN
Tel: (01792) 367723

Steve and Kate Maloney continue as ever at this cheerful wine bar-cum-restaurant in the commercial centre of Mumbles. Fish specials such as whole roast sea bass with king prawns and a spring onion and ginger sauce supplement a regularly changing menu of dishes like chargrilled chicken and chorizo skewer with chilli dressing (£5.25) and wild boar steak on a bed of avocado, tomato and mango salsa (£12.50). Desserts could include dark chocolate, Malibu and coconut torte. Bargain lunches (£7.95/£9.95), and around four dozen wines from £9.95. Closed Sun D.

MAP 7 **Trearddur Bay**
ISLE OF ANGLESEY

Waterfront Restaurant

Lôn Isallt, Trearddur Bay LL65 2UW
Tel: (01407) 860006

A minimalist dining room with bags of potential and a great location overlooking Trearddur Bay. Raw materials are good, and the dinner menu promises everything from saddle of venison with glazed onions and home-made plum chutney (£13) to fillet of sea bass with clam chowder and chicory (£13). Welsh rarebit potato cake with piccalilli and beetroot (£5) is an intriguing starter, and desserts might include iced vanilla soufflé with fruit and spiced madeleines (£4.50). Light meals and a café atmosphere at lunchtime. Workaday wines from around £10.

MAP 4 **Tredunnock**
MONMOUTHSHIRE

Newbridge Inn

AR

Tredunnock NP15 1LY
Tel: (01633) 451000

Out in the wilds by a bridge over the Usk, this pebbledash inn flies the flag for native Welsh food. Seared fillet of Carmarthenshire beef with celeriac purée and thyme jus (£18.50) is typical, but reporters have also endorsed seared scallops with pease pudding and red wine reduction (£8), 'superbly cooked' monkfish on truffle and herb risotto, and an assiette of white, milk and dark chocolate (£6). Lengthy global wine list, with house selections from £12.50. Accommodation. Open all week.

MAP 4 **Welsh Hook**
PEMBROKESHIRE

Stone Hall

AR

Welsh Hook SA62 5NS
Tel: (01348) 840212

Marion Evans (ex-Three Main Street, Fishguard) is cooking at this 600-year-old manor house on the back roads of central Pembrokeshire. Uncomplicated French cooking based on local produce is the order of the day: start with confit of duck salad with organic leaves and Puy lentils (£6.75), move on to roast monkfish with shallots and lardons, or flash-roast venison with a rich game sauce (£18), and finish with Gallic classics like profiteroles or crème brûlée (£5.50). House wines £15.10. Accommodation. Open Tue to Sat D only.

MAP 2 **Whitebrook**
MONMOUTHSHIRE

Crown at Whitebrook

Whitebrook NP25 4TX
Tel: (01600) 860254
Website: www.crownatwhitebrook.co.uk

Cooking 4 | Modern European | £40–£51

Billed as a French-style auberge in the heart of Wales, this long, low building is set alongside a narrow road within a heavily wooded valley. Inside, the atmosphere is decidedly homely, and guests are served in a pale corn-coloured dining room enlivened with decorous paintings of female nudes.

Meals are peppered with a cavalcade of incidentals – a plate of nibbles ('four in a row'), an amuse bouche, mid-course sorbet, five sorts of home-baked bread: the cumulative effect can seem over-complicated but no one can doubt the honest endeavour. Main-event dishes are also fancy and labour intensive: a ballottine of sea bass, langoustine and monkfish is served with pistachio and pink grapefruit vinaigrette and 'very decorative bits and bobs', while the trio theme re-surfaces in the shape of seared Welsh lamb fillet with a cutlet, pan-fried liver, white onion purée and tarragon jus. Desserts could range from a combo of sweet spiced chilli parfait with Sauternes-braised fruit to yet another trio – in this case involving toffee. The wine list is arranged by grape varietals, with a good range of half-bottles, and plenty to catch the eye around the £20 mark.

Chef: James Sommerin **Proprietor:** Jonathon Davies **Open:** all week exc Sun D 12 to 1.45, 7 to 8.45 **Meals:** alc L (main courses £13 to £20). Set D £35 **Service:** not inc **Cards:** Diners, Maestro, MasterCard, Visa **Details:** 35 seats. 16 seats outside. Private parties: 22 main room. Car park. Vegetarian meals. No smoking. No music. No mobile phones **Accommodation:** 8 rooms, all with bath/shower. TV. Phone. B&B £60 to £120. Swimming pool. Fishing

Channel Islands

MAP 1 Beaumont JERSEY

Bistro Soleil

La Route de la Haule, Beaumont,
St Peter JE3 7BA
Tel: (01534) 720249

Cooking 4 | Bistro/Seafood | £22–£50

A bistro named in honour of the sun naturally has a small courtyard for al fresco dining under parasols, and also a large, brightly decorated L-shaped dining room, should the weather not oblige. Locally sourced seafood forms the backbone of Ian Jones's extensive menus. Oysters might be grilled and served with garlic butter, bacon and Cheddar with a finishing kick of chilli, mussels are steamed and served in marinière fashion with white wine, onion, garlic and good Jersey cream, while main-course offerings might encompass a partnership of sea bass and turbot with crushed Jersey Royals, crème fraîche and spring onions. Meat-eaters might opt instead for roast rump of lamb with garlic flageolet mash and rosemary jus, or chateaubriand for two. Finish simply with a meringue nest of whipped cream and raspberry compote, or a selection of ice creams in a brandy-snap basket. A laminated wine list dips into southern parts as well as France and Italy, with house wines at £10.95 and £11.95.

Chef: Ian Jones **Proprietor:** Chris Power **Open:** Tue to Sun L 12.30 to 2, Tue to Sat D 6.45 to 9.30 **Closed:** 25 and 26 Dec, bank hols **Meals:** alc (not Sun L; main courses £13 to £18). Set L £12.75 (2 courses) to £14.75, Set D £24.50. Terrace L menu available in summer **Service:** not inc **Cards:** Maestro, MasterCard, Visa **Details:** 60 seats. 40 seats outside. Private parties: 60 main room. Car park. Vegetarian meals. Children's helpings. No cigars/pipes in dining room. Wheelchair access (not WC). Music

MAP 1 Gorey JERSEY

Jersey Pottery, Garden Restaurant

Gorey Village, JE3 9EP
Tel: (01534) 850850
Website: www.jerseypottery.com

Cooking 2 | Modern British/Seafood | £30–£70

This lush, greenery-filled restaurant at a popular pottery feels light and airy. Seafood plays a prominent role in modern dishes showing Mediterranean and more distant influences: starters of creamy crab risotto teamed with seared scallops and basil pesto, perhaps, or home-made sushi and sashimi with pickled ginger and wasabi, while among main courses might be whole Jersey lobster with a garden salad, or grilled Dover sole with herb butter. Meat mains are by no means neglected, witness confit of duck with roast apple, black pudding, sauté potatoes and a grain mustard and shallot dressing, and there is always a beef dish, say, ribeye steak with béarnaise sauce. The compact, globetrotting wine list starts at £12.95 and stays largely under £20.

Chef: Tony Dorris **Proprietor:** the Jones Family **Open:** Tues to Sun L only 12 to 2.30 **Closed:** 24 Dec to Feb/Mar **Meals:** alc L (main courses £11 to £31.50). Set L £15.50 (2 courses) to £19.95 **Service:** net prices, card slips closed **Cards:** Delta, Maestro, MasterCard, Visa **Details:** 180 seats. 40 seats outside. Private parties: 300 main room, 20 to 100 private rooms. Car park. Vegetarian meals. Children's helpings. No smoking. Wheelchair access (also WC). Music

Suma's

Gorey Hill, St Martin, Gorey JE3 6ET
Tel: (01534) 853291

Cooking 5 | Modern European | £24–£65

The appeal of this restaurant overlooking the harbour and Mont Orgeuil Castle is obvious. The

dining room is simple, elegant, unfussy, and Daniel Ward's sharp focus on local suppliers and prime ingredients, combined with his light touch, produces fresh and lively food. The raw materials are spun into fish dishes like salmon tortellini with a pea velouté, or grilled red mullet, prawn, scallop and spring onion fricassée with basil oil. And the kitchen's ability to tread the fine line between interesting treatment and necessary restraint produces some appealing combinations: for example, sea bass with sauerkraut, plum and onion compote and a warm garden pea dressing, or fillets of Dover sole with lightly curried crab parcels and a tomato and basil sauce. Meaty items might include loin of pork with roast potatoes, glazed apples and red onion and deep-fried sage, or pot-roast guinea fowl with herb potato purée, wild mushrooms and broad beans, or, on the Sunday set lunch menu, roast rib of beef with Yorkshire pudding and horseradish hollandaise.

Traditional desserts like profiteroles compete with slightly more cosmopolitan bitter lemon tart, or vanilla pannacotta with morello cherry compote. Some eighty wines are well varied in terms of style and origin and, like the food, fairly priced. House Spanish red is £14, French white £13.

Chef: Daniel Ward **Proprietors:** Malcolm Lewis and Sue Dufty **Open:** all week 12 to 2.30, 6.15 to 9.30 **Closed:** 22 Dec to 20 Jan **Meals:** alc (main courses £13 to £20). Set L £12.50 (2 courses) to £15, Set L Sun £20, Set D Mon to Sat 6.15 to 6.45 £12.50 (2 courses) to £15, Set D Sun to Thur £25 **Service:** net prices, card slips closed **Cards:** Amex, Delta, Diners, Maestro, MasterCard, Visa **Details:** 40 seats. 16 seats outside. Private parties: 40 main room. Vegetarian meals. Children's helpings. Smoking bar area only. Music. No mobile phones. Air-conditioned

MAP 1 St Martin's GUERNSEY

Auberge

Jerbourg Road, St Martin's GY4 6BH
Tel: (01481) 238485
Website: www.theauberge.gg

Cooking 5 | Modern British-Plus | £32–£48

Smartly redesigned in sleek minimalist style, this one-time pub on the cliffs is now a much-sought-after Guernsey destination. The location may be rural, but the interior feels metropolitan with its long bar, blond-wood tables and intriguing Mexican fireplace. From the floor-to-ceiling window there are views of the bay that was – reputedly – the number one smugglers' haunt in the area.

The contemporary style of the place is echoed by the food, which pulls in influences from near and far. Thai-marinated tuna comes with coriander rice, peanut sprouts and baby corn, while tournedos of salmon is served on spiced lentils and figs with foie gras parfait and crab bisque. Elsewhere conventional ideas might be given a twist, as in carpaccio of beef with wasabi cream and crispy capers, or roast loin of lamb with a cavalcade of components including a Mediterranean 'pizza', tomato chutney, cream cheese and basil ravioli and caramelised onion sauce. Desserts are showy offerings like pineapple beignet with mango and coconut salsa and lemongrass ice cream. The wine list covers a lot of ground in a small space, with prices from £12.60.

Chef: Paul Olliver **Proprietor:** Ian Irving-Walker **Open:** all week 12 to 2.30, 6 to 9.30 **Closed:** Sun D from Nov to Mar **Meals:** alc (main courses £10 to £14.50) **Service:** not inc **Cards:** Amex, Delta, Diners, Maestro, MasterCard, Visa **Details:** 70 seats. 40 seats outside. Private parties: 100 main room. Car park. Vegetarian meals. Children's helpings. No smoking. Wheelchair access (also WC). Music. Air-conditioned

MAP 1 St Helier JERSEY

Bohemia

AR

Green Street, St Helier, JE2 4UH
Tel: (01534) 880588

A class act – a modern, urbane dining room – with seafood playing a big part on Shaun Rankin's menus. A starter of blanquette of scallops and langoustines with cucumber and ginger (£11) impressed a reporter, as did a main course roast sea bass with Jersey Royals, scallops and sauce vierge (£18). Otherwise, the kitchen turns its hand to slow-cooked belly and glazed cheek of pork, roast rump of lamb, and fillet of beef Rossini (£19.50), followed by lemon soufflé with milk chocolate cappuccino and pecan biscotti (£6). Well-chosen wines from £13.50. Accommodation. Closed Sun. Reports, please.

Not a full entry but provisionally recommended (known as 'round-ups' in previous editions, these 'also recommended' establishments are now integrated throughout the book).

MAP 1 **St Peter Port** GUERNSEY

La Frégate

Les Cotils, St Peter Port GY1 1UT
Tel: (01481) 724624
Website: www.lafregatehotel.com

Cooking 4 | Modern European | £27–£82

Magical views over St Peter Port Bay and ancient Castle Cornet are among the selling points at this plush hotel high up on the capital's winding, narrow streets. In contrast to the oak-panelled traditionalism of the hotel itself, the restaurant puts on a modern suit of clothes, and it's no surprise that the kitchen majors in local seafood; 'weather permitting', expect anything from sea bass and skate to lobster, served with appropriately luxurious sauces. The extensive carte offers meat and fish in equal measure, beginning with, perhaps, a piscine hotpot scented with saffron and lemongrass, or peppered smoked chicken salad with Caesar dressing. Mains continue the classical French theme with fillet of beef bordelaise or a medley of grilled fish with a champagne and lobster cream, while desserts bring on board dramatically flambéed crêpes suzette and hot chocolate fondant with caramel sauce. The carefully selected, old-school wine list draws heavily on France; prices start at £12.50.

Chef: Neil Maginnis **Proprietor:** Guernsey Summer Holidays Limited **Open:** all week 12 to 2, 7 to 9.45 **Closed:** first week Jan **Meals:** alc (main courses £12 to £30). Set L £18.50, Set D £26.50 **Service:** not inc **Cards:** Amex, Maestro, MasterCard, Visa **Details:** 80 seats. 35 seats outside. Private parties: 80 main room, 4 to 38 private rooms. Car park. Vegetarian meals. No smoking. No music. Air-conditioned **Accommodation:** 13 rooms, all with bath/shower. TV. Phone. B&B £85 to £185. Rooms for disabled. Baby facilities

Da Nello

AR

46 The Pollet, St Peter Port, GY1 1WF
Tel: (01481) 721552

Highly popular, renowned Italian in an attractively modernised, centuries-old cellar with shipwreck timbers, rough-stone walls and a Neapolitan décor. Guernsey seafood points up a dyed-in-the-wool trattoria menu that covers carpaccio (£6.75), pastas and risottos, chargrilled steaks, dry-fried scallops meunière (£13.50), and monthly specials like brill with mussels and saffron sauce. To finish, 'meringue du chef' (£4.50) is greatly appreciated. Professional service, jolly atmosphere. House Italian £10.95. Open all week.

MAP 1 **St Saviour** JERSEY

Longueville Manor

St Saviour JE2 7WF
Tel: (01534) 725501
Website: www.longuevillemanor.com

Cooking 5 | Modern European | £29–£85

The venerable Manor looks every inch the part, from its welcoming, rather than imposing, stone façade to the oak-panelled dining room reserved for non-smokers. Here, the furnishings are as soft as the napery is starch-stiff, and the approach of the staff is consummately smart and professional.

Andrew Baird runs an industrious kitchen, harvesting soft fruits, vegetables and salad leaves from the Manor garden, and capitalising on the abundance of fresh seafood that washes up at his door. Local lobster is stuffed into ravioli, and served enterprisingly with pineapple and a shellfish cream sauce infused with sherry and cocoa. Fish generally comes in for the innovative treatment, as in main courses like sea bass with cauliflower purée, grilled black figs and a cep emulsion, while meats may be more traditional – perhaps Angus beef fillet partnered with fondant potato, braised oxtail and a creamy sauce of morels. The house assiette of desserts will prove a temptation to those who find themselves dithering between Valrhona orange chocolate pyramid with wattle-seed ice cream or crème brûlée with Granny Smith sorbet and apple soup.

The wine list has all the top Bordeaux and champagne that you might expect in such surroundings, supported by a sound international selection. Wines by the glass are a speciality, from house vin de pays at £4.25 (£19 a bottle) to intense white Burgundy by Ramonet at £14 (£59).

Chef: Andrew Baird **Proprietor:** Malcolm Lewis **Open:** all week 12.30 to 2, 7 to 9.30 **Meals:** alc (main courses £28 to £30). Set L £12.50 (2 courses) to £15, set L Sun £27.50. **Service:** net prices, card slips closed **Cards:** Amex, Delta, Diners, Maestro, MasterCard, Visa **Details:** 70 seats. 40 seats outside. Private parties: 70 main room, 2 to 24 private rooms. Car park. Vegetarian meals. Children's helpings. No smoking in 1 dining room. Wheelchair access (not WC). No music. No mobile phones **Accommodation:** 31 rooms, all with bath/shower. TV. Phone. B&B £175 to £700. Rooms for disabled. Baby facilities. Swimming pool

 This symbol means that accommodation is available at this establishment.

MAP 16 **Bangor** CO DOWN

Shanks

The Blackwood Golf Centre, 150 Crawfordsburn Road, Bangor BT19 1GB
Tel: (028) 9185 3313
Website: www.shanksrestaurant.com

Cooking 5 | Modern European | £40–£83

A stylish, ambitious restaurant set on a golf course (listen out for the shouts of 'Fore!'), Shanks boasts some original David Hockney pictures, as well as an almost equally diverting view of its kitchen staff hard at work. Game from nearby estates features strongly: venison from Clandeboye and pheasant from Barons Court among the high points. A light midweek supper menu has now been introduced to supplement the main fixed-price affair, which changes to reflect the seasons.

A bowl of soup is an event, a curried cauliflower version appearing with cinnamon-spiced apples and coriander crème fraîche, while smoked goose breast forms the centrepiece of a salad that also encompasses grilled figs, celeriac rémoulade, toasted hazelnuts and Cumberland dressing. As may be appreciated, the cooking aims for intricacy, treating monkfish in the meaty way with buttery champ, wild mushrooms, crunchy cabbage and a red-wine sauce, while that pheasant might appear in winter as a serving of the breast, in the cold-weather company of spätzli, chestnuts, apples, Brussels sprouts, madeira and thyme. A salad of exotic fruits is a good way to finish in the months when home produce is thin on the ground, especially when it comes with mango and lychee sorbet and coconut macaroons. France turns up lots of exciting reds to go with the game dishes, and other countries on the polished list are packed with good names. Bottles start at £15.

Chef: Robbie Millar **Proprietors:** Robbie and Shirley Millar **Open:** Tue to Fri L 12.30 to 2.30, Tue to Sat D 7 to 10 **Closed:** 24 to 26 and 31 Dec, 1 Jan, Easter Sun to Wed, 1st 2 weeks July **Meals:** Set L £21 (2 courses) to £26.75, Set D Tue to Thur 7 to 10 £21 (2 courses) to £48.50. **Service:** not inc, 10% for parties of 6 or more **Cards:** Amex, Delta, Maestro, MasterCard, Visa **Details:** 70 seats. Private parties: 10 main room, 12 to 36 private rooms. Car park. Vegetarian meals. Children's helpings. No smoking in 1 dining room. Wheelchair access (also WC). Music. Air-conditioned

MAP 16 **Belfast** CO ANTRIM

Aldens

229 Upper Newtownards Road, Belfast BT4 3JF
Tel: (028) 9065 0079
Website: www.aldensrestaurant.com

Cooking 2 | Modern Irish | £29–£47

The colour purple dominates this 'stylish restaurant on a distinctly unstylish road' some way out of the city. Pleasant Mediterranean combos and deli assemblages feature strongly on the menu (anchovies seem to show up a lot) and the kitchen also embraces a broad repertoire of global dishes from roast haunch of rabbit with lentils and wild garlic salsa verde to mushroom curry with braised rice. Reporters have liked confit of duck on a niçoise salad bolstered by chorizo and olives, and pan-fried sea bass fillet with sun-dried tomato and roasted peppers. Meals begin with splendid breads, although desserts such as sticky toffee pudding, and meringues with vanilla ice cream and hot passion-fruit sauce, have disappointed.

A lively and good-value selection of wines mixes reliable bistro standards like Madfish Unwooded Chardonnay (£17.95) with top-rated new stars including Loimer's Kaferberg Grüner

	This symbol means that the wine list is well above the average.
	This symbol means that the restaurant has a truly outstanding wine cellar.

Veltliner (£29.95) from Austria. France is strong too.

Chef: Cathy Gradwell **Proprietor:** Jonathan Davis **Open:** Mon to Fri L 12 to 2.30, Mon to Sat D 6 to 10 (11 Fri and Sat) **Closed:** 2 weeks July, bank hols **Meals:** alc (main courses L £6.50 to £17, D £8 to £17). Set D (exc Fri after 7 and Sat) £17.50 (2 courses) to £21.95 **Service:** not inc **Cards:** Amex, Delta, Maestro, MasterCard, Visa **Details:** 70 seats. Private parties: 80 main room. Vegetarian meals. Children's helpings. No-smoking area. Wheelchair access (also WC). Music. Air-conditioned

Cayenne

7 Ascot House, Shaftesbury Square,
Belfast BT2 7DB
Tel: (028) 9033 1532
Website: www.rankingroup.co.uk

Cooking 4 | Fusion | £26–£59

With some twenty items on the carte, plus fixed-price lunch and dinner menus, a separate vegetarian menu and desserts to attend to, the kitchen still manages to produce robust and good-looking food on a consistent basis. Paul Rankin is an enthusiast for contemporary international ideas, and under his direction the menu moves freely from crab and avocado California rolls with ginger, soy, wasabi and radish to dry-aged Irish sirloin with potato and horseradish gratin, from pea and ham hock risotto to grilled sake-marinated monkfish with prawn dumplings, spring carrots and shiso broth. A clear focus and confident execution make the most of flavour combinations and texture contrasts: for example, crispy aromatic pork belly served with sweet potato purée, pak choi and five-spice apples. Vegetables are (like bread) charged extra, but may not be necessary.

Relatively conventional desserts might include rhubarb and apple crumble, or spiced banana and pecan cake with bourbon crème fraîche and toffee sauce. A snappy contemporary mix of wines is listed by variety and priced mostly under £30. A separate page of fine wines adds polish. Paul and Jeanne Rankin also run Rain City and Roscoff Brasserie in the city (see below).

Chefs: Danny Millar **Proprietor:** Paul and Jeanne Rankin **Open:** Mon to Fri L 12 to 2.15, all week D 6 (5 Sun) to 10.15 (11.15 Fri/Sat, 8.45 Sun) **Closed:** 25 and 26 Dec, 1 Jan, 12 July **Meals:** alc (main courses £8.50 to £18). Set L £12 (2 courses) to £15.50, Set D Mon to Thur 7 to 10.15 £19.50 **Service:** not inc, 10% (optional) for parties of 6 or more, card slips closed **Cards:** Amex, Delta, Diners, Maestro, MasterCard, Visa **Details:** 120 seats. Private parties: 70 main room, 18 private room. Vegetarian meals. Children's helpings. Wheelchair access (also WC). Music. Air-conditioned

James Street South NEW ENTRY

21 James Street South, Belfast BT2 7GA
Tel: (028) 9043 4310
Website: www.jamesstreetsouth.co.uk

Cooking 5 | Modern European | £27–£61

A relative newcomer to Belfast's urban dining scene, this French-inspired restaurant offers a relaxed atmosphere and 'exquisitely light' modern cuisine in stark white surroundings. Kitchen techniques are well-honed, and garnishes and spices are handled with restraint and discrimination. A top local supplier delivers fish daily, while game is well hung and precision-timed (as one should expect from a chef who trained with Ladenis and Marco Pierre White). Thick-cut smoked salmon is counterpointed by a feather-light crab beignet, rosy beetroot roundels and lamb's lettuce. Rhubarb and red onion cut the richness of foie gras, while flavoursome squab breast combines with a salad including poached apricots and walnut and decorated with delicately spliced chive stems and flowers. Monkfish, crab and razor clam formed a successful main-course trio at inspection, set on gentle garlic cream slaked with fish juices; roast saddle of rabbit with baby carrots, cider jus and celeriac purée has also attracted favourable comment.

For pudding, try lime meringue in a pastry case with tangy gin-and-tonic sorbet, or 'delectable' confit pineapple with 'creamy, not cloying' coconut bavarois and coconut parfait. Coffee is reported excellent. Extras, including breads and some of the extra vegetables, may disappoint, but the champ is highly recommended. The shortish, eclectic wine list seems pricey at the low end, and bottles under £20 aren't numerous, though house red costs £15, and single glasses start from £4.50.

Chef: Niall McKenna **Proprietors:** Niall and Joanne McKenna **Open:** Mon to Sat L 12 to 2.45, all week D 5.45 to 10.45 (5.30 to 9 Sun) **Closed:** 25 and 26 Dec, 11 to 13 July **Meals:** alc L and D (main courses £13 to £17.50). Set L £13.50 (2 courses) to £15.50, Pre-theatre set D Mon to Thur £15.50 (2 courses) to £17.50. Bar menu available **Service:** not inc **Cards:** Amex, Delta, Maestro, MasterCard, Visa **Details:** 70 seats. Private parties: 76 main room. Vegetarian meals. Children's helpings. No-smoking area. Music. Air-conditioned

Metro Brasserie AR

13 Lower Crescent, Belfast BT7 1NR
Tel: (028) 9032 3349

Refurbished contemporary brasserie in the stylish Crescent Townhouse Hotel near the university.

Weekday 'early-bird' menus (5.45 to 7.15) are good value (£11.95/£14.50), and the carte treads a similar culinary path with, perhaps, smoked chicken Caesar salad with crispy prosciutto (£6.25) and sesame-steamed hake with spiced pak choi, fragrant rice and satay sauce (£12.50), followed by desserts like white and dark chocolate cheesecake with raspberry sorbet (£5). Separate vegetarian menu. Wines from £13. Closed Sat L and Sun L.

Nick's Warehouse

35 Hill Street, Belfast BT1 2LB
Tel: (028) 9043 9690
Website: www.nickswarehouse.co.uk

Cooking 3 | Modern Irish | £27–£52

Nick and Cathy Price's former whiskey warehouse stands close to St Anne's Cathedral in a district of old Belfast. The kitchen pays proper attention to local supplies in dishes such as grilled loin of Gloucester Old Spot pork (provided by 'a lady near Dundrum') on mash with shallot and balsamic jus, and the menu takes a brasserie jaunt through seared sesame beef with grilled chilli and frisée salad, salmon fillet on bacon and leek risotto, and desserts such as rhubarb cornmeal cake. Similar dishes can be eaten in the relaxed downstairs wine bar, which has been given a youthful facelift. Service can seem 'distinctly offhand', although the live wire wine list makes amends with eclectic drinking bolstered by some additional Spanish stuff; house wines are £11.95.

Chefs: Gerard Sands and Sean Craig **Proprietors:** Nick and Kathy Price **Open:** Mon to Fri L 12 to 3, Tue to Sat D 6 to 9.30 (10 Fri and Sat) **Closed:** 25 and 26 Dec, 1 Jan, Easter Mon and Tue, 1 May, 30 May, 12 July **Meals:** alc (main courses £7 to £17.50) **Service:** not inc, 10% (optional) for parties of 5 or more **Cards:** Amex, Delta, Diners, Maestro, MasterCard, Visa **Details:** 185 seats. Private parties: 90 main room, 10 to 50 private rooms. Children's helpings. No cigars/pipes. Wheelchair access (also WC). Music. Air-conditioned

Rain City

33–35 Malone Road, Belfast BT9 6RU
Tel: (028) 9068 2929
Website: www.rankingroup.co.uk

Cooking 3 | International | £26–£50

(£)

'The closest you'll get to an American diner this side of the Atlantic' is the claim made by Paul and Jeanne Rankin of their casual venue (see also Cayenne and Roscoff Brasserie), where fast, friendly service and a cool, laid-back atmosphere are what to expect. All-day dining from a versatile range of menus, including brunch at weekends and a children's menu, make this an ideal choice for young families or large informal groups. Main courses could be as simple as a burger in a toasted bun with melted Cheddar and fries, or Asian-style chicken and noodle salad. Those with more substantial appetites might opt for a starter of seafood chowder or steamed mussels, followed by crispy duck confit with red onion marmalade, rocket salad and sautéed potatoes. To finish, choices range from sticky toffee pudding to raspberry and almond tart. The wine list offers about a dozen varied choices of each colour (three of each by the glass from £3.50), with house selections starting at £15.50.

Chef: Gareth Magill **Proprietors:** Paul and Jeanne Rankin **Open:** all week 12 (10 Sat and Sun) to 10.30 **Closed:** 25 Dec **Meals:** alc (main courses £7.50 to £13.50) **Service:** not inc, card slips closed, 10% for parties of 6 or more **Cards:** Amex, Delta, Diners, Maestro, MasterCard, Visa **Details:** 90 seats. 25 seats outside. Private parties: 50 main room, 50 private room. Vegetarian meals. Children's helpings. No-smoking area. Wheelchair access (also WC). Music. Air-conditioned

Restaurant Michael Deane

36–40 Howard Street, Belfast BT1 6PF
Tel: (028) 9033 1134
Website: www.michaeldeane.co.uk

Cooking 6 | Modern European-Plus | £51–£92

Michael Deane's two-tier operation occupies a corner site on a busy city centre street, in the lee of the Belfast City Hall. The ground floor is taken up by a buzzy, informal brasserie, while the first floor is devoted to grand dining in the modern style, and it is the latter to which our rating applies. Derek Creagh arrived in 2004 to assist the proprietor in the kitchens, and the cooking is characterized as before by great polish and refinement.

Dinners might begin with an up-to-the-minute assemblage of scallops, black pudding and cauliflower, given an Irish tilt with potato bread and a brown butter dressing, and proceed to fried bream served with ravioli of smoked chicken and tarragon, with leeks and morels poached in vanilla, or beef fillet with a pasty made of the shin meat, served with horseradish mash and a bourguignon sauce. At dessert stage, the menu retreats into almost complete taciturnity, the options being

'Chocolate', 'Lemon', 'Pear' or 'Fromage'. France and Australia are the focus of a wine list that features a host of good options in the £20–£25 range, including Vacheron's Sancerre (£25) and Coldstream Hills Chardonnay (£22). There are smart mature bottles too, and ten by the glass.

Chefs: Michael Deane and Derek Creagh **Proprietor:** Michael Deane **Open:** Wed to Sat D 7.30 to 9 **Meals:** Set L £35 to £37, Set D £45 to £47 **Service:** not inc, 10% for parties of 6 or more, card slips closed **Cards:** Amex, Delta, Maestro, MasterCard, Visa **Details:** 35 seats. Private parties: 35 main room. Children's helpings. Smoking at bar only. Music. No mobile phones. Air-conditioned

Roscoff Brasserie

NEW ENTRY

7–11 Linenhall Street, Belfast
BT2 8AA
Tel: (028) 9031 1150
Website: www.rankingroup.co.uk

Cooking 5 | Modern European | £31–£79

'Belfast and its visitors have reason to rejoice in Rankin's return in peak form to the city centre,' concluded a reporter after visiting this new venture close to the Ulster Hall. The dream team of Paul and Jeanne Rankin with chef Andrew Rea is on song, and their agreeably furnished brasserie is exactly what fans were hoping for. Everything here exudes class and polish, from the warmth of the welcome and the stylish décor to the beautifully judged treatment of each ingredient – whether it's the outstanding breads, the chips served with three-inch-thick grilled fillet of beef, or the delicate Gruyère croûtons accompanying a warm salad of roast butternut squash.

Fish predominates on the menu: delicate crab ravioli is enhanced by a sharp curry and chive vinaigrette, while pan-fried whole lemon sole is set off by capers, wild mushrooms and steamed ratte potatoes. Rankin's 'flagship' confit of duck (detached from its skin) is a 'splendidly croustillant' creation enhanced by a little cep oil, and there are simple vegetarian delights in the shape of potato and goats' cheese flan with roast red peppers and rocket. Desserts have all the skill and assurance you might expect: for example, bittersweet dark chocolate tart with tangy orange ice cream, and exquisitely thin slices of pineapple carpaccio scattered with 'jewelled redcurrants' surrounding a single scoop of gin and tonic sorbet. Wines are a contemporary mix from £15.50, with sound names like Errázuriz and the Turckheim co-op in Alsace. See entries for Cayenne and Rain City (both in Belfast) for the other links in the Rankin chain.

Chef: Andrew Rea **Proprietors:** Paul and Jeanne Rankin **Open:** Sun to Fri L 12 to 2.15, all week D 6 to 10.15 **Closed:** 25 and 26 Dec, 1 Jan, 12 July **Meals:** alc (main courses £16 to £24). Set L £15.25 (2 courses) to £19.50, Set D Sun to Thur £21.50 (2 courses) to £27 **Service:** not inc, 10% for parties of 6 or more **Cards:** Amex, Delta, Diners, Maestro, MasterCard, Visa **Details:** 86 seats. Private parties: 80 main room. Vegetarian meals. Children's helpings. No-smoking area. Wheelchair access (also WC). Music. Air-conditioned

Ta Tu

AR

701 Lisburn Road, Belfast BT9 7GU
Tel: (028) 9038 0818

Fashionably chic 'Bar and Grill' that functions as a minimalist crowd-puller on Belfast's south side. A new chef arrived in 2005, but the kitchen continues to deliver a modish cocktail of fusion ideas built around decent ingredients: roast sweet potato, coconut and chilli soup (£4.50), scallops with mussel, crab and prawn risotto, curry oil and sweet soy (£17), braised lamb shank ragoût, and white chocolate torte with mango sorbet (£5) are typical. Global wines from £11.95. Open all week.

MAP 16 Gilford CO DOWN

Oriel

2 Bridge Street, Gilford BT63 6HF
Tel: (028) 3883 1543
Website: www.orielrestaurant.com

Cooking 4 | Modern Irish | £30–£70

Barry Smyth has plied his trade at this unassuming small-town restaurant since 1999. The overall impression is of unadorned simplicity – the place exudes honesty and lack of pretension – with the focus firmly on the food. The repertoire suggests lively endeavour, loyalty to local ingredients (supplemented by a weekly delivery from Rungis Market in Paris) and a modern outlook. The upshot might be shredded duck confit salad with pine nuts and oven-dried tomatoes, or warm salad of goats' cheese and beetroot purée to start, or maybe terrine of local prawn and lobster with a Jersey Royal salad. Then there might be herb roast loin of pork with braised swede, confit shallot, croquette potato and madeira jus, with five-spice-roast Gressingham duck breast accompanied by fondant potato and sauté cabbage. There's fish too, of course: say, pan-roasted marinated sardine fillets with roast Mediterranean vegetables, or turbot with baby leeks, asparagus, spinach and shellfish cream.

Desserts have featured a ginger-scented crème brûlée with pineapple granita, as well as white peach parfait with poached peaches and a champagne sorbet. Traditional French regions predominate on a wine list that hits its stride at £20; house Bordeaux and South African Chardonnay are £14.95.

Chef/Proprietor: Barry Smyth **Open:** Fri to Sun L 12.30 to 2.30, Thur to Sat D 6.30 to 9.30 (10 Sat), Sun D 5.30 to 8.30 **Meals:** alc D (main courses £16.50 to £20). Set L and D £15.95 (2 courses) to £19.95, Set D £50 **Service:** not inc, card slips closed **Cards:** Amex, Maestro, MasterCard, Visa **Details:** 60 seats. Private parties: 50 main room. Vegetarian meals. Children's helpings. Music. Air-conditioned

MAP 16 **Kircubbin** CO DOWN

Paul Arthurs

NEW ENTRY

66 Main Street, Kircubbin BT22 2SP
Tel: (028) 4273 8192
Website: www.paularthurs.com

Cooking 3 | Seafood/Mod European | £20–£49

What the advertising doesn't tell you about this eponymous restaurant in the village overlooking picturesque Strangford Lough is that it has one of the more unusual locations for fine dining, namely, above a fish-and-chip shop and an amusement arcade. However, there's no cause for concern; chef-patron Paul Arthurs has pedigree, serving his apprenticeship under Michael Deane (see Restaurant Michael Deane, Belfast) and Robbie Millar (see Shanks, Bangor), and, being on the lough shore and close to Portavogie, has access to the freshest fish and shellfish. The 'catch of the day' main dish changes to reflect quality and season, perhaps showcasing seared scallops served with truffle mash and toasted hazelnut butter, while starters on the compact, modern-focused menus could feature a richly flavoured chunky smoked haddock chowder, or 'fantastic' cracked crab claws with chopped chilli, lemongrass, garlic and coriander. Grilled ribeye with a red-wine jus and classic béarnaise might feature among the meaty options, while the homely desserts could deliver a hot chocolate pudding or raspberry pavlova. The compact, fashionable and affordable globetrotting wine list comes ordered by price and opens at £9.95.

Chef/Proprietor: Paul Arthurs **Open:** Tue to Sun L 12 to 2.30, Tue to Sat D 5 to 9 **Closed:** all Jan **Meals:** alc (main courses L £6 to £9.50, D £13 to £15) **Service:** not inc **Cards:** Amex, Delta, Diners, Maestro, MasterCard, Visa **Details:** 45 seats. 20 seats outside. Private parties: 45 main room. Car park. Children's helpings. Music. Air-conditioned

Index